The Fermilab Meeting

DPF 92

INTERNATIONAL ADVISORY COMMITTEE

G. Bellettini	INFN, Pisa
E. L. Berger	ANL
K. Berkelman	Cornell U.
J. D. Bjorken	SLAC
E. Eichten	FNAL
M. K. Gaillard	LBL
P. Grannis	SUNY at Stony Brook
K. Kondo	U. of Tsukuba, Japan
L. M. Lederman	Illinois Inst. of Tech.
V. S. Narasimham	Tata Inst., Bombay
J. Peoples	FNAL
N. W. Reay	Ohio State U.
C. Rubbia	CERN

LOCAL ORGANIZING COMMITTEE

		M. Abolins	Michigan State U.
	Secretary	C. H. Albright	Northern Illinois U.
		J. A. Appel	FNAL
		E. L. Berger	ANL
		D. Buchholz	Northwestern U.
		G. Feldman	Harvard U.
		S. Holmes	FNAL
		P. Kasper	FNAL
		H. Neal	U. of Michigan
		S. Parke	FNAL
		L. Pondrom	U. of Wisconsin
	Co-chair	R. Raja	FNAL
Conference Coordinator		C. M. Sazama	FNAL
		M. Shochet	U. of Chicago
		A. Tollestrup	FNAL
	Co-chair	J. Yoh	FNAL

PARALLEL SESSION CONVENERS AND LIAISONS

	D. S. Ayres	ANL
*	W. A. Bardeen	FNAL
	R. M. Barnett	LBL
*	E. L. Berger	ANL
	C. Bernard	Washington U.
	I. I. Bigi	U. of Notre Dame
*	D. Buchholz	Northwestern U.
	N. H. Christ	Columbia U.
	S. Dawson	BNL
*	J. Frieman	FNAL
	T. Gaisser	Bartol Research Inst.
*	W. Giele	FNAL
	H. Gordon	BNL
	B. Grinstein	SSCL
	M. Harrison	BNL
	J. A. Harvey	U. of Chicago
*	G. Hockney	FNAL
*	C. Hojvat	FNAL
*	S. D. Holmes	FNAL
*	P. Kasper	FNAL
	L. S. Littenberg	BNL
	M. Mangano	INFN, Pisa
	R. J. Morrison	U. of California, Santa Barbara
*	S. Parke	FNAL
	S. D. Protopospescu	BNL
*	R. Raja	FNAL
	J. L. Rosner	U. of Chicago
	R. Ruth	SLAC
	B. Sadoulet	LBL
	H. Satz	CERN/U. of Bielefeld
	A. B. Seiden	U. of California, Santa Cruz
	M. H. Shaevitz	Columbia U.
	M. D. Shapiro	LBL
	P. Sikivie	U. of Florida
	T. Sjöstrand	CERN
	G. Sterman	SUNY at Stony Brook
	A. P. White	U. of Texas, Arlington
*	A. B. Wicklund	ANL
*	B. Winstein	U. of Chicago
*	J. Yoh	FNAL

* Liaison

TABLE OF CONTENTS

Volume 1

Preface	v
International Advisory Committee	vii
Local Organizing Committee	vii
Parallel Session Conveners and Liaisons	viii
DPF92 Conference Schedule	xxxii
DPF92 Plenary Session Program	xxxiii
DPF92 Parallel Session Program	xxxv
Experimental Collaboration Lists	lxv

PLENARY SESSION PRESENTATIONS

Avi Yagil	Highlights from CDF	3
Ronald J. Madaras	Highlights from D0	19
Frank J. Sciulli	Recent Results from H1 and ZEUS at HERA	37
Samuel C. C. Ting	New Results from LEP Experiments	53
Charles Baltay	Results from SLD at the SLAC Linear Collider	109
Daniel Sinclair	The High Energy Physics-Astrophysics Connection	123
John F. Wilkerson	Results from Non-accelerator Experiments	137
Maury Tigner	Recent Developments in Accelerators	155
Murdock G. D. Gilchriese	Detector Developments*	165
R. Keith Ellis	Status of QCD	167
William J. Marciano	Status of Electroweak Measurements	185
John P. Cumalat	Recent Results in Charm Physics	197
David G. Cassel	b Physics	213
Walter H. Toki	The Tau of Particle Physics	235
Stephen R. Sharpe	Recent Progress in Lattice QCD	247
David J. Gross	Recent Developments in Abstract Theory	265
Leon M. Lederman	The Conventional Visionary Talk	277

* Oral presentation only.

PARALLEL SESSION CONTRIBUTIONS

A. Electroweak including τ and W/Z Physics

A1. τ Physics

R. Kowalewski	A Precise Determination of g_τ/g_μ and a Measurement of the Tau Polarization in Z^0 Decays	289
M. Schmitt	Tau Polarization in ALEPH	293
J. S. Conway	A Neural Network Approach to Charged Particle Identification in Low- Multiplicity ALEPH Events	298
M. Walsh	Tau Branching Ratios in ALEPH	301
P. Fisher	A Measurement of τ Polarization in Z^0 Decays	305
R. McNulty	Measurements of the Topological Branching Fractions and the Lifetime of the Tau Lepton	308
G. Crawford	Recent CLEO Results on Tau Decays	314
S. Henderson	A Measurement of the Tau Lepton Mass and a Limit on the Tau Neutrino Mass	318
S. Xue	τ Mass Measurement from $e\mu$, $e\pi$ and $(\mu\pi, \mu\mu, \pi\pi)$ Channels at BES/BEPC	321

A2. Asymmetries; Electroweak Tests Using b's and c's

L. Mirabito	A Measurement of $A_{FB}^{b\bar{b}}$ Using Prompt Leptons and of $A_{FB}^{c\bar{c}}$ Using D^* in the DELPHI Experiments at LEP	325
D. Wright	Asymmetry and Mixing in $Z \to b\bar{b}$ and $Z \to c\bar{c}$ Decays	329
D. Hinshaw	Measurements of $\Gamma(Z \to b\bar{b})$ and $\Gamma(Z \to c\bar{c})$ at LEP from OPAL	332
P. Wells	The Forward-Backward Asymmetry of Quarks in Z^0 Decays at OPAL	335
L. Bellantoni	A Study of $\Gamma(b\bar{b})/\Gamma$ (had) and $\Gamma(c\bar{c})/\Gamma$ (had) and the Forward-Backward Asymmetry in $Z^0 \to b\bar{b}$	338
D. Su	A Preliminary Measurement of $R_b = \frac{\Gamma(Z^0 \to b\bar{b})}{\Gamma(Z^0 \to hadrons)}$ at SLD	342
B. A. Schumm	First Measurement of the Left-Right Cross Section Asymmetry in Z Boson Production at $E_{CM} = 91.55$ GeV	348

A3a. Mini-reviews on Electroweak Theory

J. L. Rosner	Electroweak Measurements and Top Quark Mass Limits	352
J. Bagger	Electroweak Symmetry Breaking at the SSC and LHC	357

A3b. Gauge Boson Couplings — Theory

U. Baur	Probing the Weak Boson Sector in $p\bar{p} \to Z\gamma$	362
M. A. Doncheski	Probing the $WW\gamma$ Vertex in $e^{\pm}p \to \nu\gamma X$	366
K. A. Peterson	Constraints on Anomalous WWγ Couplings from $e\gamma$ Collisions	370
D. Zeppenfeld	One-Loop Constraints on the Electroweak Triple Gauge Boson Vertex	374

A4a. Multi-particle Final States and Searches at LEP

J. Marco	Radiative Leptonic Events in DELPHI	378
A. R. White	The η_6 and Massive Photon Pairs at LEP	383

A4b. Electroweak results from Hadron Colliders

N. A. Graf	W and Z Decays to Electrons in D0	387
D. Wood	W and Z Decays to Muons at D0	390
R. Markeloff	An Analysis of the CDF Monojet Data	393

A5a. Electroweak Properties of the Z

J. L. Harton	Review of Electroweak Properties of the Z Resonance from LEP	397
R. Jacobsen	Measuring the Mass of the Z Boson at LEP	405
B. Howell	Limits on Extra Z Bosons from e^+e^- Reactions Below the Z^0 Pole	408

A5b. Electroweak Results from Neutrino Experiments

R. Bernstein	Measurement of the Weak Mixing Angle in Neutrino-Nucleon Scattering by CCFR	411
G. Rädel	Neutrino-Electron Scattering with Charm II Recent Results	415
R. Brock	A Measurement of $\sin^2\theta_W$ from Deep Inelastic ν_μ-Nucleon Scattering in a Fine-Grained Detector at the Tevatron	421

B. Top and Higgs Physics

B1. Top Search: Theory

M. Mangano	Associated Production of W and Bottom Quark Pairs in Hadronic Collisions	427
L. H. Orr	Top Width Effects in Soft Gluon Radiation	432

P. Jain	Infrared Corrections to the Top Quark Width	436
J. H. Kuhn	Toponium Production at Hadron Colliders	439
G. Pancheri	Toponium Production at Hadron Colliders	443
G. W. Hou	Large Flavor Changing Neutral Couplings of the Top Quark	446

B2. Top and Higgs Search: Experiment

J. Incandela	The UA2 Search for $H^{\pm}$ from t-Quark Decay	450
B. Klima	Top Quark Search in D0 from the Lepton + Jets Mode	453
R. Partridge	Search for the Top Quark in Dilepton Events with D0	456
N. M. Shaw	Search for the Top Quark at CDF	459
L. Song	Top Search in the High P_T Dilepton Channel at CDF	464
B. Zhou	Search for the SM Higgs at LEP with the L3 Detector	467
A. Sopczak	Search for Non-Minimal Higgs Bosons in Z^0 Decays with the L3 Detector at LEP	470

B3. Top and Higgs Physics: Theory

E. Ma	Hints within the Standard Model on the Top-Quark and Higgs-Boson Masses	474
D. E. Kahana	Top and Higgs Masses in a Composite Boson Model	477
K. Riesselmann	Two-Loop Unitarity Constraints on the Higgs Boson Mass	481
J. M. Johnson	W, Z and Higgs Scattering at SSC Energies	484
S. Dawson	QCD Corrections to Higgs Boson Production	487
R. M. Barnett	Top Quark and Charged Higgs Measurements at the SSC	491
J. L. Hewett	Constraints on the Charged Higgs Sector from B Physics	496

C. Bottom, Charm and Strange Physics

C1. Quarkonia

U. Heintz	Spectroscopy from the $\Upsilon(3S)$ State	501
Q. Wu	Study of $\pi\pi$ Transitions from the $\Upsilon(3S)$ State	504
J. E. Fast	Precision Measurements of Charmonium States Formed in Proton-Antiproton Annihilations	507
A. K. Grant	Quarkonium and Power Law Potentials	511
N. Brambilla	Retardation Corrections to the Quarkonium Spectrum	515
P. Jain	$q\bar{q}$ Bound States in the Bethe-Salpeter Formalism	518

| L. P. Fulcher | A Comparison of Salpeter's and Schrödinger's Equations in Heavy-Light Systems | 521 |
| C. L. Olson | QCD Structure of Quarkonium Spin Spectra | 524 |

C2. Bottom Physics I

K. Edwards	Two Studies of $\bar{B}^0 \to D^{*+}\ell\bar{\nu}$	527
S. Ball	Hadronic B Meson Decays Testing Factorization and HQET	533
B. Blok	Nonperturbative QCD Effects in Weak Nonleptonic Decays	537
Y. Shen	Calculating the Isgur-Wise Function on the Lattice	541
R. Stephens	A Study of Exclusive Decays of B Mesons to D_s Mesons and Pions	545
R. Mir	Measurements of b-Flavoured Baryons and Strange b-Flavoured Mesons Produced in Z^0 Decays at LEP	548

C3. Bottom Physics II

Y. Gao	Evidence for Λ_b Baryon in Z Decays	553
F. Weber	Evidence for the B_s Meson and Measurement of the B_s and Λ_b Lifetimes	558
D. Vilanova	Production of B_s^0 and Λ_b Production in Z^0 Hadronic Decays	563
G. Maehlum	Lifetimes of Charged and Neutral B Hadrons Produced in Z^0 Decays	567
F. Weber	A Measurement of the B^0 and B^+ Meson Lifetimes	571
L. Taylor	Measurement of the Average B Hadron Lifetime Using the L3 Detector at LEP	576
J. Duboscq	A Precise Measurement of the Average B Hadron Lifetime with the OPAL Detector at LEP	579
L. Di Ciaccio	Inclusive Measurement of the Average B-Hadron Lifetime with the DELPHI Detector	583
I. C. Brock	Measurement of the b Semileptonic Branching Ratio and $\Gamma_{b\bar{b}}$ with L3	587
L. Bellantoni	Measurement of the Semileptonic Branching Ratios $Br(b \to \ell\nu X)$ and $Br(c \to \ell\nu X)$ and B-$\bar{B}$ Mixing	590

C4. Semileptonic Decays

D. Potter	A Study of the Semimuonic Decays of the D_s^+	594
A. Bean	Measurement of $B(D^+ \to \pi^0 l^+\nu)/B(D^+ \to \bar{K}^0 \ell^+\nu)$	597
R. Culbertson	Four Body Semileptonic Charm Decays	600

W. E. Johns	Recent Results on the Semileptonic Decay $D^0 \to K^-\mu^+\nu_\mu$	604
J. F. Amundson	Semileptonic Decays of D Mesons and the Heavy Quark Effective Theory	607
I. Bigi	A QCD 'Manifesto' on Inclusive Decays of Beauty & Charm	610
F. Muheim	Confirmation of Charmless Semileptonic Decays of B Mesons	614
J. Richman	Search for Exclusive $b \to u$ Semileptonic Decays of B Mesons	618

C5. Strange Physics I

R. P. Johnson	Ξ and Ω Production in Z Decays	621
D. M. Woods	Preliminary Results from Fermilab E-800 on the Polarization of Ξ^-'s and Ω^-'s Produced by Polarized and Unpolarized Neutral Beams	624
G. M. Guglielmo	Preliminary Results from Fermilab E-800 on the Decay Asymmetry of the Ξ^- Hyperon	627
N. B. Wallace	Preliminary Results from Fermilab E-800 on the Magnetic Moment of Ω^- Produced by a Neutral Beam	630
Y. T. Gao	Preliminary Results from Fermilab E-800 on a Search for Charged Dibaryons	633
V. J. Smith	Polarization of Σ^+ and Anti (Σ^+) Produced by 800 GeV/c Protons	636
T. Dubbs	Measurement of the Branching Ratio for $\Xi^- \to \Sigma^-\gamma$	639
A. Morelos	Magnetic Moment Measurements of Σ^+ and $\bar\Sigma^-$	642
S. Timm	Preliminary Measurement of Branching Ratio in the Radiative Decay of the Σ^+ Hyperon	645

C6. Bottom Physics III

D. Perticone	Measurements of $B^0\bar{B}^0$ Mixing and the Lifetime Ratio $\tau(B^+)/\tau(B^0)$ with the CLEO II Detector	648
J. F. Kral	Measurement of $B^0\bar{B}^0$ Mixing in OPAL Hadronic Z Decays	651
T. Han	Electromagnetic Mass Differences for Heavy-Light Mesons	655
J. L. Rosner	Heavy Meson Masses and Decay Constants	658
M. Avila	Covariant Description of Hydrogen-Like Mesons	662
J. L. Rosner	Test for Right-Handed b Quark Decays	666
G. W. Hou	In Case the b Quark Decays Right-Handedly	669

C7. Charm Physics

R. A. Sidwell	E791 Status Report	672
S. Shukla	Recent Results on L=1 Charmed Mesons	675
D. Puseljic	Lifetime Determination for $D_s^\pm$ Mesons	678
M. V. Purohit	A Dalitz Plot Analysis of $D \to K\pi\pi$ Decays Using E691 Data	681
P. Baringer	Recent Results on Charmed Mesons from CLEO II	684
G. Kim	Branching Ratios for $D_s^\pm$ and $D^\pm$ Decays to $\pi^\pm\pi^+\pi^-$	688
C. Dallapiccola	Recent Results on Charmed Baryons	691
B. Nemati	Recent Charmed Baryon Results from CLEO	694

C8. Heavy Quark Production I

E. P. Hartouni	Preliminary Results from FNAL E690	698
W. Selove	Di-Muon and Single-Muon Events from a Beauty Experiment	701
M. H. Schub	First Results from Fermilab Experiment 789	704
P. A. Pomianowski	Double Semi-Leptonic Charm Decay in HELIOS-I 450 GeV/c p-Be Data	708
S. W. Delchamps	Production of States with Hidden Charm in 300 GeV/c π^+, π^-, p, and $\bar{p}$ Collisions with Nuclei	711
N. R. Stanton	Heavy Quark Production Results from Fermilab E653: Beauty Pairs, and Limits on Diffractive Charm	715
G. Alves	Atomic Mass Dependence of $D^\pm$ and D^0, $\bar{D}^0$ Production in 250 GeV $\pi^\pm$-Nucleon Interactions	718
S. F. Takach	Feynman-x and Transverse Momentum Dependence of $D^\pm$, $D^0/\bar{D}^0$, and $D^{*\pm}$ Production in 250 GeV π-N Interactions	721
C. Darling	A Study of Beauty and Charm Production in 250 GeV π^+-nucleon Interactions Using Semi-electronic Decays	725
T. J. Weiler	Measuring Charm and Bottom Quark Masses	728

C9. Strange Physics II

M. Kalelkar	Neutral Strange-Particle Production in Neutrino-Neon Charged-Current Interactions at the Fermilab Tevatron	731
D. Aston	Evidence for Two $J^P = 2^-$ Strange Meson States in the $K_2(1770)$ Region Decaying $K^-\omega$	734
A. Bazarko	Measurement of the Strange Sea Content of the Nucleon by CCFR	738

G. Pancheri	Vector Meson and Chiral Loop Contributions to the Decays $V^0 \to P^0 P^0 \gamma$	741
P. J. Franzini	Solving the f_0 Puzzle at DAΦNE	744
S. Dell'Agnello	SVX b Physics Prospects	747
K. A. Bazizi	Inclusive Single Muons at D0	750
S. Igarashi	Dimuon Production in D0	753

C10. Heavy Quark Production II

H. Mendez	Hadronic Production of χ_c Mesons	756
L. Dauwe	Hadronic Production of B Mesons	759
R. Gardner	Studies of Fully Reconstructed $D\bar{D}$ Events in High Energy Photoproduction	762
T. Fuess	Inclusive $J/\psi, \psi(2S)$ and b-Quark Production in $\bar{p}p$ Collisions at $\sqrt{s} = 1.8$ TeV	765
C. Boswell	Inclusive χ_c Production in $\bar{p}p$ Collisions at $\sqrt{s} = 1.8$ TeV	768
B. T. Huffman	The Bottom Quark Cross Section in $P-\bar{P}$ Collisions from Inclusive Decays to Muons	771
Y. Chang	Production of J/ψ in Z^0 Decays	774
E. Sather	The Rate for $e^+e^- \to BB^\pm \pi^\mp$ and Its Implication for the Study of CP Violation	778

D. Rare Decays, CP and T Violation

D1. CP-Violation and Rare K Decay

V. A. Kostelecky	Stringy CPT Violation and the $K\bar{K}$ System	783
D. Zimmerman	Preliminary Results from the Analysis of K^0 and $\bar{K}^0$ Semileptonic Decays from the CPLEAR Collaboration	786
L. K. Gibbons	New Measurements of Re(ε'/ε) and Other $K \to \pi\pi$ Decay Parameters	791
E. J. Ramberg	Measurement of the Properties of the Decay $K_{L,S} \to \pi^+\pi^-\gamma$	795
G. D. Makoff	Study of the Decay $K_L \to \pi^\pm \pi^0 e^\mp \nu(\bar{\nu})$	799
A. Deshpande	Determination of Branching Ratio of the Decay $\pi^0 \to e^+e^-$ *	802
K. S. McFarland	A New Measurement of the Branching Ratio of $\pi^0 \to e^+e^-$	805
P. Gu	A Measurement of the Branching Ratio of $K_L \to e^+e^-e^+e^-$	809

R. Tschirhart	Measurement of the $K_L \to \mu^+\mu^-\gamma$ Branching Fraction, and Search for $K_L \to \pi^0\mu^+\mu^-$ Decay	813

D2a. K and η Decay

A. Schwartz	Measurement of $BR(K_L \to \mu^+\mu^-)$: Overall Results from BNL E791	816
J. Lee-Franzini	Physics at DAΦNE	821
B. Nefkens	Rare η Decays	824

D2b. Atomic Parity Violation, Electron Dipole Moments, and Strong CP-violation

J. Sapirstein	Atomic Physics Calculations of Weak Interaction Effects	827
R. Sachs	The Origin of Strong CP Violation	831
D. Chang	Recent Progress in CP Violating Gluonic Operators and Neutron Electric Dipole Moment	834
M. J. Booth	Dimension Eight Operators, CP Violation and the Neutron Electric Dipole Moment	837

D3. Rare Z and B Decays, Top and CP

K. Osterberg	A Search for Lepton Flavour Violation in Z^0 Decays	840
D. Cinabro	Search for Leptonic B Decays and $\tau^- \to \mu^-\gamma$ at CLEO	843
S. M. Playfer	Rare Hadronic Decays of B Mesons	848
J. M. Soares	Radiative Decays of the B-Mesons: CP Violation and Constraints on $|V_{td}|$	852
N. Uraltsev	FSI Phases and CP Asymmetries in Beauty: QCD Point of View	855
J. F. Gunion	Using Gluon Fusion to Probe CP Violation in the Higgs Sector	858
J. Liu	Final-State Interactions in the Top-Quark Semileptonic Decay	861
D. Atwood	CP Violating Effective Gluon-Top Quark Couplings	864
D. Hochberg	CP-Mixed Toponia States	867
C. Im	Could Large CP Violation Be Detected at Colliders?	870

AUTHOR INDEX

Volume 2

E. QCD and Hadron Physics

E1a. QCD near the Z^0 Mass

M. Dhina	Measurement of the Strong Coupling Constant with the L3 Detector at LEP	875
J. A. Lauber	A Study of Jet Rates and Measurement of α_s at the Z^0 Resonance	881
T. Junk	A Test of the Flavor Independence of α_s at the Z^0 Resonance	884
Y. Li	A Determination of α_s from e^+e^- Collisions at Tristan Energies	887
B. A. Schumm	Heavy Quark Event Multiplicities in e^+e^- Annihilation	890

E1b. Jets in e^+e^-

M. Hahn	QCD at DELPHI	893
C. Fan	Measurements of Gluon Spin-Sensitive Quantities at the Z^0 Resonance	898
Z. Bern	The Five Gluon Amplitude and One-Loop Integrals	901

E2a. e^+e^- and Related Cross Sections

L. R. Surguladze	$O(\alpha_s^3)$ Analytical Perturbative Calculations of $\sigma_{tot}(e^+e^- \to hadrons)$ and $\Gamma(\tau^- \to \nu_\tau + hadrons)$	906
A. C. Mattingly	Applying Optimized Perturbation Theory to QCD at Low Energies	909
S. Sanghera	A Test of Optimized Perturbative QCD to $O(\alpha_s^2)$ and $O(\alpha_s^3)$ from Z^0 Decays and a Method to Deal with the Renormalization Scale Ambiguity	912
H. J. Lu	QCD without Scale-Scheme Ambiguity	917

E2b. Structure Functions and Deep Inelastic Scattering

S. Fuess	Structure Functions from Neutrino/Nucleon Scattering in a Fine Grained Detector at the Tevatron	920
W. G. Seligman	Quantum Chromodynamics Fits to Neutrino-Iron Singlet and Non-Singlet Structure Functions	923
D. Lincoln	On Determining x_{Bj} from Jet Measurements	926

J. J. Ryan	A-Dependence of Fragmentation in Deep Inelastic Scattering	929
M. Baker	Azimuthal Asymmetry and Transverse Momentum in Deep Inelastic Muon Scattering	932
W. Sakumoto	Neutrino Production of Same-Sign Dimuons at the Fermilab Tevatron	935

E3a. Low-x, Gluon Distributions and Nuclear Scattering

E. Levin	Anomalous Dimension of Twist Four Gluonic Operator	938
R. D. Kennedy	Measurement of the Ratio of the Neutron and Proton Cross Sections to Very Low X_{Bj} Using Inelastic Muon Scattering	942
Q. Zhu	A Study of Photon-Nucleus Collisions at High Transverse Energy	945
D. Naples	A-Dependence and $K_{t\phi}$ of Photoproduced Jets	948
M. Luo	Cronin Effect in Photoproduction and Deeply Inelastic Scattering	951
R. Meng	The Gluon Density	954

E3b. Direct Photon Production

J. Qiu	Direct Photon Production	957
O. Rind	Isolated Hard Photon Emission in Hadronic Z Decays	961
J. M. Dunlea	Large P_T Production of Direct Photons and π^0 Mesons at 500 GeV/c	965
D. S. Brown	A Study of π^0 + jet and γ + jet Events Produced in 500 GeV Hadron-Nucleon Collisions	968
G. R. Snow	Direct Photon Production from D0	971
R. M. Harris	Isolated Double Prompt Photon Production at CDF	975
P. Maas	Isolated Prompt Photon Production at CDF	978

E4a. Hadronic Hard Scattering Cross Sections

F. I. Olness	A Unified QCD Fromulation of Charged Current and Neutral Current Heavy Quark Production in Deep Inelastic Scattering	981
S. Riemersma	Charm Production at HERA	984
E. Laenen	Resummation for Drell-Yan Differential Distributions	987
V. Del Duca	Jet Inclusive Cross Sections	990
R. V. Astur	Inclusive Jet Cross Sections at the D0 Detector	993
G. C. Blazey	Two Jet Energy and Rapidity Distributions	996

E4b. Final States in Hadronic Interactions

S. Behrends	Scaling Behavior of Jet Production at CDF	999
L. Keeble	A Study of Four-Jet Events and Search for Double Parton Interactions at $\sqrt{s} = 1.8$ TeV	1002
G. A. Smith	Neutral Light Quark Spectroscopy in Antiproton-Proton Annihilation at $\sqrt{s} \simeq 3000$ MeV	1005
R. Veenhof	Low Mass Lepton Pair Production in 450 GeV p-Be Collisions	1008
R. Raja	Confirmation of a Scaling Law for Particle Fragmentation	1012

E5a. Transverse Momentum Distributions and Resummation

D. D. Weerasundara	Production of Jets Recoiling From Large $P_T \pi^0$ Mesons and Direct Photons in 500 GeV/c Hadron-Nucleon Collisions	1016
J. M. Conrad	Jet Production in Deep Inelastic Muon Scattering	1020
R. Kauffman	W and Z p_T	1023
S. Willenbrock	QCD Correction to Vector-Boson Scattering	1026
C. Yuan	Kinematics of the Higgs Boson at Hadron Colliders: Gluon Resummation	1029

E5b. Spin in Inclusive and Exclusive Scattering

J. Collins	Spin in Perturbative QCD; Coherent Hard Diffraction	1032
X. Ji	Probing the Nucleon's Transversity Distribution in High-Energy Scattering Processes	1036
M. A. Doncheski	Double Photon Production in Polarized Proton-Proton Collisions	1039
H. F. Contopanagos	The Asymptotic S Matrix and Its Physical Consequences in QCD	1042
J. Ralston	High Energy Hadronic Helicity Violation: What Helicity Flip Form Factors Measure	1045

E6a. Elastic Scattering and Decays

H. Worden	Study of $\pi\pi$ Transitions from $\Upsilon(3S)$	1048
B. Ong	Two-Photon Production of $p\bar{p}$ and χ_{c2} Final States	1053
H. Li	Sudakov Effects in Elastic Form Factors	1057
A. S. Kronfeld	QCD Results for Nucleon Compton Scattering	1060
G. T. Bodwin	Rigorous QCD Predictions for Decays of P-Wave Quarkonia	1063

E6b. Vacuum Structure and Nonperturbative Effects

E. Shuryak	Correlation Functions in the QCD Vacuum and Instantons	1067
V. Elias	Full Contributions of Dimension -3 and -4 QCD-Vacuum Condensates to Current-Current Correlation Functions and Feynman Amplitudes	1071
A. B. Wakely	Pseudoscalar Glueball Wave Functions From QCD Sum Rules and Two-Photon Production of Glueballs	1074
I. Balitsky	Instanton-Induced Effects in QCD Cross Sections	1077
K. Kang	Color-Sextet Quark Condensation in QCD	1082
G. M. Prosperi	Flux Tube Model and Quark-Antiquark Potential	1086

F. QCD and Particle Production Monte Carlos

F1. QCD and Particle Production Monte Carlos

J. Benlloch	Comparisons of W+Jets CDF Data and M.E. M.C.'s Interfaced with Fragmentation Models	1091
J. Yu	Production of Jets in Association with W Vector Bosons in the D0 Dectector	1094
T. Rodrigo	Jet Multiplicity in $W \to \ell\nu$ At $\sqrt{s} = 1.8$ TeV $p\bar{p}$ Collisions	1097
W. Wittek	Bose-Einstein Correlations in Muon-Nucleon Interactions	1101
J. Schwiening	$K_s^0 K_s^0$ Bose-Einstein Correlations in e^+e^- Annihilations	1104
O. Tchikilev	Measurement of Inclusive Production of Light Meson Resonances and Multiplicity Fluctuations in Hadronic Final States from the Decay of the Z^0	1107
T. Sjostrand	The Pythia and Jetset Programs	1111
P. Leblanc	Studies of Soft Gluon Coherence in Hadronic Decays of the Z^0	1114
E. Meschi	Color Coherence in Multijet Events at CDF	1117
N. Wainer	Quark and Gluon Jets at CDF	1120

G. Heavy Ions

G1a. Hard Probes

S. Gupta	Gluon Shadowing in Charmonium/Bottomium Production and J/ψ Suppression in Nuclear Collisions	1125
M. B. Gay-Ducati	Small-x Behavior in DIS, Lepton Pair and Heavy Flavor Production in Nuclear Targets	1135
S. R. Klein	An Experimental Test of the LPM Effect: Bremsstrahlung Suppression at High Energies	1138
T. Fields	Nuclear Rescattering Effects in $pA \rightarrow$ Dihadrons	1141

G1b. Soft Photons

E. Shuryak	Two-Stage Equilibration in High Energy Heavy Ion Collisions	1144
P. Jain	Interpretation of the Color Transparency Experiments	1148
E. Shuryak	Photon Production Through A_1 Resonance in High Energy Heavy Ion Collisions	1152
C. Loomis	Soft Photon Production from Proton-Antiproton Collisions at $\sqrt{s} = 1.8$ TeV	1155

G2a. Correlations

J. Pan	Fluctuations and Scaling in High Energy Hadronic and Nuclear Collisions	1158
E. Hartouni	A High Statistics Study of Like-Sign Pion Pair Correlations	1161
T. Alexopoulos	A Study of Source Size in $\bar{p}p$ Collisions at $\sqrt{s} = 1.8$ TeV Using Pion Interferometry	1164
L. Wiencke	Observation of Coulomb Effects in Production of $\pi^+\pi^-$, $p\pi^-$ pK^-, and K^+K^- Pairs in pp Collisions at 27.5 GeV/c	1167

G2b. New and Future Experimental Results

M. Gonin	Baryon Spectra in Au+Au Collisions: Preliminary Results from E-866	1170
M. Cherney	Enhanced Strangeness Production at Mid-Rapidity	1177
T. Hallman	The Solenoidal Tracker at RHIC (STAR)	1179

H. Non-Standard Model Physics

H1. Theory: Supersymmetry

J. Hewett	Signals for Virtual Leptoquark Exchange at Colliders	1185
H. Baer	Experimental Consequences of Supersymmetry at the Tevatron Collider	1188
C. Kao	Searching for the Higgs Bosons of Minimal Supersymmetry	1191
M. A. Diaz	The Radiatively Corrected Charged Higgs Sector of the Minimal Supersymmetric Model	1194
P. Nath	SUSY-Mass Spectrum in SU(5) Supergravity Grand Unification — Summary and Results	1197
D. Kennedy	Spontaneously Broken Technicolor	1200
S. Nandi	Collider Implications of Singlet Fermions	1203
V. Elias	On-Mass-Shell Renormalization of the $(\bar{t}t)$ Contribution to the $\Delta I = 1/2$ s $\leftrightarrow$ d Self-Energy Transition	1206
M. Worah	Model of the Quark Mixing Matrix	1209

H2. Experiment: Heavy Neutrals and Supersymmetry

Y. Yuan	Detecting Long-Lived Heavy Leptons	1212
A. Weber	The L3 Collaboration Search for Neutralinos	1215
E. Gallas	A Search for Massive Neutral Particles in the Fermilab Wide Band Neutrino Beam	1218
A. Lopez-Fernandez	Search for Sleptons and Neutralinos Using the Delphi Detector	1221
C. Y. Chang	Search for Massive Unstable $\bar{\gamma}$'s that Violate R Parity	1225
M. Paterno	A Search for Squarks and Gluinos in $p\bar{p}$ Collisions at $\sqrt{s} = 1.8$ TeV with the D0 Detector	1228

H3. Theory: New Guage Bosons, Anomalous Couplings and Heavy Fermions

J. F. Gunion	Searching for the Minimal Supersymmetric Model Higgs Bosons	1231
M. B. Einhorn	Beyond the Standard Model with Effective Lagrangians	1234
G. Valencia	Vector Boson Versus Gluon Fusion at the SSC Using Effective Lagrangians	1237
E. Nardi	New Flavor Changing Interactions in Extended Gauge Models	1240
M. M. Nojiri	The Neutralino Relic Density in Minimal N = 1 Supergravity	1244

I. G. Knowles	Heavy Fermion Mass Predictions and Renormalization Group Equations	1247
D. Chang	$\mu \to e\gamma$ and Flavor Changing Couplings of Neutral Higgs Bosons	1250
H. Lew	Quark-Lepton Symmetry	1253
G. Jungman	Fermion Masses in SO(10)	1256
P. H. Frampton	On the Properties of Dileptons	1259

H4. Experiment: Technicolor, Supersymmetry, Z^0/Photon

T. Papadopoulou	Limits on the Production of Scalar Leptoquarks from Z^0 Decays at LEP I	1262
K. W. Merritt	A Search for Scalar Leptoquarks in D0	1265
S. Moulding	New Limits on Generation-1 Leptoquarks	1268
G. Crosetti	Neutral Higgs Boson Search in a Two Doublet Model	1271
R. Keranen	Search for a Light Stop	1275
T. Coan	Hard Photon Production as a Probe of Non-Standard Model Physics	1278
F. Barao	Search for New Phenomena with Photon Channels from Z^0 Decays	1281
C. Spartiotis	Final State Photon Physics through the Reaction $e^+e^- \to \gamma\gamma(\gamma)$	1286

I. Non-Accelerator Physics

I1. Neutrino Oscillations

F. Boehm	Reactor Based Neutrino-Oscillation Experiments	1291
R. I. Steinberg	Perry — A Reactor Neutrino Oscillation Experiment Sensitive to $\Delta m^2 = 10^{-4}$ eV^2	1296
M. Goodman	Interactions of Atmospheric ν_μ and ν_e Observed in Soudan 2	1300
J. Engel	Neutrino Interactions with Oxygen and the Atmospheric Neutrino Problem	1303
G. McGrath	Search for Neutrino Oscillations in IMB	1306
T. Stanev	Atmospheric Neutrinos	1308
K. S. Babu	Unified Description of Solar and Atmospheric Neutrino Oscillations	1311
K. S. Babu	Predictive Neutrino Spectrum in Minimal SO(10) Grand Unification	1314
J. Pantaleone	Gravitationally Induced Mixing of Solar and Terrestrial Neutrinos	1317
J. Pantaleone	Solar Neutrinos with Three-Flavor Mixings	1320

| D. G. Michael | Searching for Oscillations of Atmospheric and Accelerator Neutrinos | 1323 |
| P. Langacker | Implications of Solar and Atmospheric Neutrinos | 1326 |

I2. Proton Decay, Double Beta Decay and 17 KeV Neutrino

W. A. Mann	Anomalously Low Atmospheric ν_μ/ν_e Ratio as Manifestation of $p \to e^+\nu\nu$	1330
C. McGrew	Recent Limits on Baryon Non-Conservation from the IMB-3 Experiment	1334
P. Halverson	Can the IMB-3 Atmospheric Muon Neutrino Deficit be Interpreted as Evidence for Proton Decay?	1337
S. Rudaz	Remarks on a Possible Leptonic Decay Mode of the Proton	1339
P. Haridas	Status of the LVD Experiment at Gran Sasso Laboratory	1342
O. Piccioni	The Einstein Podolsky Rosen Paradox (EPR) as a Particle Physics Subject, Without Bell Inequalities	1346
A. Hime	Do Scattering Effects Resolve the 17-keV Conundrum?	1349
D. O. Caldwell	Status of the 17-keV Neutrino	1353
J. M. Cline	A New Paradigm for Majorons and Neutrinoless Double Beta Decay	1358

I3. Cosmic Ray Physics

S. Biller	Daily Search for UHE Radiation From Point-Sources with the Cygnus Array	1361
S. Klein	MILAGRO: A Low Threshold Water Cerenkov Air Shower Array	1364
K. D. Green	A Search for 100 TeV Gamma Rays from Cygnus X-3 and the Crab with CASA-MIA	1367
T. A. McKay	An All Sky Survey for Sources of 100 TeV Gamma Radiation by the UMC Collaboration	1370
N. P. Longley	Ultra High Energy Cosmic Ray Composition from EAS/Underground Muon Studies at Soudan 2	1373
E. Kearns	Search for Slow Ionizing Penetrating Particles with the MACRO Detector	1376
R. Cormack	Widely Separated Muons in the Macro Detector	1379
H. Dai	Cosmic Ray Composition Around 10^{18} eV	1382
D. J. Bird	The HiRes Fly's Eye (HiRes) Prototype Detector	1385
J. Boyer	Limits on the Expected Rate of Cosmic Ray Neutrinos at the HiRes Fly's Eye	1388

| F. Halzen | Observation of TeV Photons from Markarian 421: Implications for Neutrino Astronomy | 1394 |

J. Particle Astrophysics

J1. Cosmological Phase Transitions, Inflation, Dark Matter

P. Huet	Aspects of the Electroweak Phase Transition	1401
A. Cohen	Baryons from Electroweak Physics	1405
M. Kamionkowski	Evolution of Electroweak Bubbles	1409
J. J. Levin	The Era of Modified Aging: A Possible New Resolution of the Horizon Problem	1412
A. Kosowsky	Gravitational Radiation from Strongly First-Order Cosmological Phase Transitions	1415
K. Cahill	Inflation Pressures	1418
J. Z. Simon	The Case Against R^2 Inflation	1421
C. Stubbs	Looking for Dark Matter: WIMPs or MACHOs or ...	1424
K. Van Bibber	A Large Scale Dark-Matter Axion Search	1428
M. T. Ressell	Nuclear Shell Model Calculations of the Spin-Dependent Neutralino-Nucleus Cross Section	1432
P. Gondolo	Indirect Detection of Heavy Unstable Dark Matter	1435

J2. Microwave Background, Gamma Rays, Solar and Supernova Neutrinos

M. Schubnell	First Detection of TeV Gamma Rays from the AGN Markarian 421	1439
R. L. Hahn	The GALLEX Solar Neutrino Experiment	1442
J. S. Nico	Recent Results from the Soviet-American Gallium Experiment	1446
E. B. Norman	The Sudbury Neutrino Observatory	1450
M. Grassi	Search for Supernova Neutrinos with the MACRO Detector	1453
A. H. Jaffe	Limits on Neutrino Radiative Decay from SN1987A	1456

K. Lattice Gauge Theory

K1. Lattice Gauge Theory I

L. Lin	Study of Yukawa Models with Mirror Fermions	1461
R. Renken	Three-Dimensional Quantum Gravity Coupled to Matter	1464
M. Golterman	The Quenched Approximation in Health and in Sickness	1467

K. Cahill	A High-Statistics Simulation of SU(2) Gauge Theory	1468
K. Liu	Sea-Quark Contribution in Nucleon	1471
K. Rajagopal	Static and Dynamic Critical Phenomena in a Second Order QCD Phase Transition	1474
R. D. Mawhinney	QCD Thermodynamics Closer to the Continuum	1478
J. Kiskis	SU(2) Flux at T_c	1481
R. Narayanan	Running Coupling in Pure Gauge Theories Using the Schrödinger Functional	1484

K2. Lattice Gauge Theory II

D. Weingarten	Valence Approximation Hadron Masses	1487
S. Kim	Quenched Hadron Spectrum of QCD	1491
T. Draper	Hadronic Multipole Moments from Lattice QCD	1494
V. Singh	Monopole Currents and Confinement in U(1) and SU(2) Lattice Gauge Theory	1497
S. Gottlieb	The QCD Teraflops Project	1500
P. B. Mackenzie	A New Action for Heavy Lattice Fermions	1503
U. Hansmann	Multicanonical and Multimagnetical Simulations	1507
W. Bürger	Fermionic Vacuum in Compact Lattice QED	1510
S. Siegemund-Broka	Finite Element Quantum Electrodynamics	1513

L. Formal Theory

L1. Mathematical Methods in Field Theory

K. Cahill	A Really Effective Potential	1519
S. Boettcher	The δ Expansion in Quantum Field Theory	1522
A. Gangopadhyaya	Application of Supersymmetry to Double Well Problems	1525
L. Di Leo	Bound and Resonant Relativistic Two-Particle States and Bound Three-Particle States in Scalar Quantum Field Theory	1528
J. P. Crawford	Local Automorphism Invariance: Massive Gauge Bosons sans Higgs	1531
J. S. R. Chisholm	Top Mass Via Spin Gauge Theory	1534
T. J. Allen	Charged Vortex Dynamics in a Ginzburg-Landau Theory of a 2+1 Dimensional Charged Scalar Field	1537
P. Jain	Consistent Quantum Expansion Around Soliton Solutions	1540
P. N. Swamy	Gauge Technique and BCS Theory of Superconductivity	1543

| H. Zhang | Global Constraints of Gauss's Law and the Solution to the Strong CP Problem | 1546 |

L2. Dynamical Aspects of Field Theories and Strings

C. M. Bender	Dimensional Expansions	1549
B. Haeri	The Cutoff Dependence of the Higgs Mass	1552
G. Bathas	Nonperturbative Effects in Chiral Yukawa Models	1555
T. R. Taylor	Low-Energy Effective Action of Superstring Theory	1558
Y. Meurice	Polyakov's Conjecture in the Light of the Hierarchical Approximation	1562
S. Rey	Protecting Invisible Axion from Planck Scale Physics	1565

L3. Quantum Black Holes and Topological Field Theory

R. Gregory	Dilatonic Black Holes	1568
J. D. Lykken	Stringy Black Holes Via Coset Current Algebra	1572
S. P. De Alwis	Quantum Aspects of Black Holes in Two Dimensions	1576
K. A. Milton	Maxwell-Chern-Simons Casimir Effect	1580
K. Haller	Gauge Theories in 2 + 1 Dimensions	1583
M. K. Falbo-Kenkel	The Exact Two Particle Scattering Amplitude in the 2+1 Dimensional Chern-Simons Gauge Theory of Gravity	1586
W. R. Lundberg	Topological Combinatorics of a Quantized String Gravitational Metric	1589

M. Accelerator Techniques

M1. e^+e^- High Luminosity Storage Rings and Linear Colliders

| D. Rice | CESR Performance and Upgrade | 1595 |
| H. Hindi | PEP-II: RF and Feedback R&D | 1599 |

M2. Hadron Accelerators and Storage Rings

C. A. Wilkinson	Monte Carlo Based Formula for Estimating Penetration of Radiation Shielding at Forward Angles	1603
S. Frankle	A Comparison of Analytic Models for Estimating Dose Equivalent Rates in Shielding with Beam Spill Measurements	1605
H. Park	Measurement of the Circulating Muon Flux in the Fermilab Debuncher Ring	1607
W. Gabella	Discrete Modulations of the RF as a Tool for Controlling Proton Diffusion	1610

C. T. Murphy	Extraction from the Tevatron using Channeling with a Bent Crystal	1615
C. Mishra	The Fermilab Main Injector	1619
S. Tepikian	Polarized Protons in Large Center of Mass Collisions	1622
T. Dombeck	Power Tests of a String of 50-mm Aperture Dipole Magnets at the Superconducting Super Collider Laboratory	1625
M. J. Syphers	SSC Design Update	1629

N. Detector Development

N1a. Triggering and Scintillating Fibers

A. M. Halling	Test of a Multiplicity Jump Trigger in the E791 Spectrometer	1635
W. Luebke	Test of Principle of an Optical Trigger for Beauty	1638
J. T. Linnemann	Triggering the D0 Experiment	1641
R. C. Chaney	Central Tracking with Scintillating Fibers in the SDC Experiment	1644
R. A. Lewis	Results of Tests of Scintillating Fibers with Visible Light Photon Counters	1647

N1b. Scintillating Fibers and Particle Identification

M. Wayne	A Scintillating Fiber Detector for the D0 Upgrade	1650
T. Henkes	Particle Identification with the Forward RICH Detector of DELPHI	1653
D. Aston	First Results from the SLD Barrel CRID	1657
L. Stutte	A Phototube RICH Detector	1661
J. Y. Oyang	Tests of Silica Aerogel as a Low-Mass Particle Identification System for the SLAC B Factory Detector	1664

N2. Calorimetry I

M. E. King	Test of a Longitudinally Segmented CsI Array for a Tau-Charm Factory Detector	1669
M. Torres	Experimental Results on Low Energy Neutron Leakage in Hadronic Showers from FNAL T-821	1672
R. W. Springer	The OPAL Silicon Tungsten Luminometer	1675
M. Narain	Electron Identification in the D0 Detector	1678
P. C. Bhat	Low Energy Response of the D0 Calorimeter and Jet Energy Measurement	1681
L. Fortney	Measurement of Localized Efficiency Loss in a Silicon Microstrip Detector Operated at High Intensity	1684

| N. Akchurin | Beam Test Results From Copper/Scintillating Fiber and Lead/Quartz Fiber Calorimeter Prototypes | 1687 |
| M. Gui | A Study of Glass-Liquid Scintillating Fibers for the Forward Calorimetry of SDC | 1690 |

N3a. Calorimetry II

H. Takai	Precision Timing with Liquid Ionization Calorimeters	1693
H. Ma	Test of an Accordion Liquid Krypton Electromagnetic Calorimeter	1696
A. Bhatti	Beam Test Results of the Preshower and Shower Maximum Detectors for the SDC	1699
P. De Barbaro	Beam Tests of Reconfigurable-Stack Calorimeter	1702

N3b. General Detector Developement

P. Avery	Distributed HEP Computing Using Netqueues	1705
J. McDonough	The Design of the Beamplug for a New $K_L \to \mu e$ Experiment	1708
P. Haridas	Behavior of Large Resistive Plate Counters	1711
J. J. Thaler	Data Acquisition Design for the SDC	1715
G. Eigen	New Studies of CsI Readout and Radiation Hardness for the SLAC B Factory Detector	1719

N4. Silicon

P. P. Allport	Double-Sided Foxfet Biassed Silicon Microstrip Detectors	1724
S. Mani	Design of an Integrated Silicon Pixel Detector	1728
A. P. Heinson	The D0 Upgrade Silicon Tracker	1731
D. Kaplan	Position Resolution and Charge Correlation Tracking Tests of Double-Sided Silicon Microstrip Arrays	1734
P. Franzini	KLOE, A General Purpose Detector for DAΦNE	1737
J. Wear	Real Life Experience with the ALEPH Silicon Vertex Detector	1740
O. Schneider	Performance of the CDF Silicon Vertex Detector	1743
M. Clemen	Beam Tests of a High Resolution Silicon Vertex Detector System with VLSI Readout	1746
W. J. Murray	The DELPHI Microvertex Detector	1749
N. Cartiglia	A Test Station for Silicon Microstrip Detectors and Associated Electronic	1752

N5. Tracking

H. Tajima	A Silicon Vertex Detector for CLEO-II	1755
M. G. Strauss	Performance of a Silicon Pixel Vertex Detector in the SLD	1758
R. Miller	Design and Performance of a Pressurized Drift Tube Chamber for the Gem Muon System	1761
R. Kass	Performance of Diamond Radiation Detectors	1765
T. Zhao	Drift Tube and Chamber Module Design for the SDC Central Muon Tracking System	1769
O. K. Baker	Resistive Kapton Straw Tube Drift Chamber Prototype	1772
D. C. Christian	High Rate Drift Chambers	1775
R. Malchow	Operation of Straw-Tube Detectors using DME	1778
H. Trost	Recent Developments on Microstrip Chambers at Texas A&M	1782
H. Ogren	The Straw Outer Tracker for SDC at the Superconducting Super Collider	1785

LIST OF PARTICIPANTS

AUTHOR INDEX

DPF92 CONFERENCE SCHEDULE

	Monday 11/9/92	Tuesday 11/10/92 Fermilab	Wednesday 11/11/92 Pheasant Run	Thursday 11/12/92 Pheasant Run	Friday 11/13/92 Pheasant Run	Saturday 11/14/92 Fermilab
Morning		Plenary Session	Parallel Session	Parallel Session	Parallel Session	Plenary Session
Afternoon	Registration at Fermilab	Plenary Session	Parallel Session	Parallel Session	Parallel Session	Plenary Session
Evening	Registration at Pheasant Run Hotel	Reception + Town Meeting	Buffet + Concert at Fermilab	Education Night at Fermilab	Banquet at Art Institute of Chicago	

Sessions in Parallel at Pheasant Run

Room Seating	GH1 250	GH2 160	GH3 160	GH4 160	GH5 160	GH6 60	NO 400	P1 160	P2 160
Wed AM	C1	B1	C2	H1	E1	G1	N1	K1	M1
PM	A1	B2	C3	H2	E2	G2	J1	K2	M2
Thurs AM	A2	B3	C4	H3	E3		J2	L1	N2
PM	A3	C5	C6	D1	E4		I1	H4	N3
Fri AM	A4	C7	C8	D2	E5		I2	L2	N4
PM	A5	C9	C10	D3	E6	F	I3	L3	N5

Room Code	Pheasant Run Location
GH1	Gallery Hall: Rembrandt
GH2	Gallery Hall: Utrillo
GH3	Gallery Hall: Vermeer
GH4	Gallery Hall: Gauguin
GH5	Gallery Hall: Renoir
GH6	Gallery Hall: Corot
NO	New Orleans Ballroom
P1	Presidents' Rooms: Washington & Lincoln
P2	Presidents' Rooms: Jefferson & Eisenhower

DPF92 PLENARY SESSION PROGRAM

- Tuesday, November 10, 09:00 - 12:30   Fermilab Auditorium

    Chairperson: Rajendran Raja
    Scientific Secretary : Patrick T. Lukens

09:00   John Peoples, FNAL, *Conference Welcome*
09:10   Avi Yagil, FNAL, *Highlights from CDF*
09:50   Ronald J. Madaras, LBL, *Highlights from D0*
10:30   Break
11:00   Frank J. Sciulli, Columbia U., *Highlights from HERA*
11:45   Samuel C. C. Ting, MIT, *Highlights from LEP*
12:30   End of Session

- Tuesday, November 10, 14:00 - 17:50   Fermilab Auditorium

    Chairperson: John Peoples
    Scientific Secretary : Meena Narain

14:00   Charles Baltay, Yale U., *First Results from SLD*
14:25   Daniel Sinclair, U. of Michigan, *HEP-Astrophysics Connection*
15:10   John F. Wilkerson, LANL, *Results from Non-accelerator Experiments*
15:50   Break

    Chairperson: Bjorn Wiik, DESY
    Scientific Secretary : Meena Narain

16:20   Maury Tigner, Cornell U., *Accelerator Developments*
17:05   Murdock G. D. Gilchriese, LBL, *Detector Developments*
17:50   End of Session

- **Saturday, November 14, 09:00 - 12:20**　　　　　Fermilab Auditorium

    Chairperson: Carl H. Albright, Northern Illinois U.

    Scientific Secretary : Darien Wood

09:00 R. Keith Ellis, FNAL, *Status of QCD*
09:45 William J. Marciano, BNL, *Status of Electroweak Measurements*
10:30 Break

    Chairperson: Peter Kasper

    Scientific Secretary : Darien Wood

11:00 John P. Cumalat, U. of Colorado, *Charm Physics*
11:40 David G. Cassel, Cornell U., *Bottom Physics*
12:20 End of Session

- **Saturday, November 14, 14:00 - 16:35**　　　　　Fermilab Auditorium

    Chairperson: John Yoh

    Scientific Secretary : Young-Kee Kim

14:00 Walter H. Toki, SLAC, *Tau Decays*
14:35 Stephen R. Sharpe, U. of Washington, *Lattice Gauge Theory*
15:10 David J. Gross, Princeton U., *Other Theoretical Developments*
15:50 Leon M. Lederman, IIT, *Visionary Talk*
16:35 End of Session

DPF92 PARALLEL SESSION PROGRAM
(Wednesday - Friday, November 11 - 13   Pheasant Run)

A. Electroweak including τ and W/Z Physics
Conveners: M. H. SHAEVITZ (Columbia U.) and J. L. ROSNER (U. of Chicago)
Liaison: R. RAJA (FNAL)

A1. τ Physics
Wednesday, November 11, 14:00 - 17:50   Gallery Hall (Rembrandt Room)
Chairperson: R. STROYNOWSKI (Southern Methodist U.)

14:00 R. KOWALEWSKI, CERN (OPAL), τ *Results from OPAL.* (407, 478)
14:25 M. SCHMITT, U. of Wisconsin (ALEPH), τ *Polarization in ALEPH.* (447)
14:45 J. CONWAY, U. of Wisconsin (ALEPH), *A Neural Network Approach to Charged Particle Identification in Low-Multiplicity Events in ALEPH.* (280)
15:00 M. WALSH, U. of Wisconsin (ALEPH), τ *Branching Ratios in ALEPH.* (558)
15:15 P. FISHER, Johns Hopkins U. (L3), τ *Polarization and Leptonic Branching Ratios in Z^0 Decays.* (131, 134)

15:40 Break

16:00 R. McNULTY, U. of Liverpool (DELPHI), τ *Multiplicity and Lifetime in DELPHI.* (141, 142)
16:25 G. CRAWFORD, Ohio State U. (CLEO), τ *Decays at CLEO.* (263, 265-267, 575)
17:00 S. HENDERSON, Harvard U. (CLEO), τ *and ν_τ Masses.* (264, 268)
17:25 L. JONES, Caltech (BES), τ *Mass Measurement at BES.* (568)

17:50 End of Session

A2. Asymmetries; Electroweak Tests Using b's and c's
Thursday, November 12, 09:00 - 12:20   Gallery Hall (Rembrandt Room)
Chairperson: M. SHAEVITZ (Columbia U.)

09:00 L. MIRABITO, Lyon (DELPHI), *Forward-Backward Asymmetry of $e^+e^- \to Z^0 \to b\bar{b}$ Using Prompt Leptons.* (161, 174)
09:25 D. WRIGHT, Princeton U. (L3), *Z Decays into $b\bar{b}$ and $c\bar{c}$* (125, 137)
09:50 D. HINSHAW, U. de Montreal (OPAL), *Measurement of $\Gamma(Z \to b\bar{b})$.* (589,590,591)
10:10 P. WELLS, CERN (OPAL), *Measurement of the Forward-Backward Asymmetry of quarks.* (570,588,594)

10:30 Break

10:50 L. BELLANTONI, U. of Wisconsin (ALEPH), *A Study of $\Gamma(b\bar{b})/\Gamma(had)$ and $\Gamma(c\bar{c})/\Gamma(had)$ and the Forward-Backward Asymmetry in Z^0.* (224)
11:05 J. NASH, Imperial College (ALEPH), *Lepton Forward-Backward Asymmetry Measurements and Electroweak Predictions from ALEPH data.* (485)
11:20 D. SU, Rutherford Lab. (SLD), *Measurement of the Branching Fraction for $Z^0 \to b\bar{b}$.* (581)
11:50 B. SCHUMM, LBL (SLD), *The SLD Measurement of the Left-Right Polarization Asymmetry (A_{LR}) with Polarized Beams at SLAC.* (610)

12:20 End of Session

A3a. **Mini-reviews on Electroweak Theory**
Thursday, November 12, 14:00 - 15:10   Gallery Hall (Rembrandt Room)
Chairperson: C. QUIGG (FNAL)

14:00 J. L. ROSNER, U. of Chicago, *Electroweak Measurements and the Top Quark.* (28)
14:35 J. BAGGER, Johns Hopkins U., *Electroweak Symmetry Breaking at SSC and LHC.* (312)
15:10 Break

A3b. **Gauge Boson Couplings - Theory**
Thursday, November 12, 16:00 - 17:40   Gallery Hall (Rembrandt Room)
Chairperson: C. QUIGG (FNAL)

16:00 U. BAUR, Florida State U., *Probing the Weak Boson Sector in $Z\gamma$ Production at Hadron Colliders.* (31)
16:25 M. DONCHESKI, U. of Wisconsin, *Probing the $WW\gamma$ Vertex in $e^{\pm}p \to \nu\gamma X$.* (221)
16:50 K. PETERSON, Carleton, *Constraints on Anomalous $WW\gamma$ Couplings from $e-\gamma$ Collisions.* (345)
17:15 D. ZEPPENFELD, U. of Wisconsin, *One-Loop Constraints on the Electroweak Triple Gauge Boson Vertex.* (579)

17:40 End of Session

A4a. **Multi-particle final states and searches at LEP**
Friday, November 13, 08:30 - 09:45   Gallery Hall (Rembrandt Room)
Chairperson: R. RAJA (FNAL)

08:30 B. WYSLOUCH, MIT (L3), $Z^0 \to \ell\ell + \gamma(\gamma)$ *and Four Fermions.* (117,132)
08:55 J. MARCO, Santander (DELPHI), $Z^0 \to$ *Leptons in DELPHI.* (140, 145, 146)
09:20 A. WHITE, ANL, *The η_6 and Massive Photon Pairs at LEP.* (664)

09:45 Break

A4b. **Electroweak Results from Hadron Colliders**
Friday, November 13, 10:00 - 11:00   Gallery Hall (Rembrandt Room)
Chairperson: R. RAJA (FNAL)

10:00 N. GRAF, BNL (D0), *W and Z Decays to Electrons in D0.* (389)
10:20 D. WOOD, FNAL (D0), *W and Z Decays to Muons at D0.* (566)
10:35 R. MARKELOFF, U. of Wisconsin (CDF), *Analysis of the CDF Monojet Data.* (515)

11:00 End of Session

A5a. Electroweak Properties of the Z
Friday, November 13, 13:00 - 14:35   Gallery Hall (Rembrandt Room)
Chairperson: J. ROSNER (U. of Chicago)

13:00   J. HARTON, U. of Wisconsin (ALEPH), *Review of Electroweak Properties of the Z^0 at LEP.* (393, 139, 597)

13:45   R. JACOBSEN, CERN, *Measuring the Mass of the Z Boson at LEP.* (181)

14:10   B. HOWELL, Purdue U. (TOPAZ), *Limits on Extra Z' Bosons from $e^+e^- \to \mu^+\mu^-$ and $e^+e^- \to \tau^+\tau^-$ Reactions.* (534)

14:35   Break

A5b. Electroweak Results from Neutrino Experiments
Friday, November 13, 15:00 - 16:30   Gallery Hall (Rembrandt Room)
Chairperson: J. ROSNER (U. of Chicago)

15:00   R. BERNSTEIN, FNAL (CCFRW), *Measurement of the Weak Mixing Angle in Neutrino-Nucleon Scattering by CCFRW.* (222)

15:30   G. RÄDEL, DESY (CHARM II), *Neutrino-Electron Scattering with Charm II: Recent Results.* (442)

16:00   R. BROCK, Michigan State U. (FMMF), *A Measurement of $\sin^2\theta_W$ from Deep Inelastic ν_μ-Nucleon Scattering in a Fine-Grained Detector at the Tevatron.* (580)

16:30   End of Session

B. Top and Higgs Physics
Conveners: R. M. BARNETT (LBL) and S. D. PROTOPOPESCU (BNL)
Liaison: A. B. WICKLUND (ANL)

B1. Top Search: Theory
Wednesday, November 11, 09:00 - 12:00   Gallery Hall (Utrillo Room)
Chairperson: R. M. BARNETT (LBL)

09:00   M. MANGANO, INFN, Pisa, *Associated Production of W and Bottom Pairs in Hadronic Collisions.* (204)

09:30   W. T. GIELE, FNAL, *Top Search in Multijet Signals.* (78)

09:50   L. H. ORR, U. of California, Davis, *Top Width Effects in Soft Gluon Radiation.* (367)

10:20   P. JAIN, U. of Kansas, *Low Momentum Corrections to the Top Quark Width.* (83)

10:30   Break

10:50   J. H. KUHN, U. Karlsruhe, *Toponium Production at Hadron Colliders.* (359)

11:10   G. PANCHERI, INFN, Frascati, *Toponium Detection at Hadron Colliders.* (10)

11:30   G. W. HOU, Taiwan U., *Large Flavor Changing Neutral Current Couplings of the Top Quark.* (193)

12:00   End of Session

B2. Top and Higgs Search: Experiment
Wednesday, November 11, 14:00 - 17:20
Chairperson: S. D. PROTOPOPESCU (BNL)   Gallery Hall (Utrillo Room)

14:00 J. INCANDELA, FNAL, *The UA2 Search for Charged Higgs from Top Quark Decay.* (650)
14:20 B. KLIMA, FNAL, *Top Search in D0 from the Lepton + Jets Mode.* (404)
14:40 R. PARTRIDGE, Brown U., *Search for the Top Quark in Dilepton Events with D0.* (437)
15:00 N. M. SHAW, Purdue U., *Search for the Top Quark at CDF.* (503)

15:25 Break

15:45 L. F. SONG, FNAL, *Top Search in the High P_t Dilepton Channel at CDF.* (572)
16:00 B. ZHOU, Boston U. (L3), *Search for the Neutral Higgs Boson at LEP.* (123)
16:20 A. SOPCZAK, U. of California, San Diego (L3), *Searches for Nonminimal Higgs Bosons in Z^0 Decays.* (133)
16:40 E. ROSENBERG, Iowa State U., Ames (DELPHI) *Search for Heavy Charged Higgs in Z^0 Hadronic Decays.* (150)
17:00 H. NGUYEN, FNAL (OPAL), *Search for Neutral Higgs Bosons in two Doublet Models.* (476,471)

17:20 End of Session

B3. Top and Higgs Physics: Theory
Thursday, November 12, 09:00 - 12:20
Chairperson: R. M. BARNETT (LBL)   Gallery Hall (Utrillo Room)

09:00 S. RABY, Ohio State U., *A Predictive Ansatz for Fermion Masses.* (672)
09:30 E. MA, U. of California, Riverside, *Hints within the Standard Model on Top and Higgs Masses.* (112)
09:50 D. E. KAHANA, Kent State U., *Top and Higgs Masses from Dynamical Symmetry Breaking.* (18)
10:00 K. RIESSELMANN, U. of Wisconsin, *Two Loop Unitarity Constraints on the Higgs Mass.* (101)
10:10 J. M. JOHNSON, Wayne State U., *One Loop Corrections to W, Z, and Higgs Scattering at SSC Energies.* (73)

10:30 Break

10:50 S. DAWSON, BNL, *QCD Corrections to Higgs Production.* (198)
11:20 R. M. BARNETT, LBL, *Top Quark and Charged Higgs Measurements at the SSC.* (691)
11:50 J. L. HEWETT, ANL, *B-Physics Constrains the Charged Higgs Sector.* (350)

12:20 End of Session

C. Bottom, Charm and Strange Physics
Conveners: R. J. MORRISON (U. of California, Santa Barbara) and B. GRINSTEIN (SSCL)
Liaison: P. KASPER (FNAL)

C1. Quarkonia
Wednesday, November 11, 09:00 - 12:20 Gallery Hall (Rembrandt Room)
Chairperson: P. RAPIDIS (FNAL)

09:00 U. HEINTZ, FNAL (CUSB), *Spectroscopy from the $\Upsilon(3S)$ State.* (540)
09:20 Q. WU, Columbia U. (CUSB), *Study of $\pi\pi$ Transitions from the $\Upsilon(3S)$ State.* (188)
09:35 J. E. FAST, U. of California, Irvine (E760), *Precision Measurements of Charmonium States Formed in $\bar{p}p$ Annihilations.* (349)
10:00 A. K. GRANT, U. of Chicago, *An Updated Description of Quarkonium Spectra by Power-law Potentials.* (25,27)

10:30 Break

11:00 N. BRAMBILLA, U. di Milano, *Retardation Correction to the Quarkonium Spectrum.* (70)
11:20 P. JAIN, U. of Kansas, *Relativistic Calculation of the Light and Heavy Meson Properties.* (84)
11:40 L. P. FULCHER, Bowling Green State U., *A Comparison of Salpeter's and Schrodinger's Equations in Heavy-Light Systems.* (333)
12:00 C. L. OLSON, U. of Wisconsin, *QCD Structure of Quarkonium Spin Spectra.* (366)

12:20 End of Session

C2. Bottom Physics I
Wednesday, November 11, 09:00 - 12:25 Gallery Hall (Vermeer Room)
Chairperson: R. J. MORRISON (U. of California, Santa Barbara)

09:00 V. SHARMA, U. of Wisconsin (ALEPH), *A Review of b Physics at LEP.* (723)
09:30 K. EDWARDS, Carleton U. (ARGUS), *Two Studies of Exclusive Semileptonic Decays of B Mesons.* (653,654,655,656,657)
09:55 S. BALL, U. of Kansas (CLEO), *Measurement of Hadronic B-meson Decays and Tests of Factorization.* (246,248,253)

10:20 Break

11:00 B. BLOK, U. of California, Santa Barbara, *Nonperturbative QCD Effects in Weak Hadronic Decays.* (37)
11:20 Y. SHEN, Boston U., *Calculating the Isgur-Wise Function on the Lattice.* (582)
11:40 R. STEPHENS, U. of Florida (CLEO), *A Study of Exclusive Decays of B Mesons to D_s Mesons and Pions.* (252)
12:00 R. MIR, CERN (OPAL), *Measurements of b-flavored Baryons and Strange b-flavored Mesons Produced in Z^0 Decays at LEP.* (50)

12:25 End of Session

C3. Bottom Physics II
Wednesday, November 11, 14:00 - 17:45   Gallery Hall (Vermeer Room)
Chairperson: P. KASPER (FNAL)

14:00 Y. S. GAO, U. of Wisconsin (ALEPH), *Evidence for Λ_b Baryon in Z Decays.* (385)
14:25 F. WEBER, U. of Wisconsin (ALEPH), *Evidence for the B_s Meson and Measurement of the B_s and Λ_b Lifetimes.* (562)
14:50 D. VILANOVA, DAPNIA, Saclay (DELPHI), *Evidence for B_s^0 Meson Production in Z^0 Decays.* (169,168,170)
15:15 G. MAELHUM, Oslo U. (DELPHI), *Measurement of B Meson Production and Lifetime Using $D\ell^-$ Events in Z^0 Decays.* (167,171)

15:35 Break

16:00 F. WEBER, U. of Wisconsin (ALEPH), *A Measurement of the B^0 and B^+ Meson Lifetimes.* (384)
16:25 L. TAYLOR, Northeastern U. (L3), *Measurement of the Average B-Hadron Lifetime in Z^0 Decays.* (116)
16:40 J. DUBOSCQ, CERN (OPAL), *A Precise Measurement of the Average B Hadron Lifetime with the OPAL Detector at LEP.* (468)
16:55 L. DICIACCIO, U. di Roma II (DELPHI), *Inclusive Measurement of the Average Lifetime of B-Hadrons Produced at the Z Peak.* (166,163)
17:15 I. BROCK, Carnegie-Mellon U. (L3), *Measurement of the Semileptonic Branching Ratios of b-Hadrons.* (119,126)
17:30 L. BELLANTONI, U. of Wisconsin (ALEPH), *Measurement of the Semileptonic Branching Ratios $Br(b \to X\ell\nu)$ and $Br(c \to X\ell\nu)$ and $B^0 - \bar{B}^0$ Mixing.* (223)

17:45 End of Session

C4. Semileptonic Decays
Thursday, November 12, 09:00 - 12:20   Gallery Hall (Vermeer Room)
Chairperson: R. J. MORRISON (U. of California, Santa Barbara)

09:00 D. POTTER, Carnegie-Mellon U. (E653), *Semimuonic Decay Modes of the D_s^+ Meson.* (179)
09:20 A. BEAN, U. of California, Santa Barbara (CLEO), *Study of Cabibbo-Suppressed Semileptonic D^+ decays.* (693)
09:35 R. CULBERTSON, U. of Illinois, Urbana (E687), *Four Body Semileptonic Charm Decays.* (281)
10:00 W. E. JOHNS, U. of Colorado (E687), *Recent Results on the Semileptonic Decay $D^0 \to K^-\mu^+\nu_\mu(+c.c.)$.* (398)

10:20 Break

11:00 J. F. AMUNDSON, U. of Chicago, *Heavy Quark Symmetry Violation in Semileptonic Decays to D Mesons.* (26)
11:20 I. BIGI, U. of Notre Dame, *Nonperturbative Corrections to Nonleptonic and Semileptonic Beauty Decays.* (680)
11:40 F. MUHEIM, Syracuse U. (CLEO), *Observation of $b \to u$ Transitions.* (247)
12:00 J. RICHMAN, U. of California, Santa Barbara (CLEO), *Search for Exclusive $b \to u$ Semileptonic Decays of B Mesons.* (251)

12:20 End of Session

C5. Strange Physics I
Thursday, November 12, 14:00 - 16:55   Gallery Hall (Utrillo Room)
Chairperson: A. VOROBYOV (Leningrad NPI)

14:00 R. P. JOHNSON, U. of California (ALEPH), Ξ and Ω Production in Z Decays. (399)
14:10 M. DITTMAR, U. of California, Riverside (OPAL), A Measurement of Strange Baryon Production in Hadronic Z^0 Decays. (593)
14:25 M. N. KREISLER, U. of Massachusetts (BNL766), Precision Measurements of the Masses of the Λ, $\overline{\Lambda}$, Ξ^-, $\overline{\Xi}^+$, Ω^-, and $\overline{\Omega}^+$ Hyperons and Tests of CPT. (538)
14:45 D. M. WOODS, U. of Minnesota (E800), Preliminary Results from Fermilab E-800 on the Polarization of Ξ^-s Produced by Polarized and Unpolarized Neutral Beams. (567)
14:55 G. M. GUGLIELMO, FNAL (E800), Preliminary Results from Fermilab E-800 on the Decay Asymmetry of the Ξ^- Hyperon. (533)
15:10 N. B. WALLACE, U of Minnesota (E800), Preliminary Results from Fermilab E-800 on the Polarization and Magnetic Moment of Ω^-'s Produced by a Neutral Beam. (557)
15:25 Y. T. GAO, FNAL (E800), Search for Charged H Dibaryons Produced by 800 GeV Protons. (477)

15:35 Break

16:00 V. J. SMITH, FNAL (E761), Polarization of Σ^+ and Σ^- Hyperons Produced by 800 GeV Protons. (455)
16:10 T. DUBBS, FNAL (E761), Measurement of the Branching Ratio for $\Xi^- \to \Sigma^- \gamma$. (288)
16:25 A. MORELOS, FNAL (E761), Magnetic Moment Measurements of Σ^+ and Σ^-. (427)
16:40 S. TIMM, Carnegie Mellon U. (E761), Meaurement of Branching Ratio in the Radiative Decay of the Σ^+ Hyperon. (554)

16:55 End of Session

C6. Bottom Physics III
Thursday, November 12, 14:00 - 17:00   Gallery Hall (Vermeer Room)
Chairperson: B. GRINSTEIN (SSCL)

14:00 D. PERTICONE, U. of Minnesota (CLEO), Measurement of $B\bar{B}$ Mixing and the B-Semileptonic Branching Fraction. (254,250,249)
14:20 J. F. KRAL, CERN (OPAL), Measurements of the $B^0\bar{B}^0$ Mixing Parameter, the Z-Boson Branching Fraction into b Hadrons and the Semileptonic Branching Ratios of b Hadrons at LEP. (408)
14:35 T. HAN, FNAL, Electromagnetic Mass Differences for Heavy-Light Mesons. (348)
14:55 J. L. ROSNER, U. of Chicago, Meson Decay Constants from Isospin Mass Splittings in the Quark Model. (22,23)

15:25 Break

16:00 M. AVILA, U. Nacional Automan de Mexico, Covariant Description of Hydrogen-Like Mesons. (88)
16:20 J. L. ROSNER, U. of Chicago, Test of a Model of Right-handed b Quark Decays. (24)
16:40 G. W. S. HOU, National Taiwan U., In Case the b Quark Decays Right-Handedly. (200)

17:00 End of Session

C7. Charm Physics
Friday, November 13, 08:30 - 11:40   Gallery Hall (Utrillo Room)
Chairperson: J. RICHMAN (U. of California, Santa Barbara)

08:30   R. A. SIDWELL, Ohio State U. (E791), *Status of the E791 Charm Experiment.* (453)
08:40   S. SHUKLA, FNAL (E687), *Recent Results on L=1 Charmed Mesons.* (452)
09:00   D. PUŠELJIĆ, U. of Notre Dame (E687), *Lifetime Determination for $D_s^\pm$ Mesons.* (441)
09:15   M. V. PUROHIT, Princeton U. (E691), *A Dalitz Plot Analysis of $D \to K\pi\pi$ Decays from E691.* (440)
09:30   P. BARINGER, U. of Kansas (CLEO), *Study of rare D^0 and D_s Decays.* (257,258,256,255)

09:55   Break

10:30   G. N. KIM, U. of Notre Dame (E687), $D_s^\pm$ *and* $D^\pm$ *Decays to* $\pi^\pm\pi^+\pi^-$. (403,505)
10:55   C. DALLAPICCOLA, U. of Colorado (E687), *Recent Results on Charmed Baryons.* (282)
11:15   B. NEMATI, SUNY at Albany (CLEO), *Study of Rare Decays of Charmed Baryons.* (577,261,260,259,262)

11:40   End of Session

C8. Heavy Quark Production I
Friday, November 13, 08:30 - 11:55   Gallery Hall (Vermeer Room)
Chairperson: J. A. APPEL (FNAL)

08:30   E. P. HARTOUNI, U. of Massachusetts (E690), *Preliminary Results from FNAL E690.* (462)
08:40   W. SELOVE, U. of Pennsylvania (E771), *Di-Muon and Single-Muon Events from a Beauty Experiment.* (499)
08:50   M. H. SCHUB, U. of Chicago (E789), *First Results on Neutral D Meson Production from Fermilab Experiment E789.* (397,448,548)
09:05   P. A. POMIANOWSKI, U. of Pittsburgh (HELIOS), *Double Semi-Leptonic Charm Decay in Helios-I 450 GeV/c p-Be Data.* (439,712,713)
09:20   S. W. DELCHAMPS, FNAL (E705), *Production of States with Hidden Charm in 300 GeV/c π^+, π^- Proton, and Anti-Proton Collisions with Nuclei.* (285)
09:35   N. STANTON, Ohio State U. (E653), *Search for Coherent Charm Production in 800 GeV/c p-Si Interactions.* (187,544)

09:55   Break

10:30   G. ALVES, CBPF (E769), *A-Dependence of Charm Production in 250 GeV $\pi^\pm$-Nucleus Interactions.* (532)
10:50   S. F. TAKACH, Yale U. (E769), *Feynman-x and Transverse Momentum Dependence of $D^\pm$, $D^{*\pm}$ Production, and $D^0/\bar{D}^0$ Production in 250 GeV π^--Nucleon Interactions.* (185,183)
11:15   C. DARLING, Yale U. (E769), *Charm and Beauty Cross Sections at $\sqrt{S}$=21.7 GeV Measured Using Semi-electronic Decays.* (283)
11:35   T. J. WEILER, Vanderbilt U., *A Model for Experimental Extraction of the Charmed Quark Mass(es).* (339)

11:55   End of Session

C9. Strange Physics II
Friday, November 13, 13:00 - 15:30   Gallery Hall (Utrillo Room)
Chairperson: J. SPALDING (FNAL)

13:00 M. KALELKAR, Rutgers U. (E632), *Neutral Strange-Particle Production in Neutrino-Neon Charged-Current Interactions at the Fermilab Tevatron.* (400)

13:15 D. ASTON, Stanford Linear Accelerator Center (LASS), *Evidence for Two $J^P = 2^-$ Strange Meson States in the $K_2(1770)$ Region.* (231)

13:25 A. BAZARKO, Columbia U. (CCFRW), *Measurements of the Strange Sea Content of the Nucleon by CCFRW.* (158)

13:40 G. PANCHERI, INFN-Lab. Nazionali di Frascati, *Vector Mesons and Chiral Loop Contributions to the Decays $V^0 \to P^0 P^0 \gamma$.* (11)

14:00 P. J. FRANZINI, ENSLAPP, *Solving the f_0 Puzzle at DAPHNE.* (92)

14:20 S. DELL'AGNELLO, INFN and U. of Pisa (CDF), *SVX Physics Prospects.* (508)

14:35 Break

15:00 A. K. BAZIZI, U. of California, Riverside (D0), *Inclusive Single Muon Production with the D0 Detector.* (286)

15:15 S. IGARASHI, FNAL (D0), *Dimuon Production in D0.* (396)

15:30 End of Session

C10. Heavy Quark Production II
Friday, November 13, 13:00 - 16:05   Gallery Hall (Vermeer Room)
Chairperson: L. GLADNEY (Penn State U.)

13:00 H. MENDEZ, U. of Illinois, Chicago (E706), *Hadronic Production of χ_c Mesons.* (423)

13:15 L. DAUWE, U. of Michigan, Flint (E706), *Hadronic Production of J/ψ and B Mesons.* (284)

13:30 R. GARDNER, U. of Illinois, Urbana (E687), *Studies of Fully Reconstructed $D\bar{D}$ Events in High Energy Photoproduction.* (386)

13:50 S. VEJCIK, U. of Michigan (CDF), *A Measurement of the b-Quark Cross Section Using the Exclusive Decay $B^0 \to J/\Psi K^{0*}$ in $p\bar{p}$ Collisions at $\sqrt{s} = 1.8$ TeV.* (585)

14:10 T. FUESS, SSCL (CDF), *Inclusive $J/\psi, \psi(2S)$ and $b-$Quark Production in $\bar{p}p$ Collisions at $\sqrt{s} = 1.8$ TeV.* (537)

14:25 Break

14:55 C. BOSWELL, Johns Hopkins U. (CDF), *Inclusive χ_c Production in $\bar{p}p$ Collisions at $\sqrt{s} = 1.8$ TeV.* (578)

15:15 B. T. HUFFMAN, Purdue U. (CDF), *Inclusive Muon Cross Section on Pbar-P Collisions with CDF.* (494)

15:30 Y. H. CHANG, MIT (L3), *A Study of the Production of J Mesons from the Z^0.* (127)

15:45 E. SATHER, M.I.T., *An Estimate of $BR(\Upsilon \to B\bar{B}\pi^\pm)$.* (225)

16:05 End of Session

D. Rare Decays, CP and T Violation

Conveners: I. I. BIGI (U. of Notre Dame) and L. S. LITTENBERG (BNL)
Liaison: B. WINSTEIN (U. of Chicago)

D1. CP-Violation and Rare K Decay
Thursday, November 12, 14:00 - 17:40 Gallery Hall (Gauguin Room)
Chairperson: L. LITTENBERG (BNL)

14:00 V. A. KOSTELECKÝ, Indiana U., *Stringy CPT Violation and the $K\bar{K}$ System.* (97)
14:15 D. ZIMMERMAN, Boston U. (CPLEAR), *The CPLEAR Experiment.* (491)
14:35 L.K. GIBBONS, U. of Chicago (E731), *CP Violation in the 2π System at Fermilab.* (576,543)
15:00 E. J. RAMBERG, FNAL (E731), *Measurement of the Properties of the Decay $K_{L,S} \to \pi^+\pi^-\gamma$.* (443)
15:15 G. D. MAKOFF, U. of Chicago (E731), *Study of the Decay $K_L \to \pi^{\pm}\pi^0 e^{\mp}\nu(\bar{\nu})$.* (417)

15:30 Break

16:00 A. DESHPANDE, Yale U. (E851), *Determination of the Branching Ratio of the Decay $\pi^0 \to e^+e^-$.* (676)
16:25 K. S. MCFARLAND, U. of Chicago (E799), *A New Measurement of the Branching Ratio of $\pi^0 \to e^+e^-$.* (429)
16:55 P. GU, Rutgers U. (E799), *Measurement of the Branching Ratio for $K_L \to e^+e^-e^+e^-$.* (390)
17:10 R. TSCHIRHART, FNAL (E799), *Measurement of the $K_L \to \mu^+\mu^-\gamma$ Branching Ratio and a Search for $K_L \to \pi^0\mu^+\mu^-$ Decay.* (555,556)

17:40 End of Session

D2a. K and η Decay
Friday, November 13, 08:30 - 09:50 Gallery Hall (Gauguin Room)
Chairperson: B. WINSTEIN (U. of Chicago)

08:30 A. J. SCHWARTZ, Princeton (E791), *Measurement of $BR(K_L \to \mu^+\mu^-)$.* (450)
08:50 P. PADLEY, TRIUMF (E787), *Results from BNL E787.* (675,674)
09:10 J. LEE-FRANZINI, INFN, Frascati (DAPHNE), *Physics at DAPHNE.* (410)
09:30 B. M. K. NEFKENS, U. of California, Los Angeles, *Eta Physics.* (673)

09:50 Break

D2b. Atomic Parity Violation, Electric Dipole Moments, and Strong CP-violation
Friday, November 13, 10:10 - 12:30   Gallery Hall (Gauguin Room)
Chairperson: B. WINSTEIN (U. of Chicago)

10:10 J. SAPIRSTEIN, U. of Notre Dame, *Atomic Physics Calculations of Weak Interaction Effects.* (615)
10:40 R. G. SACHS, U. of Chicago, *The Origin of Strong CP Violation.* (203)
10:55 D. CHANG, Northwestern U., *Recent Developments in CP Violating Gluonic Operators Related to the Neutron Electric Dipole Moment.* (317)
11:15 M. J. BOOTH, U. of Chicago, *Dimension Eight Operators, CP Violation and the Neutron Electric Dipole Moment.* (314,315)

12:30 End of Session

D3. Rare Z and B Decays, Top and CP
Friday, November 13, 13:00 - 16:05   Gallery Hall (Gauguin Room)
Chairperson: I. I. BIGI (U. of Notre Dame)

13:00 K. OSTERBERG, Helsinki U. (DELPHI) *A Search for Lepton Flavour Violation in Z^0 Decays.* (147)
13:20 D. CINABRO, Harvard U. (CLEO) *Searches for $B^+ \to e^+\nu$, $\mu^+\nu$, and $\tau^+\nu$, and $\tau \to \mu\gamma$.* (242,244,245)
13:45 S. PLAYFER, Syracuse U. (CLEO) *Search for Charmless Hadronic and c-Penguin Decays of B Mesons.* (243)
14:10 A. SONI, BNL, *Calculation of $B \to K^*\gamma$ on the Lattice.* (379)
14:20 J. M. SOARES, Carnegie-Mellon U., *Radiative Decays of the B-Mesons: CP Violation and Constraints on $|V_{td}|$.* (55)

14:30 Break

14:45 N. URALTSEV, U. of Notre Dame, *FSI Phases and CP Asymmetries in Beauty: QCD Point of View.* (718)
15:00 J. F. GUNION, U. of California, Davis, *Probing CP Violation in the Higgs Sector.* (194)
15:10 J. LIU, U. of Pennsylvania *Final-State-Interaction Simulation of T-Violation in the Top-Quark Semileptonic Decay.* (209)
15:25 D. ATWOOD, SLAC, *CP Violating Effective Gluon-Top Quark Couplings.* (310)
15:40 D. HOCHBERG, Vanderbilt U., *CP-Mixed Toponia States.* (342)
15:50 C. IM, U. of Michigan, *Could Large CP Violation Be Detected at Colliders.* (353)

16:05 End of Session

E. QCD and Hadron Physics
Conveners: M. D. SHAPIRO (LBL) and G. STERMAN (SUNY at Stony Brook)
Liaisons: E. BERGER (ANL), W. GIELE (FNAL)

E1a. QCD Near the Z^0 Mass
Wednesday, November 11, 09:00 - 10:24   Gallery Hall (Renoir Room)
Chairperson: G. STERMAN (SUNY at Stony Brook)

09:00 M. DHINA, ETH, Zurich (L3), α_s at the Z^0 Resonance. (118, 129)
09:24 J. A. LAUBER, SLAC (SLD), Jet Rates and α_s at the Z_0 Resonance. (409)
09:42 T. JUNK, SLAC (SLD), Measurement of α_s in b quark events. (535)
10:00 Y. LI, U. of Rochester (AMY), α_s From Higher-Order QCD and TRISTAN Data. (413)
10:12 B. A. SCHUMM, LBL (MARK II), Charged Multiplicity of Events Containing Bottom Hadrons at $E_{cm}=91$ GeV. (449)

10:24 Break

E1b. Jets in e^+e^-
Wednesday, November 11, 10:40 - 12:35   Gallery Hall (Renoir Room)
Chairperson: M. D. SHAPIRO (LBL)

10:40 M. HAHN, U. Karlsruhe (DELPHI) α_s Measurements from Delphi. (151,152, 154, 138)
11:20 C. FAN, U. of Colorado (SLD), Measurments of Gluon Spin-Sensitive Quantities at the Z^0 Resonance. (341)
11:34 Z. BERN, U. of California, Los Angeles, The five-gluon Amplitude and One-loop Integrals. (313)
12:00 W. GIELE, FNAL, Higher-order Corrections for Jet and Lepton Production in Hadron Colliders. (79, 80)

12:35 End of Session

E2a. e^+e^- and Related Cross Sections (Continued)
Wednesday, November 11, 14:00 - 15:35   Gallery Hall (Renoir Room)
Chairperson: G. STERMAN (SUNY at Stony Brook)

14:00 E. BRAATEN, Northwestern U., Precise Determination of the Strong Coupling Constant from Tau Decays. (82)
14:22 L. R. SURGULADZE, U. of Oregon, $O(\alpha_s)$ Analytical Perturbative Calculations of $\sigma_{total}(e^+e^- \to hadrons)$ and $\Gamma(\tau^- \to \nu_\tau + hadrons)$ in QCD. (338)
14:44 A. C. MATTINGLY, Rice U., Applying Optimized Perturbation Theory to QCD at Low Energies. (16)
15:01 S. SANGHERA, Southern Methodist U., Optimized Perturbative QCD in Z^0 and Tau Decays. (229, 602)
15:18 H. J. LU, U. of Maryland, QCD Without Scale Ambiguity. (201)

15:35 Break

E2b. Structure Functions and Deeply Inelastic Scattering
Wednesday, November 11, 15:45 - 17:10 Gallery Hall (Renoir Room)
Chairperson: M. D. SHAPIRO (LBL)

15:45 S. FUESS, FNAL (FMMF), *Structure Functions from Neutrino/Nucleon Scattering in a Fine Grained Detector at Fermilab.* (357)
16:02 B. SELIGMAN, Columbia U. (CCFR), *Quantum Chromodynamics Fits to Neutrino-Iron Singlet and non-Singlet Struture Functions..* (451)
16:16 D. LINCOLN, FNAL (E683), *Measurement of the Photon Structure Function.* (411)
16:30 J. RYAN, MIT (E665), *A-Dependence of Fragmentation in Deep Inelastic Scattering.* (445)
16:44 M. BAKER, MIT (E665), *Azimuthal Asymmetry and Transverse Momentum in Deep Inelastic Muon Scattering.* (234)
16:58 W. SAKUMOTO, U. of Rochester (CCRF), *Neutrino Production of Same-Sign Dimuons.* (446)

17:10 End of Session

E3a. Low-x, Gluon Distributions and Nuclear Scattering
Thursday, November 12, 09:00 - 10:45 Gallery Hall (Renoir Room)
Chairperson: M. D. SHAPIRO (LBL)

09:00 E. M. LEVIN, FNAL and St. Petersburg Nuclear Physics Institute, *Anomalous Dimension of Twist Four Gluon Operator.* (604)
09:25 R. KENNEDY, FNAL (E665), *Measurement of the Ratio of the Neutron and Proton Differential Cross-Sections to very low x_{BJ}.* (275,402)
09:45 Q. ZHU, Rice U. (E683), *A Study of Photon-Nucleus Collisions at High Transverse Energy.* (525)
10:02 D. NAPLES, FNAL (E683), *A-Dependence of $k_\perp$ of Photoproduced Jets.* (432)
10:16 M. LUO, Iowa State U., *Nuclear Dependence at Large Transverse Momentum.* (363)
10:30 R. MENG, ANL, *Constraints on the Gluon Density from Bottom Quark and Prompt Photon Production.* (614)

10:45 Break

E3b. Direct Photon Production
Thursday, November 12, 11:00 - 12:50 Gallery Hall (Renoir Room)
Chairperson: M. D. SHAPIRO (LBL)

11:00 J. QIU, Iowa State U., *Hadronic Direct Photon Production.* (369)
11:25 O. RIND, U. of Michigan (L3), *Isolated Hard Photon Emission and π^0 and η Production in Z^0 Decays.* (135,136)
11:42 J. DUNLEA, FNAL (E706), *Large P_t Production of π^0 Mesons and Direct Photons at 500 GeV/c.* (289)
11:56 D. BROWN, FNAL (E706) *A Study of π^0 + jet and γ + Jet Events in 500 GeV Hadron Nucleon Collisions.* (273)
12:10 G. SNOW, U. of Michigan (D0), *Direct Photon Production from the D0 Experiment.* (456)
12:24 R. HARRIS, FNAL (CDF), *Isolated Double Prompt Photon Production at CDF.* (392)
12:36 P. MAAS, FNAL (CDF), *Recent Photon Results from CDF.* (510)

12:50 End of Session

E4a. Hadronic Hard Scattering Cross Sections
Thursday, November 12, 14:00 - 15:35 Gallery Hall (Renoir Room)
Chairperson: G. STERMAN (SUNY at Stony Brook)

14:00 F. OLNESS, SMU, *Unified QCD Analysis of Charged Current and Neutral Current Heavy Quark Production in Deeply Inelastic Scattering.* (213)
14:20 S. RIEMERSMA, SUNY at Stony Brook, *On the Heavy Quark Content of the Nucleon.* (373)
14:35 E. LAENEN, FNAL, *Factorization and Resummation of Large Corrections in Drell-Yan.* (361)
14:47 V. DEL DUCA, SLAC, *Jet Inclusive Cross Sections and Minijet Production.* (670)
15:04 R. ASTUR, FNAL (D0), *Inclusive Jet Cross Sections in D0.* (233)
15:21 G. BLAZEY, FNAL (D0), *Dijet Angular Distributions in the D0 Experiment.* (270)

15:35 Break

E4b. Final States in Hadronic Interactions
Thursday, November 12, 15:55 - 17:26 Gallery Hall (Renoir Room)
Chairperson: M. D. SHAPIRO (LBL)

15:55 S. BEHRENDS, Brandeis U. (CDF), *Scaling Behavior of Jet Production at CDF.* (463)
16:12 M. INCAGLI, INFN, Pisa (CDF), *Dijet Invarient Mass Spectrum at CDF.* (496)
16:26 L.J. KEEBLE, Texas A & M U. (CDF), *A Study of Four-Jet Events and Search for Double-Parton Interactions at CDF.* (502)
16:40 G. SMITH, Penn State U. (E760), *Neutral Light Quark Spectroscopy at $p\bar{p}$ annihilation at $\sqrt{s} = 3000$ MeV.* (454)
16:54 R. VEENHOF, CERN (Helios), *Low Mass Di-Lepton Production in 450 GeV pBe Collisions.* (712)
17:06 R. RAJA, FNAL, *Confirmation of a Scaling Law for Particle Fragmentation.* (182)

17:26 End of Session

E5a. Transverse Momentum Distributions and Resummation
Friday, November 13, 08:30 - 10:10 Gallery Hall (Renoir Room)
Chairperson: G. STERMAN (SUNY at Stony Brook)

08:30 D. WEERASUNDARA, FNAL (E706), *Production of Jets Recoiling From Large P_T π^0 Mesons and Direct Photons in 500 GeV Hadron-Nucleon Collisions.* (561)
08:44 J. CONRAD, FNAL (E665), *Measurement of the Q^2 dependence of α_s from Jet P_t in Deep-Inelastic Muon-Proton Scattering.* (279,421)
09:06 R. P. KAUFFMAN, BNL, *W and Z p_T.* (192)
09:28 S. WILLENBROCK, BNL, *QCD Correction to Vector-Boson Scattering.* (382)
09:50 C.-P. YUAN, Michigan State U., *Kinematics of the Higgs Boson at Hadron Colliders: NLO QCD Gluon Resummation.* (340)

10:10 Break

E5b. Spin in Inclusive and Exclusive Scattering
Friday, November 13, 10:25 - 12:05   Gallery Hall (Renoir Room)
Chairperson: G. STERMAN (SUNY at Stony Brook)

10:25   J. C. COLLINS, Penn State U., *Recent Developments in Polarized Hard Scattering in QCD.* (197,319)
10:55   X. JI, MIT, *Probing the Nucleon's Transversity Distribution.* (659)
11:15   M. A. DONCHESKI, U. of Wisconsin, *Double Photon Production in Polarized Proton-Proton Collisions.* (72)
11:30   H. P. CONTOPANAGOS, SUNY at Stony Brook, *The Asymptotic S Matrix and its Physical Consequences in QCD.* (320)
11:45   J. RALSTON, U. of Kansas, *High Energy Helicity Violation in Hard Exclusive Processes.* (370,371)

12:05   End of Session

E6a. Elastic Scattering and Decays
Friday, November 13, 13:00 - 14:45   Gallery Hall (Renoir Room)
Chairperson: M. D. SHAPIRO (LBL)

13:00   H. WORDEN, Cornell U. (CLEO) *Study of $\pi\pi$ Transitions from $\Upsilon(3S)$.* (240, 241)
13:22   B. ONG, U. of California, San Diego (CLEO), *Charmonium and $p\bar{p}$ Production from Two Photon Interactions.* (238,239)
13:44   H.-N. LI, Academia Sinica, Taipei, *Sudakov Effects in Elastic Form factors.* (662)
14:05   A. S. KRONFELD, FNAL, *Nucleon Compton Scattering in Perturbative QCD.* (603)
14:25   G. T. BODWIN, ANL, *Rigorous QCD Predictions for Decays of P-Wave Quarkonia.* (89)

14:45   Break

E6b. Vacuum Structure and Nonperturbative Effects
Friday, November 13, 15:00 - 16:42   Gallery Hall (Renoir Room)
Chairperson: G. STERMAN (SUNY at Stony Brook)

15:00   E. SHURYAK, SUNY at Stony Brook, *Correlation Functions in the QCD Vacuum.* (110, 111)
15:30   V. ELIAS, U. of Western Ontario, *Full Contributions of Dimension-3 and 4 QCD Vacuum Condensates to Current-current Correlation Functions.* (323)
15:42   A. B. WAKELY, Coll. of William and Mary, *Pseudoscalar Glueball Wave Functions from QCD Sum Rules.* (107)
15:52   I. BALITSKY, Penn State U., *Instanton Induced Effects in QCD Cross Sections.* (531)
16:07   K. KANG, Brown U., *Color-Sextet Quark Condensation in QCD.* (190)
16:22   G. M. PROSPERI, U. di Milano, *Flux-tube Model and Quark-Antiquark Potential.* (76)

16:42   End of Session

F. QCD and Particle Production Monte Carlos

Conveners: M. MANGANO (INFN, Pisa) and T. SJÖSTRAND (CERN)
Liaison: W.T. GIELE (FNAL)

Friday, November 13, 13:00 - 16:20   Gallery Hall (Corot Room)
Chairperson: T. SJÖSTRAND (CERN)

13:00 J. BENLLOCH, FNAL (CDF), *Results on Interfaced Matrix Elements (VECBOS) and Parton Shower (HERWIG) MC's for the Production of W + Jets*. (237)
13:15 J. YU, FNAL (D0), *Measurement of W boson + Jet Production with the D0 Detector*. (569)
13:30 T. RODRIGO, FNAL (CDF), *Jet Multiplicity in W → lν events*. (542)
13:45 W. WITTEK, MPI, Munich (E665), *Bose-Einstein Correlations in Muon-Nucleon Interactions*. (564)
14:00 J. SCHWIENING, U. Bonn (OPAL), $K_S^0 K_S^0$ *Bose-Einstein Correlations in Hadronic Z^0 Decays*. (596)
14:10 O. TCHIKILEV, Serpukhov (DELPHI), *Measurement of Inclusive Production of Light Meson Resonances and Multiplicity Fluctuations in Hadronic Final States from the Decay of the Z^0*. (157,159)

14:35 Break

Chairperson: M. MANGANO (INFN, Pisa)

15:00 T. SJÖSTRAND, CERN, *The Pythia and Jetset Programs*. (377)
15:15 Ph. LEBLANC, Montreal (OPAL), *Studies of Soft Gluon Coherence in e^+e^- Annihilation*. (592)
15:30 E. MESCHI, SNS, Pisa (CDF), *Color Coherence in Multi-Jet Events at CDF*. (519)
15:45 N. WAINER, FNAL (CDF), *Quark and Gluon Jets at CDF*. (516)
16:00 C. JUI, U. of California, Riverside (OPAL), *A study of Differences between Quark and Gluon Jets at LEP*. (474,595)

16:20 End of Session

G. Heavy Ions

Convener: H. SATZ (CERN and U. Bielefeld)
Liaison: C. HOJVAT (FNAL)

G1a. Hard Probes

Wednesday, November 11, 09:00 - 11:55   Gallery Hall (Corot Room)
Chairperson: H. SATZ (CERN and U. Bielefeld)

09:00 S. GUPTA, HLRZ/Jülich, *Gluon Shadowing in Charmonium/Bottomium Production and J/ψ Suppression in Nuclear Collisions*. (220)
09:35 M. B. GAY DUCATTI, U. of Wisconsin, *Small x Behavior in DIS, Lepton Pair and Heavy Flavor Production in Nuclear Targets*. (321)
09:55 S. R. KLEIN, U. of California, Santa Cruz, *An Experimental Test of the Landau-Pomeranchuk-Migdal Effect*. (406)
10:15 T. FIELDS, ANL, *Nuclear Rescattering Effects in Massive Dihadron Production*. (178)

10:35 Break

11:00 E. SHURYAK, SUNY at Stony Brook, *Two-stage Equilibration in High Energy Heavy Ion Collisions.* (103)

11:35 P. JAIN, U. of Kansas, *Correlated Independent Scattering Processes in Hadron-Nucleus Collisions, What Color Transparency Measures.* (93, 94)

G1b. Soft Photons
Wednesday, November 11, 11:55 - 12:35   Gallery Hall (Corot Room)
Chairperson: H. SATZ (CERN and U. Bielefeld)

11:55 E. SHURYAK, SUNY at Stony Brook, *Photon Production Through A1 Resonance in High Energy Heavy In Collisions.* (104)

12:15 C. LOOMIS, Jr., Duke U., *Soft Photon Production From Proton-Antiproton Collisions at $\sqrt{s} = 1.8\ TeV$.* (416)

12:35 End of Session

G2a. Correlations
Wednesday, November 11, 14:00 - 15:40   Gallery Hall (Corot Room)
Chairperson: C. HOJVAT (FNAL)

14:00 J. PAN, U. of Oregon, *Fluctuations and Scaling in High Energy Nuclear Collisions.* (100)

14:20 E. P. HARTOUNI, U. of Massachusetts, *A High Statistics Study of Like-sign Pion Pair Correlations.* (492)

14:40 O. TCHIKILEV, Serpukhov (DELPHI), *Bose-Einstein Correlations in the Hadronic Decays of the Z^0.* (155)

15:00 T. ALEXOPOULOS, U. of Wisconsin, *A Study of Source Size in $\bar{p}p$ Collisions at $\sqrt{s} = 1.8 TeV$ Using Pion Interferometry.* (176)

15:20 L. R. WIENCKE, Columbia U., *Observation of Coulomb Effects in Production of $\pi^+\pi^-$, $p\pi^-$ and K^+K^- Pairs in pp Collisions at 27.5 GeV/c.* (563)

15:40 Break

G2b. New and Future Experimental Results
Wednesday, November 11, 16:00 - 17:40   Gallery Hall (Corot Room)
Chairperson: C. HOJVAT (FNAL)

16:00 M. GONIN, BNL, *Au-Au Collisions at the AGS: First Results from E866.* (546)

16:35 M. CHERNEY, Creighton U. (NA36) *Enhanced Strangeness Production at Mid-Rapidity.* (276)

16:55 S. WHITE, Rockefeller U., *The PHENIX experiment at RHIC.* (710)

17:20 T. HALLMAN, U. of California, Los Angeles (STAR), *The Solenoidal Tracker at RHIC.* (730)

17:40 End of Session

H. Non-Standard Model Physics

Conveners: S. DAWSON (BNL) and A. P. WHITE (U. of Texas, Arlington)
Liaison: J. YOH (FNAL)

H1. Theory: Supersymmetry
Wednesday, November 11, 09:00 - 12:15   Gallery Hall (Gauguin Room)
Chairperson: A. WHITE (U. of Texas, Arlington)

09:00   J. HEWETT, ANL, *Signals for Virtual Leptoquark Exchange at Colliders.* (208)
09:20   H. BAER, Florida State U., *Experimental Consequences of Supersymmetry.* (327)
09:40   C. KAO, Florida State U., *Searching for the Higgs Bosons of Minimal Supersymmetry.* (354)
10:00   M. DIAZ, Vanderbilt U., *The Radiatively Corrected Charged Higgs Sector of the Minimal Supersymmetric Model.* (328)
10:15   P. NATH, Northeastern U., *SUSY Mass Spectrum in SU(5) Supergravity.* (6)

10:30   Break

11:00   D. KENNEDY, FNAL, *Large-N Dynamics of Techni-Vector Mesons and Electroweak Observables.* (351)
11:20   S. NANDI, Oklahoma State U., *Collider Implications of Singlet Fermions.* (211)
11:35   V. ELIAS, U. of Western Ontario, *On-shell Renormaliztion of the $t\bar{t}$ Contribution to the $\Delta I = 1/2$ s-d Self-Energy Transition.* (324)
11:55   M. WORAH, U. of Chicago, *Models of the Quark Mixing Matrix.* (29)

12:15   End of Session

H2. Experiment: Heavy Neutrals and Supersymmetry
Wednesday, November 11, 14:00 - 17:20   Gallery Hall (Gauguin Room)
Chairperson: S. DAWSON (BNL)

14:00   Y. YUAN, Coll. of William and Mary, *Detecting Long-lived Heavy Leptons.* (212)
14:20   A. WEBER, Aachen (L3), *Search for Neutralinos at LEP.* (750)
14:40   F. MERRITT, U. of Chicago (OPAL), *Search for Neutral Heavy Leptons in OPAL.* (481)
15:00   E. GALLAS, Michigan State U. (E733), *A Search for Massive Neutral Particles in the Fermilab Wide Band Neutrino Beam.* (360)
15:20   A. FERNANDO-LOPEZ, CERN and U. de Madrid (DELPHI), *Search for Z0 Decays into Sleptons and Neutralinos Using the DELPHI detector.* (143)

15:40   Break

16:00   C. Y. CHANG, U. of Maryland (OPAL), *Search for Massive Unstable Photinos that violate R-parity.* (475)
16:20   M. PATERNO, SUNY at Stony Brook (D0), *Search for Squarks and Gluinos with the D0 Detector.* (438)
16:40   J.T. WHITE, Texas A&M (D0), *Search for Wino-Zino Production in D0.* (518)
17:00   D. KIM, FNAL (CDF), *Perspective on a Search for Squarks and Gluinos at CDF.* (504)

17:20   End of Session

H3. Theory: New Gauge Bosons, Anomalous Couplings and Heavy Fermions
Thursday, November 12, 09:00 - 12:15   Gallery Hall (Gauguin Room)
Chairperson: A. WHITE (U. of Texas, Arlington)

09:00 J. GUNION, U. of California, Davis, *Searching for the Supersymmetric Higgs Boson.* (199)
09:20 M. EINHORN, U. of Michigan, *Beyond the Standard Model with Effective Lagrangians.* (322)
09:40 G. VALENCIA, FNAL, *Vector-Boson vs Gluon Fusion at Hadron Colliders.* (381)
10:00 E. NARDI, U. of Michigan, *New Flavor Changing Interactions in Extended Gauge Models.* (365)
10:15 M. NOJIRI, U. of Wisconsin, *The Neutralino Relic Density in Minimal N=1 Supergravity.* (99)

10:30 Break

11:00 I. KNOWLES, ANL, *Heavy Fermion Mass Predictions and the Renormalization Group Equations.* (332)
11:15 D. CHANG, Northwestern U., $\mu \to e\gamma$ and *Mass-Dependent Flavor Changing Neutral Couplings of Higgs Bosons.* (219)
11:30 H. LEW, Purdue U., *Quark Lepton Symmetry.* (216)
11:45 G. JUNGMAN, U. of Chicago, *Fermion Masses in $SO(10)$.* (96)
12:00 P. FRAMPTON, U. of North Carolina, *Chiral Dilepton Model and the Flavor Question.* (329)

12:15 End of Session

H4. Experiment: Technicolor, Supersymmetry, Z^0/Photon
Thursday, November 12, 14:00 - 17:00   Presidents' Rooms (Washington & Lincoln)
Chairperson: J. YOH (FNAL)

14:00 T. PAPADOPOULOU, NTU of Athens (DELPHI), *Limits on the Production of Scalar Leptoquarks from Z^0 Decay at LEP1.* (149)
14:20 K. W. MERRITT, FNAL (D0), *Leptoquark search in D0.* (424)
14:40 S. MOULDING, Brandeis U. (CDF), *New Limits on Generation-1 Leptoquarks.* (524)
15:00 G. CROSSETTI, INFN, Genova (DELPHI), *Neutral Higgs Bosons in a two-Doublet Model.* (148)
15:20 R. KERANEN, CERN and U. of Helsinki (DELPHI), *Light Scalar Top at LEP Energies.* (153)

15:40 Break

16:00 T. COAN, LANL (L3), *Hard Photon Production as a Probe of Non-Standard Model Physics.* (120)
16:20 F. BARAO, LIP, Lisbon (DELPHI), *Search for New Phenomena with Photon Channels from Z^0 Decays.* (144)
16:40 C. SPARTIOTIS, Johns Hopkins U. (L3), *Final State Photon Physics through the Reaction $e^+e^- \to \gamma\gamma(\gamma)$.* (121)

17:00 End of Session

I. Non-Accelerator Physics

Conveners: D. S. AYRES (ANL) and T. GAISSER (Bartol Research Institute)
Liaison: S. PARKE (FNAL)

I1. Neutrino Oscillations
Thursday, November 12, 14:00 - 17:40   New Orleans Ballroom
Chairperson: S. PARKE (FNAL)

14:00   F. BOEHM, Caltech, *Reactor Based Neutrino Oscillation Experiments.* (271)
14:25   R. STEINBERG, Drexel U., *Perry - a Reactor Neutrino Oscillation Experiment Sensitive to $\delta m^2 \sim 10^{-4}$ eV^2.* (584)
14:35   M. GOODMAN, ANL, *Atmospheric Muon Neutrino and Electron Neutrino Rates as Observed in Soudan 2.* (387)
14:55   J. ENGEL, Bartol, *Neutrino Interactions with Oxygen, and the Atmospheric Neutrino Problem.* (668)
15:10   G. McGRATH, U. of Hawaii, *Neutrino Oscillations in IMB.* (430)
15:25   T. STANEV, Bartol, *Atmospheric Neutrinos.* (202)

15:40   Break

16:00   K. BABU, Bartol, *From Fermion Mass Matrices to Neutrino Oscillations.* (5)
16:10   K. BABU, Bartol, *Predictive Neutrino Spectrum in Minimal SO(10) Grand Unification.* (215)
16:20   J. PANTALEONE, Indiana U., *Gravitationally Induced Mixing of Solar and Terrestrial Neutrinos.* (368)
16:30   J. PANTALEONE, Indiana U., *Solar Neutrinos with Three Flavor Mixings.* (54)
16:40   W. REAY, Ohio State U., *Neutrino Oscillation Experiments with the Fermilab Main Injector.* (444)
17:05   D. MICHAEL, Caltech, *Searching for Oscillations of Atmospheric and Accelerator Neutrinos.* (425)
17:15   P. LANGACKER, U. of Pennsylvania, *Implications of Solar and Atmospheric Neutrinos.* (666)

17:40   End of Session

I2. Proton Decay, Double Beta Decay and 17 KeV Neutrino
Friday, November 13, 8:30 - 12:00   New Orleans Ballroom
Chairperson: D. S. AYRES (ANL)

08:30   W. MANN, Tufts U., *The Atmospheric flux ν_μ / ν_e anomaly as manifestation of Proton Decay $p \to e^+ \nu \nu$.* (419)
08:45   C. McGREW, U. of California, Irvine, *Recent limits on Baryon Non-conservation from the IMB-3 Experiment.* (431)
09:00   P. HALVERSON, U. of California, Irvine, *Can the IMB-3 Atmospheric Muon Neutrino Flux Deficit be Interpreted as Evidence for Proton Decay?* (665)
09:15   S. RUDAZ, U. of Minnesota, *Proton Decay Theory.* (630)
09:35   P. HARIDES, MIT, *Status of the LVD Experiment at Gran Sasso Laboratory.* (391)
09:45   O. PICCIONI, U. of California, San Diego, *The Einstein Podolsky Rosen Paradox as a Particle Physics Subject without Bell Inequalties.* (217)

10:00   Break

10:30 S. FREEDMAN, ANL and LBL, *Evidence against the 17 KeV Neutrino from Beta-Decay.* (658)
10:45 A. HIME, LANL, *Do Scattering Effects Resolve the 17 KeV Conundrum?* (613)
11:00 D. CALDWELL, U. of California, Santa Barbara, *Status of the 17 KeV Neutrino.* (177)
11:25 J. CLINE, U. of Minnesota, *Majorons from Double Beta Decay.* (529)
11:35 F. AVIGNONE, U. of South Carolina, *Double Beta Decay in Nuclear Physics: Recent Results and Projections.* (667)

12:00 End of Session

I3. Cosmic Ray Physics
Friday, November 13, 13:00 - 16:30   New Orleans Ballroom
Chairperson: T. GAISSER (Bartol)

13:00 S. BILLER, U. of California, Irvine, *Daily Search for Ultra High Energy Radiation from Point Sources.* (587)
13:15 S. KLEIN, U. of California, Santa Cruz, *MILAGRO: A Low Threshold Water Cerenkov Air Shower Detector.* (405)
13:25 K. GREEN. U. of Michigan, *A Search for 100 TeV Gamma Rays from Cygnus X-3 and the Crab with CASA-MIA.* (483)
13:40 T. McKAY, U. of Chicago, *An All Sky Survey for Sources of 100 TeV Gamma Radiation by the UMC Collaboration.* (526)
13:50 S. KASAHARA, U. of Minnesota, *Underground Muons Observed with the Soudan 2 Detector.* (517)
14:05 N. LONGLEY, U. of Minnesota and Carleton Coll., *Ultra High Energy Cosmic Ray Composition from EAS/Underground Muon Studies at Soudan 2.* (479)
14:15 E. KEARNS, Boston U., *Search for Slow Ionizing Penetrating Particles with the MACRO Detector.* (467)

14:25 Break

14:50 R. CORMACK, Boston U., *Multiple Muons at Large Separation in the MACRO Detector.* (457)
15:05 H. DAI, U. of Utah, *Cosmic Ray Composition around 1 EeV.* (469)
15:20 P. SOKOLSKY, U. of Utah, *The Cosmic Ray Spectrum above 0.1 EeV: Present Data, Future Prospects.* (512)
15:45 D. BIRD, U. of Illinois, Urbana, *The HiRes Fly's Eye Prototype Detector.* (466)
15:55 J. BOYER, Columbia U., *Limits on the Expected Rate of Cosmic Ray Neutrinos at the HiRes Fly's Eye.* (316)
16:05 F. HALZEN, U. of Wisconsin, *High Energy Neutrino Astronomy.* (565)

16:30 End of Session

J. Particle Astrophysics

Conveners: B. SADOULET (LBL) and P. SIKIVIE (U. of Florida)
Liaison: J. FRIEMAN (FNAL)

J1. Cosmological Phase Transitions, Inflation, Dark Matter
Wednesday, November 11, 14:00 - 17:40   New Orleans Ballroom
Chairperson: P. SIKIVIE (U. of Florida)

14:00   P. HUET, SLAC, *Aspects of the Electroweak Phase Transition.* (574)
14:25   A. COHEN, Boston U., *Baryons from Electroweak Physics.* (722)
14:50   M. KAMIONKOWSKI, Institute for Advanced Study, Princeton, *Instability and Subsequent Evolution of Electroweak Bubbles.* (35)
15:05   J. LEVIN, MIT, *The MAD Era: A Possible New Resolution to the Horizon, Flatness, and Monopole Problems.* (770)
15:20   A. KOSOWSKY, U. of Chicago, *Gravitational Radiation from First-Order Cosmological Phase Transitions.* (74)
15:30   K. CAHILL, U. of New Mexico, *Inflation Pressures.* (226)

15:40   Break

16:00   J. SIMON, U. of Maryland, *The Case against R^2 Inflation.* (210)
16:15   C. STUBBS, U. of California, Santa Barbara, *Searching for Dark Matter: WIMPs or MACHOs?* (719)
16:45   K. VAN BIBBER, Livermore, *A Large Scale Dark-Matter Axion Search.* (720)
17:10   T. RESSELL, Livermore, *Nuclear Shell Model Calculations of the Spin-Dependent Neutralino-Nucleus Cross Section.* (372)
17:25   P. GONDOLO, Uppsala U., *Indirect Detection of Unstable Heavy Dark Matter.* (330)

17:40   End of Session

J2. Microwave Background, Gamma Rays, Solar and Supernova Neutrinos
Thursday, November 12, 09:00 - 12:50   New Orleans Ballroom
Chairperson: J. FRIEMAN (FNAL)

09:00   M. TURNER, U. of Chicago and FNAL, *Inflation after COBE.* (725)
09:25   S. DODELSON, FNAL, *Small-scale anisotropies in light of COBE.* (714)
09:40   A. STEBBINS, FNAL, *Topological Defects after COBE.* (724)
10:00   S. MEYER, MIT, *Microwave Background Anisotropy Experiments.* (715)
10:25   M. SCHUBNELL, U. of Michigan, *First Detection of TeV Gamma Rays from the AGN Markarian 421.* (717)

10:40   Break

11:00   D. LAMB, U. of Chicago, U., *Gamma Ray Bursts: Galactic or Cosmological in Origin?* (716)
11:25   R. HAHN, BNL, *The Gallex Solar Neutrino Experiment.* (612)
11:45   J. NICO, LANL, *Recent Results from the Soviet-American Gallium Experiment.* (434)
12:05   E. NORMAN, LBL, *The Sudbury Neutrino Observatory.* (435)
12:25   M. GRASSI, INFN, Pisa, *Search for Supernova Neutrinos with MACRO.* (465)
12:40   A. JAFFE, U. of Chicago, *Limits on Neutrino Radiative Decay from SN1987A.* (726)

12:50   End of Session

K. Lattice Gauge Theory

Conveners: C. BERNARD (Washington U., St. Louis) and N. H. CHRIST (Columbia U.)
Liaison: G. HOCKNEY (FNAL)

K1. Lattice Gauge Theory I

Wednesday, November 11, 09:00 - 12:30   Presidents' Rooms (Washington & Lincoln)
Chairperson: C. BERNARD (Washington U., St. Louis)

09:00   L. LIN, U. of Münster, *Study of Yukawa Models with Mirror Fermions.* (75)
09:20   R. L. RENKEN, U. of Florida, *Three-Dimensional Quantum Gravity Coupled to Ising Matter.* (77)
09:40   M. GOLTERMAN, Washington U., St. Louis, *Chiral Perturbation Theory for the Quenched Approximation.* (678)
10:00   K. CAHILL, U. of New Mexico, *A High-Statistics Simulation of SU(2) Gauge Theory at Strong Coupling.* (228)
10:15   K.-F. LIU, U. of Kentucky, *Sea-Quark Contributions in Nucleon.* (56)

10:30   Break

11:00   K. RAJAGOPAL, Princeton U., *Static and Dynamical Critical Phenomena in a Second Order QCD Phase Transition.* (660)
11:25   R. D. MAWHINNEY, Columbia U., *QCD Thermodynamics Closer to the Continuum.* (679)
11:45   J. KISKIS, U. of California, Davis, *SU(2) Adjoint Wilson Line at T^c.* (356)
12:05   R. S. NARAYANAN, Rutgers U., *Running Coupling in Pure Gauge Theories Using the Schrödinger Functional.* (17)

12:30   End of Session

K2. Lattice Gauge Theory II

Wednesday, November 11, 14:00 - 17:40   Presidents' Rooms (Washington & Lincoln)
Chairperson: G. HOCKNEY (FNAL)

14:00   D. WEINGARTEN, IBM Research, *Infinite Volume, Continuum Limit of Hadron Masses in the Valence Approximation.* (692)
14:25   S. KIM, ANL, *Quenched Hadron Spectrum of QCD.* (355)
14:45   T. DRAPER, U. of Kentucky, *Hadronic Multiple Moments from Lattice QCD.* (600)
15:05   V. SINGH, Louisiana State U., *Monopole Currents and Confinement in Lattice Gauge Theory.* (583)
15:25   S. GOTTLIEB, Indiana U., *The QCD Teraflops Project.* (681)

15:40   Break

16:00   P. B. MACKENZIE, FNAL, *Heavy Quarks on the Lattice.* (677)
16:25   A. X. EL-KHADRA, FNAL, *A Determination of the Strong Coupling Constant from the Charmonium Spectrum.* (671)
16:45   U. HANSMANN, SCRI, *Multicanonical and Multimagnetical Simulations.* (331)
17:10   W. BÜRGER, U. Wien, *Fermionic Vacuum in Compact Lattice QED.* (39)
17:25   S. SIEGEMUND-BROKA, U. of Oklahoma, *Finite Element Quantum Electrodynamics.* (375)

17:40   End of Session

L. Formal Theory

Conveners: W.A. BARDEEN (FNAL) and J. A. HARVEY (U. of Chicago)
Liaison: W.A. BARDEEN (FNAL)

L1. Mathematical Methods in Field Theory
Thursday, November 12, 09:00 - 12:30   Presidents' Rooms (Washington & Lincoln)
Chairperson: J.D. LYKKEN (FNAL)

09:00 K.E. CAHILL, U. of Mexico, *A More Effective Potential*. (227)
09:15 S. BOETTCHER, Washington U., St. Louis, *The Delta Expansion in Quantum Field Theory*. (196)
09:30 A. GANGOPADHYAYA, Loyola U., *Supersymmetry and the Tunnelling Problem in an an Asymmetric Double Well*. (573)
09:45 L. DI LEO, York U., *Bound and Resonant Relativistic Two-Particle States and Bound Three-Particle States in Scalar Quantum Field Theory*. (71)
10:00 J.P. CRAWFORD, Penn State U., Fayette, *Massive Gauge Bosons sans Higgs*. (19)
10:15 J.S.R. CHISHOLM, U. of Kent, *Top Mass via Spin Gauge Theory*. (318)

10:30 Break

11:00 P. SIKIVIE, U. of Florida, *Casimir Forces Induced by String Fluctuations*. (530)
11:30 T.J. ALLEN, U. of Wisconsin, *Charged Vortex Dynamics in a Ginsburg-Landau Theory of (2+1) Dimensions*. (326)
11:45 P. JAIN, U. of Kansas, *Consistent and Covariant Quantum Expansion around Soliton Solutions*. (95)
12:00 N.P. SWAMY, Southern Illinois U., *Gauge Technique and BCS Theory of Superconductivity*. (380)
12:15 H. ZHANG, Jackson State U., *Global Constraints of Gauss' Law and the Solution to the Strong CP Problem*. (86)

12:30 End of Session

L2. Dynamical Aspects of Field Theories and Strings
Friday, November 13, 08:30 - 11:40   Presidents' Rooms (Washington & Lincoln)
Chairperson: W.A. BARDEEN (FNAL)

08:30 C.M. BENDER, Washington University, St. Louis, *Dimensional Expansions*. (90)
08:50 B. HAERI, Purdue U., *The Cutoff Dependence of the Higgs Mass*. (114)
09:10 G. BATHAS, Rutgers U., *Nonperturbative Effects in Chiral Yukawa Models*. (115)
09:30 T.R. TAYLOR, Northeastern U., *Low Energy Effective Action of Superstring Theory*. (105)

10:00 Break

10:30 D.J. GROSS, Princeton U., *Induced QCD*. (661)
11:00 Y. MEURICE, U. of Iowa, *Polyakov's Conjecture in the Light of the Hierarchical Approximation*. (364)
11:20 S-J. REY, Princeton U., *Protecting Invisible Axions from Near-Planck Scale Physics*. (346)

11:40 End of Session

L3. Quantum Black Holes and Topological Field Theory
   Friday, November 13, 13:00 - 16:20   Presidents' Rooms (Washington & Lincoln)
   Chairperson: J.A. HARVEY (U. of Chicago)

13:00 R. GREGORY, U. of Chicago, *Black Holes with a Massive Dilaton.* (721)
13:30 J.D. LYKKEN, FNAL, *Stringy Black Holes via Coset Current Algebra.* (98)
14:00 S.P. DE ALWIS, U. of Colorado, *Quantum Black Holes in Two Dimensions.* (91)

14:30 Break

15:00 K.A. MILTON, U. of Oklahoma, *Maxwell-Chern-Simons-Casimir Effect.* (335)
15:20 K. HALLER, U. of Connecticut, *Gauge Theories in (2+1) Dimensions.* (20)
15:40 M.K. FALBO-KENKEL, U. of Cincinnati, *The Exact Two Particle Scattering Amplitude in the (2+1) Dimensional Chern-Simons Theory of Gravity.* (599)
16:00 W.R. LUNDBERG, Wright State U., *Quantized String Gravitational Metric Evolves to Standard Physics.* (214)

16:20 End of Session

M. Accelerator Techniques
   Conveners: R. RUTH (SLAC) and M. HARRISON (BNL)
   Liaison: S. D. HOLMES (FNAL)

M1. e^+e^- High Luminosity Storage Rings and Linear Colliders
   Wednesday, November 11, 09:00 - 10:30   Presidents' Rooms (Jefferson and Eisenhower)
   Chairperson: R. RUTH (SLAC)

09:00 D. RICE, Cornell U., *CESR Performance and Upgrades.* (682)
09:20 H. YAMAMOTO, Harvard U., *CESR/CLEO IR Upgrade.* (489)
09:35 M. SULLIVAN, U. of California, San Diego, *PEP II: B-Factory.* (683)
09:55 H. HINDI, SLAC, *PEP II: RF and Feedback R&D.* (684)
10:10 A. ZHOLENTS, LBL, *Tau/Charm Factory.* (685)

10:30 Break

   Wednesday, November 11, 11:00 - 12:40   Presidents' Rooms (Jefferson and Eisenhower)
   Chairperson: M. TIGNER (Cornell U.)

11:00 N. WALKER, SLAC, *The SLC Performance and Future Plans.* (686)
11:20 D. PREPOST, SLAC, *The Polarized Beam Facility of the SLC.* (687)
11:40 R. RUTH, SLAC, *Next Linear Collider Development at SLAC.* (688)
12:00 B. WIIK, DESY, *TESLA.* (689)
12:20 G. LOEW, SLAC, *Linear Collider Scaling and Costs.* (690)

12:40 End of Session

M2. Hadron Accelerators and Storage Rings
Wednesday, November 11, 14:00 - 17:30   Presidents' Rooms (Jefferson and Eisenhower)
Chairperson: M. HARRISON (BNL)

14:00 C. WILKINSON, LANL, *Monte Carlo Based Formula for Estimating Penetration of Radiation Shielding at Forward Angles.* (523)

14:10 S. FRANKLE, LANL, *A Comparison of Analytic Models for Estimating Dose Equivalent Rates in Shielding with Beam Split Measurements.* (473)

14:20 H. PARK, FNAL, *Measurement of the Circulating Muon Flux in the Fermilab Debuncher Ring.* (436)

14:40 W. GABELLA, U. of California, Los Angeles, *RF Voltage Modulation at Discrete Frequencies with Applications to Crystal Channelling Extraction.* (336)

15:05 T. MURPHY, FNAL, *Extraction from the Tevatron Using Channeling with a Bent Crystal.* (484,464)

15:30 Break

16:00 S. MISHRA, FNAL, *The Fermilab Main Injector.* (522)

16:20 S. TEPIKIAN, BNL, *Polarized Protons in Large Center of Mass Collisions.* (552)

16:40 T. DOMBEK, SSCL, *Power Tests of a String of 50 mm Aperture Dipole Magnets at the Superconducting Super Collider Laboratory.* (287,547)

17:05 M. SYPHERS, SSCL, *SSC Design Update.* (652)

17:30 End of Session

N. Detector Development
Conveners: A. B. SEIDEN (U. of California, Santa Cruz) and H. GORDON (BNL)
Liaison: D. BUCHHOLZ (Northwestern U.)

N1a. Detector Development: Triggering and Scintillating Fibers
Wednesday, November 11, 09:00 - 10:35   New Orleans Ballroom
Chairperson: D. BUCHHOLZ (Northwestern U.)

09:00 A. M. HALLING, FNAL (E791), *Test of a Multiplicity Jump Trigger Using the E791 Spectrometer.* (487)

09:20 W. LUEBKE, Northern Illinois U., *Test of Principle of an Optical Trigger for Beauty.* (506)

09:40 J. T. LINNEMANN, Michigan State U. (D0), *Triggering the D0 Detector.* (414)

09:55 R. CHANEY, Texas, Dallas Richardson (SDC), *Central Tracking with Scintillating Fibers in the SDC Experiment.* (551)

10:15 R. LEWIS, Penn State U. (SDC), *Results of Test of Scintillating Fibers with Visible Light Photon Counters.* (545,549,550)

10:35 Break

N1b. Detector Development: Scintillating Fibers and Particle Identification
Wednesday, November 11, 11:00 - 12:35   New Orleans Ballroom
Chairperson: D. BUCHHOLZ (Northwestern)

11:00 M. WAYNE, U. of Notre Dame (D0), *A Scintillating Fiber Detector for the D0 Upgrade.* (559)

11:15 T. HENKES, CERN (DELPHI), *Particle Identification with the Forward RICH Detector of DELPHI.* (175)

11:35 D. ASTON, SLAC (SLD), *First Results from the SLD Barrel CRID.* (232)

11:55 L. STUTTE, FNAL, *Prototype RICH Detector.* (1)

12:15 J.T. OYANG, Caltech, *Tests of Silica Aerogel as a Low-Mass Particle Identification System for the SLAC B Factory Detector.* (528)

12:35 End of Session

N2. Detector Development: Calorimetry
Thursday, November 12, 9:00 - 12:35   Presidents' Rooms (Jefferson & Eisenhower)
Chairperson: H. GORDON (BNL)

09:00 J. F. BOUDREAU, CERN (ALEPH), *A Silicon-Tungsten Calorimeter for a Precise Measurement of Luminosity at ALEPH.* (272)

09:20 M. KING, SLAC (US Tau-Charm Factory), *Performance of a Longitudinally Segmented CsI Calorimeter for a Tau Charm Factory Detector.* (493)

09:40 M. TORRES, FNAL (T821), *Experimental Results on Low Energy Neutron Leakage in Hadronic Showers from FNAL T-821.* (482)

10:00 SPRINGER, CERN (OPAL), *The OPAL Silicon-Tungsten Luminometer.* (651)

10:20 S. LOKOS, SUNY at Stony Brook (D0), *Upgraded D0 Calorimeter Electronics for Short Tevatron Bunch Space and the Effect of Pile-Up on the W Mass Measurement.* (415)

10:35 Break

11:00 M. NARAIN, FNAL (D0), *Electron Identification in the D0 Detector.* (433)

11:15 P. BHAT, FNAL (D0), *Low Energy Response of the D0 Calorimeter and Jet Energy Measurement.* (269)

11:30 L. FORTNEY, Duke U., *Measurement of Localized Efficiency Loss in a Silicon Microstrip Detector Operated at High Intensity.* (751)

11:50 N. AKCHURIN, U. of Iowa, (SSCintCAL), *Beam Test Results From Copper/Scintillating Fiber and Lead/Quartz Fiber Calorimeter Prototypes.* (458,571)

12:10 M. GUI, Texas A & M U. (SDC), *A Study of Glass-Liquid Scintillating Fibers for the Forward Calorimetry of SDC.* (180)

12:35 End of Session

N3a. Detector Development: Calorimetry
  Thursday, November 12, 14:00 - 15:40   Presidents' Rooms (Jefferson & Eisenhower)
  Chairperson: H. GORDON (BNL)

14:00 H. TAKAI, BNL, *Precision Timing Measurements with a Liquid Ionization Calorimeter*. (488)
14:20 H. MA, BNL, *Test of Prototype Liquid Ionization Accordion Calorimeters*. (509)
14:40 L. SULAK, Boston U. (GEM), *The Fiber Hadron Detector for the GEM Hybrid Calorimeter*. (663)
15:00 A. BHATTI, Rockefeller U. (SDC), *Shower-Maximum and Preshower Detectors for SDC*. (422)
15:20 P. de BARBARO, U. of Rochester (SDC), *Beam Test of Reconfigurable-Stack Calorimeter*. (611)

15:40 Break

N3b. Detector Development: General
  Thursday, November 12, 16:00 - 17:50   Presidents' Rooms (Jefferson & Eisenhower)
  Chairperson: H. GORDON (BNL)

16:00 P. AVERY, U. of Florida, *A New Approach to Distributed Computing in High Energy Physics*. (460)
16:20 J. McDONOUGH, U. of Texas, *The Design of the Beamplug for a New $K_L \to \mu e$ Experiment*. (428)
16:40 P. HARIDAS, MIT (GEM), *Behavior of Large Resistive Plate Counters*. (490)
17:00 J. THALER, U. of Illinois (SDC), *Data Acquisition Design for the SDC*. (186)
17:20 G. EIGEN, Caltech (SLAC B Factory), *New Studies of CSI Readout and Radiation Hardness for the SLAC B Factory Detector*. (470)
17:40 R. CARRIGAN, FNAL (E761), *First Observation of Magnetic Moment Precession of Channeled Particles in Bent Crystals*. (274)

17:50 End of Session

N4. Detector Development: Silicon
  Friday, November 13, 08:30 - 10:05   Presidents' Rooms (Jefferson & Eisenhower)
  Chairperson: A. SEIDEN (U. of California, Santa Cruz)

08:30 P. P. ALLPORT, Cavendish Lab. (OPAL), *Double-Sided Foxfet Biassed Silicon Microstrip Detectors*. (230, 459)
08:50 S. MANI, U. of California, Davis, *A Monolithic Silicon Pixel Detector Using BE-Silicon-On-Insulator*. (418)
09:10 S. SHAPIRO, SLAC, *Measurement of Spatial Resolution Using Silicon Hybrid Pixel Arrays*. (501)
09:30 A. HEINSON, U. of California, Riverside (D0), *The D0 Upgrade Silicon Tracker*. (394)
09:45 D. H. KAPLAN, U. of Oklahoma, *Position Resolution and Charge Correlation Tracking Tests of Double-Sided Silicon Microstrip Arrays*. (401)

10:05 Break

Friday, November 13, 10:25 - 12:15   Presidents' Rooms (Jefferson & Eisenhower)
Chairperson: R. SCHINDLER (SLAC)

10:25 P. FRANZINI, INFN, Frascati (KLOE), *KLOE, A General Purpose Detector for DAPHNE.* (189)
10:45 J. WEAR, U. of California, Santa Cruz (ALEPH), *Real Life Experience with the ALEPH Silicon Vertex Detector.* (560)
11:05 O. SCHNEIDER, LBL (CDF), *Performance of the CDF Silicon Vertex Detector.* (497)
11:20 M. CLEMEN, Carnegie-Mellon U. (E781), *Beam Studies of a Software Trigger Sector Using a High Resolution Silicon Vertex Detector System with VLSI Readout.* (278, 553)
11:40 W. MURRAY, Rutherford Lab. (DELPHI), *The DELPHI Microvertex Detector.* (160)
12:00 N. CARTIGLIA, U. of California, Santa Cruz, *A Test Station for Silicon Silicon Microstrip Detectors and Associated Electronics.* (809)
12:15 End of Session

N5. Detector Development: Tracking
Friday, November 13, 13:00 - 15:00   Presidents' Rooms (Jefferson & Eisenhower)
Chairperson(tentative): H. OGREN (Indiana U.)

13:00 H. TAJIMA, U. of California, Santa Barbara (CLEO II), *A Silicon Vertex Detector for CLEO II.* (486)
13:20 M. STRAUSS, U. of Massachusetts, Amherst (SLD), *Performance of a Silicon CCD Pixel Vertex Detector in the SLD.* (495)
13:40 R. MILLER, Michigan State U. (GEM), *Design and Performance of a Pressurized Drift Tube Chamber for the Gem Muon System.* (426)
14:00 R. KASS, Ohio State U., *Performance of Diamond Radiation Detectors.* (498)
14:20 T. ZHAO, U. of Washington (SDC), *SDC Central Muon Tracking System.* (51, 586)
14:40 O. K. BAKER, Hampton U., *Resistive Kapton Straw Tube Drift Chamber Prototype.* (235)
15:00 Break

Friday, November 13, 15:20 - 16:40   Presidents' Rooms (Jefferson & Eisenhower)
Chairperson(tentative): H. KAGAN (Ohio State U.)

15:20 D. C. CHRISTIAN, FNAL (E690), *High Rate Drift Chambers.* (277)
15:40 R. MALCHOW, Ohio State U. (CLEO II), *Operation of Straw-Tube Detectors Using DME.* (513)
16:00 H. TROST, Texas A&M U., *Recent Developments on Microstrip Chambers at Texas A&M.* (514)
16:20 H. OGREN, Indiana U. (SDC), *SDC-Outer Straw Tracker.* (527)
16:40 End of Session

The ALEPH COLLABORATION

D. Buskulic, D. Decamp, C. Goy, J.-P. Lees, M.-N. Minard, B. Mours, B. Pietrzyk
  Laboratoire de Physique des Particules (LAPP), IN^{2}P^3-CNRS, 74019 Annecy-le-Vieux Cedex, France

R. Alemany, F. Ariztizabal, P. Comas, J.M. Crespo, M. Delfino, E. Fernandez, V. Gaitan, Ll. Garrido, T. Mattison, A. Pacheco, C. Padilla, A. Pascual
  Institut de Fisica d'Altes Energies, Universitat Autonoma de Barcelona, 08193 Bellaterra (Barcelona), Spain

D. Creanza, M. de Palma, A. Farilla, G. Iaselli, G. Maggi, M. Maggi, S. Natali, S. Nuzzo, M. Quattromini, A. Ranieri, G. Raso, F. Romano, F. Ruggieri, G. Selvaggi, L. Silvestris, P. Tempesta, G. Zito
  INFN Sezione di Bari e Dipartimento di Fisica dell' Università, 70126 Bari, Italy

H. Hu, D. Huang, X. Huang, J. Lin, J. Lou, T. Wang, Y. Xie, D. Xu, R. Xu, J. Zhang, W. Zhao
  Institute of High-Energy Physics, Academia Sinica, Beijing, The People's Republic of China

L.A.T. Bauerdick,[10] E. Blucher, G. Bonvicini, J. Boudreau, D. Casper, H. Drevermann, R.W. Forty, G. Ganis, C. Gay, R. Hagelberg, J. Harvey, S. Haywood, J. Hilgart, R. Jacobsen, B. Jost, J. Knobloch, I. Lehraus, T. Lohse,[17] A. Lusiani, M. Martinez, P. Mato, H. Meinhard, A. Minten, R. Miquel, H.-G. Moser, P. Palazzi, J.A. Perlas, J.-F. Pusztaszeri,[15] F. Ranjard, G. Redlinger,[11] L. Rolandi, J. Rothberg,[2] M. Saich, D. Schlatter, M. Schmelling, F. Sefkow, W. Tejessy, H. Wachsmuth, W. Wiedenmann, T. Wildish, W. Witzeling, J. Wotschack
  European Laboratory for Particle Physics (CERN), 1211 Geneva 23, Switzerland

Z. Ajaltouni, F. Badaud, M. Bardadin-Otwinowska, R. El Fellous, A. Falvard, P. Gay, C. Guicheney, P. Henrard, J. Jousset, B. Michel, J-C. Montret, D. Pallin, P. Perret, J. Proriol, F. Prulhière, G. Stimpfl
  Laboratoire de Physique Corpusculaire, Université Blaise Pascal, IN^{2}P^3-CNRS, Clermont-Ferrand, 63177 Aubière, France

T. Fearnley, J.D. Hansen, J.R. Hansen,[1] P.H. Hansen, R. Møllerud, B.S. Nilsson[1]
  Niels Bohr Institute, 2100 Copenhagen, Denmark

I. Efthymiopoulos, A. Kyriakis, E. Simopoulou, A. Vayaki, K. Zachariadou
  Nuclear Research Center Demokritos (NRCD), Athens, Greece

J. Badier, A. Blondel, G. Bonneaud, J.C. Brient, G. Fouque, S. Orteu, A. Rougé, M. Rumpf, R. Tanaka, M. Verderi, H. Videau
  Laboratoire de Physique Nucléaire et des Hautes Energies, Ecole Polytechnique, IN^{2}P^3-CNRS, 91128 Palaiseau Cedex, France

D.J. Candlin, M.I. Parsons, E. Veitch
  Department of Physics, University of Edinburgh, Edinburgh EH9 3JZ, United Kingdom

L. Moneta, G. Parrini
  Dipartimento di Fisica, Università di Firenze, INFN Sezione di Firenze, 50125 Firenze, Italy

M. Corden, C. Georgiopoulos, M. Ikeda, J. Lannutti, D. Levinthal, M. Mermikides[†], L. Sawyer, S. Wasserbaech

Supercomputer Computations Research Institute and Dept. of Physics, Florida State University, Tallahassee, FL 32306, USA

A. Antonelli, R. Baldini, G. Bencivenni, G. Bologna,[4] F. Bossi, P. Campana, G. Capon, F. Cerutti, V. Chiarella, B. D'Ettorre-Piazzoli,[12] G. Felici, P. Laurelli, G. Mannocchi,[5] F. Murtas, G.P. Murtas, L. Passalacqua, M. Pepe-Altarelli, P. Picchi[4]

Laboratori Nazionali dell'INFN (LNF-INFN), 00044 Frascati, Italy

P. Colrain, I. ten Have, J.G. Lynch, W. Maitland, W.T. Morton, C. Raine, P. Reeves, J.M. Scarr, K. Smith, M.G. Smith, A.S. Thompson, R.M. Turnbull

Department of Physics and Astronomy, University of Glasgow, Glasgow G12 8QQ, United Kingdom

B. Brandl, O. Braun, C. Geweniger, P. Hanke, V. Hepp, E.E. Kluge, Y. Maumary, A. Putzer, B. Rensch, A. Stahl, K. Tittel, M. Wunsch

Institut für Hochenergiephysik, Universität Heidelberg, 6900 Heidelberg, Fed. Rep. of Germany

A.T. Belk, R. Beuselinck, D.M. Binnie, W. Cameron, M. Cattaneo, D.J. Colling, P.J. Dornan, S. Dugeay, A.M. Greene, J.F. Hassard, N.M. Lieske,[19] J. Nash, D.G. Payne, M.J. Phillips, J.K. Sedgbeer, I.R. Tomalin, A.G. Wright

Department of Physics, Imperial College, London SW7 2BZ, United Kingdom

E. Kneringer, D. Kuhn, G. Rudolph

Institut für Experimentalphysik, Universität Innsbruck, 6020 Innsbruck, Austria

C.K. Bowdery, T.J. Brodbeck, A.J. Finch, F. Foster, G. Hughes, D. Jackson, N.R. Keemer, M. Nuttall, A. Patel, T. Sloan, S.W. Snow, E.P. Whelan

Department of Physics, University of Lancaster, Lancaster LA1 4YB, United Kingdom

K. Kleinknecht, J. Raab, B. Renk, H.-G. Sander, H. Schmidt, F. Steeg, S.M. Walther, R. Wanke, B. Wolf

Institut für Physik, Universität Mainz, 6500 Mainz, Fed. Rep. of Germany

J-J. Aubert, A.M. Bencheikh, C. Benchouk, A. Bonissent, J. Carr, P. Coyle, J. Drinkard,[3] F. Etienne, D. Nicod, S. Papalexiou, P. Payre, L. Roos, D. Rousseau, P. Schwemling, M. Talby

Centre de Physique des Particules, Faculté des Sciences de Luminy, IN^{2}P^3-CNRS, 13288 Marseille, France

S. Adlung, R. Assmann, C. Bauer, W. Blum, D. Brown, P. Cattaneo,[16] B. Dehning, H. Dietl, F. Dydak,[9] M. Fernandez-Bosman, M. Frank, A.W. Halley, J. Lauber, G. Lütjens, G. Lutz, W. Männer, R. Richter, H. Rotscheidt, J. Schröder, A.S. Schwarz, R. Settles, H. Seywerd, U. Stierlin, U. Stiegler, R. St. Denis, G. Wolf

Max-Planck-Institut für Physik, Werner-Heisenberg-Institut, 8000 München, Fed. Rep. of Germany[16]

J. Boucrot,[1] O. Callot, A. Cordier, M. Davier, L. Duflot, J.-F. Grivaz, Ph. Heusse, D.E. Jaffe, P. Janot, D.W. Kim, F. Le Diberder, J. Lefrançois, A.-M. Lutz, M.-H. Schune, J.-J. Veillet, I. Videau, Z. Zhang

Laboratoire de l'Accélérateur Linéaire, Université de Paris-Sud, IN^2P^3-CNRS, 91405 Orsay Cedex, France

D. Abbaneo, S.R. Amendolia, G. Bagliesi, G. Batignani, L. Bosisio, U. Bottigli, C. Bozzi, C. Bradaschia, M. Carpinelli, M.A. Ciocci, R. Dell'Orso, I. Ferrante, F. Fidecaro, L. Foà, E. Focardi, F. Forti, A. Giassi, M.A. Giorgi, F. Ligabue, E.B. Mannelli, P.S. Marrocchesi, A. Messineo, F. Palla, G. Rizzo, G. Sanguinetti, P. Spagnolo, J. Steinberger, R. Tenchini, G. Tonelli, G. Triggiani, C. Vannini, A. Venturi, P.G. Verdini, J. Walsh

Dipartimento di Fisica dell'Università, INFN Sezione di Pisa, e Scuola Normale Superiore, 56010 Pisa, Italy

A.P. Betteridge, J.M. Carter, M.G. Green, P.V. March, Ll.M. Mir, T. Medcalf, I.S. Quazi, J.A. Strong, L.R. West

Department of Physics, Royal Holloway & Bedford New College, University of London, Surrey TW20 0EX, United Kingdom

D.R. Botterill, R.W. Clifft, T.R. Edgecock, M. Edwards, S.M. Fisher, T.J. Jones, P.R. Norton, D.P. Salmon, J.C. Thompson

Particle Physics Dept., Rutherford Appleton Laboratory, Chilton, Didcot, Oxon OX11 0QX, United Kingdom

B. Bloch-Devaux, P. Colas, H. Duarte, W. Kozanecki, E. Lançon, M.C. Lemaire, E. Locci, P. Perez, F. Perrier, J. Rander, J.-F. Renardy, A. Rosowsky, A. Roussarie, J.-P. Schuller, J. Schwindling, D. Si Mohand, B. Vallage

Service de Physique des Particules, DAPNIA, CE-Saclay, 91191 Gif-sur-Yvette Cedex, France

R.P. Johnson, A.M. Litke, G. Taylor, J. Wear

Institute for Particle Physics, University of California at Santa Cruz, Santa Cruz, CA 95064, USA[14]

J.G. Ashman, W. Babbage, C.N. Booth, C. Buttar, R.E. Carney, S. Cartwright, F. Combley, F. Hatfield, L.F. Thompson[1]

Department of Physics, University of Sheffield, Sheffield S3 7RH, United Kingdom

E. Barberio, A. Böhrer, S. Brandt, G. Cowan, C. Grupen, G. Lutters, F. Rivera, U. Schäfer

Fachbereich Physik, Universität Siegen, 5900 Siegen, Fed. Rep. of Germany

R. Della Marina, G. Giannini, B. Gobbo, F. Ragusa[8]

Dipartimento di Fisica, Università di Trieste e INFN Sezione di Trieste, 34127 Trieste, Italy

L. Bellantoni, W. Chen, D. Cinabro,[13] J.S. Conway,[18] D.F. Cowen,[7] Z. Feng, D.P.S. Ferguson, Y.S. Gao, J. Grahl, J.L. Harton, R.C. Jared,[6] B.W. LeClaire, C. Lishka, A. Miotto, Y.B. Pan, J.R. Pater, T. Ruan, Y. Saadi, V. Sharma, M. Schmitt, Z.H. Shi, A.M. Walsh, F.V. Weber, M.H. Whitney, Sau Lan Wu, X. Wu, G. Zobernig

Department of Physics, University of Wisconsin, Madison, WI 53706, USA

†*Deceased.*
[1] *Now at CERN, PPE Division, 1211 Geneva 23, Switzerland.*
[2] *Permanent address: University of Washington, Seattle, WA 98195, USA.*
[3] *Now at University of California, Irvine, CA 92717, USA.*
[4] *Also Istituto di Fisica Generale, Università di Torino, Torino, Italy.*
[5] *Also Istituto di Cosmo-Geofisica del C.N.R., Torino, Italy.*
[6] *Permanent address: LBL, Berkeley, CA 94720, USA.*
[7] *Now at California Institute of Technology, Pasadena, CA 91125, USA.*
[8] *Now at Dipartimento di Fisica, Università di Milano, Milano, Italy.*
[9] *Also at CERN, PPE Division, 1211 Geneva 23, Switzerland.*
[10] *Now at DESY, Hamburg, Germany.*
[11] *Now at TRIUMF, Vancouver, B.C., Canada.*
[12] *Also at Università di Napoli, Dipartimento di Scienze Fisiche, Napoli, Italy.*
[13] *Now at Harvard University, Cambridge, MA 02138, U.S.A.*
[14] *Supported by the US Department of Energy, grant DE-FG03-92ER40689.*
[15] *Visitor from University of Wisconsin, Madison, WI 53706, USA.*
[16] *Now at Università di Pavia, Pavia, Italy.*
[17] *Now at Max-Planck-Institut f. Kernphysik, Heidelberg, Germany.*
[18] *Now at Rutgers University, Piscataway, NJ 08854, USA.*
[19] *Now at Oxford University, Oxford OX1 3RH, U.K.*

ARGUS COLLABORATION

H. Albrecht,[1] H. Ehrlichmann,[1] T. Hamacher,[1] R. P. Hofmann,[1] T. Kirchhoff,[1] A. Nau,[1] S. Nowak,[2] H. Schröder,[1] H. D. Schulz,[1] M. Walter,[2] R. Wurth,[1] C. Hast,[3] H. Kolanoski,[3] A. Kosche,[3] A. Lange,[3] A. Lindner,[3] R. Mankel,[3] M. Schieber,[3] T. Siegmund,[3] B. Spaan,[3] H. Thurn,[3] D. Töpfer,[3] D. Wegener,[3] M. Bittner,[4] P. Eckstein,[4] M. Paulini,[5] K. Reim,[5] H. Wegener,[5] R. Mundt,[6] T. Oest,[6] R. Reiner,[6] W. Schmidt-Parzefall,[6] W. Funk,[7] J. Stiewe,[7] S. Werner,[7] K. Ehret,[8] W. Hofmann,[8] A. Hüpper,[8] S. Khan,[8] K. T. Knöpfle,[8] M. Seeger,[8] J. Spengler,[8] D. I. Britton,[9,10] C. E. K. Charlesworth,[9,11] K. W. Edwards,[9,12] E. R. F. Hyatt,[9,10] H. Kapitza,[9,12] P. Krieger,[9,11] D. B. MacFarlane,[9,10] P. M. Patel,[9,10] J. D. Prentice,[9,11] P. R. B. Saull,[9,10] K. Tzamariudaki,[9,10] R. G. Van de Water,[9,11] T.-S. Yoon,[9,11] D. Reßing,[13] M. Schmidtler,[13] M. Schneider,[13] K. R. Schubert,[13] K. Strahl,[13] R. Waldi,[13] S. Weseler,[13] G. Kernel,[14] P. Križan,[14] E. Križnič,[14] T. Podobnik,[14] T. Živko,[14] V. Balagura,[15] I. Belyaev,[15] S. Chechelnitsky,[15] M. Danilov,[15] A. Droutskoy,[15] Yu. Gershtein,[15] A. Golutvin,[15] G. Kostina,[15] D. Litvintsev,[15] V. Lubimov,[15] P. Pakhlov,[15] F. Ratnikov,[15] S. Semenov,[15] A. Snizhko,[15] V. Soloshenko,[15] I. Tichomirov,[15] Yu. Zaitsev [15]

[1] *DESY, Hamburg, Germany*
[2] *DESY, IfH Zeuthen, Germany*
[3] *Institut für Physik, Universität Dortmund, Germany*
[4] *Institut für Kern- und Teilchenphysik, Technische Universität Dresden, Germany*
[5] *Physikalisches Institut, Universität Erlangen-Nürnberg, Germany*
[6] *II. Institut für Experimentalphysik, Universität Hamburg, Germany*
[7] *Institut für Hochenergiephysik, Universität Heidelberg, Germany*
[8] *Max-Planck-Institut für Kernphysik, Heidelberg, Germany*
[9] *Institute of Particle Physics, Canada*
[10] *McGill University, Montreal, Quebec, Canada*
[11] *University of Toronto, Toronto, Ontario, Canada*
[12] *Carleton University, Ottawa, Ontario, Canada*
[13] *Institut für Experimentelle Kernphysik, Universität Karlsruhe, Germany*
[14] *Institut J. Stefan and Oddelek za fiziko, Univerza v Ljubljani, Ljubljana, Slovenia*
[15] *Institute of Theoretical and Experimental Physics, Moscow, Russia*

BES COLLABORATION

J. Z. Bai,[1] O. Bardon,[6] R. A. Becker-Szendy,[7] A.Breakstone,[9] T. H. Burnett,[11] J. S. Campbell,[10] S. J. Chen,[1] S. M. Chen,[1] Y. Q. Chen,[1] Z. D. Cheng,[1] J. A. Coller,[2] R. F. Cowan,[6] H. C. Cui,[1] X. Z. Cui,[1] H. L. Ding,[1] Z. Z. Du,[1] W. Dunwoodie,[7] C. Fang,[1] M. J. Fero,[6] M. L. Gao,[1] S. Q. Gao,[1] W. X. Gao,[1] Y. N. Gao,[1] J. H. Gu,[1] S. D. Gu,[1] W. X. Gu,[1] Y. N. Guo,[1] Y. Y. Guo,[1] Y. Han,[1] M. Hatanaka,[3] J. He,[1] D. G. Hitlin,[3] G. Y. Hu,[1] T. Hu,[1] D. Q. Huang,[1] Y. Z. Huang,[1] J. M. Izen,[10] Q. P. Jia,[1] C. H. Jiang,[1] Z. J. Jiang,[1] A. S. Johnson,[2] L. A. Jones,[3] M. H. Kelsey,[3] Y. F. Lai,[1] P. F. Lang,[1] A. Lankford,[4] F. Li,[1] J. Li,[1] P. Q. Li,[1] Q. M. Li,[1] R. B. Li,[1] W. Li,[1] W. D. Li,[1] W. G. Li,[1] Y. S. Li,[1] S. Z. Lin,[1] H. M. Liu,[1] Q. Liu,[1] R. G. Liu,[1] Y. Liu,[1] B. Lowery,[10] J. G. Lu,[1] D. H. Ma,[1] E. C. Ma,[1] J. M. Ma,[1] M. Mandelkern,[4] H. Marsiske,[7] H. S. Mao,[1] Z. P. Mao,[1] X. C. Meng,[1] H. L. Ni,[1] S.Olsen,[9] L. J. Pan,[1] J. H. Panetta,[3] F. C. Porter,[3] E. N. Prabhakar,[3] N. D. Qi,[1] Y. K. Que,[1] J. Quigley,[6] G. Rong,[1] B. Schmid,[4] J. Schultz,[4] J. T. Shank,[2] Y. Y. Shao,[1] D. L. Shen,[1] H. Y. Sheng,[1] H. Z. Shi,[1] A. Smith,[4] E. Soderstrom,[7] X. F. Song,[1] D. P. Stoker,[4] H. S. Sun,[1] J. Synodinos,[7] W. H. Toki,[5] G. L. Tong,[1] E. Torrence,[6] L. Z. Wang,[1] M. Wang,[1] P. Wang,[1] P. L. Wang,[1] T. J. Wang,[1] Y. Y. Wang,[1] J. S. Whitaker,[2] R. J. Wilson,[5] W. J. Wisniewski,[8] X. D. Wu,[1] D. M. Xi,[1] X. M. Xia,[1] P. P. Xie,[1] X. X. Xie,[1] R. S. Xu,[1] Z. Q. Xu,[1] S. T. Xue,[1] R. K. Yamamoto,[6] J. Yan,[1] W. G. Yan,[1] C. M. Yang,[1] C. Y. Yang,[1] H. B. Yao,[1] M. H. Ye,[1] S. Z. Ye,[1] Z. Q. Yu,[1] B. Y. Zhang,[1] C. C. Zhang,[1] D. H. Zhang,[1] H. L. Zhang,[1] H. Y. Zhang,[1] J. W. Zhang,[1] L. S. Zhang,[1] S. Q. Zhang,[1] Y. Zhang,[1] D. X. Zhao,[1] M. Zhao,[1] P. D. Zhao,[1] W. R. Zhao,[1] J.P. Zheng,[1] L. S. Zheng,[1] Z. P. Zheng,[1] G. P. Zhou,[1] H. S. Zhou,[1] L. Zhou,[1] L. Zhou,[1] X. F. Zhou,[1] Y. H. Zhou,[1] Q. M. Zhu,[1] Y. C. Zhu,[1] Y. S. Zhu,[1] and G. Zioulas[4]

[1] *Institute of High Energy Physics, Beijing 100039, People's Republic of China.*
[2] *Boston University, Boston MA 02215, USA.*
[3] *California Institute of Technology, Pasadena, CA 91125, USA.*
[4] *University of California, Irvine, CA 92717, USA.*
[5] *Colorado State University, Fort Collins, CO 80523, USA.*
[6] *Massachusetts Institute of Technology, Cambridge, MA 02139, USA.*
[7] *Stanford Linear Accelerator Center, Stanford University, Stanford, CA 94309, USA.*
[8] *Superconducting Super Collider Laboratory, Dallas TX 75237-3946, USA.*
[9] *University of Hawaii, Honolulu, HI 96822, USA.*
[10] *University of Texas at Dallas, Richardson, TX 75083-0688, USA.*
[11] *University of Washington, Seattle, WA 98195, USA.*

CDF COLLABORATION

F. Abe,[11] M. Albrow,[6] D. Amidei,[14] C. Anway-Wiese,[3] G. Apollinari,[22] M. Atac,[6] P. Auchincloss,[21] P. Azzi,[16] A. R. Baden,[8] N. Bacchetta,[15] W. Badgett,[14] M. W. Bailey,[20] A. Bamberger,[6,a] P. de Barbaro,[21] A. Barbaro-Galtieri,[12] V. E. Barnes,[20] B. A. Barnett,[10] G. Bauer,[13] T. Baumann,[8] F. Bedeschi,[19] S. Behrends,[2] S. Belforte,[19] G. Bellettini,[19] J. Bellinger,[27] D. Benjamin,[26] J. Benlloch,[6,a] J. Bensinger,[2] A. Beretvas,[6] J. P. Berge,[6] S. Bertolucci,[7] K. Biery,[17,a] S. Bhadra,[9] M. Binkley,[6] D. Bisello,[16] R. Blair,[1] C. Blocker,[2] A. Bodek,[21] V. Bolognesi,[19] A. W. Booth,[6] C. Boswell,[10] G. Brandenburg,[8] D. Brown,[8] E. Buckley-Geer,[6] H. S. Budd,[21] G. Busetto,[16] A. Byon-Wagner,[6] K. L. Byrum,[1] C. Campagnari,[6] M. Campbell,[14] A. Caner,[6] R. Carey,[8] W. Carithers,[12] D. Carlsmith,[27] J. T. Carroll,[6] R. Cashmore,[6,a] A. Castro,[16] F. Cervelli,[19] K. Chadwick,[6] J. Chapman,[14] G. Chiarelli,[7] W. Chinowsky,[12] S. Cihangir,[6] A. G. Clark,[6] M. Cobal,[19] D. Connor,[17] M. Contreras,[4] J. Cooper,[6] M. Cordelli,[7] D. Crane,[6] J. D. Cunningham,[2] C. Day,[6] F. DeJongh,[6] S. Dell'Agnello,[19] M. Dell'Orso,[19] L. Demortier,[22] B. Denby,[6] P. F. Derwent,[14] T. Devlin,[23] D. DiBitonto,[24] M. Dickson,[21] R. B. Drucker,[12] K. Einsweiler,[12] J. E. Elias,[6] R. Ely,[12] S. Eno,[4] S. Errede,[9] A. Etchegoyen,[6,a] B. Farhat,[13] M. Frautschi,[15] G. J. Feldman,[8] B. Flaugher,[6] G. W. Foster,[6] M. Franklin,[8] J. Freeman,[6] H. Frisch,[4] T. Fuess,[6] Y. Fukui,[11] A. F. Garfinkel,[20] A. Gauthier,[9] S. Geer,[6] D. W. Gerdes,[4] P. Giannetti,[19] N. Giokaris,[22] P. Giromini,[7] L. Gladney,[17] M. Gold,[15] J. Gonzalez,[17] K. Goulianos,[22] H. Grassmann,[16] G. M. Grieco,[19] R. Grindley,[17,a] C. Grosso-Pilcher,[4] C. Haber,[12] S. R. Hahn,[6] R. Handler,[27] K. Hara,[25] B. Harral,[17] R. M. Harris,[6] S. A. Hauger,[5] J. Hauser,[3] C. Hawk,[23] T. Hessing,[24] R. Hollebeek,[17] L. Holloway,[9] S. Hong,[14] G. Houk,[17] P. Hu,[18] B. Hubbard,[12] B. T. Huffman,[18] R. Hughes,[21] P. Hurst,[8] J. Huth,[6] J. Hylen,[6] M. Incagli,[19] T. Ino,[25] H. Iso,[25] H. Jensen,[6] C. P. Jessop,[8] R. P. Johnson,[6] U. Joshi,[6] R. W. Kadel,[12] T. Kamon,[25] S. Kanda,[25] D. A. Kardelis,[9] I. Karliner,[9] E. Kearns,[8] L. Keeble,[24] R. Kephart,[6] P. Kesten,[2] R. M. Keup,[9] H. Keutelian,[6] D. Kim,[6] S. B. Kim,[14] S. H. Kim,[25] Y. K. Kim,[12] L. Kirsch,[2] K. Kondo,[25] J. Konigsberg,[8] K. Kordas,[17,a] E. Kovacs,[6] M. Krasberg,[14] S. E. Kuhlmann,[1] E. Kuns,[23] A. T. Laasanen,[20] S. Lammel,[3] J. I. Lamoureux,[27] S. Leone,[19] J. D. Lewis,[6] W. Li,[1] P. Limon,[6] M. Lindgren,[3] T. M. Liss,[9] N. Lockyer,[17] M. Loreti,[16] E. H. Low,[17] D. Lucchesi,[19] C. B. Luchini,[9] P. Lukens,[6] P. Maas,[27] K. Maeshima,[6] M. Mangano,[19] J. P. Marriner,[6] M. Mariotti,[19] R. Markeloff,[27] L. A. Markosky,[27] J. Matthews,[15] R. Mattingly,[2] P. McIntyre,[24] A. Menzione,[19] E. Meschi,[19] T. Meyer,[24] S. Mikamo,[11] M. Miller,[4] T. Mimashi,[25] S. Miscetti,[7] M. Mishina,[11] S. Miyashita,[25] Y. Morita,[25] S. Moulding,[2] J. Mueller,[23] A. Mukherjee,[6] T. Muller,[3] L. F. Nakae,[2] I. Nakano,[25] C. Nelson,[6] D. Neuberger,[3] C. Newman-Holmes,[6] J. S. T. Ng,[8] M. Ninomiya,[25] L. Nodulman,[1] S. Ogawa,[25] R. Paoletti,[19] V. Papadimitriou,[6] A. Para,[6] E. Pare,[8] S. Park,[6] J. Patrick,[6] G. Pauletta,[19] L. Pescara,[16] G. Piacentino,[19] T. J. Phillips,[5] F. Ptohos,[8] R. Plunkett,[6] L. Pondrom,[27] J. Proudfoot,[1] G. Punzi,[19] D. Quarrie,[6] K. Ragan,[17,a] G. Redlinger,[4] J. Rhoades,[27] M. Roach,[26] F. Rimondi,[6,a] L. Ristori,[19] W. J. Robertson,[5] T. Rodrigo,[6] T. Rohaly,[17] A. Roodman,[4] W. K. Sakumoto,[21] A. Sansoni,[7] R. D. Sard,[9] A. Savoy-Navarro,[6] V. Scarpine,[9] P. Schlabach,[8] E. E. Schmidt,[6] O. Schneider,[12] M. H. Schub,[20] R. Schwitters,[8] A. Scribano,[19] S. Segler,[6] S. Seidel,[15] Y. Seiya,[25] G. Sganos,[17,a] M. Shapiro,[12] N. M. Shaw,[20] M. Sheaff,[27] M. Shochet,[4] J. Siegrist,[12] A. Sill,[21] P. Sinervo,[17,a] J. Skarha,[10] K. Sliwa,[26] D. A. Smith,[19] F. D. Snider,[10] L. Song,[6] T. Song,[14] M. Spahn,[12] A. Spies,[10] P. Sphicas,[13] R. St. Denis,[8] L. Stanco,[6,a] A. Stefanini,[19] G. Sullivan,[4] K. Sumorok,[13] R. L. Swartz, Jr.,[9] M. Takano,[25] K. Takikawa,[25] S. Tarem,[2] F. Tartarelli,[19] S. Tether,[13] D. Theriot,[6] M. Timko,[26] P. Tipton,[21] S. Tkaczyk,[6] A. Tollestrup,[6] J. Tonnison,[20] W. Trischuk,[8] Y. Tsay,[4] J. Tseng,[10] N. Turini,[19] F. Ukegawa,[25] D. Underwood,[1] S. Vejcik, III,[14] R. Vidal,[6] R. G. Wagner,[1] R. L. Wagner,[6] N. Wainer,[6] R. C. Walker,[21] J. Walsh,[17] G. Watts,[21] T. Watts,[23] R. Webb,[24] C. Wendt,[27] H. Wenzel,[19] W. C. Wester, III,[12] T. Westhusing,[9] S. N. White,[22] A. B. Wicklund,[1] E. Wicklund,[6] H. H. Williams,[17] B. L. Winer,[21] P. Wolinski,[24] D. Y. Wu,[14] X. Wu,[19] J. Wyss,[16] A. Yagil,[6] K. Yasuoka,[25] Y. Ye,[17,a] G. P. Yeh,[6] C. Yi,[17] J. Yoh,[6] M. Yokoyama,[25] J. C. Yun,[6] A. Zanetti,[19] F. Zetti,[19] S. Zhang,[14] W. Zhang,[16] S. Zucchelli[6,a]

[1] *Argonne National Laboratory, Argonne, Illinois 60439*
[2] *Brandeis University, Waltham, Massachusetts 02254*
[3] *University of California at Los Angeles, Los Angeles, California 90024*
[4] *University of Chicago, Chicago, Illinois 60637*
[5] *Duke University, Durham, North Carolina 27706*
[6] *Fermi National Accelerator Laboratory, Batavia, Illinois 60510*
[7] *Laboratori Nazionali di Frascati, Istituto Nazionale di Fisica Nucleare, Frascati, Italy*
[8] *Harvard University, Cambridge, Massachusetts 02138*
[9] *University of Illinois, Urbana, Illinois 61801*
[10] *The Johns Hopkins University, Baltimore, Maryland 21218*
[11] *National Laboratory for High Energy Physics (KEK), Japan*
[12] *Lawrence Berkeley Laboratory, Berkeley, California 94720*
[13] *Massachusetts Institute of Technology, Cambridge, Massachusetts 02139*
[14] *University of Michigan, Ann Arbor, Michigan 48109*
[15] *University of New Mexico, Albuquerque, NM 87131*
[16] *Universita di Padova, Instituto Nazionale di Fisica Nucleare, Sezione di Padova, I-35131 Padova, Italy*
[17] *University of Pennsylvania, Philadelphia, Pennsylvania 19104*
[18] *University of Pittsburgh, Pittsburgh, PA 15260*
[19] *Istituto Nazionale di Fisica Nucleare, University and Scuola Normale Superiore of Pisa, I-56100 Pisa, Italy*
[20] *Purdue University, West Lafayette, Indiana 47907*
[21] *University of Rochester, Rochester, New York 15627*
[22] *Rockefeller University, New York, New York 10021*
[23] *Rutgers University, Piscataway, New Jersey 08854*
[24] *Texas A&M University, College Station, Texas 77843*
[25] *University of Tsukuba, Tsukuba, Ibaraki 305, Japan*
[26] *Tufts University, Medford, Massachusetts 02155*
[27] *University of Wisconsin, Madison, Wisconsin 53706*

CHARM II COLLABORATION

B. Akkus,[10] E. Arik,[10] R. Beyer,[2] F.W. Büsser,[3] A. Capone,[8] M. Caria,[7] A.G. Cocco,[7] D. De Pedis,[8] E. Di Capua,[9] U. Dore,[8] A. Ereditato,[7] D. Favart,[4] G. Fiorillo,[7] W. Flegel,[2] C. Foos,[3] A. Frenkel-Rambaldi,[8] L. Gerland,[3] P. Gorbunov,[5] G. Grégoire,[4] E. Grigoriev,[5] H. Grote,[2] K. Hiller,[11] V. Khovansky,[5] E. Knoops,[4] T. Layda,[3] V. Lemaître,[4] W. Lippich,[6] P.F. Loverre,[8] D. Macina,[8] F. Marchetti-Stasi,[7] A. Maslennikov,[5] T. Mouthuy,[2] R. Nahnhauer,[11] A. Nathaniel,[6] F. Niebergall,[3] H. Øverås,[2] V. Palladino,[7] J. Panman,[2] G. Piredda,[8] G. Rädel,[3] S. Ricciardi,[9] H. Roloff,[11] A. Rozanov,[2] B. Saitta,[9] R. Santacesaria,[8] M. Serin-Zeyrek,[10] R. Sever,[10] P. Stähelin,[3] A. Staude,[6] P. Strolin,[7] P. Tolun,[10] P. Vilain,[1] J. Vogt,[6] T. Voss,[3] G. Wilquet,[1] K. Winter,[2] G. Zacek,[2] V. Zacek[2]

[1] *Inter-University Institute for High Energies (ULB-VUB), Brussels, Belgium*
[2] *CERN, Geneva, Switzerland*
[3] *II. Institut für Experimentalphysik Universität Hamburg, Hamburg, Germany*
[4] *Université Catholique de Louvain, Louvain-la-Neuve, Belgium*
[5] *Institute for Theoretical and Experimental Physics, Moscow, Russian Federation*
[6] *Sektion Physik* der Universität München, Munich, Germany*
[7] *Università e Istituto Nazionale di Fisica Nucleare (INFN), Naples, Italy*
[8] *Università 'La Sapienza' e Istituto Nazionale di Fisica Nucleare (INFN), Rome, Italy*
[9] *Università di Ferrara e Istituto Nazionale di Fisica Nucleare (INFN), Ferrara, Italy*
[10] *YEFAM, Turkey*
[11] *DESY-Institut für Hochenergiephysik, Zeuthen, Germany*

CLEO COLLABORATION

D.S. Akerib[1] B. Barish[1] M. Chadha[1] S. Chan[1] D.F. Cowen[1] G. Eigen[1] J.S. Miller[1] J. Urheim[1]
A.J. Weinstein[1] D. Acosta[2] M. Athanas[2] G. Masek[2] B. Ong[2] H. Paar[2] M. Sivertz[2] A. Bean[3]
J. Gronberg[3] R. Kutschke[3] S. Menary[3] R.J. Morrison[3] S. Nakanishi[3] H.N. Nelson[3] T.K. Nelson[3]
J.D. Richman[3] H. Tajima[3] D. Schmidt[3] D. Sperka[3] M.S. Witherell[3] M. Procario[4] S. Yang[4]
R. Balles[5] K. Cho[5] M. Daoudi[5] W.T. Ford[5] D.R. Johnson[5] K. Lingel[5] M. Lohner[5] P. Rankin[5]
J.G. Smith[5] J.P. Alexander[6] C. Bebek[6] K. Berkelman[6] D. Besson[6] T.E. Browder[6] D.G. Cassel[6]
H.A. Cho[6] D.M. Coffman[6] P.S. Drell[6] R. Ehrlich[6] R.S. Galik[6] M. Garcia-Sciveres[6] B. Geiser[6]
B. Gittelman[6] S.W. Gray[6] D.L. Hartill[6] B.K. Heltsley[6] K. Honscheid[6] C.D. Jones[6] S.L. Jones[6]
J. Kandaswamy[6] N. Katayama[6] P.C. Kim[6] D.L. Kreinick[6] G.S. Ludwig[6] J. Masui[6] J. Mevissen[6]
N.B. Mistry[6] C.R. Ng[6] E. Nordberg[6] M. Ogg*[6] C. O'Grady[6] J.R. Patterson[6] D. Peterson[6]
D. Riley[6] M. Sapper[6] M. Selen[6] H. Worden[6] M. Worris[6] F.Würthwein[6] P. Avery[7] A. Freyberger[7]
J. Rodriguez[7] R. Stephens[7] J. Yelton[7] D. Cinabro[8] S. Henderson[8] K. Kinoshita[8] T. Liu[8] M. Saulnier[8]
R. Wilson[8] H. Yamamoto[8] A. J. Sadoff[9] R. Ammar[10] S. Ball[10] P. Baringer[10] D. Coppage[10]
N. Copty[10] R. Davis[10] N. Hancock[10] M. Kelly[10] N. Kwak[10] H. Lam[10] Y. Kubota[11] M. Lattery[11]
J.K. Nelson[11] S. Patton[11] D. Perticone[11] R. Poling[11] V. Savinov[11] S. Schrenk[11] R. Wang[11]
M.S. Alam[12] I.J. Kim[12] B. Nemati[12] J.J. O'Neill[12] V. Romero[12] H. Severini[12] C.R. Sun[12]
M.M. Zoeller[12] G. Crawford[13] R. Fulton[13] K.K. Gan[13] H. Kagan[13] R. Kass[13] J. Lee[13] R. Malchow[13]
F. Morrow[13] Y. Skovpen**[13] M. Sung[13] C. White[13] J. Whitmore[13] P. Wilson[13] F. Butler[14]
X. Fu[14] G. Kalbfleisch[14] M. Lambrecht[14] W.R. Ross[14] P. Skubic[14] J. Snow[14] P.L. Wang[14]
M. Wood[14] D. Bortoletto[15] D.N. Brown[15] J. Dominick[15] R.L. McIlwain[15] T. Miao[15] D.H. Miller[15]
M. Modesitt[15] S.F. Schaffner[15] E.I. Shibata[15] I.P.J. Shipsey[15] P.N. Wang[15] M. Battle[16] J. Ernst[16]
H. Kroha[16] S. Roberts[16] K. Sparks[16] E.H. Thorndike[16] C.H. Wang[16] S. Sanghera[17] T. Skwarnicki[17]
R. Stroynowski[17] M. Artuso[18] M. Goldberg[18] N. Horwitz[18] R. Kennett[18] G.C. Moneti[18] F. Muheim[18]
S. Playfer[18] Y. Rozen[18] P. Rubin[18] S. Stone[18] M. Thulasidas[18] G. Vasseur[18] G. Zhu[18] A.V. Barnes[19]
J. Bartelt[19] S.E. Csorna[19] Z. Egyed[19] V. Jain[19] P. Sheldon[19]

[1] California Institute of Technology, Pasadena, California 91125
[2] University of California, La Jolla, California 92093
[3] University of California, Santa Barbara, California 93106
[4] Carnegie-Mellon University, Pittsburgh, Pennsylvania 15213
[5] University of Colorado, Boulder, Colorado 80309-0390
[6] Cornell University, Ithaca, New York 14853
[7] University of Florida, Gainesville, Florida 32611
[8] Harvard University, Cambridge, Massachusetts 02138
[9] Ithaca College, Ithaca, New York 14850
[10] University of Kansas, Lawrence, Kansas 66045
[11] University of Minnesota, Minneapolis, Minnesota 55455
[12] State University of New York at Albany, Albany, New York 12222
[13] Ohio State University, Columbus, Ohio, 43210
[14] University of Oklahoma, Norman, Oklahoma 73019
[15] Purdue University, West Lafayette, Indiana 47907
[16] University of Rochester, Rochester, New York 14627
[17] Southern Methodist University, Dallas, Texas 75275
[18] Syracuse University, Syracuse, New York 13244
[19] Vanderbilt University, Nashville, Tennessee 37235
* Permanent address: Carleton University, Ottawa, Canada
** Permanent address: Budker Institute of Nuclear Physics, Novosibirsk-90, Russia

DELPHI COLLABORATION

P. Abreu,[20] W. Adam,[7] T. Adye,[36] E. Agasi,[30] I. Ajinenk,[41] R. Aleksan,[38] G. D. Alekseev,[14] A. Algeri,[13] P. Allen,[47] S. Almehed,[23] S. J. Alvsvaag,[4] U. Amaldi,[7] E. G. Anassontzis,[3] A. Andreazza,[27] P. Antilogus,[24] W-D. Apel,[15] R. J. Apsimon,[36] Y. Arnoud,[38] B. Åsman,[43] J-E. Augustin,[18] A. Augustinus,[30] P. Baillon,[7] P. Bambade,[18] F. Barao,[20] R. Barate,[12] G. Barbiellini,[45] D. Y. Bardin,[14] G. J. Barker,[33] A. Baroncelli,[39] O. Barring,[7] J. A. Barrio,[25] W. Bartl,[48] M. J. Bates,[36] M. Battaglia,[13] M. Baubillier,[22] K-H. Becks,[50] C. J. Beeston,[33] M. Begalli,[35] P. Beilliere,[6] Yu. Belokopytov,[41] P. Beltran,[9] D. Benedic,[8] A. C. Benvenuti,[5] M. Berggren,[18] D. Bertrand,[2] F. Bianchi,[44] M. S. Bilenky,[14] P. Billoir,[22] J. Bjarne,[23] D. Bloch,[8] S. Blyth,[33] V. Bocci,[37] P. N. Bogolubov,[14] T. Bolognese,[38] M. Bonesini,[27] W. Bonivento,[27] P. S. L. Booth,[21] G. Borisov,[41] H. Borner,[7] C. Bosio,[39] B. Bostjancic,[42] S. Bosworth,[33] O. Botner,[46] B. Bouquet,[18] C. Bourdarios,[18] T. J. V. Bowcock,[21] M. Bozzo,[11] S. Braibant,[2] P. Branchini,[39] K. D. Brand,[34] R. A. Brenner,[7] H. Briand,[22] C. Bricman,[2] R. C. A. Brown,[7] N. Brummer,[30] J-M. Brunet,[6] L. Bugge,[32] T. Buran,[32] H. Burmeister,[7] J. A. M. A. Buytaert,[7] M. Caccia,[7] M. Calvi,[27] A. J. Camacho Rozas,[40] R. Campion,[21] T. Camporesi,[7] V. Canale,[37] F. Cao,[2] F. Carena,[7] L. Carroll,[21] M. V. Castillo Gimenez,[47] A. Cattai,[7] F. R. Cavallo,[5] L. Cerrito,[37] V. Chabaud,[7] A. Chan,[1] M. Chapkin,[41] Ph. Charpentier,[7] L. Chaussard,[18] J. Chauveau,[22] P. Checchia,[34] G. A. Chelkov,[14] L. Chevalier,[38] P. Chliapnikov,[41] V. Chorowicz,[22] J. T. M. Chrin,[47] M. P. Clara,[44] P. Collins,[33] J. L. Contreras,[25] R. Contri,[11] E. Cortina,[47] G. Cosme,[18] F. Couchot,[18] H. B. Crawley,[1] D. Crennell,[36] G. Crosetti,[11] M. Crozon,[6] J. Cuevas Maestro,[40] S. Czellar,[13] E. Dahl-Jensen,[28] B. Dalmagne,[18] M. Dam,[32] G. Damgaard,[28] G. Darbo,[11] E. Daubie,[2] A. Daum,[15] P. D. Dauncey,[33] M. Davenport,[7] P. David,[22] J. Davies,[21] W. Da Silva,[22] C. Defoix,[6] D. Delikaris,[7] S. Delorme,[7] P. Delpierre,[6] N. Demaria,[44] A. De Angelis,[45] H. De Boeck,[2] W. De Boer,[15] C. De Clercq,[2] M. D. M. De Fez Laso,[47] N. De Groot,[30] C. De La Vaissiere,[22] B. De Lotto,[45] A. De Min,[27] H. Dijkstra,[7] L. Di Ciaccio,[37] F. Djama,[8] J. Dolbeau,[6] M. Donszelmann,[7] K. Doroba,[49] M. Dracos,[7] J. Drees,[50] M. Dris,[31] Y. Dufour,[6] F. Dupont,[12] L-O. Eek,[46] P. A. -M. Eerola,[7] R. Ehret,[15] T. Ekelof,[46] G. Ekspong,[43] A. Elliot Peisert,[34] J-P. Engel,[8] N. Ershaidat,[22] D. Fassouliotis,[31] M. Feindt,[7] A. Fenyuk,[41] M. Fernandez Alonso,[40] A. Ferrer,[47] T. A. Filippas,[31] A. Firestone,[1] H. Foeth,[7] E. Fokitis,[31] F. Fontanelli,[11] K. A. J. Forbes,[21] J-L. Fousset,[26] S. Francon,[24] B. Franek,[36] P. Frenkiel,[6] D. C. Fries,[15] A. G. Frodesen,[4] R. Fruhwirth,[48] F. Fulda-Quenzer,[18] K. Furnival,[21] H. Furstenau,[15] J. Fuster,[7] D. Gamba,[44] C. Garcia,[47] J. Garcia,[40] C. Gaspar,[7] U. Gasparini,[34] Ph. Gavillet,[7] E. N. Gazis,[31] J-P. Gerber,[8] P. Giacomelli,[7] R. Gokieli,[49] B. Golob,[42] V. M. Golovatyuk,[14] J. J. Gomez Y Cadenas,[7] A. Goobar,[43] G. Gopal,[36] M. Gorski,[49] V. Gracco,[11] A. Grant,[7] F. Grard,[2] E. Graziani,[39] G. Grosdidier,[18] E. Gross,[7] P. Grosse-Wiesmann,[7] B. Grossetete,[22] J. Guy,[36] U. Haedinger,[15] F. Hahn,[50] M. Hahn,[15] S. Haider,[30] Z. Hajduk,[16] A. Hakansson,[23] A. Hallgren,[46] K. Hamacher,[50] G. Hamel De Monchenault,[38] W. Hao,[30] F. J. Harris,[33] V. Hedberg,[23] T. Henkes,[7] J. J. Hernandez,[47] P. Herquet,[2] H. Herr,[7] T. L. Hessing,[21] I. Hietanen,[13] C. O. Higgins,[21] E. Higon,[47] H. J. Hilke,[7] S. D. Hodgson,[33] T. Hofmokl,[49] R. Holmes,[1] S-O. Holmgren,[43] D. Holthuizen,[30] P. F. Honore,[6] J. E. Hooper,[28] M. Houlden,[21] J. Hrubec,[48] K. Huet,[2] P. O. Hulth,[43] K. Hultqvist,[43] P. Ioannou,[3] D. Isenhower,[7] P-S. Iversen,[4] J. N. Jackson,[21] P. Jalocha,[16] G. Jarlskog,[23] P. Jarry,[38] B. Jean-Marie,[18] E. K. Johansson,[43] D. Johnson,[21] M. Jonker,[7] L. Jonsson,[23] P. Juillot,[8] G. Kalkanis,[3] G. Kalmus,[36] F. Kapusta,[22] B. A. Khomenko,[14] E. Karvelas,[9] S. Katsanevas,[3] E. C. Katsoufis,[31] R. Keranen,[13] J. Kesteman,[2] B. A. Khomenko,[14] N. N. Khovanski,[14] B. King,[21] N. J. Kjaer,[7] H. Klein,[7] W. Klempt,[7] A. Klovning,[4] P. Kluit,[30] A. Koch-Mehrin,[50] J. H. Koehne,[15] B. Koene,[30] P. Kokkinias,[9] M. Koratzinos,[32] K. Korcyl,[16] A. V. Korytov,[14] V. Kostioukhine,[41] C. Kourkoumelis,[3] O. Kouznetsov,[14] P. H. Kramer,[50] J. Krolikowski,[49] I. Kronkvist,[23] U. Kruener-Marquis,[50] W. Krupinski,[16] K. Kulka,[46] K. Kurvinen,[13] C. Lacasta,[47] C. Lambropoulos,[9] J. W. Lamsa,[1] L. Lanceri,[45] V. Lapin,[41] J-P. Laugier,[38] R. Lauhakangas,[13] G. Leder,[48] F. Ledroit,[12] R. Leitner,[29] Y. Lemoigne,[38] J. Lemonne,[2]

G. Lenzen,[50] V. Lepeltier,[18] T. Lesiak,[16] J. M. Levy,[8] E. Lieb,[50] D. Liko,[48] J. Lindgren,[13]
R. Lindner,[50] A. Lipniacka,[49] I. Lippi,[34] B. Loerstad,[23] M. Lokajicek,[14] J. G. Loken,[33] A. Lopez-
Fernandez,[7] M. A. Lopez Aguera,[40] M. Los,[30] D. Loukas,[9] J. J. Lozano,[47] P. Lutz,[6] L. Lyons,[33]
G. Maehlum,[32] J. Maillard,[6] A. Maio,[20] A. Maltezos,[9] F. Mandl,[48] J. Marco,[40] M. Margoni,[34]
J-C. Marin,[7] A. Markou,[9] T. Maron,[50] S. Marti,[47] L. Mathis,[1] F. Matorras,[40] C. Matteuzzi,[27]
G. Matthiae,[37] M. Mazzucato,[34] M. Mc Cubbin,[21] R. Mc Kay,[1] R. Mc Nulty,[21] G. Meola,[11]
C. Meroni,[27] W. T. Meyer,[1] M. Michelotto,[34] I. Mikulec,[48] L. Mirabito,[24] W. A. Mitaroff,[48]
G. V. Mitselmakher,[14] U. Mjoernmark,[23] T. Moa,[43] R. Moeller,[28] K. Moenig,[7] M. R. Monge,[11]
P. Morettini,[11] H. Mueller,[15] W. J. Murray,[36] B. Muryn,[16] G. Myatt,[33] F. L. Navarria,[5] P. Negri,[27]
B. S. Nielsen,[28] B. Nijjhar,[21] V. Nikolaenko,[41] P. E. S. Nilsen,[4] P. Niss,[43] V. Obraztsov,[41]
A. G. Olshevski,[14] R. Orava,[13] A. Ostankov,[41] K. Osterberg,[13] A. Ouraou,[38] M. Paganoni,[27]
R. Pain,[22] H. Palka,[30] Th. D. Papadopoulou,[31] L. Pape,[7] F. Parodi,[11] A. Passeri,[39] M. Pegoraro,[34]
J. Pennanen,[13] L. Peralta,[20] H. Pernegger,[48] M. Pernicka,[48] A. Perrotta,[5] C. Petridou,[45]
A. Petrolini,[11] T. E. Pettersen,[34] F. Pierre,[38] M. Pimenta,[20] O. Pingot,[2] S. Plaszczynski,[18]
O. Podobrin,[15] M. E. Pol,[7] G. Polok,[16] P. Poropat,[45] P. Privitera,[15] A. Pullia,[27] D. Radojicic,[33]
S. Ragazzi,[27] H. Rahmani,[31] P. N. Ratoff,[19] A. L. Read,[32] N. G. Redaelli,[27] M. Regler,[48] D. Reid,[21]
P. B. Renton,[33] L. K. Resvanis,[3] F. Richard,[18] M. Richardson,[21] J. Ridky,[10] G. Rinaudo,[44]
I. Roditi,[17] A. Romero,[44] I. Roncagliolo,[11] P. Ronchese,[34] C. Ronnqvist,[13] E. I. Rosenberg,[1]
S. Rossi,[7] U. Rossi,[5] E. Rosso,[7] P. Roudeau,[18] T. Rovelli,[5] W. Ruckstuhl,[30] V. Ruhlmann-
Kleider,[38] A. Ruiz,[40] K. Rybicki,[16] H. Saarikko,[13] Y. Sacquin,[38] G. Sajot,[12] J. Salt,[47] J. Sanchez,[25]
M. Sannino,[11] S. Schael,[7] H. Schneider,[15] B. Schulze,[37] M. A. E. Schyns,[50] G. Sciolla,[44] F. Scuri,[45]
A. M. Segar,[33] A. Seitz,[15] R. Sekulin,[36] M. Sessa,[45] G. Sette,[11] R. Seufert,[15] R. C. Shellard,[35]
I. Siccama,[30] P. Siegrist,[38] S. Simonetti,[11] F. Simonetto,[34] A. N. Sisakian,[14] G. Skjevling,[32]
G. Smadja,[38,24] G. R. Smith,[36] R. Sosnowski,[49] D. Souza-Santos,[35] T. S. Spassoff,[12] E. Spiriti,[39]
S. Squarcia,[11] H. Staeck,[50] C. Stanescu,[39] S. Stapnes,[32] G. Stavropoulos,[9] F. Stichelbaut,[2]
A. Stocchi,[18] J. Strauss,[48] J. Straver,[7] R. Strub,[8] B. Stugu,[4] M. Szczekowski,[7] M. Szeptycka,[49]
P. Szymanski,[49] T. Tabarelli,[27] O. Tchikilev,[41] G. E. Theodosiou,[9] A. Tilquin,[26] J. Timmermans,[30]
V. G. Timofeev,[14] L. G. Tkatchev,[14] T. Todorov,[8] D. Z. Toet,[30] O. Toker,[13] B. Tome,[20]
E. Torassa,[44] L. Tortora,[39] D. Treille,[7] U. Trevisan,[11] W. Trischuk,[7] G. Tristram,[6] C. Troncon,[27]
A. Tsirou,[7] E. N. Tsyganov,[14] M. Turala,[16] M-L. Turluer,[38] T. Tuuva,[13] I. A. Tyapkin,[22]
M. Tyndel,[36] S. Tzamarias,[21] S. Ueberschaer,[50] O. Ullaland,[7] V. Uvarov,[41] G. Valenti,[5]
E. Vallazza,[44] J. A. Valls Ferrer,[47] C. Vander Velde,[2] G. W. Van Apeldoorn,[30] P. Van Dam,[30]
M. Van Der Heijden,[30] W. K. Van Doninck,[2] P. Vaz,[7] G. Vegni,[27] L. Ventura,[34] W. Venus,[36]
F. Verbeure,[2] M. Verlato,[34] L. S. Vertogradov,[14] D. Vilanova,[38] P. Vincent,[24] L. Vitale,[13]
E. Vlasov,[41] A. S. Vodopyanov,[14] M. Vollmer,[50] G. Voulgaris,[3] M. Voutilainen,[13] V. Vrba,[39]
H. Wahlen,[50] C. Walck,[43] F. Waldner,[45] M. Wayne,[1] A. Wehr,[50] M. Weierstall,[50] P. Weilhammer,[7]
J. Werner,[50] A. M. Wetherell,[7] J. H. Wickens,[2] G. R. Wilkinson,[33] W. S. C. Williams,[33] M. Winter,[8]
M. Witek,[16] G. Wormser,[18] K. Woschnagg,[46] N. Yamdagni,[43] P. Yepes,[7] A. Zaitsev,[41] A. Zalewska,[16]
P. Zalewski,[18] D. Zavrtanik,[42] E. Zevgolatakos,[9] G. Zhang,[50] N. I. Zimin,[14] M. Zito,[38] R. Zuberi,[33]
R. Zukanovich Funchal,[6] G. Zumerle,[34] J. Zuniga[47]

[1] *Ames Laboratory and Department of Physics, Iowa State University, Ames IA 50011, USA*
[2] *Physics Department, Univ. Instelling Antwerpen, Universiteitsplein 1, B-2610 Wilrijk, Belgium*
and IIHE, ULB-VUB, Pleinlaan 2, B-1050 Brussels, Belgium
and Faculté des Sciences, Univ. de l'Etat Mons, Av. Maistriau 19, B-7000 Mons, Belgium
[3] *Physics Laboratory, University of Athens, Solonos Str. 104, GR-10680 Athens, Greece*
[4] *Department of Physics, University of Bergen, Allégaten 55, N-5007 Bergen, Norway*
[5] *Dipartimento di Fisica, Università di Bologna and INFN, Via Irnerio 46, I-40126*

Bologna, Italy
[6] Collège de France, Lab. de Physique Corpusculaire, IN2P3-CNRS, F-75231 Paris Cedex 05, France
[7] CERN, CH-1211 Geneva 23, Switzerland
[8] Centre de Recherche Nucléaire, IN2P3 - CNRS/ULP - BP20, F-67037 Strasbourg Cedex, France
[9] Institute of Nuclear Physics, N.C.S.R. Demokritos, P.O. Box 60228, GR-15310 Athens, Greece
[10] FZU, Inst. of Physics of the C.A.S. High Energy Physics Division, Na Slovance 2, CS-180 40, Praha 8, Czechoslovakia
[11] Dipartimento di Fisica, Università di Genova and INFN, Via Dodecaneso 33, I-16146 Genova, Italy
[12] Institut des Sciences Nucléaires, IN2P3-CNRS, Université de Grenoble 1, F-38026 Grenoble, France
[13] Research Institute for High Energy Physics, SEFT, Siltavuorenpenger 20 C, SF-00170 Helsinki, Finland
[14] Joint Institute for Nuclear Research, Dubna, Head Post Office, P.O. Box 79, 101 000 Moscow, Russian Federation
[15] Institut für Experimentelle Kernphysik, Universität Karlsruhe, Postfach 6980, D-7500 Karlsruhe 1, Germany
[16] High Energy Physics Laboratory, Institute of Nuclear Physics, Ul. Kawiory 26 a, PL-30055 Krakow 30, Poland
[17] Centro Brasileiro de Pesquisas Físicas, rua Xavier Sigaud 150, RJ-22290 Rio de Janeiro, Brazil
[18] Université de Paris-Sud, Lab. de l'Accélérateur Linéaire, IN2P3-CNRS, Bat 200, F-91405 Orsay, France
[19] School of Physics and Materials, University of Lancaster - Lancaster LA1 4YB, UK
[20] LIP, IST, FCUL - Av. Elias Garcia, 14 - 1°, P-1000 Lisboa Codex, Portugal
[21] Department of Physics, University of Liverpool, P.O. Box 147, GB - Liverpool L69 3BX, UK
[22] LPNHE, IN2P3-CNRS, Universités Paris VI et VII, Tour 33 (RdC), 4 place Jussieu, F-75252 Paris Cedex 05, France
[23] Department of Physics, University of Lund, Sölvegatan 14, S-22363 Lund, Sweden
[24] Université Claude Bernard de Lyon, IPNL, IN2P3-CNRS, F-69622 Villeurbanne Cedex, France
[25] Universidad Complutense, Avda. Complutense s/n, E-28040 Madrid, Spain
[26] Univ. d'Aix - Marseille II - CPP, IN2P3-CNRS, F-13288 Marseille Cedex 09, France
[27] Dipartimento di Fisica, Università di Milano and INFN, Via Celoria 16, I-20133 Milan, Italy
[28] Niels Bohr Institute, Blegdamsvej 17, DK-2100 Copenhagen 0, Denmark
[29] NC, Nuclear Centre of MFF, Charles University, Areal MFF, V Holesovickach 2, CS-180 00, Praha 8, Czechoslovakia
[30] NIKHEF-H, Postbus 41882, NL-1009 DB Amsterdam, The Netherlands
[31] National Technical University, Physics Department, Zografou Campus, GR-15773 Athens, Greece
[32] Physics Department, University of Oslo, Blindern, N-1000 Oslo 3, Norway
[33] Nuclear Physics Laboratory, University of Oxford, Keble Road, GB - Oxford OX1 3RH, UK
[34] Dipartimento di Fisica, Università di Padova and INFN, Via Marzolo 8, I-35131 Padua, Italy
[35] Depto. de Fisica, Pontificia Univ. Católica, C.P. 38071 RJ-22453 Rio de Janeiro,

Brazil
[36] Rutherford Appleton Laboratory, Chilton, GB - Didcot OX11 OQX, UK
[37] Dipartimento di Fisica, Università di Roma II and INFN, Tor Vergata, I-00173 Rome, Italy
[38] Centre d'Etude de Saclay, DSM/DAPNIA, F-91191 Gif-sur-Yvette Cedex, France
[39] Istituto Superiore di Sanità, Ist. Naz. di Fisica Nucl. (INFN), Viale Regina Elena 299, I-00161 Rome, Italy
[40] Facultad de Ciencias, Universidad de Santander, av. de los Castros, E - 39005 Santander, Spain
[41] Inst. for High Energy Physics, Serpukow P.O. Box 35, Protvino, (Moscow Region), Russian Federation
[42] J. Stefan Institute and Department of Physics, University of Ljubljana, Jamova 39, SI-61000 Ljubljana, Slovenia
[43] Institute of Physics, University of Stockholm, Vanadisvägen 9, S-113 46 Stockholm, Sweden
[44] Dipartimento di Fisica Sperimentale, Università di Torino and INFN, Via P. Giuria 1, I-10125 Turin, Italy
[45] Dipartimento di Fisica, Università di Trieste and INFN, Via A. Valerio 2, I-34127 Trieste, Italy
and Istituto di Fisica, Università di Udine, I-33100 Udine, Italy
[46] Department of Radiation Sciences, University of Uppsala, P.O. Box 535, S-751 21 Uppsala, Sweden
[47] IFIC, Valencia-CSIC, and D.F.A.M.N., U. de Valencia, Avda. Dr. Moliner 50, E-46100 Burjassot (Valencia), Spain
[48] Institut für Hochenergiephysik, Österr. Akad. d. Wissensch., Nikolsdorfergasse 18, A-1050 Vienna, Austria
[49] Inst. Nuclear Studies and, University of Warsaw, Ul. Hoza 69, PL-00681 Warsaw, Poland
[50] Fachbereich Physik, University of Wuppertal, Postfach 100 127, D-5600 Wuppertal 1, Germany

DZero COLLABORATION

B. Gomez, B. Hoeneisen, D. Mendoza, J.P. Negret, J. Roldan
Universidad de los Andes, Bogota Colombia

J. Chen, D. Fein, G. Forden, E. James, K. Johns, P. Loch, L. Markovsky, B. May, A. Milder, J. Rutherfoord, M. Shupe, A. Smith, C. Zeitnitz
University of Arizona

S. Aronson, M. Fatyga, J. Featherly, B. Gibbard, H. Gordon, N. Graf, J.M. Guida, W. Guryn, S. Kahn, S. Protopopescu, P. Yamin
Brookhaven National Laboratory

J. Bantly, D. Cullen-Vidal, D. Cutts, J. Hoftun, R. Lanou, F. Nang, D. Nesic
Brown University

K. Bazizi, B. Choudhary, J. Ellison, R. E. Hall, A. Heinson, T. Huehn, A. Khachatouran, A. Kernan, A. Klatchko, S. J. Wimpenny
University of California, Riverside

G. Alves ,G. Lima, A.K.A. Maciel, V. Oguri, A. Santoro, M. Souza, M. Vaz
Centro Brasiliero de Pesquisas Fisicas, Rio de Janeiro Brazil

H. Castilla, G. Herrera
CINVESTAV, Mexico City Mexico

I. Adam, P. Franzini, U. Heintz, S. Kanekal, P.M. Tuts
Columbia University

V. Kapoor, R. K. Shivpuri
Delhi University, Delhi India

N. Amos, S. Abachi, S. Ahn, J.F. Bartlett, P. Bhat, D. Boggert, F. Borcherding, A. Brandt, A. Bross, J.M. Butler, J. Christenson, W.E. Cooper, M. Demarteau, K. Denisenko, N. Denisenko, H.T. Diehl, M. Diesburg, R. Dixon, G. Dugan, D. Eartly, D. Elvira, D. Finley, H.E. Fisk, S. Fuess, C. Gao, K. Genser, C. Gerber, D. R. Green, H. Greenlee, H. Haggerty, S. Igarashi, A.S. Ito, M. Johnson, A. Jonckheere, H. Jostlein, B. Klima, S. Krzywdzinski, R. Li, Q.Z. Li-Demarteau, R. Lipton, P. Lucas, L. Lueking, E. Malamud, I. Manning, H.-S. Mao, M. I. Martin, P.S. Martin, H. Melanson, X.-C. Meng, W. Merritt, S. Mishra, H.E. Montgomery, C.T. Murphy, M. Narain, N. Oshima, A. Para, C. H. Park, A. Peryshkin, H. Prosper, Y. Que, P. Quintas, P. Rapidis, R. Raja, A.L. Read, W. Smart, R.P. Smith, D. Stewart, A. Taketani, M. Tartaglia, D.-C. Wang, L. Wang, D. Wood, P. Xie, R. Yamada, M.-J. Yang, Y. Zhou, Y. Zhu
Fermi National Accelerator Laboratory

W. Dharmaratna, M. Goforth, S. Hagopian, V. Hagopian, S. Linn, R. Madden, H. Piekarz, H. Wahl, J. Womersley, D. Xiao, S. Youssef
Florida State University

J. Balderston, R. Cence, M. Cummings, M. Jones, M. Peters, C. Yoshikawa
   University of Hawaii

M. Adams, H. Goldberg, S. Margulies, J. Solomon
   University of Illinois, Chicago

G. Alvarez, T. Marshall, H. J. Martin, C. Murphy, D. Zieminska, A. Zieminski
   Indiana University

E. W. Anderson, J. M. Hauptman, M. Pang, A. Zinchenko
   Iowa State University

H. Aihara, J. Bendich, L.-P. Chen, A.R. Clark, O.I. Dahl, A. Goldschmidt, P. Grudberg, L. Kerth, S.C. Loken, R.J. Madaras, E. Oltman, N.A. Roe, A.L. Spadafora, M.L. Stevenson, M. Strovink, T. Trippe
   Lawrence Berkeley Laboratory

A. Baden, W.G. Cobau, N. Hadley, S. Kunori, D. Norman, K. Streets
   University of Maryland

K. De, T. L. Geld, H.A. Neal, L. Oesch, G.R. Snow, S. Zhang
   University of Michigan

M. Abolins, R. Brock, D. Edmunds, S. Fahey, E. Flattum, R. Genik, N. Grossman, J. Linnemann, J. McKinley, P. Mooney, D. Owen, B. Pi, B. Pope, H. Weerts, Y. Xia
   Michigan State University

P. Ermolov, Y. Fisyak, A. Leflat, S. Rusin, E. Shabbalina
   Moscow State University, Russia

J. Kourlas, A. Mincer, M. Mudan, P. Nemethy, J. Sculli, J. Yang, Q. Zhu
   New York University

R. Demina, M. Glaubman, S. Reucroft, T. Yasuda
   Northeastern University

M. Fortner, J. Green, D. Hedin, R. Markeloff, V. Sirotenko, S. Willis
   Northern Illinois University

R. E. Avery, S. Blessing, D. Buchholz, B. Gobbi, Y.-C. Liu, T. Joffe-Minor, H. Schellman
   Northwestern University

V. Balamurali, N. Biswas, J. Jaques, R. Kehoe, M. Kelly, R. Ruchti, J. Warchol, M. Wayne
   University of Notre Dame

V. Bhatnagar, S. Chopra, J. Kohli, J. B. Singh
   Panjab University, Chandigarh India

Y. Antipov, B. Baldin, V. Bezzubov, N. Bozko, V. Burtovoy, S. Chekulaev, D. Denisov, S. Denisov, A. Efimov, O. Eroshin, V. Evdokimov, A. Kirunin, B. Klochkov, V. Klyukhin, I. Kotov, V. Kochetkov, E. Kozlovsky, A. Mayorov, Y. Pischalnikov, V. Podstavkov, V. Riadovikov, A. Shkurenkov, D. Stoyanova, A. Suhanov, A. Vorobiev

Institute for High Energy Physics, Protvino, Russia

B. Abbott, D. Koltick, R. McIlwain

Purdue University

D. Adams, G. Eppley, H. Miettinen, J. Skeens

Rice University

G. Blazey, J. Borders, C. Cretsinger, S. Durston, G. Fanourakis, T.Ferbel, S. Gruenendahl, R. Hirosky, K. Hodel, F. Lobkowicz, P. Slattery

University of Rochester

Y. Ducros, J. Glicenstein, J.R. Hubbard, P. Mangeot, B. Mansoulie, A. Pluquet, J. Teiger, A. Zylberstejn

CEN Saclay, France

R. Astur, D. Chakraborty, W. Chen, D. Claes J. Cochran, R. Engelmann, S. Feher, G. Finocchiaro, M.L. Good, P. Grannis, J. A. Guida, T. Heuring, J. Jiang, C. K. Jung, C. Klopfenstein, S. Lami, G. Landsberg, J. Lee-Franzini, S. Lokos, M. Marx, R. McCarthy, K. Ng, M. Paterno, D. Pizzuto, S. Rajagopalan, L. Rasmussen, M. Rijssenbeek, P. Rubinov, R.D. Schamberger, S. Snyder, J. Thompson, C. Yanigasawa, J. Yu

State University of New York - Stony Brook

A. Booth, M. Botlo, L. Cormell, P. Dingus, H. Fenker, S. Fredricksen, V. Glebov, H. Johnstad, J. Kotcher, K. McFarlane, C. Milner, T. Pal, L. Roberts, I. Sheer, F. Stocker, M. Takashima, E. Wang

Superconducting Supercollider Laboratory, Dallas

B. S. Acharya, M. R. Krishnaswamy, N. K. Mondal, V.S. Narasimham, M. V. S. Rao, P. R. Vishwanath

Tata Institute of Fundamental Research, Bombay India

P. Draper, J. Li, L. Sawyer, M. Sosebee, A. White

University of Texas - Arlington

A. Boehnlein, R. Huson, J.T. White, J. Wightman

Texas A&M University

FNAL E653 COLLABORATION

K. Kodama,[1] N. Ushida,[1] A. Mokhtarani,[2] V.S. Paolone,[2] J.T. Volk,[2] J.O. Wilcox,[2] P.M. Yager,[2] R.M. Edelstein,[3] A.P. Freyberger,[3] D.B. Gibaut,[3] R.J. Lipton,[3] W.R. Nichols,[3] D.M. Potter,[3] J.S. Russ,[3] C. Zhang,[3] Y. Zhang,[3] H.I. Jang,[4] J.Y. Kim,[4] T.I. Kim,[4] I.T. Lim,[4] M.Y. Pac,[4] B.R. Baller,[5] R.J. Stefanski,[5] K. Nakazawa,[6] K.S. Chung,[7] S.H. Chung,[7] D.C. Kim,[7] I.G. Park,[7] M.S. Park,[7] J.S. Song,[7] C.S. Yoon,[7] M. Chikawa,[8] T. Abe,[9] T. Fujii,[9] G. Fujioka,[9] K. Fujiwara,[9] H. Fukushima,[9] T. Hara,[9] Y. Takahashi,[9] K. Taruma,[9] Y. Tsuzuki,[9] C.Yokoyama,[9] S.D. Chang,[10] B.G. Cheon,[10] J.H. Cho,[10] J.S. Kang,[10] C.O. Kim,[10] K.Y. Kim,[10] T.Y. Kim,[10] J.C. Lee,[10] S.B. Lee,[10] G.Y. Lim,[10] S.W. Nam,[10] T.S. Shin,[10] K.S. Sim,[10] J.K. Woo,[10] Y. Isokane,[11] Y. Tsuneoka,[11] S. Aoki,[12] A. Gauthier,[12] K. Hoshino,[12] H. Kitamura,[12] M. Kobayashi,[12] M. Miyanishi,[12] K. Nakamura,[12] M. Nakamura,[12] Y. Nakamura,[12] S. Nakanishi,[12] K. Niu,[12] K. Niwa,[12] M. Nomura,[12] H. Tajima,[12] S. Yoshida,[12] M. Aryal,[13] J.M. Dunlea,[13] S.G. Frederiksen,[13] S. Kuramata,[13] B.G. Lundberg,[13] G.A. Oleynik,[13] N.W. Reay,[13] K. Reibel,[13] R.A. Sidwell,[13] N.R. Stanton,[13] K. Moriyama,[14] H. Shibata,[14] G.R. Kalbfleisch,[15] P. Skubic,[15] J.M. Snow,[15] S.E. Willis,[15] O. Kusumoto,[16] K. Nakamura,[16] T. Okusawa,[16] M. Teranaka,[16] T. Tominaga,[16] T. Yoshida,[16] H. Yuuki,[16] H. Okabe,[17] J. Yokota,[17] M. Adachi,[18] M. Kazuno,[18] E. Niu,[18] H. Shibuya,[18] S. Watanabe,[18] I. Ohtsuka,[19] Y. Sato,[19] I. Tezuka,[19] S.Y. Bahk,[20] and S.K. Kim[20]

[1] *Aichi University of Education, Kariya 448, JAPAN*
[2] *University of California (Davis), Davis, CA 95616, USA*
[3] *Carnegie-Mellon University, Pittsburgh, PA 15213, USA*
[4] *Chonnam National University, Kwangju 500-757, KOREA*
[5] *Fermi National Accelerator Laboratory, Batavia, IL 60510, USA*
[6] *Gifu University, Gifu 501-11, JAPAN*
[7] *Gyeongsang National University, Jinju 660-300, KOREA*
[8] *Kinki University, Higashi-Osaka 577, JAPAN*
[9] *Kobe University, Kobe 657, JAPAN*
[10] *Korea University, Seoul 136-701, KOREA*
[11] *Nagoya Institute of Technology, Nagoya 466, JAPAN*
[12] *Nagoya University, Nagoya 464, JAPAN*
[13] *The Ohio State University, Columbus, OH 43210, USA*
[14] *Okayama University, Okayama 700, JAPAN*
[15] *University of Oklahoma, Norman, OK 73019, USA*
[16] *Osaka City University, Osaka 558, JAPAN*
[17] *Science Education Institute of Osaka Prefecture, Osaka 558, JAPAN*
[18] *Toho University, Funabashi 274, JAPAN*
[19] *Utsunomiya University, Utsunomiya 321, JAPAN*
[20] *Wonkwang University, Iri 570-749, KOREA*

FNAL E665 COLLABORATION

M. R. Adams,[7] S. Aïd,[11] P. L. Anthony,[12,10] D. A. Averill,[7] M. D. Baker,[12] B. R. Baller,[5]
A. Banerjee,[16] J. Bartlett,[5] A. A. Bhatti,[17] U. Bratzler,[17] H. M. Braun,[18] H. Breidung,[18] W. Busza,[12]
T. J. Carroll,[7] H. L. Clark,[15] J. M. Conrad,[6] G. Coutrakon,[5] R. Davisson,[17] I. Derado,[13]
S. K. Dhawan,[19] F. S. Dietrich,[10] W. Dougherty,[17] T. Dreyer,[1] K. Dziunikowska,[9] V. Eckardt,[13]
U. Ecker,[18] M. Erdmann,[1] A. Eskreys,[8] G. F. Fang,[6] J. Figiel,[8] R. W. Finlay,[15] H. J. Gebauer,[13]
D. F. Geesaman,[2] R. Gilman,[2] M. C. Green,[2] K. A. Griffioen,[16] R. S. Guo,[7] J. Haas,[1] C. Halliwell,[7]
J. Hanlon,[5] D. Hantke,[13] K. H. Hicks,[15] V. W. Hughes,[19] H. E. Jackson,[2] D. E. Jaffe,[7] G. Jancso,[13]
D. M. Jansen,[17] Z. Jin,[17] S. Kaufman,[2] R. D. Kennedy,[3] E. Kinney,[2,4] T. Kirk,[5,2] H. G. E. Kobrak,[3]
A. Kotwal,[6] S. Krzywdzinski,[5] S. Kunori,[11] M. Lenski,[1] J. J. Lord,[17] H. J. Lubatti,[17] T. McKibben,[7]
D. McLeod,[7] P. Madden,[3] S. Magill,[7] P. Malecki,[8] A. Manz,[13] H. Melanson,[5] D. G. Michael,[6]
W. Mohr,[1] H. E. Montgomery,[5] J. G. Morfin,[5] R. B. Nickerson,[6] S. O'Day,[11] K. Olkiewicz,[8]
L. Osborne,[12] R. Otten,[18] V. Papavassiliou,[19,2] B. Pawlik,[8,14] F. M. Pipkin,[6,†] D. Potterveld,[2]
E. J. Ramberg,[11] A. Röser,[18] J. J. Ryan,[12] C. Salgado,[5] A. Salvarani,[3,m] H. Schellman,[5,14]
M. Schmitt,[6] N. Schmitz,[13] K. P. Schüler,[19] G. Seigert,[1] H. J. Seyerlein,[13] A. Skuja,[11]
G. A. Snow,[11] S. Söldner-Rembold,[13] P. Spentzouris,[14] P. H. Steinberg,[11,†] H. E. Stier,[1,†] P. Stopa,[8]
R. A. Swanson,[3] R. Talaga,[11] S. Tentindo-Repond,[2] H.-J. Trost,[2] H. Venkataramania,[19] M. Vidal,[13]
M. Wilhelm,[1] J. Wilkes,[17] Richard Wilson,[6] W. Wittek,[13] S. A. Wolbers,[5] A. Zghiche,[2] T. Zhao[17]

[1] *Albert-Ludwigs-Universität Freiburg i. Br., Germany*
[2] *Argonne National Laboratory, Argonne IL USA*
[3] *University of California, San Diego, CA USA*
[4] *University of Colorado, Boulder, CO USA*
[5] *Fermi National Accelerator Laboratory, Batavia, IL USA*
[6] *Harvard University, Cambridge, MA USA*
[7] *University of Illinois, Chicago, IL USA*
[8] *Institute for Nuclear Physics, Krakow, Poland*
[9] *Institute for Nuclear Physics, Academy of Mining and Metallurgy, Krakow, Poland*
[10] *Lawrence Livermore National Laboratory, Livermore, CA USA*
[11] *University of Maryland, College Park, MD USA*
[12] *Massachusetts Institute of Technology, Cambridge, MA USA*
[13] *Max-Planck-Institut für Physik, Munich, Germany*
[14] *Northwestern University, Evanston, IL USA*
[15] *Ohio University, OH USA*
[16] *University of Pennsylvania, Philadelphia PA USA*
[17] *University of Washington, Seattle, WA USA*
[18] *University of Wuppertal, Wuppertal, Germany*
[19] *Yale University, New Haven, CT USA*

FNAL E683 COLLABORATION

S. Ahmad,[6] N. Akchurin,[3] P. Birmingham,[7] H. Breuer,[5] C. C. Chang,[4] S. Cihangir,[2] M. D. Corcoran,[6] W. Davis,[1] R. Gustafson,[5] H. Holmgren,[4] P. Kasper,[2] D. Lincoln,[6] M. Longo,[5] J. Marraffino,[2] J. McPherson,[3] G. Morrow,[6] G. S. Mutchler,[6] D. Naples,[4] Y. Onel,[3] J. Skeens,[6] G. P. Thomas,[1] M. Traynor,[6] J. Waters,[7] M. Webster,[7] J. P. Xu[6]

[1] *Ball State University*
[2] *Fermilab*
[3] *University of Iowa*
[4] *University of Maryland*
[5] *University of Michigan*
[6] *Rice University*
[7] *Vanderbilt University*

FNAL E687 COLLABORATION

P. L. Frabetti
  Dip. di Fisica dell'Università and INFN - Bologna, I-40126 Bologna, Italy

H. W. K. Cheung, J. P. Cumalat, C. Dallapiccola, J. F. Ginkel, S. V. Greene, W. E. Johns, M. S. Nehring
  University of Colorado, Boulder, CO 80309

J. N. Butler, S. Cihangir, I. Gaines, L. Garren, P. H. Garbincius, S. A. Gourlay, D. J. Harding, P. Kasper, A. Kreymer, P. Lebrun, S. Shukla
  Fermilab, Batavia, IL 60510

S. Bianco, F. L. Fabbri, S. Sarwar, A. Zallo
  Laboratori Nazionali di Frascati dell'INFN, I-00044 Frascati, Italy

R. Culbertson, R. W. Gardner, R. Greene, J. Wiss
  University of Illinois at Urbana-Champaign, Urbana, IL 61801

G. Alimonti, G. Bellini, B. Caccianiga, L. Cinquini, M. Di Corato, M. Giammarchi, P. Inzani, F. Leveraro, S. Malvezzi, D. Menasce, E. Meroni, L. Moroni, D. Pedrini, L. Perasso, A. Sala, S. Sala, D. Torretta[a], M. Vittone[a]
  Dip. di Fisica dell'Università and INFN - Milano, I-20133 Milan, Italy

D. Buchholz, D. Claes, B. Gobbi, B. O'Reilly
  Northwestern University, Evanston, IL 60208

J. M. Bishop, N. M. Cason, C. J. Kennedy, G. N. Kim, T. F. Lin, D. L. Pušeljić, R. C. Ruchti, W. D. Shephard, J. A. Swiatek, Z. Y. Wu
  University of Notre Dame, Notre Dame, IN 46556

V. Arena, G. Boca, C. Castoldi, R. Diaferia, G. Gianini, S. P. Ratti, C. Riccardi, P. Vitulo
  Dip. di Fisica dell'Università and INFN - Pavia, I-27100 Pavia, Italy

A. Lopez
  University of Puerto Rico at Mayaguez, Puerto Rico

G. P. Grim, V. S. Paolone, P. M. Yager
  University of California-Davis, Davis, CA 95616

J. R. Wilson
  University of South Carolina, Columbia, SC 29208

P. D. Sheldon
  Vanderbilt University, Nashville, TN 37235

F. Davenport
  University of North Carolina-Asheville, Asheville, NC 28804

J. F. Filasetta
  Northern Kentucky University, Highland Heights, KY 41076

G. R. Blackett, T. Handler, M. Pisharody
  University of Tennessee, Knoxville, TN 37996

B. G. Cheon, J. S. Kang, K. Y. Kim
  Korea University, Seoul 136-701, Korea

FNAL E706 COLLABORATION

G. Alverson,[6] W. F. Baker,[3] G. Ballocchi,[10,a] R. Benson,[5,b] D. Berg,[3] S. Blusk,[9] C. Bromberg,[4] D. Brown,[4] D. Carey,[3] T. Chand,[2] C. Chandlee,[10] B. C. Choudhary,[2,c] W. H. Chung,[9] L. de Barbaro,[10] W. DeSoi,[10] W. Dlugosz,[6] J. Dunlea,[10] S. Easo,[8,d] E. Engels, Jr.,[9] W. Faissler,[6] G. Fanourakis,[10] T. Ferbel,[10] D. Garelick,[6] G. Ginther,[10] G. Glass,[6] M. Glaubman,[6] P. Gutierrez,[7] K. Hartman,[8,e] J. Huston,[4] C. Johnstone,[3] V. Kapoor,[2] I. Kourbanis,[6,f] A. Lanaro,[10] C. Lirakis,[6] F. Lobkowicz,[10] P. Lukens,[5,f] S. Mani,[1] A. Maul,[4] J. Mansour,[10,g] R. Miller,[4] C. A. Nelson, Jr.,[3] B. Y. Oh,[8] D. Orris,[9,f] E. Pothier,[6] E. Prebys,[10,h] B. M. Rajaram,[2,i] R. Roser,[10] K. Ruddick,[5] P. Shepard,[9] R. K. Shivpuri,[2] A. Sinanidis,[6] D. Skow,[10,f] P. Slattery,[10] L. Sorrell,[4] W. Toothacker,[8] N. Varelas,[10] D. Weerasundara,[9] J. Whitmore,[8] G. Wu,[6,f] T. Yasuda,[6] C. Yosef,[6,g] M. Zieliński[10]

[1] University of California, Davis
[2] University of Delhi, Delhi, India
[3] Fermi National Accelerator Laboratory
[4] Michigan State University
[5] University of Minnesota
[6] Northeastern University
[7] University of Oklahoma
[8] Pennsylvania State University
[9] University of Pittsburgh
[10] University of Rochester
[a] Current Address: CERN, 1211 Geneva 23, Switzerland
[b] Current Address: LeCroy Corporation, Chestnut Ridge, NY
[c] Current Address: University of California, Riverside
[d] Current Address: INFN University of Perugia, Perugia, Italy
[e] Current Address: Stanford University
[f] Current Address: Fermi National Accelerator Laboratory
[g] Current Address: Michigan State University
[h] Current Address: Princeton University
[i] Current Address: L. B. and S. B. S. College, Sagar, Karnatka 577401, India

FNAL E731 COLLABORATION

A.R. Barker,[1,a] R.A. Briere,[1] L. K. Gibbons,[1] G. Makoff,[1] V. Papadimitriou,[1,b] J. R. Patterson,[1,c] S. V. Somalwar,[1] Y. W. Wah,[1] B. Winstein,[1] R. Winston,[1] M. Woods,[1,d] H. Yamamoto,[1,e] E. C. Swallow,[2] G. J. Bock,[3] R. Coleman,[3] J. Enagonio,[3] Y. B. Hsiung,[3] E. Ramberg,[3] K. Stanfield,[3] R. Tschirhart,[3] T. Yamanaka,[3,f] G. D. Gollin,[4,g] M. Karlsson,[4,h] J. K. Okamitsu,[4,i] P. Debu,[5] B. Peyaud,[5] R. Turlay,[5] B. Vallage[5]

[1] *Enrico Fermi Institute and the Department of Physics, The University of Chicago, Chicago, IL 60637*
[2] *Department of Physics, Elmhurst College, Elmhurst, IL 60126, and The Enrico Fermi Institute, The University of Chicago, Chicago, IL 60637*
[3] *Fermi National Accelerator Laboratory, Batavia, Il 60510*
[4] *Department of Physics, Princeton University, Princeton,NJ 08544*
[5] *Department de Physique des Particules Elementaires, Centre d'Etudes Nucleaires de Saclay, F-91191 Gif-sur-Yvette CEDEX, France*
[a] *Current Address: University of Colorado, Boulder, CO 80309*
[b] *Current Address: Fermi National Accelerator Laboratory, Batavia, IL 60510*
[c] *Current Address: Cornell University, Ithaca, NY 14853*
[d] *Current Address: Stanford Lin.Acc.Cen.,P.O.Box 4349, Stanford, CA 94309*
[e] *Current Address: Harvard University, Cambridge, MA 02139*
[f] *Current Address: Osaka University, Toyonaka, Osaka 560 Japan*
[g] *Current Address: University of Illinois, Urbana, IL 61801*
[h] *Current Address: CERN, CH1211, Geneva 23, Switzerland*
[i] *Current Address: Princeton Combustion Res.Lab,Monmouth Junction,NJ 08852*

FNAL E760 COLLABORATION

T.A. Armstrong,[6] D. Bettoni,[2] V. Bharadwaj,[1] C. Biino,[7] G. Borreani,[2] D. Broemmelsiek,[4] A. Buzzo,[3] R. Calabrese,[2] A. Ceccucci,[7] R. Cester,[7] M. Church,[1] P. Dalpiaz,[2] P.F. Dalpiaz,[2] R. Dibenedetto,[7] D. Dimitroyannis,[5] M.G. Fabbri,[2] J. Fast,[4] S. Ferroni,[3] A. Gianoli,[2] C.M. Ginsburg,[5] K. Gollwitzer,[4] A. Hahn,[1] M. Hasan,[6] S. Hsueh,[1] R. Lewis,[6] E. Luppi,[2] M. Macrí,[3] A.M. Majewska,[6] M. Mandelkern,[4] F. Marchetto,[7] M. Marinelli,[3] J. Marques,[4] W. Marsh,[1] M. Martini,[2] M. Masuzawa,[5] E. Menichetti,[7] A. Migliori,[7] R. Mussa,[7] M. Pallavicini,[3] S. Palestini,[7] N. Pastrone,[7] C. Patrignani,[3] J. Peoples Jr.,[1] L. Pesando,[7] F. Petrucci,[2] M.G. Pia,[3] S. Pordes,[1] P. Rapidis,[1] R. Ray,[5,1] J. Reid,[6] G. Rinaudo,[7] B. Roccuzzo,[7] J. Rosen,[5] A. Santroni,[3] M. Sarmiento,[5] M. Savrie',[2] A. Scalisi,[3] J. Schultz,[4] K.K. Seth,[5] A. Smith,[4] G.A. Smith,[6] M. Sozzi,[7] S. Trokenheim,[5] M.F. Weber,[4] S. Werkema,[1] Y. Zhang,[6] J. Zhao,[5] G. Zioulas[4]

[1] *Fermi National Accelerator Laboratory, Batavia, Illinois 60510, U.S.A.*
[2] *I.N.F.N. and University of Ferrara, 44100 Ferrara, Italy*
[3] *I.N.F.N. and University of Genoa, 16146 Genoa, Italy*
[4] *University of California at Irvine, California 92717, U.S.A.*
[5] *Northwestern University, Evanston, Illinois 60201, U.S.A.*
[6] *Pennsylvania State University, University Park, Pennsylvania 16802, U.S.A.*
[7] *I.N.F.N. and University of Turin, 10125 Turin, Italy*

FNAL E761 COLLABORATION

R. Carrigan,[1] P.S. Cooper,[1] H. Gottschalk,[1] J. Lach,[1] A. Morelos,[1] Li Yunshan,[2] Tang Fukun,[2] Lang Pengfei,[2] Li Chengze Shi Huanzhang,[2] Zhao Wenheng,[2] Dia Lisheng,[2] Zheng Shuchen,[2] Zhong Yuanyuan,[2] Yan Jie,[2] V. Baublis,[3] N.F. Bondar,[3] A.S. Denisov,[3] A. Dobrovolsky,[3] V.L. Golovtsov,[3] V.T. Grachev,[3] A.V. Khanzadeev,[3] N. Kuropatkin,[3] V.M. Samsonov,[3] V. Schegelsky,[3] N.K. Terentyev,[3] I.I. Tkatch,[3] L.N. Uvarov,[3] A.A. Vorobyov,[3] P.A. Goritchev,[4] M.A. Kubantsev,[4] V.N. Lebedenko,[4] T. Dubbs,[5] E. McCliment,[5] C. Newsom,[5] I.F. Alburquerque,[6] C. Escobar,[6] P. Gouffon,[6] J. Mahon,[6] M. Foucher,[7] A.M.F. Endler,[8] M.C. Pommot Maia,[9] D. Chen,[10] V.J. Smith,[11] S. Timm,[12] M. Luksys[13]

[1] *Fermilab, Batavia, Illinois 60510*
[2] *Institute of High Energy Physics, Beijing, PRC*
[3] *St. Petersburg Nuclear Physics Institute, St. Petersburg, Russia*
[4] *Institute of Theoretical and Experimental Physics, Moscow, Russia*
[5] *University of Iowa, Iowa City, Iowa 42242*
[6] *University of Sao Paulo, Brazil*
[7] *Yale University, New Haven, Connecticut 06511*
[8] *Centro Brasileiro de Pesquisas Fisicas, Rio de Janeiro, Brazil*
[9] *Conselho Nacional de Pesquisa - CNPq, Rio de Janeiro, Brazil*
[10] *State University of New York - Albany, Albany, New York 12222*
[11] *H.H. Wills Physics Laboratory, University of Bristol, United Kingdom*
[12] *Carnegie Mellon University, Pittsburgh, PA 15213*
[13] *Universidade Federal da Paraiba, Paraiba Brazil*

FNAL E769 COLLABORATION

G. A. Alves,[1] S. Amato,[1] J. C. Anjos,[1] J. A. Appel,[2] S. B. Bracker,[5] L. M. Cremaldi,[3] C. L. Darling,[8] R. L. Dixon,[2] D. Errede,[7,a] H. C. Fenker,[2,b] C. Gay,[5,c] D. R. Green,[2] R. Jedicke,[5] D. Kaplan,[4,d] P. E. Karchin,[8] S. Kwan,[2] I. Leedom,[4] L. H. Lueking,[2] G. J. Luste,[5] P. M. Mantsch,[2] J. R. T. de Mello Neto,[1,e] J. Metheny,[6] R. H. Milburn,[6] J. M. de Miranda,[1] H. da Motta Filho,[1] A. Napier,[6] A. B. d'Olivera,[f] A. Rafatian,[3] A. C. dos Reis,[1] S. Reucroft,[4] W. R. Ross,[8,d] A. F. S. Santoro,[1] M. Sheaff,[7] M. H. G. Souza,[1] W. J. Spalding,[2] C. Stoughton,[2] M. E. Streetman,[2] D. J. Summers,[3] S. F. Takach,[8] Z. Wu[8,g]

[1] *Centro Brasileiro de Pesquisas Fisicas, Rio de Janeiro, Brazil*
[2] *Fermi National Accelerator Laboratory, Batavia, Illinois 60510*
[3] *University of Mississippi, Oxford, Mississippi 38677*
[4] *Northeastern University, Boston, Massachusetts 02115*
[5] *University of Toronto, Toronto, Ontario, Canada, M5S 1A7*
[6] *Tufts University, Medford, Massachusetts 02155*
[7] *University of Wisconsin, Madison, Wisconsin 53706*
[8] *Yale University, New Haven, Connecticut 06511*
[a] *Now at University of Illinois, Urbana, IL 61801*
[b] *Now at SSC Laboratory, Dallas, TX 75237*
[c] *Now at CERN, CH-1211, Geneve 23, Switzerland*
[d] *Now at University of Oklahoma, Norman, OK 73071*
[e] *Now at University Estadual do Rio de Janeiro, RJ, Brazil*
[f] *Now at University of Cincinnati, Cincinnati, OH 45221*
[g] *Now at Rockefeller University, New York, NY 10021*

FNAL E771 COLLABORATION

T. Alexopoulos,[1] L. Antoniazzi,[2] M. Arenton,[3] C. Ballagh,[4] H. Bingham,[4] A. Blankman,[5] M. Block,[6] A. Boden,[7] S. Borodin,[21] J. Budagov,[8] Z. Cao,[9] G. Cataldi,[10] T. Chen,[11] K. Clark,[12] D. Cline,[7] S. Conetti,[3] M. Cooper,[13] G. Corti,[20] B. Cox,[3] P. Creti,[14] E. Dukes,[3] C. Durandet,[1] V. Elia,[19] A. Erwin,[1] L. Fortney,[15] S. Golovatyuk,[3] E. Gorini,[14] F. Grancagnolo,[14] M. Haire,[16] P. Hanlet,[3] M. He,[9] G. Introzzi,[2] M. Jenkins,[12] J. Jennings,[1] D. Judd,[16] T. Kaeding,[4] W. Kononenko,[5] W. Kowald,[15] A. Lanza,[2] K. Lau,[17] G. Liguori,[2] J. Lys,[4] P. Mazur,[10] A. McManus,[3] S. Misawa,[4] G. Mo,[17] T. Murphy,[10] K. Nelson,[3] M. Newcomer,[5] M. Panareo,[14] S. Ramachandran,[7] M. Recagni,[3] J. Rhoades,[7] J. Segal,[3] W. Selove,[5] R. Smith,[10] L. Spiegel,[10] J. Sun,[3] S. Tokar,[7] P. Torre,[2] J. Trischuk,[18] T. Trojak,[5] E. Tsyganov,[8] L. Turnbull,[16] R. VanBerg,[5] D. Wagoner,[16] C. Wang,[9] H. Wang,[6] C. Wei,[9] W. Yang,[10] N. Yao,[11] N. Zhang,[9] S. Zhang,[5] B. Zou[15]

[1] *Univ. of Wisconsin*
[2] *Univ. and INFN of Pavia, Italy*
[3] *University of Virginia*
[4] *Univ. of California at Berkeley*
[5] *Univ. of Pennsylvania*
[6] *Northwestern University*
[7] *Univ. of California at Los Angeles*
[8] *JINR, Dubna, Russia*
[9] *Shandong University, P. R. of China*
[10] *Fermilab*
[11] *Nanjing University, P. R. C.*
[12] *Univ. of South Alabama*
[13] *Vanier College, Canada*
[14] *Univ. and INFN of Lecce, Italy*
[15] *Duke University*
[16] *Prairie View A & M University*
[17] *Univ. of Houston*
[18] *McGill University, Canada*
[19] *Fermilab, and INFN of Lecce, Italy*
[20] *Northwestern University and INFN of Pavia, Italy*
[21] *Univ. of Pennsylvania and JINR, Dubna, Russia*

FNAL E789 COLLABORATION

J. Boissevain,[1] C. N. Brown,[2] G. Brown,[3] T. A. Carey,[1] Y. C. Chen,[4,5] R. L. Childers,[6] W. E. Cooper,[2] C. W. Darden,[6] G. Gidal,[7] H. D. Glass,[2] K. N. Gounder,[2] P. M. Ho,[7] L. D. Isenhower,[3] D. M. Jansen,[1] R. Jeppesen,[1] D. M. Kaplan,[8] J. S. Kapustinsky,[1] G. C. Kiang,[4] M. S. I. Kowitt,[10] D. W. Lane,[1] L. M. Lederman,[9] M. J. Leitch,[1] J. W. Lillberg,[1] W. Luebke,[8] K. B. Luk,[7,10] V. M. Martin,[8] P. L. McGaughey,[1] C. S. Mishra,[2] J. M. Moss,[1] R. S. Preston,[8] D. Pripstein,[10] J. Sa,[8] M. E. Sadler,[3] R. Schnathorst,[3] M. H. Schub,[9] R. Schwindt,[3] D. Snodgrass,[6] W. E. Sondhein,[1] V. Tanikella,[8] P. K. Teng,[4] J. R. Wilson[6]

[1] *Los Alamos National Laboratory*
[2] *Fermilab*
[3] *Abilene Christian University*
[4] *Academia Sinica, Taiwan*
[5] *National Cheng Kung University, Taiwan*
[6] *University of South Carolina*
[7] *Lawrence Berkeley Laboratory*
[8] *Northern Illinois University*
[9] *University of Chicago*
[10] *University of California at Berkeley*

FNAL E791 COLLABORATION

E. M. Aitala,[7] S. Amato,[2] J. C. Anjos,[2] J. A. Appel,[5] M. Aryal,[8] D. Ashery,[11] J. Astorga,[13] S. Banerjee,[5] I. Bediaga,[2] G. Blaylock,[1] S. B. Bracker,[12] P. R. Burchat,[1] R. A. Burnstein,[6] T. Carter,[5] H. S. Carvalho,[10] I. Costa,[2] L. M. Cremaldi,[7] K. Denisenko,[5] A. Fernandez,[4,a] P. Gagnon,[1] S. Gerzon,[11] K. Gounder,[7] D. Granite,[8] M. Halling,[5] C. James,[5] P. A. Kasper,[6] S. Kwan,[5] D. C. Langs,[9] J. Leslie,[1] J. Lichtenstadt,[11] B. Lundberg,[5] A. Manacero,[5] S. MayTal-Beck,[11] B. Meadows,[3] J. R. T. de Mello Neto,[2] R. H. Milburn,[13] J. M. de Miranda,[2] A. Napier,[13] A. Nguyen,[8] A. B. d'Oliveira,[3] K. C. Peng,[6] L. P. Perera,[3] M. V. Purohit,[9] B. Quinn,[7] S. Radeztsky,[14] A. Rafatian,[7] A. J. Ramalho,[10] N. W. Reay,[8] K. Reibel,[8] J. J. Reidy,[7] A. C. dos Reis,[2] H. A. Rubin,[6] A. K. S. Santha,[3] A. F. S. Santoro,[2] A. Schwartz,[9] M. Sheaff,[14] R. Sidwell,[8] A. J. Slaughter,[15] J. G. Smith,[8] M. D. Sokoloff,[3] M. H. G. Souza,[2] N. Stanton,[8] K. Sugano,[1] D. J. Summers,[7] K. Thorne,[5] A. Tripathi,[8] D. Trumer,[11] S. Watanabe,[14] J. Wiener,[9] N. Witchey,[8] E. Wolin,[15] D. Yi[7]

[1] *University of California, Santa Cruz, CA, USA*
[2] *Centro Brasileiro de Pesquisas Fisicas, Rio de Janeiro, Brazil*
[3] *University of Cincinnati, Cincinnati, OH, USA*
[4] *CINVESTAV, Mexico*
[5] *Fermilab, Batavia, IL, USA*
[6] *Illinois Institute of Technology, Chicago, IL, USA*
[7] *University of Mississippi, Oxford, MS, USA*
[8] *Ohio State University, Columbus, OH, USA*
[9] *Princeton University, Princeton, NJ, USA*
[10] *Universidade Federal do Rio de Janeiro, Brazil*
[11] *Tel Aviv University, Tel Aviv, Israel*
[12] *317 Belsize Drive, Toronto, Canada*
[13] *Tufts University, Medford, MA, USA*
[14] *University of Wisconsin, Madison, WI, USA*
[15] *Yale University, New Haven, CT, USA*
[a] *Permanent Address: Facultad de Ciencias Fisico-Matematicas de la Universidad Autonoma de Puebla, Mexico*

FNAL E799 COLLABORATION

K. Arisaka,[1] D. Roberts,[1] W. Slater,[1] M. Weaver,[1] R. Briere,[2] E. Cheu,[2] D. Harris,[2] G. Makoff,[2] K. McFarland,[2] A. Roodman,[2] P. Shawhan,[2] B. Schwingenheuer,[2] S. Somalwar,[2] Y. Wah,[2] B. Winstein,[2] R. Winston,[2] T. Barker,[3] E. Swallow,[4] G. Bock,[5] R. Coleman,[5] M. Crisler,[5] J. Enagonio,[5] R. Ford,[5] Y. B. Hsiung,[5] D. Jensen,[5] E. Ramberg,[5] R. Tschirhart,[5] E. Collins,[6] G. Gollin,[6] T. Nakaya,[7] T. Yamanaka,[7] P. Haas,[8] W. P. Hogan,[8] S. Kim,[8] J.N. Matthews,[8] S. S. Myung,[8] P. Gu,[8] S. Schnetzer,[8] G. Thomson,[8] Y. Zou[8]

[1] *University of California at Los Angeles*
[2] *University of Chicago*
[3] *University of Colorado*
[4] *Elmhurst College*
[5] *Fermi National Accelerator Laboratory*
[6] *University of Illinois*
[7] *Osaka University*
[8] *Rutgers University*

LASS E135 COLLABORATION

D. Aston,[1] N. Awaji,[2] T. Bienz,[1] F. Bird,[1] J. D'Amore,[3] W. Dunwoodie,[1] R. Endorf,[3] K. Fujii,[2] H. Hayashii,[2] S. Iwata,[2] W.B. Johnson,[1] R. Kajikawa,[2] P. Kunz,[1] Y. Kwon,[1] D.W.G.S. Leith,[1] L. Levinson,[1] J. Martinez,[3] T. Matsui,[2] B.T. Meadows,[3] A. Miyamoto,[2] M. Nussbaum,[3] H. Ozaki,[2] C.O. Pak,[2] B.N. Ratcliff,[1] P. Rensing,[1] D. Schultz,[1] S. Shapiro,[1] T. Shimomura,[2] P. K. Sinervo,[1] A. Sugiyama,[2] S. Suzuki,[2] G. Tarnopolsky,[1] T. Tauchi,[2] N. Toge,[1] K. Ukai,[4] A. Waite,[1] S. Williams[1]

[1] *Stanford Linear Accelerator Center, Stanford University, CA 94309, USA*
[2] *Department of Physics, Nagoya University, Nagoya 464, Japan*
[3] *Department of Physics, University of Cincinnati, OH 45221, USA*
[4] *Inst. for Nuclear Study, University of Tokyo, Tokyo 188, Japan*

L3 COLLABORATION

O.Adriani,[14] M. Aguilar-Benitez,[23] S. Ahlen,[9] J. Alcaraz,[15] A. Aloisio,[26] G. Alverson,[10] M. G. Alviggi,[26] G. Ambrosi,[31] Q. An,[16] H. Anderhub,[45] A. L. Anderson,[13] V. P. Andreev,[35] L. Antonov,[39] D. Antreasyan,[7] P. Arce,[23] A. Arefiev,[25] A. Atamanchuk,[35] T. Azemoon,[3] T. Aziz,[1,8] P. V. K. S. Baba,[16] P. Bagnaia,[34] J. A. Bakken,[33] L. Baksay,[41] R. C. Ball,[3] S. Banerjee,[8] J. Bao,[5] R. Barillère,[15] L. Barone,[34] A. Baschirotto,[24] R. Battiston,[31] A. Bay,[17] F. Becattini,[14] U. Becker,[13,45] F. Behner,[45] J. Behrens,[45] Gy. L. Bencze,[11] J. Berdugo,[23] P. Berges,[13] B. Bertucci,[31] B. L. Betev,[39,45] M. Biasini,[31] A. Biland,[45] G. M. Bilei[31] R. Bizzarri,[34] J. J. Blaising,[4] G. J. Bobbink,[15,2] R. Bock,[1] A. Böhm,[1] B. Borgia,[34] M. Bosetti,[24] D. Bourilkov,[28] M. Bourquin,[17] D. Boutigny,[4] B. Bouwens,[2] E. Brambilla,[26] J. G. Branson,[36] I. C. Brock,[32] M. Brooks,[21] A. Bujak,[42] J. D. Burger,[13] W. J. Burger,[17] J. Busenitz,[41] X. D. Cai,[16] M. Capell,[20] M. Caria,[31] G. Carlino,[26] A. M. Cartacci,[14] R. Castello,[24] M. Cerrada,[23] F. Cesaroni,[34] Y. H. Chang,[13] U. K. Chaturvedi,[16] M. Chemarin,[22] A. Chen,[47] C. Chen,[6] G. M. Chen,[6] H. F. Chen,[18] H. S. Chen,[6] M. Chen,[13] W. Y. Chen,[47] G. Chiefari,[26] C. Y. Chien,[5] M. T. Choi,[40] S. Chung,[13] C. Civinini,[14] I. Clare,[13] R. Clare,[13] T. E. Coan,[21] H. O. Cohn,[29] G. Coignet,[4] N. Colino,[15] A. Contin,[7] X. T. Cui,[16] X. Y. Cui,[16] T. S. Dai,[13] R. D'Alessandro,[14] R. de Asmundis,[26] A. Degré,[4] K. Deiters,[43] E. Dénes,[11] P. Denes,[33] F. DeNotaristefani,[34] M. Dhina,[45] D. DiBitonto,[41] M. Diemoz,[34] H. R. Dimitrov,[39] C. Dionisi,[34,15] L. Djambazov,[45] M. T. Dova,[16] E. Drago,[26] T. Driever,[28] D. Duchesneau,[17] P. Duinker,[2] I. Duran,[37] S. Easo,[31] H. El Mamouni,[22] A. Engler,[32] F. J. Eppling,[13] F. C. Erné,[2] P. Extermann,[17] R. Fabbretti,[43] M. Fabre,[43] S. Falciano,[34] S. J. Fan,[38] O. Fackler,[20] J. Fay,[22] M. Felcini,[15] T. Ferguson,[32] D. Fernandez,[23] G. Fernandez,[23] F. Ferroni,[34] H. Fesefeldt,[1] E. Fiandrini,[31] J. Field,[17] F. Filthaut,[28] G. Finocchiaro,[34] P. H. Fisher,[5] G. Forconi,[17] T. Foreman,[2] K. Freudenreich,[45] W. Friebel,[44] M. Fukushima,[13] M. Gailloud,[19] Yu. Galaktionov,[25,13] E. Gallo,[14] S. N. Ganguli,[15,8] P. Garcia-Abia,[23] D. Gele,[22] S. Gentile,[34,15] S. Goldfarb,[10] Z. F. Gong,[18] E. Gonzalez,[23] A. Gougas,[5] D. Goujon,[17] G. Gratta,[30] M. Gruenewald,[30] C. Gu,[16] M. Guanziroli,[16] J. K. Guo,[38] V. K. Gupta,[33] A. Gurtu,[8] H. R. Gustafson,[3] L. J. Gutay,[42] K. Hangarter,[1] A. Hasan,[16] D. Hauschildt,[2] C. F. He,[38] J. T. He,[6] T. Hebbeker,[1] M. Hebert,[36] G. Herten,[13] A. Hervé,[15] K. Hilgers,[1] H. Hofer,[45] H. Hoorani,[17] G. Hu,[16] G. Q. Hu,[38] B. Ille,[22] M. M. Ilyas,[16] V. Innocente,[15] H. Janssen,[15] S. Jezequel,[4] B. N. Jin,[6] L. W. Jones,[3] A. Kasser,[19] R. A. Khan,[16] Yu. Kamyshkov,[29] P. Kapinos,[35,44] J. S. Kapustinsky,[21] Y. Karyotakis,[15] M. Kaur,[16] S. Khokhar,[16] M. N. Kienzle-Focacci,[17] J. K. Kim,[40] S. C. Kim,[40] Y. G. Kim,[40] W. W. Kinnison,[21] D. Kirkby,[30] S. Kirsch,[44] W. Kittel,[28] A. Klimentov,[13,25] A. C. König,[28] E. Koffeman,[2] O. Kornadt,[1] V. Koutsenko,[13,25] A. Koulbardis,[35] R. W. Kraemer,[32] T. Kramer,[13] V. R. Krastev,[39,31] W. Krenz,[1] A. Krivshich,[35] H. Kuijten,[28] K. S. Kumar,[12] A. Kunin,[12,25] G. Landi,[14] D. Lanske,[1] S. Lanzano,[26] P. Lebrun,[22] P. Lecomte,[45] P. Lecoq,[15] P. Le Coultre,[45] D. M. Lee,[21] I. Leedom,[10] C. Leggett,[3] J. M. Le Goff,[15] R. Leiste,[44] M. Lenti,[14] E. Leonardi,[34] X. Leytens,[2] C. Li,[18,16] H. T. Li,[6] P. J. Li,[38] J. Y. Liao,[38] W. T. Lin,[47] Z. Y. Lin,[18] F. L. Linde,[15] B. Lindemann,[1] L. Lista,[26] Y. Liu,[16] W. Lohmann,[44,15] E. Longo,[34] Y. S. Lu,[6] J. M. Lubbers,[15] K. Lübelsmeyer,[1] C. Luci,[34] D. Luckey,[7,13] L. Ludovici,[34] L. Luminari,[34] W. Lustermann,[44] J. M. Ma,[6] W. G. Ma,[18] M. MacDermott,[45] P. K. Malhotra,[8†] R. Malik,[16] A. Malinin,[25] C. Maña,[23] M. Maolinbay,[45] P. Marchesini,[45] F. Marion,[4] A. Marin,[9] J. P. Martin,[22] L. Martinez-Laso,[23] F. Marzano,[34] G. G. G. Massaro,[2] K. Mazumdar,[8] P. McBride,[12] T. McMahon,[42] D. McNally,[45] M. Merk,[32] L. Merola,[26] M. Meschini,[14] W. J. Metzger,[28] Y. Mi,[19] G. B. Mills,[21] Y. Mir,[16] G. Mirabelli,[34] J. Mnich,[1] M. Möller,[1] B. Monteleoni,[14] R. Morand,[4] S. Morganti,[34] N. E. Moulai,[16] R. Mount,[30] S. Müller,[1] A. Nadtochy,[35] E. Nagy,[11] M. Napolitano,[26] F. Nessi-Tedaldi,[45] H. Newman,[30] C. Neyer,[45] M. A. Niaz,[16] A. Nippe,[1] H. Nowak,[44] G. Organtini,[34] D. Pandoulas,[1] S. Paoletti,[14] P. Paolucci,[26] G. Pascala,[34] G. Passaleva,[14,31] S. Patricelli,[26] T. Paul,[5] M. Pauluzzi,[31] C. Paus,[1] F. Pauss,[45] Y. J. Pei,[1] S. Pensotti,[24] D. Perret-Gallix,[4] J. Perrier,[17] A. Pevsner,[5] D. Piccolo,[26] M. Pieri,[15] P. A. Piroué,[33] F. Plasil,[29] V. Plyaskin,[25] M. Pohl,[45] V. Pojidaev,[25,14] H. Postema,[13] Z. D. Qi,[38] J. M. Qian,[3] K. N. Qureshi,[16] J. Raghavan,[8] G. Rahal-Callot,[45] P. G. Rancoita,[24] M. Rattaggi,[24] G. Raven,[2] P. Razis,[27] K. Read,[29] D. Ren,[45] Z. Ren,[16] M. Rescigno,[34] S. Reucroft,[10] A. Ricker,[1] S. Riemann,[44] B. C. Riemers,[42] K. Riles,[3] O. Rind,[3] H. A. Rizvi,[16] F. J. Rodriguez,[23]

B. P. Roe,[3] M. Röhner,[1] S. Röhner,[1] L. Romero,[23] J. Rose,[1] S. Rosier-Lees,[4] R. Rosmalen,[28] Ph. Rosselet,[19] A. Rubbia,[13] J. A. Rubio,[15] H. Rykaczewski,[45] M. Sachwitz,[44] J. Salicio,[15] J. M. Salicio,[23] G. S. Sanders,[21] A. Santocchia,[31] M. S. Sarakinos,[13] G. Sartorelli,[7,16] M. Sassowsky,[1] G. Sauvage,[4] V. Schegelsky,[35] D. Schmitz,[1] P. Schmitz,[1] M. Schneegans,[4] H. Schopper,[46] D. J. Schotanus,[28] S. Shotkin,[13] H. J. Schreiber,[44] J. Shukla,[32] R. Schulte,[1] S. Schulte,[1] K. Schultze,[1] J. Schwenke,[1] G. Schwering,[1] C. Sciacca,[26] I. Scott,[12] R. Sehgal,[16] P. G. Seiler,[43] J. C. Sens,[15,2] L. Servoli,[31] I. Sheer,[36] D. Z. Shen,[38] S. Shevchenko,[30] X. R. Shi,[30] E. Shumilov,[25] V. Shoutko,[25] D. Son,[40] A. Sopczak,[36] C. Spartiotis,[5] T. Spickermann,[1] P. Spillantini,[14] R. Starosta,[1] M. Steuer,[7,13] D. P. Stickland,[33] F. Sticozzi,[13] H. Stone,[33] K. Strauch,[12] B. C. Stringfellow,[42] K. Sudhakar,[8] G. Sultanov,[16] L. Z. Sun,[18,16] H. Suter,[45] J. D. Swain,[16] A. A. Syed,[28] X. W. Tang,[6] L. Taylor,[10] G. Terzi,[24] Samuel C. C. Ting,[13] S. M. Ting,[13] M. Tonutti,[1] S. C. Tonwar,[8] J. Tóth,[11] A. Tsaregorodtsev,[35] G. Tsipolitis,[32] C. Tully,[33] K. L. Tung,[6] J. Ulbricht,[45] L. Urbán,[11] U. Uwer,[1] E. Valente,[34] R. T. Van de Walle,[28] I. Vetlitsky,[25] G. Viertel,[45] P. Vikas,[16] U. Vikas,[16] M. Vivargent,[4] H. Vogel,[32] H. Vogt,[44] I. Vorobiev,[25] A. A. Vorobyov,[35] L. Vuilleumier,[19] M. Wadhwa,[4] W. Wallraff,[1] C. Wang,[13] C. R. Wang,[18] G. H. Wang,[32] X. L. Wang,[18] Y. F. Wang,[13] Z. M. Wang,[16,18] A. Weber,[1] J. Weber,[45] R. Weill,[19] T. J. Wenaus,[20] J. Wenninger,[17] M. White,[13] C. Willmott,[23] F. Wittgenstein,[15] D. Wright,[33] S. X. Wu,[16] B. Wysłouch,[13] Y. Y. Xie,[38] J. G. Xu,[6] Z. Z. Xu,[18] Z. L. Xue,[38] D. S. Yan,[38] B. Z. Yang,[18] C. G. Yang,[6] G. Yang,[16] C. H. Ye,[16] J. B. Ye,[18] Q. Ye,[16] S. C. Yeh,[47] Z. W. Yin,[38] J. M. You,[16] N. Yunus,[16] M. Yzerman,[2] C. Zaccardelli,[30] P. Zemp,[45] M. Zeng,[16] Y. Zeng,[1] D. H. Zhang,[2] Z. P. Zhang,[18,16] B. Zhou,[9] G. J. Zhou,[6] J. F. Zhou,[1] R. Y. Zhu,[30] A. Zichichi,[7,15,16] B. C. C. van der Zwaan[2]

[1] *I. Physikalisches Institut, RWTH, W-5100 Aachen, FRG*
   III. Physikalisches Institut, RWTH, W-5100 Aachen, FRG
[2] *National Institute for High Energy Physics, NIKHEF, NL-1009 DB Amsterdam, The Netherlands*
[3] *University of Michigan, Ann Arbor, MI 48109, USA*
[4] *Laboratoire d'Annecy-le-Vieux de Physique des Particules, LAPP,IN2P3-CNRS, BP 110, F-74941 Annecy-le-Vieux CEDEX, France*
[5] *Johns Hopkins University, Baltimore, MD 21218, USA*
[6] *Institute of High Energy Physics, IHEP, 100039 Beijing, China*
[7] *INFN-Sezione di Bologna, I-40126 Bologna, Italy*
[8] *Tata Institute of Fundamental Research, Bombay 400 005, India*
[9] *Boston University, Boston, MA 02215, USA*
[10] *Northeastern University, Boston, MA 02115, USA*
[11] *Central Research Institute for Physics of the Hungarian Academy of Sciences, H-1525 Budapest 114, Hungary*
[12] *Harvard University, Cambridge, MA 02139, USA*
[13] *Massachusetts Institute of Technology, Cambridge, MA 02139, USA*
[14] *INFN Sezione di Firenze and University of Florence, I-50125 Florence, Italy*
[15] *European Laboratory for Particle Physics, CERN, CH-1211 Geneva 23, Switzerland*
[16] *World Laboratory, FBLJA Project, CH-1211 Geneva 23, Switzerland*
[17] *University of Geneva, CH-1211 Geneva 4, Switzerland*
[18] *Chinese University of Science and Technology, USTC, Hefei, Anhui 230 029, China*
[19] *University of Lausanne, CH-1015 Lausanne, Switzerland*
[20] *Lawrence Livermore National Laboratory, Livermore, CA 94550, USA*
[21] *Los Alamos National Laboratory, Los Alamos, NM 87544, USA*
[22] *Institut de Physique Nucléaire de Lyon, IN2P3-CNRS,Université Claude Bernard, F-69622 Villeurbanne Cedex, France*
[23] *Centro de Investigaciones Energeticas, Medioambientales y Tecnologicas, CIEMAT, E-28040*

    Madrid, Spain
[24] INFN-Sezione di Milano, I-20133 Milan, Italy
[25] Institute of Theoretical and Experimental Physics, ITEP, Moscow, Russia
[26] INFN-Sezione di Napoli and University of Naples, I-80125 Naples, Italy
[27] Department of Natural Sciences, University of Cyprus, Nicosia, Cyprus
[28] University of Nymegen and NIKHEF, NL-6525 ED Nymegen, The Netherlands
[29] Oak Ridge National Laboratory, Oak Ridge, TN 37831, USA
[30] California Institute of Technology, Pasadena, CA 91125, USA
[31] INFN-Sezione di Perugia and Universitá Degli Studi di Perugia, I-06100 Perugia, Italy
[32] Carnegie Mellon University, Pittsburgh, PA 15213, USA
[33] Princeton University, Princeton, NJ 08544, USA
[34] INFN-Sezione di Roma and University of Rome, "La Sapienza", I-00185 Rome, Italy
[35] Nuclear Physics Institute, St. Petersburg, Russia
[36] University of California, San Diego, CA 92093, USA
[37] Dept. de Fisica de Particulas Elementales, Univ. de Santiago, E-15706 Santiago de Compostela, Spain
[38] Shanghai Institute of Ceramics, SIC, Shanghai, China
[39] Bulgarian Academy of Sciences, Institute of Mechatronics, BU-1113 Sofia, Bulgaria
[40] Center for High Energy Physics, Korea Advanced Inst. of Sciences and Technology, 305-701 Taejon, Republic of Korea
[41] University of Alabama, Tuscaloosa, AL 35486, USA
[42] Purdue University, West Lafayette, IN 47907, USA
[43] Paul Scherrer Institut, PSI, CH-5232 Villigen, Switzerland
[44] DESY-Institut für Hochenergiephysik, O-1615 Zeuthen, FRG
[45] Eidgenössische Technische Hochschule, ETH Zürich, CH-8093 Zürich, Switzerland
[46] University of Hamburg, W-2000 Hamburg, FRG
[47] High Energy Physics Group, Taiwan, China
† Deceased.

OPAL COLLABORATION

P.D. Acton,[25] G. Alexander,[23] J. Allison,[16] P.P. Allport,[5] K.J. Anderson,[9] S. Arcelli,[2] A. Astbury,[28] D. Axen,[29] G. Azuelos,[18,a] G.A. Bahan,[16] J.T.M. Baines,[16] A.H. Ball,[17] J. Banks,[16] R.J. Barlow,[16] S. Barnett,[16] J.R. Batley,[5] G. Beaudoin,[18] A. Beck,[23] G.A. Beck,[13] J. Becker,[10] T. Behnke,[27] K.W. Bell,[20] G. Bella,[23] P. Bentkowski,[18] P. Berlich,[10] S. Bethke,[11] O. Biebel,[3] U. Binder,[10] I.J. Bloodworth,[1] P. Bock,[11] B. Boden,[3] H.M. Bosch,[11] H. Breuker,[8] P. Bright-Thomas,[25] R.M. Brown,[20] A. Buijs,[8] H.J. Burckhart,[8] C. Burgard,[27] P. Capiluppi,[2] R.K. Carnegie,[6] A.A. Carter,[13] J.R. Carter,[5] C.Y. Chang,[17] D.G. Charlton,[8] S.L. Chu,[4] P.E.L. Clarke,[25] I. Cohen,[23] J.C. Clayton,[1] W.J. Collins,[5] J.E. Conboy,[15] M. Cooper,[22] M. Coupland,[14] M. Cuffiani,[2] S. Dado,[22] G.M. Dallavalle,[2] S. De Jong,[13] L.A. del Pozo,[5] H. Deng,[17] A. Dieckmann,[11] M. Dittmar,[4] M.S. Dixit,[7] E. do Couto e Silva,[12] J.E. Duboscq,[8] E. Duchovni,[26] G. Duckeck,[11] I.P. Duerdoth,[16] D.J.P. Dumas,[6] P.A. Elcombe,[5] P.G. Estabrooks,[6] E. Etzion,[23] H.G. Evans,[9] F. Fabbri,[2] M. Fierro,[2] M. Fincke-Keeler,[28] H.M. Fischer,[3] D.G. Fong,[17] M. Foucher,[17] A. Gaidot,[21] O. Ganel,[26] J.W. Gary,[4] J. Gascon,[18] R.F. McGowan,[16] N.I. Geddes,[20] C. Geich-Gimbel,[3] S.W. Gensler,[9] F.X. Gentit,[21] G. Giacomelli,[2] R. Giacomelli,[2] V. Gibson,[5] W.R. Gibson,[13] J.D. Gillies,[20] J. Goldberg,[22] M.J. Goodrick,[5] W. Gorn,[4] C. Grandi,[2] F.C. Grant,[5] J. Hagemann,[27] G.G. Hanson,[12] M. Hansroul,[8] C.K. Hargrove,[7] P.F. Harrison,[13] J. Hart,[8] P.M. Hattersley,[1] M. Hauschild,[8] C.M. Hawkes,[8] E. Heflin,[4] R.J. Hemingway,[6] R.D. Heuer,[8] J.C. Hill,[5] S.J. Hillier,[8] T. Hilse,[10] D.A. Hinshaw,[18] J.D. Hobbs,[8] P.R. Hobson,[25] D. Hochman,[26] R.J. Homer,[1] A.K. Honma,[28,a] R.E. Hughes-Jones,[16] R. Humbert,[10] P. Igo-Kemenes,[11] H. Ihssen,[11] D.C. Imrie,[25] A.C. Janissen,[6] A. Jawahery,[17] P.W. Jeffreys,[20] H. Jeremie,[18] M. Jimack,[2] M. Jobes,[1] R.W.L. Jones,[13] P. Jovanovic,[1] C. Jui,[4] D. Karlen,[6] K. Kawagoe,[24] T. Kawamoto,[24] R.K. Keeler,[28] R.G. Kellogg,[17] B.W. Kennedy,[15] S. Kluth,[5] T. Kobayashi,[24] D.S. Koetke,[8] T.P. Kokott,[3] S. Komamiya,[24] L. Köpke,[8] J.F. Kral,[8] R. Kowalewski,[6] J. von Krogh,[11] J. Kroll,[9] M. Kuwano,[24] P. Kyberd,[13] G.D. Lafferty,[16] R. Lahmann,[17] F. Lamarche,[18] J.G. Layter,[4] P. Leblanc,[18] A.M. Lee,[17] M.H. Lehto,[15] D. Lellouch,[26] C. Leroy,[18] J. Letts,[4] S. Levegrün,[3] L. Levinson,[26] S.L. Lloyd,[13] F.K. Loebinger,[16] J.M. Lorah,[17] B. Lorazo,[18] M.J. Losty,[7] X.C. Lou,[12] J. Ludwig,[10] M. Mannelli,[8] S. Marcellini,[2] G. Maringer,[3] C. Markus,[3] A.J. Martin,[13] J.P. Martin,[18] T. Mashimo,[24] P. Mättig,[3] U. Maur,[3] J. McKenna,[28] T.J. McMahon,[1] J.R. McNutt,[25] F. Meijers,[8] D. Menszner,[11] F.S. Merritt,[9] H. Mes,[7] A. Michelini,[8] R.P. Middleton,[20] G. Mikenberg,[26] J. Mildenberger,[6] D.J. Miller,[15] R. Mir,[12] W. Mohr,[10] C. Moisan,[18] A. Montanari,[2] T. Mori,[24] M. Morii,[24] T. Mouthuy,[12,b] B. Nellen,[3] H.H. Nguyen,[9] M. Nozaki,[24] S.W. O'Neale,[1] F.G. Oakham,[7] F. Odorici,[2] H.O. Ogren,[12] C.J. Oram,[28,a] M.J. Oreglia,[9] S. Orito,[24] J.P. Pansart,[21] B. Panzer-Steindel,[8] P. Paschievici,[26] G.N. Patrick,[20] N. Paz-Jaoshvili,[23] P. Pfister,[10] J.E. Pilcher,[9] J. Pinfold,[31] D. Pitman,[28] D.E. Plane,[8] P. Poffenberger,[28] B. Poli,[2] A. Pouladdej,[6] T.W. Pritchard,[13] H. Przysieznak,[18] G. Quast,[27] M.W. Redmond,[9] D.L. Rees,[8] G.E. Richards,[16] D. Robinson,[8] A. Rollnik,[3] J.M. Roney,[28,c] E. Ros,[8] S. Rosskagi,[10] A.M. Rossi,[2] M. Rosvick,[28] P. Routenburg,[6] K. Runge,[10] O. Runolfsson,[8] D.R. Rust,[12] M. Sasaki,[24] C. Sbarra,[8] A.D. Schaile,[10] O. Schaile,[10] W. Schappert,[6] P. Scharff-Hansen,[8] P. Schenk,[4] B. Schmitt,[3] H. von der Schmitt,[11] S. Schreiber,[3] C. Schwick,[27] J. Schwiening,[3] W.G. Scott,[20] M. Settles,[12] T.G. Shears,[5] B.C. Shen,[4] C.H. Shepherd-Themistocleous,[7] P. Sherwood,[15] R. Shypit,[29] A. Simon,[3] P. Singh,[13] G.P. Siroli,[2] A. Skuja,[17] A.M. Smith,[8] T.J. Smith,[28] G.A. Snow,[17] R. Sobie,[28,c] R.W. Springer,[17] M. Sproston,[20] K. Stephens,[16] J. Steuerer,[28] R. Ströhmer,[11] D. Strom,[30] T. Takeshita,[24,d] P. Taras,[18] S. Tarem,[26] M. Tecchio,[9] P. Teixeira-Dias,[11] N. Tesch,[3] N.J. Thackray,[1] M.A. Thomson,[15] E. Torrente-Lujan,[22] G. Transtromer,[25] N.J. Tresilian,[16] T. Tsukamoto,[24] M.F. Turner,[8] G. Tysarczyk-Niemeyer,[11] C. Van den plas,[18] R. Van Kooten,[27] G.J. VanDalen,[4] G. Vasseur,[21] C.J. Virtue,[7] A. Wagner,[27] D.L. Wagner,[9] C. Wahl,[10] J.P. Walker,[1] C.P. Ward,[5] D.R. Ward,[5] P.M. Watkins,[1] A.T. Watson,[1] N.K. Watson,[8] M. Weber,[11] P. Weber,[6] P.S. Wells,[8] N. Wermes,[3] M.A. Whalley,[1] G.W. Wilson,[4] J.A. Wilson,[1] V-H. Winterer,[10] T. Wlodek,[26] S. Wotton,[11] T.R. Wyatt,[16] R. Yaari,[26] A. Yeaman,[13] G. Yekutieli,[26] M. Yurko,[18] W. Zeuner,[8] G.T. Zorn[17]

c

[1] School of Physics and Space Research, University of Birmingham, Birmingham, B15 2TT, UK
[2] Dipartimento di Fisica dell' Università di Bologna and INFN, Bologna, 40126, Italy
[3] Physikalisches Institut, Universität Bonn, D-5300 Bonn 1, FRG
[4] Department of Physics, University of California, Riverside, CA 92521 USA
[5] Cavendish Laboratory, Cambridge, CB3 0HE, UK
[6] Carleton University, Dept of Physics, Colonel By Drive, Ottawa, Ontario K1S 5B6, Canada
[7] Centre for Research in Particle Physics, Carleton University, Ottawa, Ontario K1S 5B6, Canada
[8] CERN, European Organisation for Particle Physics, 1211 Geneva 23, Switzerland
[9] Enrico Fermi Institute and Department of Physics, University of Chicago, Chicago Illinois 60637, USA
[10] Fakultät für Physik, Albert Ludwigs Universität, D-7800 Freiburg, FRG
[11] Physikalisches Institut, Universität Heidelberg, Heidelberg, FRG
[12] Indiana University, Dept of Physics, Swain Hall West 117, Bloomington, Indiana 47405, USA
[13] Queen Mary and Westfield College, University of London, London, E1 4NS, UK
[14] Birkbeck College, London, WC1E 7HV, UK
[15] University College London, London, WC1E 6BT, UK
[16] Department of Physics, Schuster Laboratory, The University, Manchester, M13 9PL, UK
[17] Department of Physics, University of Maryland, College Park, Maryland 20742, USA
[18] Laboratoire de Physique Nucléaire, Université de Montréal, Montréal, Quebec, H3C 3J7, Canada
[20] Rutherford Appleton Laboratory, Chilton, Didcot, Oxfordshire, OX11 0QX, UK
[21] DAPNIA/SPP, Saclay, F-91191 Gif-sur-Yvette, France
[22] Department of Physics, Technion-Israel Institute of Technology, Haifa 32000, Israel
[23] Department of Physics and Astronomy, Tel Aviv University, Tel Aviv 69978, Israel
[24] International Centre for Elementary Particle Physics and Dept of Physics, University of Tokyo, Tokyo 113, and Kobe University, Kobe 657, Japan
[25] Brunel University, Uxbridge, Middlesex, UB8 3PH UK
[26] Nuclear Physics Department, Weizmann Institute of Science, Rehovot, 76100, Israel
[27] Universität Hamburg/DESY, II Inst für Experimental Physik, 2000 Hamburg 52, Germany
[28] University of Victoria, Dept of Physics, P O Box 3055, Victoria BC V8W 3P6, Canada
[29] University of British Columbia, Dept of Physics, 6224 Agriculture Road, Vancouver BC V6T 1Z1, Canada
[30] University of Oregon, Dept of Physics, Eugene, Oregon 97403, USA
[31] University of Alberta, Dept of Physics, Edmonton AB T6G 2J1, Canada

[a] Also at TRIUMF, Vancouver, Canada V6T 2A3
[b] Now at Centre de Physique des Particules de Marseille, Faculté des Sciences de Luminy, Marseille
[c] And IPP, University of Victoria, Dept of Physics, P O Box 3055, Victoria BC V8W 3P6, Canada
[d] Also at Shinshu University, Matsumoto 390, Japan

SLD COLLABORATION

K. Abe,[20] I. Abt,[29] P.D. Acton,[3] G. Agnew,[3] C. Alber,[26] P. Antilogus,[19] C. Arroyo,[5] W.W. Ash,[19]
A. Astbury,[33] D. Aston,[19] D.A. Axen,[24] N. Bacchetta,[10] K.G. Baird,[17] C. Baltay,[37] H.R. Band,[35]
G.J. Baranko,[26] O. Bardon,[15] R. Battiston,[28] A.O. Bazarko,[5] A. Bean,[22] G. Beer,[33] R.J. Belcinski,[30]
R. Ben-David,[37] A.C. Benvenuti,[8] S. Bethke,[14] M. Biasini,[28] T. Bienz,[19] G.M. Bilei,[28] F. Bird,[19]
D. Bisello,[10] G. Blaylock,[23] T. Bolton,[5] S. Bougerolle,[24] J. E. Brau,[31] M. Breidenbach,[19]
W.M. Bugg,[32] D. Burke,[19] T.H. Burnett,[34] P.N. Burrows,[15] W. Busza,[15] A. Calcaterra,[7]
D.O. Caldwell,[22] D. Calloway,[19] B. Camanzi,[9] M. Carpinelli,[12] J. Carr,[26] S. Cartwright,[30]
R. Cassell,[19] R. Castaldi,[12,27] A. Castro,[10] M. Cavalli-Sforza,[23] G.B. Chadwick,[19] O. Chamberlain,[14]
L. Chen,[36] P.E.L. Clarke,[3] R. Claus,[19] H.O. Cohn,[32] J.A. Coller,[2] V. Cook,[34] R. Cotton,[3]
R.F. Cowan,[15] P.A. Coyle,[23] D.G. Coyne,[23] C.J.S. Damerell,[18] S. Dasu,[19] R. De Sangro,[7]
P. De Simone,[7] S. De Simone,[7] R. Dell'Orso,[12] Y.C. Du,[32] R. Dubois,[19] W. Dunwoodie,[19]
D.D. Durrett,[26] G. Eigen,[4] B.I. Eisenstein,[29] R. Elia,[19] E. Erdos,[26] C. Fan,[26] M.J. Fero,[15]
T. Fieguth,[19] K.M. Fortune,[29] R. Frey,[31] J.I. Friedman,[15] J. Fujimoto,[13] K. Furuno,[31] M. Gallinaro,[7]
T. Gillman,[18] G. Gladding,[29] S. Gonzalez,[15] G.D. Hallewell,[19] T. Hansl-Kozanecka,[15] E.L. Hart,[32]
K. Hasegawa,[20] Y. Hasegawa,[20] S. Hedges,[3] S.S. Hertzbach,[30] M.D. Hildreth,[19] D.G. Hitlin,[4]
A. Honma,[33] J. Huber,[31] E.W. Hughes,[19] H. Hwang,[31] E. Hyatt,[5] Y. Iwasaki,[20] J.M. Izen,[29]
P. Jacques,[17] A.S. Johnson,[2] J.R. Johnson,[35] R.A. Johnson,[25] T. Junk,[19] S. Kaiser,[19] R. Kajikawa,[16]
M. Kalelkar,[17] I. Karliner,[29] H. Kawahara,[19] R.K. Keeler,[33] M.H. Kelsey,[4] H.W. Kendall,[15]
H.Y. Kim,[34] P.C. Kim,[19] R. King,[19] M. Klein,[4] R.R. Kofler,[30] M. Kowitt,[14] N.M. Krishna,[26]
R.S. Kroeger,[32] P.F. Kunz,[19] Y. Kwon,[19] J.F. Labs,[19] M. Langston,[31] A. Lath,[15] J.A. Lauber,[26]
D.W.G. Leith,[19] X. Liu,[23] M. Loreti,[10] A. Lu,[22] H.L. Lynch,[19] J. Ma,[34] W.A. Majid,[29]
G. Mancinelli,[28] S. Manly,[37] G. Mantovani,[28] T.W. Markiewicz,[19] T. Maruyama,[19] G.R. Mason,[33]
H. Masuda,[19] A. Mazzucato,[10] E. Mazzucato,[9] J.F. McGowan,[29] A.K. McKemey,[3] B.T. Meadows,[25]
D.J. Mellor,[29] R. Messner,[19] A.I. Mincer,[4] P.M. Mockett,[34] K.C. Moffeit,[19] R.J. Morrison,[22]
B. Mours,[19] G. Mueller,[19] D. Muller,[19] T. Nagamine,[19] U. Nauenberg,[26] R. Neal,[19] M. Nussbaum,[25]
C. Oram,[21] L.S. Osborne,[15] R.S. Panvini,[36] H. Park,[31] M. Pauluzzi,[28] T.J. Pavel,[19] F. Perrier,[19]
I. Peruzzi,[7,28] L. Pescara,[10] D. Peters,[24] M. Petradza,[19] M. Piccolo,[7] L. Piemontese,[9] E. Pieroni,[12]
K.T. Pitts,[31] R.J. Plano,[17] P.R. Poffenberger,[33] R. Prepost,[35] C.Y. Prescott,[19] D. Pripstein,[14]
G.D. Punkar,[19] B.N. Ratcliff,[19] T.W. Reeves,[36] P.E. Rensing,[19] J.D. Richman,[22] L.P. Robertson,[33]
L.S. Rochester,[19] L. Rosenson,[15] J.E. Rothberg,[34] P.C. Rowson,[5] J.J. Russell,[19] D. Rust,[6]
P. Saez,[19] B. Saitta,[9] A.K. Santha,[25] A. Santocchia,[28] T. Schalk,[23] P.R. Schenk,[33] R.H. Schindler,[19]
U. Schneekloth,[15] D. Schultz,[19] B.A. Schumm,[14] A. Seiden,[23] L. Servoli,[28] M.H. Shaevitz,[5]
J.T. Shank,[2] G. Shapiro,[14] S.L. Shapiro,[19] D.J. Sherden,[19] A. Shoup,[25] R.L. Shypit,[24]
C. Simopoulos,[19] S.R. Smith,[19] J.A. Snyder,[37] R. Sobie,[24] M.D. Sokoloff,[25] P. Stamer,[17] H. Steiner,[14]
R. Steiner,[1] I.E. Stockdale,[25] M.G. Strauss,[30] D. Su,[18] F. Suekane,[20] A. Sugiyama,[16] S. Suzuki,[16]
M. Swartz,[19] A. Szumilo,[34] T. Takahashi,[19] F.E. Taylor,[15] M. Tecchio,[10] J.J. Thaler,[29] N. Toge,[19]
M. Turcotte,[33] J.D. Turk,[37] T. Usher,[19] J. Va'Vra,[19] C. Vannini,[12] E. Vella,[34] J.P. Venuti,[36]
R. Verdier,[15] P.G. Verdini,[12] A.P. Waite,[19] S.J. Watts,[3] A.W. Weidemann,[32] J.S. Whitaker,[2]
S.L. White,[32] F.J. Wickens,[18] D.A. Williams,[23] D.C. Williams,[15] R.W. Williams,[34] S.H. Williams,[19]
R.J. Wilson,[2] W.J. Wisniewski,[4] M.S. Witherell,[22] M. Woods,[19] G.B. Word,[17] J. Wyss,[10]
R.K. Yamamoto,[15] J.M. Yamartino,[15] S.J. Yellin,[22] C.C. Young,[19] H. Yuta,[20] G. Zapalac,[35]
R.W. Zdarko,[19] C. Zeitlin,[31] J. Zhou,[31] M. Zolotorev,[19] P. Zucchelli[9]

[1] *Adelphi University*
[2] *Boston University*
[3] *Brunel University*
[4] *California Institute of Technology*
[5] *Columbia University*

[6] *Indiana University*
[7] *INFN Lab. Nazionali di Frascati*
[8] *INFN Sezione di Bologna*
[9] *INFN Sezione di Ferrara and Università di Ferrara*
[10] *INFN Sezione di Padova and Università di Padova*
[11] *INFN Sezione di Perugia and Università Perugia*
[12] *INFN Sezione di Pisa and Università di Pisa*
[13] *KEK National Laboratory*
[14] *Lawrence Berkeley Laboratory, University of California*
[15] *Massachusetts Institute of Technology*
[16] *Nagoya University*
[17] *Rutgers University*
[18] *Rutherford Appleton Laboratory*
[19] *Stanford Linear Accelerator Center*
[20] *Tohoku University*
[21] *TRIUMF*
[22] *University of California, Santa Barbara*
[23] *University of California, Santa Cruz*
[24] *University of British Columbia*
[25] *University of Cincinnati*
[26] *University of Colorado*
[27] *Università di Genova*
[28] *Università di Perugia*
[29] *University of Illinois*
[30] *University of Massachusetts*
[31] *University of Oregon*
[32] *University of Tennessee*
[33] *University of Victoria, TRIUMF*
[34] *University of Washington*
[35] *University of Wisconsin*
[36] *Vanderbilt University*
[37] *Yale University*

The SOUDAN 2 COLLABORATION

J. L. Thron,[1] W. W. M. Allison,[3] G. J. Alner,[4] I. Ambats,[1] D. S. Ayres,[1] L. J. Balka,[1] G. D. Barr,[3,a] W. L. Barrett,[8,1] D. Benjamin,[5] P. M. Border,[2] C. B. Brooks,[3] J. H. Cobb,[3] D. J. A. Cockerill,[4] H. Courant,[2] J. W. Dawson,[1] D. M. Demuth,[2] V. W. Edwards,[4] B. Ewen,[5] T. H. Fields,[1] C. Garcia-Garcia,[4,b] R. H. Giles,[3] G. L. Giller,[3] M. C. Goodman,[1] R. N. Gray,[2] S. Heilig,[6,1] N. Hill,[1] J. Hoftiezer,[1,c] D. J. Jankowski,[1] K. Johns,[2,d] T. Kafka,[5] S. M. S. Kasahara,[2] J. Kochocki,[5,f] W. Leeson,[5] P. L. Litchfield,[4] N. P. Longley,[2,7] F. V. Lopez,[1] M. J. Lowe,[2,g] W. A. Mann,[5] M. L. Marshak,[2] E. N. May,[1] D. Maxam,[2] L. McMaster,[5] R. Milburn,[5] W. H. Miller,[2] C. P. Minor,[2] A. Napier,[5] W. P. Oliver,[5] G. F. Pearce,[4] D. H. Perkins,[3] E. A. Peterson,[2] L. E. Price,[1] D. M. Roback,[2] D. B. Rosen,[2,h] K. Ruddick,[2] B. Saitta,[5,i] D. Schmid,[2] J. Schlereth,[1] J. Schneps,[5] P. D. Shield,[3] M. A. Shupe,[2,d] N. Sundaralingam,[5] M. Thomson,[3,k] L. Tupper,[3,e] G. Villaume,[2] S. Werkema,[2,j] N. West,[3] and C. A. Woods[4,a]

[1] Argonne National Laboratory, Argonne, IL 60439, USA
[2] University of Minnesota, Minneapolis, MN 55455, USA
[3] Department of Physics, University of Oxford, Oxford OX1 3RH, UK
[4] Rutherford Appleton Laboratory, Chilton, Didcot, Oxfordshire, OX11 0QX, UK
[5] Tufts University, Medford, MA 02155, USA
[6] Grinnell College, Grinnell, IA 50112, USA
[7] Carleton College, Northfield, MN 55057, USA
[8] Western Washington University, Bellingham, WA 98225, USA
[a] Now at CERN, CH-1211, Geneva 23, Switzerland
[b] Now at IFIC, E-46100 Burjassot, Valencia, Spain
[c] Now at LeCroy Corporation, Chestnut Ridge, NY 10977, USA
[d] Now at University of Arizona, Physics Department, Tucson, AZ 85721, USA
[e] Now at University of Oxford, Department of Physiology, Oxford, UK
[f] Now at Virginia Polytechnic Institute, Blacksburg, VA 24061, USA
[g] Now at Rice University, Houston, TX 77251, USA
[h] Now at Boston University, Boston, MA 02215, USA
[i] Now at Univ. di Ferrara, Dipartimento di Fisica, 44100 Ferrara, Italy
[j] Now at FNAL, Batavia, Il 60510, USA
[k] Now at Department of Physics and Astronomy, University College London, London WC1E 6BT, UK

TOPAZ COLLABORATION

K. Abe[1], I. Adachi[2], M. Aoki[3], R. Belusevic[2], K. Emi[1], R. Enomoto[2], H. Fujii[2], K. Fujii[2], T. Fujii[4], J. Fujimoto[2], N. Fujiwara[5], H. Hayashii[5], B. Howell[6], N. Iida[5], H. Ikeda[2], R. Itoh[2], H. Iwasaki[2], M. Iwasaki[5], R. Kajikawa[3], S. Kato[7], S. Kawabata[2], H. Kichimi[2], T. Kishida[4], M. Kobayashi[2], D. Koltick[6], I. Levine[6], K. Miyabayashi[3], A. Miyamoto[2], K. Muramatsu[5], K. Nagai[8], T. Nagira[5], E. Nakano[3], O. Nitoh[1], S. Noguchi[5], F. Ochiai[9], Y. Ohnishi[3], H. Okuno[7], T. Okusawa[10], K. Shimozawa[3], A. Sugiyama[3], N. Sugiyama[11], S. Suzuki[3], K. Takahashi[1], T. Takahashi[10], M. Takemoto[5], T. Tanimori[11], T. Tauchi[2], F. Teramae[3], Y. Teramoto[10], T. Toyama[3], T. Tsukamoto[2], S. Uno[2], Y. Watanabe[11], A. Yamamoto[2], S. Yamamoto[4], M. Yamauchi[2]

[1] *Tokyo Univ. of Agriculture and Technology, Japan*
[2] *KEK National Laboratory for High Energy Physics, Japan*
[3] *Nagoya University, Japan*
[4] *University of Tokyo, Japan*
[5] *Nara Women's University, Japan*
[6] *Purdue University*
[7] *Institute for Nuclear Study, University of Tokyo, Japan*
[8] *Kobe Univiversity, Japan*
[9] *Tezukayama University, Japan*
[10] *Osaka City University, Japan*
[11] *Tokyo Institute of Technology, Japan*

Plenary Sessions

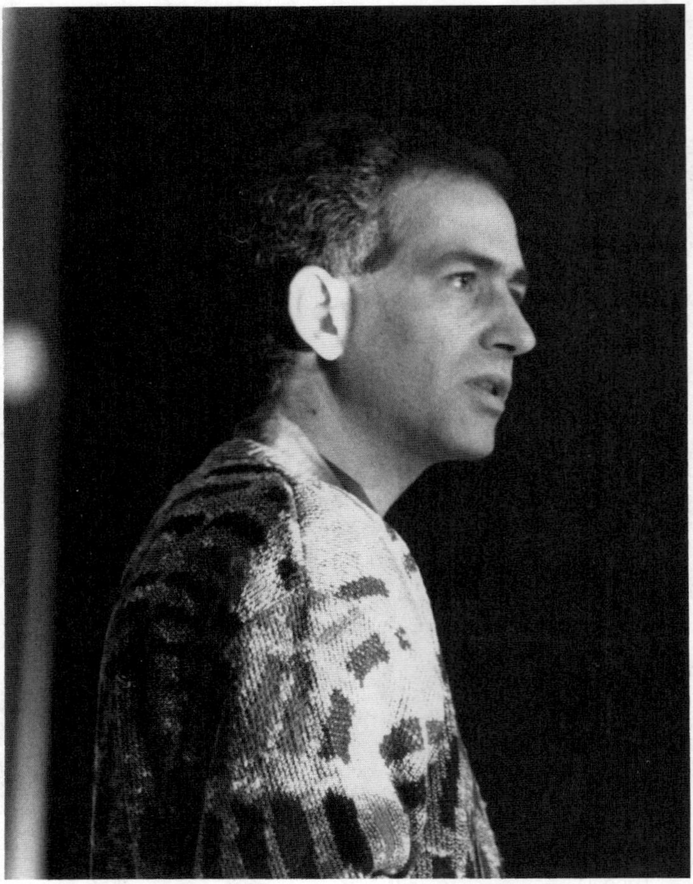

HIGHLIGHTS FROM CDF

AVI YAGIL
The CDF Collaboration
Fermi National Accelerator Laboratory
Batavia, IL 60510 USA

ABSTRACT

After a hiatus of 3 years, CDF is again taking data. Many of the upgrades made to the detector during this period are described here, along with some preliminary indications of their performance. A brief survey of the new data is presented. Prospects for the current run are discussed.

1. Introduction

The CDF detector has begun to collect data again starting in the summer of 1992, after a shutdown of 3 years. The current run is proceeding well, and will be briefly discussed in section 2. During the 3 years since the last run (1988-9), there have been a large number of upgrades, which enhance the performance of the detector in acceptance, triggering, and event information. We describe in section 3 the important upgrades, as well as some preliminary indication of their performances from data collected in this run. We show in section 4 preliminary physics results from this current run, and compare some of them with results from last run. In addition, we include a few new results from more thorough analysis of the data from the 88-89 run. Finally, we give some indications of the prospects for various physics goals that might be achievable in this run.

2. Operations

The Fermilab Tevatron collider resumed operation on May 12, 1992, when it started delivering $p\bar{p}$ collisions to the CDF detector, as well as the new D0 detector. The time period berween May 12 and August 26 1992 was taken to comission the CDF detector, including those components of the detector that were added for the 1992 run.

The performances of the Tevatron collider and CDF had sufficiently matured by August 26, 1992 that good quality data begun to be recorded. As of this date (November 1992), the Fermilab Tevatron achieved a peak luminosity of $4.5 \cdot 10^{30}$, three times higher than the peak luminosity of the last run. In the period August 26, 1992 to November 12, 1992, the Tevatron has delivered an integrated luminosity of 3.2 pb^{-1}, with CDF recording 2.3 pb^{-1} on tape, more than 1/2 of the data sample from the last run; this was achieved with an average initial luminosity of around $2 \cdot 10^{30}$; thus, the recent factor of 3 increase in initial luminosity bodes well for the future. Figure 1 shows the delivered and recorded integrated luminosity versus time.

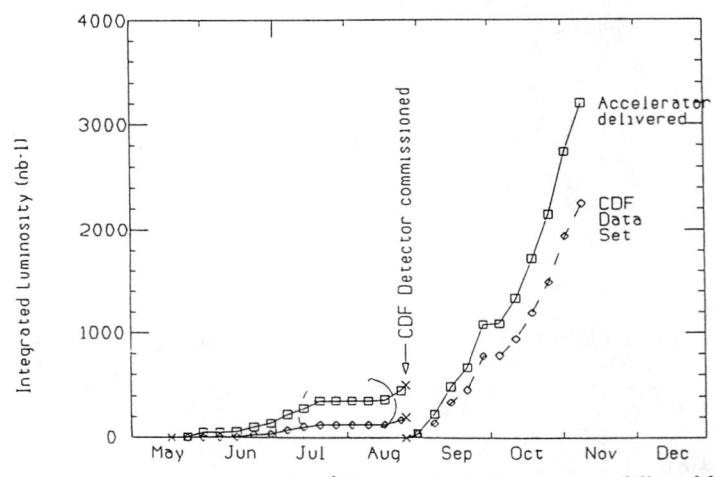

Figure 1: The integrated luminosity (pb^{-1}) versus time. The boxes are delivered luminosity, and the diamonds are the luminosity CDF wrote to tape.

3. Upgrades

3.1 Central Muon Upgrade (CMP)

The original CDF Central Muon detector (CMU), which covers the pseudorapidity region $|\eta| < 0.6$, has been complemented by the addition of four layers of drift tubes behind 2 feet of steel. As a result, hadronic punch-through backgrounds to the muon signal have been considerably reduced. This is illustrated in Figure 2 where we compare the energy deposited in the calorimeter by muon candidates with and without a requirement of hits in the CMP system. The minimum ionizing component is greatly enhanced. The addition of the CMP improves the muon identification capabilities of CDF.

3.2 Central Muon Extension (CMX)

We have also added layers of drift tubes outside the calorimeter in the pseudorapidity region of $0.6 < |\eta| < 1.0$. This increases the muon coverage in CDF by 50%. Figure 3 illustrates the increased acceptance to $J/\psi \to \mu^+\mu^-$ events using the CMX system.

3.3 Central PreRadiator (CPR)

The Central PreRadiator (CPR) system consists of a set of MWPCs mounted between the solenoid's coil (≈ 1.1 radiation lengths) and the central Electro-Magnetic

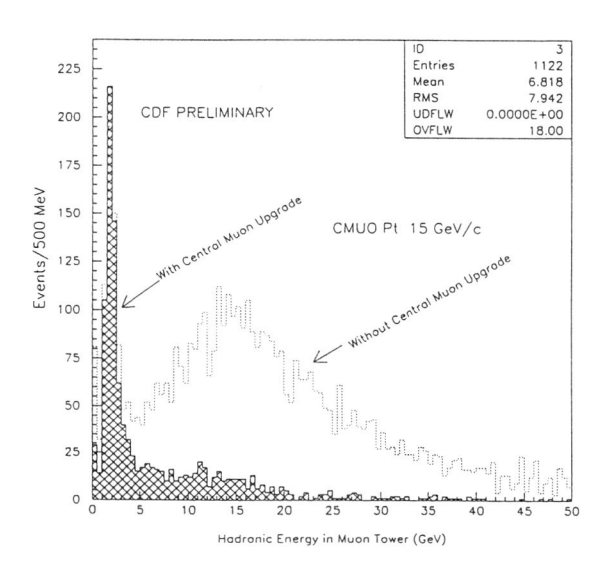

Figure 2: Hadronic Energy deposited in the muon tower: open histogram is for tracks with a stub in the Central Muon system (CMU), and the shaded area is that for tracks that have a stub in the Central Muon Upgrade (CMP)

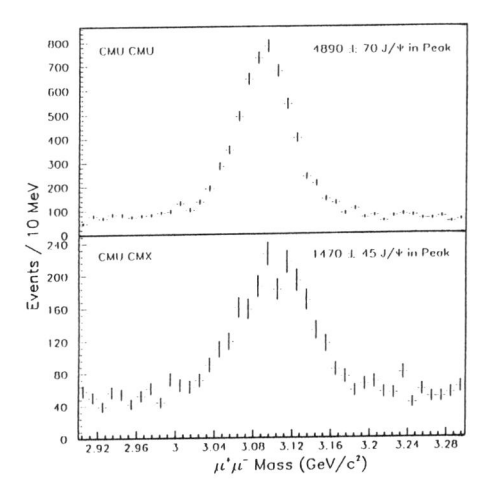

Figure 3: $M(\mu^+\mu^-)$ in the J/ψ region; shown are dimuon combinations of CMU-CMU (both muons in the Central Muon) and CMU-CMX (one muon in the Central Muon Extension)

calorimeter. The CPR gives an additional factor of 2-3 in pion-electron separation. It will also reduce the systematic uncertainties in the prompt-photon cross section measurement by a factor of 5 due to the enhanced γ/π^0 separation. The performance of the CPR is illustrated in Figure 4.

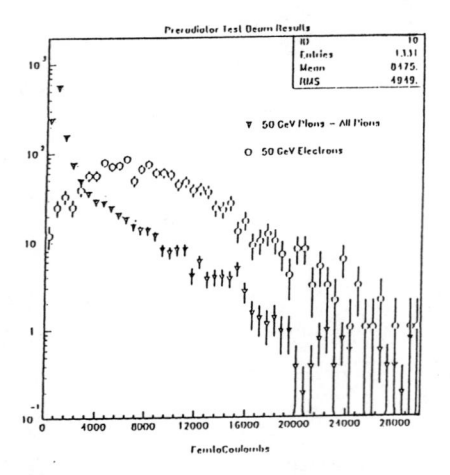

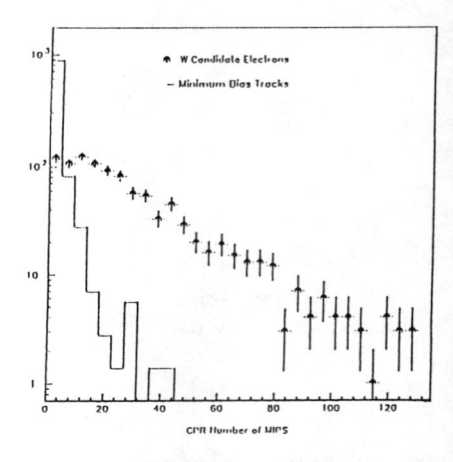

Figure 4: A comparison of the observed charge in the Central PreRadiator between electrons and pions is shown for: a) Testbeam and b) collider data.

3.4 Silicon Vertex Detector (SVX)

Four layers of DC coupled, single sided, silicon detectors with $R - \phi$ readout and $\approx 60\mu$ pitch have been added around the beam-pipe. The SVX covers the region of $|z| < 26$ cm around the interaction point (the luminous region has a width of ≈ 30 cm). The impact parameter resolution is better than 40μ (15μ) for tracks with $P_T > 1$ GeV/c ($P_T > 10$ GeV/c). Despite the large number of channels (46K), the readout is fast due to the sparsification performed on the readout chips. For tracks within the SVX fiducial volume the reconstruction efficiency is > 92%. The performance of the device is illustrated in Figure 5.

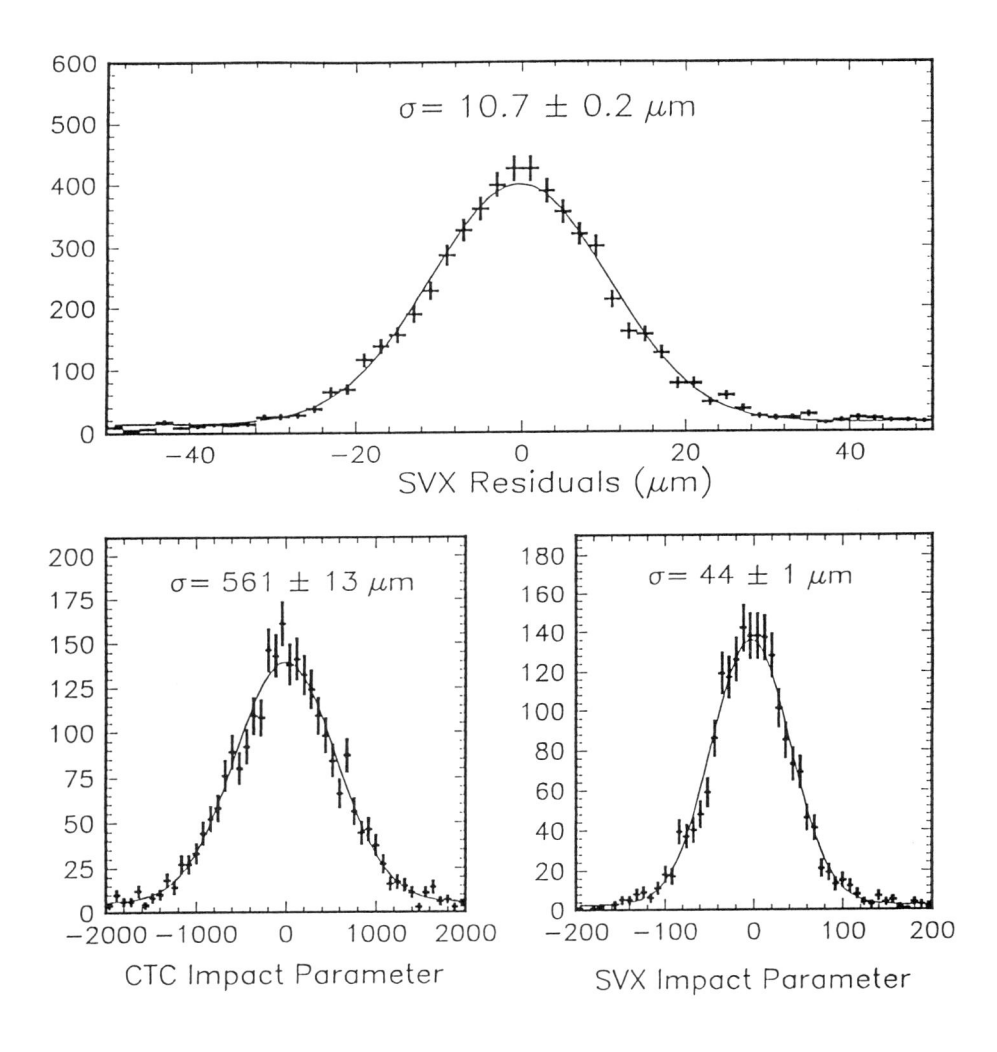

Figure 5: The Silicon Vertex performance is illustrated by: a). SVX track residual distribution (the observed resolution corresponds to spatial resolution of $\approx 13\mu$. b). Comparison of Impact Parameter as measured by the Central Tracker (CTC), and the CTC+SVX.

3.5 dE/dx in the Central Tracker

The outermost 54 (out of 84) layers of the Central Tracking Chamber (CTC) have been instrumented to measure charge deposition on the wires. The goals of the dE/dx system are to improve the e/π separation for $P_T < 4$ GeV/c and to assist in identifying kaons below 700 MeV/c. The expected resolution in the dE/dx measurement is $\approx 10\%$; calibration of this system is still underway, and a 13-15% resolution has already been achieved (see Figure 6).

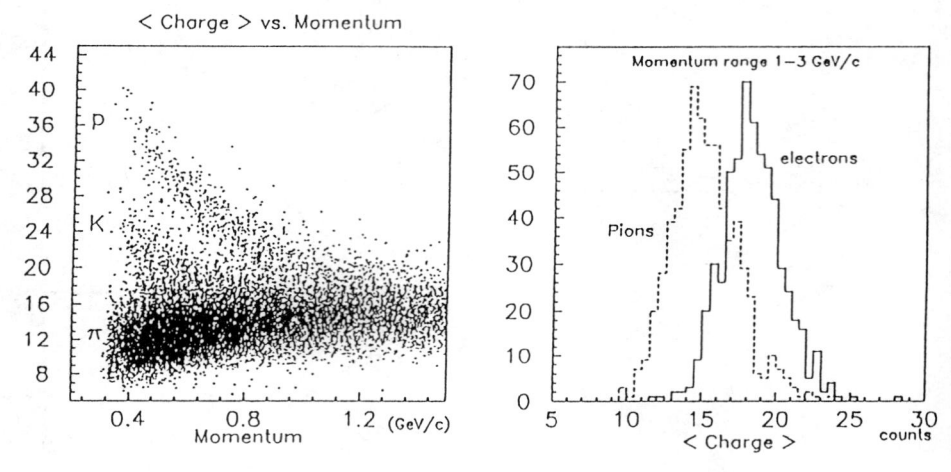

Figure 6: a).Mean charge Vs. momentum of CTC tracks. b). Electron/pion mean charge distribution ($1 < P_T < 3$ GeV/c).

3.6 Trigger

A number of changes to the trigger were implemented for the 1992 run, resulting in improved purity of the data written to tape and lower trigger thresholds for electrons and muons (see Figure 7). Hardware improvements included new triggers for the CMP and CMX systems, a better plug electromagnetic trigger, addition of a second processor to reduce the L2 decision time, a neural net (NN) based isolated photon trigger, as well as a NN electron trigger. In addition, a completely new software level 3 system using SiG computers replaced the old ACP based system.

3.7 Offline

Between 1989 and 1992, all of CDF's reconstruction code was ported to UNIX (both SiG and IBM), enabling us to run the offline code as part of the level 3 trigger.

Large fraction of the 1992 code is new (for new detectors: VTX, SVX, CPR, CMP and CMX). Many changes to the reconstruction code for existing detectors

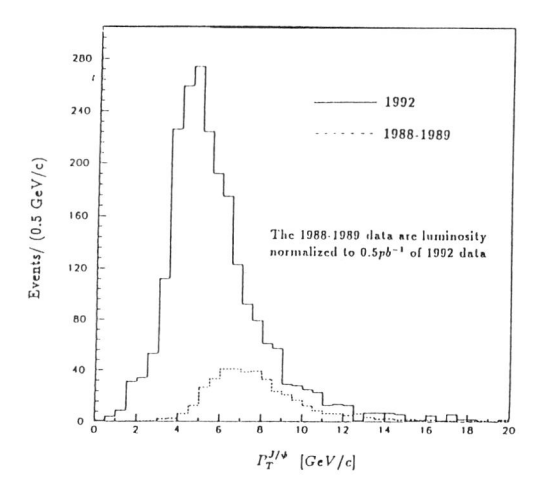

Figure 7: Comparison of J/ψ P_T spectrum using 88/89 data and 92 data - luminosity normalized.

were made based on the data collected in the 88/89 run. A new data compression scheme is being used, to accomodate the expected large size of the data set.

Full reconstruction of all CDF data is complete within two days of data taking, using 1000 MIPS from a SiG farm, while approximatley 5-10% of the data, including the most interesting events, are reconstructed and available within a few hours of data taking.

Utilities have been developed to distribute and maintain code across three hardware platforms (SiG, IBM and VAX) as well as computer systems at remote institutions.

4. Data

We will now turn to a discussion of the physics capabilities of CDF, as well as a brief review of selected results from the 1988/89 run.

4.1 QCD

In the past five years we have performed several tests of QCD using CDF data. The main goals for the 1992 run are to exploit the increase in statistics to improve the sensitivity to quark compositness and to combine our data on direct photons, Drell-Yan and jets in order to better constrain the understanding of parton distribution functions. In addition, the new CPR (see section 3.3) in conjunction with a lower photon-trigger threshold will allow us to greatly improve on our previous measurement of the direct photon cross section. In Figures 8 and 9, we show comparisons of 1992 and 1988/89 jet data. Figure 10 provides a demonstration of the capabilities of the CDF detector in photon physics.

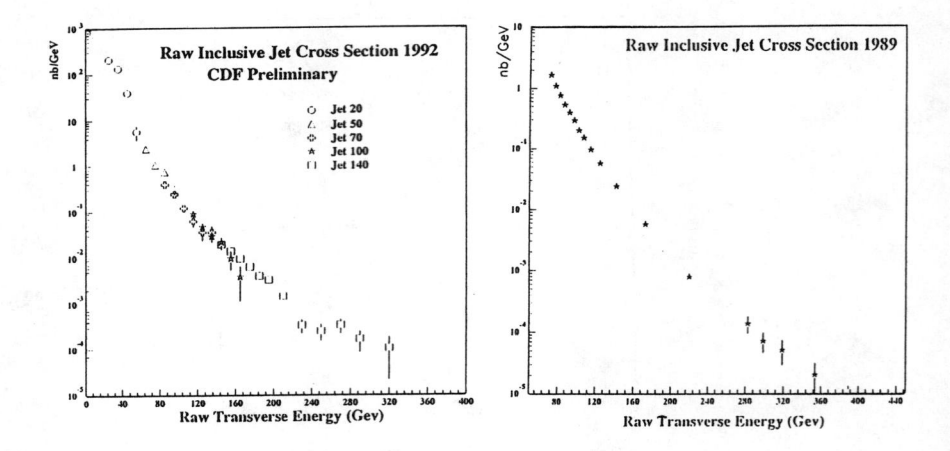

Figure 8: Comparison of RAW jet cross section for the 88/89 and 1992 data.

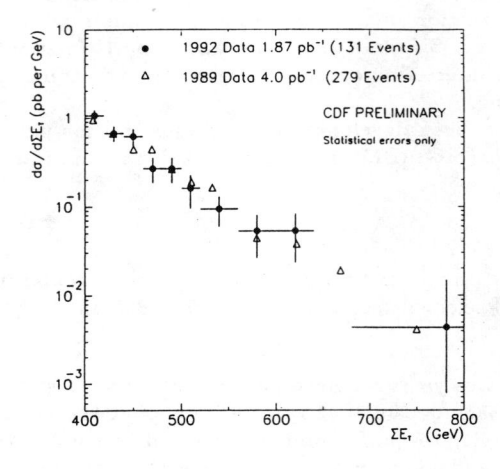

Figure 9: Comparison of the Total Transverse Energy (ΣE_T) cross section, for the 88/89 and 1992 data.

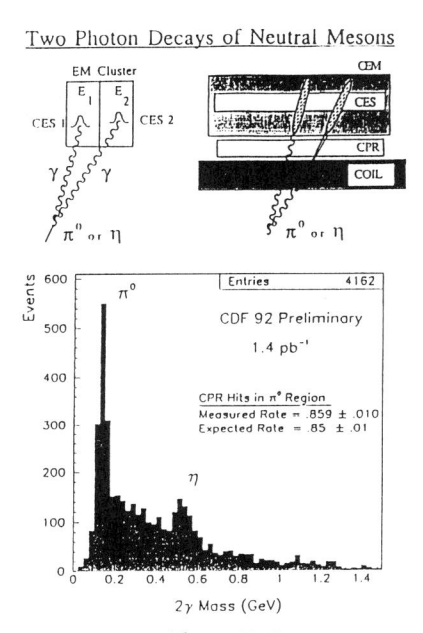

Figure 10: 2γ mass spectrum

4.2 Exotic Physics

Since the Tevatron collider provide antiproton-proton collisions with an unprecedented high center-of-mass energy of 1.8 TeV, it has open up a new mass window where exotic physics beyond the Minimal Standard Model could manifest themselves. With every substantial increase in integrated luminosity, additional regions of the mass windows are reached. Thus, one of the most important goals of CDF is to search for new physics, perhaps even in those topologies that theorists have not mentioned.

In previous runs, CDF have searched for Squarks and Gluinos, as well as for heavy stable charged particles. Results from a search for a 1st generation Lepto-Quark is close to publication. Many other topics are under study, including the search for τ's from the decay of charged Higgs, which itself could come from the decay of a top quark.

4.3 Electro-Weak Physics

In the field of Electro-Weak physics, the main goal of CDF is to increase the accuracy of the W mass measurement. This is a very important topic since within the framework of the standard model there is a well defined relationship between the masses of the W, the top quark and the Higgs boson. In addition, we plan to improve our previous measurements of W/Z production cross sections, W/Z transverse momenta, W asymmetry and Drell-Yan. We will also be searching for diboson production ($W\gamma, Z\gamma, WW, WZ, ZZ$) as well as new heavy intermediate vector

and $W \to \mu\nu$ candidates and the invariant mass of Z candidates using 1.43 pb^{-1} of 1992 data.

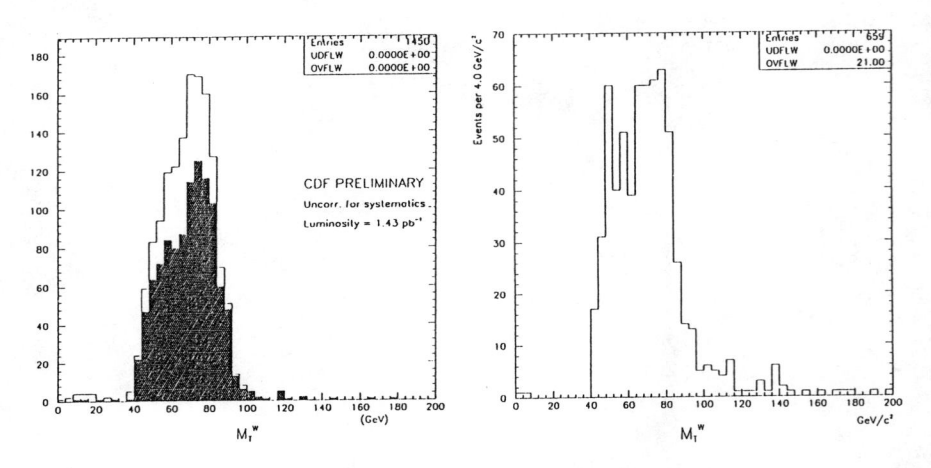

Figure 11: W Transverse Mass: a). $W \to e\nu$, the shaded area is central electrons and the open represents the histogram is contribution of plug electrons. b). $W \to \mu\nu$

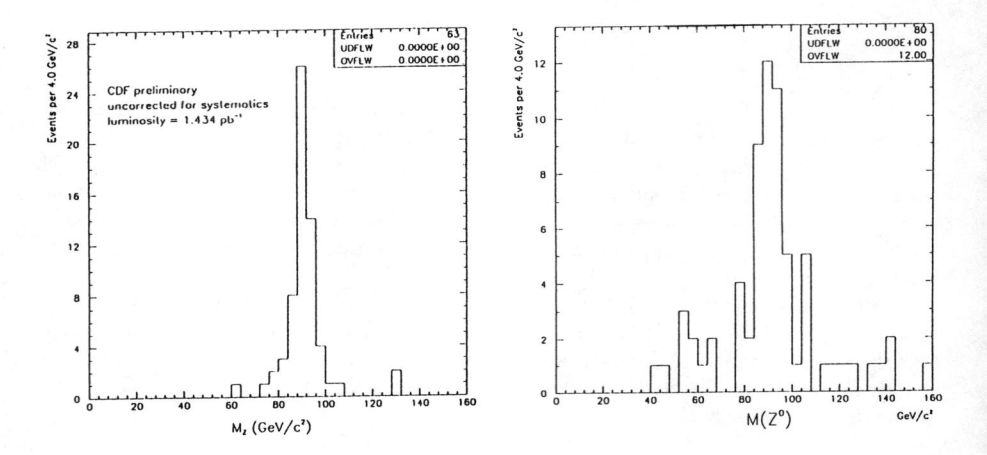

Figure 12: Z^0 Invariant Mass: a). $Z \to ee$ b). $W \to \mu\mu$

4.4 B Physics

b-quarks are copiously produced in $p\bar{p}$ collisions. Over the last few years, much interest has emerged within the HEP community at the prospect of exploiting this large cross section to study b production and decay at the Tevatron.

Using the data from the 1988/89 run, we have measured the b-quark production cross section with electron, muon and J/ψ data (see Figure 13). We have also reconstructed exclusive final states ($B \to \psi K, \psi K^*$), and have mesured $B\bar{B}$ mixing.

With the addition of the SVX, the b-physics capabilities of CDF will be greatly enhanced. We expect to search for, and measure the mass of the B_s, Λ_b and possibly B_c. We will also measure the lifetime for inclusive b-hadrons from electron, muon and J/ψ data, as well as the individual lifetimes of B_u, B_d and B_s. We plan to improve our measurement of the mixing parameter, to search for rare B decays, to study $b\bar{b}$ correlations, and to perform engineering studies aimed at an eventual CP violation experiment.

In Figure 14, we show the improvement in mass resolution achieved with the usage of the SVX information. In Figure 15 we demonstrate the power of the SVX in reducing combinatorial backgrounds in a spectroscopy-type analysis, and in Figure 16 we illustrate the cleanliness of a b-lifetime measurement from inclusive $J/\psi \to \mu^+\mu^-$.

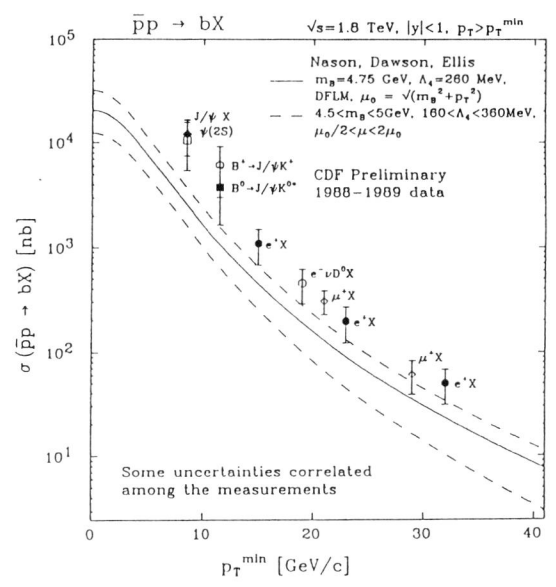

Figure 13: Summary of CDF's various b cross section measurements.

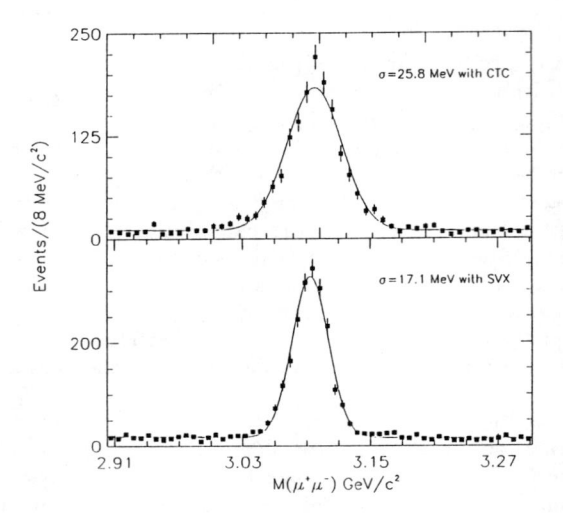

Figure 14: Improvement in Mass Resolution due to the SVX: $M(\mu^+\mu^-)$ compared for CTC only and CTC+SVX tracking.

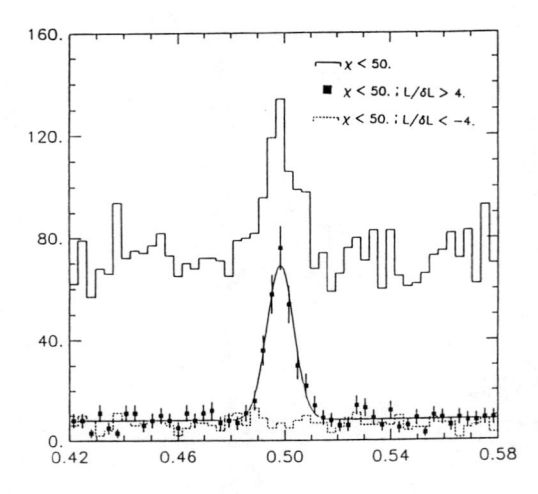

Figure 15: Reduction of combinatorial background due to the SVX: $M(\pi^+\pi^-)$, with no displaced vertex cut and a 4σ cut on the decay length.

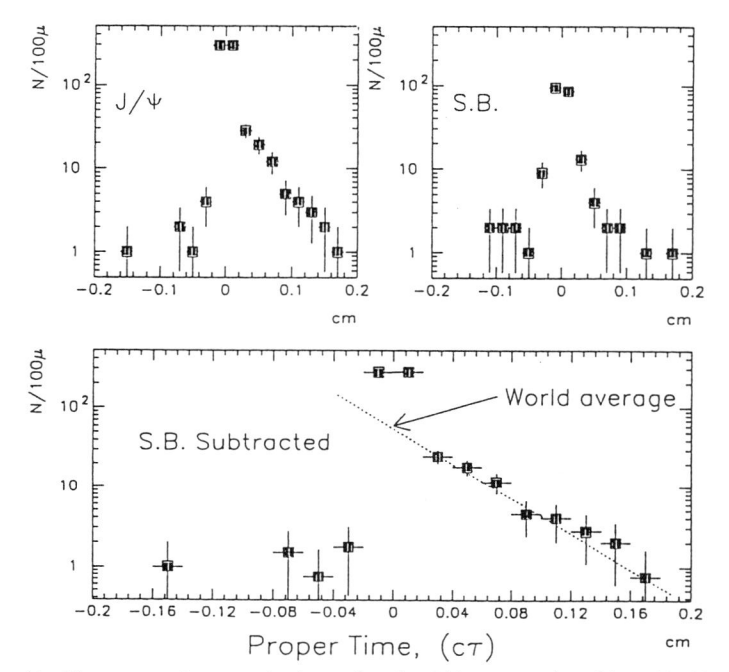

Figure 16: The proper time, $c\tau$, is shown for a). J/ψ mass region, b). J/ψ side band, and c). background subtracted J/ψ.

4.5 Top Search

At Tevatron energies, Standard Model top quarks are expected to be pair produced, through quark annihilation and gluon fusion. The decay of a Standard Model top quark is expected to proceed via $t \to W + b$. The W can then decay into quarks or lepton-neutrino. Decay modes with no leptons have the highest branching ratio, but are very hard to distinguish from multi-jet QCD backgrounds. Final states with one W decaying into lepton-neutrino and the other W decaying into quarks also have a large branching ratio, and have to be separated from the $p\bar{p} \to W + jets$ background by tagging the b-quarks in top events. This can be achieved either by using the SVX to reconstruct a displaced vertex or by searching for an additional (soft) lepton (e or μ) from semileptonic b-decays (see figures 17 and 18).

The cleanest $t\bar{t}$ events, with the least amount of backgrounds but the smallest branching ratio, are those with both W's decaying into electrons or muons. The (small) backgrounds in this channel arise from the decay of $Z \to \tau\tau$, as well as WZ and WW production. Once again, b-tagging can provide the required background rejection.

With a 25 pb^{-1} data set, we expect to be able to claim a top discovery up to $M_{Top} \leq 130~GeV/c^2$.

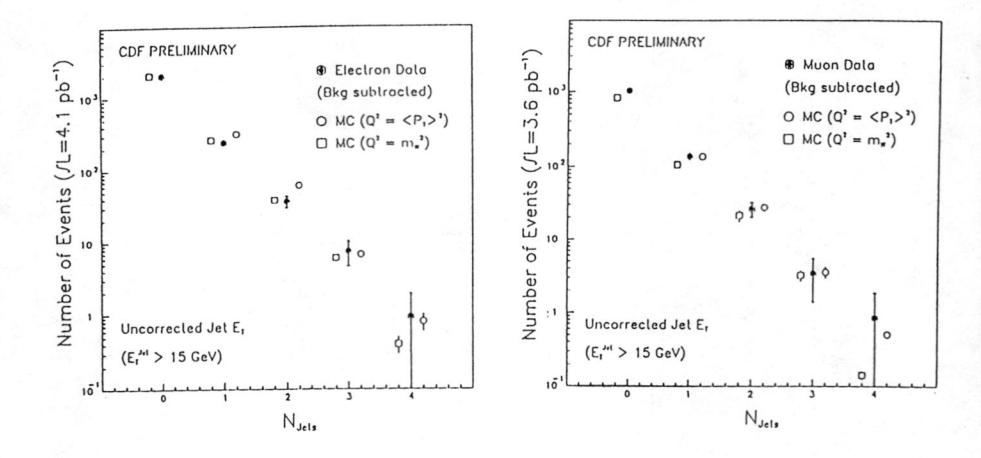

Figure 17: Jet multiplicity in W+Jet events: a). Electrons, and b). Muons. compared with VECBOS calculation.

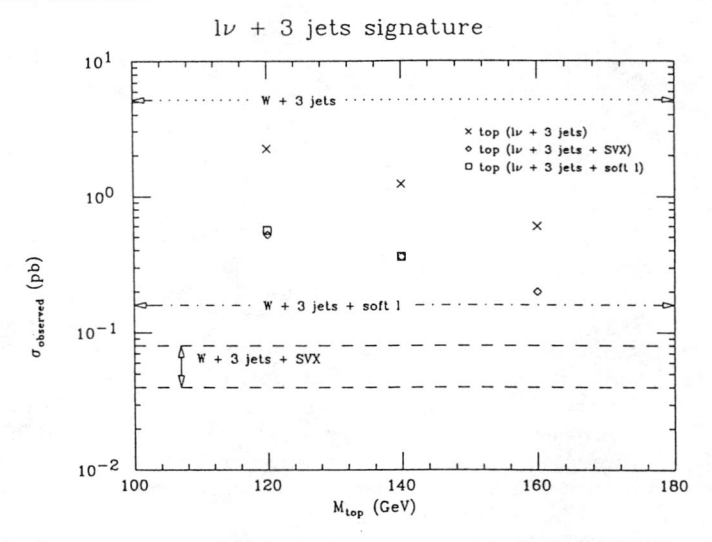

Figure 18: Expected cross sections for $t\bar{t}$ and W+jets using the high P_T lepton+3 Jets signature. The crosses are for $t\bar{t}$, before b tagging. The diamonds represent the $t\bar{t}$ rate after an SVX tag is added. The area bounded by the dotted lines shows the rate for W+jets+SVX. The squares are for $t\bar{t}$ using the soft lepton tag. The dot-dashed line show the W+jets rate for this tagging technique.

5. Conclusion and Prospects

CDF is begining to accumulate a large sample of data. During the last 2-1/2 months, we have already accumulated data which corresponds to more than 1/2 of the data sample of the last run. With the recent improvement in Tevatron luminosity, the Tevatron's goal of delivering 25 pb-1 appears likely to be met.

Based on a first look at the data, the performance of the CDF detector and its various upgrades appears to be very good. The agreement of the preliminary physics results from the new data with those from the 1988/89 run is encouraging. While many further studies need to be carried out, the indications are that CDF is able to study a variety of important physics goals with improved acceptance, more information on the event properties (such as the ability to provide secondary vertex tagging for b jets), and other improvements in triggering, event selection and data handling.

We are optimistic that with the data sample that we expect to accumulate, CDF will be able to address some of the most critical issues in High Energy physics. Along with the possibility of the discovery of top, we would be able to make much progress in understanding B-mesons and hadrons, precisely measuring the W mass, searching for exotic physics, and many other areas.

6. Acknowledgements

I would like to thank the many people who have assisted me in the preparation of this talk, particularly C. Campagnari, J. Yoh, Y.K. Kim and K. Maeshima.

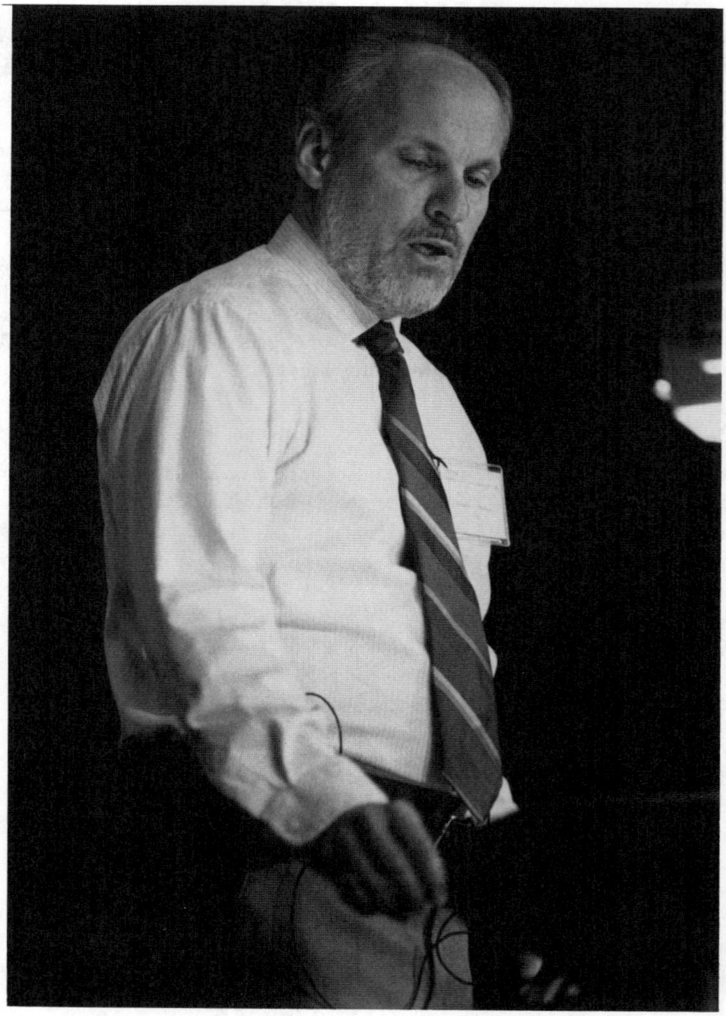

HIGHLIGHTS FROM DØ

RONALD J. MADARAS
Lawrence Berkeley Laboratory, University of California
Berkeley, CA 94720, USA

for the D0 Collaboration

ABSTRACT

The DØ Experiment is a new, large multipurpose experiment at the Tevatron Proton-Antiproton Collider at the Fermi National Accelerator Laboratory. From the analysis of data taken during August–October, 1992, a selection of preliminary physics results will be given on inclusive jet production, direct photon production, the production and decay properties of the W and Z bosons, the search for the top quark in the dilepton and lepton + jets channels, B physics and searches for new particles.

1. The DØ Detector

The primary goal of the DØ Experiment[1,2] is the precision study of high mass, large transverse momentum phenomena with particular emphasis on measurements of leptons (electrons and muons), photons, jets (clusters of produced particles), and missing transverse momentum indicative of penetrating particles (such as neutrinos). To accomplish this goal, the detector design stresses uniform, hermetic, fine-grained calorimetry, large solid angle coverage and excellent muon detection. The Detector is shown in Fig. 1. It includes three major components: the outer Muon System, the inner Central Tracking System, and the liquid argon Calorimeter System.

1.1. Muon System

The Muon System[3] consists of five iron toroids, 1.1–1.5 meters thick, and three layers of proportional drift tube (PDT) chambers. The central toroid surrounds the calorimeter and covers angles down to 45°. The end toroids and the small angle muon system cover the forward region down to 5°. Thus there is full muon coverage for $|\eta| \leq 3.2$. The momentum of a muon is determined by using the PDT chambers to measure the deflection of the muon trajectory in the 1.9 T steel toroids. The momentum resolution, typically 20%, is dominated by multiple scattering for momenta < 80 GeV/c. The combined calorimeter plus toroid thickness

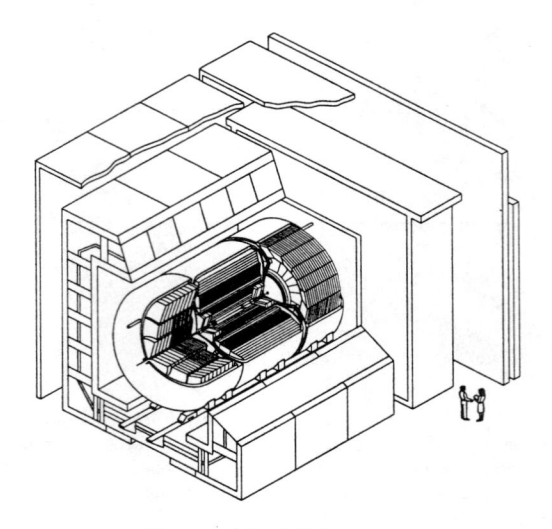

Figure 1: The DØ Detector

varies from 14 λ in the central region to 19 λ in the end regions. This thickness reduces backgrounds from hadronic punchthroughs to a negligible level.[4]

1.2. Central Tracking System

The Central Tracking System,[5] shown in Fig. 2, consists of four main components: Vertex Chamber, Transition Radiation Detector, Central Drift Chamber and two sets of Forward Drift Chambers.

The Vertex Chamber[6] has three cylindrical layers of jet-type cells, and every cell in a layer has eight sense wires. It provides precision charged particle tracking with good azimuthal spatial resolution (60 μm) and good two-track resolution (0.6 mm). Charge division is used to measure the axial coordinate with a resolution of about 1 cm. The chamber is also used to find secondary vertices, and reject photon conversions which can give a fake electron signal.

The Transition Radiation Detector[7] provides additional rejection of pions in the identification of central electrons. It has three cylindrical layers, each layer consisting of a set of polypropylene foils surrounded by a radial drift X-ray detector. A pion rejection factor of 50 was achieved in a test beam for an electron efficiency of 90%.

The Central Drift Chamber[8] has four cylindrical layers of jet-type cells, and every cell in a layer has seven sense wires. Its azimuthal spatial resolution is 150 μm. The axial position of tracks is measured with delay lines, with a resolution of 4 mm. Measurements of dE/dx are used to help identify conversions.

The Forward Drift Chambers[9] cover angles down to 5°, and include two

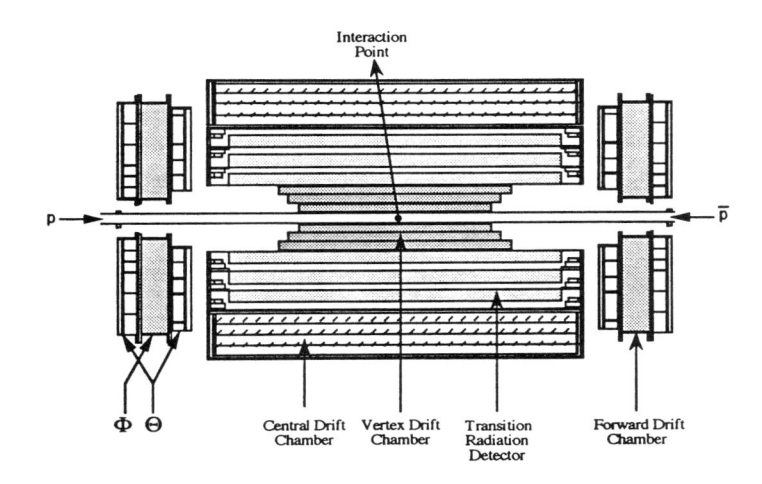

Figure 2: The DØ Central Tracking System.

types of units. The Φ units have radial sense wires, with 16 measurements along each track. The Θ units have sense wires oriented transversely to the beam, with 8 measurements along each track in each of the two units. The spatial resolution in each unit is 200 μm.

1.3. Calorimeter System

The DØ calorimeters are sampling calorimeters using uranium as the absorbing material and liquid argon as the sampling medium. The use of uranium not only leads to a compact calorimeter design, but it helps in equalizing the calorimeter response to electrons and hadrons. This is important for minimizing the fluctuations in the observed energies of jets, whose particle content may vary. Liquid argon is used as the active ionization medium because of its ease of calibration, its stability and uniformity of response, and its radiation hardness.

The DØ Calorimeter System,[10,11] shown in Fig. 3, consists of a cylindrical Central Calorimeter and two End Calorimeters covering angles down to within 1° of the beamline. Each of the three calorimeters contains an electromagnetic section with thin uranium plates, a fine hadronic section with thick uranium plates, and a coarse hadronic section with very thick copper or steel plates. Printed circuit boards with segmented detection pads are interleaved between the absorber plates to detect the ionization in the liquid argon. All of the DØ calorimeter modules use a uniform technology to facilitate the relative calibration between modules. The calorimeters are designed with minimal cracks and other uninstrumented regions in order to provide essentially hermetic coverage.

DØ LIQUID ARGON CALORIMETER

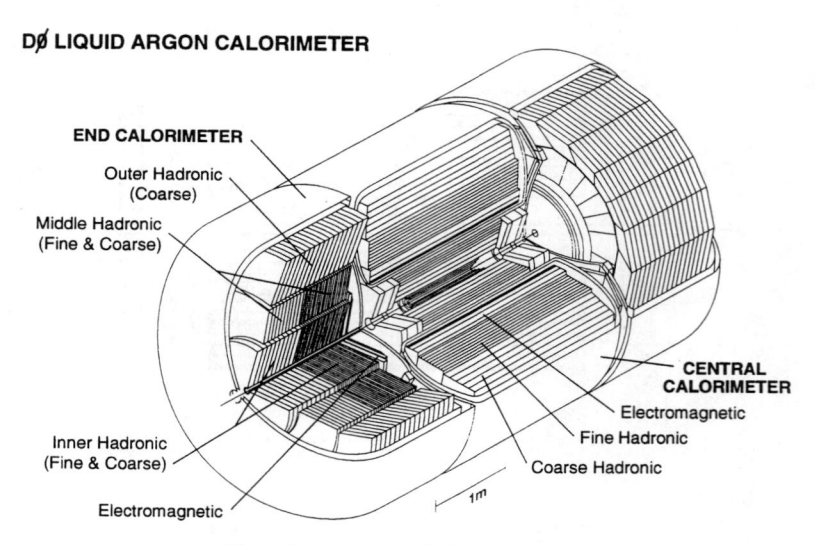

Figure 3: The DØ Calorimeter System.

The calorimeters are finely segmented both longitudinally and transversely. Longitudinally, each electromagnetic section is divided into 4 readout depths (for a total of 21 X_o), and the hadronic sections are divided into 4–5 depths (for a total of 7–9 λ). The transverse segmentation is 0.1×0.1 for $\Delta\eta \times \Delta\phi$, except in the third electromagnetic longitudinal section (where shower maximum occurs), where the segmentation is increased to 0.05×0.05 for better shower position resolution. The readout cells are arranged in semi-projective towers.

Typical electromagnetic and hadronic calorimeter modules have been extensively tested with electrons and pions from 2 to 150 GeV in a test beam at FNAL.[10,12,13] The fractional energy resolution of electrons in the calorimeters is $15\%/\sqrt{E}$, and of pions is $50\%/\sqrt{E}$. The spatial position resolution for electrons is 1–2 mm, for energies above 50 GeV. Using the transverse and longitudinal shower shape information from the electromagnetic and hadronic modules, a pion rejection factor of greater than 1000 has been measured for a 95% electron efficiency. The e/π response of the calorimeter system is energy dependent but varies within the range 1.04–1.12 for energies between 10 and 100 GeV.

The missing transverse energy $\rlap{/}{E}_T$ resolution of the DØ Calorimeter System, important for new particle searches and the precision measurement of the mass of the W boson, is excellent because of the calorimeter's hermeticity and uniformity. Figure 4a shows the distribution of the signed x component of the $\rlap{/}{E}_T$ for minimum bias collider data, for a total scalar transverse energy interval of 60–70 GeV. The distribution is well fit with a Gaussian, with a resolution of 2.3 GeV. The standard deviation of the x component of the $\rlap{/}{E}_T$ is plotted as a function of total scalar E_T

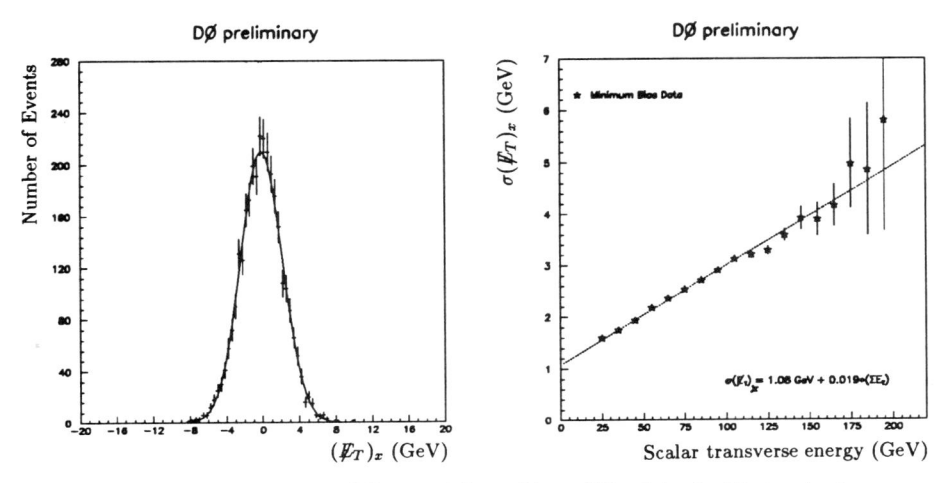

Figure 4: a) Signed x component of $\not{E}_T$ for minimum bias collider data, for 60 < scalar transverse energy < 70 GeV. b) The standard deviation of the x component of the $\not{E}_T$ as a function of scalar transverse energy. The line is a linear fit to the data.

in Fig. 4b. One sees that the $\not{E}_T$ resolution is 2–4 GeV for scalar E_T in the range 50–150 GeV.

1.4. Trigger

The DØ Trigger System[14] is outlined in Fig. 5. The initial (Level 0) trigger uses scintillation counters on both sides of the interaction point to determine if a beam-beam interaction occurred during a particular beam crossing. This rate depends on the luminosity, but is typically 100 kHz. The next (Level 1) trigger[15] is a hardware trigger using information from the Muon System and Calorimeter. Part of the calorimeter signal is split off, and electromagnetic and hadronic energy is summed separately for $\Delta\eta \times \Delta\phi = 0.2 \times 0.2$ trigger towers. The Level 1 trigger can then make cuts on various combinations of counts of EM and jet towers above E_T thresholds, missing and total scalar E_T above thresholds, and the number of muons. The Level 1.5 trigger uses more detailed information from the muon chambers to make a P_T cut for muon triggers. The Level 1/1.5 rate at the present time is 70 Hz, which will be increased to 200 Hz in the near future.

The Level 2 trigger[16] is a software filter running on a farm of VAX 4000/60 microprocessors. There the full event readout is used, and fully developed algorithms identify and measure electrons, photons, jets and muons, and calculate more accurately the event missing E_T and total scalar E_T. The filter then makes cuts on various combinations of these objects, with various thresholds. The events passing Level 2 are written to tape. The Level 2 event rate is currently 2 Hz, which will be

D0 Trigger

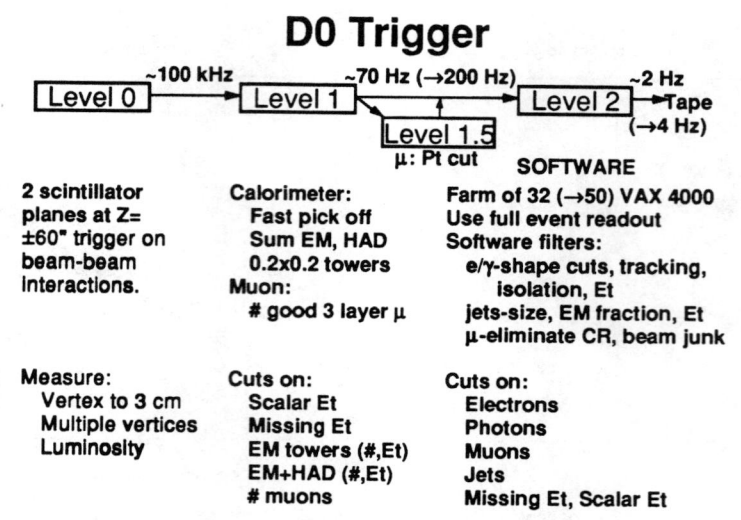

Level 0	~100 kHz →	Level 1	~70 Hz (→200 Hz) →	Level 2	~2 Hz → Tape (→4 Hz)
			Level 1.5 µ: Pt cut		

Level 0:
2 scintillator planes at Z= ±60" trigger on beam-beam interactions.

Measure:
Vertex to 3 cm
Multiple vertices
Luminosity

Level 1:
Calorimeter:
Fast pick off
Sum EM, HAD
0.2x0.2 towers
Muon:
good 3 layer µ

Cuts on:
Scalar Et
Missing Et
EM towers (#,Et)
EM+HAD (#,Et)
muons

Level 2: SOFTWARE
Farm of 32 (→50) VAX 4000
Use full event readout
Software filters:
  e/γ-shape cuts, tracking, isolation, Et
  jets-size, EM fraction, Et
  µ-eliminate CR, beam junk

Cuts on:
Electrons
Photons
Muons
Jets
Missing Et, Scalar Et

Figure 5: The DØ Trigger System.

increased to 4 Hz in the near future.

1.5 Operation at the Tevatron Collider

The DØ Detector saw its first $p\bar{p}$ collisions at the Fermilab Collider in May, 1992, when commissioning of the detector began with detailed studies of the trigger, backgrounds, and various detector elements. In August, 1992, we started our first physics data taking run with this detector. By the end of October, 1992, we had accumulated data on tape representing an integrated luminosity of 1.1 pb^{-1}. All of the results presented in the next section are based on data from that sample, and are preliminary.

2. Physics Analysis Highlights

2.1 Electroweak

Both $W \to \mu\nu$ and $Z \to \mu\mu$ have been detected in DØ. Initial results[17] for $W \to \mu\nu$ are given here for a luminosity of 410 nb^{-1}. The muons in this sample have $|\eta| < 1.0$, have a match to a central detector track, and have $P_T > 20$ GeV/c. The missing P_T is > 20 GeV/c for the events. QCD background has been eliminated by requiring that the muon track be isolated in the calorimeter, and cosmic ray background has been reduced using drift timing from the muon chambers. Figure 6a shows the P_T spectrum for the muons, and Fig. 6b shows the W transverse mass for this sample of muons. In both cases, the Monte Carlo prediction (normalized to the luminosity) agrees with the data. The observed number of events is 25, including 6

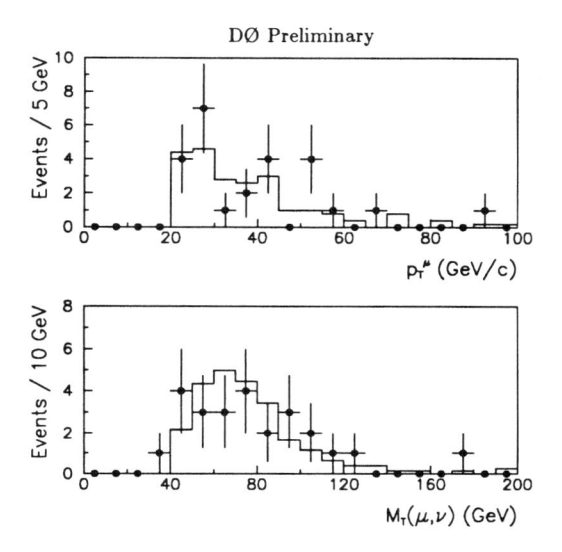

Figure 6: a) P_T spectrum for the muons in W boson events. b) W transverse mass for $W \to \mu\nu$ events. In both figures the points are data and the histogram is Monte Carlo.

background events, for a total of 19 W events. The expected number of W events, based on the luminosity, is 22 ± 5 events.

A clean $Z \to ee$ peak is seen in the data.[18] Figure 7 shows the invariant mass distribution for di-electrons, in the 1.1 pb^{-1} data sample, with both electrons having $E_T > 20$ GeV. The electrons were identified as electromagnetic clusters having < 10% of their energy in the hadronic calorimeter sections, having a transverse and longitudinal cluster shape χ^2 which agrees with test beam expectations,[19] and being isolated from the rest of the event. In addition, for one of the electrons a track was required to be found in the tracking chambers and to point to the calorimeter cluster. This tracking requirement was relaxed for the second electron. A Breit-Wigner fit to the 72 events, shown in Fig. 7, gives a peak at about 86 GeV. This is using the energy scale calibration directly from the test beam, without any corrections for the collider data, and is currently estimated to be correct to about 5%. Studies are underway to obtain a more precise energy scale.

A search[18] for $W \to e\nu$ was made in the same 1.1 pb^{-1} sample that was used for the Z bosons. In addition to the cuts on the electron described in the preceeding paragraph (including the tracking requirement), it was required that the event have $\rlap{\,/}E_T > 20$ GeV. The resulting electron E_T spectrum is shown in Fig. 8. It falls off sharply at about 40 GeV, as expected for W events. The W transverse mass distribution for the 882 events is shown in Fig. 9, along with a fit to a curve whose shape is determined by Monte Carlo. It is seen that the expected shape, including the sharp Jacobian edge, agrees well with the distribution of the data points. One cannot extract a value for the W mass until the energy scale questions discussed

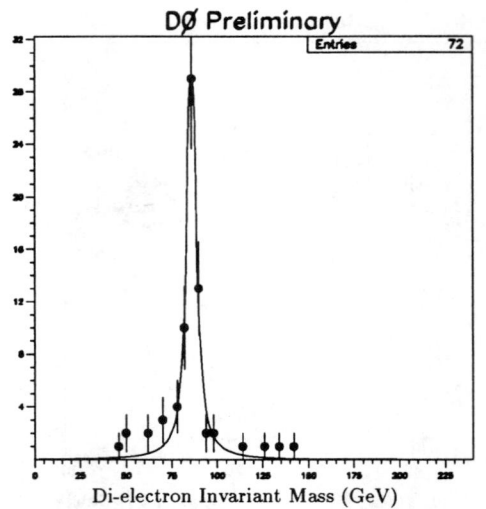

Figure 7: Di-electron invariant mass distribution, with a Breit-Wigner fit.

above are resolved. The cross section for W production times the branching ratio for $W \to e\nu$ is calculated from the above sample of events to be 2.3 ± 0.5 nb, in good agreement with published values.

2.2 Top

At the Tevatron Collider, top quark production and decay is expected to proceed via:

$$p\bar{p} \to t\bar{t} \to W^+W^-b\bar{b}$$

with the W bosons decaying into either lepton + neutrino, or jets. Thus in the final state one expects:

dileptons + jets + $\not{E}_T$, or

lepton + jets + $\not{E}_T$, or

all jets.

The search for top exploits the DØ detector's large angular acceptance for electrons, jets and muons, and its excellent missing E_T resolution.

A search for top was made in the di-electron channel.[20] Each electron was required to have a transverse and longitudinal shower shape χ^2 which agrees with test beam expectations,[19] to be isolated from the rest of the event, and to have $E_T > 15$ GeV. Only one of the electrons was required to have a matching track. The dependence on azimuthal angle between electrons and the $\not{E}_T$ for the resulting sample of 139 events is shown in Fig. 10. One sees a concentration of events from $Z \to ee$ in the upper left corner, and no events for $\Delta\phi(ee) < 160°$ and $\not{E}_T > 20$ GeV. One would expect roughly 0.9 events in that region if the top quark mass were

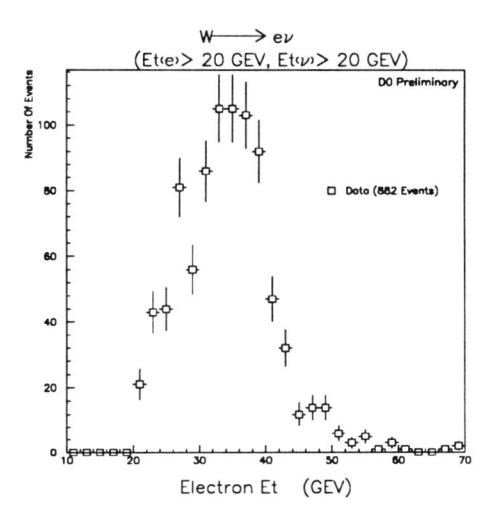

Figure 8: E_T spectrum for electrons in W boson events.

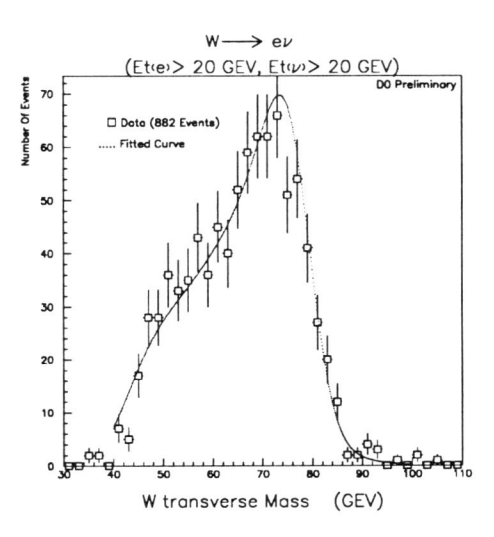

Figure 9: W transverse mass for $W \rightarrow e\nu$ events. The fit is discussed in the text.

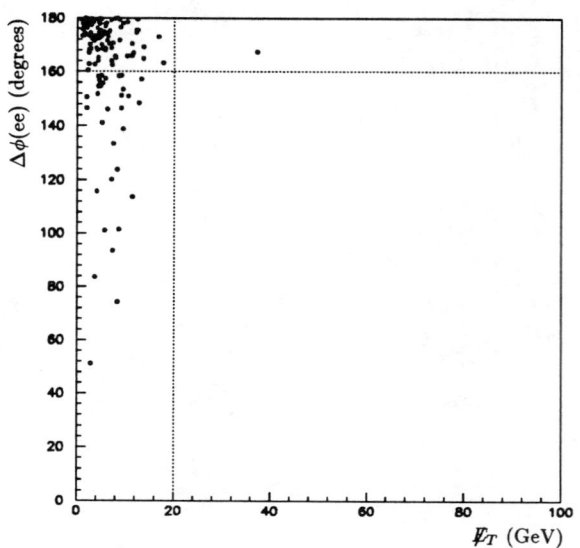

Figure 10: Azimuthal angle between di-electrons vs. $\not{E}_T$.

80 GeV.

A search was also made in the electron-muon channel.[20] Again the electron was required to have a shower shape χ^2 which agrees with test beam expectations,[19] and to be isolated. But now $E_T > 8$ GeV, and the electron was not required to have a matching track. For the muons we required that $P_T > 8$ GeV, that the muon pointed back to the vertex, that there was a match between the muon track and the central tracking chambers, that there was no back-to-back track in the central tracker (to reject cosmic rays), and that the energy deposit in the calorimeter was appropriate for a muon. This resulted in a sample of six events. Figure 11 is a scatter plot for those events of the muon P_T and the electron E_T. It is seen that there are no events for $P_T(\mu) > 20$ GeV and $E_T(e) > 20$ GeV. One would expect roughly 0.6 events in that region if the top quark mass were 80 GeV.

Finally, a search was made in the electron+jets channel.[21] The electron was required to pass the above shower shape and track matching cuts, and have $E_T > 20$ GeV. The number of jets with $E_T > 25$ GeV was required to be 3, and the $\not{E}_T > 20$ GeV. No events were left after these cuts. One would expect 2.6 ± 1.2 events after these cuts if the top quark mass were 80 GeV.

2.3 QCD

DØ, with its hermetic and finely segmented calorimeters, is ideal for a study of jet distributions. A particularly advantageous feature of DØ is its ability to

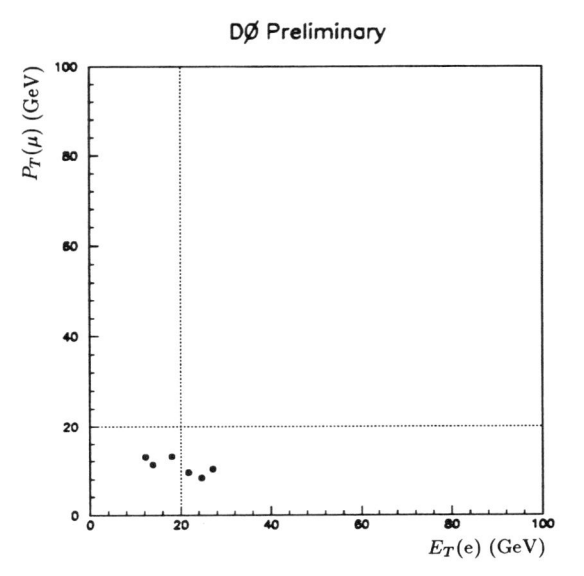

Figure 11: Muon P_T vs. electron E_T.

trigger on jets all the way down to $|\eta|= 3.2$. The preliminary inclusive jet cross section[22] is shown in Fig. 12 for a data sample corresponding to 130 nb^{-1} of luminosity. The jets were reconstructed using a cone algorithm, with the cone radius = 0.7 (in $\eta - \phi$ space). The band in Fig. 12 is the upper and lower limit for the cross section including the current energy scale uncertainty. We have also measured the 2-jet double differential cross-sections[23] out to rapidities of 3.2 where the structure functions have considerable impact upon the results.

The full coverage of the DØ calorimeters to $|\eta|= 4.0$ and their fine segmentation and good energy resolution allow us to make a good measurement of direct photon production. Direct photons in the central region ($|\eta|< 0.9$) and in the P_T range of 14–90 GeV/c were searched for in the same 130 nb^{-1} sample of data used for the jet studies. The photons were required to have a transverse and longitudinal shape χ^2 which agrees with test beam expectations,[19] to be isolated in a cone of $R = 0.4$ from the rest of the event, and to not have a track nearby. Backgrounds due to π^0 which pass the cuts were estimated through study of the ratio of 1-photon and 2-photon conversions in the tracking material, and by Monte Carlo simulations. Both methods are in agreement, finding that the fraction of photons in the candidate sample is 0.42 ± 0.14. The resulting direct photon cross section[24] is shown in Fig. 13. The errors include an estimate of the systematic errors. It is seen that the data agree well with a next to leading order calculation.[25]

The measurement of W+Jet production is a good tool for testing QCD, as the

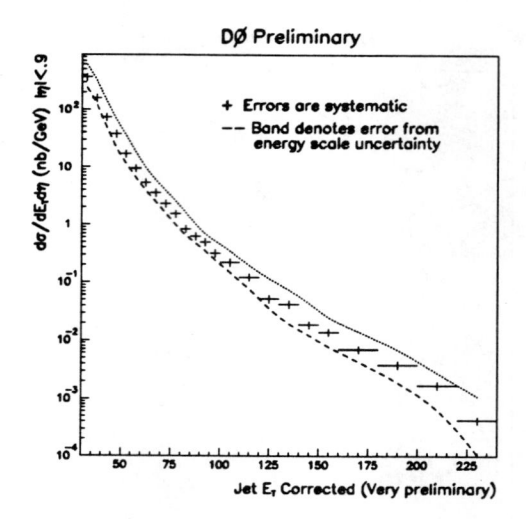

Figure 12: Inclusive jet cross section vs. jet E_T.

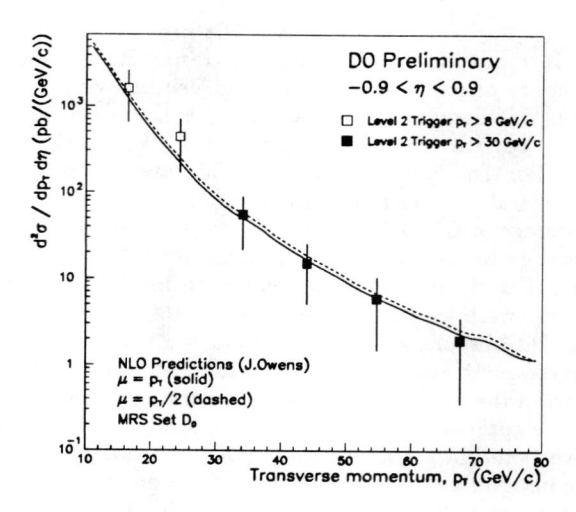

Figure 13: Direct photon cross section vs. photon P_T.

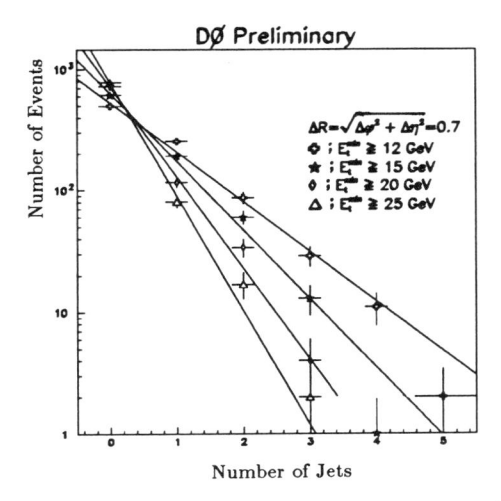

Figure 14: Jet multiplicity distribution for W events, for various values of the minimum E_T of the jets. The lines are logrithmic fits to the data.

next to leading order theoretical prediction for $W+0Jet$ and $W+1Jet$ is now available. In addition, one can use $W+Jet$ production to measure the strong coupling constant, α_s. The jet multiplicity distribution was studied[26] for the 882 $W \to e\nu$ event sample described above in the electroweak section. Figure 14 shows the number of events as a function of the number of jets associated with the W boson, for various values of the minimum E_T of the jets. It is seen that the distributions become steeper as the minimum jet E_T increases. This behavior will enable us to both test QCD and eventually measure α_s.

2.4 B Physics

The DØ detector has excellent muon coverage for the full solid angle ($|\eta| <$ 3.2), and with the toroids we can measure the charge and momentum of the muons. Because of the muon system's compactness and large number of interaction lengths of material, the backgrounds from decay in flight and punchthrough are small. In addition, muons can be identified within jets. Inclusive single muon production has been measured,[27] and the P_T spectrum is shown in Fig. 15. These muons had hits in all three muon chamber layers, a track pointing back to the vertex, an appropriate energy deposit in the calorimeter, a central tracking chamber track match, and were not back-to-back with other tracks. Jets were found using a cone algorithm with a cone radius of 0.7 (in $\eta - \phi$ space), and at least one jet was required to be near the muon track. Also shown in Fig. 15 is the Monte Carlo expectation from b and c quarks, normalized to the total number of events. It is seen that the shapes agree well.

We have also observed dimuon production with jets,[28] and our measurement

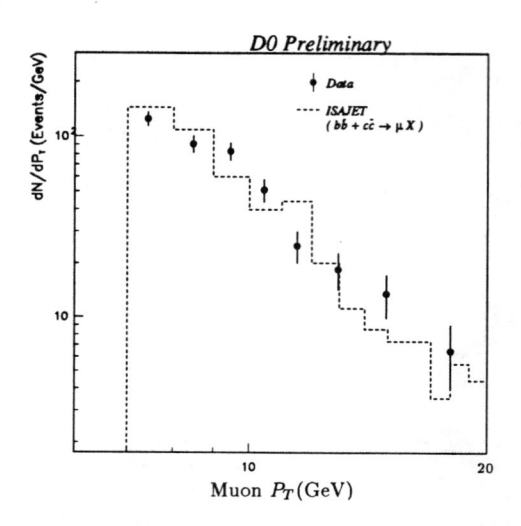

Figure 15: Inclusive muon P_T spectrum.

of the ratio of same sign events to opposite sign events is consistent with previous measurements of $B_0\bar{B}_0$ mixing.

Electrons can also be used to study b quark systems. In Fig. 16 we see a plot of the invariant mass of di-electrons, showing a clear $\Upsilon \to ee$ signal.

2.5 New Particle Searches

In the minimal supersymmetric extension of the Standard Model, gluinos and squarks either "decay directly" into the lightest neutralino (with large $\not{E}_T$ and high E_T jets) or "cascade decay" through several supersymmetric particles and finally into the lightest neutralino (with less $\not{E}_T$, softer jets, and possible leptons). Thus the DØ detector's excellent $\not{E}_T$ resolution and acceptance for multijets and leptons will play an important role here. A search for squarks and gluinos was done,[29] involving purely hadronic decays, with a data sample corresponding to 140 nb^{-1}. We required three jets in the event (with each jet having $E_T > 20$ GeV), $\not{E}_T > 30$ GeV, and angular cuts on the jets and $\not{E}_T$ to remove QCD backgrounds. No events were left after these cuts. These results clearly rule out squark and gluino masses both equal to 100 GeV/c^2, for which we would expect 6.9 ± 2.2 events after the above cuts.

Leptoquarks carry both color quantum numbers and lepton quantum numbers, and can decay, for example, into a lepton and a quark. In composite models, leptoquarks are the natural result of different combinations of the constituents of quarks and leptons. A search was done[30] for scalar leptoquarks, looking for events with 2 electrons and 2 jets, with a data sample corresponding to 0.8 pb^{-1}. Both

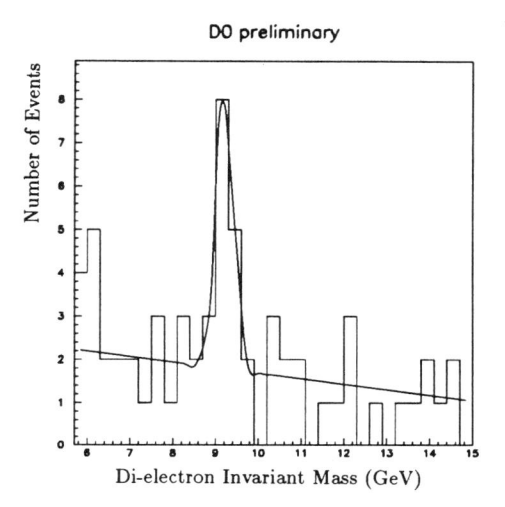

Figure 16: Di-electron invariant mass distribution.

electrons and jets were required to have $E_T > 20$ GeV. The electrons were required to be clean, isolated electrons. After removing one event that was consistent with $Z(\to ee) + 2jets$, no events were left after these cuts. Assuming a 100% branching ratio into the electron + quark decay mode, we have used this result to set a lower leptoquark limit of 74 GeV, at 95% CL.

3. Conclusion

The DØ Detector has been installed at the Fermilab Tevatron Collider, and is currently taking physics data. Preliminary physics results, based on the first three months of data taking after commissioning, have been presented in the areas of electroweak, QCD, B physics, top and new particle searches. We have rapidly begun to use DØ to do exciting physics.

4. Acknowledgements

I am indebted to the many DØ physicists who presented the latest DØ physics results at the DPF meeting and made their results available to me for this summary, and to all the members of the DØ Collaboration for their successful efforts in bringing the DØ Experiment to its productive physics phase. I would also like to thank Tony Spadafora for his help with the electronic integration of many of the figures used here, and Tony, Paul Grannis and David Buchholz for their critical reading of this paper. This work was supported by the U.S. Department of Energy and the National Science Foundation.

5. References

1. Design report for the DØ Experiment at the Fermilab Antiproton-Proton Collider, Fermilab, November 1984 (unpublished).
2. P.D. Grannis, in the *Proceedings of Les Rencontres de Physique de la Vallee d'Aoste on Results and Perspectives in Particle Physics, La Thuile*, March 1987, edited by M. Greco (Editions Frontieres, 1987) p. 253.
3. C. Brown, et al., *Nucl. Instr. and Meth.* **A279** (1989) 331; J.M. Butler, et al., *Nucl. Instr. and Meth.* **A290** (1990) 122.
4. D. Green, et al., *Nucl. Instr. and Meth.* **A244** (1985) 356.
5. A.R. Clark et al., *Nucl. Instr. and Meth.* **A279** (1989) 243.
6. A.R. Clark et al., *Nucl. Instr. and Meth.* **A315** (1992) 193.
7. J.F. Detoeuf et al., *Nucl. Instr. and Meth.* **A265** (1988) 157.
8. T. Behnke, Ph.D. Thesis, SUNY, Stony Brook (1989); D. Pizzuto, Ph.D. Thesis, SUNY, Stony Brook (1991).
9. R.E. Avery et al., DØ Note 1567, to be published in the *IEEE Trans. in Nucl. Sci.*
10. H. Aihara et al., LBL-31378 (July 1992), to be published in *Nucl. Instr. and Meth.*
11. J. Christenson, to be published in the *Proceedings of the Third International Conference on Calorimetry in High Energy Physics, Corpus Christi, Texas*, September, 1992.
12. S. Abachi et al., FNAL-PUB-92/162, to be published in *Nucl. Instr. and Meth.*
13. P. Bhat, "Low Energy Response of the DØ Calorimeter and Jet Energy Measurement", these Proceedings.
14. Jan Guida, DØ Note 1510, to be published in the *Proceedings of the Third International Conference on Calorimetry in High Energy Physics, Corpus Christi, Texas*, September, 1992.
15. M. Abolins et al., *Nucl. Instr. and Meth.* **A289** (1990) 543.
16. J. Linnemann, DØ Note 1519, to be published in the *Proceedings of the Conference on Computing in High Energy Physics, Annecy, France*, September, 1992; and also these Proceedings.
17. D. Wood, "W and Z Decays to Muons at DØ", these Proceedings.
18. N. Graf, "W and Z Decays to Electrons at DØ", these Proceedings.
19. M. Narain, "Electron Identification in the DØ Detector", these Proceedings.

20. R. Partridge, "Search for the Top Quark in Dilepton Events with DØ", these Proceedings.
21. B. Klima, "Search for the Top Quark in Electron+Jets Events in DØ", these Proceedings.
22. R. Astur, "Inclusive Jet Distributions at DØ", these Proceedings.
23. G. Blazey, "Dijet Differential Distributions", these Proceedings.
24. G. Snow, "Direct Photon Production at DØ", these Proceedings.
25. H. Baer, J. Ohnemus, J.F. Owens, *Phys. Lett.* **B234** (1990) 127, and private communication.
26. J. Yu, "W+Jet Production with DØ", these Proceedings.
27. K. Bazizi, "Inclusive Single Muon Production with DØ", these Proceedings.
28. S. Igarashi, "Dimuon Production at DØ", these Proceedings.
29. M. Paterno, "A Search for Squarks and Gluinos with DØ", these Proceedings.
30. W. Merritt, "Search for Scalar Leptoquarks in DØ", these Proceedings.

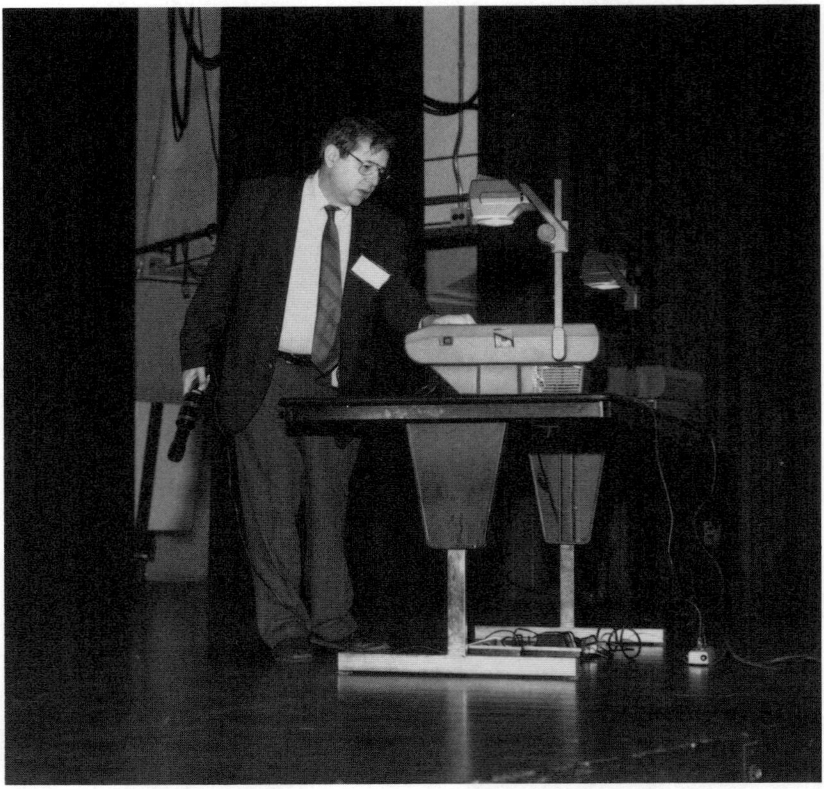

RECENT RESULTS FROM H1 AND ZEUS AT HERA

FRANK SCIULLI
Columbia University and Nevis Laboratory
New York, NY 10533

1. HERA

1.1. Schedule

Eight years ago HERA, the first electron-proton collider, was approved to proceed with construction and the two experimental groups, H1 and ZEUS, also began forming in earnest. The last several years have seen great excitement: tunnel completion in December 1987; electron beam in August 1988; proton ring completed in November 1989; and one year ago, the first electron-proton collisions. In November 1991, the machine began operating with 10 bunches of electrons and protons.

The experiments moved into their collision regions soon afterwards; installation was completed in April 1992. On May 5 of this year, collisions between 26.7 GeV electrons and 820 GeV protons were observed in both detectors. The collider has continued to operate at these energies since May. The design luminosity of 1.5×10^{31} cm^{-2} sec^{-1}, or about 100 pb^{-1} per year, will come more gradually.

1.2. Luminosity

During July both experiments were commissioned with data; preliminary results from this run were presented[1] at the Dallas meeting, and that data forms the principal base for this talk. About $\int \mathcal{L} dt \sim 3$ nb^{-1} were delivered to the experiments in July and most resulted in recorded data.

Since restarting operations in mid-September, the accelerator has operated at increased luminosity: about 60 nb^{-1} delivered to date. Though this luminosity still represents about two orders of magnitude less than the design goal, the present event rate actually well matches the learning curve for the experiments in dealing with it. Even with the data from summer commissioning, though, exciting new physics was explored: the order of magnitude luminosity increase in the fall promises yet another physics regime to explore. Running will begin again in the spring when another factor of ten rate increase should be obtained. It is expected that, over the next year or two, the luminosity will continue to increase at approximately this geometric rate.

To achieve design luminosity, HERA incorporates a timing structure for collisions that is a new, but not unique, problem for experiments. The bunches, which will total 210 at design, are spaced by 96 ns. This structure requires that experimental data be buffered while trigger decisions are being made. The accelerator has mostly operated with 9 paired electron and proton bunches, one unpaired electron "pilot" bunch and one proton pilot bunch.

1.3. Polarization

Among the unique potential tools of HERA, the availability of longitudinally polarized electrons for studies of the chiral structure of scattering currents is one of the most promising. To achieve it requires that circulating electrons develop transverse polarization through the Sokholov-Ternov effect, and that this polarization be preserved during rotation to the longitudinal direction. While polarization through this mechanism has been achieved elsewhere, the large polarizations necessary for use at HERA had not yet been demonstrated. A record transverse polarization[2] of 58% for a circulating electron beam has been observed at HERA and has been sustained over several hours.

2. Experimental Techniques

2.1. Experiments - H1 and ZEUS

The experiments at the HERA collider look superficially like those at other collider facilities: precision vertex detectors, tracking chambers in magnetic fields, hermetic calorimeters, and muon detection. They differ in that the HERA detectors are asymmetric so as to optimize operation with asymmetric beams. They differ from each other in the emphasis: H1 opted for fine segmentation with liquid argon calorimetry and ZEUS for precision compensated calorimetry. Though all active components of both detectors were in place last summer, readout for the ZEUS tracking was not yet complete (only the trigger readout of the central tracking was installed), muon tracking readout was still being installed, and the trigger was preliminary; for H1 a small fraction of the muon tracking and of the forward tracking readout were missing.

2.2. Luminosity Measurements

Luminosity is measured with bremsstrahlung events

$$e^- + p \to e^- + p + \gamma \tag{1}$$

which will occur with the calculable rate of ≈ 50 kHz at design luminosity. Both experiments have monitors (LUMI) along the electron beam directions which detect the electron (at ≈ 40 m) and the photon (at ≈ 100 m) in coincidence; as expected, the energy sums are found to equal the electron beam energy. Since bremsstrahlung also occurs from nuclei of gas atoms at rest in the beam pipe, these background are subtracted from measurements made with an electron "pilot bunch".

2.3. Event Topologies

Deep inelastic scattering (DIS) reactions are the principal foci for HERA. The reaction that occurs with high rate at low Q^2 is the deep-inelastic neutral current (NC) process

$$e^- + p \to e^- + X \tag{2}$$

from exchange of a virtual photon. Here, the final state electron tends to peak in the backward (or electron beam) direction for low Q^2 scatters. At higher Q^2, the NC reaction (2) will have contributions from Z^0 exchange.

Another DIS process expected at high Q^2 is the charged current (CC) reaction

$$e^- + p \to \nu_e + X \tag{3}$$

as a consequence of W^- exchange. The rate is such that, in a run of 3 nb^{-1} (like the past summer) only about 0.1 events are expected. Such events will be characterized by an energetic jet of hadrons and large missing transverse momentum.

A reaction that occurs at high rate, even at low luminosity, is the photoproduction (γp) process, wherein a virtual photon very near the mass shell collides with the proton. HERA provides the capability to investigate this process at much higher center-of-mass energies than previously possible.

Finally, there are exotic possibilities that are unique to HERA or that complement searches done elsewhere. In the longer term, these will include sensitive searches for R-violating SUSY processes and neutral leptons. At startup luminosity, efforts have concentrated on states decaying into lepton and quark (leptoquarks) and on excited electrons; these are characterized by high rate and large transverse momentum decay products.

2.3. Triggering and Backgrounds

The interesting high rate processes (NC and γp) will occur at several Hz when design luminosity is achieved. The ability to trigger on these and rarer processes is an important requirement for the detectors, since the rates for other (less interesting) reactions occur orders-of-magnitude more frequently: background triggers include cosmic ray showers and interactions of the beams with inert gas in the beam pipe. The interaction of protons with gas nuclei has the highest rate: the task of triggering on events of interest in the presence of many kHz of beam gas interactions, and subsequently separating these events, is an important task for the detectors. To handle this, several levels of triggering are incorporated online, and several levels of filtering are utilized offline.

Energy clusters in the calorimeter, are important trigger inputs for both detectors. Last summer, the ZEUS experiment required minimal energy in tower groups of calorimeter cells for DIS events. For photoproduction, a trigger with reduced thresholds and a coincident tagged electron in the LUMI detector was operated during short dedicated runs. (The trigger has been improved since then to permit simultaneous recording of DIS and photoproduction events.) The H1 experiment required an electron trigger based on cluster energies in the calorimeters or electron tagger and a trigger based on vertex-finding from the central tracking chambers. In both experiments, timing is an important element of the trigger and precision time measurements of calorimeter energy deposits are essential.

Proton beam-induced backgrounds most often originate upstream of the detector and deposit energy around the beam pipe calorimeter cells in the forward (proton direction) and rear (electron direction) calorimeters. The energy in the rear direction is out-of-time by about 12 ns relative to that from events originating at a vertex within the detector volume. Hence, a clear separation of events is possible, as shown in figure 1a for the ZEUS detector.[3] The difference in the times measured in the forward and rear calorimeter versus the time measured in the rear calorimeter demonstrates that the large number of beam gas background events is clearly separated from events originating within the detector volume.

2.4. Kinematic Constraints

Redundancy in event reconstruction is important both to ensure the cleanliness of event samples and to corroborate calibrations. (This redundancy is an important element, for example, in the "cleanliness" of e^+e^- colliders.) For HERA events in which there are no non-interacting particles (e.g. neutrinos), like neutral current or tagged photoproduction events, such constraints exist.

Consider the following sums over calorimeter cells:

$$\vec{p} = \sum_{cells}^{CAL} E_i \vec{n}_i \qquad (4)$$

where $\vec{n}_i$ is a unit vector from the vertex in the direction of cell i and E_i is the measured energy in that cell. For events in which all final state energies are observed except in the direction of the proton beam, the transverse components should be zero ($p_x = 0$ and $p_y = 0$) and a single longitudinal combination is conserved:

$$E - p_z = 2E_e \qquad (5)$$

where $E = \sum E_i$ and $E_e = 26.7$ GeV is the incident electron beam energy. The mean value of the quantity (5) for NC events can provide an important check on calibration which is largely independent of physics assumptions.

Proton beam gas, the most pernicious triggering background, will on average give transverse components (p_x and p_y) zero, but the magnitude of the measured quantity, $E-p_z$, will not be as predicted from (5). In fact, since upstream interactions produce energy in calorimeter cells near the beam pipe, then one measures for such events, $E - p_z \approx 2E_{REAR}$, where E_{REAR} is the energy deposited in the beam-pipe calorimeter cells in the backward or electron beam direction. But as discussed above, the accurate time measures for finite E_{REAR} permit rejection of this background.

The ZEUS distributions of $E - p_z$ (figure 1b) and beam vertex coordinate (figure 1c) clearly demonstrate that the selected DIS events are made inside the detector volume and dominantly arise from the NC process (2).

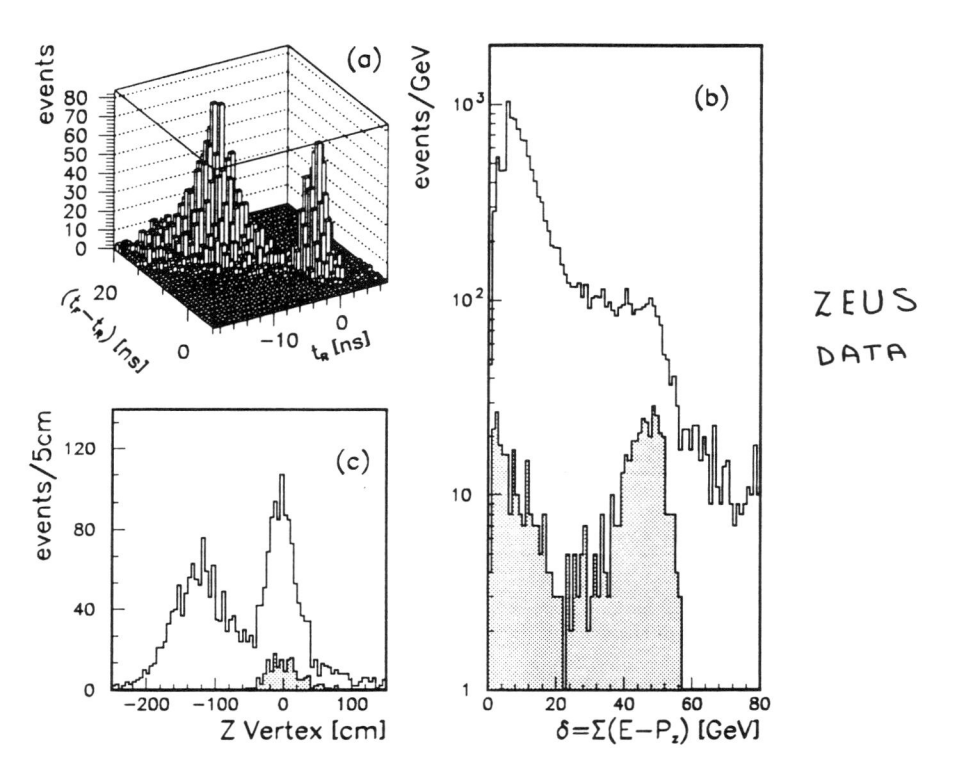

Figure 1: (a) Distribution of times for preselected DIS triggers in the ZEUS experiment. The time difference between forward and rear calorimeters is plotted against the rear calorimeter time. The peak at the origin contains DIS events; the other peak is due to upstream proton beam interactions. (b) The distribution in $E - p_z$ at the preselection level (unshaded) and after all selections other than $E - p_z$ (shaded). The timing cuts have produced a clear peak from DIS NC events. (c) The beam coordinate distribution of vertices at the preselection level (upper) and after final selections (lower). The large background from beam gas, with vertex coordinates below $-50\ cm$, are clearly visible in the unselected sample but have been removed after selections.

3. Photoproduction

HERA, operating at the commissioning luminosity, has already made important contributions to the measurement of the photoproduction reaction

$$\gamma + p \to \text{anything} \tag{6}$$

in a new kinematic region. Previous measurements of (6) utilized fixed target photon beams for center-of-mass energies, W, up to 20 GeV. At HERA, virtual photons very near the mass shell ($Q^2 \leq 10^{-2}$ GeV^2 for electrons tagged in the LUMI), but with large photon energy, provide $100 < W < 250$ GeV. Photon energies of about 30 TeV would be required to provide this W at fixed target machines.

3.1. Total Cross Section Measurements

Measurements[4,5] of the total photoproduction cross-section, $\sigma_{\gamma p}$, are obtained from data triggered with minimal activity in the detectors coincident with detection of an electron in the forward electron detector of the LUMI. The total electron-proton cross-section σ_{ep} for such events is obtained after dividing by the measured luminosity. The photoproduction cross-section is obtained from

$$\sigma_{ep} = \sigma_{\gamma p} F(E_{min}, E_{max}) \tag{7}$$

where the flux factor, F, is calculated from the minimum and maximum final state electron energies corresponding to the geometry and detection efficiency of the forward electron detector. For the geometry of the LUMI at HERA, $F \approx .015$.

The result depends on the efficiency for triggering on the various photoproduction final states in the main detector. Because this triggering efficiency is low for elastic and diffractive final states with little energy in the main detectors ($\epsilon \approx .20$), $\sigma_{\gamma p}$ is sensitive to the fraction of such processes. Cross-sections are reported assuming the fraction to be $26 \pm 6\%$ ($20 \pm 10\%$) in the H1 (ZEUS) experiments. These numbers are consistent with the (small) numbers of observed events that are consistent with being elastic or diffractive.

The photoproduction cross-sections from summer operation are shown in table 1. Differences in the input numbers of the table arise from several sources. The smaller luminosity used in the ZEUS experiment was occasioned by the need for a dedicated run with a separate trigger for the photoproduction measurement. The proportionately larger error on the observed number of events in the H1 measurement was due to the (30%) statistical subtraction of electron beam gas events in random coincidence with a LUMI-detected electron. This background in the ZEUS case was measured to be less than 5% and ignored.

Figure 2 shows the results for the total photoproduction cross-sections versus center-of-mass energy. The lower energy measurements of fixed target experiments are also shown. Various model extrapolations are also shown: the solid curves, labelled DL[6] and ALLM[7], are Regge extrapolations from lower energy data. The

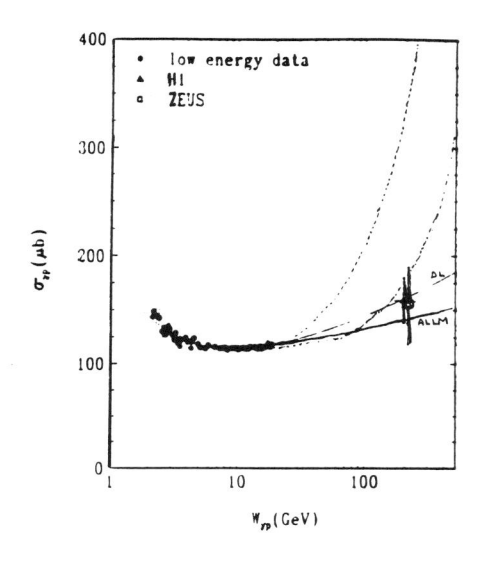

Figure 2: Total γp cross section results from ZEUS and H1. See text.

dotted (higher) curves utilize a "minijet" calculation[8] with specific assumptions for the structure functions of the proton[9] and of the photon[10]. These predictions depend on a cutoff parameter (p_T^{min}); the upper (lower) curve corresponds to $p_T^{min} =$ 1.4 GeV(2.0 GeV). The measurement demonstrates that predictions of a sharply rising cross-section over the decade beyond the fixed target experiments are not correct.

3.2. Hard processes

The historical success of vector-dominance models (VDM) to describe photon-hadron interactions leads us to expect that such reactions, like the hadron-hadron case, will include hard collisions. Some events should have jets of high p_T. The HERA experiments have demonstrated that such hard processes exist in photoproduction, and have begun to investigate their details. For the γp studies, event samples both with and without LUMI tags were used.

Figure 3a shows the H1 distribution[11] (data points) of charged track density versus p_T^2, the square of the track transverse momentum, in photoproduction events.

Table 1: Photoproduction Results from HERA

Experiment	$\int \mathcal{L}dt \ \mu b^{-1}$	N_{obs}	ϵ_{expt}	$\sigma_{\gamma p}(tot)$
H1	994 ± 100	602 ± 61	55 ± 4	$150 \pm 15 \pm 19$
ZEUS	227 ± 25	182 ± 14	59 ± 9	$154 \pm 16 \pm 32$

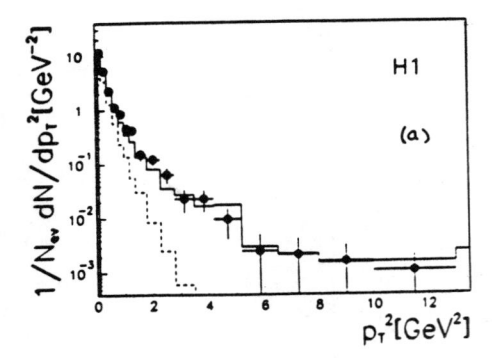

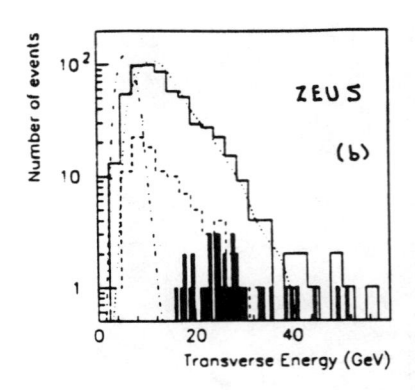

Figure 3: Evidence for hard scattering in photoproduction from H1 and ZEUS. See text for description. The dashed histograms in (b) are the subset with LUMI electron tags, and the filled histogram contains the events with jet candidates.

The dashed histogram shows the expected distribution from "soft" processes; the solid histogram gives the expectation after inclusion of hard scattering mechanisms. Figure 3b is the ZEUS[12] distribution (solid histogram) of selected photoproduction events versus E_T, the net transverse energy in the event. The dash-dotted curve indicates the expected distribution calculated assuming only "soft" processes, while the dotted curve is the prediction including hard scattering mechanisms between the proton constituents and the photon or its constituents. The rates for these hard processes appear to be substantial, accounting for approximately 20% of the total photoproduction cross-section.

Both experiments have applied "jet-finding" algorithms to these data. The number of found 2-jet events agrees with the Monte Carlo predictions and the events have characteristics expected for such events, such as the colinearity of the two jets in azimuth. If the 2-jet events are caused by hard scattering between proton and photon constituents, the kinematics of HERA permit one to search for an important expected property. The high p_T scattering of two quark constituents leads to a proton remnant jet along the proton direction, as is well known; it might be expected that a photon remnant would also appear along the direction of the virtual photon (the same as the beam electron). Such an effect is characteristic of "resolved photon" diagrams[13] for photoproduction. Indeed in the ZEUS data, for 15 cases in which both jets are in the general direction of the beam proton, the events contain substantial additional energy, more than a few GeV, along the electron direction. A similar effect attributed to the resolved photon diagram is seen in the energy flow and in the correlation between polar angles of the two jets in the H1 data.

Hard scattering mechanisms are definitely seen with substantial rate in the photoproduction reactions at HERA, including events with jets. Furthermore, there is strong indication that the hard scatters involve only a fraction of the photon energy, and so correspond to interactions of the photon's point-like hadronic constituents. More data will help us to pursue this interesting question.

4. Deep Inelastic Scattering

DIS has been of fundamental interest since the discovery of scaling more than 20 years ago. Such processes are described by the *Bjorken* x variable, the fraction of the proton momentum carried by the struck constituent, and the y variable, the fraction of the lepton energy transferred to the nucleon in its own rest frame.

HERA permits the study of DIS processes in new regions. Many high Q^2 events will be seen as the luminosity increases, but another important new kinematic regime is available now: events with very low x but Q^2 high enough to be calculable in QCD. This region is particularly interesting because of the unknown behaviour of the nucleon's gluon distribution, $G(x)$, at small values of x. From a practical viewpoint, understanding the gluon structure function is necessary in order to predict event rates for anticipated phenomena at the SSC and LHC colliders. Besides wide disparities among different extrapolations of $G(x)$, there are exciting conjectures about whether the gluon distribution will saturate or exhibit "hot spots".

At small x, estimates of the quark structure functions, $F_2(x)$ and $F_L(x)$, which determine the ep differential cross-section, depend strongly on this gluon density. The study of the "small x" region will be an important area of research for years to come. At the moment, the data allow us to begin this study, demonstrate that events can be separated from backgrounds, and see if there are any major surprises.

4.1. Early DIS results.

Both the ZEUS[3] and H1[14] groups have analyzed data taken during July 1992. The selection procedures, involving timing and other criteria, have succeeded in removing backgrounds induced by beam collisions with gas as demonstrated by studies of unpaired pilot bunches. Other sources of background, like cosmic rays, pileup, *etc.* are also small. The most significant background in the samples is due to photoproduction.

Figure 4a shows the selected ZEUS *NC* events plotted on log scales of Q^2 vs. x. In previous experiments, data with $Q^2 \approx 10\,GeV^2$ had $x \geq 10^{-2}$. The data from HERA populate the region $10^{-4} \leq x \leq 10^{-2}$ at this Q^2. The projections along the Q^2 and x axes are shown in figures 4b and c, respectively; the histograms on these figures show predictions of Monte Carlo calculations using the MRSD0 parametrization. Figure 4d gives the absolutely normalized differential cross-sections from these data, for the boxes outlined in figure 4a, as data points. The predictions of three different structure function parametrizations are superimposed in 4d.

Figure 5a shows the normalized cross-sections versus $\log x$ and Q^2 from events selected by the H1 experiment. Also shown are comparisons with various parametrizations of the structure functions. The data of figures 4 and 5 are in reasonable

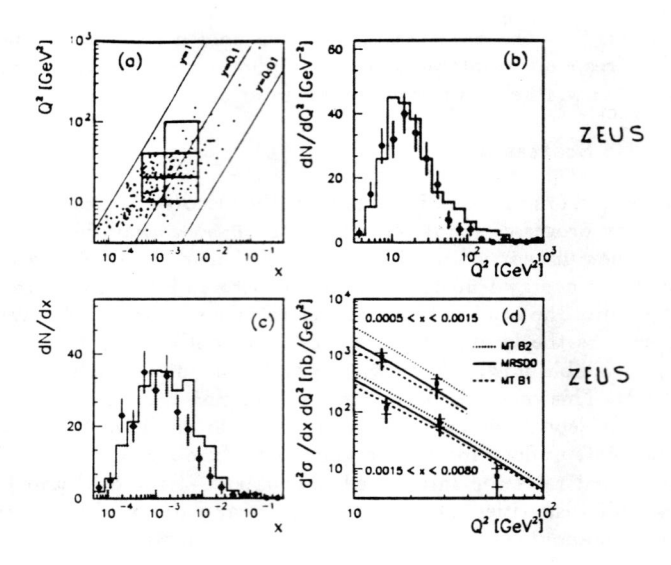

Figure 4: Deep inelastic neutral current data from the ZEUS experiment taken during the summer running. See text for the description of the various plots.

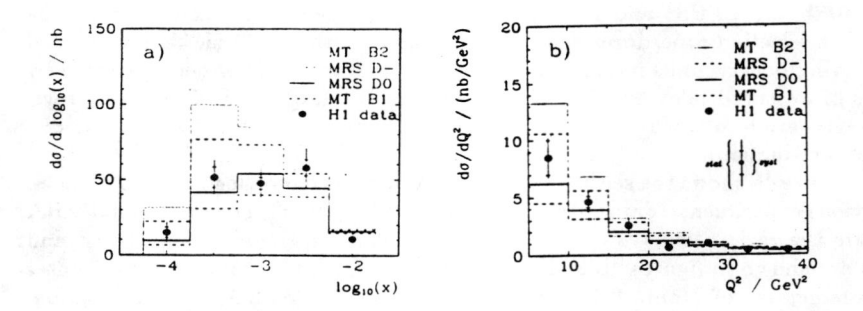

Figure 5: Deep inelastic neutral current data from the H1 experiment taken during the summer 1992 running. See text for a description of the various plots.

agreement with expectations. No major surprises are yet evident.

The most serious background to the NC small-x signal comes from photoproduction processes in which the recoil electron proceeds down the beam pipe but is missed by the electron detector of the LUMI. A fraction of such events will have an electromagnetic cluster misidentified as the scattered electron. For the samples shown in figures 4 and 5, these backgrounds have been largely, though not completely, removed by cuts on $E - p_z$ of equation 5, or equivalently on comparisons of calculations of the scaling variable y, using the electron and the hadrons in the final state. Photoproduction backgrounds primarily contain apparent electrons of low final state energy. DIS events with high Q^2 and small x also have electrons of low energy. A challenge for the future is to maximize sensitivity at low x and high Q^2 by identifying low energy electrons in DIS samples with little photoproduction background.

These first observations of DIS events at HERA indicate that QCD-extrapolated structure functions qualitatively agree with expectations. The separation of NC events from background, the measurement of luminosity, and the measurement of cross-sections in the new low-x domain has begun. Results with higher statistics are eagerly anticipated.

4.2. Hadronic final states.

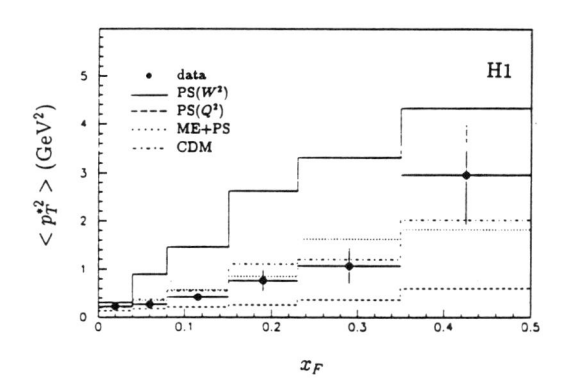

Figure 6: Transverse momentum rms for final state tracks in DIS events from the H1 experiment. See text for discussion.

The H1 experiment has made extensive studies[15] of the tracks reconstructed in final states of selected NC events. The data are in good agreement with QCD expectations, though some model calculations of the descriptions agree better than others. The particularly sensitive plot of figure 6, the mean of the squares of transverse momenta $<p_T^2>$ versus Feynman variable, x_F, illustrates this. Comparisons are made with leading log parton shower (PS) models using scales Q^2 and W^2, along with the color dipole model (CDM), and a model entailing exact order α_s matrix elements with soft emissions added from the parton shower model (ME+PS). Such comparisons will improve with more data.

5. Exotic Processes

Even at very low luminosity, the high energy of HERA permits unique searches for new particles, such as excited electrons (e^*) and bound states of leptons and hadronic constituents, like the leptoquarks (LQ). The latter have been proposed[16] to mediate new forces between leptons and quarks in extensions of the standard model. Both e^* and LQ have been sought at LEP, where s-channel production of e^* has been ruled out to masses at the kinematic limit. Point-like LQ have not been observed at either LEP or at hadron colliders. The most stringent limit comes from the CDF experiment which limits the mass to $M_{LQ} > 113~GeV$.[17]

There is wonderful complementarity between searches for leptoquarks at electron and hadron colliders, on the one hand, to those at HERA on the other. Production of <u>point-like</u> leptoquarks acting as gauge bosons <u>must</u> occur in pairs (given enough energy) at LEP because of the weak charge carried by the LQ and at CDF/D^0 because of the net colour. Such production is independent of the coupling of the leptoquark to lepton and quark. Leptoquarks of <u>finite</u> size may well <u>not</u> be produced with observable rates at electron or hadron colliders. Also, model-dependent limits[18] on the couplings of leptoquark states from low energy experiments apply only to point-like leptoquarks.

Production of resonant lepton-quark states <u>must</u> occur at HERA whether these states are point-like or not. Such s-channel production depends on the coupling strength, g, between the LQ and the lepton-quark in the initial state. In order to compare LQ searches between hadron colliders and HERA, one must assume <u>point-like</u> leptoquarks of known coupling. Conventionally, this coupling is taken to be "electroweak": $g_{EW} = \sqrt{4\pi\alpha_{EW}} \approx 0.31$.

The signature of flavour-conserving leptoquarks at HERA is spectacular. They will be created when the center-of-mass energy between the beam electron and a quark in the beam proton are at the resonant mass, or when x is equal to

$$x_0 = \frac{M_{LQ}^2}{s}. \tag{8}$$

where s is the square of the center-of-mass energy from the incident electron and proton. Production of a leptoquark is therefore signalled by a peak in the x-distribution.

The cross-section to produce a resonant state of electron and u-quark is given by[19]

$$\sigma = \frac{\pi}{4s}g^2 u(x_0) \tag{9}$$

where $u(x_0)$ is the differential probability for finding a u-quark of momentum fraction, x_0. The decay widths of leptoquarks to which these searches are sensitive are large enough so that all decays are prompt, and small enough so that the measurement resolution of x dominates over intrinsic widths. Leptoquarks must decay back to the initial state and would manifest as NC events (2). The only other flavour-conserving final state would appear as the CC process (3) if this decay is permitted by helicity, *etc.* Hence, the branching ratio to the NC mode is either 1/2 or 1.

Analysis of the summer data from H1 and ZEUS resulted in limits on LQ masses below 100 GeV for $g = g_{EW}$. The fall data, with ten times more luminosity permits a much more sensitive search. Preliminary analyses (with similar conclusions) have been performed with this sample by both the H1 and ZEUS groups; only the latter will be discussed here.

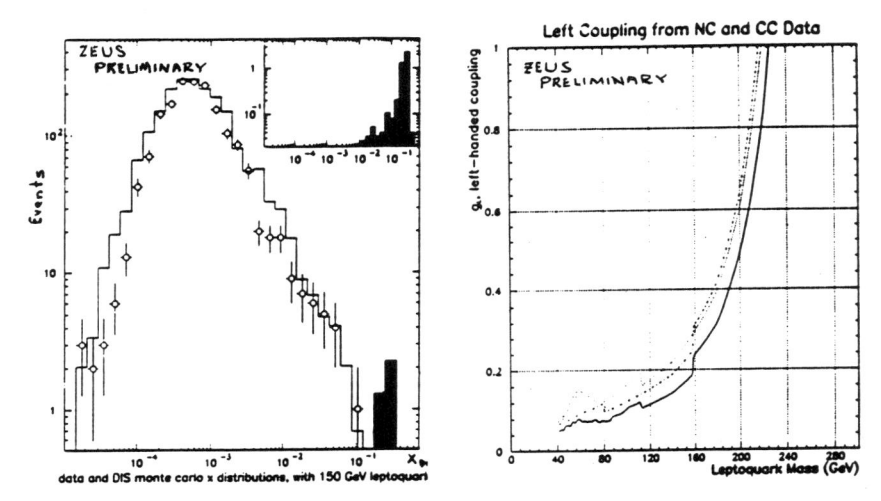

Figure 7: Preliminary ZEUS leptoquark analysis. (a) The x distribution for selected NC candidates. (b) Limits on leptoquark-electron-quark coupling versus leptoquark mass. (See text for details.)

The preliminary ZEUS analysis has resulted in selection of the 1659 NC events with $y > .1$ and electron energy, $E > 10$ GeV, shown plotted versus x in figure 7a. The data are shown with statistical error bars; the predicted Monte Carlo distribution normalized to the measured total luminosity of 26 ± 5 nb^{-1}, is shown as the unshaded histogram. The shaded histogram on the figure and in the upper inset illustrate the expected signal for a leptoquark with $M_{LQ} = 150$ GeV and coupling $g = g_{EW}$. There is no indication in this data for a leptoquark.

The CC selection from the same data sample has resulted in two charged current candidates, with an expectation of 1.1 events. One of these is a spectacular high Q^2 event with an unbalanced transverse momentum of about 90 GeV.

These data have permitted the limits shown in figure 7b for a left-handed (eu) spin-0 leptoquark decaying into both NC and CC channels. The figure gives the 90% confidence limit on the coupling versus leptoquark mass. The dotted curve shows the limit from the NC sample, the dash-dotted curve from the CC sample, and the solid curve from the combined samples. The mass limit for a leptoquark of coupling $g = g_{EW}$ is $M_{LQ} > 177$ GeV. Table 2 gives the mass limits for electroweak coupling of various scalar leptoquarks with $SU3 \times SU2 \times U1$ couplings[19] of both helicities. The resonant quark type and branching ratio into the initial state are also shown.

Table 2: Mass Limits (GeV) on Various Scalar Leptoquark

Type	Left-handed			Right-handed		
	Quark	$B(e^-q)$	Limit	Quark	$B(e^-q)$	Limit
S_1	u	1/2	177	u	1	184
S_3	$u + 2d$	1/2	190	—	—	—
$\tilde{S}_3$	—	—	—	d	1	147
R_2	$\bar{u}$	1	99	$\bar{u} + \bar{d}$	1	119
$\tilde{R}_2$	$\bar{d}$	1	99	—	—	—

Preliminary analyses of the fall running of ZEUS and H1 on e^* production with decays into $e + \gamma$ provide limits well above the 90 GeV s-channel mass limits of LEP.

6. Conclusions

The new era of electron-proton beam collisions has begun! In about a month of data-taking during commissioning, with only about 10^{-3} of the design luminosity, physics has been explored in new kinematic regimes.

Photoproduction total-cross sections have been measured at center-of-mass energies ten times those previously studied. Hard-scattering properties have been identified in the data; a wealth of information should soon become available on the hard-scattering mechanisms from data in hand.

Deep inelastic neutral current events have been separated from backgrounds. The high rate events have moderate Q^2 but in lie a new regime of x_{Bj}: $10^{-4} \leq x \leq 10^{-2}$. Studies begin to understand the gluon distribution in this small x region from the substantially increased data sample of the fall running.

The first charged current event at HERA has been observed in the fall data of ZEUS. Preliminary analysis of this data provides limits on leptoquark masses in excess of the 100 GeV mass scale for electroweak coupling.

The rate of luminosity increase bodes well for future studies of NC and CC processes at high Q^2 and for exotic searches. The next run should begin in spring 1993; we anticipate about an order-of-magnitude increase in the event sample beyond that obtained this fall. This increase will provide a yet deeper level of sensitivity for physics and will well match the capabilities of the experiments. We expect the next run and thereafter will provide continuing excitement and challenges for us at HERA.

References

1. Status of HERA, experimental results, and detector descriptions were presented as invited talks and will appear in *Proceedings of the 26th International Conference on High Energy Physics* **Dallas** (August 1992) by B. Wiik (HERA), B. Löhr (ZEUS results), F. Eisele (H1 results), A. Caldwell (ZEUS detector), and F. W. Brasse (H1 detector).
2. D.P. Barber, et al, *The HERA Polarimeter and the First Observation of Electron Spin Polarization at HERA* **DESY 92-136** (October 1992).
3. ZEUS Coll: M. Derrick, et al, *Initial Study of Deep Inelastic Scattering with ZEUS at HERA* **DESY 92-180** (December 1992), submitted to *Phys. Lett.*
4. ZEUS Coll: M. Derrick, et al, *Phys. Lett.* **B293** (1992) 465.
5. H1 Coll: T. Ahmed, et al, *Total Photoproduction Cross Section Measurement at HERA Energies* **DESY 92-160** (November 1992), submitted for publication.
6. A. Donnachie and P.V. Landshoff, *Nucl. Phys.* **B231** (1984) 189.
7. H. Abramowicz, et al., *Phys. Lett.* **B269** (1991) 465.
8. M. Drees and F. Halzen, *Phys. Rev. Lett.* **61** (1988) 275.
   R. Ghandi and I. Sarcevic, *Phys. Rev.* **D44** (1991) R10.
9. J. Kwiecinski, et al., *Phys. Rev.* **D42** (1990) 3645.
10. M. Drees and K. Grassie, *Z. Phys.* **C28** (1985) 451.
11. H1 Coll: T. Ahmed, et al, *Hard Scattering in γp Interactions* **DESY 92-160** (October 1992), submitted for publication.
12. ZEUS Coll: M. Derrick, et al, *Phys. Lett.* **B297** (1992) 404.
13. E. Witten, *Nucl. Phys.* **B120** (1977) 189.
14. H1 Coll: T. Ahmed, et al, *Observation of Deep Inelastic Scattering at Low x* **DESY 92-164** (November 1992), submitted to *Phys. Lett. B.*
15. H1 Coll: T. Ahmed, et al, *Measurement of the Hadronic Final State in Deep Inelastic Scattering at HERA* **DESY 92-162** (November 1992), submitted for publication.
16. See reference 19 and references therein.
17. CDF Coll: J. Freeman, (private communication).
18. W. Buchmüller and D. Wyler. *Phys. Lett.* **B177** (1986) 377.
19. W. Buchmüller, et al., *Phys. Lett.* **B191** (1987) 442.

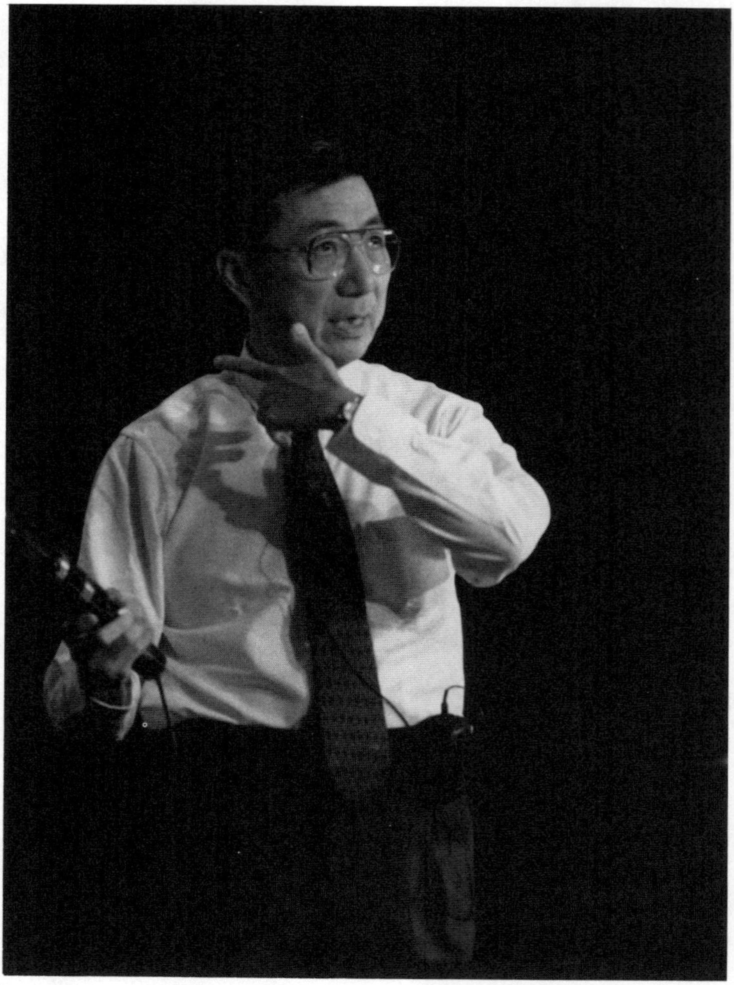

NEW RESULTS FROM LEP EXPERIMENTS

SAMUEL C.C. TING

CERN, 1211 Geneva, Switzerland

and

Laboratory for Nuclear Science
Massachusetts Institute of Technology
Cambridge, MA 02139, USA

ABSTRACT

In the years 1989 to 1992, LEP has delivered to each of the four experiments ALEPH, DELPHI, L3 and OPAL more than 1 million Z events. With such high statistics, a stringent test of the Standard Model has been performed and its parameters have been measured with very high precision. In this paper I will present a few new results from each of the four LEP experiments on the electroweak interaction, QCD and new particle searches. I will also comment on the future plans of LEP.

1 Introduction

1.1 LEP Performance

The Large Electron Positron (LEP) collider, which has been operating since August 1989, is located at the French and Swiss border near Geneva (see Figure 1). The machine is in a tunnel of 27 km circumference and is one of the largest colliders developed for experimental high energy physics. Bunches of electrons and positrons circulate in opposite directions with an energy of ≈ 45 GeV.

In 1992 the LEP collider continued to demonstrate excellent performance and delivered to each of the four experiments an integrated luminosity of 28 pb^{-1}. Some machine time was spent to commission a new mode of operation: 8×8 bunch collisions in a so-called Pretzel scheme. This new mode is expected to provide a luminosity increase of about a factor two. Figure 2 shows the integrated luminosity seen by the experiments from 1990 to 1992. Progress from year to year is clearly seen.

In 1991, the technique of resonant depolarization was used to determine the beam energy by measuring the frequency with which the spins of transversely polarized electrons precess around the vertical axis. Also the properties of the LEP magnets and RF system were studied and better understood in detail. A precise absolute energy scale of the LEP beams was achieved. The relative precision was

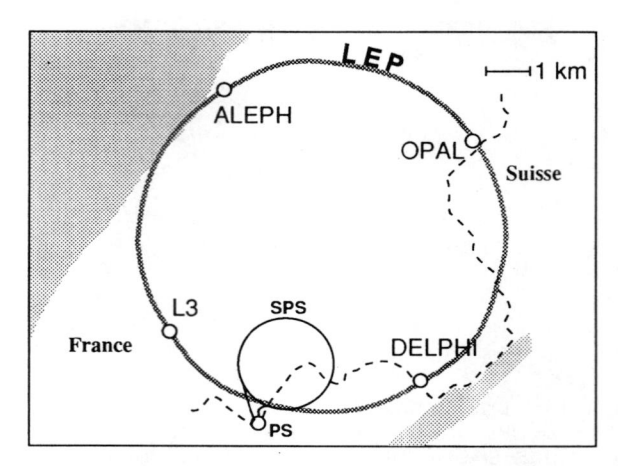

Figure 1: The LEP collider at CERN

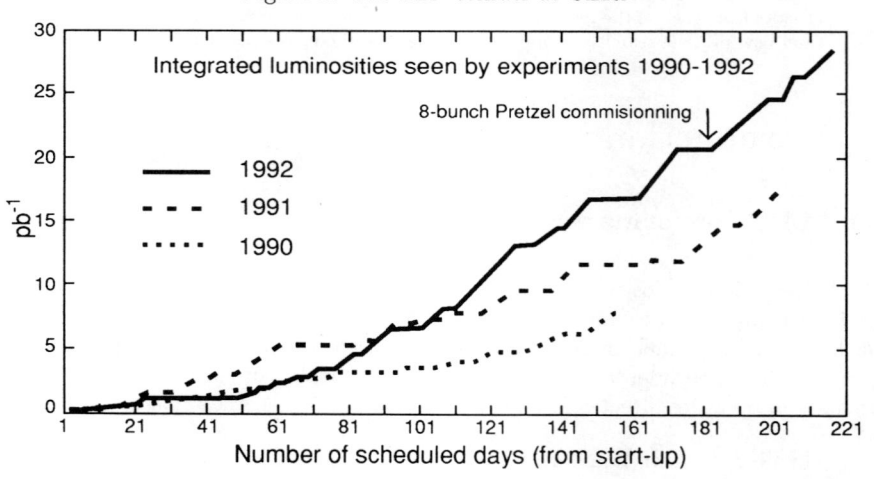

Figure 2: Integrated luminosity seen by the experiments in 1990 to 1992 at LEP

reduced from $\pm 22. \times 10^{-5}$ in 1990 to $\pm 5.7 \times 10^{-5}$ in 1991. At a center-of-mass energy of 93 GeV, this corresponds to ± 5.3 MeV. Adding the energy uncertainties of LEP beams from other sources leads an uncertainty of ± 6.3 MeV on the Z mass.

1.2 LEP Experiments

Nearly 2000 physicists are working at the four LEP experiments: ALEPH (see Figure 3), DELPHI (see Figure 4), L3 (see Figure 5) and OPAL (see Figure 6), each with its own unique detector capabilities and each with a set of unique beautiful physics results. In the last few years, many outstanding papers have been published by the four LEP collaborations. Rather than give a quick summary of all the results, I decided to contact the spokesmen of the collaborations, Professor Jacques Lefrançois of ALEPH, Professor Ugo Amaldi of DELPHI and Professor Aldo Michelini of OPAL to invite them to give me a few examples of interesting results from their collaborations. I present some of these results here.

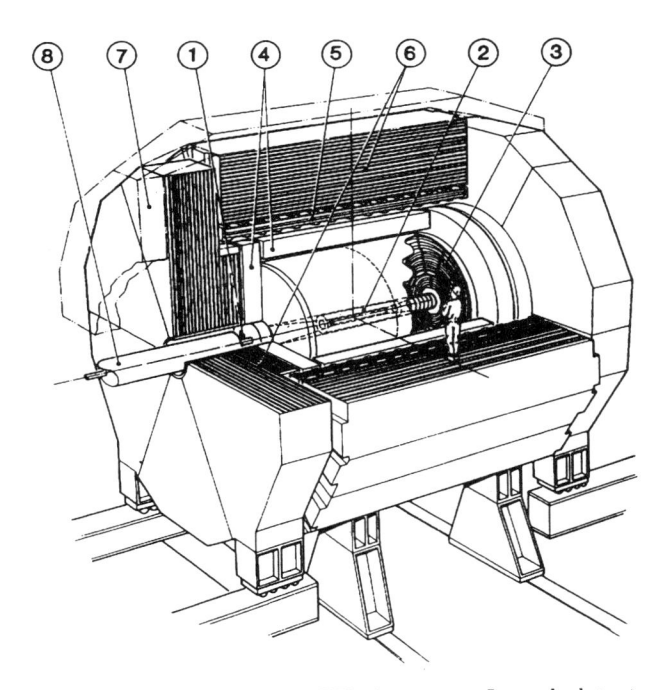

Figure 3: General view of the ALEPH detector. Its sub-detector components are: (1) Luminosity Calorimeter, (2) Inner Tracking Chamber, (3) Time Projection Chamber, (4) Electromagnetic Calorimeter, (5) Superconducting Coil, (6) Hadron Calorimeter and (7) Muon Chambers. Also shown are LEP superconducting quadrupoles (8).

Table 1: The performance of the ALEPH detector

Momentum :	$\Delta p/p =$	2.7% at 45 GeV
Impact Parameter:		25 μm at 45 GeV
Invariant Mass :	$J/\psi \to \mu\mu$	25 MeV
b-Decay Length :	$\sigma_\parallel =$	300 μm
	$\sigma_\perp =$	30 μm
τ-Decay Length :	$\sigma_\parallel =$	740 μm
	$\sigma_\perp =$	25 μm
Energy Flow :	$\Delta E =$	6.8% at 91 GeV
Electromag. Shower :	$\Delta E/E =$	$0.18/\sqrt{E(\text{GeV})}$
Luminosity error (exp.)	$\Delta L/L =$	0.5%
Lepton Identification :	Efficiency	Miss-ident. Prob.	
Electrons:	85%	5×10^{-3}	ECAL only
	75%	1×10^{-3}	ECAL only + dE/dX
Muons:	88%	1×10^{-3}	
Two Track Separation:	100%	at 2 deg	(TPC)
	50%	at 1 deg	(TPC)

An improved running efficiency was also demonstrated by all four LEP experiments. As an example, Table 1 demonstrates the outstanding level of performance achieved by the ALEPH detector. Another example of progress in the year 1992 is shown in Figure 7 which illustrates the beautiful performance of the DELPHI silicon microvertex detector. This device allows much better determination of, for example, secondary vertices and lifetimes of shortlived particles. The L3 detector is designed to measure both the energy and direction of leptons and photons with high precision. Figure 8 illustrates the achieved energy resolution with the electromagnetic calorimeter, where two-photon mass spectra from hadronic events are presented. OPAL installed an additional set of forward-backward drift chambers for their luminosity monitor in the year 1992 to improve the luminosity measurement.

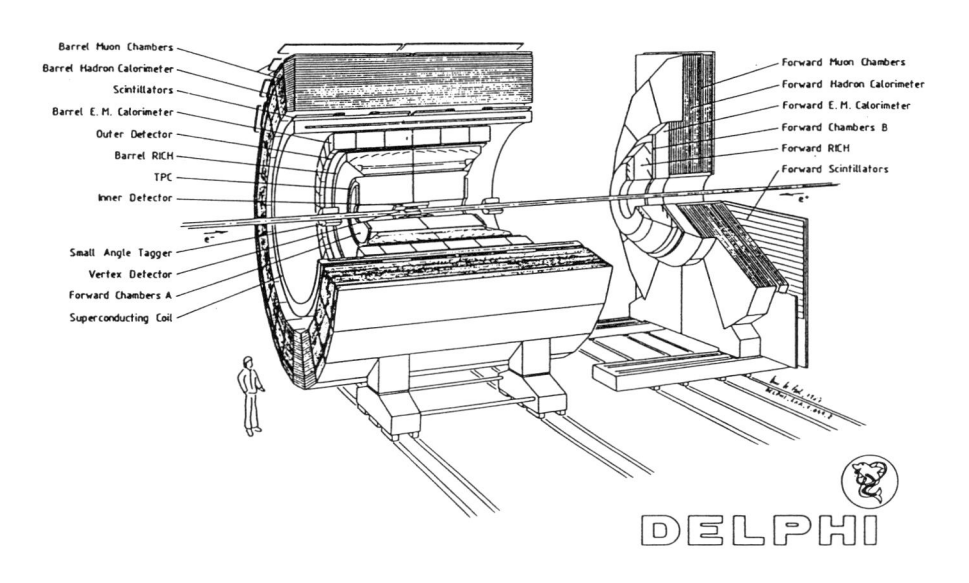

Figure 4: General view of the DELPHI detector

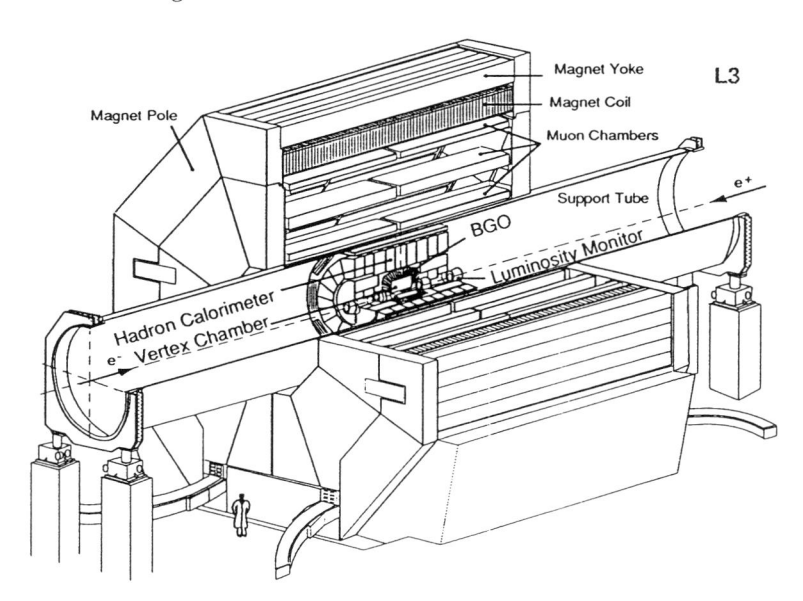

Figure 5: Overview of the L3 detector

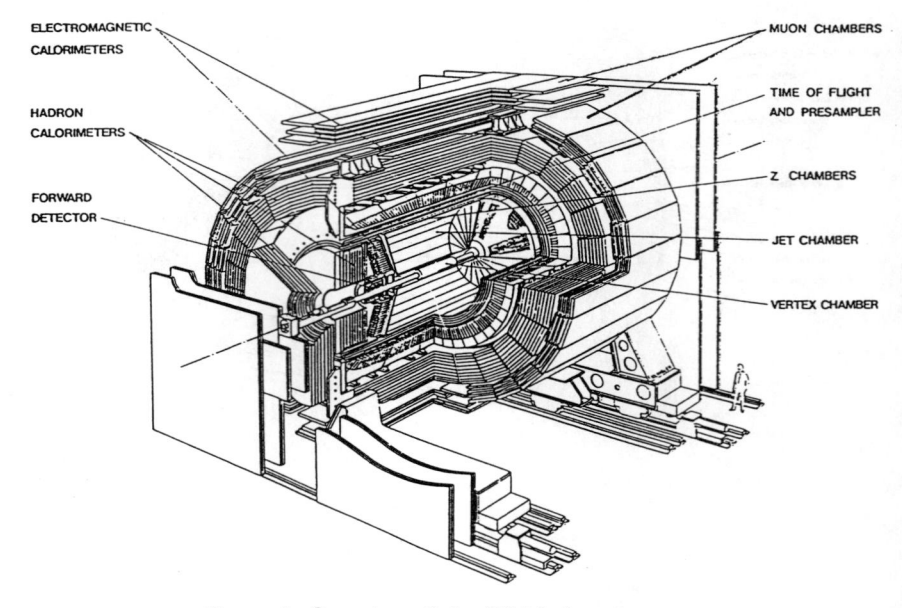

Figure 6: Overview of the OPAL detector

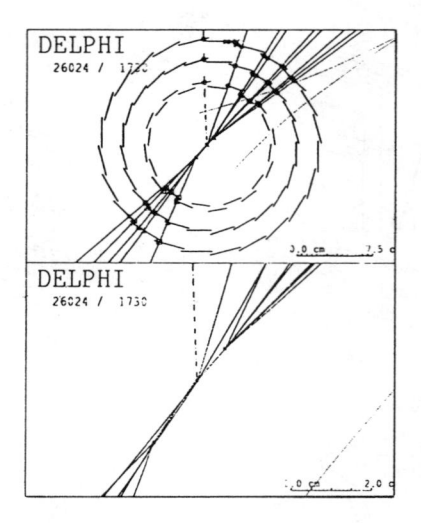

Figure 7: The Silicon Microvertex Detector of the DELPHI experiment and an example of a reconstructed event with primary and secondary vertices.

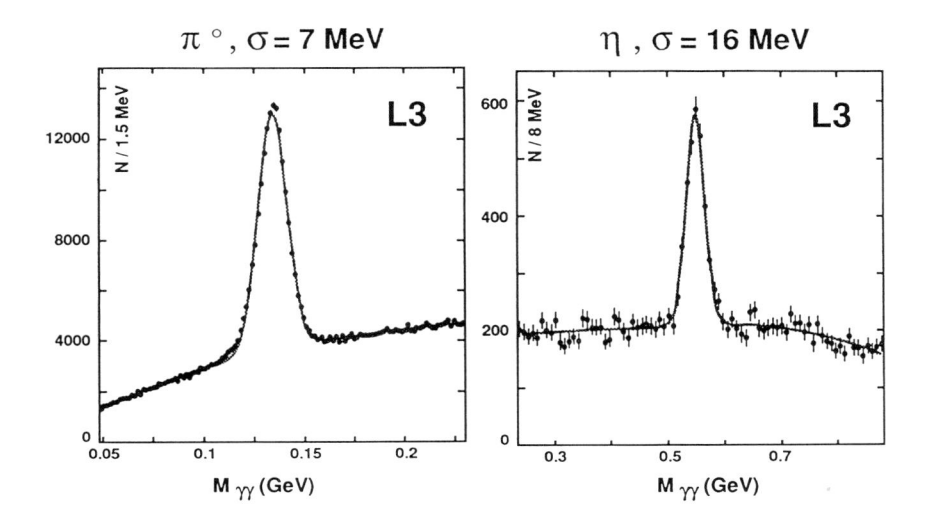

Figure 8: Measured $\gamma\gamma$ mass spectra from $q\bar{q}$ events at LEP, by L3

2 Electroweak Interaction

The total number of Z events collected in 1989 to 1991 by the four LEP experiments is given in Table 2. A total of 1.7 million hadronic and 180 thousand leptonic Z decays have been analyzed.

Table 2: The number of Z events collected by the four LEP experiments during 1989 to 1991.

Type	ALEPH	DELPHI	L3	OPAL	Total
$q\bar{q}$	452 K	368 K	425 K	454 K	1699 K
e^+e^-	19 K	10 K	16 K	16 K	61 K
$\mu^+\mu^-$	19 K	15 K	13 K	21 K	68 K
$\tau^+\tau^-$	17 K	10 K	10 K	16 K	53 K
Total	507 K	403 K	464 K	507 K	1.9×10^6

2.1 Electroweak Parameters from Z Decays

Due to increased statistics, better understanding of the detectors and the improvement in the energy calibration of the LEP beams, the measurement accuracy of the electroweak parameters is substantially improved. To determine the electroweak parameters of Z decays, the four LEP experiments have performed model-independent fits to leptonic cross sections and forward-backward asymmetries, and to hadronic cross sections. Figure 9 shows the measured hadronic cross sections at different center-of-mass energies and the result of the fit. Table 3 lists the values of the Z mass and width as measured by OPAL from the model-independent fit to the hadronic and leptonic cross sections. Corresponding L3 results are shown in Table 4. One can see that the Z mass is determined with a relative precision of about 10^{-4}.

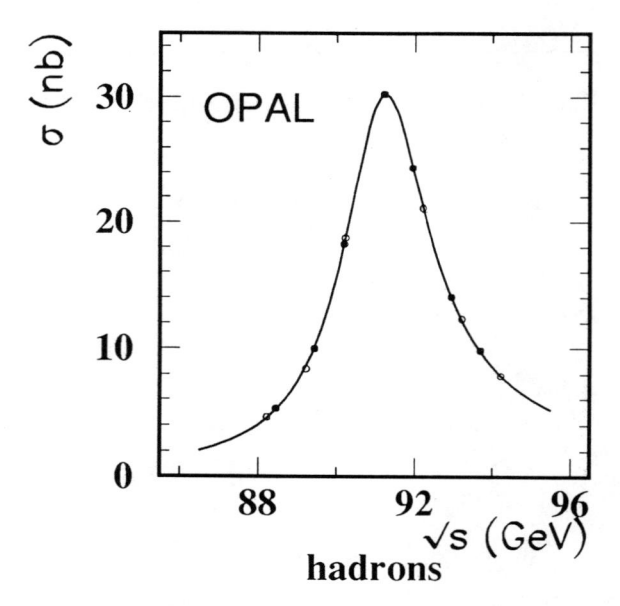

Figure 9: The hadronic cross section around the Z resonance measured by OPAL

Table 3: The OPAL lineshape results

M_Z	$91.181 \pm 0.007(exp.) \pm 0.006(LEP)$ GeV
Γ_Z	$2.483 \pm 0.011(exp.) \pm 0.004(LEP)$ GeV
$R_Z = \Gamma_{had}/\Gamma_{ll}$	20.88 ± 0.013

Table 4: The Z parameters measured by L3

M_Z	91.195 ± 0.009 GeV
Γ_Z	2490.0 ± 11.0 MeV
Γ_{had}	1747.0 ± 11.0 MeV
Γ_{lep}	83.1 ± 0.5 MeV
Γ_{inv}	494.0 ± 9.6 MeV
N_ν	2.98 ± 0.06
R_{had}	21.00 ± 0.015
σ_{had}	41.34 ± 0.28 (nb)

The L3 forward-backward asymmetry data for the years 1990 and 1991 are given in Figure 10 and demonstrate the reproducibility of the detector. By assuming lepton universality, the Z vector and axial vector coupling constants to leptons have been derived from leptonic forward-backward asymmetries A_{FB} in addition to the total cross section data, as shown in Figure 10. With the assumption of lepton universality, L3 has determined g_a and g_v by including the τ-polarization measurement. The measured results are:

$$g_a = -0.4986 \pm 0.0015 \qquad g_v = -0.040^{+0.006}_{-0.005} \qquad (1)$$

The number of light neutrino families measured by all four LEP experiments is illustrated by Figure 11, and the averaged value is:

$$N_\nu = 3.00 \pm 0.04 \qquad (2)$$

The accuracy of this number averaged over all four experiment is approaching 1%. The summary of lepton widths averaged over all four LEP experiments is given in Figure 12. The accuracy of the measurement is very high. It is better than 1% for any of the three charged leptons and, if one assumes lepton universality, the accuracy is better than 0.5%. The measured electroweak parameters are compared with the Standard Model values in Table 5, where the SM predictions are obtained by using the parameters $M_Z = 91.188 \pm 0.007$ GeV, $M_{top} = 150^{+100}_{-60}$ GeV, $M_{Higgs} = 300^{+700}_{-240}$ GeV and $\alpha_s(M_Z) = 0.118 \pm 0.007$. The agreement between measured values and their theoretical expectations is quite spectacular.

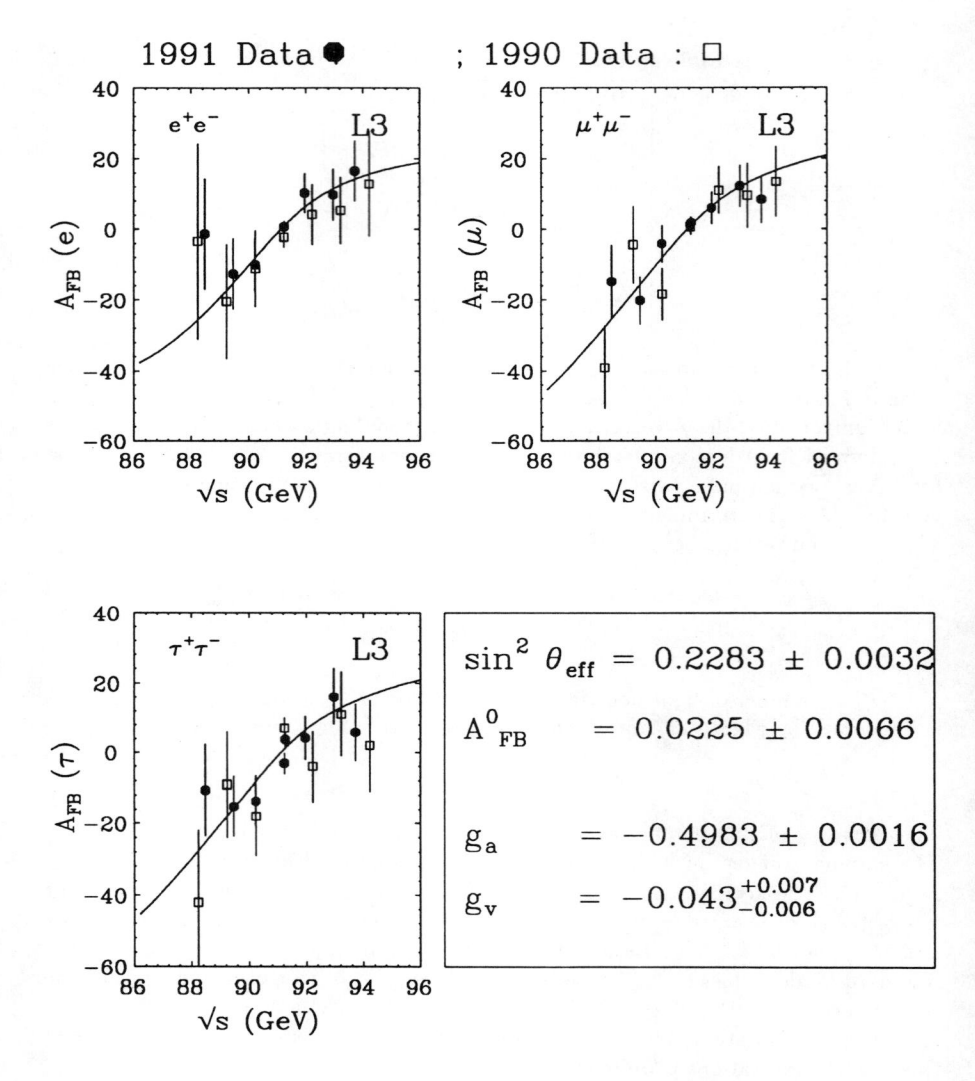

Figure 10: The leptonic forward-backward asymmetries as a function of the center of mass energy and the measured electroweak coupling constants by L3.

Table 5: The measured Z parameters from LEP compared with the Standard Model

Parameters	LEP values	Standard Model
M_Z (GeV)	91.188 ± 0.007	
Γ_Z (MeV)	2493.0 ± 7.0	2487^{+38}_{-20}
Γ_{had} (MeV)	1742.0 ± 6.8	1736^{+28}_{-15}
Γ_{lep} (MeV)	83.4 ± 0.38	$83.7^{+1.3}_{-0.5}$
Γ_{inv} (MeV)	500.8 ± 5.8	$500.3^{+6.1}_{-2.7}$
N_ν	3.00 ± 0.04	3
R_{had}	20.88 ± 0.07	$20.73^{+0.08}_{-0.10}$
σ^0_{had}	41.26 ± 0.18	$41.47^{+0.12}_{-0.07}$
$|g_a|$	0.5001 ± 0.0009	$0.5007^{+0.003}_{-0.001}$
$|g_v|$	0.0362 ± 0.0031	$0.034^{+0.010}_{-0.004}$
$\sin^2\theta_{\text{eff}}$	0.2324 ± 0.0011	$0.2330^{+0.0022}_{-0.0051}$

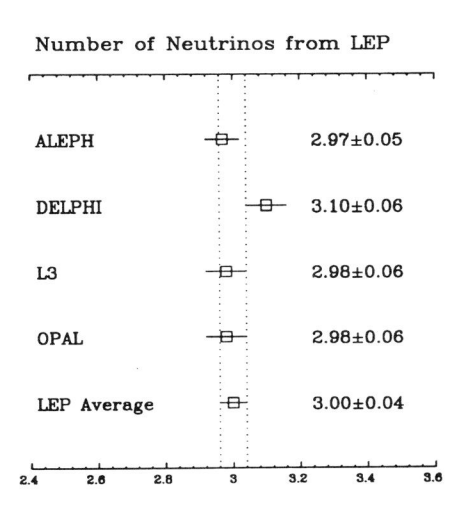

Number of Neutrinos from LEP

ALEPH		2.97 ± 0.05
DELPHI		3.10 ± 0.06
L3		2.98 ± 0.06
OPAL		2.98 ± 0.06
LEP Average		3.00 ± 0.04

Figure 11: Number of light neutrino species from the four LEP experiments

Γ_e, Γ_μ and Γ_τ

Γ_e 83.19±0.36

Γ_μ 83.69±0.53

Γ_τ 83.49±0.63

Γ_{lepton} 83.4±0.3

Γ_{lep} (MeV)

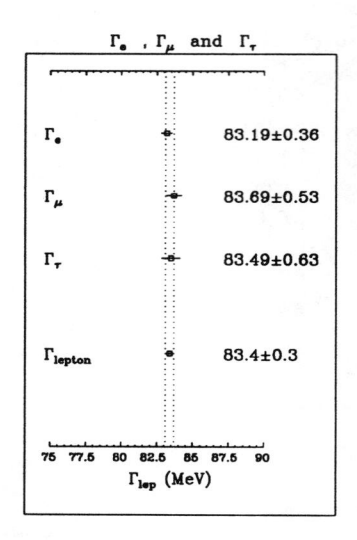

Figure 12: The Z leptonic decay width measured by the LEP experiments

2.2 $e^+ e^- \to \nu \nu \gamma$

Single photon events originating from initial state radiation (see Figure 13) are used for a direct measurement of the Z width into neutrinos and hence the number of light neutrino types. The measured single photon energy spectrum from L3 has been compared with Monte Carlo predictions for three light neutrino species, together with the expected backgrounds. The theoretical expectations are in good agreement with the data. The measured cross sections, which are energy dependent, are shown in Figure 14 together with the result of a maximum likelihood fit for the number of light neutrino types and the expected Standard Model cross sections for two, three and four light neutrino families. The measurements are in very good agreement with $N_\nu = 3$. The fit results are:

$$N_\nu = 3.14 \pm 0.024 \ (stat.) \pm 0.012 \ (sys.) \tag{3}$$

This corresponds to an invisible width of the Z:

$$\Gamma_{inv} = 524 \pm 40 \ (stat.) \pm 20 \ (sys.) \quad \text{MeV} \tag{4}$$

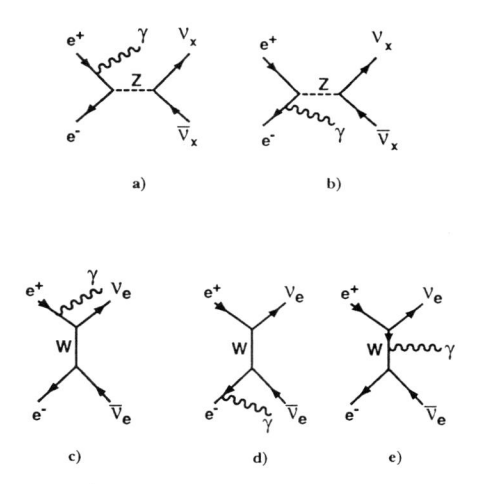

Figure 13: Lowest order Feynman diagrams contributing to $e^+e^- \to \nu\bar{\nu}\gamma$

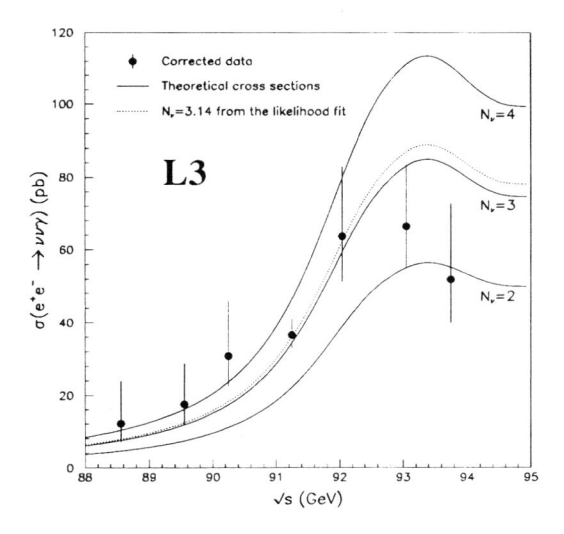

Figure 14: The single photon cross sections as a function of the center of mass energy. The maximum likelihood fit result (dashed line) corresponds to the L3 measurement $N_\nu = 3.14 \pm 0.24(stat)$. The predicted SM cross sections for 2, 3 and 4 light neutrino species are also shown (solid lines).

3 Quantum Chromodynamics

3.1 Measurement of α_s

OPAL has measured the strong coupling constant $\alpha_s(M_Z)$, from a study of 15 different observables in hadronic Z decays. Based on $\mathcal{O}(\alpha_s^2)$ QCD calculation, $\alpha_s(M_Z)$ is determined from studying the following variables :

- Global event shape variables, including C-parameter (C), Oblateness (O) and event Thrust (T) distribution

- Jet masses, where particles in an event are grouped to form two jets with invariant masses M_H (high mass) and M_L (low mass). The two jets are separated using either a plane orthogonal to the Thrust axis or by minimizing $M_H^2 + M_L^2$, therefore four variables, $M_H^{(T)}$, $M_D^{(T)}$, $M_H^{(M)}$ and $M_D^{(M)}$, can be used for studying the strong coupling constant, where $M_D = \sqrt{M_H^2 - M_L^2}$.

- Jet production rates, where all scaled jet pair masses, $y_{ij} = M_{ij}^2/s$, of resolvable jets i and j are required to exceed a certain value y_{cut}. Jets or particles with $y_{ij} \leq y_{cut}$ are put into a single jet. The value of $\alpha_s(M_Z)$ is determined from the differential jet production rate distribution as a function of the y variable. The E0-, E-, p- and Durham (D) schemes of jet production rate analysis are explored.

- Energy correlations, including the asymmetry distribution of energy-energy correlation (AEEC) and the planar triple-energy correlation (PTEC).

Determination of $\alpha_s(M_Z)$ from the hadronic width of Z decays and τ decays are based on $\mathcal{O}(\alpha_s^3)$ QCD calculations. In the Standard Model, the QCD correction to the hadronic Z width can be measured directly from:

$$R_Z \equiv \frac{\Gamma_{had}}{\Gamma_{lep}} = R_Z^0 \cdot (1 + \delta_{QCD}) \tag{5}$$

The value of R_Z^0 (19.95) is determined by the SM with little uncertainty (only $\pm$ 0.02) due to the unknown masses of the top quark and the Higgs. The QCD correction, calculated to $\mathcal{O}(\alpha_s^3)$, may be parametrized as:

$$\delta_{QCD} = 1.05\frac{\alpha_s}{\pi} + 0.9(\frac{\alpha_s}{\pi})^2 - 13(\frac{\alpha_s}{\pi})^3 \tag{6}$$

Therefore a precise measurement of R_Z is a clean and precise way to determine $\alpha_s(M_Z)$. OPAL also measured $\alpha_s(M_Z)$ from the ratio of the hadronic and leptonic

τ decay widths. All OPAL measurements of $\alpha_s(M_Z)$ are summarized in Figure 15. The experimental uncertainties are much less than the theoretical ones except for the values from the Z and τ hadronic widths. The averaged $\alpha_s(M_Z)$ value from OPAL is:

$$\alpha_s(M_Z) = 0.122^{+0.006}_{-0.005} \tag{7}$$

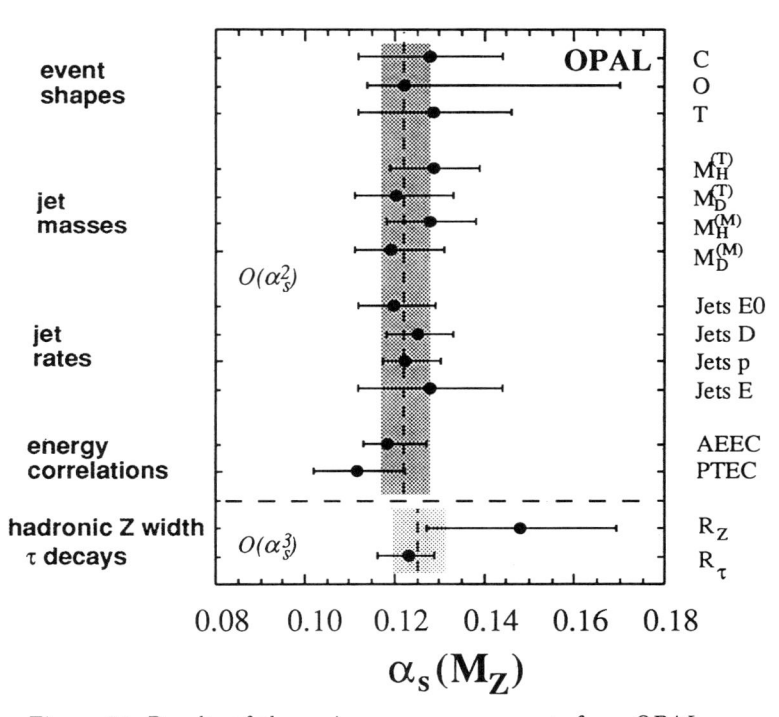

Figure 15: Results of the various α_s measurements from OPAL

In QCD, gluon radiation leads to logarithmic scaling violation, i.e., the momentum distributions expressed as fractions of the beam energy are dependent on energy. Therefore the strong coupling constant can be determined from the measurement of scaling violations. DELPHI has presented data on $\alpha_s(M_Z)$ extracted from the scaling violation in the fragmentation functions describing inclusive hadron production (see Figure 16). The result is:

$$\alpha_s(M_Z) = 0.119 \pm 0.006 \tag{8}$$

L3 has tested the flavor independence of $\alpha_s(M_Z)$ by using hadron samples containing events with high p_t muons or electrons which are therefore enriched with b-quarks. The result is:

$$\alpha_s^b / \alpha_s^{udsc} = 1.00 \pm 0.08 \qquad (9)$$

L3 also performed a measurement of $\alpha_s(M_\tau)$ from τ decays (see Figure 17) and confirmed the energy dependence of α_s predicted by QCD. The measurement gives:

$$\alpha_s(M_\tau = 1.78 \text{ GeV}) = 0.36 \pm 0.09 \qquad (10)$$

Extrapolating the α_s value from M_τ to M_Z assuming the energy dependence of α_s as predicted by QCD yields:

$$\alpha_s(M_Z) = 0.122 \pm 0.009, \qquad (11)$$

in good agreement with the α_s values measured at the Z resonance.

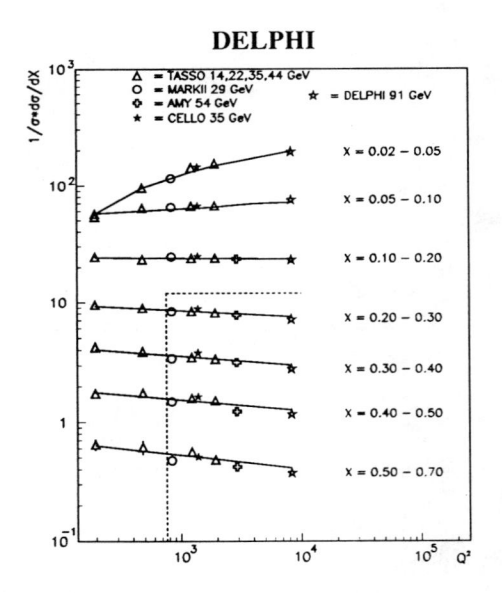

Figure 16: Combining low energy experiment results with DELPHI measurements, the Q^2 dependence of the inclusive momentum cross section is shown in the plot. Only the data at high Q^2 and high x have been used for the determination of α_s, as indicated by the dashed line.

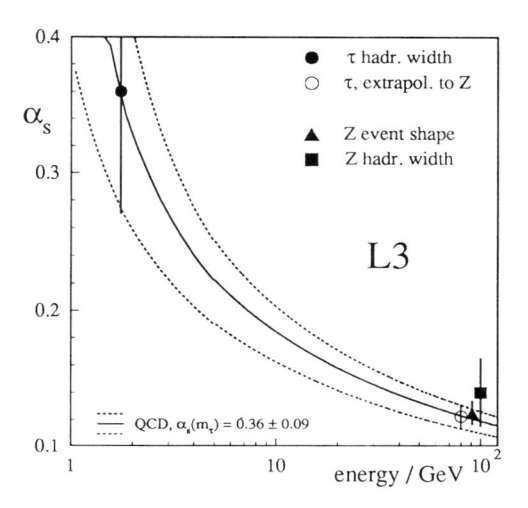

[Figure: plot of α_s vs energy/GeV showing L3 measurements]

Figure 17: Measured $\alpha_s(M_\tau)$ from the hadronic τ width by L3, extrapolated to $\alpha_s(M_Z)$ and compared to results from Z event shape variables and from the Z hadronic width. The energy dependence of α_s is clearly demonstrated.

3.2 Gluon Self-coupling

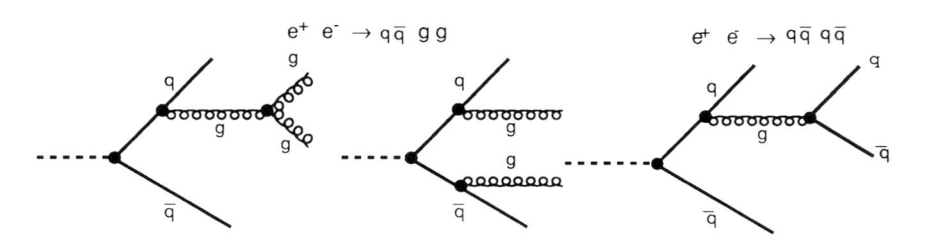

[Figure: Feynman diagrams for $e^+e^- \to q\bar{q}gg$ and $e^+e^- \to q\bar{q}q\bar{q}$]

Figure 18: The Feynman diagrams for four-jet events production

The test of gluon self-coupling was performed with four-jet events. The basic Feynman diagrams to produce four-jet events are shown in Figure 18. The four-jet production cross section, corresponding to the Feynman diagrams in Figure 18, is a function of the Casimir factors C_A, C_F and T_F which are the coupling strengths for the triple-gluon vertex, gluon radiation from quarks and gluon splitting into a quark pair, respectively. The values of C_A, C_F and T_F are shown in table 6 for QCD, an abelian model and QED. From a fit to the measured differential four-jet cross sections one

Table 6: Comparison between QCD, an abelian model and QED for the coupling strength parameters C_F, C_A and T_F

	C_A	C_F	T_F
QCD	3	4/3	1/2
abelian	0	1	3
QED	0	1	1

can determine C_A/C_F and T_F/C_F. Both ALEPH and DELPHI identify directly the contribution from the triple gluon vertex without comparing with a specific non-QCD model. ALEPH has performed a five-dimensional analysis using invariant masses y_{ij} while DELPHI used a two-dimensional representation corresponding to two angles between jets. The results of the DELPHI analysis are shown in Figure 19. They are in good agreement with QCD predictions and rule out several other models. The measured values of C_A/C_F and N_C/N_A are:

$$C_A/C_F = 2.12 \pm 0.35 \qquad N_C/N_A = 0.46 \pm 0.19 \qquad (12)$$

where N_C is the number of quark colors and N_A is the number of gluons.

The corresponding L3 result derived from the distribution of the so-called Bengtsson-Zerwas angle χ_{BZ} is shown in Figure 20. The quantity χ_{BZ} is the angle between the plane spanned by the two most energetic jets and the plane containing the other two jets. The measurements are in agreement with QCD, while they are incompatible with the expectation from an abelian model.

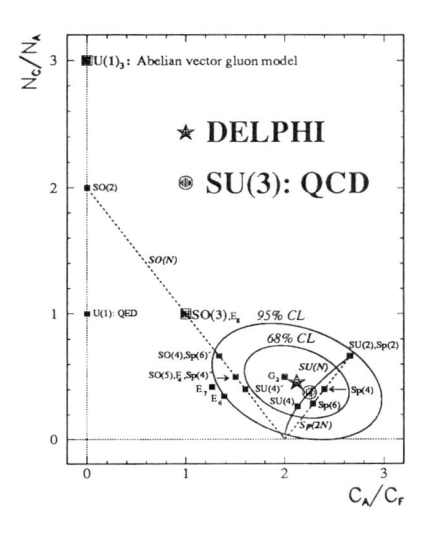

Figure 19: The allowed region in the C_A/C_F versus N_C/N_A plane from DELPHI, where the measured values and various theoretical predictions are indicated. They agree well with QCD and rule out several other models.

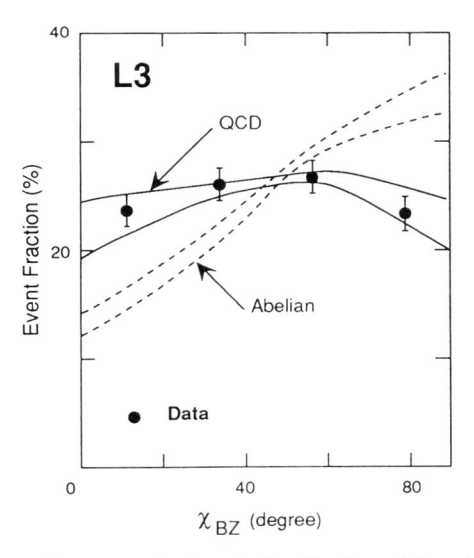

Figure 20: Bengtsson-Zerwas angle (χ_{BZ}) distribution of four-jet events from L3

3.3 Direct Measurement of Quark-Gluon Fragmentation Differences

By analyzing three-jet events, OPAL was able to directly compare quark and gluon jets. In this analysis, the angles between the highest energy jet and each of the two lower energy jets were required to be approximately the same. Because gluons are produced from the primary quarks, which come directly from Z decay, the most energetic jet is identified as a quark or an anti-quark jet with high probability. The second quark jet is required to contain a high energy lepton, which comes predominantly from the semileptonic decay of the heavy quark. The third jet is regarded as the gluon jet. Figure 21 shows the mean energy of the particles at different azimuthal angles ψ in the three-jet event plane, where ψ is the angle in the event plane between the highest energy jet axis and the particle. A "jet peak" region is defined by $110° < \psi < 180°$ in the analysis, as delineated by the dashed line in Figure 21. One can see from Figure 21 that the mean energy of particles in quark jets is higher than in gluon jets.

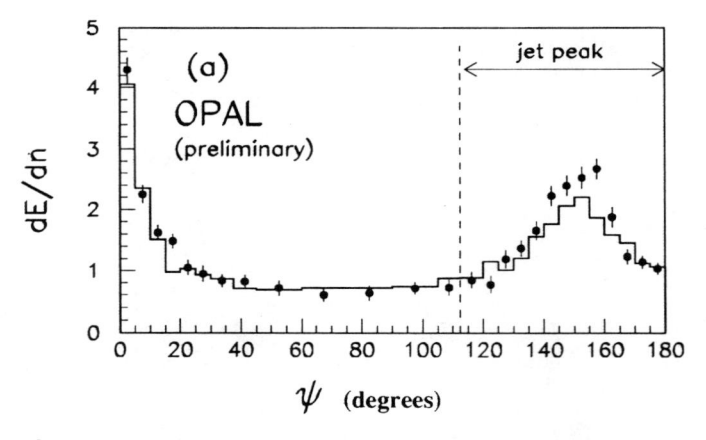

Figure 21: Comparison of the mean energy of particles between quark jets and gluon jets in three jet events from OPAL with dots for quark jets and a solid line for gluon jets.

3.4 Isolated Hard Photons

L3 has studied the production of isolated hard photons in hadronic Z decays, where the photons are mainly emitted from the primary quark pairs. The L3 data on isolated hard photons have been compared to three different MC generators and an $\mathcal{O}(\alpha\alpha_s)$ matrix element calculation. There is good agreement between data and the next-to-leading order calculation in which the quark electroweak couplings are not constrained to their Standard Model values. A fit to the direct photon distribution gives a linear constraint on the quark electroweak couplings to the Z. A second independent linear constraint on the coupling is derived from the L3 measurement of the total hadronic width of Z decays. By combining these two limits, L3 obtains the individual values of the u- and d-type quark electroweak couplings:

$$c_u = 0.92 \pm 0.22 \qquad c_d = 1.63 \pm 0.15 \qquad (13)$$

where $c_{u,d} = 4(\bar{g}_V^2 + \bar{g}_A^2)_{u,d}$. The results are consistent with the Standard Model as illustrated in Figure 22.

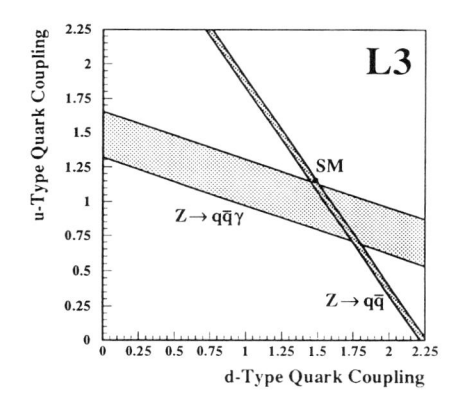

Figure 22: The measurement of the d-type quark and u-type quark coupling to the Z by the L3 experiment

OPAL also studied the production of energetic photons. A typical $qq\gamma$ event is shown in Figure 23. The production rates of jet plus photon are studied from the E0 and Durham schemes for various y_{cut} values for which data and MC are in good agreement. The measurement of the photon rate at a certain value of y_{cut}, where the theoretical and experimental errors are smallest, gives a linear constraint on the quark electroweak couplings to the Z. Combining it with the OPAL Γ_{had} measurement and assuming the electroweak couplings of all u-type and all d-type quarks to be the same, as expected to within 2-3%, OPAL obtains from the E0 scheme:

$$c_u = 0.94 \pm 0.18 \qquad c_d = 1.62 \pm 0.12 \qquad (14)$$

corresponding to

$$\Gamma_u = 242 \pm 46 \text{ MeV} \qquad \Gamma_d = 419 \pm 30 \text{ MeV} \qquad (15)$$

The analysis has repeated using the Durham scheme and the results are consistent. The measurements are in good agreement with the Standard Model predictions and the results of other LEP experiments. The results are shown in Figure 23. As one can see the OPAL measurement from final state photons has a comparable precision to the results for c and b quarks obtained from various methods and by combining results from all LEP experiments, given the current precision on the c and b semileptonic branching ratio.

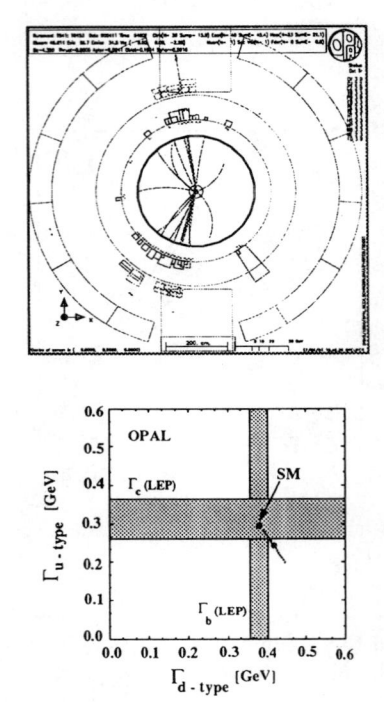

Figure 23: The top figure shows an observed $q\bar{q}\gamma$ event from the OPAL experiment. The bottom one shows the LEP results on the Z partial widths to up-type and down-type quarks from direct c-, b-quark tagging and the OPAL measurement from $q\bar{q}\gamma$ events (point with error bar).

4 Inclusive Production of Hadrons

Inclusive particle production in hadronic events is measured by all LEP experiments. From $\pi^+\pi^-$ and $K^\pm\pi^\mp$ final states, DELPHI has studied the light meson resonances of ρ^0, $f_0(975)$, $f_2(1270)$ and K^{*0} in hadronic decays. The observed resonances are shown in Figure 24, where the background including the contribution due to a particle being wrongly identified are subtracted using a fitting procedure. The average meson

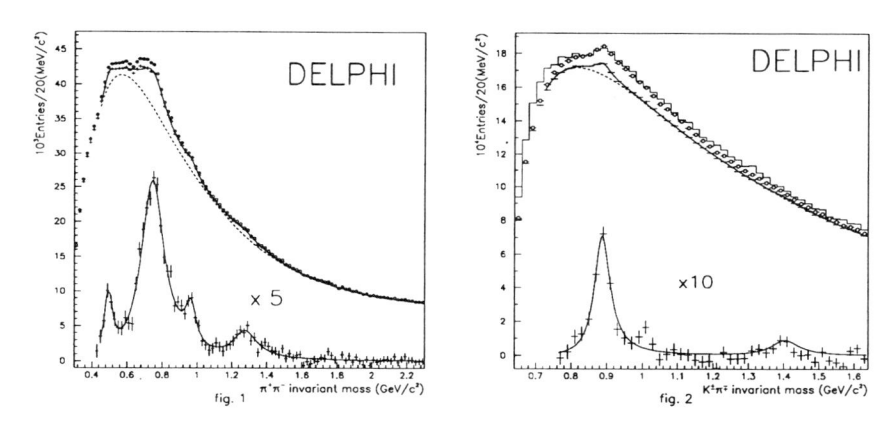

Figure 24: The plots show individual mass spectra in $\pi^+\pi^-$ and $K^\pm\pi^\mp$ final states from DELPHI. Open dots are raw data, and crosses with error bars are corrected after background subtraction.

multiplicities per hadronic event of the ρ^0, $f_0(975)$, $f_2(1270)$ and K^{*0} have been measured. They are consistent with MC predictions. The measurements of differential cross sections, $1/\sigma_{hadr} \cdot d\sigma/dx_p$, for these mesons are shown in Figure 25 together with the JETSET and HERWIG expectations, where x_p is the ratio of the particle momentum to the beam energy. There is an impressive agreement between data and MC predictions. As one can see the shape of $1/\sigma_{hadr} \cdot d\sigma/dx_p$ distributions for $f_0(975)$ and $f_2(1270)$ are quite similar in the data.

L3 has reconstructed η mesons from photon pairs measured in the electromagnetic calorimeter. The measured invariant mass spectra of the photon pairs are shown in Figure 8. The width of the η peak is $\sigma = 16.1$ MeV. The differential cross sections for η are measured by correcting the data, as a function of momentum, for detector and initial and final state photon emission effects. The measured inclusive η production rates are given in Figure 26 and compared with different Monte Carlo

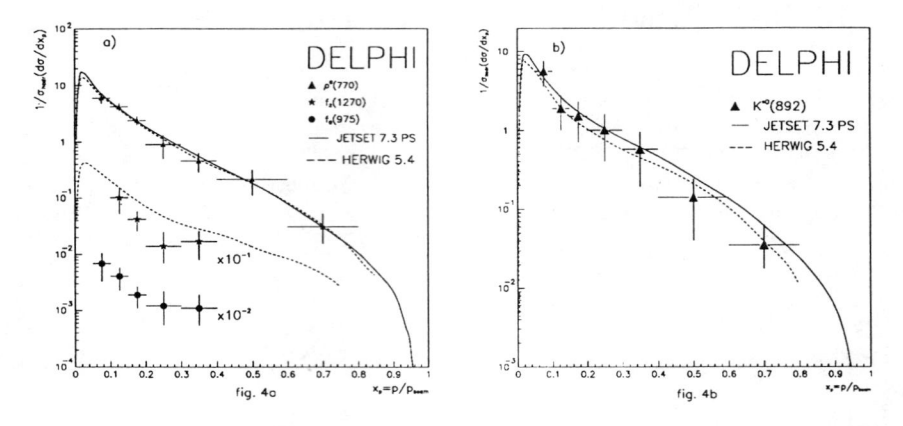

Figure 25: The differential cross sections for ρ^0, $f_0(975)$, $f_2(1270)$ and K^{*0}, where the distributions for $f_0(975)$ and $f_2(1270)$ are lowered by a factor 10 and 100, respectively. The inclusive production rates from two different Monte Carlo predictions are shown in the plots.

predictions. Data are in good general agreement with QCD expectations.

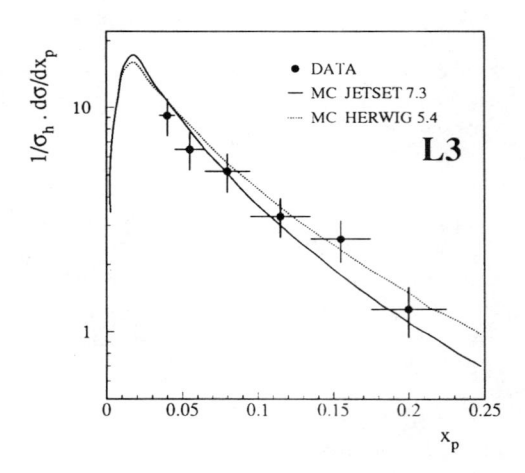

Figure 26: The L3 measured inclusive η production rate at different x_p.

5 B Physics

The b-quark properties are measured by using inclusive lepton events. Due to the hard fragmentation of b-quarks, the b-hadrons carry most of the initial b-quark energy (on average $\approx 70\%$). Since the b-quark is heavy, the products of b-decay have a large transverse momentum with respect to the initial parton direction. Therefore the leptons which come from the semileptonic decay of the b-quark ($b \to l\nu X$) via the weak charged current, have high momentum and high transverse momentum. Thus $b\bar{b}$ events can be separated from background by selecting high momentum and high transverse momentum leptons, where the transverse momentum is computed with respect to the nearest hadronic jet. This is illustrated in Figure 27 where the measured p and p_t distributions of electrons and muons for data and Monte Carlo are shown, together with the contributions from the signal and backgrounds. By adjusting p and p_t cuts one can achieve a $b\bar{b}$ purity better than 80%. Also one can

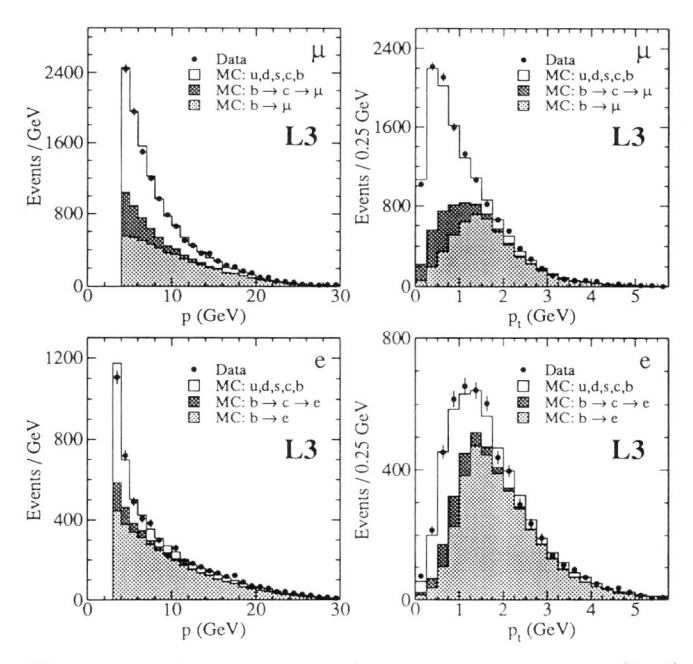

Figure 27: The measured momentum and transverse momentum distributions for inclusive lepton events from L3

use a secondary vertex to tag b-hadrons. Typically a leading b-hadron has a decay length of a few mm.

5.1 Measurement of the b-hadron semileptonic branching ratio.

Based on lepton (muon or electron) tagging, L3 has determined the semileptonic branching ratio of b-hadrons using two different methods. The first method is a so-called double tagging method. The b semileptonic branching ratio is measured from the ratio R of the accepted number of dilepton events to single lepton events. To first order, this ratio is proportional to $Br(b \to l \nu X)$ and independent of the partial width of Z decays into $b\bar{b}$. By fitting the ratio R, L3 obtained the preliminary result:

$$Br(b \to l) = 0.118 \pm 0.005(stat) \pm 0.006(sys) \qquad (16)$$

In the second method, the b semileptonic branching ratio is extracted from an event-by-event unbinned maximum likelihood fit, with the b semileptonic branching ratio as a free parameter and all other parameters fixed to their nominal values. This method uses mainly the single lepton events and has a smaller statistical error compared to the first method. By fitting to the observed p and p_t spectra for inclusive lepton events, L3 has measured (preliminary):

$$Br(b \to l) = 0.119 \pm 0.001(stat) \pm 0.006(sys) \qquad (17)$$

ALEPH has reported the first measurement of the branching ratio of $b \to \tau^- \bar{\nu}_\tau + X$. The value predicted by the Standard Model is $(2.83 \pm 0.31)\%$, and in certain two Higgs doublet models it could be as high as 10-20%. Since in the final state there are only hadrons and missing energy (from neutrinos), one needs good jet energy resolution which in ALEPH is 6.2 GeV at 91 GeV. One also needs a good e, μ veto from particle identification. Above 0.25 GeV the electron identification by the e.m. calorimeter together with dE/dx in the TPC is 90-98% efficient. Above 1 GeV the muon identification by the hadronic calorimeter and the muon chambers has an efficiency of 88-98%. The vertex detector is used to identify b quark events from the displaced vertex. The resulting efficiency is 63%, for a b purity of 80%. The result, from a fit to the missing energy distribution for $E_{miss} > 12$ GeV is:

$$Br(b \to \tau^- \bar{\nu}_\tau + X) = (4.08 \pm 0.76 \; (stat) \pm 0.60 \; (sys))\% \qquad (18)$$

5.2 Lifetime of B-Hadrons

The b-hadron lifetime can be measured with high precision at LEP. Recently, all LEP experiments have improved their measurements of the b-hadron lifetime. L3 has extracted the b-lifetime from a maximum likelihood fit to the signed impact parameter distribution of the lepton tracks from semileptonic b-decays. The impact parameter δ is defined as the distance of closest approach of the lepton track to the estimated primary event vertex (as shown in Figure 28) and carries b-hadron lifetime information. The b-hadron direction is approximated by the jet axis. In case the lepton track intersects with the jet axis in the opposite flight direction of the b-hadron, the impact parameter is taken to be negative. The lepton impact parameter distribution is fitted to the sum of the contributions of the four lepton sources, weighted by their corresponding fractions which are estimated from Monte Carlo. The results for muons and electrons are shown in Figure 29, where the

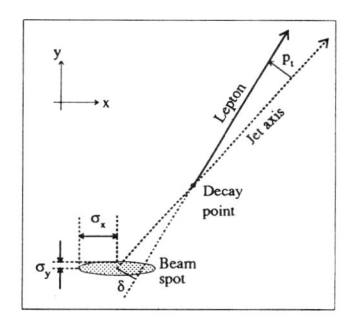

Figure 28: The definition of the impact parameter δ

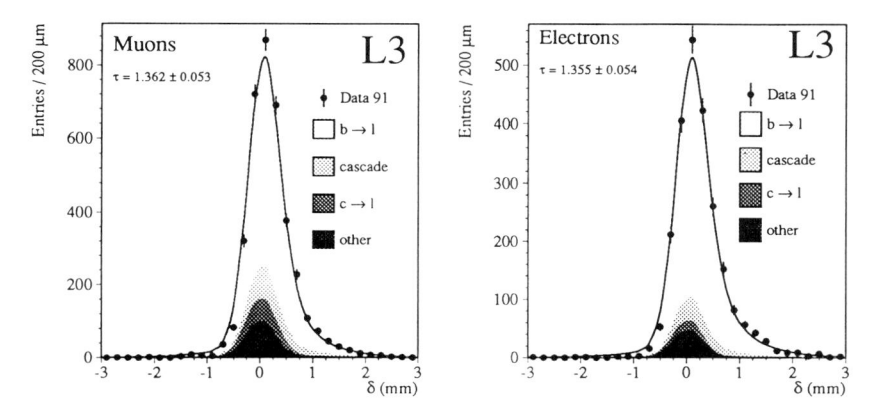

Figure 29: The impact parameter distribution of selected muon and electron tracks from the L3 data (dots) with the fitted results (solid line). The various lepton contributions are shown.

contributions of the four lepton sources are also indicated. The combined muon and electron analysis gives:

$$\tau_B = (1.358 \pm 0.038 \pm 0.058) \ ps \qquad (19)$$

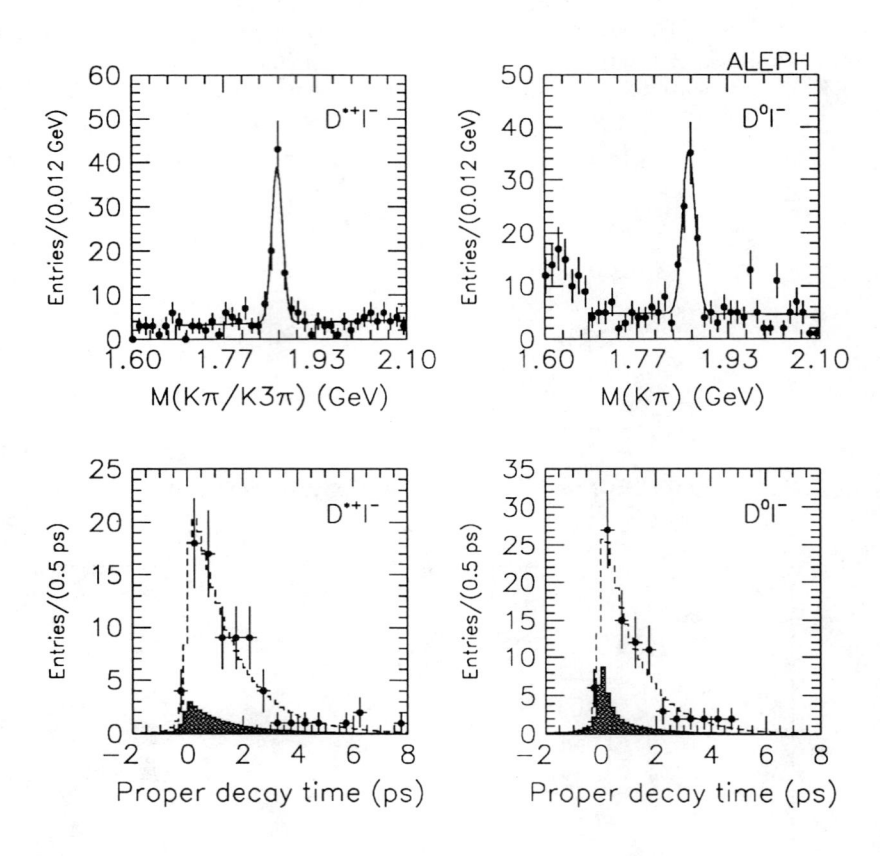

Figure 30: The observed invariant mass peaks and decay time distributions for B^0 and B^- mesons by ALEPH

ALEPH presented a beautiful measurement of the lifetimes for B^0 and B^- mesons which was performed by partial reconstruction of the decays: $\bar{B}^0 \to D^{*+}l^-\nu X$ and $B^- \to D^0 l^-\nu X$, where the D mesons are reconstructed from the $K\pi$ and $K3\pi$ final states (see Figure 30). The B decay vertex was reconstructed from the lepton and D meson track, enabling a direct measurement of the B decay length and hence the B lifetime to be made. The extracted B^0 and B^- lifetimes from B decay time distributions using a maximum likelihood method are shown in Figure 30, where the background contributions are indicated. The results are:

$$\tau(B^0) = (1.56 \pm 0.19 \pm 0.07) \ ps \qquad (20)$$

$$\tau(B^-) = (1.34 \pm 0.20 \pm 0.07) \ ps \qquad (21)$$

ALEPH also observed B_s mesons from their decay channel, $B_s \to D_s^\pm l^\mp \nu X$, where D_s was reconstructed from $\phi\pi$ and K^*K final states. The B_s lifetime was measured from the B_s flight distance using a maximum likelihood fit, as shown in Figure 31. The measured B_s lifetime is:

$$\tau(B_s) = (1.02 \pm 0.39 \pm 0.10) \ ps \qquad (22)$$

Evidence for Λ_b baryon production in Z decays has been reported by ALEPH (see

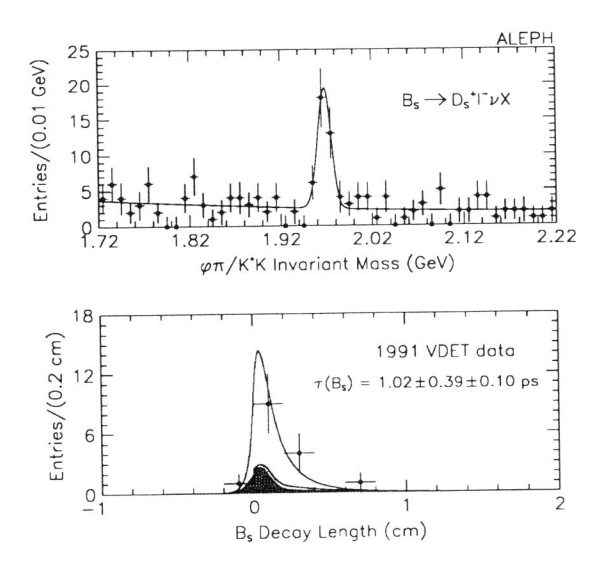

Figure 31: The observation of B_s meson in Z decays and its decay length distribution by ALEPH

Figure 32). The observed signal from the decay $\Lambda_b \to \Lambda_c^+ l^- \bar{\nu}$ followed by the decay $\Lambda_c \to \Lambda X$ consists of a Λ and a negative lepton (or $\bar{\Lambda}l^+$), with the Λ decaying to $p\pi^-$.

The Λ_b lifetime was extracted from a fit to the impact parameter distribution of the leptons in the data sample. The result is:

$$\tau(\Lambda_b) = (1.12 \pm 0.30 \pm 0.16)\ ps \tag{23}$$

Evidence for B_s production was also given by DELPHI and OPAL.

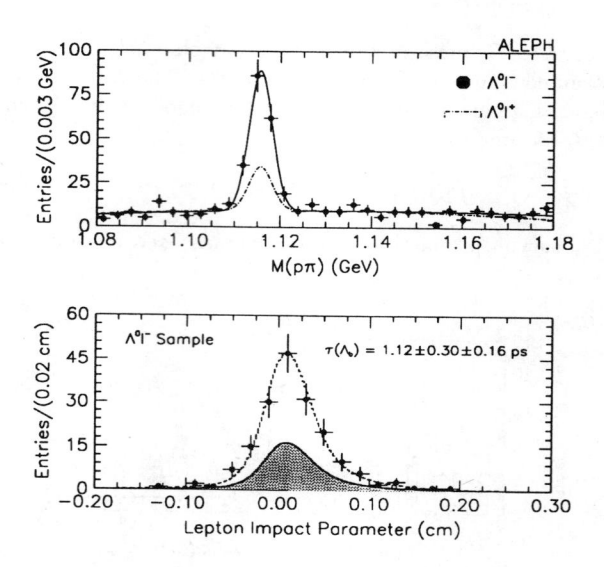

Figure 32: The observation of Λ_b mesons in Z decays and the lepton impact parameter distributions for Λl^-, together with the results of the unbinned maximum likelihood fits by ALEPH.

5.3 $|V_{cb}|$ Determination

The combined LEP measurements of the mean b-hadron lifetime, $\tau_B = 1.40 \pm 0.04\ ps$, and of the semileptonic branching ratio, $Br(b \to l) = 0.112 \pm 0.006$, are used to extract the value of the Cabbibo-Kobayashi-Maskawa matrix element $|V_{cb}|$. The semileptonic decay width of b-hadrons is related to the semileptonic branching ratio and τ_B and to the CKM matrix elements by:

$$\Gamma(b \to l) = Br(b \to l)/\tau_B = \frac{G_F^2 m_b^5}{192\pi^3}(f_c|V_{cb}|^2 + f_u|V_{ub}|^2), \tag{24}$$

where f_c and f_u account for the phase space corrections due to quarks masses and the QCD corrections. The result is shown in Figure 33 as a curve in the $|V_{cb}|$ versus $|V_{ub}|$ plane. The numerical values of various parameters used in the calculation are also shown in the figure. The combined LEP result is:

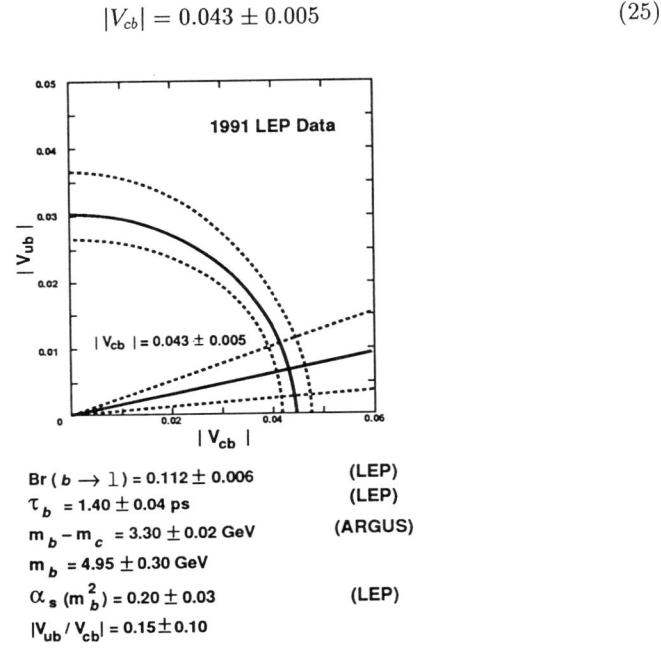

$$|V_{cb}| = 0.043 \pm 0.005 \tag{25}$$

Figure 33: Allowed region in the V_{cb} versus V_{ub} plane from measurements at LEP and by ARGUS/CLEO. The solid curves are measurements and the dashed curves correspond to the one standard deviation limits.

5.4 Forward-Backward Charge Asymmetry A_{FB}

Forward-backward asymmetry measurements for both b and c quarks are presented by OPAL. The b quarks are tagged using their semileptonic decays, and the direction is approximated by the thrust direction. By fitting the b production angle distribution of the data, which is corrected for angular acceptance and non-b background, $A_{FB}(b\bar{b})$ is directly measured. The angular distribution is shown in Figure 34 both for muon and electron data. The combined OPAL result is:

$$A_{FB}(b\bar{b}) = 0.099 \pm 0.018(stat) \pm 0.012(syst) \tag{26}$$

where a correction for $B^0\bar{B}^0$ mixing has been applied. The corresponding Standard Model prediction for $M_{top} = 132$ GeV is $A_{FB}(b\bar{b}) = 0.085$.

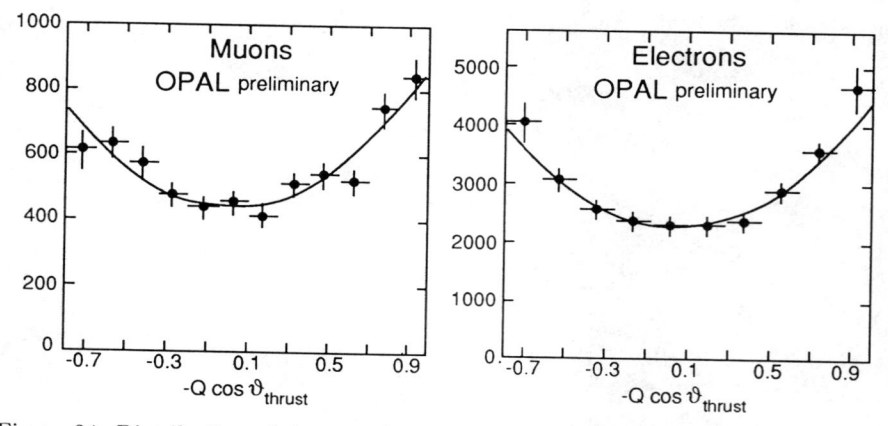

Figure 34: Distribution of the measured b production angle for the inclusive muon and electron samples of OPAL, after backgrounds and acceptance corrections. The solid curve shows the results of the fits.

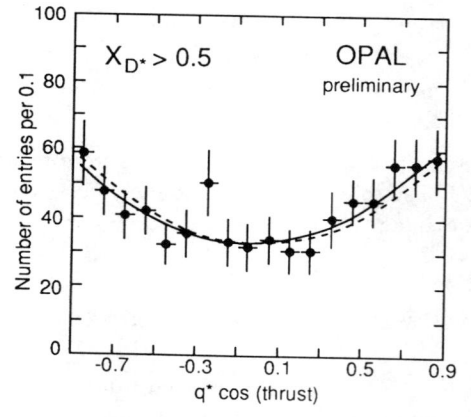

Figure 35: Distribution of measured c production angle for $D^* \to D\pi$ sample of OPAL, after background and acceptance corrections. The solid curve shows the fitted results, and the dashed line is the expected distribution with $A_{FB}(c\bar{c}) = 0.054$

By using $D^* \to D\pi$ decays to tag c-quarks (this gives smaller systematic errors than by tagging c-quarks with leptons), OPAL obtained the following result:

$$A_{FB}(c\bar{c}) = 0.064 \pm 0.049(stat) \pm 0.022(syst) \tag{27}$$

The data and fitted result are shown in Figure 35. The corresponding Standard Model prediction is $A_{FB}(c\bar{c}) = 0.054$ for $M_{top} = 132$ GeV.

A similar analysis was performed by L3 with high p_t ($> 1\ GeV$) lepton events and gave the observed $b\bar{b}$ forward-backward asymmetry, i.e, without correction for $B^0\bar{B}^0$ mixing:

$$A_{FB}^{obs}(b\bar{b}) = 0.062 \pm 0.013\ (stat) \tag{28}$$

The angular distribution is shown in Figure 36 together with the fit results. In order

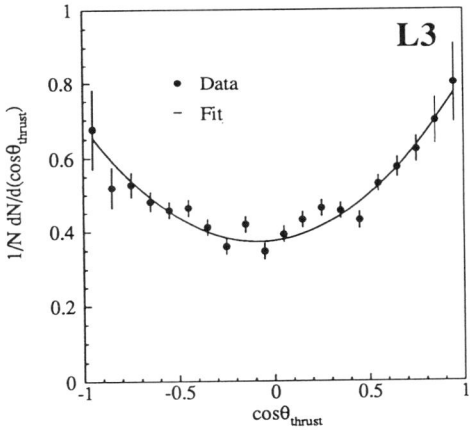

Figure 36: Distribution of the measured b production angle from high p_t inclusive lepton events obtained by L3, after background and acceptance corrections. The solid curve show the fit result.

to use the full statistics of all the p and p_t lepton events and measure $A_{FB}(c\bar{c})$, L3 has performed an event by event maximum likelihood fit in the p-p_t plane to determine $A_{FB}(b\bar{b})$ and $A_{FB}(c\bar{c})$. The observed $b\bar{b}$ forward-backward asymmetry is $A_{FB}^{obs}(b\bar{b}) = 0.066 \pm 0.011\ (stat)$ in good agreement with the previous direct measurement. After correcting $A_{FB}^{obs}(b\bar{b})$ for the effect of $B^0\bar{B}^0$ oscillation, the final results are:

$$A_{FB}(c\bar{c}) = 0.083 \pm 0.038\ (stat) \pm 0.027\ (sys) \tag{29}$$

$$A_{FB}(b\bar{b}) = 0.086 \pm 0.015\ (stat) \pm 0.007\ (sys) \tag{30}$$

Figure 37 shows the measured $\sqrt{s}$-dependent $A_{FB}(b\bar{b})$ of L3 compared to the Standard Model expectations with $\sin^2\theta_W = 0.2336$. The Standard Model predictions are in good agreement with the data.

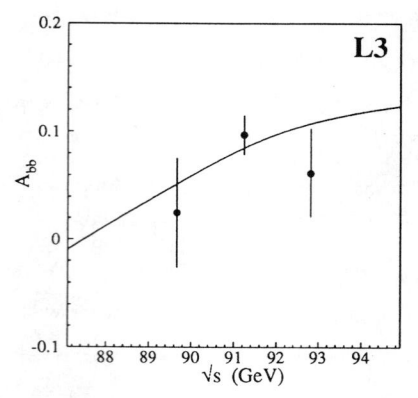

Figure 37: Comparison between the measured $A_{b\bar{b}}$ and the Standard Model predictions with $\sin^2\bar{\theta}_W = 0.2336$ at different center of mass energies around the Z mass.

5.5 Measurement of $B^0 - \bar{B}^0$ Mixing

Higher order flavor changing weak interactions induce an oscillation between B^0 and $\bar{B}^0$. The experimental signature of mixing is the observation of like sign dileptons from the decays $B^0 \to l^+$ and $\bar{B}^0 \to B^0 \to l^+$. The amount of $B^0 - \bar{B}^0$ mixing is measured by determining the mixing parameter:

$$\chi_B = \frac{Br(b \to \bar{B}^0 \to B^0 \to l^+ X)}{Br(b \to b - hadron \to l^\pm X)} \quad (31)$$

where equal semileptonic branching ratios for all b-hadrons are assumed. Measurements of χ_B around the Z peak are sensitive to both B_d^0 and B_s^0 mixing,

$$\chi_B = f_d \chi_d + f_s \chi_s \quad (32)$$

where χ_d and χ_s are mixing parameters and f_d and f_s are the production fractions of B_d^0 and B_s^0 mesons. The L3 data for the measured minimum p_t spectra of like-sign and opposite sign dileptons are shown in Figure 38 together with Monte Carlo expectations. The mixing parameter χ_B is determined to be:

$$\chi_B = 0.121 \pm 0.017\,(stat.) \pm 0.006\,(sys.) \quad (33)$$

The systematic effects are evaluated by varying parameters with one standard deviation or more of their known or estimated errors. Figure 39 shows the dependence of χ_s on $\gamma_s = f_s/f_d$, up to the SU(3) flavor symmetry limit $\gamma_s = 1$. The one σ limits, which include a 50% uncertainty on the b-baryon production fraction (f_B), are shown in the figure also. In the analysis, f_B is assumed to be 0.08 ± 0.04. The value of χ_s is consistent with maximal mixing for any reasonable choice of f_d, f_s and f_B, as expected from the CKM matrix and χ_d measurement.

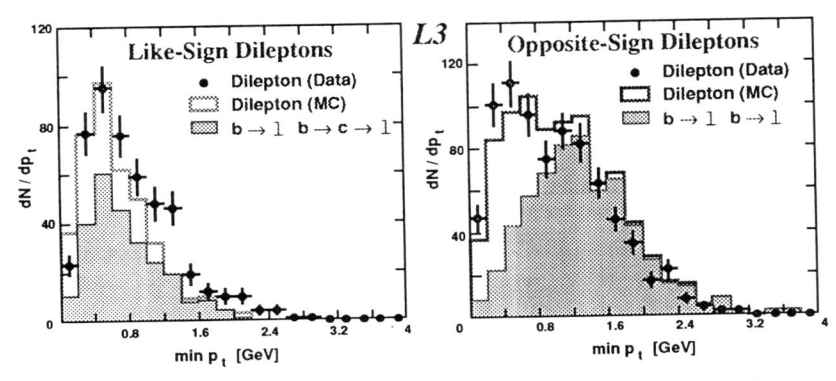

Figure 38: The minimum transverse momentum of the two leptons in opposite hemispheres for like-sign and unlike-sign dileptons compared to the Monte Carlo expectations with no mixing. The excess of like-sign data events, and the shortage of unlike-sign data events are evidence for mixing.

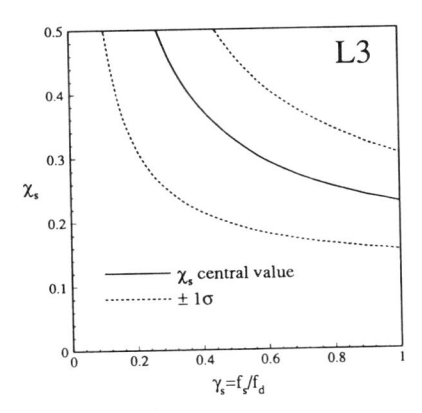

Figure 39: The B-mixing parameter of χ_s versus $\gamma_s = f_s/f_d$ for the L3 measurement of χ_B (solid curve). The dashed curves correspond to the one standard deviation limits. Here χ_d is constrained by measurements of ARGUS/CLEO.

5.6 Double tagging

OPAL made a measurement of $\Gamma_{b\bar{b}}/\Gamma_{had}$ using both the semileptonic decays of b-hadrons and by exploiting the long decay distances of b hadrons compared to hadrons containing only lighter quarks. In the analysis, events are divided into two hemisphere and are tagged in the following five categories:

- one hemisphere with a secondary vertex tag
- both hemispheres with a secondary vertex tag
- one hemisphere with a lepton tag
- both hemispheres with a lepton tag
- one hemisphere with a lepton tag and the other with a secondary vertex tag

Figure 40 illustrates an example of the tagging topologies. The measured $\Gamma_{b\bar{b}}/\Gamma_{had}$ is

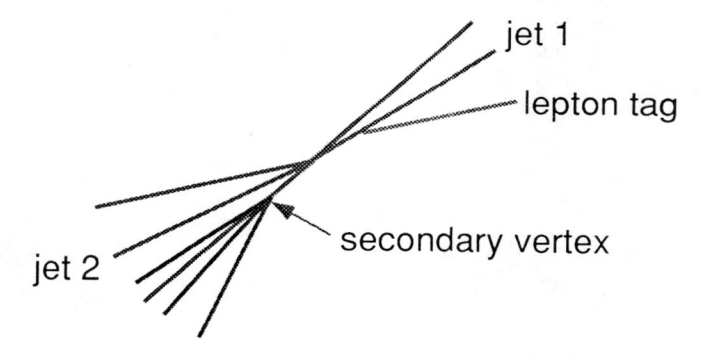

Figure 40: The event topology, where one jet contains a lepton and the other jet has a secondary vertex

insensitive to Monte Carlo modeling, such as the b fragmentation, branching ratio of the b semileptonic decay and the b-hadron lifetime. Hence the measurement has a small systematic error. The preliminary result from the double tagging method is:

$$\frac{\Gamma_{b\bar{b}}}{\Gamma_{had}} = 0.218 \pm 0.013(stat) \pm 0.010(sys) \qquad (34)$$

The expected value of $\Gamma_{b\bar{b}}/\Gamma_{had}$ in the Standard Model is 0.217.

6 τ Physics

In the past few years, all LEP experiments have made great efforts to measure the τ lepton properties. $Z \to \tau^+\tau^-$ events are selected by exploiting the characteristic low multiplicities, missing energy and only odd number of charged particles from a τ decay. In the electroweak interaction section, the partial width of Z decays into τ pair and the forward-backward charge asymmetry have been presented. In this section, the τ decay properties which are measured by the LEP experiments will be shown.

6.1 Branching ratios of τ Decays

The OPAL $\tau\tau$ sample consists of 12707 events with an estimated background of 1.9%. The inclusive and exclusive branching ratios of the τ lepton decays are measured from this data sample. The inclusive branching fractions of the τ lepton to one, three and five charged particles are determined to be:

$$\begin{aligned} B_1 &= (84.48 \pm 0.27 \ (stat) \pm 0.23 \ (sys))\% \\ B_3 &= (15.26 \pm 0.26 \ (stat) \pm 0.22 \ (sys))\% \\ B_5 &= (\ 0.26 \pm 0.06 \ (stat) \pm 0.05 \ (sys))\% \end{aligned} \quad (35)$$

$B_1 + B_3 + B_5$ is constrained to equal one in the fit. There is a strong anti-correlation between B_1 and B_3, while B_5 is relatively independent of B_1 and B_3. The measurements are in agreement with other LEP results. Electrons, muons and charged ρ's, π's from τ 1-prong decays are identified. Background fractions and tagging efficiencies are estimated from Monte Carlo. After subtracting the background and taking into account the efficiency corrections, OPAL extracts the exclusive branching ratios of τ lepton decays:

$$\begin{aligned} Br(\tau \to \mu\nu_\mu\nu_\tau) &= (16.8 \pm 0.3 \ (stat) \pm 0.3 \ (sys))\% \\ Br(\tau \to e\nu_e\nu_\tau) &= (17.5 \pm 0.3 \ (stat) \pm 0.3 \ (sys))\% \\ Br(\tau \to \rho\nu_\tau) &= (23.8 \pm 0.6 \ (stat) \pm 0.7 \ (sys))\% \\ Br(\tau \to \pi\nu_\tau) &= (12.2 \pm 0.3 \ (stat) \pm 0.4 \ (sys))\% \end{aligned} \quad (36)$$

6.2 τ Lifetime

In the framework of the Standard Model, there is a well-defined relation between the lifetime of the τ lepton, its exclusive electronic and muonic branching fractions and its mass. The theoretical expectation is:

$$\tau_\tau = \tau_\mu \left(\frac{G_\mu}{G_\tau}\right)^2 \left(\frac{M_\mu}{M_\tau}\right)^5 Br(\tau \to e\nu_e\nu_\tau) \tag{37}$$

where G_μ and G_τ are the Fermi coupling constants of μ and τ determined from μ and τ decays. Precise measurements of the lifetime of the τ lepton, $Br(\tau \to e\nu_e\nu_\tau)$ and its mass give a stringent test of the μ-τ universality.

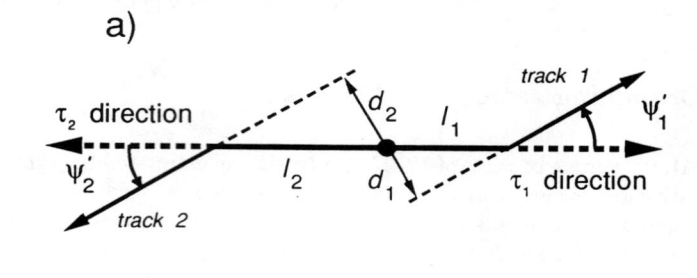

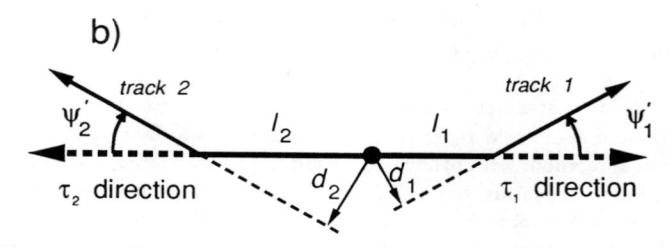

Figure 41: The topology where both τ's decay into single charged particles and the DCA measurement (d_1, d_2).

New results on the τ lifetime have been reported by ALEPH, DELPHI and OPAL. ALEPH used three different techniques to measure the τ lifetime, two for one prong decays and one for three prong decays. Figure 41 shows the event topologies where both τ's decay into a single charged particle. The τ lifetime is measured from one-prong τ decay events by two independent methods. First is the measurement using the "sum of impact parameters (δ)" distribution shown in Figure 42, where 2479 events are used. The fitted result is:

$$\tau_\tau = (288.3 \pm 7.5 \pm 5.1)\, fs \tag{38}$$

The second measurement of the τ lifetime comes from the "difference of impact pa-

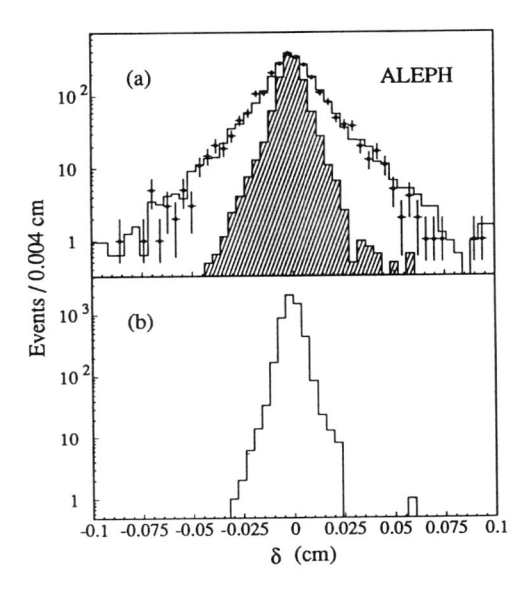

Figure 42: The sum of impact parameters, δ, distribution from ALEPH for (a) τ data (dots) and τ Monte Carlo (solid line). The hatched histogram from zero-lifetime τ Monte Carlo. (b) dimuon data from Z decays.

rameters (Y)" as shown in Figure 43. Using 3205 events, it yields the result:

$$\tau_\tau = (310.5 \pm 13.0 \pm 3.5)\, fs \tag{39}$$

The ALEPH collaboration has also collected 909 three-prong τ events, where the decay vertices are reconstructed. Together with the beam position and its size, the τ flight distance is determined. By fitting the distribution of the τ decay length (see Figure 44), the τ lifetime is determined to be:

$$\tau_\tau = (298.0 \pm 10.6 \pm 4.5)\, fs \tag{40}$$

Combining these three ALEPH results and their 1990 measurements, one gets:

$$\tau_\tau = (294.7 \pm 5.4 \pm 3.0)\, fs \tag{41}$$

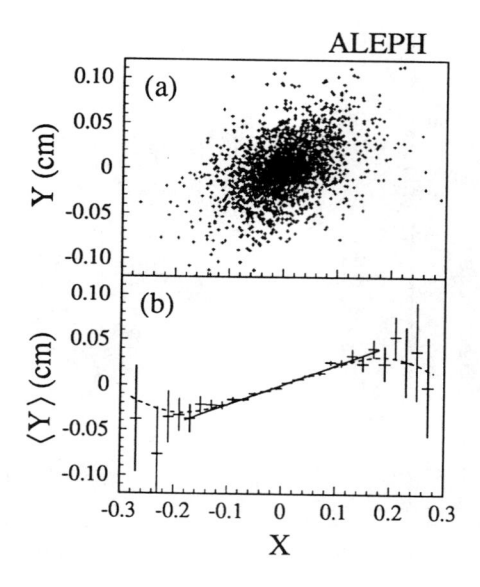

Figure 43: The measurement of the τ lifetime from the difference of impact parameters Y as a function of acoplanarity X by ALEPH. (a) Scatter plots of accepted events (b) The data distribution and fitted result (solid curve). The dashed curve shows the expected distribution from Monte Carlo.

By comparing τ_τ and τ_μ ALEPH has tested μ-τ universality, where $M_\tau = 1777.1 \pm 0.5$ MeV and $B_{\tau e} = (17.99 \pm 0.19)\%$ are used. The measured ratio of coupling constants of the weak charged current is:

$$\frac{G_\tau}{G_\mu} = 0.998 \pm 0.012 \tag{42}$$

in agreement with μ-τ universality.

OPAL also measured the τ lifetime by fitting the impact parameter distributions of one-prong τ decays, and the flight distance distributions from three-prong τ decays. The two statistically independent analyses give results:

$$\begin{aligned}\tau_\tau(one-prong) &= (296.4 \pm 7.1\ (stat) \pm 3.8\ (sys))\ fs \\ \tau_\tau(three-prong) &= (286.3 \pm 7.4\ (stat) \pm 5.2\ (sys))\ fs\end{aligned} \tag{43}$$

Figure 45 shows the measurement from the decay length of three-prong τ decays.

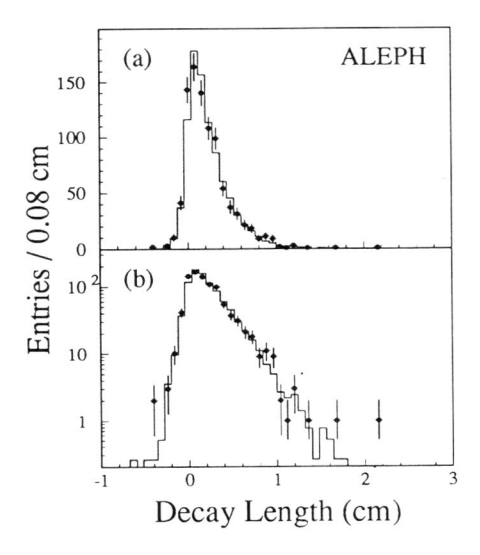

Figure 44: The τ decay length distributions for data (dots) and Monte Carlo (solid line) from ALEPH (a) linear scale, (b) log scale. The generated τ lifetime is 304 fs.

Combining both OPAL measurements, one obtains:

$$\tau_\tau = (291.9 \pm 5.1\ (stat) \pm 3.1\ (sys))\ fs \qquad (44)$$

together with the OPAL measurement of the τ electronic branching ratio and the τ mass determined by BES/ARGUS collaborations, one finds:

$$\frac{G_\tau}{G_\mu} = 0.985 \pm 0.017 \qquad (45)$$

The result is shown in Figure 45 and is consistent with the μ-τ universality.

The DELPHI result from fitting the impact parameter distributions is presented (see Figure 46), the determined τ lifetime is:

$$\tau_\tau = (294 \pm 9(stat) \pm 4(sys))\ fs \qquad (46)$$

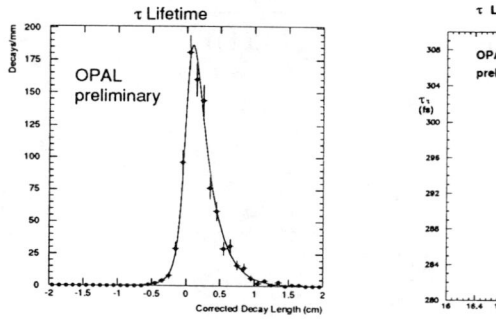

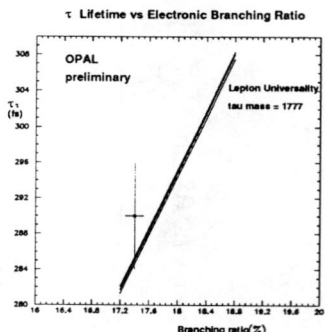

Figure 45: The distribution of the τ decay length for data (dots) and fitted curve (solid line) from OPAL. The right plot shows the measured values of τ lifetime and $\tau \to e$ branching ratio and the predictions with the assumption of μ-τ universality.

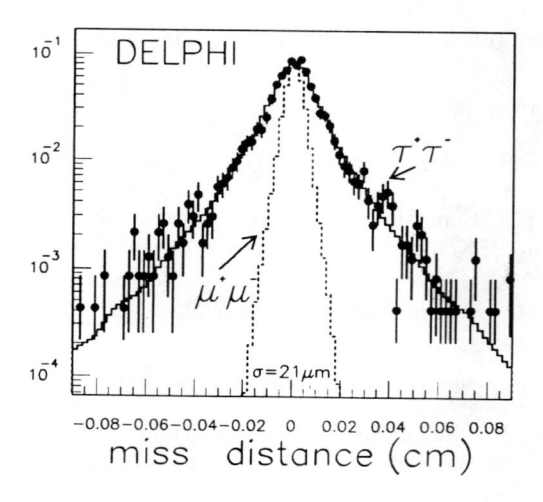

Figure 46: The distribution of the impact parameter for data (dots) from the DELPHI experiment. Also the fitted curve (solid line) is shown, which yields $\tau_\tau = 294 \pm 9(stat) \pm 4(sys)$ fs. The dashed line is from dimuon data.

6.3 τ Polarization

The average polarization of the τ lepton is a parity violating observable defined as:

$$P_\tau = \frac{\sigma(h=+1) - \sigma(h=-1)}{\sigma(h=+1) + \sigma(h=-1)} \tag{47}$$

where σ is the cross section and h is helicity. In the improved Born approximation, the τ-polarization on the peak of the Z can be expressed in terms of τ couplings to the Z:

$$P_\tau = -A_\tau = -\frac{2\bar{g}_V^\tau \cdot \bar{g}_A^\tau}{(\bar{g}_V^\tau)^2 + (\bar{g}_A^\tau)^2} \tag{48}$$

In the Standard Model,

$$P_\tau \simeq -2(1 - 4\sin^2\theta_{\text{eff}}) \tag{49}$$

Hence a measurement of P_τ can determine not only $\sin^2\theta_{\text{eff}}$, but also the relative sign of the Z vector and axial vector coupling constants.

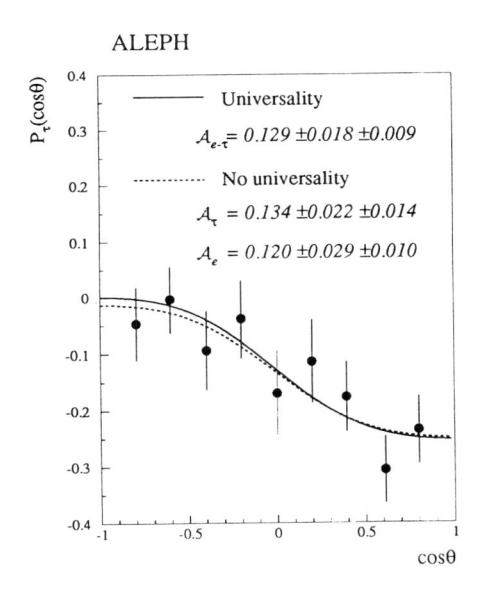

Figure 47: The polar angle dependence of the τ polarization measurement by ALEPH, where A_e and A_τ can be obtained independently.

Recently, ALEPH has performed a preliminary measurement of the polar angle dependence of the τ polarization. The polar angle dependent τ polarization can be

expressed as:
$$P_\tau(cos\theta) \simeq -A_\tau(1 + \cos^2\theta) - 2A_e \cos\theta \qquad (50)$$
where
$$A_e = \frac{2g_V^e g_A^e}{(g_V^e)^2 + (g_A^e)^2} \qquad (51)$$

Figure 47 shows the results of the ALEPH measurement for both electron and τ asymmetries. The data are fitted both with and without the e-τ universality assumption. The results are consistent with each other, thus the measurements support the e-τ universality hypothesis. Assuming e-τ universality, the leptonic asymmetry is measured to be:
$$A_{e\tau} = 0.129 \pm 0.018 \; (stat) \pm 0.009 \; (sys) \qquad (52)$$

L3 and OPAL have determined the average τ polarization from a fit to the energy spectrum for the τ decay modes $\tau \to e(\mu)\nu_{e,\mu}\nu_\tau$, $\tau \to \pi\nu_\tau$ and to the distributions in the two angles for modes $\tau \to \rho(a_1)\nu_\tau$. OPAL results are listed in Table 7. From the polarization data, OPAL finds:
$$\sin^2\theta_{\text{eff}} = 0.2356 \pm 0.0058 \qquad (53)$$

Table 7: The measured τ polarization results from OPAL

Decay Channel	Polarization
$\mu^-\bar{\nu}_\mu\nu_\tau$	$-0.18 \pm 0.08 \pm 0.06$
$e^-\bar{\nu}_e\nu_\tau$	$0.05 \pm 0.07 \pm 0.06$
$\rho^-\nu_\tau$	$-0.18 \pm 0.06 \pm 0.04$
$\pi^-\nu_\tau$	$-0.09 \pm 0.06 \pm 0.05$
Average	-0.115 ± 0.046

The L3 τ-polarization results are shown in Figure 48 and summarized in Table 8, where the first error is statistical and the second one is systematic. The weighted mean value of the τ polarization over all five decay modes gives:
$$P_\tau = -0.132 \pm 0.026 \; (stat.) \pm 0.021 \; (sys.) \qquad (54)$$
Extraction of the electroweak parameters yields:
$$\frac{\bar{g}_V^\tau}{\bar{g}_A^\tau} = +0.069 \pm 0.017 \qquad (55)$$
as the ratio of the effective τ coupling to the weak neutral current, and the electroweak mixing angle is determined to be:
$$\sin^2\theta_{\text{eff}} = 0.2326 \pm 0.0043 \qquad (56)$$

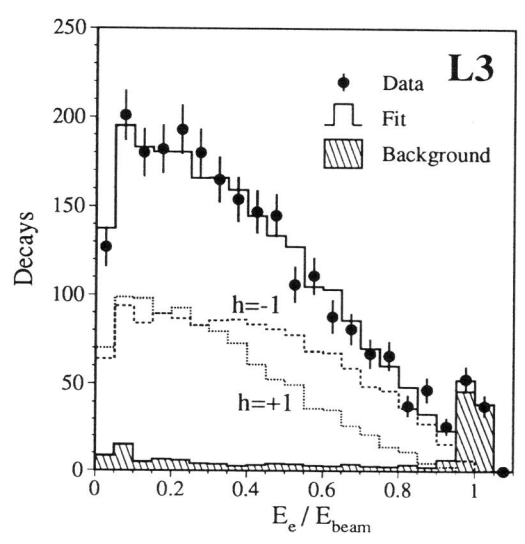

Figure 48: The L3 measurement of the electron energy spectrum for $\tau^\pm \to e^\pm \nu_e \nu_\tau$ and the τ polarization.

Table 8: The L3 τ-polarization results

Decay Channel	Polarization
$e^- \bar{\nu}_e \nu_\tau$	$-0.127 \pm 0.097 \pm 0.062$
$\mu^- \bar{\nu}_\mu \nu_\tau$	$-0.020 \pm 0.101 \pm 0.055$
$\pi^-(K^-)\nu_\tau$	$-0.148 \pm 0.046 \pm 0.033$
$\rho^- \nu_\tau$	$-0.152 \pm 0.035 \pm 0.029$
$a_1 \nu_\tau$	$0.105 \pm 0.164 \pm 0.093$
all	$-0.132 \pm 0.026 \pm 0.021$

7 $\sin^2 \theta_{\text{eff}}$ from LEP

The effective electroweak mixing angle can be measured using several independent methods, such as,

- leptonic cross sections and asymmetries;
- $b\bar{b}$ forward-backward asymmetry;
- τ polarization;

- forward-backward asymmetry of τ polarization;
- forward-backward quark charge asymmetry;
- M_Z, Γ_l relation.

Figure 49 summarizes the $\sin^2\theta_{\text{eff}}$ measurements of the four LEP experiments and shows the excellent agreement between the independent determinations of $\sin^2\theta_{\text{eff}}$. All measurements are consistent with the Standard Model prediction.

$\sin^2\theta_{\text{eff}}$ from LEP

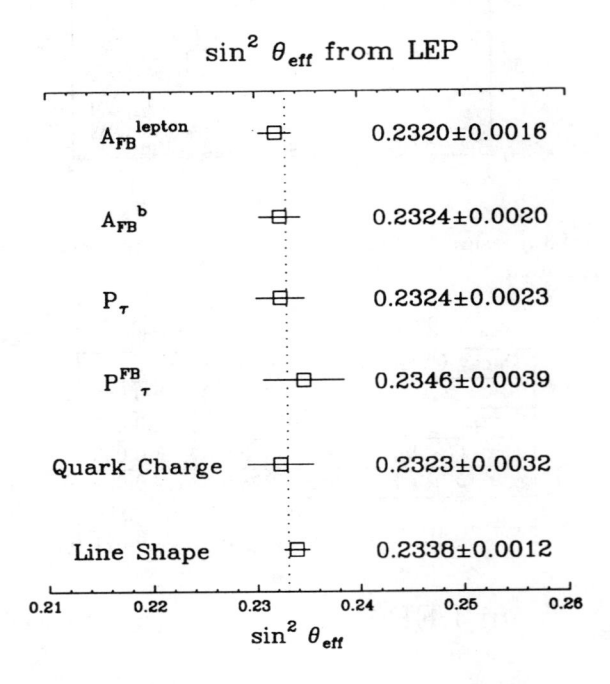

A_{FB}^{lepton}		0.2320 ± 0.0016
A_{FB}^{b}		0.2324 ± 0.0020
P_τ		0.2324 ± 0.0023
P_τ^{FB}		0.2346 ± 0.0039
Quark Charge		0.2323 ± 0.0032
Line Shape		0.2338 ± 0.0012

Figure 49: Average $\sin^2\theta_{\text{eff}}$ value from various measurements by LEP experiments

8 New Particles

8.1 Higgs Search

If the Higgs boson is lighter than the Z, the Higgs boson will be produced at LEP, predominantly through the bremsstrahlung process:

$$e^+e^- \to Z \to H^0 + Z^* \to H^0 + f\bar{f} \qquad (57)$$

The four LEP experiments have searched for the Higgs boson up to $M_{H^0} \approx 60$ GeV. OPAL reported a lower limit on the mass of the Higgs bosons of 54 GeV. The most recent L3 lower mass limit for the Higgs is:

$$M_{H^0} > 57.7 \text{ GeV} \qquad (58)$$

at the 95% confidence level. The total number of expected events for L3 from all channels is shown in Figure 50 together with the individual channel contributions.

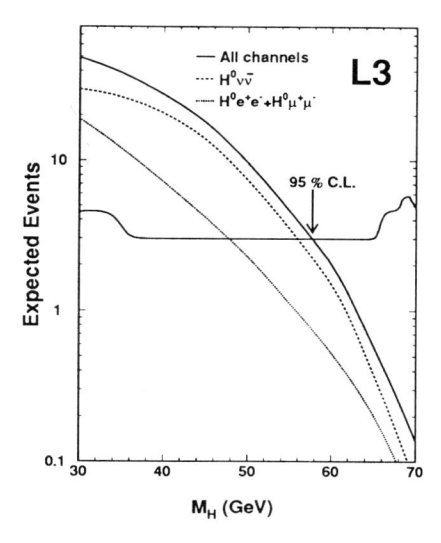

Figure 50: The expected number of Higgs events as a function of the Higgs mass in different channels. The experimental lower limit with 95% CL is indicated, it is 57.7 GeV.

$M_{\mu\mu} = 20.0 \pm 0.4$ GeV

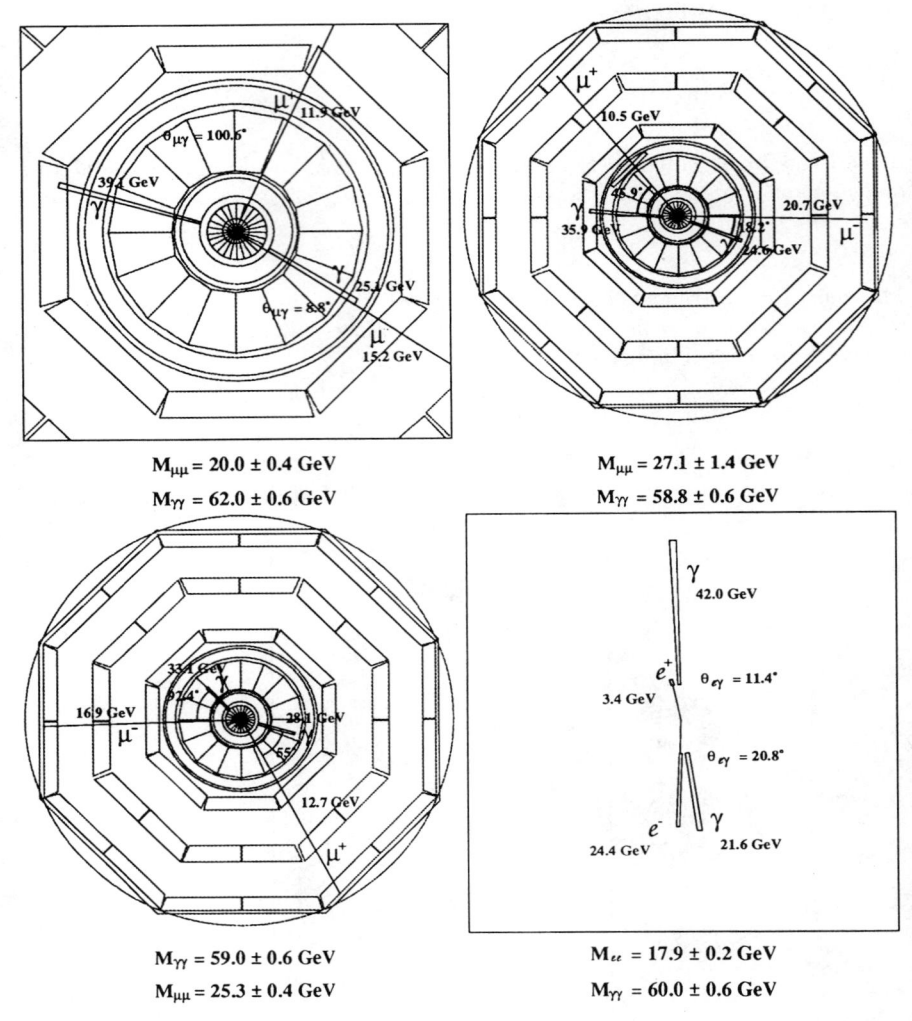

$M_{\gamma\gamma} = 62.0 \pm 0.6$ GeV

$M_{\mu\mu} = 27.1 \pm 1.4$ GeV

$M_{\gamma\gamma} = 58.8 \pm 0.6$ GeV

$M_{\gamma\gamma} = 59.0 \pm 0.6$ GeV

$M_{\mu\mu} = 25.3 \pm 0.4$ GeV

$M_{ee} = 17.9 \pm 0.2$ GeV

$M_{\gamma\gamma} = 60.0 \pm 0.6$ GeV

Figure 51: Four observed $ll\gamma\gamma$ events by L3, where the photon pair has a high invariant mass. Their characteristics and invariant mass are indicated in the pictures.

8.2 High Mass Photon Pairs in $l^+l^-\gamma\gamma$ Events at LEP

The process $e^+e^- \to l^+l^-(n\gamma)$ is well understood by QED and can be accurately predicted. Therefore, from an analysis of $l^+l^-(n\gamma)$ events one can test QED. Furthermore an excess in $l^+l^-(n\gamma)$ events would imply new physics. L3 has observed four $l^+l^-\gamma\gamma(l = e, \mu)$ events with an invariant mass of the two isolated photons close to 60 GeV in a data sample corresponding to a total integrated luminosity of 40 pb^{-1} or 1,600,000 produced Z's. The event pictures are shown in Figure 51. The relevant numerical data are also given in the figure. These events were selected from a sample of multiphoton events and, for events with more than two photons, the highest invariant mass of any combination was taken as $M_{\gamma\gamma}$. Figure 52 shows the two dimensional plot of $M_{\gamma\gamma}$ versus M_{ll}. The four events clustering around 60 GeV are well separated from the others. The energy distribution of the most energetic photon and the sec-

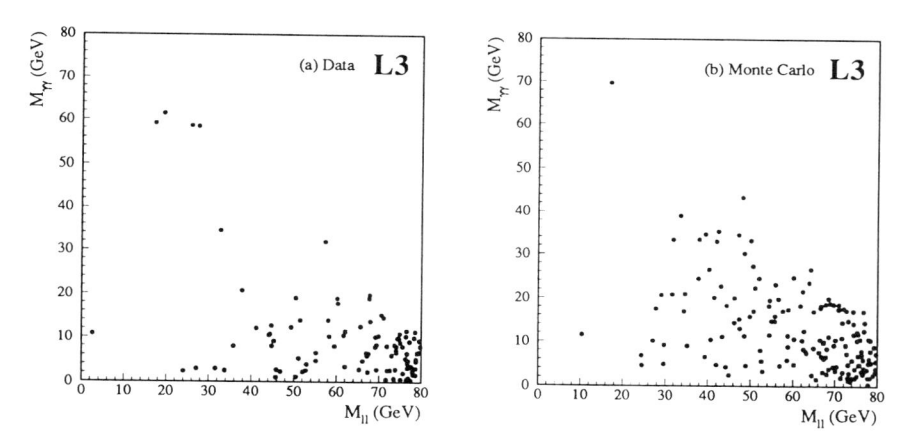

Figure 52: The scatter plot of $M_{\gamma\gamma}$ versus M_{ll} from L3 (a) data, and (b) QED Monte Carlo

ond most energetic photon for events with one or more photons in the final state are compared with a QED Monte Carlo in Figure 53 (a) and (b). The Monte Carlo is in good agreement with the data. Figure 54 shows the $M_{\gamma\gamma}$ distribution compared with QED which of course does not predict clustering of $M_{\gamma\gamma}$ around 60 GeV. L3 determines the probability for observing four or more events around 60 GeV from a QED fluctuation. The probability for observing four or more clustered events, all with $M_{\gamma\gamma} > 50$ GeV, is found to be $\mathcal{O}(10^{-2})$. The photon pairs could come from the decay of a massive particle, although one can not rule out a QED fluctuation. In the near future with more data one can find out the origin of these events. A similar search has been done in the hadronic data sample with an integrated luminosity of 13 pb^{-1} and in the $e^+e^- \to \nu\bar{\nu}\gamma\gamma$ data sample with all collected events. No isolated photon pair with $M_{\gamma\gamma} > 40$ GeV has been observed in the data.

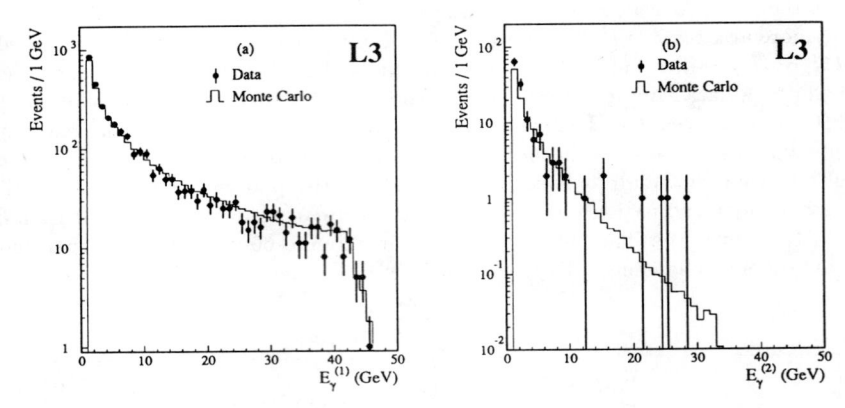

Figure 53: The energy distribution of (a) the most energetic, (b) the second most energetic photon from $Z \to l^+l^-$ ($l = e, \mu$) from L3. Data and MC show good agreement.

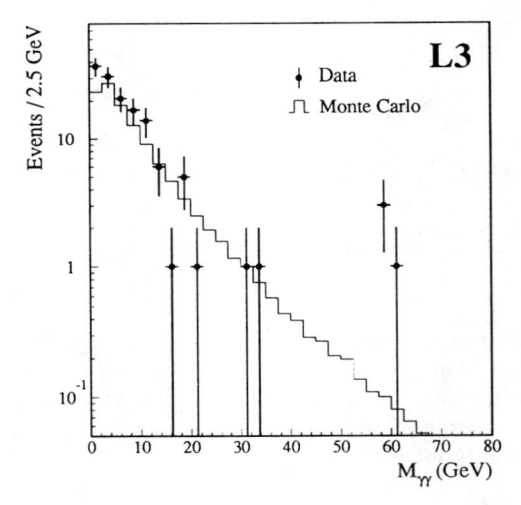

Figure 54: The measured two photon invariant mass spectrum from L3 compared with the QED Monte Carlo expectations.

DELPHI also observed two such events with $M_{\gamma\gamma}$ close to 60 GeV. The event pictures are shown in Figure 55. The invariant mass of the photon pair is $M_{\gamma\gamma} = 58.4\pm$

1.0 GeV and $M_{\gamma\gamma} = 59.0 \pm 0.7$ GeV for the two observed events. The corresponding $M_{\gamma\gamma}$ distribution is given in Figure 56 compared with the Monte Carlo expectation, where the different lepton channel contributions are indicated.

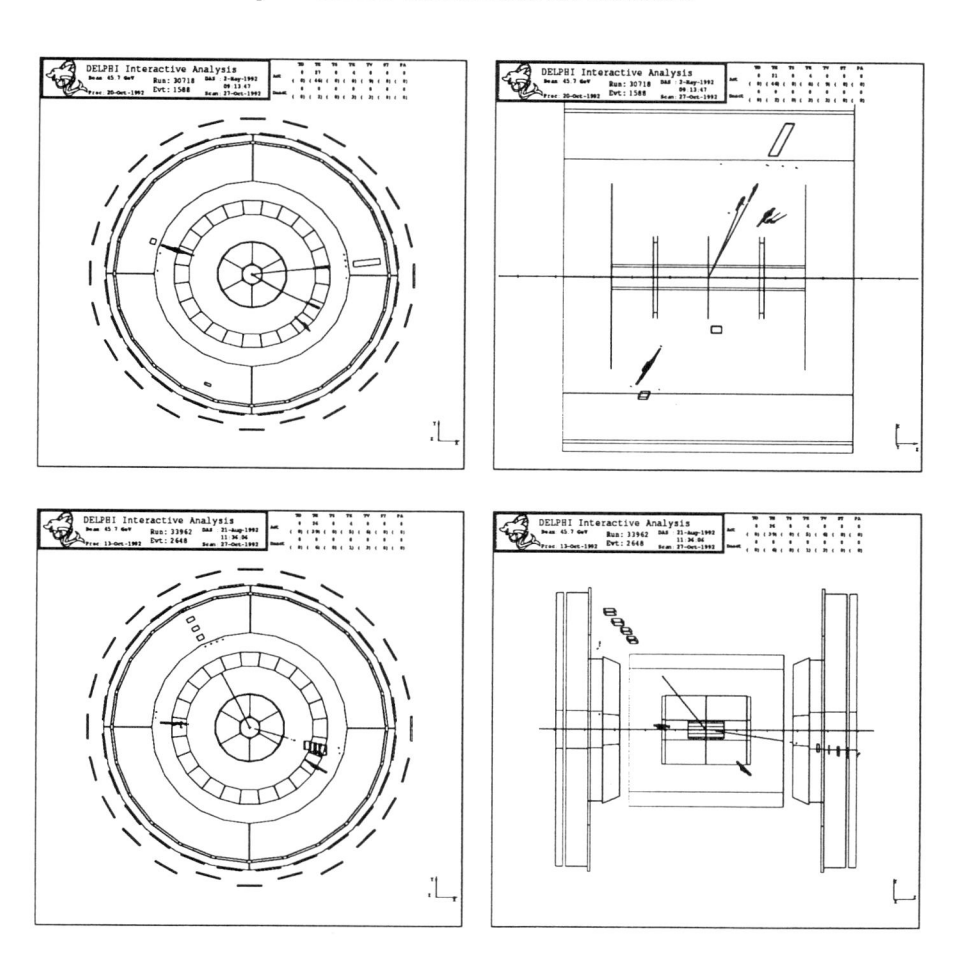

Figure 55: Two observed $ll\gamma\gamma$ events by DELPHI, in which the photon pair has a high invariant mass. The upper pictures show the x-y and x-z views of the first event, having $M_{\gamma\gamma} = 58.4 \pm 1.0$ GeV. The lower pictures show the x-y and y-z views of the second event, having $M_{\gamma\gamma} = 59.0 \pm 0.7$ GeV.

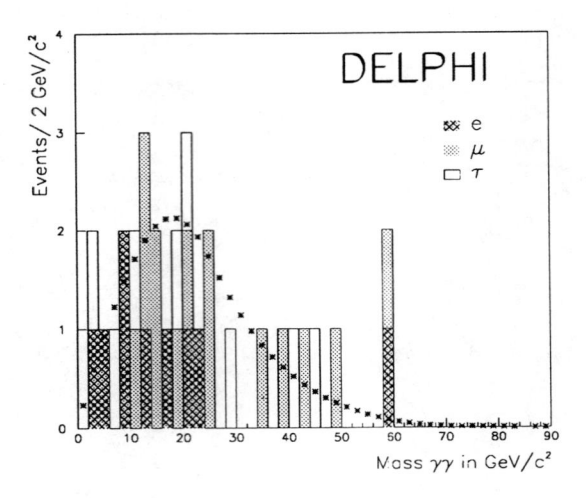

Figure 56: The measured spectrum of two photon invariant mass by DELPHI compared with Monte Carlo expectation, where the different channel contributions in the data are indicated.

9 Future plans

LEP will be running in the Z mass region in 1993 and 1994 to allow each experimental group to collect a total of 4×10^6 events. In the years 1995, 1996 and 1997 LEP will be running at energies above the W^+W^- threshold for a total of 500 pb^{-1} per LEP collaboration. The foreseen increase of the LEP energy above the W^+W^- threshold will open up a new field of physics. For example, if $\sqrt{s}$ would be 200 GeV we shall be able to reach $M_{H^0} \approx 100$ GeV. We shall be able to test the corner stone of the Electroweak theory: gauge cancellations. As seen from Figure 58 the cross sections of W^+W^- production as a function of $\sqrt{s}$ are quite sensitive to the detailed contributions of each of the Feynman diagrams. The huge destructive interference of the cross sections coming from the ZWW vertex is characteristic of the Standard Model. The triple boson coupling constant g_{ZWW} can be obtained by measuring the

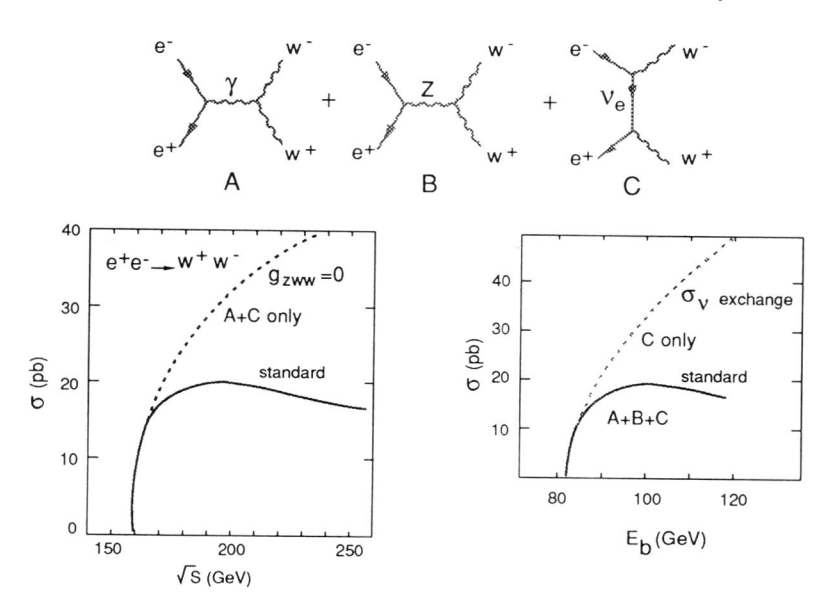

Figure 57: The lowest order Feynman diagrams contributing to W^+W^- production, and the expected gauge cancellations effect on the W^+W^- production cross-section.

angular distribution of W^+W^- production, as illustrated in Figure 59. 1000 events of the type $e^+e^- \rightarrow W^+W^- \rightarrow \mu^{\pm}\nu X$ will be collected over 3 years of running with an integrated luminosity of 500 pb^{-1}. In the backward region ($133° < \theta_\mu < 160°$) the Standard Model predicts 41 events, the absence of triple boson coupling will increase this number to 125.

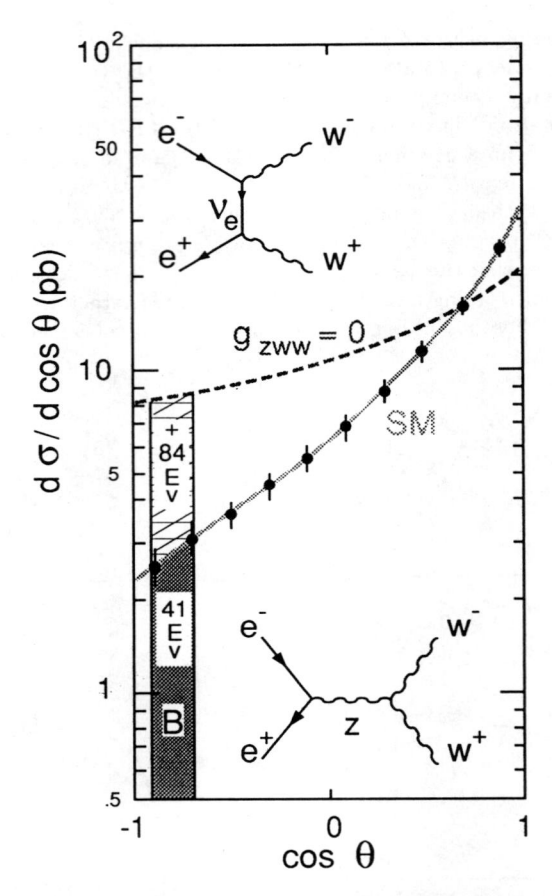

Figure 58: Angular distribution μ for both the Standard Model (solid line) and the abelian model (dashed line). The triple boson coupling constant g_{ZWW} can be measured from $e^+e^- \to W^+W^- \to \mu^\pm \nu X$

10 Estimation of M_{top} from the LEP data

In order to constrain the top quark mass, a simultaneous fit to the LEP data in the framework of the Standard Model has been performed, using the following measurements:

- Cross sections $\sigma_{had}, \sigma_{ee}, \sigma_{\mu\mu}$ and $\sigma_{\tau\tau}$ as function of $\sqrt{s}$.
- Three lepton asymmetries: A_{FB}^e, A_{FB}^μ and A_{FB}^τ as function of $\sqrt{s}$
- Tau polarization
- Forward-backward tau polarization asymmetry
- A_{FB}^b

In the fit, there are four parameters: M_Z, M_{H^0}, M_t and α_s. The fit is carried out by fixing the mass of the Higgs boson and constraining the value of α_s to 0.118 ± 0.007. The central value of M_t quoted below corresponds to $M_{H^0} = 300$ GeV. The uncertainty due to the Higgs mass is determined by varying its mass from 60 GeV to 1000 GeV. The derived quantities are:

$$M_W = 80.21 \pm 0.15 \pm 0.02 \text{ GeV} \tag{59}$$

$$\sin^2\theta_W = 0.2263 \pm 0.0028 \pm 0.0003 \tag{60}$$

$$\sin^2\theta_{\text{eff}} = 0.2327 \pm 0.0008 \pm 0.0002 \tag{61}$$

and the top quark mass:

$$M_{top} = 157^{+22+18}_{-25-21} \, (M_{H^0}) \text{ GeV} \tag{62}$$

where the spread from varying M_{H^0} from 60 to 1000 GeV is shown separately.

Therefore it is most likely the next major advance in physics will be the discovery of the top quark at FNAL.

Acknowledgments

I wish to acknowledge the support of the spokesmen of the other three LEP collaborations, Professor Jacques Lefrançois, Professor Ugo Amaldi, Professor Aldo Michelini as well as Professor Yuri Galaktionov, Dr. T.S. Dai, Professor L. Taylor and Dr. M. Pohl for their work in helping me to prepare this manuscript.

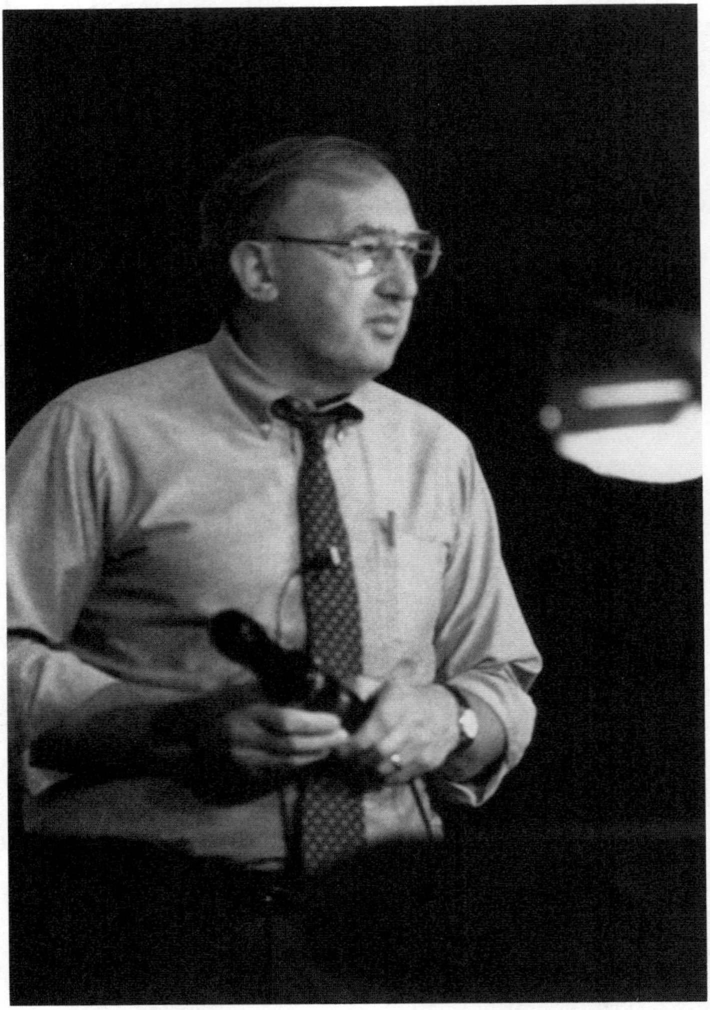

RESULTS FROM SLD AT THE SLAC LINEAR COLLIDER
THE SLD COLLABORATION*
presented by C. Baltay
Department of Physics, Yale University, New Haven, Connecticut 06511
ABSTRACT

1 Introduction

The first physics run of the SLD detector at the SLAC Linear Collider (the SLC) took place from April to September of 1992 with polarized incident electrons. The run resulted in approximately 11,000 Z° decays recorded on tape by SLD.

The SLC was typically running with $\sim 3 \times 10^{10}$ particles per bunch with spot sizes at the interaction point of ~ 2 μm or smaller. This resulted in somewhat over 20 Z°'s per hour, with a peak rate of 28 Z°'s per hour. The SLC was colliding beams around 75 to 80% of the scheduled time, and the SLD data taking efficiency was around 85 to 90% for a combined efficiency of $\sim 70\%$. The total number of Z°'s per week written on tape increased steadily during the run, reaching ~ 1300 Z°'s per week toward the end of the run. The polarization of the incident e^- beam at the interaction point was typically around 22%.

2 Performance of the SLD Detector

The SLD detector has been described previously [1] a quadrant view of the detector is shown in Figure 1. The entire SLD detector is complete, and all components were taking data in the 1992 run with the exception of the End Cap Cerenkov Counters which are still being commissioned.

The innermost detector element is the Vertex Detector, [2] located between 2.5 cm and 6 cm in radius. It consists of two logical layers of Silicon CCD pixel detectors with 20 μm $\times$ 20 μm sized pixels. The high precision, three dimensional spatial resolution (~ 6 μm) of this device, with the innermost layer very close to the interaction point, combined with the very small beam size at the SLC provide excellent secondary vertex detection. A close up of a $Z^0 \to \tau^+\tau^-$ event is shown in Figure 2a, and a hadronic event, probably a $Z^0 \to b\bar{b}$, is shown in Figure 2b. The secondary vertices are clearly resolved in these events.

Charged particle tracking is done in the 6 kg axial magnetic field of SLD by the Central Drift chamber which is located between 20 cm and 100 cm in radius and is 200 cm long. It consists of 640 vector cells with 8 sense wires each arranged in 10 concentric superlayers. The spatial resolution of this device is around 100 μm,

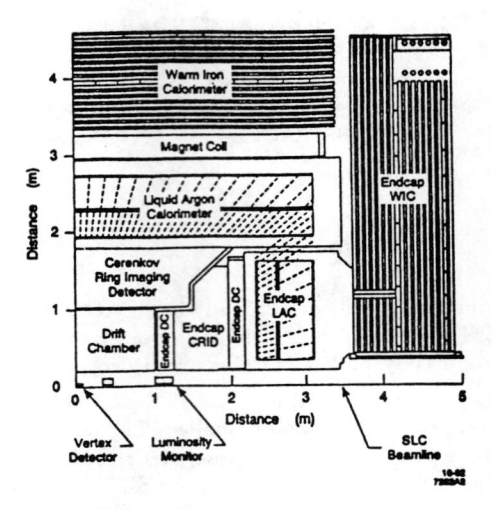

Figure 1: Quadrant view of the SLD Detector

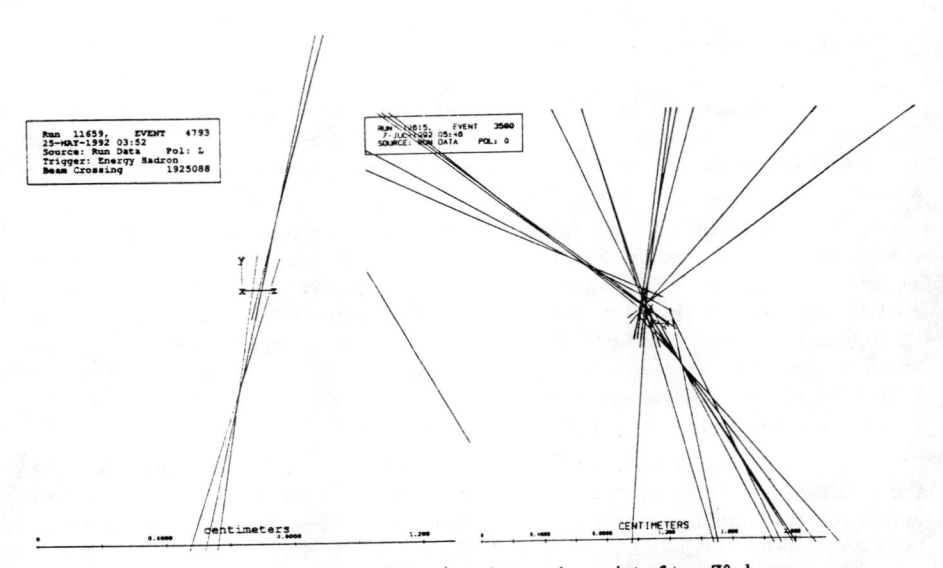

Figure 2: Close-up views of the $e^+\,e^-$ interaction point of two Z^0 decays

as shown in Figure 3.

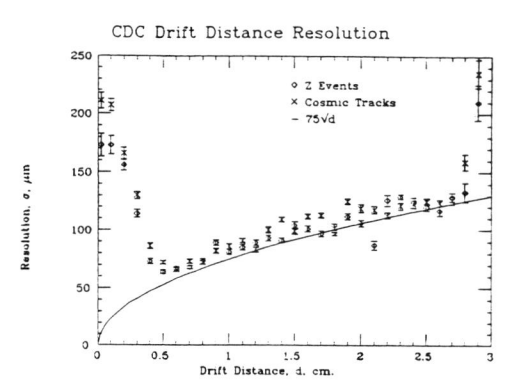

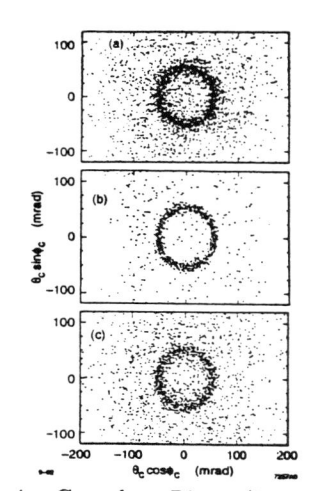

Figure 3: The measured spatial resolution of the SLD Central Drift Chamber

Figure 4: Cerenkov Rings (integrated over many events from the gas radiator seen in the CRID detector a) from cosmic rays b) for Bhabha events and c: from hadronic Z° decays

The barrel Cerenkov Ring Imaging Detector (CRID) [3] started taking data in this run with both the liquid and gas radiator systems operational with good photo electron yields. Typical rings seen in the electron detectors are shown in Figure 4.

The SLD calorimetry consists of a ~ 3 interaction lengths, finely segmented, projective tower geometry lead-liquid argon calorimeter [4] followed by ~ 5 interaction lengths of 5 cm iron plates instrumented with Iarocci gas chambers. The iron calorimeter also served as the magnet flux return iron and the muon identification and tracking system. The resolution for single hadrons in this combined calorimeter is shown in Figure 5 and is approximately $55\%/\sqrt{E}$.

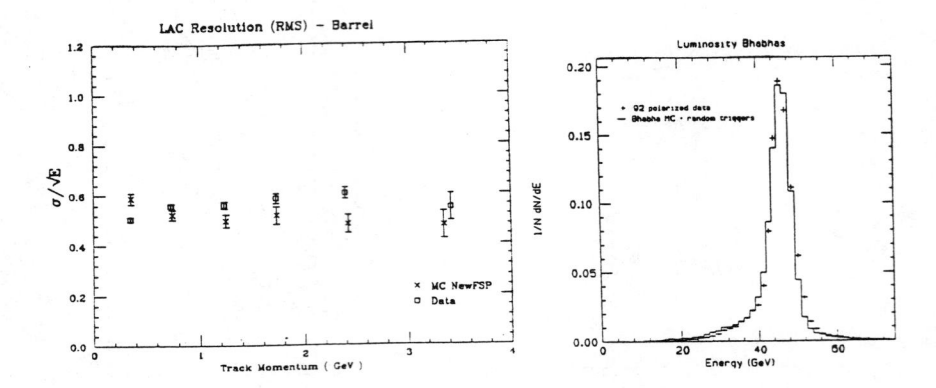

Figure 5: Measured energy resolution of the SLD Calorimeter

Figure 6: Energy resolution of the SLD Luminosity monitor for Bhabha events

The SLD Luminosity Monitor [5] consisted of tungsten plates with silicon detector readout. The energy resolution of this device for 45 GeV electrons from Bhabha events is shown in Figure 6.

Overall the performance of the SLD detector in this first data run was very satisfactory; however, much remains to be done to optimize the efficiency and resolution of all of the components.

3 Polarization at the SLC

The SLAC Linear Collider (SLC) was designed to produce, accelerate, and collide a spin-polarized electron beam. [6] A diagram of the SLC is shown in Figure 7. The polarized electron source consists of a GaAs photocathode that is illuminated by a circularly polarized laser beam. [7] The emitted electrons are longitudinally polarized, and the electron helicity is changed randomly on a cycle-by-cycle basis (the SLC operates at 120 Hz). The polarization of the emitted electrons was typically 28% during the 1992 run.

A system composed of the dipole magnets in the transfer line from the linac to the damping rings, and a superconducting solenoid magnet, is used to rotate the longitudinal polarization of the beam into the vertical direction to preserve polarization during storage in the damping ring. A system composed of two superconducting solenoids and the dipole magnets in the return line to the linac is used

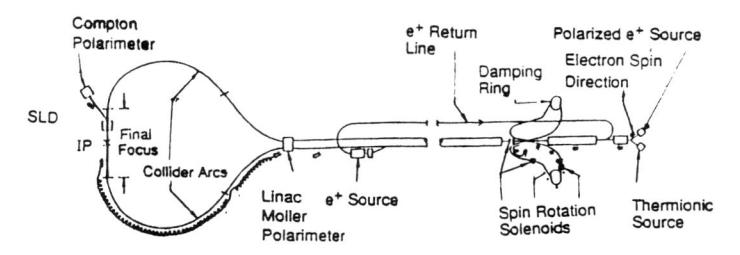

POLARIZATION IN THE OVERALL SLC LAYOUT

Figure 7: Schematic of the SLC. The electron spin direction is indicated by the double arrows.

to reorient the polarization vector upon extraction from the damping ring. This system has the ability to provide nearly all polarization orientations in the linac. A fractional polarization loss of 5% occurs in the damping ring.

The electron pulse is transported through the North Arc and Final Focus systems of the SLC to the interaction point (IP) of the machine. Polarization loss in the arcs due to energy dispersion is expected to be 5-10% fractionally, while the net spin rotation due to the arc system is sensitive to the parameters of the orbit and is measured empirically. The spin rotation system is adjusted to maximize the longitudinal polarization at the IP. After passing through the interaction point, the longitudinal component of the electron beam polarization is measured with a Compton polarimeter. The electron and positron beams are then transported to the south and north beam dumps, respectively, where precision energy spectrometers [8] are located upstream of the beam dumps and monitor the beam energies continually. The mean electron and positron energies were measured to be 45.71 GeV and 45.84 GeV, respectively. The mean center-or-mass energy was $E_{cm} = 91.55 \pm 0.04$ GeV.

The Compton polarimeter continually monitors the longitudinal polarization of the electron beam after it has passed through the IP and before it is deflected by dipole magnets. Polarimeter data are acquired continually for intervals of 20,000 SLC cycles ($\sim$ 3 min) and are logged in summary form onto SLD data tapes. The electron beam collides with a circularly polarized photon beam which is produced by a frequency-doubled Nd:YAG laser of wavelength 532 nm. The scattered and unscattered beams remain unseparated until they pass through a pair of dipole magnets. The scattered electrons are dispersed horizontally and exit the vacuum system through a thin window. Electrons in the energy interval 15-30 GeV are detected and momentum analyzed by a pair of redundant multichannel detectors (a

Cherenkov detector and a proportional tube detector). We measure the counting rates in the detectors for anti-parallel and parallel photon/electron beam helicities; given the laser polarization. The asymmetry formed from these rates determines the electron beam polarization. The circular polarization of the laser beam at the Compton IP was measured to be 93 ± 2%. The absolute helicity of the laser polarization was determined from comparison with a calibrated quarter-wave plate. In order to avoid systematic effects, the sign of the circular polarization is changed randomly on sequential laser pulses. Including effects due to the Compton polarimeter spectrometer and laser systems, we estimate the total relative systematic error on the polarization ($\frac{\delta P}{P}$) to be 3%.

4 First Physics Results

The sample of Z° decays used was selected via a calorimetric analysis based largely upon the LAC. The calorimetric analysis must distinguish Z° events from

several backgrounds that are unique to the operation of a linear collider and differ from those encountered at e^+e^- storage rings. The backgrounds fall into two major categories: those due to low energy electrons and photons that scatter from various beamline elements and apertures, and those due to high energy muons that traverse the detector parallel to the beam axis (due to the low average current in the SLC, backgrounds caused by beam collisions with residual gas in the beamline are negligible). We make use of the fine segmentation and tower geometry of the LAC to suppress both backgrounds. All electromagnetic and hadronic LAC towers used in the analysis are required to satisfy a combination of tower threshold cuts and criteria that select against radially isolated energy deposition in a combined electromagnetic-hadronic tower. All events are required to satisfy a set of global event cuts based on total visible energy and energy balance.

In this overview report three physics measurements are summarized. These results are presented in more detail in these proceedings. [9]

4.1 Measurement of α_s from a study of jet rates

The number and properties of hadronic jets produced in Z° decays are sensitive to the strong coupling constant α_s.

The analysis presented here used charged tracks measured in the Central Drift Chamber (CDC). In addition to the calorimetric event selection described above, a set of cuts was applied to select well measured tracks and events well contained within the acceptance of the detector. 5500 events survived these cuts with a total background estimated to be at the level of 0.3%. Jets were reconstructed by using variations of the JADE algorithm. Pairs of tracks i and j are combined and their effective mass M_{ij} are calculated. More tracks are added, and a jet is defined

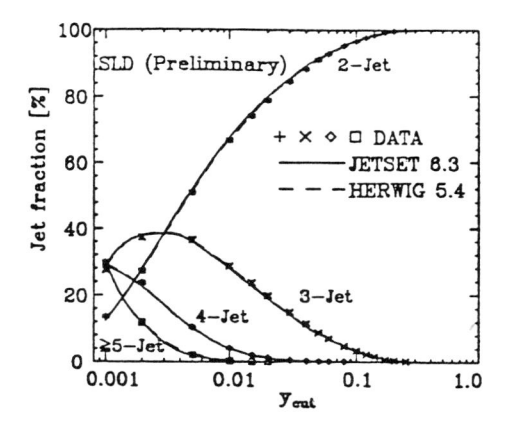

Figure 8: Jet rates measured in SLD as a function of the parameter Y_{cut}

to consist of those tracks whose combined effective mass ΣM_{ij} is below some cut Y_{cut} times the total energy E_{tot} of the event $\Sigma M_{ij} \leq Y_{cut} \cdot E_{tot}$.

The data were corrected by standard procedures for the effects of initial state radiation, detector acceptance and resolution, anaylsis cuts, unmeasured neutral particles, decays of unstable particles and hadronization.

The number of jets found as a function of the parameter Y_{cut} is shown in Figure 8. Also shown on this figure are the predictions of the JETSET 6.3 and HERWIG 5.3 perturbative QCD plus fragmentation Monte Carlo programs, which are in good agreement with the data.

From a fit to this data, we obtain the following result

$$\alpha_s(M_{Z^0}) = 0.119 \pm 0.002(stat) \pm 0.003(expt.syst) \pm 0.014(theory)$$

The largest contribution to the error comes from the theoretical uncertainties associated with the QCD renormalization scale. This result is in good agreement with the results of similar analyses obtained in Z° decays at LEP, [10] which have about the same total errors due to the same theoretical uncertainties.

4.2 Measurement of the branching ratio $\Gamma(Z^0 \to b + \bar{b})/\Gamma(Z^0 \to hadrons)$

Most of the previous measurements of this ratio used high P_t leptons in one way or another to tag $Z^0 \to b\bar{b}$ decays. The first SLD analysis presented here relies entirely on the vertex detector and does not use lepton tags at all.

In addition to the Z⁰ selection cuts discussed above, cuts were imposed to select events with well measured tracks which were within the acceptance of the Vertex Detector as well as the Central Drift Chamber. A sample of 4684 hadronic decays were thus selected.

All of the charged tracks identified in the CDC were extrapolated through the Vertex Detector to the interaction point and the impact parameter and its error, $b \pm \delta b$, were calculated. The position of the interaction point was determined precisely (to $\sim 10~\mu$ m in the transverse dimensions) by averaging over many Z⁰ decay events occurring in the same run. Tracks that missed the e⁺e⁻ interaction point by more than three standard deviations (i.e. $b/\delta b \geq 3$) were selected as candidates coming from secondary vertices. Monte Carlo simulations indicate that $b\bar{b}$ events have more tracks coming from secondary vertices than $c\bar{c}$ or light quark events. Thus, events were tagged as $Z^0 \to b\bar{b}$ if the number of tracks with $b/\delta b \geq 3$ was larger than some number N_{cut}. As N_{cut} is increased the purity of the $Z^0 \to b\bar{b}$ sample is increased but the tagging efficiency decreases. $N_{cut}=3$ was used as a good compromise. This resulted in a sample of 786 $Z^0 \to b\bar{b}$ decays, with a calculated tagging efficiency of 54%, and a sample purity of 71%.

We thus obtain the branching ratio

$$R = \frac{\Gamma(Z^0 \to b\bar{b})}{\Gamma(Z^0 \to hadrons)} = 0.218 \pm 0.013(stat) \pm 0.026(syst).$$

The large systematic error is due to the uncertainty in the Monte Carlo calculation of the tagging efficiency and the sample purity and includes uncertainties in B decay parameters such as multiplicity, and the uncertainty in the Central Drift Chamber track reconstruction efficiency. At this time the error is dominated by the latter, and we believe that with further study this error can be reduced by about a factor of two.

The result quoted above is in good agreement with the results from the LEP experiments, [11] although at this time our error is considerably larger than theirs.

4.3 Measurement of the Polarization Asymmetry A_{LR}

The polarization left-right asymmetry is defined as follows:

$$A_{LR} \equiv \frac{\sigma(e^+e^-_L \to Z^0) - \sigma(e^+e^-_R \to Z^0)}{\sigma(e^+e^-_L \to Z^0) + \sigma(e^+e^-_R \to Z^0)},$$

where $\sigma(e^+e^-_L \to Z^0)$ and $\sigma(e^+e^-_R \to Z^0)$ are the production cross section for Z⁰ bosons with left-handed and right-handed electrons, respectively. Within the context of the Standard Model, this quantity is a sensitive function of the electroweak mixing parameter $sin^2\theta_w$, [12]

$$A_{LR} = \frac{2v_e a_e}{v_e^2 + a_e^2} = \frac{2[1 - 4sin^2\theta_w]}{1 + [1 - 4sin^2\theta_w]^2},$$

where v_e and a_e are the vector and axial vector coupling constants of the Z° boson to the electron current. Note that A_{LR} is sensitive to the initial state couplings and is insensitive to the final state couplings. The left-right asymmetry has the following properties: it is sensitive to virtual electroweak corrections; it is insensitive to real radiative corrections; it is a weak function of center-of-mass energy, E_{cm}, near the Z° pole; and it is expected to be relatively large, in the range 0.10-0.15.

We measured A_{LR} by counting all hadronic decay modes of the Z° boson (the sample also contains $\tau^+\tau^-$ final states) for each of the two longitudinal polarization states of the electron beam. The measurement does not require an absolute luminosity measurement or any knowledge of the absolute detector acceptance and efficiency.

In this analysis, Z° decays were selected by the calorimetric trigger described above. The only additional cut was to remove e^+e^- events since these have a background from Bhabha scattering. Each Z° produced was tagged by the polarization of the incident electron for that pulse (the polarization of the electrons from the polarized gun was reversed randomly from pulse to pulse). This resulted in a sample of 10,224 Z° decays with 5,226 produced by left-handed electrons and 4,998 produced by right-handed electrons.

The polarization of the electrons at the interaction point for this run was very stable between 20 and 24%, with an average weighted by the number of Z° decays of P=0.224 ±0.007.

Many detailed calculations and consistency checks show that the luminosities and polarization were the same for left and right-handed electrons and that detector acceptances, efficiencies, and background effects cancel out in the asymmetry to an approximation much better then we need with our present statistics. We can thus write the asymmetry as

$$A_{LR} = \left(\frac{1}{P}\right)\frac{N_L - N_R}{N_L + N_R} = \left(\frac{1}{0.224 \pm .007}\right)\frac{5,226 - 4,998}{5,226 + 4,998}$$

$$A_{LR} = 0.100 \pm 0.044(stat) \pm 0.003(syst)$$

The systematic error is dominated by the error on the measurement of the polarization.

From this measurement of A_{LR} we calculate the electroweak mixing angle to be

$$sin^2\theta_w = 0.2378 \pm 0.0056$$

where the error includes both statistical and systematic errors (but is dominated by the statistical error). A small correction (+0.0003) has been applied to correct the value of $sin^2\theta_w$ from our center of mass energy of 91.55 GeV to the central energy of the Z° pole.

The measurement of A_{LR} is unique to an e^+e^- collider with polarized incident electrons. However, the electron couplings to the Z° measured by A_{LR} can also

A_{FB} for $Z^\circ \to e^+e^-$

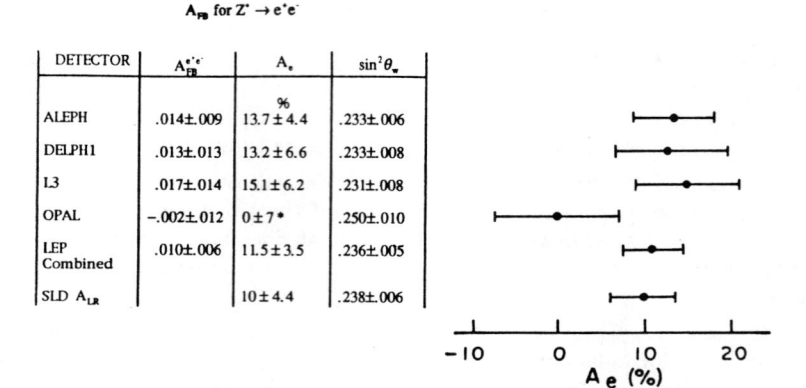

DETECTOR	$A_{FB}^{e^+e^-}$	A_e %	$\sin^2\theta_w$
ALEPH	.014±.009	13.7±4.4	.233±.006
DELPHI	.013±.013	13.2±6.6	.233±.008
L3	.017±.014	15.1±6.2	.231±.008
OPAL	−.002±.012	0±7*	.250±.010
LEP Combined	.010±.006	11.5±3.5	.236±.005
SLD A_{LR}		10±4.4	.238±.006

Figure 9: Comparison of the A_{LR} measurement from SLD with the A_{FB} (e^+e^-) measurements from the four detectors at LEP

be obtained from the forward-backward asymmetry A_{FB} for electron pairs, and, assuming lepton universality, from A_{FB} for muon and tau pairs and the tau polarization in Z° decays with unpolarized electrons. The comparison with the LEP results [13] $A_{LR}^{e^+e^-}$ and $P(\tau)$ are shown in Figures 9 and 10. The errors from the SLD A_{LR} measurement is similar to those obtained for a single measurement by one of the LEP experiments. However, the combined error from all four LEP detectors for all of the various measurements is considerably smaller than the present error on the A_{LR} measurement.

5 Future Prospects for SLD/SLC

The 1992 run was considered to be sufficiently successful to schedule a 1993 run, and assuming continued good performance, a 1994 run. The 1993 run is presently scheduled to be approximately thirty-six weeks with an estimated 2,000 Z°'s per week written to SLD tape. The 1994 run is expected to be similar, hopefully with further improvements in the number of Z°'s per week.

The polarization in the 1993 run is expected to be ~ 40% with the use of thin GaAs or cooled bulk GaAs photocathodes in the polarized electron source. A further improvement to a polarization of 65 to 70% at the interaction point might be possible by the use of GaAs photocathodes with a "strained lattice". Such cathodes have produced up to 90% polarizations in the lab; however, much work remains to be done in turning these strained lattice cathodes into devices that produce sufficient currents under real life conditions at the SLC.

A_τ from Tau Polarization

DETECTOR	$A_{\tau\alpha\epsilon}$
ALEPH	−0.138±.031
DELPH1	−0.235±.074
L3	−0.139±.034
OPAL	−.065±.063
LEP Combined	−.138±.021
SLD A_{LR}	0.100±.044

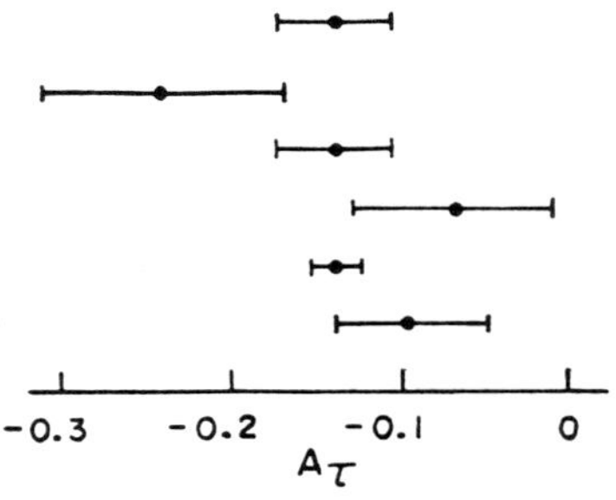

Figure 10: Comparison of the A_{LR} measurement from SLD with the tau polarization measurements from the four detectors at LEP

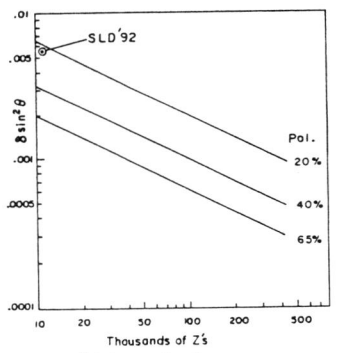

Figure 11: Expected error on $sin^2\theta$ from the A_{LR} measurement from the 1993-94 SLD/SLC run

As an example of the kind of result that we can expect from the 1993-94 SLD/SLC run; we show in Figure 11 the anticipated error on $sin^2\theta_w$ obtained from the A_{LR} measurement with the expected members of Z°'s and the increased polarizations. We can hope to reach an error in $sin^2\theta_w$ well below 0.001.

References

1. The SLD Design Report, SLAC Report 273, 1984.
2. VXD paper at Dallas.
3. J. V'avra et al, SLAC-PUB-5945, October 1992.
4. D. Axeu et al, SLAC PUB-5354 (1992) and E. Vella, SLAC-PUB-5953 (1992).
5. S.C. Berridge et al, Proceedings of the 1991 Nuclear Science Symposium, Santa Fe, N.M. Vol 1 p. 495, also SLAC-PUB 5694.
6. D. Blockus et al, Proposal for Polarization of the SLC, April 1986.

7. The SLC polarized electron source is described in D. Schultz, et al, SLAC-PUB-5768 (1992) and the laser system is described in J. Frisch et al, SLAC-PUB-5965 (1992).
8. J. Kent et al, SLAC-PUB-4922 (March 1989).
9. See the papers by Jan Lauber et al, Su Dong et al and Bruce Schumm et al in these proceedings.
10. S. Bethke, Plenary talk of the XXVI the International Conference on HEP, Dallas, August 1992.
11. S. Bethke, Plenary talk at the XXVI the International Conference on HEP, Dallas, August 1992.
12. We define the parameter $sin^2\theta$ in this paper in terms of the ratio of the vector and axial vector coupling strength of the Z° to leptons: $sin^2\theta_w \equiv \frac{1}{4}(1 - \frac{v}{a})$.
13. L. Rolandi, Plenary talk at the XXVI the International Conference on HEP, Dallas, August 1992.

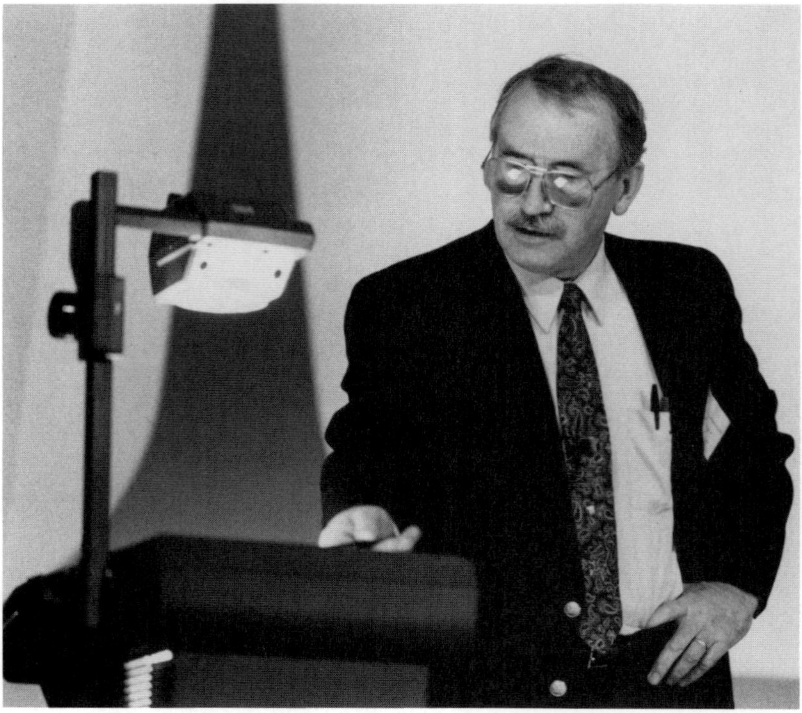

THE HIGH ENERGY PHYSICS–ASTROPHYSICS CONNECTION

DANIEL SINCLAIR
Department of Physics, University of Michigan
Ann Arbor, Michigan USA

ABSTRACT

Techniques developed for experiments in high energy physics are used to do high energy γ-ray astronomy. In the first part of my talk I review the history of this field, the experimental techniques, the discoveries and the prospects. Radiation from space can provide unique conditions for experiments in high energy physics. Neutrinos from the sky travel distances (between production and detection) much greater than neutrinos studied at accelerators, making the experiments more sensitive to changes in the neutrino's flavor. In the second part of my talk I examine the 'too few ν_μ' problem.

1. High Energy γ-Ray Astronomy

1.1. Historical Highlights

The field of high energy γ-ray astronomy began in 1965 when R.J. Gould[1] calculated that a detectable flux of γ-rays, perhaps up to ~1 TeV in energy, would be emitted by the Crab Nebula. This is a supernova remnant, fairly nearbye by galactic standards (~1 kpc). At its core is a rotating neutron star, the Crab Pulsar. It has long been known that the nebula contains high energy electrons, and that these electrons, bending in the magnetic field of the Nebula, are the source of the observed synchrotron radiation. In the model, the γ-rays are produced by the electrons colliding with the synchrotron photons and boosting their energies up to the TeV region. The calculated flux of photons above 1 TeV was within a factor 10 of that which was ultimately measured. However, almost a quarter centry elapsed before a reliable measurement was available. In the meantime, the field took a remarkable turn.

In 1983 the Kiel group reported[2] the observation of cosmic ray showers with energies in excess of 1 PeV (1 PeV $\equiv 10^{15}$ eV) coming from the x-ray source Cygnus X-3. This source is at a distance of ~10 kpc and presumably consists of a neutron star and an ordinary star orbiting around their common center of mass. The observed signal was enhanced when the showers were selected by 'phase locking' their arrival times to the 4.8 h orbital period of the binary system. The Kiel result was remarkable because γ-rays of such high energy and such high intensity are unlikely to come from the Compton-synchrotron process. It was also puzzling, because the muon content of the showers coming from the direction of the source was not low[3] as would be expected for showers initiated by γ-rays.

Though this result was followed by other observations[4] there was always considerable doubt about this source because all of the observations were of low

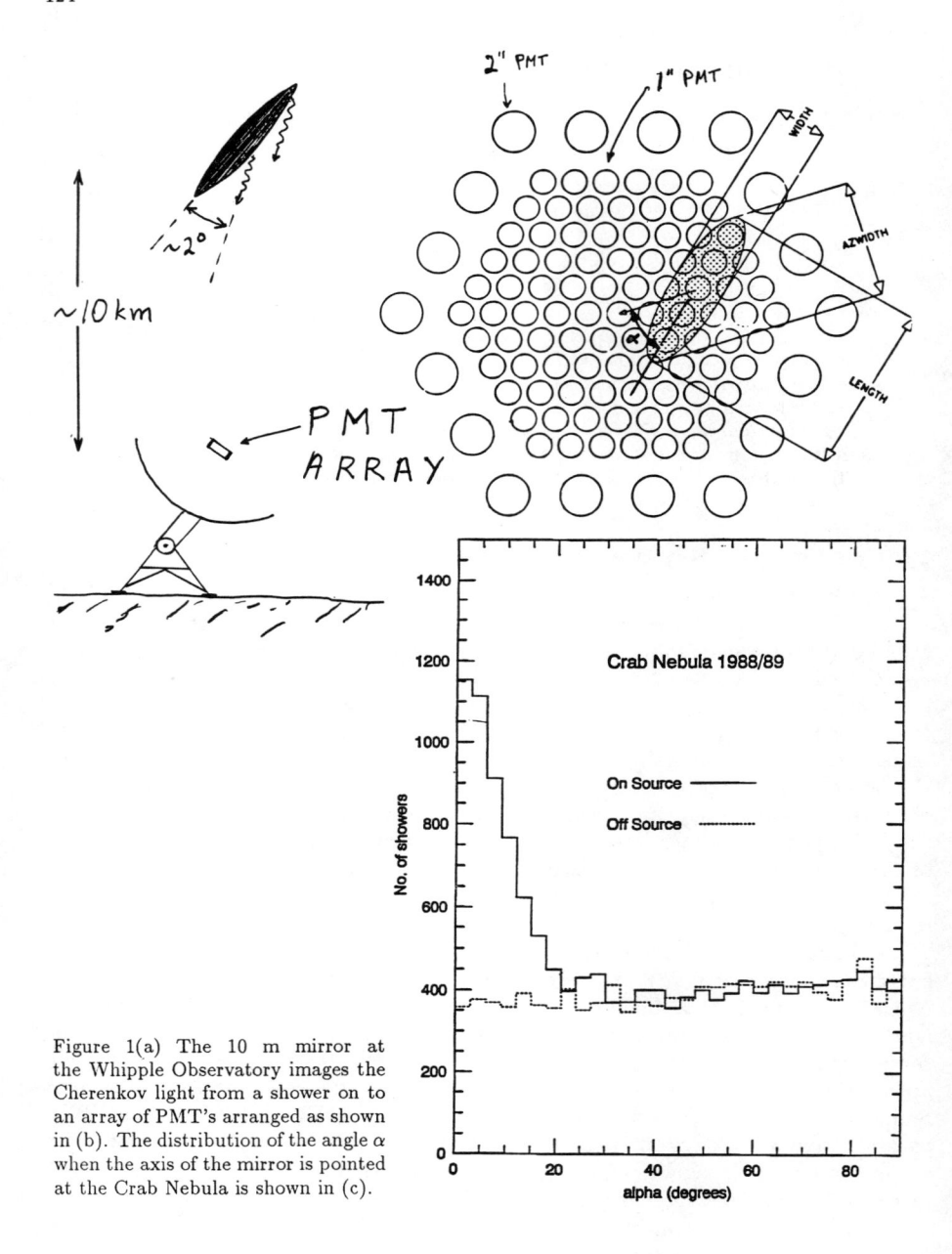

Figure 1(a) The 10 m mirror at the Whipple Observatory images the Cherenkov light from a shower on to an array of PMT's arranged as shown in (b). The distribution of the angle α when the axis of the mirror is pointed at the Crab Nebula is shown in (c).

statistical significance. Indeed, in the decate of the '80's there were many sightings of different sources at both TeV and PeV energies, but always with low statistical significance (a few σ). Sometimes the radiation was steady, sometimes pulsed, sometimes episoidal and sometimes with properties unlike that of photons, for example penetrating deep underground or producing showers that were not muon-poor. But there were no observations that were clearly beyond the possibility of statistical fluctuations.

In 1989 the situation changed dramatically. Two groups[5] using Cherenkov imaging reflectors, detected clear and unquivocal signals from the Crab Nebula. These observations were characterized by high statistics and signals which met the criteri for TeV γ-rays coming from a compact source. The radiation was not pulsed so presumably the source was the Nebula and not the Pulsar. Meanwhile, working at higher energies, arrays of scintillators, some with muon counters to veto hadron showers began publishing[6] upper limits on Cygnus X-3 which were substantially below the level of previous sightings.

Recently, the Whipple Group made another dramatic discovery[7] when they observed TeV γ-rays from the Active Galactic Nucleus (AGN) Markarian 421.

1.2. Experimental Techniques

γ-rays are only a small fraction of the cosmic radiation. Most cosmic rays striking the earth's atmosphere are protons and other light nuclei. These charged particles are bent by the magnetic field of the galaxy. Their direction of motion bears no relation to the direction of their source. To detect sources of γ-rays, instruments must discriminate against this cosmic background, either by angular resolution or by rejecting hadrons, or both. The techniques used in γ-ray astronomy at TeV energies and above, are summarized below.

Cherenkov cameras	$3 \times 10^{11} - 3 \times 10^{12}$ eV
Cherenkov arrays	$3 \times 10^{12} - 3 \times 10^{13}$ eV
Scintillator arrays	$10^{13} - 10^{15}$ eV

The best example of a Cherenkov camera is the 10 m reflector[8] operated by the Whipple Group on Mount Hopkins. The operation of this instrument is illustrated in Figure 1. The number of charged particles (and hence the production of Cherenkov photons) is maximum at an altitude of ~10 km for a 1 TeV shower. Using the Cherenkov light, the reflector forms an image of the shower at its focal plane. This image, which is eleptical in shape, is detected by an array of photomultiplier tubes (PMT). If the camera is pointed precisely at the source, the axis of the elipse passes through the axis of the camera. The angle α is a measure of the angle between the optical axis of the telescope and the direction of the particle which produced the shower. Figure 1(c) shows the distribution of α when the axis of the telescope is pointed at the Crab Nebula.

The Themistocle Cherenkov timing array[9] makes use of the property that the Cherenkov photons generated by a shower arrive in a well defined plane (actually a wide-angle cone). These photons are detected by an array of PMT's with good timing resolution ($\sigma \sim 0.35$ ns) spaced ~50 m apart. The concept is shown in Figure 2.

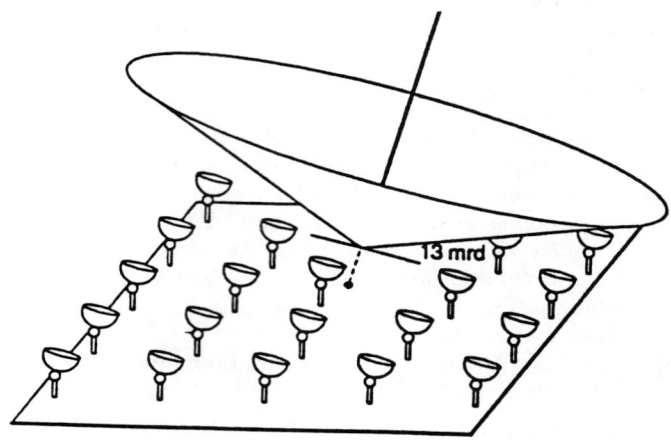

Figure 2. The diagram illustrates the operating principle of a Cherenkov timing array of spherical mirrors each with a PMT at its focus. The PMT's measure the arrival times of the Cherenkov photons generated by the shower. This allows the shape of the Cherenkov light front (actually a wide angle cone) to be reconstructed.

The leading surface of Cherenkov photons is well defined so Cherenkov timing arrays are capable of extremely good angular resolution. It has been estimated that an array of 300 mirrors could attain an angular resolution of 0.01°. A small array consisting of 18 mirrors is in use and has an angular resolution of 0.035°. The energy range of this array is 3–30 TeV.

The largest scintillator array in operation is CASA-MIA (Chicago Air Shower Array-Michigan Anti) at Dugway, Utah. It is shown in Figure 3. It consists of 1089 scintillator stations on the ground, which detect mainly the electrons in the shower to measure its size and direction. Buried 3 m below the surface are 1024 counters grouped in 16 patches. These are used to detect the muons in the shower and hence veto hadron induced showers. The threshold energy is 10^{14} eV and the angular resolution is in the range 1° to 0.5° depending on the size of the shower.

In comparing a scintillator array such as CASA-MIA with the Cherenkov timing array (Themistocle), one striking difference is the very much better angular resolution of the latter (0.035° vs. 1°). There are several reasons for this. There are many more Cherenkov photons than electrons in a shower. They are spread over a larger area and the PMT's detect the photons directly without the time-smearing effect of the scintillator. Of course one disadvantage of the Cherenkov timing array

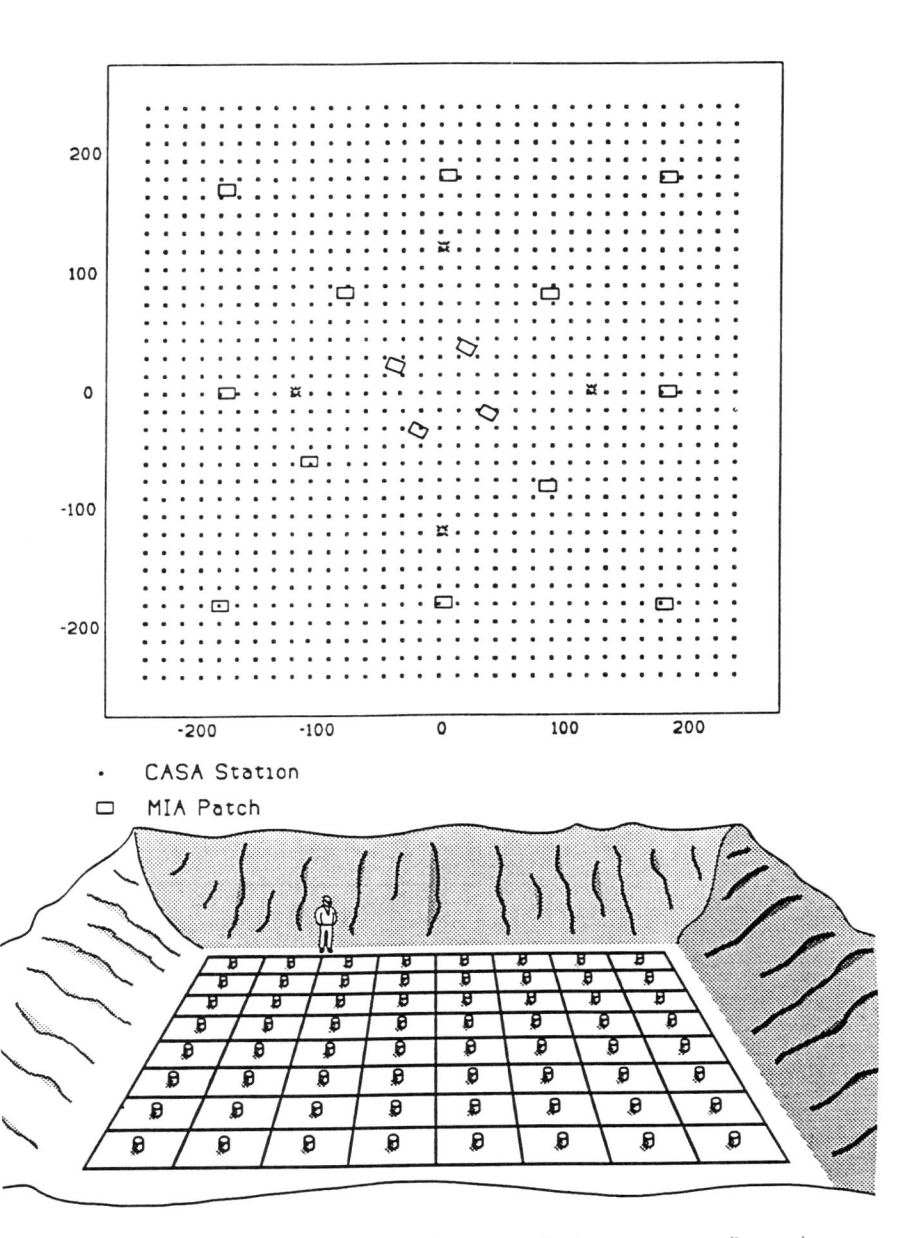

Figure 3. The CASA-MIA array (top) and a patch of muon counters (bottom).

is that it can only work on dark cloudless nights, about 8% of the time.

1.3. Discoveries

The most interesting discoveries in gamma-ray astronomy have been made by the EGRET experiment aboard the Compton Gamma Ray Observatory. This experiment has detected[10] GeV photons from numerous extra-galactic objects identified as AGN's. However at higher energies, TeV and above, most searches have turned up negative. There are really only two clearly identified sources at TeV energies and, interestingly one of them is the AGN Markarian 421[7], which is at a distance of ~100 Mpc! The other is the Crab Nebula[5,11].

The sightings of the Crab Nebula and Pulsar at GeV and TeV energies are summarized in Figure 4 which was provided by C. Akerlof.

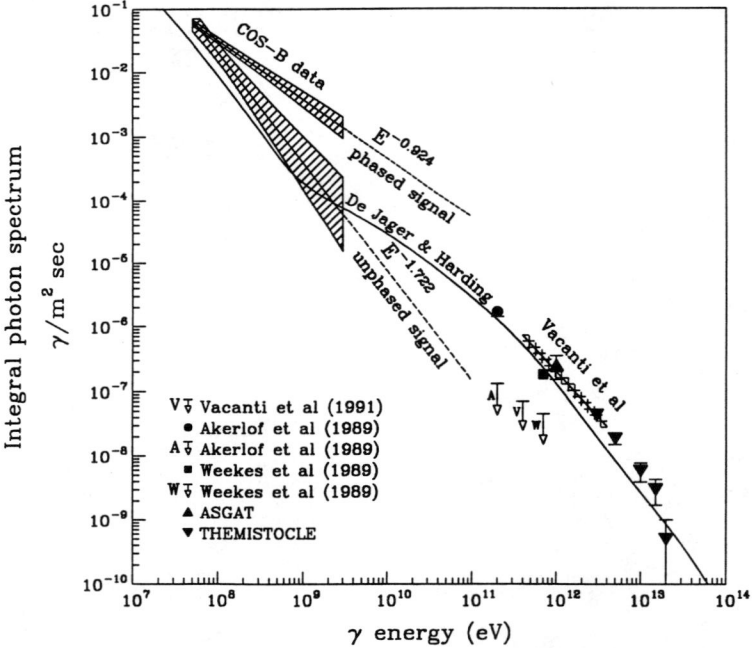

Figure 4. Compilation of data on the Crab Nebula and Pulsar. The phased signal from the pulsar is observed at energies below a Gev. In the TeV region there are only upper limits on the phased signal, denoted by the points A, V and W.

It is interesting to note that there are two components to the radiation at GeV energies[12]. The stronger component is modulated in phase with the Crab Pulsar. However, at energies above 10^{11} eV, only the unphased component is observed. Indeed, the limits on the strength of the phased component lie an order of magnitude below the intensity of the unphased component at TeV energies[11]. The solid line shown in Figure 4 is calculated using the Compton-synchrotron model.[13]

In the energy region accessible to ground based arrays (10^{13}–10^{15} eV) there are only upper limits on the intensity of γ-rays from the Crab Nebula, and these do not seriously challenge the Compton-synchrotron model, though they are expected to do so within a couple of years. The best limits[14] come from the As γ array in Tibet, the CASA-MIA array in Utah, and the Cygnus array in New Mexico.

The source *Markarian 421* was reported[10] at GeV energies by the EGRET group. It was subsequently detected[7] by the Whipple group at TeV energies. (See Figure 5)

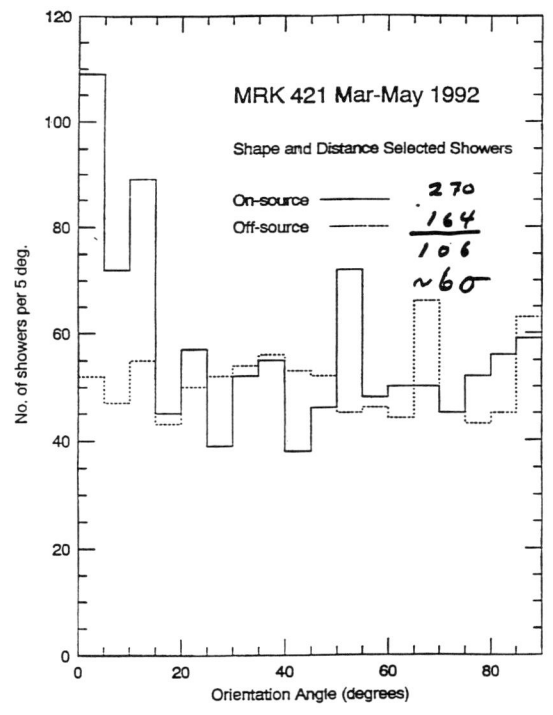

Figure 5. Distribution of the angle α (see Figure 1) when the axis of the Whipple 10 m reflector is pointed at Mk 423.

These are truly remarkable discoveries because of the level of intensities observed and the great distance of the source. The EGRET experiment report an intensity $\phi \approx 1 \times 10^{-7}$ photons/cm^2.s above 10^8 eV and the Whipple Group report $\phi \approx 1.2 \times 10^{-11}$ photons/cm^2.s above 5×10^{11} eV. These measurements correspond to a spectral index equal to -1.1 which is much harder than the cosmic ray spectrum.

The source *Cygnus X-3* is not seen at TeV energies and above in recent experiments. The upper limit set by the Whipple group[11] is 30 times lower than the signals reported before 1985. A similar situation exists at higher energies. Limits[14] set by the Tibetan array, CASA-MIA, and others are well below previously reported sightings. Of course, it is possible that Cygnus X-3 is a sporadic source of very high energy γ-rays, which is recently in a dormant phase. But another possibility is that earlier "sightings" were due to an optimistic interpretation of statistically shaky data.

1.4. Prospects

Clearly the most interesting development of the past year has been the discovery of intense sources of high energy γ-rays at cosmological distances. Unfortunately, the presence of the microwave background radiation precludes the detection of these sources at energies above 100 TeV because the interaction $\gamma\gamma \to e^+e^-$ absorbs the γ-rays. Indeed, since the only extragalactic source observed at TeV energies is the closest such source, the implication is that another absorptive process is at work, perhaps the production of e^+e^- pairs from collisions with infrared photons. Thus, if progress is to be made, the energy threshold of the Cherenkov camera must be lowered to 100 TeV of less. This may be accomplished by collecting more photons (larger focussing mirrors or more of them) and by improving the angular resolution.

As far as galactic sources are concerned the Crab Nebula may be the only source observable at TeV energies with existing techniques. An interesting question here concerns the energy dependence of the signal. Does it 'die' at 10 TeV or will it be detected at 100 TeV by CASA-MIA? In the GeV energy region we can look for more information about both the phased and unphased signal from the EGRET experiment.

2. Atmospheric Neutrinos and the Too Few ν_μ Problem

Large underground detectors (designed to look for proton decay) detect the interactions of neutrinos which (presumably) come from the decay of kaons, pions and muons made in the atmosphere by cosmic rays. These atmospheric neutrinos are not quite isotropic, but nearly so. They are detected in two ways:

1. They interact in the detector.

2. They interact in the rock surrounding the detector producing muons which penetrate the rock and enter the detector.

Obviously method (2) detects only ν_μ, and only upward or horizontal ν_μ can be measured because of the huge background of down-going cosmic ray muons.

The following measurements are made and the results compared with Monte Carlo simulations:

1. The rate of ν_e charged current interactions inside the detector.

2. The rate of ν_μ charged current interactions inside the detector.

3. The rate of upgoing muons which pass through the detector.
4. The rate of upgoing muons which stop in the detector.

Some of the uncertainties associated with the Monte Carlo calculations are removed when ratios are compared. Table 1[15] shows results from the Kamiokande[16] and IMB[17] experiments for the ratio (2)/(1), designated $R\left(\frac{\mu}{e}\right)$.

Ratio	KAM 4.9 kton-yr	IMB 7.7 kton-yr	Conditions
$R_{data}\left(\frac{\mu}{e}\right)$	0.72 ± 0.09	0.56 ± 0.05	$100 < p_e < 1200$ MeV/c
			$300 < p_\mu < 1200$ MeV/c
$R_{MC}\left(\frac{\mu}{e}\right)$	1.11	1.04	as in $R_{data}\left(\frac{\mu}{e}\right)$
$R_{MC}^{data}\left(\frac{\mu}{e}\right)$	$0.65 \pm 0.08 \pm 0.06$	$0.54 \pm 0.05 \pm 0.12$	$100 < p_e < 1200$ MeV/c
			$300 < p_\mu < 1200$ MeV/c

Table 1.

Clearly the measured values of this ratio do not agree with the predictions of the model. A similar result is reported at this meeting by the Soudan experiment, namely

$$R_{MC}^{data}\left(\frac{\mu}{e}\right) = 0.55 \pm 0.27 \pm 0.10$$

The Soudan result is statistically weak at present, but more data is forthcoming. It is significant because it comes from a different kind of detector, not a water Cherenkov detector.

However, if we look at the ratio (4)/(3), that is stopping muons versus through-going muons we find good agreement between experiment and simulation. These data[18] come from the IMB experiment which finds

$$R_{data}\left(\frac{stop}{thru}\right) = \frac{85 \pm 9}{532 \pm 23} = 0.160 \pm 0.019$$

$$R_{MC}\left(\frac{stop}{thru}\right) = 0.162$$

The error on $R_{MC}\left(\frac{stop}{thru}\right)$ is estiamted to be 7%. This agreement excludes, at the 90% confidence level, the small Δm^2 region shown in Figure 6.

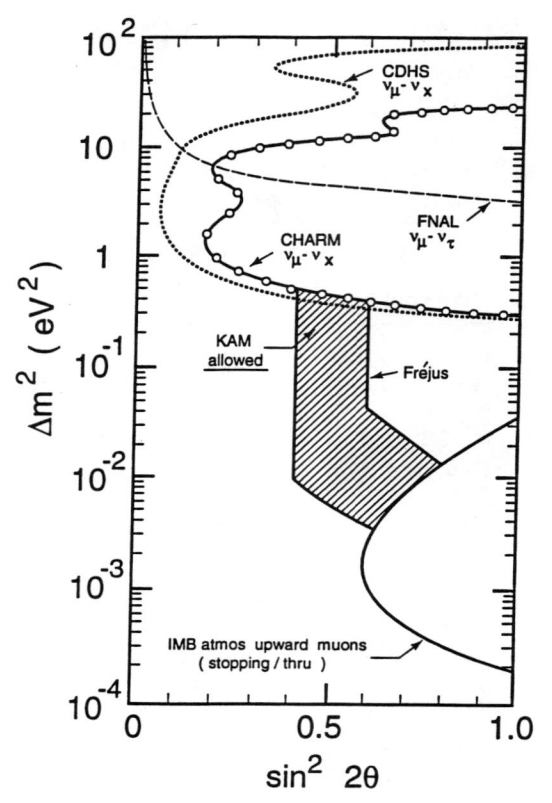

Figure 6. The allowed (shaded) and excluded regions of parameter space for $\nu_\mu \to \nu_\tau$. The figure is from reference 15.

What are we to make of this? The differences between experiment and simulation for the ratio $R\left(\frac{\mu}{e}\right)$ are too large to be statistical fluctuations. The combined discrepancy in the case of the IMB and Kameoka results amounts to $\sim 13\sigma$. One possibility is that muon neutrinos change flavor to tau neutrinos which would not be observable in these experiments. This would imply values of Δm^2 and $\sin^2 2\theta$ indicated by the shaded region in Figure 6.

Recently, another suggestion[19] was made. It is that the experiments are not observing a deficit of muon events, but are, instead, observing a surplus of electron events, and these excess electron events are not due to neutrino interactions but are, instead, due to proton decay! According to this suggestion, protons decaying by the mode $p \to e\nu\bar{\nu}$ create a surplus of single track showering events. However, there is a problem with this suggestion. The momentum distribution of the single track showering events measured in the IMB experiment does not agree with it. The data and the Monte Carlo simulation shown in Figure 7 are taken from reference 17.

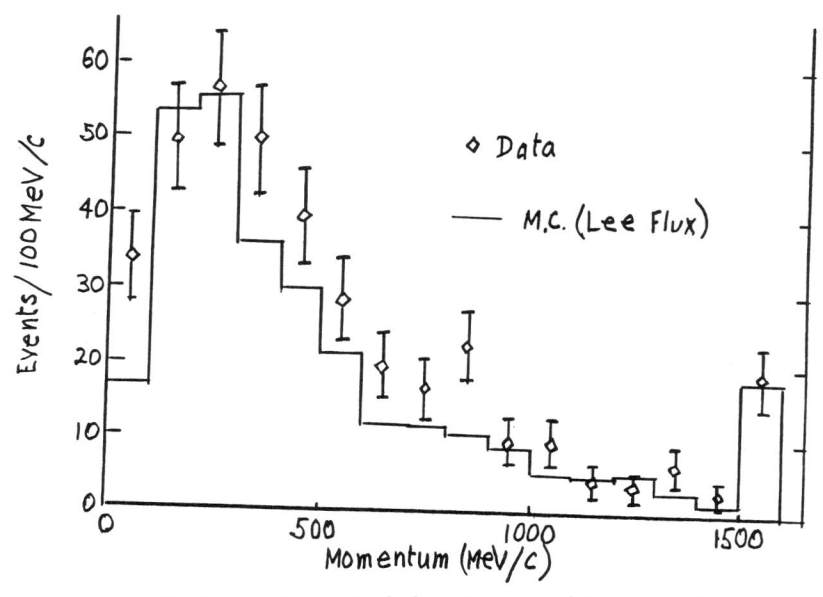

Figure 7. Momentum distribution of single track showering events (electrons) in the IMB detector. The histogram is the result of a Monte Carlo simulation. The figure is from reference 17.

Note that there is fairly good agreement between the data and the simulation which is calculated on the assumption of no proton decay, and no neutrino flavor changing. Scaling down the simulation, to get the ratio $R\left(\frac{\mu}{e}\right)$ right, would produce an excess of showering events but this excess would not be confined to the region below 400 MeV/c as expected if the surplus was due to proton decay.

Acknowledgements

I am grateful for the assistance of several members of the University of Michigan Physics Department in preparing this report. Carl Akerlof provided Figure 4 and much help was obtained from Jim Matthews, Don Meyer, Mike Schubnell and Jack van der Velde.

References

1. R.J. Gould, *Phys. Rev. Lett.* **15**, (1965) 511.
2. M. Samorski and W. Stamm, *Ap. J.* **268** (1983) 117.
3. M. Samorski and W. Stamm, *Proc. 18th Int. Cosmic Ray Conf.* **11** (Bangalore, 1983) 244.
4. For review of the sightings of Cygnus X-3 see W. Hermsen et al., *Astron. Astrophys.* **175** (1987) 141; A.A. Watson, *Proc. 19th int. Cosmic Ray Conf.* **9** (La Jolla, 1985) 111.
5. C.W. Akerlof et al., 1989, in *proc. of Gamma-Ray Observatory Workshop*, ed. W.N. Johnson (Greenbelt: NRL) pp. 4–49; T.C. Weekes et al., *Ap. J.* **342**, (WEA89) 379.
6. D. Ciampa et al., *Phys. Rev. D* **42**, (1990) 281; See also ref. 14.
7. M. Punch et al., *Nature* **358** (1992) 477.
8. M.F. Cawley et al., *Exper. Astr.* **1**, (1990) 173.
9. G. Fontaine, College de France preprint.
10. P.F. Michelson et al., IAU Circular 5470 (1992) 1.
11. G. Vacanti et al., *Ap. J.* **377** (1991) 467.
12. J. Clear et al., *Astron. Astrophys.* **174** (1987) 85.
13. O.C. DeJegar and A.K. Harding, *22nd Int. Cosmic Ray Conf.* **1** (Dublin, 1991) 572.
14. M. Amenomori et al., *Phys. Rev. Lett.* **69** (1992) 2468; G.M. Dion, Ph.D. Thesis, University of California; T.A. McKay Ph.D. Thesis, University of Chicago.
15. Table 1 and Figure 6 are from the draft of a paper by W. Frati et al. See also an analysis by E.W. Beier et al., *Phys. Lett. B* **283** (1992) 446.
16. K.S. Hirata et al., *Phys. Lett. B* **280** (1992) 146.
17. R. Becker-Szendy et al., *Phys. Rev. D* **46** (1992) 3720.
18. R. Becker-Szendy et al., *Phys. Rev. Lett.* **69** (1992) 1010.
19. W.A. Mann et al., *Phys. Lett. B* **291** (1992) 200.

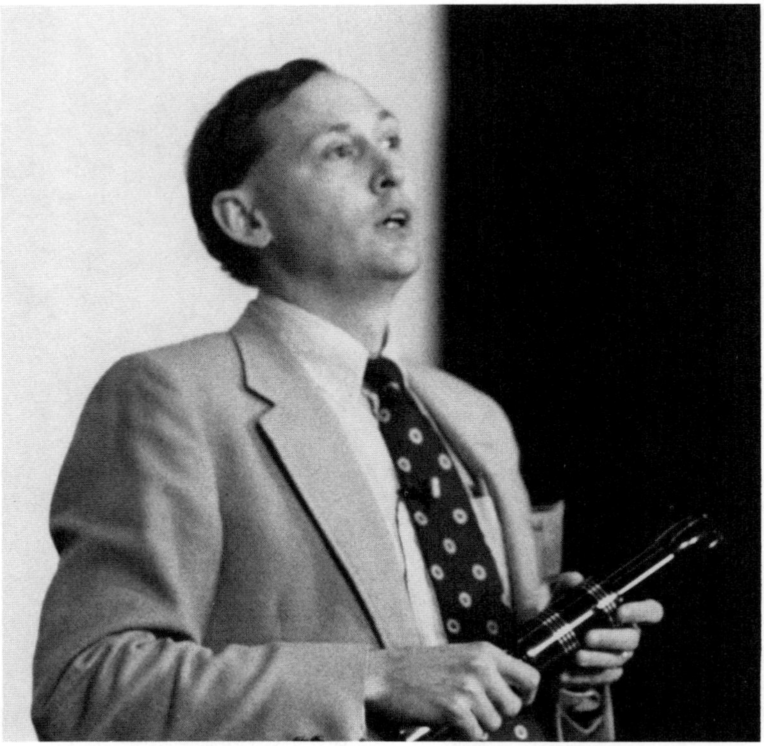

RESULTS FROM NON-ACCELERATOR EXPERIMENTS

J.F. WILKERSON
Physics Division, Los Alamos National Laboratory
Los Alamos, NM 87545 USA

ABSTRACT

The diversity of non-accelerator experiments is at first look both dazzling and even daunting. However, nearly all of these experiments strive to attain the same goal, to search for new physics, beyond the current Standard Model. These measurements are also unified in the fact that their results are often dominated by systematic uncertainties. This review necessarily covers only a limited subset of non-accelerator experiments, and will concentrate on the experimental areas where there has been significant recent progress. The topics reviewed include neutrino mass, double beta decay, solar neutrino, and long-baseline neutrino oscillation measurements.

1. Introduction

Non-accelerator experiments not only span a broad range of topics, they also cover a wide scale of physics, including the atomic, nuclear, and particle regimes. Table 1 offers a current list of topics that non-accelerator measurements are probing. On first inspection of this list, it is difficult to recognize a unifying theme. However closer examination reveals that nearly all of these experiments are searching for the same thing, new physics, not predicted or expected within the framework of the current Standard Model.

There has also been another, somewhat less fortunate thread connecting this field. During the past two decades, while the Standard Model has been verified to higher and higher levels of precision, there have been occasional announcements of "hints" of new physics, and the accompanying high expectations and excitement, from a few of these non-accelerator measurements. However, in all of the cases thus far, the initial high hopes been followed by eventual disappointment, as none of these "hints" has proven true and the Standard Model has held firm. The reason these hints seem to spring up and then disappear is related to the fact that most of these experiments share the characteristics that they are precision experiments attempting to measure very minute quantities with uncertainties that are usually dominated by systematics. As we will demonstrate throughout this review, enormous attention must be paid to understanding systematic uncertainties and their possible impact on the interpretation of results.

This review concentrates on non-accelerator measurements in the neutrino sector, in part because this is an area where there has been recent progress and also because the neutrino sector seems to be a likely place where physics not predicted by the Standard Model may be manifested. This is at least partly due to the rather

Table 1: Summary of Non-Accelerator Measurement Topics.

Topic	Discussed here
Atmospheric Neutrinos	No[1]
Dark Matter	No
Double beta decay	Yes
CP-Violation (neutron and atomic EDM, TRIV, ...)	No
Gravitational interactions (torsion balance, ...)	No
Neutrino Mass Searches	Yes
Neutrino oscillations (long baseline reactor experiments)	Yes
Proton Decay	No
Solar Neutrinos	Yes

arbitrary manner in which the Standard Model deals with neutrinos. In particular, the Standard Model requires that neutrinos be massless, although there are no strong theoretical justifications to do so. However, neutrino masses arise quite naturally within most current theoretical attempts at unification of the electroweak and strong forces, thus offering additional motivation for experimentalists to further probe neutrino properties.

2. Neutrino Mass

2.1. The 17 KeV Neutrino

The claim of the existence of a 17 keV neutrino has waxed and waned over the past eight years. The controversy started in 1985, when John Simpson[2], claimed that a distortion that he had observed in the low-energy end of the tritium beta decay spectrum was best explained by an admixture of a heavy neutrino. If the kink in the beta spectrum was from a neutrino, Simpson determined that it would have a mass of 17.1 keV and be admixed at a level of 3%. Simpson's early claim was not supported by any of the initial measurements made in ^{35}S and ^{63}Ni during the next two years (see Table 2 for a summary of all the 17 keV measurements) and the 17 keV neutrino issue seemed to have died out by 1988.

However, in 1989 Simpson revisited the problem, reporting the results from a series of new measurements and pointing out that there were possible serious systematic problems with all of the earlier null measurements that had ruled out his 17 keV neutrino[3,4]. Motivated by these new claims, a number of groups once again became involved in trying to sort out the problem. By early 1992 there were a host of results supporting the 17 keV neutrino and a slightly larger number ruling out the 17 keV neutrino. A particularly convincing positive result came from Oxford, where Andrew Hime, who had earlier worked with Simpson, presented new measurements made on ^{35}S decay[14]. This result not only had strong statistical sensitivity at the 8 sigma level, but most critics could find no serious flaw in the measurement. The positive results occurred within a wide variety of nuclei, including ^{3}H, ^{14}C, ^{35}S, ^{45}Ca, ^{63}Ni, and ^{71}Ge. All of the positive results were in good agreement for their values of the best fit neutrino mass and the level of heavy neutrino admixture. An

Table 2: Experiments on the 17-keV neutrino.

Collaboration	Source	Method	m_ν, keV	$\sin^2 2\theta$	Ref.
Simpson	T in Si	Crystal	17.1(2)	0.03	2
Haxton		Exchange Corrections			5
Lindhard & Hansen		Screening Corrections			6
Simpson (revised)	T in Si	Crystal	17.1(2)	0.011(3)	3,4
Altzitzoglou et al.	^{35}S	Magnetic		<0.004 99% CL	7
Ohi et al.	^{35}S	Crystal		<0.0015 90% CL	8
Apalikov et al.	^{35}S	Magnetic		<0.0017 90% CL	9
Datar et al.	^{35}S	Crystal		<0.006 90% CL	10
Markey & Boehm	^{35}S	Magnetic		<0.003 90% CL	11
Hetherington et al.	^{63}Ni	Magnetic		<0.003 90% CL	12
Hime & Simpson	T in Ge	Crystal	16.9(1)	0.011(5)	3
Simpson & Hime	^{35}S	Crystal	16.9(4)	0.0073(9,6)	13
Hime & Jelley	^{35}S	Crystal	17.2(5)	0.0085(6,5)	14
Sur et al.	^{14}C	Crystal	17.1(6)	0.012(3)	15
Becker et al.	^{35}S	Magnetic		<0.006 90% CL	16
Zlimen et al.	^{71}Ge (IB)	Crystal	17.2(12)	0.016(7)	17
Schonert et al.	^{177}Lu	Magnetic		<0.004 68% CL	18
Hime & Jelley	^{63}Ni	Crystal	16.8(4)	0.0099(12,18)	19
diGregorio et al.	^{71}Ge (IB)	Crystal	13.8(18)	0.0080(25)	20
Bahran & Kalbfleisch	T_2 gas	Prop. Ctr.		<0.004 98% CL	21
Hargrove et al.	T_2 gas	Prop. Ctr.		(in progress)	22
Wark	^{35}S	Magnetic		(in progress)	23
Freedman et al.	^{35}S	Mag.+Cryst.		<0.0025 95 % CL	24
Simpson	^{45}Ca	Crystal	16.1(8)	0.008(?)	25
Chen et al.	^{35}S	Magnetic		<0.002 90% CL	26
Stoeffl & Decman	T_2 gas	Magnetic		(in progress)	27
Ohshima et al.	^{63}Ni	Magnetic		<0.00073 95% CL	28
Norman et al.	^{55}Fe (IB)	Crystal		(no effect seen)	29

interesting feature of all the positive results was that they had used solid state counters in measuring the beta spectrum. While all measurements made using magnetic spectrometers had reported null results.

By this point, given the abundance of both statistically significant positive and null results, it had become clear that at least one of the problems facing the interpretation of 17 keV neutrino results, was understanding and accounting for systematic uncertainties. To the unbiased observer it was not clear which measurements had problems and which were correct. For example, Bonvicini[30] made a critical study of the analysis methods used in the magnetic spectrometer measurements where shape-correction parameters are used. This study indicated that nearly all of the spectrometer based studies had at best overestimated their sensitivity, and at worst could have easily washed-out a 17 keV neutrino kink. There were also possible problems in the positive solid state based measurements. Piilonen and Abashian[31] performed detailed Monte Carlo studies that indicated that small second order scattering effects might give rise to kinks in the beta spectrum.

What was disappointing was that up to this point, none of the experiments had attempted to make a direct calibration of their apparatus to prove the sensitivity to positive or null results. The suggestions had been made earlier that experiments should calibrate their detectors. Experiments finding null results could make a mixed source by adding a small admixture (1%) of a source having a lower endpoint energy[32]. These experiments should prove they had the sensitivity to observe the expected kink at the endpoint of the lower energy source. Experiments finding a positive result or kink, could simultaneously measure another beta source with a higher endpoint energy. This higher energy source should have a smooth spectrum in the same energy region where the original source exhibited a kink[33].

Today, the question of the existence of a 17 keV at the 1% level has been clearly answered. Two new measurements designed to eliminate many of the systematic problems encountered in earlier experiments, have now presented results that clearly rule out a 17 keV neutrino well below the 1% level. A group at Argonne National Laboratory designed a clever experiment that combined the best features of magnetic spectrometers and solid state detectors[24]. By using a magnetic solenoid, they were able to transport the betas emerging from their ^{35}S source to a solid state detector without any baffles or slits. Their measurement yielded a limit of $\leq 0.25\%$ admixture of a 17 keV neutrino at the 95% CL. More importantly, the group tested their sensitivity by making a composite source containing by fraction of total decays 1.34% of ^{14}C, which has an endpoint 11 keV below that of ^{35}S. Their best fit to the fraction of ^{14}C in the mixed source was $1.4 \pm 0.1\%$ of ^{14}C, in excellent agreement with the expected value. The results from both their measurements are shown in Figure 1.

The other experiment to produced a null result was a magnetic spectrometer based measurement on ^{63}Ni made at the Institute for Nuclear Studies in Tokyo[28]. This experiment reduced the problem of sensitivity to shape correction parameters by acquiring extremely high statistics over a very narrow energy range centered about the energy region where the 17 keV kink was expected to appear. Their announced statistical limit $\leq 0.073\%$ admixture of a 17 keV neutrino at the 95% CL does not contain any estimates of systematic uncertainties. However, given the narrow energy range measured, it is unlikely that the type of problems Bonvicini pointed out would obscure a 17 keV neutrino. Nevertheless, the Tokyo group will hopefully present a final analysis that includes realistic estimates of systematic uncertainties.

The final blow to the 17 keV neutrino comes from a reanalysis by Hime of the positive Oxford results[34]. Hime's new analysis indicates that Piilonen and Abashian were correct in worrying about second order scattering effects. The reanalysis indicates that the kink observed in the Oxford data could indeed arise entirely from multiple scattering on slits and baffles in the Oxford measurement chamber. What was especially surprising was the fact that the experiment was found to be extremely insensitive to first order scattering effects, but not second order ones. Hime demonstrated that this sensitivity arises mainly because of the unfavorable energy dependence of the multiple scattering.

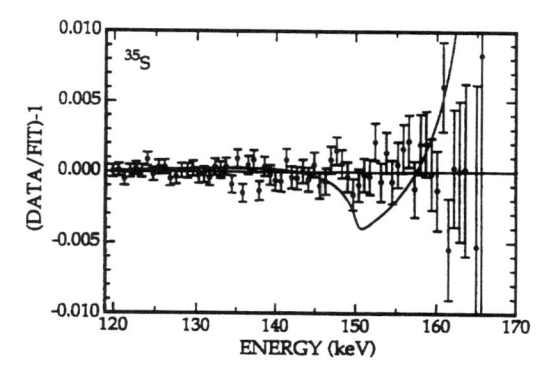

Figure 1. (a) Residuals from Freedman et al. ^{35}S measurement for a fit to data assuming no massive neutrino. The solid curve represents the residuals expected for decay with a 17 keV neutrino and $\sin^2 2\theta = 0.85\%$ mass.

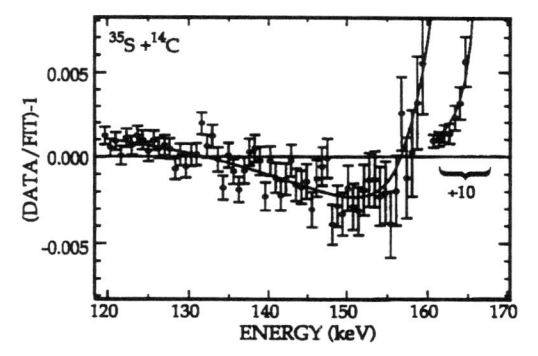

Figure 1. (b) Residuals from Freedman et al. ^{35}S and ^{14}C measurement. The fit assumed no ^{14}C present.

Even though the 17 keV neutrino has been laid to rest, one can see that precision measurements of the beta spectrum shape can offer a sensitive method of searching for new physics. The key is that one must have a thorough understanding of all possible shape effects and one must not overestimate an experiment's sensitivity. It is important to not rely on calculations, but to find methods that allow one to directly measure an experiment's sensitivity.

2.2. Direct Measurements of Neutrino Mass

Direct searches for neutrino mass have the advantage that there are few, if any, theoretical assumptions involved. Unlike the indirect searches where one is forced to assume the non-conservation of total lepton number or lepton family, the direct searches are based on purely kinematical considerations. The current best limits on neutrino mass from published measurements are $m_\nu < 9.3$ eV (95% CL)

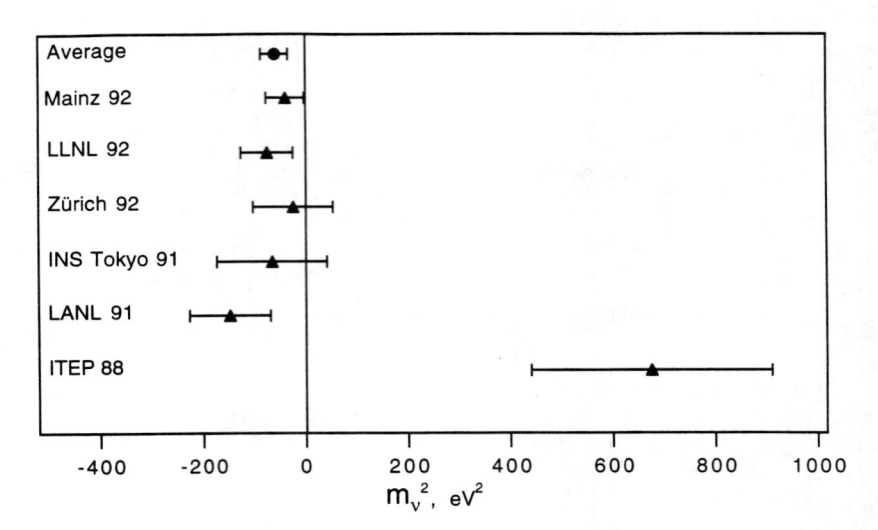

Figure 2. Tritium Beta Decay Neutrino Mass^2 Results.

for the electron neutrino[35], < 270 keV (90% CL) for the muon neutrino[36,37], and < 35 MeV (95% CL) for the tau neutrino[38]. The limits on the μ_ν and τ_ν neutrinos come from accelerator based measurements and will not be discussed here. Detailed reviews of direct neutrino mass measurements can be found in the literature[39–41].

Nuclear beta decay experiments set the most stringent limits on the mass of the electron neutrino (actually antineutrino, we make no distinction here). These experiments are sensitive to the neutrino mass in the energy region of the beta spectrum from a few m_ν below the endpoint to the endpoint energy, E_o, of the decay. Essentially the search for neutrino mass in beta decay is simply a search for a distortion in the shape of the spectrum in the endpoint region. The low endpoint energy of 18.58 keV for the decay of tritium plus the fact that it is an allowed decay makes it an ideal source to search for neutrino mass. A report in 1980 by Lyubimov et al. of a 35 eV electron neutrino mass[42] spurred nearly two dozen groups around the world to attempt and verify this significant result. Over a decade later just three groups from Los Alamos[35], Zurich[43], and Tokyo[44] have published results. In addition a group from Lawrence Livermore[45] and a group from Mainz[46] have recently reported results at conferences. The results from the five groups, all upper limits, are in clear disagreement with and rule out the revised ITEP value[47] of 26 eV (see Figure 2).

Although the five recent results seem to definitively rule out the ITEP non-zero value, they all share the troubling feature that they have negative m_ν^2 values giving a mean value of
$$m_\nu^2 = -59 \pm 26 \text{ eV}^2,$$

which is 2.3σ from 0. Thus, one must consider possible mechanisms that might cause all five values to be negative.

Statistical There is only a 1.2% probability that the effect arises from statistics.

Systematics There are certainly a large number of possibilities here. To solve the problem, at least several of the experiments must suffer from a systematic shape effect that results in a negative value. Or all of them may be suffering from the same not understood systematic problem. On the other hand the two measurements that lie closest to zero have the greatest systematic uncertainties.

Models incorrect Perhaps we do not understand some fundamental physics interaction that is modifying the shape near the endpoint.

Note that these five independent measurements vary enormously, there are 4 different types of sources used and three totally different momentum analyzing spectrometers.

Precisely characterizing all possible processes that modify the shape of the observed beta spectrum is required in making an accurate measurement of neutrino mass. We know from the example of comparing the ITEP result to any of the other five recent tritium measurements that two statistically significant results can be in total disagreement. It is also important to recognize that as one attempts to increase sensitivity and measure smaller values of m_ν^2 that the total uncertainty budget varies as the square of the neutrino mass sensitivity. This budget is the sum of both statistical and systematic uncertainties. Thus, while a 30 eV mass limit has a total uncertainty budget of 900 eV^2, a measurement with 8 eV sensitivity has a total uncertainty budget of 64 eV^2. In retrospect, the early claims from some groups that they planned to make measurements to 1 eV sensitivity were clearly not realistic. Pushing down to 5-6 eV sensitivity is going to be very difficult and there is the real concern that groups must not underestimate the possible systematic errors in their experiment.

There are a four primary process that contribute to modifying the shape of the observed beta spectrum: energy loss, instrumental resolution, energy dependent efficiencies of the analyzing system, and atomic final state effects. All of these shape effects must be correctly accounted for before one can extract a neutrino mass from the beta spectrum. Because the elimination of most of these systematic shape effects is impossible, one must minimize and accurately account for them in a model independent manner where possible. Usually this means that one should attempt to perform a measurement of the particular shape modifying process. The Los Alamos experiment set the standard in becoming the first measurement to break the 10 eV sensitivity barrier. In doing so they implemented a number of new techniques to reduce or eliminate systematics, including; building the first gaseous molecular tritium source; discovering an ideal calibration source of ^{83}Kr^m that allowed both a direct energy calibration and a direct measurement of the instrumental resolution function; and performing the first in-situ energy loss measurements for their source[35,48]. By making these direct measurements, the LANL results only had to rely on a calculation of the final state corrections for the molecular tritium source, the simplest source used in any tritium measurements to date. Initially, LANL's negative mass squared value and the endpoint energy value led critics to say that the experiment must be wrong. However, the LANL results have been confirmed both for the mass squared value and the endpoint value, and the two most recent experiments at LLNL and Mainz have adopted nearly all of the Los Alamos measurement innovations.

However, the question remains why does the measured beta spectrum shape curve the "wrong way" giving a negative value? There are a number of speculative physics explanations that have been proposed including interactions with relic neutrinos, neutrino magnetic moments, tachyonic neutrinos, and a possible new a scalar particle that only interacts with neutrinos. However, until further experimental measurements have been done it is premature to accept any of the above explanations. What is needed is for the next generation experiments including those at LLNL and Mainz that are now running to not only acquire more statistics, but to actively search for possible systematic effects. In particular, attention should be concentrated on the possible impact of atomic final states, since these along with Fermi beta decay theory are really the only calculations on which the measurements depend. Ultimately, to reach a sensitivity of 5 eV will require that these experiment determine the shape dependent effects that modify the beta spectrum to a new degree of accuracy. It will certainly be interesting to see what the final results of the new generation of these experiments turn out to be.

3. Double Beta Decay

In some radioactive nuclei, ordinary beta decay is energetically forbidden, while the two neutrino double beta decay mode

$$Nucleus(Z, A) \rightarrow Nucleus(Z+2, A) + 2e^- + 2\nu_e$$

is energetically allowed by standard electroweak theory. This mode has now been observed in ^{76}Ge, ^{82}Se, ^{100}Mo, and ^{150}Nd nuclei[49,50]. The 0ν double beta decay mode

$$Nucleus(Z, A) \rightarrow Nucleus(Z+2, A) + 2e^-$$

while favored by phase space considerations over the 2ν mode, can only occur if the neutrino has mass and the neutrino is a Majorana particle (the particle and antiparticle are indistinguishable, which requires that lepton number is violated). The 0ν mode would appear as a monoenergetic decay line, and is thus quite distinct from the 2ν mode. At present, all double beta decay experiments searching for the 0ν decay mode set upper limits on the half-life for the decay of the parent nuclei to be on the order of $> 10^{22} - 10^{24}$ years. The most sensitive to these measurements have been achieved using enriched ^{76}Ge detectors[50,51], where the Majorana neutrino mass, if the decay mode were to be allowed, is now constrained to be $< 2 \pm 1 eV$.

Recently, several experiments searching for 0ν double beta decay have reported observing some excess counts in the energy region just below the endpoint[49-51].

Some observers have interpreted these excess counts as arising from the existence of a massless Goldstone boson or "Majoron" that couples to the neutrinos. However, even though the anomalous results are being seen by three different groups, one must once again be very cautious when considering possible systematics. The Irvine group[49], which has the data of greatest statistical significance, is making no claims of new physics and has started to probe for a number of possible experimental systematic problems. They have increased the magnetic field of their TPC in order to increase energy resolution and have prepared a new more intense ^{100}Mo source. They hope to announce new results by mid-1993. It will be interesting to see the future results from all of the double beta decay measurements.

4. Solar Neutrinos

Bruno Pontecorvo's rather radical proposition of observing neutrinos produced in the sun in 1946, was motivated by the desire to learn about the physics going on at the core of the sun[52]. Unlike the photons, which take on average of 10,000 years to diffuse out from the core, the neutrinos escape the sun's core essentially instantaneously with no scattering. Pontecorvo's dream of looking for solar neutrinos was not realized until over 20 years later when Ray Davis began his ambitious chlorine based solar neutrino experiment at the Homestake gold mine in South Dakota[53] using the reaction:

$$^{37}\text{Cl} + \nu_e \rightarrow {}^{37}\text{Ar} + e^-.$$

From the late-1960's until the mid-1980's the Davis experiment endured as the only solar neutrino measurement in existence. The tantalizing result from this measurement is that the deduced solar neutrino signal is about three times lower than the signal predicted by solar models. This discrepancy between the experimental observations and the standard solar model (SSM) predictions has become known as the solar neutrino problem.

However, the Davis radiochemical measurement cannot yield any information that tells us if its observed signal is actually coming from the sun. Perhaps for this reason the experiment was slow to arouse wide interest. It was not for another 20 years, until December of 1986, that a second solar neutrino experiment started taking data. This new experiment, a water Cerenkov detector known as Kamiokande II, was originally built to search for proton decay in the Kamioka mine in Japan. The reaction it utilizes,

$$\nu_e + e^- \rightarrow \nu_e + e^-,$$

does have directional sensitivity to neutrino interactions, and after several years of acquiring data, Kamiokande convincingly demonstrated that neutrinos were being emitted from the sun[54]. Of equal significance, the experiment observed less than half the number of predicted neutrinos, thus confirming the Davis result.

These two results motivated a number of theoretical speculations that include solar physics based solutions and particle physics solutions. These speculations raised the question as to whether the "solar neutrino problem" is a problem with our understanding of solar physics or arises from unexpected neutrino properties. The cornerstone of current predictions for solar neutrino flux is Bethe's seminal 1939 explanation of energy generation in stars[55]. The standard solar models are based on a foundation of exhaustive experimental nuclear physics measurements as well as theoretical predictions of how the sun works. Currently there are two detailed SSM based calculations that predict the solar neutrinos fluxes, the Bahcall - Pinsonneault[56] (B-P) and Turck-Chiezé[57] (T-C) models. These two models are in reasonable agreement, with most discrepancies arising from slightly different interpretations of experimental data. Within this paper where not specified we use the B-P calculations.

Most of the solar physics explanations to the solar neutrino problem are based on the fact that both the Davis and Kamiokande experiments are not sensitive to the low-energy neutrinos emitted by the proton - proton (pp) reaction,

$$p + p \rightarrow {}^2H + e^+ + \nu_e,$$

which is the primary fusion reaction thought to occur in the sun. Both Davis and Kamiokande are primarily sensitive to neutrinos created from the ^8B reaction,

$$^8B \rightarrow {}^7Be + e^+ + \nu_e.$$

This reaction has a very small total branching fraction of 0.01 % of the neutrinos leaving the sun, but more importantly is also a reaction that is highly dependent on the assumed core temperature of the sun varying approximately as $\sim T^{18}$. Thus, most non-standard solar models account for the discrepancy between observed and predicted solar neutrino flux by lowering the core temperature.

Most of the particle physics solutions to the solar neutrino problem have relied on introducing new neutrino properties to account for the missing solar neutrinos. In most cases the original electron neutrinos are induced by some mechanism to change neutrino flavor before reaching the earth. Possible mechanisms to cause neutrinos to change flavors are interactions with the neutrino magnetic moment, vacuum oscillations, and matter enhanced neutrino oscillations that would occur primarily in the sun. All of these mechanisms would require that the neutrinos have mass and be able to change flavor and thus require new properties beyond the current standard model of particle physics.

At present the most popular theoretical explanation for the missing neutrinos is the idea of matter enhanced neutrino oscillations, or MSW effect[58,59]. The basic idea uses the fact that as neutrinos propagate thorough the sun the electron neutrinos experience both charge current and neutral current interactions and see a varying interaction potential because of the change in the density of matter in the sun. However, the mu or tau neutrinos only undergo neutral current interactions and see a differently varying interaction potential. These two different interaction potentials then give rise to a two-state quantum mechanical level crossing, where mixing between flavors could occur. One of the reasons that the MSW solution is so popular is that in addition to being able to accommodate the data from all of

Table 3: Solar Neutrino Experiments.

Collaboration	Target	Threshold (MeV)	Measured Flux/SSM	Total Counts	Year of Operation
Homestake	^{37}Cl	≥ 0.814	0.28 ± 0.03	530	1969
Kamiokande	e^-	≥ 7.5	$0.49 \pm 0.04 \pm 0.06$	380	1986
SAGE	^{71}Ge	≥ 0.233	$0.44 +0.13/-0.18 \pm 0.11$	25	1990
GALLEX	^{71}Ge	≥ 0.233	$0.63 \pm 0.14 \pm 0.06$	70	1991

the current experiments, it is also yields values of the mixing angle and neutrino masses that are reasonable in most grand unified theories.

In order to try and understand the origin of the solar neutrino problem, one needs a method to observe the low-energy pp neutrinos. The reaction

$$^{71}\text{Ga} + \nu_e \rightarrow\ ^{71}\text{Ge} + e^-,$$

with an energy threshold of 233 keV allows one to do this. The SSM predicts that nearly 60% of the predicted neutrinos observed in the gallium experiments should come from the pp neutrinos. Since the predicted pp neutrino flux is strongly linked to the luminosity output of the sun, it would be very difficult for any type of solar model to reduce the pp flux substantially. In fact, if the gallium experiments observe less than 60% of the predicted SSM neutrino flux, it would be a strong indication of new neutrino properties. (The uncertainties in the expected neutrino flux from the pp reaction are minimal and estimated[60] to be about 2%.)

There are currently two gallium experiments underway, a Russian-US collaboration known as SAGE and a European-US effort known as GALLEX. The SAGE collaboration announced their first results in 1990 from 6 months of data taken using a target of 30 tons of gallium metal[61]. Their result for the ratio of measured flux to the predicted SSM flux was 0.15. In terms of counts, this corresponded to observing 2.6 decays instead of the predicted 17 decays. Given the very limited statistics, a more meaningful number emphasized was the upper limit the experiment placed on the ratio of the observed to predicted neutrino flux of $< .60$ (90% CL). The group reported the results with the proviso that an assumption is made that the extraction efficiency for the ^{71}Ge produced by solar neutrinos is the same as from the natural Ge carrier. SAGE spent most of the following year performing a number of calibrations and tests to try and verify their measurements. All of the calibrations were consistent with the system operating correctly.

In June 1992, the GALLEX collaboration announced their first results from measurements made on 30 tons of gallium in the form of a solution GaCl$_4$. The experiment had been delayed by about one year because of a problem with the removal of ^{68}Ge, an isotope with a 271 day half-life that is formed while the gallium is on the surface exposed to cosmic rays. (It is difficult to distinguish ^{68}Ge from the ^{71}Ge decays of interest.) The GALLEX group verified that the ^{68}Ge retention problem was a chemical one by heating their solution and were able to reduce this problem. Their initial results[62] are that the ratio of observed to predicted SSM

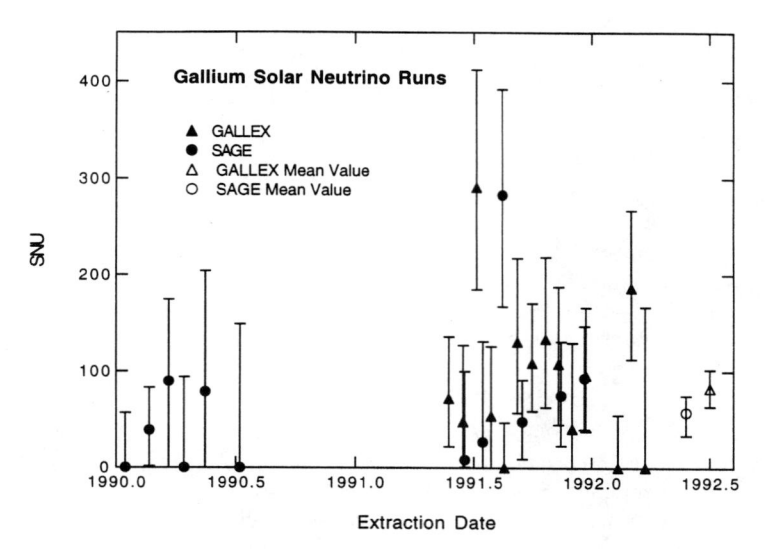

Figure 3. Gallium Solar Neutrino Results.

neutrino flux is 0.63. The collaboration presented convincing evidence that they were seeing decays of the 11.43 day half life ^{71}Ge and had thus clearly seen pp neutrinos. Two months later, in August 1992, the SAGE collaboration announced new results based on 6 additional measurements taken during 1991. Four of these measurements had been taken with 57 tons of gallium metal. The result for the combined analysis of all data sets gave a measured flux/SSM flux ratio of 0.44.

The SAGE and GALLEX results are shown in Figure 3. Both experiments plan to acquire additional statistics as well as to calibrate the detectors using a direct neutrino source of ^{51}Cr. This source gives off a monoenergetic neutrinos of 746 keV (90%) and 426 keV (10%). The lower energy line lies just above the maximum energy of the pp neutrinos. Because of the interesting region in which the gallium results lie, it is still possible to accommodate both solar physics and neutrino physics solutions to the solar neutrino problem. As shown in Figure 4, the MSW solution still has two allowed regions for solutions[63].

As one can see in Table 3, all the measurements to date suffer from very limited statistics. In addition, radiochemical experiments have the limitation that they are unable to demonstrate that their signal is generated by solar neutrinos. Motivated by these factors and by the now persistent ambuguity as to the correct solution to the solar neutrino problem, a number of new solar neutrino experiments are now being constructed or developed, three of which are described below.

Sudbury Neutrino Observatory (SNO) A Canadian - US collaboration is building a heavy water (D$_2$0) based Cerenkov detector in Sudbury, Ontario. The unique

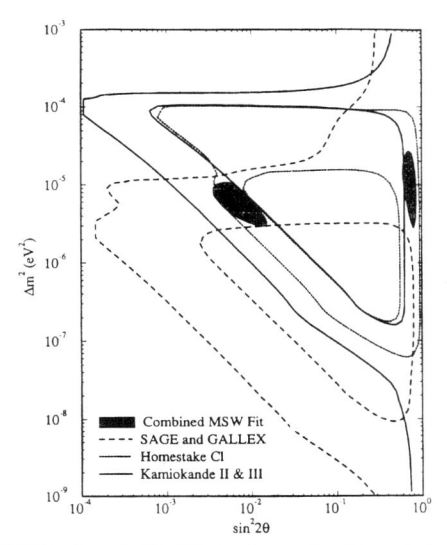

Figure 4. Allowed MSW Regions (90% CL) for fits to Combined Solar Neutrino Measurements[63].

feature of this detector is that it can detect not only the electron neutrinos, but more importantly it can also detect electron, mu, and tau neutrinos by neutral current neutrino disintegration of deuterium. Thus, SNO is uniquely positioned to be able to distinguish particle physics from solar physics solutions. This experiment, expected to turn on in late 1995, also will be one of the first to have good statistical sensitivity. Assuming a rate of 0.46 times the SSM predicted flux (scaling to Kamiokande II) with no MSW effect SNO should see (with a 5 MeV threshold) about 5000 charged current events per year and 1200 neutral current events. If the MSW effect is correct, SNO should observe 4000 charged current events and 2800 neutral current events. Finally, the measurement should be able to obtain information about the spectral shape of the ^{8}B neutrinos.

SuperKamiokande The Japanese are now constructing a new 22,000 ton volume light water detector, similar to the original Kamiokande detector. The SSM predicted event rate, depending on the achieved energy detection threshold, will be between 7000 - 18000 counts per year. The experiment is slated to start acquiring data by late 1995 or early 1996.

BOREXINO An Italian - US - USSR collaboration is starting to prototype a 100 ton liquid scintillator based detector. This detector has the feature that it should be sensitive to the ^{7}Be neutrinos, which are emitted as a monoenergetic line. If the collaboration can obtain the extremely high purities required, then the detector would be expected from the SSM to observe about 18000 events per year. This detector would be very sensitive to MSW effects and able to help restrict the possible MSW solutions. The group has an even more ambitious kiloton scintillator based project known as BOREX which would make precise measurements of the ^{8}B neutrino spectrum.

The main limitation of the new generation of detectors is that they cannot detect the low energy pp neutrinos. Clearly the ideal solar neutrino detector would be one that would have the ability to detect these neutrinos in real-time with high statistical accuracy; have good background rejection; and neutral current detection. Such a detector has not yet been designed, but efforts to research new ideas are underway. One particularly promising effort that would be sensitive to the pp neutrinos in real time is an attempt to use a superfluid He based detector being worked on at Brown University[64]. With a 10 ton detector it is estimated that one could observe 20 events per day. It may be that cryogenic based detectors will be the detectors of the next decade.

The quest to observe solar neutrinos from the sun has evolved from a lone experiment with a handful of researchers in a remote gold mine in South Dakota to a worldwide effort with multiple experiments and scores of researchers. With the gallium experiments continuing to acquire further statistics and planning calibrations in 1994, and with SNO, Super Kamiokande, and BOREXINO detectors turning on in the mid-1990's it seems likely that the long standing mystery of missing solar neutrino flux will be solved during the decade of the 90's.

5. Long-baseline Neutrino Oscillation Searches

If at least one flavor of neutrino has mass, and if any conservation of lepton number is violated, than neutrino oscillations are possible. Even though there are claimed "hints" of neutrino oscillations from solar neutrino and atmospheric neutrino observations[1], there is at present no positive evidence from neutrino oscillations searches performed at accelerators and reactors. (There have been several instances in the past when terrestrial source experiments did have positive results, but in all cases these positive results turned out to arise from systematic problems.) Unfortunately, the regions where the solar and atmospheric neutrino oscillations are claimed to occur are regions that have been inaccessible to the terrestrial source experiments.

However, there are now a number of long-baseline neutrino oscillation experiments that have been proposed to be built at both accelerators and reactors. These experiments would be able to probe Δm^2 in the region of $10^{-1} - 10^{-3}$ eV^2. This is the region where the atmospheric neutrino oscillations are claimed to occur. There is one reactor based experiment under construction near the San Onofre power plant in California[65]. Two other experiments are at the proposal stage, one to be located near a nuclear power plant near Chooz, France[66], and the other at the Morton Fairport mine in Ohio[67]. These experiments, with detectors located at distances about 1 km away from the reactors, should be able to test and verify the atmospheric neutrino oscillation claims.

6. Conclusions

The thriving field of non-accelerator physics continues to probe the limits of the Standard Model. As we have seen for nearly all the areas discussed, one must perform these measurements with careful attention to possible systematic problems. Before the current "hints" of new physics in solar neutrino, atmospheric neutrino, and double beta decay experiments can be believed, much additional work needs to be completed.

7. References

1. D. Sinclair plenary talk, these proceedings.
2. J.J. Simpson, *Phys. Rev. Lett.* **54** (1985) 1891.
3. A. Hime and J.J. Simpson, *Phys. Rev.* **D39** 1837 (1989).
4. J.J. Simpson, *Phys. Lett.* **B174** (1986) 113.
5. W.C. Haxton, *Phys. Rev. Lett.* **55** (1985) 807.
6. J. Lindhard and P.G. Hansen, *Phys. Rev. Lett.* **57** (1986) 965; B. Eman and D. Tadic, *Phys. Rev.* **C33** (1986) 2128.
7. T. Altzitzoglou et al., *Phys. Rev. Lett.* **55** (1985) 799.
8. T. Ohi et al., *Phys. Lett.* **B160** (1985) 322.
9. A. Apalikov et al., *JETP Lett.* **42** (1985) 289; V.A. Lyubimov, contr. to *Workshop on the 17 keV Neutrino Question*, Berkeley, CA, December 18-20, 1991 (unpublished).
10. V.M. Datar et al., *Nature* **318** (1985) 547.
11. J. Markey and F. Boehm, *Phys. Rev.* **C32** (1985) 2215.
12. D.W. Hetherington et al., *Phys. Rev.* **C36** (1987) 1504.
13. J.J. Simpson and A. Hime, *Phys. Rev.* **D39** (1989) 1825.
14. A. Hime and N.A. Jelley, *Phys. Lett.* **B257** (1991) 441.
15. B. Sur et al., *Phys. Rev. Lett.* **66** (1991) 2444.
16. H. Becker et al., *Caltech preprint CALT-63-605* (1991).
17. I. Zlimen et al., *Phys. Rev. Lett.* **67** (1991) 560.
18. S. Schonert et al., in *Int. Workshop on Electroweak Physics beyond the Standard Model*, Valencia, Spain, October 2-5, 1991.
19. A. Hime and N.A. Jelley, *Oxford preprint OUNP 91-21* (1991).
20. D.E. DiGregorio et al., *TANDAR preprint LNY584 L-1 SB* (1991).
21. M. Bahran and G.R. Kalbfleisch, *Oklahoma preprint OKHEP 91-005* (1991).
22. C.K. Hargrove, in *Beyond the Standard Model III*, Ottawa, Canada, June 22-24, 1992 (to be published).

23. D.L. Wark, in *Workshop on the 17 keV Neutrino Question*, Berkeley, CA, December 18-20, 1991 (unpublished).
24. S.J. Freedman, these proceedings; Mortara et al., *ANL Preprint* (1992).
25. J.J. Simpson, in *Beyond the Standard Model III*, Ottawa, Canada, June 22-24, 1992 (to be published).
26. M. Chen, in *CalTech preprint CALT-63-638* (1992).
27. W. Stoeffl and D. Decman, in *The Many Aspects of Neutrino Physics*, Fermilab Workshop, Batavia, IL, Nov. 14-17, 1991 (unpublished).
28. T. Ohshima, *KEK preprint 92-120* (1992).
29. E.B. Norman, *Proceedings of the 26th International Conference on High Energy Physics* Dallas, Texas, August 6-12,1992 (to be published).
30. G. Bonvicini, *CERN preprint CERN EP-92/xx* (1992).
31. L. Piilonen and M. Abashian, *preprint VPI-IHEP-92/6* (1992).
32. S.R. Elliott, private communication, (1991).
33. J.F. Wilkerson, in *XIII International Workshop on Weak Interactions and Neutrino Physics*, Gran Sasso Italy, July 7-13, 1991 (unpublished).
34. A. Hime, *LANL preprint LA-UR-92-3087* (1992) and these proceedings.
35. R. G. H. Robertson et al., *Phys. Rev. Lett.* **67** (1991) 957.
36. R. Abela et al., *Phys. Lett.* **B146** (1984) 149.
37. B. Jeckelmann et al., *Phys. Rev. Lett.* **56** (1986) 1444.
38. A. Albrecht et al., *Phys. Lett.* **B202** (1988) 149.
39. R.G.H. Robertson and D. A. Knapp, *Ann. Rev. Nucl. Part. Sci.* **38** (1988) 185.
40. E. Holzschuh, *Rep. Prog. Phys.* **55** (1992) 1035.
41. J.F. Wilkerson, in *Proc. XV Int. Conf. on Neutrino Physics and Astrophysics "Neutrinos '92"*, Granada, Spain, June 6-11, 1992 (to be published).
42. V. A. Lyubimov et al., *Phys. Lett.* **B94** (1980) 266.
43. E. Holzschuh et al., *Phys. Lett.* **B287** (1992) 381.
44. H. Kawakami et al., *Phys. Lett.* **B256** (1991) 105.
45. W. Stoeffl, *Bull. Am. Phys. Soc.* **37** (1992) 925.
46. H. Backe et al., in *Proc. XV Int. Conf. on Neutrino Physics and Astrophysics "Neutrinos '92"*, Granada, Spain, June 6-11, 1992 (to be published); A. Picard et al., *Nucl. Instr. and Methods in Phys. Research* **B63** (1992) 345.
47. S. Boris et al., *Pis'ma Zh. Eksp. Teor. Fiz.* **45** (1987) 267; *Sov. Phys. JETP Lett* **45** (1987) 333; *Phys. Rev. Lett.* **58** (1987) 2019; V.A. Lyubimov, *Proc. Int. Conf. Neutrino '88*, ed. J. Schneps et al. (World Scientific, Singapore, 1989), p. 2.
48. J. F. Wilkerson et al., *Nucl. Phys.* **B19** *Proc. Suppl.* (1991) 215.

49. M.K. Moe, M.A. Nelson, M.A. Vient, and S.R. Elliott, in *Proc. XV Int. Conf. on Neutrino Physics and Astrophysics "Neutrino '92"*, Granada, Spain, June 6-12, 1992 (to be published).
50. F.T. Avignone III, et al. *Phys. Lett.* **B256** (1991) 559 and these proceedings.
51. A. Balysh et al., *Phys. Lett.* **B283** (1992) 32; A. Piepke, *Proceedings of the 26th International Conference on High Energy Physics* Dallas, Texas, August 6-12,1992 (to be published).
52. B. Pontecorvo, *Inverse Beta Decay*, Chalk River report PD-205 (1946); *Usp. Fiz. Nauk.* **141**, (1983) 675 [*Sov. Phys. Usp.* **26** (1982) 1087].
53. R. Davis et al., *Phys. Rev. Lett.* **20** (1968) 1205; K. Lande et al.,*Proc. XV Int. Conf. on Neutrino Physics and Astrophysics "Neutrinos '92"*, Granada, Spain, June 6-11, 1992 (to be published).
54. K.S. Hirata et al., *Phys. Rev. Lett.* **19** (1989) 77; T. Kajita, *Proceedings of the 26th International Conference on High Energy Physics* Dallas, Texas, August 6-12,1992 (to be published).
55. H. A. Bethe and C.L. Critchfield, *Phys. Rev.* **54** (1938) 248; H. A. Bethe, *Phys. Rev.* **55** (1939) 434.
56. J.N. Bahcall and H.M. Pinsonneault, *Rev. Mod. Phys.* **64** (1992) 885.
57. S. Turck-Chiezé, S. Cahen, M. Casse, and C. Doom, *Ap. J.* **335** (1988) 415.
58. S.P. Mikheyev and A. Yu. Smirnov, *Yad. Phys.* **42** (1985) 1441; *Sov. J. Nucl. Phys.* **42** (1985) 913.
59. L. Wolfenstein, *Phys. Rev.* **D17** (1978) 2369.
60. J.N. Bahcall, *Neutrino Astrophysics* (Cambridge University Press, Cambridge 1989).
61. A.I. Abazov et al., *Phys. Rev. Lett.* **67** (1991) 3332; V.A. Gavrin, in *Proceedings of the 26th International Conference on High Energy Physics* Dallas, Texas, August 6-12,1992 (to be published).
62. P. Anselmann et al., *Phys. Lett.* **B285** (1992) 376; P. Anselmann et al., *Phys. Lett.* **B285** (1992) 390, D. Vignaud, in *Proceedings of the 26th International Conference on High Energy Physics* Dallas, Texas, August 6-12,1992 (to be published).
63. S.A. Bludman et al., *Pennsylvania preprint UPR-0516T* (1992).
64. R.E. Lanou et al.,*Phys. Rev. Lett.* **58** (1987) 2498.
65. F. Boehm, these proceedings.
66. Y. Declais et al., *Letter of Intent: Search for Neutrino Oscillations at a Distance of 1 km from Two Power Reactors at Chooz*, 1992 (unpublished).
67. R.I. Steinberg, these proceedings.

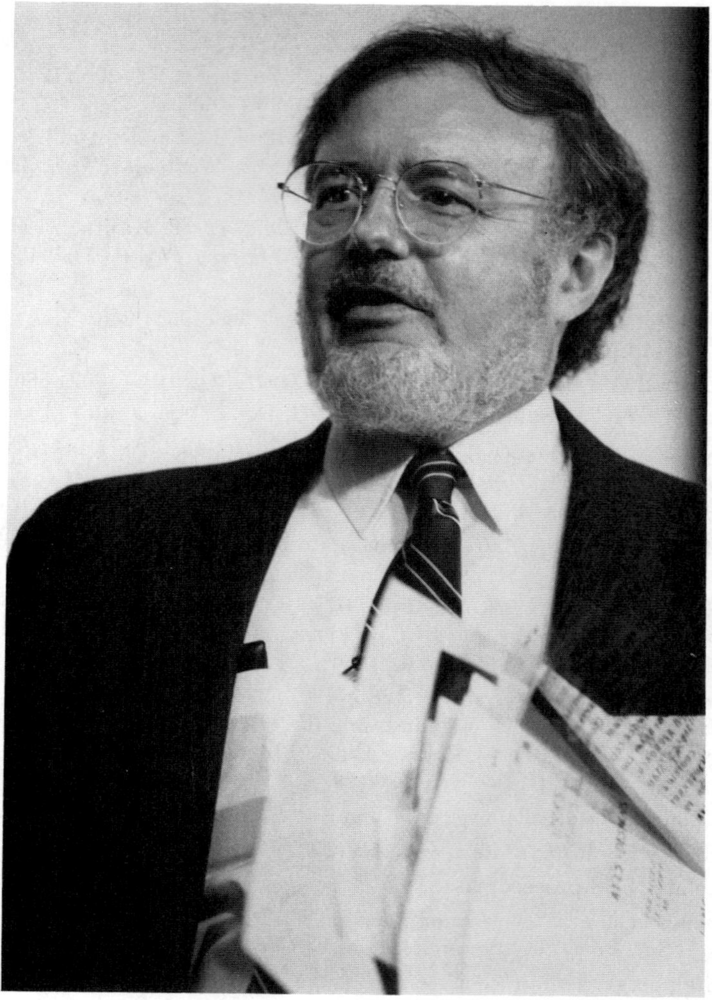

RECENT DEVELOPMENTS IN ACCELERATORS

MAURY TIGNER[1]
Floyd R. Newman Laboratory of Nuclear Studies, Cornell University
Ithaca, New York 14853-5001, USA

ABSTRACT

Accelerator development activity worldwide is intense. Some of these developments in the areas of superconducting magnet materials, "factories," linear colliders, and "new accelerator concepts" are briefly reviewed.

1. Magnet Materials

The classic low temperature material NbTi shows continued improvement in current carrying capacity. If we tabulate the current density at quench of commercially available wire for 1980, 1986, 1991 at $5T$, $4.2K$ we find, 1800, 3200 and $5200 A/mm^2$ respectively. As the temperature is lowered below $2K$, $10T$ magnets of this material have become practical.

This progress owes its strength to increasingly sophisticated methods for precipitating pinning centers at the microscopic scale, homogeneously throughout the material. A new invention, the installation of pinning centers at the macroscopic scale promises still further improvements.

Application of these improvements to I.P. focusing and dipoles will enable significant improvement to existing accelerators, both e and p as well as make possible new accelerators with improved performance.

2. Factories

Need to probe the Standard Model more deeply has inspired designs for accelerators at special energies. Their design luminosities are 10 to 100 times that now achieved. Such accelerators are called "factories" e.g. phi factories, tau-charm factories, and B factories. Figure 1 shows the target luminosities (roughly) for these machines against the backdrop of existing machines. In all there are at least 14 such proposals, each well developed.

While each of these factories has its own particular technical challenges and for each have been developed particular tricks for surmounting them, we take the B factory as our paradigm for this review.

2.1. B Factory Physics Requirements and Technical Approach

The physics objectives for B factories require luminosities in the 3×10^{33} to 10^{34} $cm^{-2}s^{-1}$ range. The CM energy must be $10.6 GeV$ with some tunability and the CM must be moving in the lab. frame. In addition, it is most important that synchrotron radiation and lost particle backgrounds be kept low.

---
[1]Supported by the National Science Foundation

Meeting those requirements leads directly to the need for two independent rings with beams colliding at one detector location. All extant proposals envision running at the single bunch, beam-beam limit with bunch intensities comparable with those now in use. The high luminosity is to be achieved by using hundreds of bunches. Each proposal plans rings of equal circumference roughly from 3/4 to 3km in length. Energy ratios between the two beams range from 7/4 to 9/3.1. Most plans, but not all, include existing tunnels and infrastructure.

2.2. Technical Challenges

The main technical challenges arise directly from the need for high beam currents, one to two amperes in most cases. These high currents require special measures to assure beam stability, to absorb the corresponding megawatts of synchrotron radiation power dissipated on vacuum chamber walls, and to keep beam produced backgrounds and irradiation of detector components at acceptable levels.

Assurance of beam stability requires new approaches to both rf system design and construction, and feedback system design and construction. The dissipation of MW x-ray power levels requires new approaches to vacuum chamber and pump technology. Good vertex measurement and low backgrounds require new approaches to IR layout and optics, to masking and shielding at the IR and to IP beam pipes and vacuum systems. Concept designs to meet all these challenges are rather well developed and the corresponding hardware is in the modeling or even prototype stage. As example, a brief description of rf system development follows.

In general one must keep impedances low at all frequencies other than that of the accelerating mode. To achieve this one needs to use as few accelerating cavities as possible and damp the parasitic cavity modes (PM) as heavily as possible. Parasitic Q's of 100 or less are sought. Two main lines of approach are being pursued, use of normal conducting cavities and use of superconducting cavities. In each, one or at most two cavity cells per accelerating unit are used to enhance parasitic mode damping.

In the normal conducting case one employs a standard cell shape to enhance coupling of the beam to the accelerating mode. For PM damping the cell walls are interrupted, typically at 3 places, at antinodes of the PM currents for extraction of PM energy. Models of such designs at SLAC and KEK show good results on damping the PM's. High power models of these cavities are expected in about a year's time.

A disadvantage of this approach is that the fundamental accelerating mode resonance is broad enough to drive nearby, longitudinal, coupled bunch instabilities. This leads to the need for an elaborate feedback system to suppress the cavity impedance close to the main resonance. The design of such a system has been demonstrated at SLAC and appears to be practical. A further disadvantage of this approach is that the number of cells is large enough that even with good PM damping, many of the longitudinal coupled bunch modes will be driven unstable thus necessitating a high power, broad band longitudinal feedback system to enforce stability. Designs and modeling by the PEP II group indicate that such a system can be realized as well. A beam test program for these feedback concepts is underway.

In the superconducting approach the inherently low wall losses are exploited to increase the voltage per cell to roughly three times what is practical in normal conducting cells. This gives a factor of three advantage in total beam impedance. An additional factor of about three can also be obtained by modifying the cell shape for low coupling impedance, another advantage afforded by the low wall losses. This, together with the narrow bandwith of the accelerating mode, means that no longitudinal feedback is required. The principal disadvantage of the superconducting approach is the relative delicacy of the superconducting state and the complexity of the cryogenic system.

The superconducting approach has been adopted by the VEPP 5 and CESR B groups and is being studied in parallel with the normal conducting approach at KEK. Both KEK and Cornell groups have demonstrated 3MV per cell accelerating voltages at Q's of 10^9 in full scale models. A high power beam test will be carried out at CESR in a year's time.

It should be noted that in both normal and superconducting cases a broad band, transverse feedback system will be required to ensure stability. Such systems are under development and will be beam tested soon.

While such rf systems are complex, work so far shows that they are practical.

3. Linear Colliders

For the somewhat farther future, worldwide efforts focus on various means for producing linear colliders. The ideas are less well formed than those for "factories" but are developing fast. A number of schemes are being pursued in parallel at the concept design and technology R/D stages.

The basic motivating idea is that Elementary Particle Physics (EPP) would benefit by adding to HERA, SSC, and LHC the ability to do e^+e^- physics at the energy frontier as defined by those facilities, i.e. elementary collision energies at 1–4 TeV(CM). Mature reflection has shown that, even with SLC experience, achievement of such an energy and luminosity in one step is too ambitious. A consensus has built that 0.5 TeV(CM) would be useful for physics and is probably a realistic first step.

In the "beginning," (say about 1982 with the Oxford Conference on the Challenge of High Energies), optimism about "New Accelerator Concepts" involving lasers, plasmas, et cetera ran high. By "Monday morning" (say 1992) much of the smoke has cleared and sobering up well set in. The main drivers for this sobering are quantitative evaluations of luminosity requirements, beam cleanliness and brightness needed, and a heightened awareness of the need for high mains power to beam power efficiency. The surviving concepts all rely in wave-particle interactions in vacuum in the presence of metallic slow wave guiding structures. All of the components of the various schemes are recognizable from the past although the range of driving wavelengths being considered is much wider than before. All frequencies are still in microwave range. Research and development now in train will determine which of these schemes are capable of realization with good probability for success. All schemes now aim at luminosities between 10^{33} and 10^{34} at 0.5 TeV(CM) and all try to envision an E^2 luminosity dependence for further extensions. Each of the schemes tries to exploit the advantages of particular technologies and operating wavelengths. While each has its own particularities and tricks in layout, the overall schemes are similar, at least in component names. Figure 2 shows a rather generic layout.

In scale, the main linacs actually dwarf the other component in most schemes. In some schemes the damping ring and compressor are very elaborate due to the very small emittances desired.

It is by now an established procedure that the proponents of the various schemes meet annually to compare notes and progress in a workshop setting. There is much international collaboration on every scale and more is anticipated.

The most recent of these workshops—LC92, sponsored by ECFA and MPI, Munich—took place at Garmisch-Partenkirchen in August. At this meeting a comparison of parameters was carried out and is abstracted below. This is just a snapshot of a fast changing scene.

Table I displays selected parameters from those schemes receiving the most attention now. The parameters are scaled to a common, 500 GeV(CM) energy.

Table 1: Linear Collider Comparative Parameters

†	TESLA	DLC	JLC(S)	JLC(C)	JLC(X)	NLC	VLEPP	CLIC
Frequency(GHz)	1.3	3	2.8	5.7	11.4	11.4	14	30
$\mathcal{L}$ With pinch (10^{33})	11	6.5	4.4	6.5	6.3	8.2	15	2.2–8.9
No. Bun. per Pulse	800	172	55	72	90	90	1	1–4
Rep. Rate (Hz)	10	50	50	100	150	180	300	1700
Active Length (km)	20	30	28	16.7	17	14	6.4	6.6
Lin. AC Pwr. (MW)	137	114	106	193	86	152	91	175
$\gamma_x/\gamma\epsilon_y(10^{-8}\text{m})$	2000/100	500/50	330/4.5	330/4.5	330/4.5	500/5	2000/2.5	180/20
$\sigma_x^*/\sigma_y^*(10^{-9}\text{m})$	640/100	400/32	300/3	260/3	260/3	300/3	2000/4	90/8

† TESLA, an international collaboration centered at DESY; DLC, a collaboration of DESY and TH Darmstadt; JLC, a Japanese collaboration centered at KEK; NLC centered at SLAC; VLEPP, collaboration of Protvino and Novosibirsk; CLIC, a CERN group.

Intense R/D is underway both in terms of accelerator physics of the various schemes and in terms of the supporting component and subsystem technologies. A partial list of R/D items follows: Accelerator produced backgrounds, final focus and collimation, alignment tolerances and assurance, accelerating structures and mode damping and tuning, microwave power sources and windows, modulators and energy storage, rf pulse compressors, particle sources, damping rings, bunch compressors, dark current, beam position and profile monitors... The interested reader is referred to LC92 Workshop Proceeding which will soon be published by MPI, Munich and ECFA, R. Settles, Editor.

As mentioned, all designs are quite fluid now, being driven by new accelerator physics findings and results of the various technological R/D programs. A good example is the recent interest in multibunch operation driven by studies of the effects of "beamstrahlung." In this process, particles in one beam are induced to radiate in the coherent field of the oncoming beam. The products of these events make backgrounds and degrade the energy spectrum of the colliding beams, "stealing" luminosity from the high energy end where it is wanted. Figure 3 shows a differential luminosity spectrum from a certain 2 TeV(CM) design studied recently. The total luminosity, which is the number computed from the simple luminosity formula, is the integral of the differential luminosity. Note that due to the "beamstrahlung" process the luminosity in this example is spread over a wide range of energies so that a large part is wasted. Worse yet this lower energy luminosity must be convolved with a E^{-2} cross-section, making large numbers of unwanted, low energy events to confuse the detection of wanted events. Note also that the "beamstrahlung" process results in a significant photon-photon luminosity at low energies producing more, largely unwanted, events. Clearly, this degradation needs to and can be controlled by limiting the bunch coherent fields through limiting the number of particles per bunch. An example of a design in which this control is achieved is show in Figure 4. The practical result is that the total charge needed to produce the target luminosity must be distributed among many bunches. This change in turn ripples down to changes throughout the whole system. Not the least of these changes is to require more effective damping of multibunch instabilities and thus make elaborate mode extraction or detuning methods than previously foreseen.

In addition to these theoretical advances, practical advances on many of the items of our list have been made. For example structures achieving 100 MV/m accelerating gradient have been demonstrated and development of power sources of useful output power coupled with other needed parameters have made significant strides in the past year. Much remains to be done but the work shows good progress.

Even if component developments are successful on their own terms, all involved are keenly aware that system performance is the ultimate measure of success. Accordingly, plans and projects for a number of system and subsystem tests are being drawn up or have already been approved. For example, a Final Focus Test Facility, engaging an international consortium is well advanced at SLAC. It will beam test a final focus system having the same demagnification as required for a 0.5 TeV(CM) machine although it will operate at 50 GeV. A damping ring with preaccelerator, compressor, test accelerator, and final focus is approved and under construction at KEK. Several test accelerators in the 500 MeV to 1 GeV range are being constructed at Protvino/Novosibirsk, SLAC, KEK, and DESY.

It is hoped by these means to arrive at some consensus so that by 1996-97 a truly international collaboration can form to put forward a viable proposal for a

0.5 TeV(CM) linear collider.

4. New Accelerator Concepts

This field is very active also, covering many fronts of theoretical and technological interest. Some areas receiving attention now are:1. rf power sources, i.e. klystrons, gyrotrons, gyrocons, FEL, TWT, and two beam accelerator schemes (TBA); 2. terawatt table top (T^3) lasers; 3. plasma beat wave (PBWA) and plasma wakefield (FWFA) accelerators; 4. inverse cerenkov accelerators; 5. inverse FEL; 6. wakefield accelerator with dielectric slow wave structure; 7. damped muon collider and much more. Several of these have recently been put to the test and more will be in the near future. An up to date report will soon be published as an AIP Conference Report of the proceedings of the Third International Workshop on Advanced Accelerator Concepts.

4.1. One example recently tested is the PBWA at UCLA.

In this accelerator a powerful laser, 100 GW, 300 ps FWHM in the present instance, is focused in the hydrogen-filled (140 mTorr) accelerator chamber. The two frequencies emitted by the laser are separated by $\Delta w = w_p$ the plasma frequency, $\eta_0 = 8 \times 10^{15}$/cc, exciting a strong, longitudinal plasma wave. This wave accelerates a beam injected into it from a linac at about 2 MeV. Electrons with 9 MeV were detected emerging from the 1 cm long accelerating volume giving an effective gradient of 0.7 GeV/m for the active length. About 3×10^4 electrons are accelerated per burst.

This is a significant accomplishment, crowning many years of hard work.

4.2. Future of Advanced Accelerator Concepts (ACC)

How the PBWA and other of the AAC's can be staged to give TeV energies with good efficiency and high luminosity with clean beams remains to be seen.

Some of the more "conventional" concepts mentioned earlier are probably capable of extension to TeV energies, giving very strong competition for the AAC's to beat.

5. Conclusions

There is intense activity in development of accelerators for EPP, both on luminosity and energy frontiers.

This activity can support the creation of "factories" before the end of the 90's. This activity is expected to support a viable proposal for an e^+e^- collider at 1/2 TeV(CM) about 1997.

There seams a good chance of e^+e^- LC extension to the energy frontier early in the 21st century.

6. Acknowledgements

I am much indebted to many persons and institutions for providing illustrative materials.

For Magnet Materials: R. Scanlan and C. Taylor, LBL; and D. Larbalestier, Univ. Wisconsin.

For "factories": H. Schwarz, J. Dorfan, SLAC; S. Kurokawa, KEK; A. Skrinsky, BINP; and H. Padamsee, Cornell Univ.

For advanced accelerator concepts: C. Joshi, UCLA.

Special thanks are due to Ron Settles, MPI Munich, for making LC92 Conclusion Transparencies available to me; and to John Nation, Cornell Univ., for making available transparencies from the Third International Workshop on Advanced Accelerator Concepts.

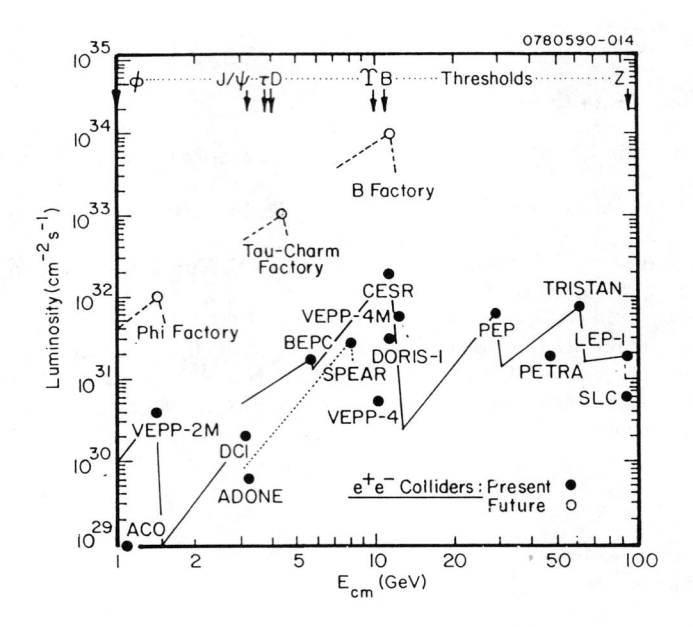

Figure 1: Planned Factories and Existing Colliders

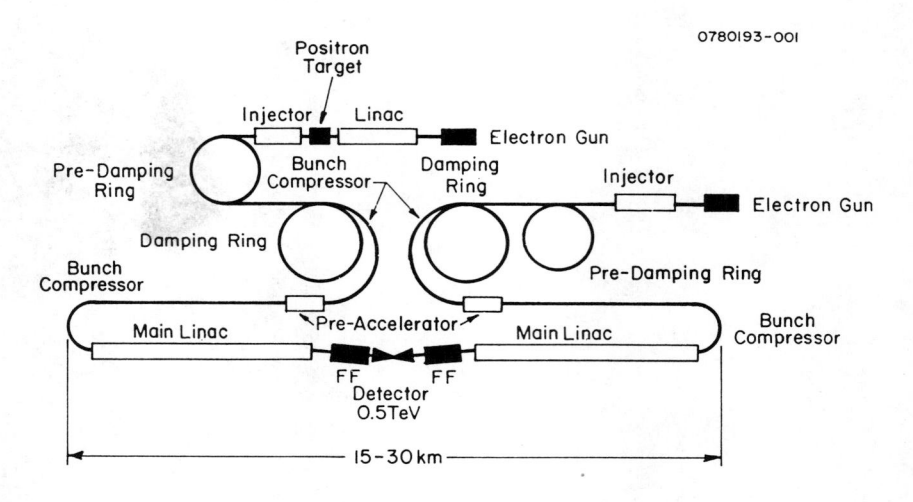

Figure 2: Generic Linear Collider Layout—Adopted from JLC-1

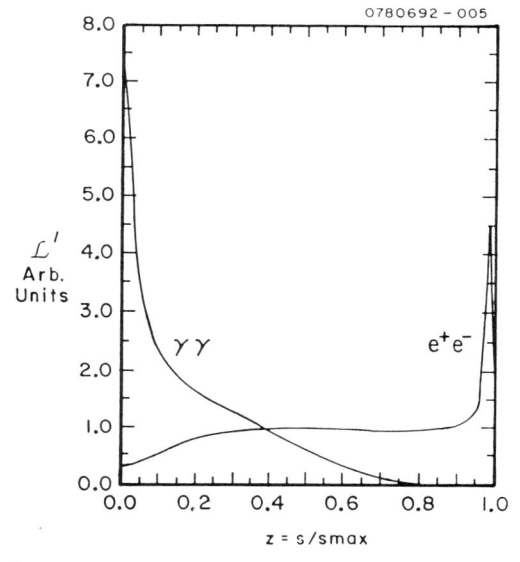

Figure 3: Differential luminosity with unfavorable parameters.

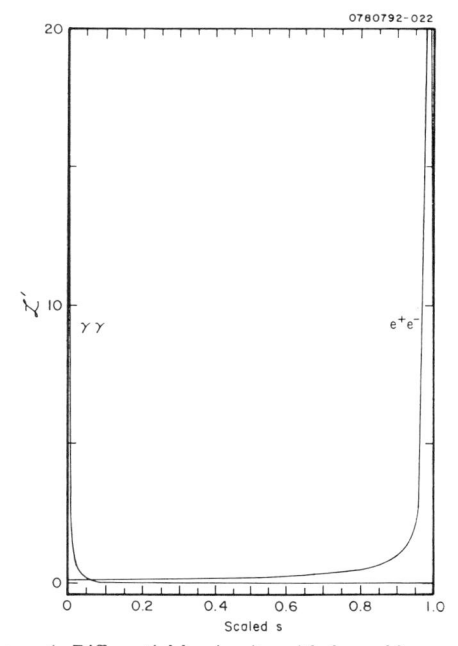

Figure 4: Differential luminosity with favorable parameters.

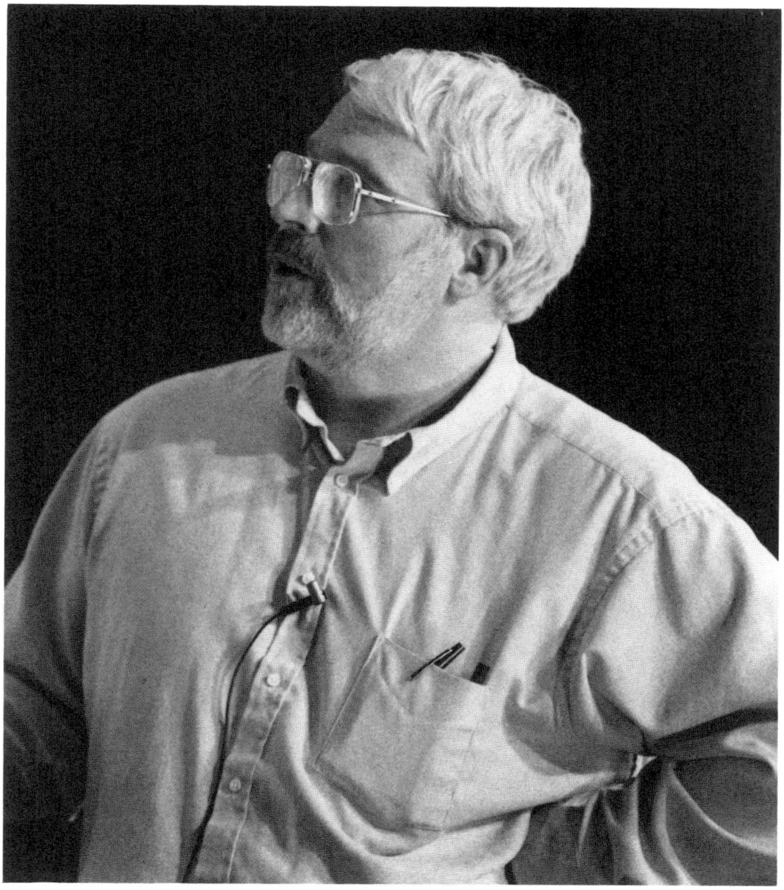

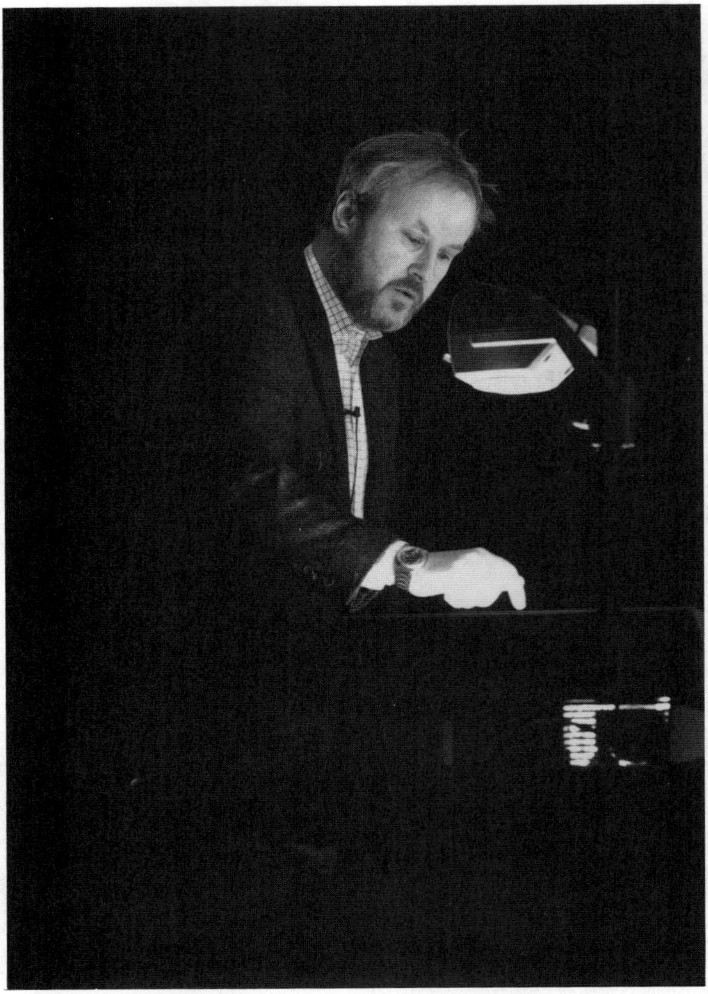

STATUS OF QCD

R. K. ELLIS
Fermi National Accelerator Laboratory, P.O. Box 500,
Batavia, IL 60510

ABSTRACT

Recent advances in perturbative QCD are reviewed. The topics discussed include structure functions, small x physics, direct photon production, heavy flavour production, jet physics and measurements of α_s.

1. Structure functions

New data on deep inelastic structure functions have been presented in 1992 by the muon experiment NMC[1] and by the neutrino experiments CCFR[2] and FFMF.[3] Fig. 1 shows a comparison of the new muon scattering data with previous results from SLAC and BCDMS. The data interpolate nicely between the lower Q^2 SLAC data and the BCDMS data. Also shown in Fig. 1 is the Q^2 dependence of xF_3 from the CCFR[2] and CDHSW[4] neutrino collaborations. The slope in Q^2 differs between the two neutrino experiments; the CCFR data has a slope more consistent with QCD. The FFMF collaboration has about 100K events so the statistical precision is much less than the other two experiments.

Data with different beams and different isoscalar targets can be compared. This comparison has been performed, for example by Virchaux.[5] First, one must apply a correction for the beams, using the mean square charge relationship,

$$F_2^{\ell\pm}/F_2^{\nu N} = \frac{5}{18}(1 - \frac{6}{5}\frac{s - \bar{c}}{q + \bar{q}}) \qquad (1)$$

Second, one should correct for nuclear effects using a parameterisation of the EMC effect.

The main conclusion to be drawn from this analysis is that the reanalysed EMC data[6] is in poor agreement with the other sets. In addition, there are less serious problems with low Q^2 CDHSW data. The CCFR data interpolates nicely between the SLAC and BCDMS data. The overall conclusion is that there is now a precise set of structure function data from SLAC, BCDMS, NMC and CCFR which are in good mutual agreement. QCD fits lead to a value of $\Lambda_{\overline{MS}} \approx 200$ MeV for four flavours. For a detailed discussion we refer the reader to the paper by Virchaux.[5]

1.1. Measurements at lower values of x

The data from NMC also extends precise measurements to lower values of x than previously available. Fig. 2 shows the parton parameterizations of Martin, Roberts and Stirling[7] of 1990 (B_0 and B_-)and 1992(D_0) compared with the older BCDMS data as well with as the new NMC data. Fig. 2 makes clear the importance

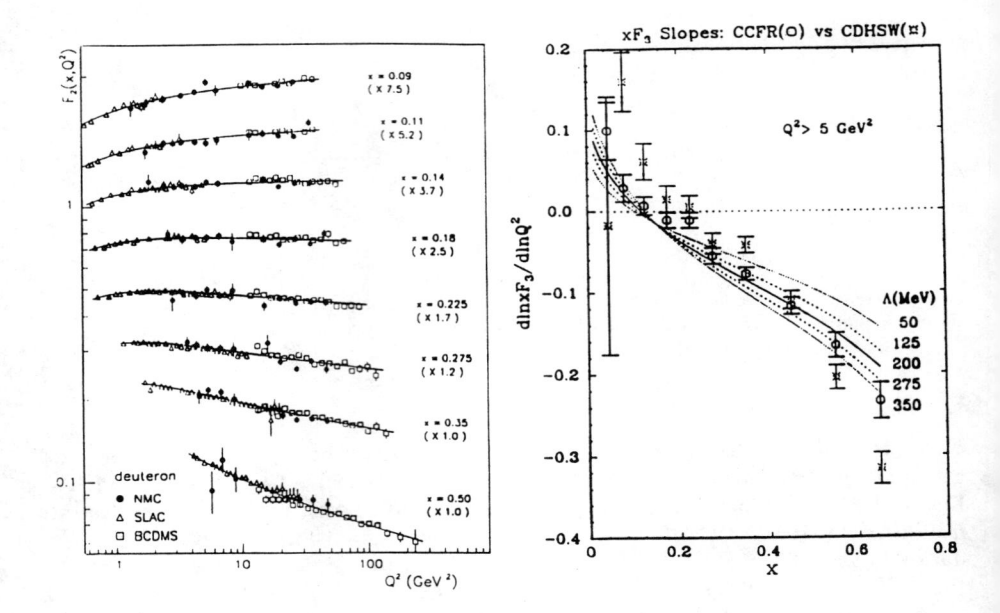

Figure 1: Comparison of lepton scattering experiments

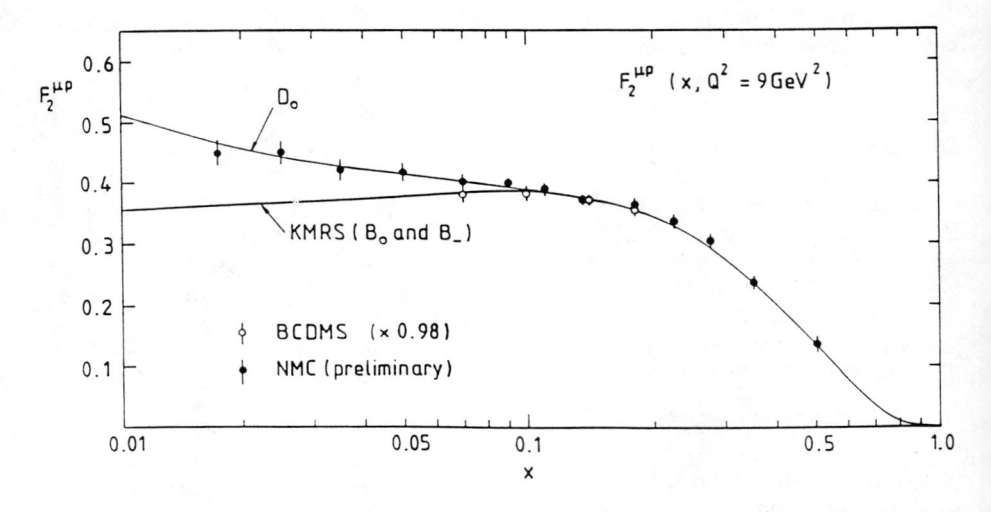

Figure 2: Comparison of NMC and BCDMS data with parton parameterizations

of experimental information in the low x region. Complete parton fits including the final NMC data are expected soon[7,8].

The NMC results indicate that parton distributions should increase for $x < 0.1$ as illustrated by Fig. 2. This change in parton distribution functions will have an impact on predictions for collider energies. At the Tevatron an object of mass 10 GeV is produced by partons with $x \approx M/\sqrt{s} = 0.006$. A W boson is produced at $x \approx 0.05$. Objects produced at large rapidities probe even lower values of x.

1.2. SU(2) Symmetric Sea and the Gottfried Sum Rule

The NMC collaboration has also published information on the Gottfried sum rule.[9] The sum rule can be derived in the context of the quark parton model,

$$\int_0^1 \frac{dx}{x}(F_2^p - F_2^n) \equiv \frac{1}{3}\int_0^1 dx\left(u_v(x) - d_v(x)\right) - \frac{2}{3}\int_0^1 dx\left(\bar{d}(x) - \bar{u}(x)\right)$$
$$= \frac{1}{3} \text{ if } \bar{u} = \bar{d} \qquad (2)$$

The NMC collaboration find

$$\int_{.004}^{0.8} \frac{dx}{x}(F_2^p - F_2^n) = 0.227 \pm 0.007 \pm 0.014 \qquad (3)$$

The estimate of the value of the integral for all x is 0.240 ± 0.016 which is significantly different from 0.33. To maintain $\bar{u} = \bar{d}$, the small x behaviour of the distributions must be modified to push the missing contribution into the unmeasured region. Simple ideas based on the Pauli principle give $\bar{u} \neq \bar{d}$. For a theoretical discussion of the Gottfried sum rule defect in the chiral quark model and references to earlier work, see Eichten et al.[10] Note that information on $\bar{d} - \bar{u}$ can be obtained in a different x region from the nuclear target dependence of the x_F distribution in lepton pair production.[11]

2. Partons Distribution in the small x Region

The physical picture of the gluon distribution is that $xg(x,\mu^2)$ is the number of gluons per unit rapidity with transverse size less than $1/\mu$ in a frame in which the hadron is fast moving. At small x it is also useful to define a more differential distribution of partons. The number of gluons with transverse momentum k_T and longitudinal fraction x is defined as $f(x, k_T^2)$. The normal gluon distribution is recovered by integrating over the transverse momentum up to scale μ.

$$g(x,\mu^2) = \int_0^{\mu^2} dk_T^2 f(x,k_T^2) \qquad (4)$$

There are three phenomena predicted theoretically in the small x region,
1.) Rapid growth of number of partons.
2.) Growth of mean transverse momentum in gluon cascade.
3.) Saturation phenomena.[12]

Fig. 3 gives a schematic map of the plane in x and Q^2. The evolution in Q^2 is

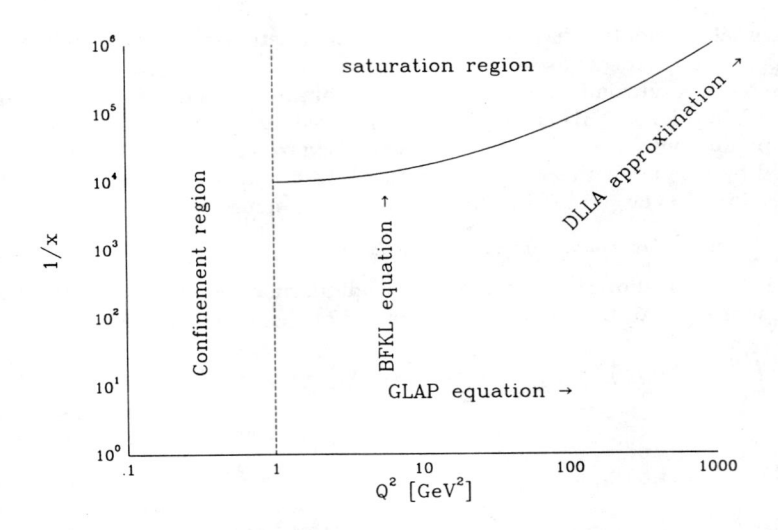

Figure 3: GLR plane showing the putative saturation region

controlled by the GLAP equation.[13] On the other hand the small x logarithms are resummed by the BFKL equation.[14] (For a unified treatment correct in both limits see the work of Marchesini and Webber[15]). If both $\ln 1/x$ and $\ln Q^2$ are large we may make a double leading logarithmic approximation (DLLA) and both equations coincide. We begin by defining moments of the gluon distribution,

$$g(j,t) = \int_0^1 dx\, x^{j-1} g(x,t) \qquad (5)$$

In terms of these moments the DLLA of the Altarelli-Parisi equation for the gluon distribution g is,

$$\frac{dg(j,t)}{dt} = \frac{\bar{\alpha}(t)}{(j-1)} g(j,t), \quad \bar{\alpha} = \frac{N\alpha_s}{\pi} \qquad (6)$$

where $N = 3$. The solution is

$$g(j,t) = g(j,t_0) \exp\frac{\xi}{b(j-1)}, \quad \xi = b\int_{t_0}^t dt'\, \bar{\alpha}_s(t') \sim \ln(\ln Q^2) \qquad (7)$$

If both ξ and $\ln 1/x$ are large, the inverse Mellin transform may be performed by saddle point methods,

$$xg(x,t) \sim \exp 2\sqrt{\frac{\xi \ln\frac{1}{x}}{b}} \qquad (8)$$

The DLLA teaches us that the gluon distribution grows very rapidly at small x. This feature is maintained in the full BFKL equation[14] which predicts a power growth at small x,

$$xg(x,t) \sim \frac{1}{x^{j_l}}, \quad j_l \sim 0.5 \qquad (9)$$

Experiment	$\sqrt{s}$ [GeV]	x-range
WA70	22	$0.35 < x_T < 0.55$
E706	31.5	$0.3 < x_T < 0.5$
UA1/UA2	630	$0.03 < x_T < 0.16$
CDF/D0	1800	$0.016 < x_T < 0.1$

Table 1: x-ranges probed by direct photon experiments

For inclusive quantities it is hard to distinguish this behaviour from the growth predicted by the GLAP equation. Methods of disentangling this behaviour from Altarelli-Parisi growth have been suggested in the literature.[16] The DLLA also teaches us that the important variables are $\ln 1/x$ and $\xi \equiv \ln \ln Q^2$. In practical situations $\ln 1/x$ is often much bigger than ξ. Thus from a practical point of view it is more important to understand small x than large Q^2.

The critical line shown in Fig. 3 is the line of constant packing fraction of partons. It corresponds to the start of parton interactions and the onset of saturation. The approach to this line from the perturbative region is governed by the equation[17] ($G(x,Q^2) \equiv xg(x,Q^2)$)

$$\frac{\partial^2 G(x,Q^2)}{\partial \ln 1/x \partial \ln Q^2} = \bar{\alpha}_s G(x,Q^2) - \frac{81}{16}\alpha_s^2 \frac{(G(x,Q^2))^2}{Q^2 R^2} \qquad (10)$$

The second term slows the growth of the parton distribution and leads to a saturation of the parton density. The observability of saturation effects[18] depends on the value for R. A uniform distribution of partons corresponds to $R \sim 1$ fm ~ 5 GeV^{-1}. If the partons are clustered in hot spots a value of $R \sim 0.2$ fm ~ 2 GeV^{-1} would be more appropriate. The theoretical status of this equation, including the first demonstration in QCD that the terms which are formally 'power suppressed' will dominate the leading terms at small x, has been reviewed by Levin.[19]

3. Direct Photon Production

Direct photon production offers a clean way of probing the gluon distribution function in a limited range of x_T. The x_T ranges measured by selected present experiments are shown in Table 1. A fairly large coverage in x_T is now available. Results from experiment E706 investigating direct photon production with 500 GeV pion and proton beams have been presented by Dunlea.[20] Some deviations from current fits of structure functions are observed at low p_T. At collider energy we must impose an isolation cut to remove bremsstrahlung contributions. The theoretical understanding of this process has been reviewed by Qiu.[21] Fig. 4 shows the data from the Tevatron collider[22] compared to the most recent theoretical predictions.[23] The preliminary analysis of the D0 collaboration is in agreement, within errors, with the published CDF results. Note that the theoretical predictions,[23] using modern structure functions, give a reasonable description of the data for both large and small p_T.

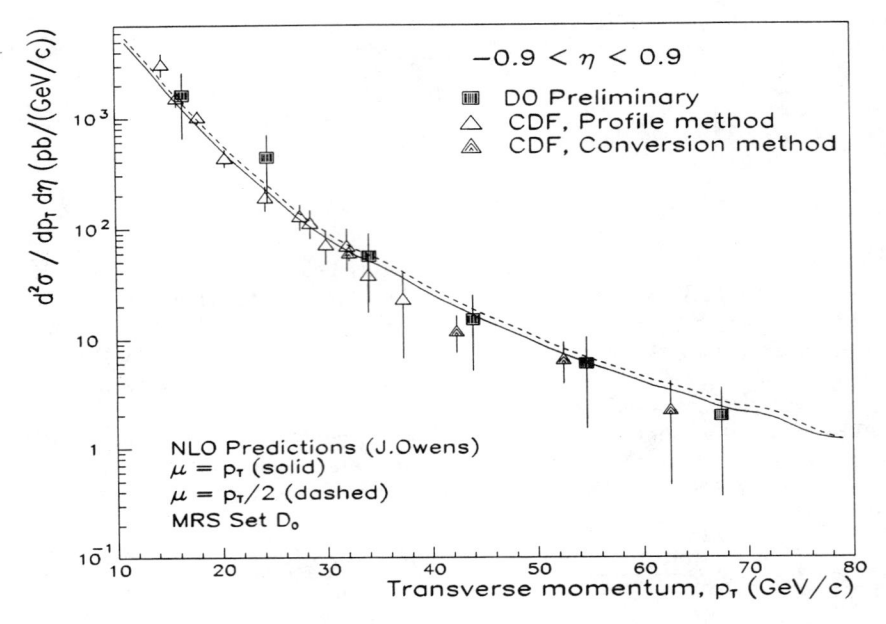

Figure 4: Tevatron results on direct photon production

4. Heavy Quark Production

Heavy quark production proceeds both by the annihilation of a light quark with a light antiquark and by gluon-gluon fusion. Cross sections for the production of hadrons containing heavy quarks are calculable in the quark parton model. The large parameter which makes perturbation theory applicable is m_Q, the mass of the heavy quark. Corrections to the QCD parton model are of order Λ/m_Q.

4.1. Production of hadrons containing charmed quarks

The mass of the charmed quark is such that the description of charmed hadron production using the heavy quark formalism is marginal. The production of charmed hadrons is interesting precisely because of the ambiguous nature of the charmed quark on the border between heavy and light quark.

At fixed target energies the theoretical prediction for total rate of charmed hadron production is extremely sensitive to the value chosen for the charm quark mass, m_c. By choosing plausible values of the charm quark mass, agreement can be found with the more recently measured values of total production cross-sections.[25] Measured differential cross sections for charmed *mesons* are in agreement with theoretical predictions for charmed *quarks*. There is no experimental evidence for the softening expected from fragmentation.

The evidence for a strong leading particle effect[26] is not confirmed by a

Figure 5: b quark production

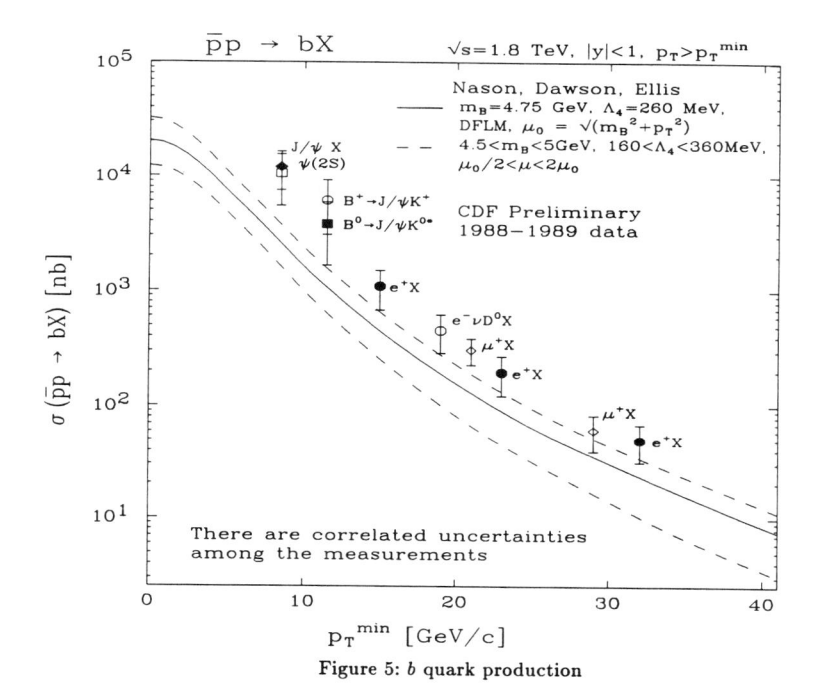

higher statistics experiment.[27] A pronounced leading particle effect would indicate interaction between the remnants of the beam and the produced charmed quark to alter the x_F distribution. The Feynman x_F distributions for the D-mesons produced in the reaction $\pi^- N \to D^\pm$ can be fitted to the form $(1 - x_F)^{n_\pm}$. The measured value[27] of the difference of the exponents for the two types of mesons is $n_+ - n_- = 1.1 \pm 0.4$.

4.2. Production of hadrons containing bottom quarks

The data on bottom production[28] at $\sqrt{s} = 1.8$ TeV is shown in Fig. 5. The data lies above the band of theoretical predictions derived from α_s^3 theory,[29] unlike the corresponding data from UA1 at $\sqrt{s} = 0.63$ TeV.[30] However several caveats are important in making this determination from Fig. 5. First, there is a large amount of manipulation of the data which goes into the determination of the bottom quark p_T distribution shown in Fig. 5. On the theoretical side the value of x at which the gluon distribution is probed is very small and the gluon distribution is not measured at such small values of x. In fact, one mechanism to accommodate the data shown in Fig. 5 is to alter the form of the gluon distribution.[31]

However the order α_s^3 theory is flawed for bottom production at $\sqrt{s} = 1.8$ TeV. The order α_s^3 terms are equal in magnitude to the cross section predicted at the Born graph level (α_s^2). Thus the perturbation series for bottom production at the Tevatron is not stable order-by-order. The reason for the large correction is understood. It is due to the fact that $\sqrt{s} \gg m \gg \Lambda$. An improved theory of this regime has yet to be worked out to the level of reliable numerical predictions. I shall try and describe the concepts required to give a description of this regime. For simplicity, consider the photoproduction of heavy quarks, since this process involves primarily photon-gluon fusion with only one gluon in the initial state.

In the standard parton model the cross section is schematically given by the product of the parton distribution and the on-shell cross section.

$$\sigma^{\gamma N} = \int_0^{m^2} dk_T^2 f(x, k_T^2) \otimes \hat{\sigma}(m^2) \equiv g(x, m^2) \otimes \hat{\sigma}(m^2) \tag{11}$$

In the region $\sqrt{s} \gg m \gg \Lambda$, the perturbation series is no longer a series in α_s but rather in $\alpha_s \ln s/m^2$. The transverse momentum of the incoming partons is no longer limited and a description in terms of an on-shell cross section is no longer appropriate. The modified form requires an off-shell cross-section (impact factor) and a distribution of gluons in x and k_T.

$$\sigma^{\gamma N} = \int_0^\infty dk_T^2 f(x, k_T^2) \otimes \hat{I}(k_T^2, m^2), \quad \hat{I}(0, m^2) = \hat{\sigma}(m^2) \tag{12}$$

How numerically important is the effect of off-shellness at practical energies[32,15]? The answer to the question depends on the importance of the tail region. This depends on the shape of the impact factor I as well as on the k_T behaviour of $f(x, k_T^2)$. The fact that the α_s^3 corrections to bottom production are large shows that these effects are important in fixed order calculations at present energies.

4.3. Top Quark Production at Tevatron

The dominant parton process in top quark production at the Tevatron depends on the mass of the top quark, m_t. If $m_t \sim 100$ GeV then the $gg \to Q\bar{Q}$ and $q\bar{q} \to Q\bar{Q}$ processes are of equal importance. For $m_t > 100$ GeV the process $q\bar{q} \to Q\bar{Q}$ dominates because of the stiffer quark distributions. Note that W gluon fusion does not lead to an observable signal[36] in 100 pb^{-1} samples at $\sqrt{s} = 1.8$ TeV. Thus the phenomenological parameters required to predict the rate of top quark production are the quark distribution at $x \sim 0.1$ and the value of α_s. There are various levels of sophistication with which we can calculate top quark cross sections. Including the α_s^3 corrections leads to a reduction in theoretical error,[33] when compared with tree graph level calculations. A partial resummation of higher order terms[34] indicates a further 10% increase. Including all known effects a reasonable estimate of the theoretical error on the top cross-section is that it is determined to ±20%.

We now consider the background which can mask the top quark signal. One of the most important applications of the multi-jet calculations is the estimate of the background to the top quark search. A $t\bar{t}$ event gives rise to an observable W + n-jet signature ($n \leq 4$) when one of the W's from top decay undergoes a semileptonic decay. The background is due to the production of a W in association with QCD jets. Fig 6 shows the cross-section for both as a function of the top quark mass.[35] Both the signal and the background are calculated at tree graph level. The jets are defined using standard cuts of the CDF collaboration (for details see Berends et

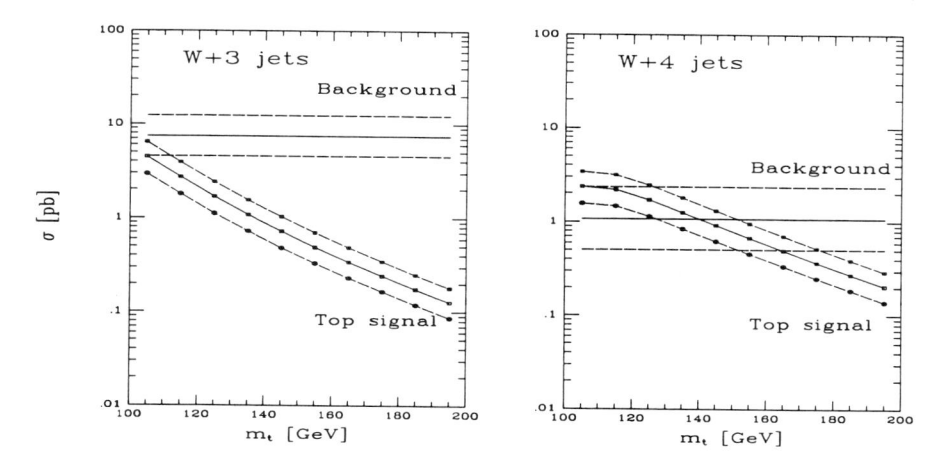

Figure 6: W + jet cross sections from background and signal

al.[35]). The theoretical uncertainty is estimated by varying the renormalisation scale between $m_t/2 < \mu < 2\sqrt{(m_t^2 + p_T^2)}$ for the signal and between $M_W/2 < \mu < 2\sqrt{(M_W^2 + p_T^2)}$ for the background. This plot shows the importance of the four jet channel for top discovery. Note however that these plots do not include the discrimination against the background obtained when a b-quark is identified. With b tagging, the $W+4$ jets background is effectively removed.

The top quark cross sections are known beyond the leading order.[33] This allows us to reduce the theoretical error on the top quark cross section shown in Fig. 6. The upper values of the top quark cross sections shown in Fig. 6 are favoured by NLO calculations.

5. Jets

Tree level predictions for jet cross sections suffer from a number of deficiencies. First, they have no parton merging cone size dependence. The number of partons in the final state determines the number of jets. Two partons which are produced close together can never be merged to give a single jet. At tree level a single parton is equivalent to a jet. Second, they are sensitive to variations of the size of the coupling constant α_s and to the choice of renormalisation scale. This is particularly true of cross-sections which begin in order α_s^n for large n. For example the W plus four jet cross section occurs in order α_s^4. A 20% uncertainty in α_s, coming from scale uncertainty and uncertainty in α_s itself, leads to a factor 2 uncertainty in the cross section. Estimates beyond leading order can be done either using a parton shower Monte-Carlo program or using fixed order perturbation theory. Both methods have their advantages. Here I describe only advances in fixed order techniques.

In fixed order perturbation theory one can sensibly define a cross section for any 'infra-red safe' quantity. This is technically complicated because it requires regulation and cancellation of contributions from real and virtual emission graphs,

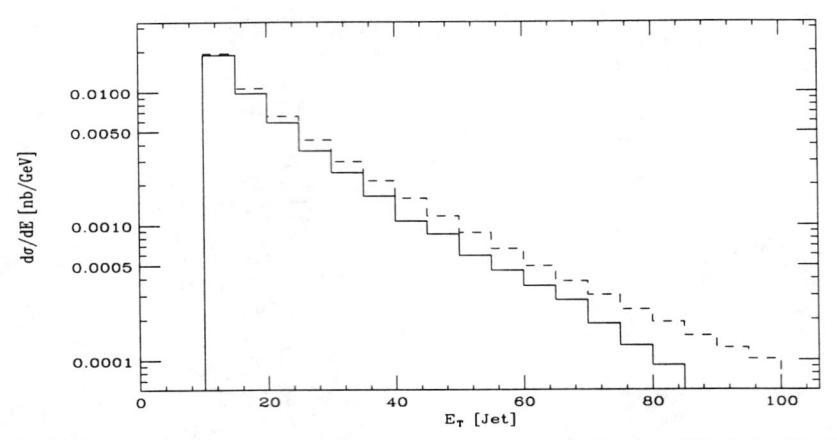

Figure 7: The $W^\pm + 1$ jet cross section vs. the transverse energy of the jet. The dashed line is leading order, the solid line is next to leading order.

but presents no conceptual difficulties. Several calculations of jet cross-sections are now available beyond leading order.[37] Fig. 7 shows an example of such a calculation[38] for a $W + 1$ jet cross-section plotted as a function of E_T. Standard CDF cuts are used. The softening of the jet E_T spectrum beyond the leading order is due to the use of a fixed E_T cut to define the jets. At high tranverse energy the accompanying soft radiation scales with E_T. Thus at higher E_T the accompanying soft radiation is much more likely to promote the event to the two jet sample, leading to a smaller $W + 1$ jet sample.

6. The measurement of α_s

6.1. α_s at low Q^2

If measurements of α_s can be performed at low energy they can be competitive with high energy measurements. A 10% measurement of α_s at 1.7 GeV coresponds to a 4% measurement at the mass of the Z, because of the focussing effect in the evolution of the coupling constant. Remarkably, it appears that the hadronic width of the τ is able to provide a believable low energy measurement[40] of α_s. The measurement begins with the ratio of the hadronic to leptonic decay widths of the τ which is given theoretically by,

$$R_\tau = \frac{\Gamma(\tau \to \text{Hadrons})}{\Gamma(\tau \to e)} = 3S_{EW}(1 + \delta_{PQCD} + \delta_{NPQCD}) \qquad (13)$$

$S_{EW} = 1.0194$ is a known electroweak correction.[41] The perturbative contribution δ_{PQCD} is known up to third order.[42]

$$\delta_{PQCD} = a + 5.2a^2 + 26.4a^3(\pm 130a^4), \quad a = \frac{\alpha_s(m_\tau)}{\pi} \qquad (14)$$

The fourth order contribution (in brackets) shows the value chosen by Braaten et al.[40] to estimate the size of error in the estimate of δ_{PQCD}. Since a will turn out to be about 0.1 it is easy to check the size of the various contributions to δ_{PQCD}. The non-perturbative corrections have also been estimated[40] and are found to be small, because of the absence of $1/m_\tau^2$ terms in the limit of zero quark masses.

$$\delta_{NPQCD} = -0.007 \pm 0.004 \tag{15}$$

Thus the unknown higher order contributions to δ_{PQCD} are largest source of theoretical uncertainty. The experimental measurement of R_τ can be derived either from the lifetime measurement, $1/\Gamma(\tau)$, and the calculated leptonic widths of the τ,

$$R_\tau^\Gamma = \frac{\Gamma(\tau) - \Gamma(\tau \to e) - \Gamma(\tau \to \mu)}{\Gamma(\tau \to e)} \tag{16}$$

or from the leptonic branching ratios

$$R_\tau^B = \frac{\Gamma(\tau) - \Gamma(\tau \to e) - \Gamma(\tau \to \mu)}{\Gamma(\tau \to e)} = \frac{1}{B_e} - 1.973 \tag{17}$$

The 1992 results for these two independent determinations are[43]

$$\begin{aligned} R_\tau^\Gamma &= 3.55 \pm 0.06 \\ R_\tau^B &= 3.63 \pm 0.03 \end{aligned} \tag{18}$$

Note that with the recent measurements of the τ mass and lifetime there is no longer a significant discrepancy between these two determinations and it is appropriate to avarage them to give $R_\tau = 3.62 \pm 0.03$. The value of the strong coupling derived from this average value is

$$\alpha_s(M_\tau) = 0.36 \pm 0.03 \to \alpha_s(M_Z) = 0.122 \pm 0.004 \tag{19}$$

A comparison with other determinations of α_s is given later.

6.2. α_s from $1P - 1S$ splitting in charmonium

The determination of α_s from the $1P - 1S$ splitting in charmonium[44] using lattice methods requires three steps. First, the determination of the lattice spacing in physical units using the measured spin splitting in the charmonium system; second, the determination of the physical coupling at a scale measured in lattice units; third, a correction for the absence of light quarks. The correction for the absence of light quarks, which is made using a QCD based potential model, is the largest source of uncertainty. It is argued that the use of the static potential is an acceptable procedure for the correction because it gives a good description of the charmonium system. When lattice calculations are performed in the future with dynamical fermions this correction will no longer be necessary. The value and estimate of the systematic error are

$$\alpha_s(5GeV) = 0.174 \pm 0.012 \to \alpha_s(M_Z) = 0.105 \pm 0.004 \tag{20}$$

6.3. Jet structure in e^+e^- annihilation

Determinations of α_s are now available using event shape variables and the high statistics data obtained at the Z pole at LEP. A complete review of these analyses is inappropriate here and we refer the reader to reviews by Bethke.[45] The connection between the perturbative results and the quantities derived from the hadrons measured experimentally is made by performing hadronisation corrections. The hadronisation corrections are examined by considering a series of Monte Carlo models. These corrections are nominally of order Λ/Q, but in practice are often found to be of order 10% or larger at LEP energies. The size of the hadronisation correction depends on the particular observable. Consider the perturbative expansion for a physical observable used to measure α_s

$$O = \alpha_s(1 + \sum c_n \alpha_s^n) \tag{21}$$

with coefficients c_n assumed to be of order 1. The coefficient c_1 is known, but c_2 is not yet calculated. Thus the first perturbative correction term is about 10% at LEP energies, comparable in size to the hadronisation correction. The statement that the dominant error on an α_s determination comes from ignorance of higher order terms such as c_2, depends on the estimate of the error on the hadronisation corrections from Monte Carlo programs. Note that despite the high energy the power suppressed terms play a more important role than in an inclusive measurement such as τ decay.

6.4. Jet clustering algorithms and resummation

Jet cross sections in e^+e^- annihilation are defined in terms of a jet resolution parameter y_{cut} and a jet recombination scheme. In the original JADE algorithm the resolution parameter is taken to be M_j^2/Q^2 where M_j is the maximum jet invariant mass. Thus in the Jade algorithm, we define,

$$y_{ij} = \frac{2E_iE_j(1-\cos\theta_{ij})}{Q^2} \tag{22}$$

The algorithm then proceeds as follows
1.) Compute y_{ij}'s
2.) Define the smallest y_{ij} to be y_{kl}; If $y_{kl} < y_{cut}$, form $p_{kl} = p_k + p_l$
3.) repeat until all $y_{ij} > y_{cut}$

Unfortunately this algorithm generates strong kinematic correlations and leads to a non-intuitive classification of some events. As a consequence, the resummation of large logarithms of y_{cut} appears theoretically hopeless in this scheme since exponentiation fails at leading log level. The modified k_T (Durham) algorithm[46] replaces Eq. (22) by

$$y_{ij} = 2(1-\cos\theta_{ij})\min(E_i^2, E_j^2)/Q^2 \simeq \frac{k_{t\,ij}^2}{Q^2} \tag{23}$$

This modified algorithm is easier to treat theoretically, and predictions which resum leading and subleading logarithms have been given. Resummed calculations are available for jet rates in this scheme, as well as for thrust, heavy jet-mass and

Process	Q [GeV]	$\alpha_s(Q)$	$\alpha_s(M_{Z^0})$	$\Delta\alpha_s(M_{Z^0})$ exp.	theor.	Theory
R_τ	1.77	0.360 ± 0.03	0.122 ± 0.004	0.002	0.004	NNLO
DIS [ν]	5.0	$0.193 {}^{+0.019}_{-0.018}$	0.111 ± 0.006	0.004	0.004	NLO
DIS [μ]	7.1	0.180 ± 0.014	0.113 ± 0.005	0.003	0.004	NLO
$c\bar{c}$ mass splitting	5.0	0.174 ± 0.012	0.105 ± 0.004	0.000	0.004	LGT
$J/\Psi + \Upsilon$ decays	10.0	$0.167 {}^{+0.015}_{-0.011}$	$0.113 {}^{+0.007}_{-0.005}$	0.001	${}^{+0.007}_{-0.005}$	NLO
e^+e^- [σ_{had}]	34.0	0.157 ± 0.018	0.131 ± 0.012	–	–	NNLO
e^+e^- [ev. shapes]	35.0	0.14 ± 0.02	0.119 ± 0.014	–	–	NLO
e^+e^- [ev. shapes]	58.0	0.130 ± 0.008	0.122 ± 0.007	0.003	0.007	NLO
$\Gamma(Z^0 \to$ had.)	91.2	0.130 ± 0.012	0.130 ± 0.012	0.011	0.004	NNLO
Z^0 [ev. shapes]	91.2	0.120 ± 0.006	0.120 ± 0.006	0.001	0.006	NLO
Z^0 [ev. shapes]	91.2	0.124 ± 0.005	0.124 ± 0.005	0.001	0.005	resum.

Table 2: Summary of α_s measurements

energy-energy correlations.[47] The resummed quantities remove the need to choose small renormalisation scales to fit the data, but the quoted error for resummed quantities still remains substantial.

6.5. Summary on α_s

Table 2, adapted from a summary by Bethke,[45] gives an overall view of the situation on α_s. This information is also presented in graphical form in Fig. 8. This figure shows the efficacy of the various measurements in determining Λ and does not directly show the error on the determination of $\alpha_s(M_Z)$. The values of $\alpha_s(M_Z)$ derived from these measurements are shown in Fig. 9.

References

1. P. Amaudruz et al., CERN-PPE-92-124 (July, 1992).
2. S.R. Mishra et al., Nevis Preprint NEVIS-1459, (June, 1992).
3. S. Fuess for the FFMF collaboration, this conference.
4. P. Berge et al. *Z. Phys.* **C49** (1991) 187.
5. M. Virchaux, proceedings of *QCD at 20*, Aachen, 1992.
6. K. Bazizi and S.J. Wimpenny, preprint UCR-DIS-91-02.

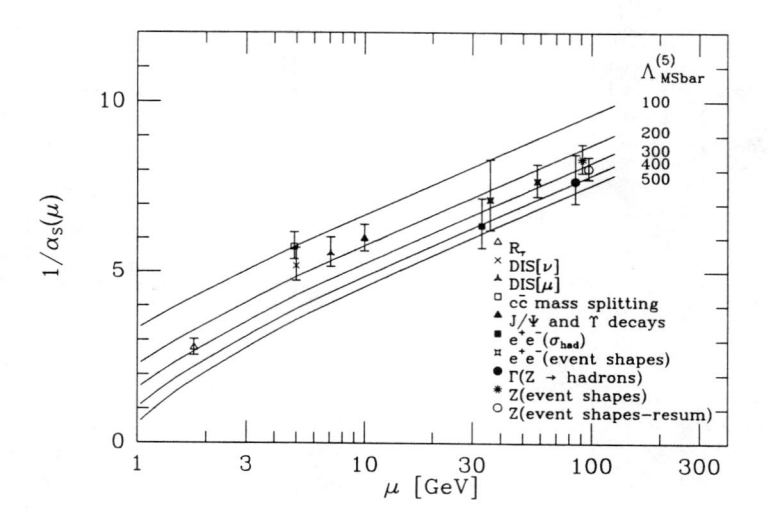

Figure 8: $1/\alpha_s$ vs $\ln \mu$

7. A.D. Martin, et al., Durham preprint, DTP-92-16 (Apr 1992) ;
   P.N. Harriman et al., *Phys. Rev.* **D42** (1990) 798.
8. J.G. Morfin and W-K. Tung, *Z. Phys.***C52** (1991) 13 and private communication.
9. P. Amaudruz et al., *Phys. Rev. Lett.* **66** (1991) 2712.
10. E.J. Eichten et al, *Phys. Rev.* **D45** (1992) 2269 and Fermilab-Pub-92/264-E, (1992).
11. P.B. Straub et al., *Phys. Rev. Lett.* **68** (1992) 452.
12. L.V. Gribov et al., *Phys. Rep.* **100** (1983) 1.
13. see, for example, G. Altarelli., *Phys. Rep.* **81** (1982) 1.
14. see for example, L.N. Lipatov in *Perturbative Quantum Chromodynamics*, World Scientific, A.H. Mueller, editor.
15. G. Marchesini and B.R. Webber, *Nucl.Phys.***B386** (1992) 215.
16. A.H. Mueller and H. Navelet, *Nucl.Phys.***B282** (1987) 727;
    J. Kwiecinski et al., *Phys. Rev.***D46** (1992) 921.
17. A.H. Mueller and J-W Qiu, *Nucl.Phys.***B268** (1986) 427
18. J. Kwiecinski et al., *Phys. Rev.***D44** (1991) 2640.
19. E.M. Levin, these proceedings;
    E.M. Levin et al., DESY-92-047 (March 1992);

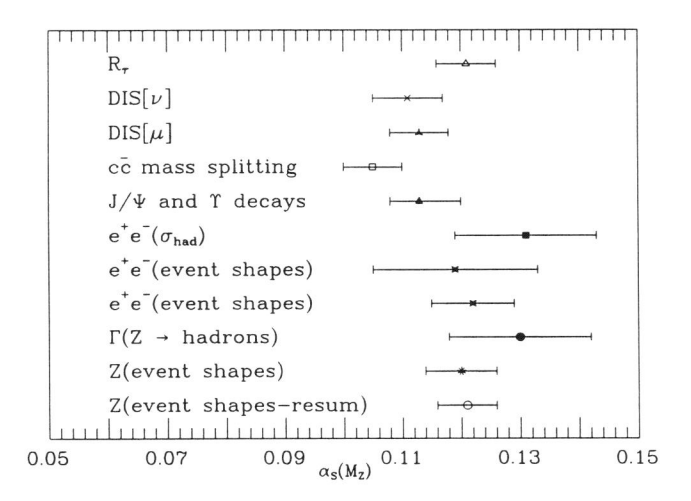

Figure 9: $\alpha_s(M_Z)$

J. Bartels, DESY-92-114 (August 1992).
20. J.M. Dunlea, this conference.
21. J-W Qiu, this conference.
22. G.R. Snow for the D0 collaboration, this conference;
    P. Maas for the CDF collaboration, this conference.
23. H. Baer, J. Ohnemus and J.F. Owens, *Phys. Rev.***D42** (1990) 61,
    J.F. Owens, private communication.
24. J. Dunlea for the E706 collaboration, this conference.
25. J. Appel, Fermilab-Pub-92/49, (1992).
26. M. Aguilar-Benitez et al., *Nucl.Phys.***B161** (1985) 400.
27. G.A. Alves et al, Fermilab-Pub-92/208-E, (1992);
28. T. Fuess, for the CDF collaboration, this conference;
    B.T. Huffman, for the CDF collaboration, this conference;
    S. Vejcik, for the CDF collaboration, this conference.
29. P. Nason et al., *Nucl.Phys.***B327** (1989) 49.
30. C. Albajar et al., *Phys. Lett.***B213** (1988) 405.
31. E.L. Berger et al., Argonne preprint, ANL-HEP-CP-92-79.
32. R.K. Ellis and D.A. Ross, *Nucl.Phys.***B345** (1990) 79;

J.C. Collins and R.K. Ellis, *Nucl.Phys.***B360** (1991) 3;
E.M. Levin et al., *Sov.J.Nucl.Phys.***54** (1991) 867;
S. Catani et al., *Nucl.Phys.***B366** (1991) 135.

33. R.K. Ellis, *Phys. Lett.* **B259** (1991) 492 and references therein.
34. E. Laenen et al., *Nucl.Phys.***B369** (1992) 543.
35. F.A. Berends et al., Fermilab-Pub-92/196-T, (1992).
36. R.K. Ellis and S. Parke, Fermilab-Pub-92-132-T (May 1992).
37. S.D. Ellis et al., *Phys. Rev. Lett.* **69**(1992) 1496;
    H. Baer et al., *Phys. Lett.* **B234** (1990) 127;
    M.L. Mangano et al., *Nucl.Phys.***B373** (1992) 295.
38. W.T. Giele et al., Fermilab-Conf-92/213-T, (1992).
39. J. Conrad for the E665 collaboration, this conference.
40. E. Braaten et al., *Nucl.Phys.***B373** (1992) 581.
41. W. Marciano and A. Sirlin, *Phys. Rev. Lett.***61** (1988) 1815.
42. L.R. Surguladze et al., *Phys. Rev. Lett.* **66** (1991) 560;
    S. Gorishny et al., *Phys. Lett.* **B259** (1991) 144.
43. A. Pich, CERN-TH 6738/92 (1992).
44. A. El-Khadra et al., *Phys. Rev. Lett.* **69** (1992) 729.
45. S. Bethke, Heidelberg preprints, HD-PY 92/12,92/13.
46. S. Catani, et al., *Phys. Lett.* **B269** (1991) 432.
47. S. Catani, et al., *Phys. Lett.* **B263** (1991)491;
    Phys. Lett. **B272** (1991)368;

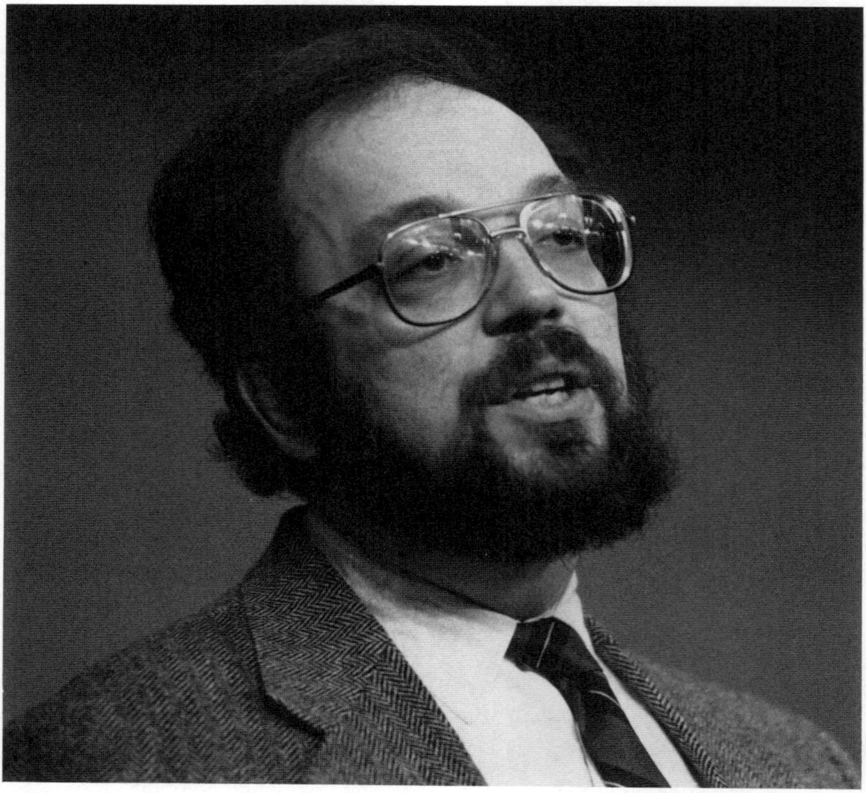

STATUS OF ELECTROWEAK MEASUREMENTS

WILLIAM J. MARCIANO*

Brookhaven National Laboratory Upton, New York 11973-5000

ABSTRACT

Precision tests of electroweak theory are discussed. The status of charged current universality is reviewed. Implications of neutral current and gauge boson mass measurements for top, Higgs, and "new physics" are described. An outlook for future expectations is given.

1. Perspective

Over the past several decades, we have witnessed tremendous advances in elementary particle physics. The standard $SU(3)_C \times SU(2)_L \times U(1)_Y$ model of strong and electroweak interactions was developed and subjected to close experimental scrutiny. It has passed all tests with flying colors. There are no experimental results that cannot be accommodated by the standard model.[1] That situation is quite remarkable when one considers the wealth of precise experimental data it has confronted. Nevertheless, we do anticipate the emergence of "new physics" beyond standard model expectations as higher energies are probed, both directly and indirectly (via precision measurements and searches for rare or forbidden reactions). That conviction stems from a general dissatisfaction with electroweak symmetry breaking and mass generation via the simple fundamental Higgs mechanism. Although that mechanism can accommodate all known particle masses and mixing (even CP violation), it does not really explain their origin. One hopes that a truly fundamental theory would have no free (arbitrary) parameters and would elucidate the origin of mass either through additional symmetry or new dynamics, perhaps both. In addition, the simple Higgs mechanism seems to be a trivial theory (when taken on its own), and exhibits fine-tuning problems when embedded in a grand unified theory.

At present, supersymmetry is the leading justification for a fundamental scalar Higgs mechanism. It is an elegant symmetry that potentially alleviates fine-tuning hierarchy problems, if the scale of supersymmetry, m_{SUSY}, is not too large ($(m_{SUSY} \leq \mathcal{O}(1 \text{ TeV}))$). Supersymmetry, so far, has no direct experimental support, although the unification of gauge couplings does work out very nicely in supersymmetric GUTS. Nevertheless, it has many theory believers (enlightened fundamentalists) who have no doubt that it is correct. Confirmation of their faith will require discovery of the plethora of new particles, sparticles, predicted by supersymmetry models. Fortunately, if supersymmetry masses are near or below 1 TeV, that new spectroscopy should be easily uncovered at the SSC.

---
*Research supported by U.S. DOE under contract DE-AC02-76CH00016.

An alternative to a fundamental Higgs mechanism is dynamical symmetry breaking via fermion-antifermion condensation. Scenarios ranging from minimal $t\bar{t}$ condensation models to complicated extended technicolor scenarios have been advocated. Although the basic idea is very attractive, no really complete models exist. It appears that new experimental discoveries are probably required to stimulate more creativity among the dynamicists. Those insights may come from probing higher collider energies, finding rare or forbidden reactions (e.g., proton decay), or making very high precision measurements.

In this talk, I will concentrate on the status of precision electroweak measurements and their implications. After reviewing the state of charged current universality tests, I will describe neutral current loop constraints on the top quark mass, hopes (delusions) regarding Higgs mass constraints, and implications for "new physics" parameterized by the Peskin-Takeuchi[2] variables S, T, and U.

2. Charged Current Universality

Weak charged current interactions are described by

$$L_{int}^{CC} = -\frac{g_2^0}{\sqrt{2}} W^\mu(x) J_\mu^{CC}(x) + h.c. \tag{1}$$

$$J_\mu^{CC} = \sum_{\ell=e,\mu,\tau} \bar{\nu}_{\ell_L} \gamma_\mu \ell_L + \sum_{\substack{q=u,c,t \\ q'=d,s,b}} \bar{q}_L V_{qq'} \gamma_\mu q'_L \tag{2}$$

where g_2^0 is a universal bare $SU(2)_L$ coupling and V is the 3 × 3 CKM matrix.

Unitarity requires

$$\sum_i V_{ij}^* V_{ik} = \sum_i V_{ji}^* V_{ki} = \delta_{jk} \tag{3}$$

and lepton universality implies

$$g_{We\nu_e} = g_{W\mu\nu_\mu} = g_{W\tau\nu_\tau} \tag{4}$$

for the renormalized couplings (assuming lepton mass effects are separated out in the extraction of couplings). A deviation from the predictions in (3) and (4) would signal "new physics".

Measurements of superallowed β-decays, K_{e3} and B decays give[3]

$$\begin{aligned} |V_{ud}| &= 0.9734 \pm 0.0007 \\ |V_{us}| &= 0.2205 \pm 0.0018 \\ |V_{ub}| &= 0.004 \pm 0.002 \end{aligned} \tag{5}$$

where the errors are primarily theoretical and therefore not really possible to treat on a gaussian basis. Nevertheless, one finds (somewhat blindly)

$$|V_{ud}|^2 + |V_{us}|^2 + |V_{ub}|^2 = 0.9962 \pm 0.0016 \tag{6}$$

The theoretical prediction of unity is tested at the ±0.16% level! A 2.4σ deviation seems to be present which could, in principle, be due to "new physics" such as heavy quark mixing. However, it is more likely that $|V_{ud}|$ (perhaps also $|V_{us}|$) lies outside the range in Eq. (5). Theoretical uncertainties in $|V_{ud}|$ are difficult to assess and thus limit the validity of Eq. (6).

Leptonic universality tests are less sensitive to theoretical uncertainties and are presently only limited by experimental errors. Comparing the recent measurements[4]

$$\frac{\Gamma(\pi \to e\nu_e(\gamma))}{\Gamma(\pi \to \mu\nu_\mu(\gamma))} = \begin{cases} 1.2265 \pm 0.0034 \pm 0.0044 \times 10^{-4} & \text{(TRIUMF)} \\ 1.2346 \pm 0.0035 \pm 0.0036 \times 10^{-4} & \text{(PSI)} \end{cases} \qquad (7)$$

and experimental averages[5]

$$B(\tau \to \nu_\tau \pi/K(\gamma)) = 0.1203 \pm 0.0026$$
$$\tau_{tau} = 2.96 \pm 0.03 \times 10^{-13} s \qquad (8)$$

with theoretical expectations[6], one finds

$$g_{We\nu_e} : g_{W\mu\nu_\mu} : g_{W\tau\nu_\tau} :: 1 : 1.0012 \pm 0.0015 : 0.996 \pm 0.013 \qquad (9)$$

Electron-Muon-Tau universality is precisely tested by those measurements for the W boson's (pseudo) *scalar* component. In that sense, the Higgs structure of the standard model is being scrutinized. The good agreement can be used to constrain heavy neutrino mixing, majoran emission, additional Higgs interactions, etc. So far, there is no hint of "new physics", but those tests can still be pushed further before theoretical uncertainties set in. (In the case of Eq. (7), the theoretical prediction[6] 1.235×10^{-4}, has less than $\pm 0.1\%$ uncertainty.)

The transverse W couplings are tested by comparing the muon decay rate with the decay rates $\Gamma(\tau \to \ell\bar{\nu}_\ell\nu_\tau), \ell = e$ or μ. Operationally, that amounts to testing the muon lifetime normalized predictions[7]

$$B(\tau \to e\bar{\nu}_e\nu_\tau(\gamma)) = 0.18131 \left(\frac{m_\tau}{1776.9 \text{ MeV}}\right)^5 \left(\frac{\tau_{tau}}{2.96 \times 10^{-13}s}\right)$$
$$B(\tau \to \mu\bar{\nu}_\mu\nu_\tau(\gamma)) = 0.17634 \left(\frac{m_\tau}{1776.9 \text{ MeV}}\right)^5 \left(\frac{\tau_{tau}}{2.96 \times 10^{-13}s}\right) \qquad (10)$$

by comparing measured leptonic branching ratios with m_τ and τ_{tau}. I note that the predictions in Eq. (10) have essentially no theoretical uncertainty. They provide pure experimental tests. A recent BES measurement[9] has now nailed down m_τ at

$$m_\tau = 1776.9 \pm 0.5 \text{ MeV}; \qquad (11)$$

however, some error still resides in τ_{tau} (see Eq. (8)) which leads to about a 1% uncertainty in Eq. (10). Those predictions are to be compared with the world averages[5]

$$B(\tau \to e\bar{\nu}_e\nu_\tau(\gamma))^{exp.} = 0.1778 \pm 0.0015$$
$$B(\tau \to \mu\bar{\nu}_\mu\nu_\tau(\gamma))^{exp} = 0.1739 \pm 0.0017 \qquad (12)$$

which I have updated to include the CLEO II result[9] $B(\tau \to e\bar{\nu}_e\nu_\tau(\gamma)) = 0.1749 \pm 0.0014 \pm 0.0022$. From those results, one finds

$$g_{We\nu_e} : g_{W\mu\nu_\mu} : g_{W\tau\nu_\tau} :: 1 : 1.0028 \pm 0.0064 : 0.991 \pm 0.006 \tag{13}$$

for the *transverse* W couplings. The small 1.5 σ discrepancy in Eq. (13) is a remnant of the tau decay puzzle[7] which has been largely resolved. A complete solution will likely require further experimental movement in the tau lifetime and/or leptonic branching ratios. Alternatively, it could still be a first hint of "new physics" at the tree or loop level. To properly address that prospect will require future measurements of τ_{tau} and $B(\tau \to \ell\bar{\nu}_\ell\nu_\tau(\gamma))$ at the $\pm 0.1\%$ level, an exciting goal. Such precision may be possible for the branching ratios at a high luminosity tau-charm factory. It is, however, unclear as to what uncertainty in τ_{tau} can be ultimately achieved. Given the lack of theoretical uncertainty in Eq. (10), efforts to test that prediction should be pushed as far as possible.

3. Neutral Current Tests

Precision measurements of m_W, m_Z, G_μ, $\sin^2\theta_W$, Γ_Z, etc. have been used to constrain m_t and "new physics" scenarios such as technicolor, Z' bosons etc. In addition, there have been claims that a relatively light Higgs, $m_H \sim 100$ GeV, is preferred by the data. I will address those issues collectively.

Loop constraints arise because of the natural relation

$$\sin^2\theta_W^0 = (e_0/g_2^0)^2 = 1 - (m_W^0/m_Z^0)^2 \tag{14}$$

which connects what could have been independent parameters. Instead, those relations are maintained after renormalization, up to finite calculable loop corrections. Experimental measurements of those quantities then constrain m_t and (perhaps) m_H through loop effects. In addition, "new physics" loop corrections to gauge boson self-energies can be similarly constrained using the Peskin-Takeuchi[10] S, T, and U parameters.

Employing the known fermion masses, along with

$$\begin{aligned} \alpha &= 1/137.036 \\ G_\mu &= 1.16639 \times 10^{-5} \text{ GeV}^{-2} \\ m_Z &= 91.187 \text{ GeV} \end{aligned} \tag{15}$$

as input and assuming (as temporary central values) m_t (defined by $\overline{MS}$ at $\mu = m_t$) = 140 GeV, $m_H = 200$ GeV, one predicts[11]

$$\sin^2 2\theta_W(m_Z)_{\overline{MS}} = \frac{4\pi\alpha}{\sqrt{2}G_\mu m_Z^2(1-\Delta\hat{r})} \tag{16}$$

$$m_W^2 = \frac{\pi\alpha}{\sqrt{2}G_\mu \sin^2\theta_W(m_Z)_{\overline{MS}}(1-\Delta r(m_Z)_{\overline{MS}})} \tag{17}$$

where[12]

$$\Delta\hat{r} = 0.0636 \pm 0.0009 + 0.011 S_Z - 0.00782 T \qquad (18)$$
$$\Delta r(m_Z)_{\overline{MS}} = 0.0701 \pm 0.0009 + 0.0084 S_W \qquad (19)$$
$$\rho^{new} = 1 + 0.00782 T \qquad (20)$$

T, $S = S_Z$, and $U = S_W - S_Z$ represent "new physics" loop effects or deviations from the assumed m_t and m_H values

$$\begin{aligned} T &\simeq \frac{3}{16\pi \sin^2\theta_W} \frac{m_t^2 - (140 \text{ GeV})^2}{m_W^2} - \frac{3}{8\pi \cos^2\theta_W} \ell n\left(\frac{m_H}{200 \text{ GeV}}\right) + \cdots \\ S &\simeq -\frac{1}{3\pi} \ell n\left(\frac{m_t}{140 \text{ GeV}}\right) + \frac{1}{6\pi} \ell n\left(\frac{m_H}{200 \text{ GeV}}\right) + \cdots \\ U &\simeq \frac{1}{\pi} \ell n\left(\frac{m_t}{140 \text{ GeV}}\right) + \cdots \end{aligned} \qquad (21)$$

where only the leading m_t and m_H dependence is exhibited and $\cdots$ represent "new physics" effects. Based on those formulas, one expects

$$\sin^2\theta_W(m_Z)_{\overline{MS}} = 0.2326 \pm 0.0003 + 0.00365 S_Z \times 0.00261 T \qquad (22)$$

$$m_W = 80.16 \mp 0.020 + 0.45 T - 0.63 S_Z + 0.34 S_W \text{ GeV} \qquad (23)$$

The uncertainties in Eqs. (22) and (23) stem from hadronic loop uncertainties in extrapolating $\alpha = 1/137.036$ to short-distances. They can be reduced, somewhat, by improved measurements of $e^+e^- \to$ hadrons data.

Before discussing the experimental tests of Eq. (22) and (23), let me make a few comments. First of all, the $\overline{MS}$ definition of $\sin^2\theta_W(m_Z)_{\overline{MS}}$ is very similar to the $\sin^2\bar{\theta}_W$ definition employed at LEP. Roughly, one finds

$$\sin^2\theta_W(m_Z)_{\overline{MS}} \simeq \sin^2\bar{\theta}_W + 0.0002 \qquad (24)$$

I will use that relation to translate LEP values.

I have normalized Eqs. (22) and (23) at $m_t(m_t)_{\overline{MS}} = 140$ GeV and refer to that parameter as m_t. If one prefers a more conventional mass definition such as the real part of the pole in the top quark propagator, then QCD corrections give

$$m_t(pole) = m_t(m_t)_{\overline{MS}} \left(1 + \frac{4}{3} \frac{\alpha_s(m_t)}{\pi} + 10.9 \left(\frac{\alpha_s(m_t)}{\pi}\right)^2 \right) \qquad (25)$$

Employing $\alpha_s(m_t) \simeq 0.11$ implies

$$m_t(pole) \simeq 1.06 m_t(m_t)_{\overline{MS}} \qquad (26)$$

The difference can be considerable, e.g., about 8.4 GeV for $m_t \simeq 140$ GeV. Therefore, one must be precise in the definition of m_t employed and cognizant of QCD effects in any extraction of m_t from experimental data or meaningful theoretical prediction.

Assuming no new physics and $m_H \simeq 200$ GeV, one finds the predictions in table 1. Because of the hadronic loop uncertainties, even a perfect (error free)

Table 1: Standard model predictions as a function of m_t, using $m_Z = 91.187$ GeV, $\alpha = 1/137.036$, $G_\mu = 1.16639 \times 10^{-5}$ GeV^{-2} as input and assuming $m_H = 200$ GeV. The uncertainties correspond to hadronic loop effects.

m_t (GeV)	$\sin^2\theta_W(m_Z)_{\overline{MS}} \pm 0.0003$	$m_W \mp 0.02$ (GeV)
100	0.2337	79.93
110	0.2334	79.99
120	0.2332	80.04
130	0.2329	80.10
140	0.2326	80.16
150	0.2322	80.23
160	0.2319	80.29
170	0.2315	80.36
180	0.2312	80.44
190	0.2307	80.52
200	0.2303	80.59
210	0.2299	80.67
220	0.2294	80.76
230	0.2289	80.84
240	0.2285	80.94
250	0.2279	81.03

measurement of $\sin^2\theta_W(m_Z)_{\overline{MS}}$ via Z decay asymmetries determines m_t to only ± 10 GeV for a given m_H. Varying m_H up or down by a factor of 4 introduces another ± 20 GeV uncertainty in m_t. One does better by measuring m_W where hadronic loop and Higgs mass uncertainties lead to ± 4 GeV and ± 13 GeV in the determination of m_t. The W mass is our most sensitive probe of m_t.

To overcome the hadronic loop uncertainties, one can use both m_W and $\sin^2\theta_W(m_Z)_{\overline{MS}}$ or a global fit to all data. Unfortunately, because of the compensating effect of m_H (see Eq. (21)), an uncertainty of about ± 18 GeV in m_Z will still result from the Higgs mass. Of course, one can hope to take advantage of that situation by measuring m_t directly (after its discovery) and then using loop effects to constrain m_H. However, only very limited information can be obtained. For example, if m_t is measured very precisely, say ± 1 GeV and $\sin^2\theta_W(m_Z)_{\overline{MS}}$ is measured to ± 0.0004, then one finds using a central value of $m_H = 200$ GeV

$$m_H \simeq 200 \text{ GeV} \exp[\pm 0.50 \pm 0.67] \tag{27}$$

where the uncertainties stem from hadronic loop effects and $\Delta \sin^2\theta_W$ respectively. The range in Eq. (27) is too broad to constrain m_H much beyond the 57 GeV $< m_H \leq$ 800 GeV range already assumed. One could eliminate the hadronic loop uncertainty by including a very precise m_W measurement in the fit. Even then, the best one can probably hope for is differentiating the heavy and light (100 GeV) Higgs scenarios.

Given the above general discussion, let me describe the present constraints that follow from existing data. My discussion will emphasize the role of some results reported at this meeting.

The CHARM II collaboration has completed their measurement of the ratio $\sigma(\nu_\mu e)/\sigma(\bar\nu_\mu e)$. From the preliminary results given by G. Rädel[13], one finds

$$\sin^2\theta_W(m_Z)_{\overline{MS}} = 0.2325 \pm 0.0092 \quad \text{(CHARM II)} \tag{28}$$

The central value is very close to the LEP average from forward-backward and polarization asymmetries[14]

$$\sin^2\theta_W(m_Z)_{\overline{MS}} = 0.2326 \pm 0.0011 \quad \text{(LEP)} \tag{29}$$

but the error in Eq. (28) is not competitive. Instead, the best use of CHARM II data is to constrain new physics scenarios such as Z' bosons which affect $\overset{(-)}{\nu}_\mu e$ scattering but not Z decays.

The LEP result in (29) sets a standard for future measurements of $\sin^2\theta_W(m_Z)_{\overline{MS}}$. The only potential challenger seems to be the SLD experiment at SLAC. On the basis of 10,000 Z decays with about 0.22 polarization, they find from the left-right asymmetry[15]

$$\sin^2\theta_W(m_Z)_{\overline{MS}} = 0.2372 \pm 0.0056 \quad \text{(SLD)} \tag{30}$$

(I have attempted to translate the $\sin^2\theta_W(SLD) = 0.2378$ to an $\overline{MS}$ definition.)

In the future they hope to significantly increase the number of Z bosons and polarization. They aim to measure $\sin^2\theta_W(m_Z)$ to ± 0.0005 or even better. That experiment provides a unique opportunity to nail down the value of $\sin^2\theta_W(m_Z)_{\overline{MS}}$ and should be pushed as far as possible.

The above $\sin^2\theta_W(m_Z)_{\overline{MS}}$ values correspond to $m_t \simeq 133 \pm 10 \pm 20^{+30}_{-40}$ GeV where the errors are due to hadronic loops, Higgs mass, and experimental uncertainties. Last year, the value of $\sin^2\theta_W(m_Z)$ coming from LEP was somewhat smaller and suggestive of a larger m_t. To compensate, the global fits to all neutral current data were forced to favor a small m_H (marginally). That is no longer the case.

A more powerful constraint on m_t comes from m_W measurements. The prevailing average[16]

$$m_W = 80.22 \pm 0.26 \text{ GeV} \tag{31}$$

corresponds to

$$m_t = 149 \pm 4 \pm 13 \pm 35 \text{ GeV} \tag{32}$$

Note the smaller uncertainties from hadronic loops and Higgs mass. In the near future one expects CDF and DØ to determine m_W to ± 100 MeV which leads to $\Delta m_t = \pm 20$ GeV.

Another good handle on m_t comes from $R_\nu \equiv \sigma(\nu_\mu N \to \nu_\mu X)/\sigma(\nu_\mu N \to \mu X)$. That ratio measures $1 - m_W^2/m_Z^2$ which indirectly gives m_W. New measurements reported at this meeting

$$\begin{aligned} 1 - m_W^2/m_Z^2 &= 0.224 \pm 0.0044 \pm 0.0047 \quad \text{(CCFRW - Preliminary}^{17}) \\ 1 - m_W^2/m_Z^2 &= 0.2342 \pm 0.011 \quad \text{(FMMF}^{18}) \end{aligned} \tag{33}$$

bring the world average from deep-inelastic neutrino scattering to

$$1 - m_W^2/m_Z^2 = 0.2304 \pm 0.0024 \pm 0.0050 \quad (R_\nu \text{ world avg.}) \tag{34}$$

Using $m_Z = 91.187$ GeV then implies

$$m_W = 80.00 \pm 0.13 \pm 0.27 \text{ GeV} \quad (\text{From } R_\nu \text{ \& } m_Z) \tag{35}$$

That determination is competitive with direct m_W measurements and corresponds (from table 1) to $m_t \simeq 112$ GeV. A future experiment, P815, at Fermilab aims to reduce the total error in Eq. (34) to ± 0.0024 which is equivalent to measuring m_W to ± 130 MeV.

Another sensitive probe of m_Z comes from LEP measurements of the Z partial and total widths.[19] Those quantities are normalized in terms of G_μ which induces a strong m_t (or T) dependence via the ρ parameter in Eq. (20). Including all Z width measurements along with m_W, $\sin^2\theta_W(m_Z)_{\overline{MS}}$, etc. one finds from a global fit[19]

$$m_t \simeq 135 \pm 26 \text{ GeV} \tag{36}$$

where the error is theoretical (including m_H uncertainty) and experimental. The corresponding top pole mass is 143 ± 26 GeV.

I now come to constraints on new physics via S, T and U. Interest in S was aroused by Peskin and Takeuchi[2][10] about two years ago when they showed how it could probe a generic technicolor feature. Each new $SU(2)_L$ chiral isodoublet of fermions contributes[20] (perturbatively) $1/6\pi$ to S. Technicolor enhancements,[10], taken in analogy with QCD, seem to increase that contribution by about a factor of 2 for technifermions. Therefore, theories such as technicolor which naturally contain many $SU(2)_L$ doublets can easily have $S \simeq +1$ or 2. A low energy signature for technicolor would then be a non-zero positive S (unless cancellations somehow occur with other new physics). Unfortunately, as we shall see, there is currently no signal for a positive non-zero S.

Employing the S, T, and U dependence in Eqs. (18)-(20) (using $S = S_Z$, $U = S_W - S_Z$) one finds the experimental constraints[1] given in table 2. A glance at that table shows no evidence in favor of $S > 0$. Taking $U = 0$, however, those constraints average to

$$S = -0.05 \pm 0.26 + 1.15T \tag{37}$$

So, an $S \simeq +1$ could still be accommodated if $T \simeq \mathcal{O}(+1)$. That is quite interesting since extended technicolor models quite naturally give $T > 0$ when they try to explain the top quark mass. One can eliminate the T dependence by comparing m_W with $\sin^2\theta_W(m_Z)_{\overline{MS}}$

$$S_W \simeq 118 \left\{ 2\left(\frac{m_W - 80.16 \text{ GeV}}{80.16 \text{ GeV}}\right) + \frac{\sin^2\theta_W(m_Z)_{\overline{MS}} - 0.2326}{0.2326} \right\} \tag{38}$$

Employing current experimental averages $m_W = 80.22 \pm 0.26$ GeV and $\sin^2\theta_W(m_Z)_{\overline{MS}} = 0.2328 \pm 0.0011$ implies

$$S_W \simeq 0.22 \pm 0.77 \pm 0.56 \tag{39}$$

Table 2: Present experimental constraints on S, T and U along with future sensitivities. Central values of $m_t = 140 GeV$ and $m_H = 200 GeV$ are assumed.

Experiment	Current Constraint	Future
$m_W = 80.22 \pm 0.26 GeV$	$T - 0.64S + 0.76U = 0.13 \pm 0.60$	± 0.16
$R_\nu = \sigma_{RC}/\sigma_{CC}$	$T - 0.4S = -0.22 \pm 0.67$	± 0.24
$R_{\bar{\nu}}$	$T - 0.028 = 1.4 \pm 1.3$	± 0.65
LEP Asymmetries	$S - 0.69T = 0 \pm 0.31$	± 0.15
$A_{LR}(SLD)$	$S - 0.69T = 1.3 \pm 1.5$	± 0.10
$\Gamma_z = 2492 \pm 7 MeV$	$T - 0.36S = 0.27 \pm 0.27$	± 0.27
$\Gamma_{\ell^+\ell^-} = 83.33 \pm 0.29 MeV$	$T - 0.23S = -0.35 \pm 0.37$	± 0.37
$Q_W(C_s) = -71.04 \pm 1.58 \pm 0.88$	$S - 0.006T = -2.7 \pm 2.0 \pm 1.1$	± 0.5

which is still (roughly) consistent with $S \simeq +1$ but not much larger. Cesium atomic parity violation[21] is also insensitive[12] to T and gives

$$S_Z = -2.7 \pm 2.0 \pm 1.1 \tag{40}$$

where the errors are experimental and atomic theory. That experiment favors a negative S but the errors are still large enough to accommodate an $S \simeq +1$. An ongoing experiment at Boulder is expected[22] to reduce the first error in Eq. (40) by a factor of 5 and the atomic theory error may be further reduced[23] by a factor of 2. That would lead to an interesting confrontation with technicolor as well as other precision measurements.

4. OUTLOOK

Precision electroweak measurements have now tested the standard model at the $0.1 \sim 1\%$ level. So far, there is no evidence for anything beyond $m_t \simeq 135 \pm 26$ GeV and $57 < m_H < 800$ GeV. A hoped for technicolor signal, $S \simeq +1 \sim 2$ has not materialized, but $S \simeq +1$ is not ruled out. A direct measurement of m_t combined with results from ongoing experiments should eventually pin S down at about the ± 0.3 level. At that point, some constraint on m_H may also be possible, but it will not be very significant. Other potential "new physics" scenarios such as Z' bosons will be severely constrained by those measurements.

In the charged current sector, new measurements of $|V_{ud}|$ via neutron decay or $\pi^+ \to \pi^0 e^+ \nu_e$ and $|V_{us}|$ via K_{e3} would be useful in clarifying the small deviation from CKM unitary presently observed. Tests of e-μ-τ universality in $\pi_{\ell 2}$ decays and $\tau \to \ell \nu \bar{\nu}$, $\ell = e$ or μ have been pushed quite far, but can still be significantly improved before theoretical uncertainties set in. Those tests and other comparable precision tests of the standard model should be pushed as far as possible. Maybe then we will start to see hints of the new surprises nature has in store for us.

References

1. W. Marciano, *Annu. Rev. Nucl. Part. Sci.* **41** (1991) 469.
2. M. Peskin and T. Takeuchi, *Phys. Rev. Lett.* **65** (1990) 964.
3. I. Towner *et al.* preprint (1992); F. Barker *et al.*, *Nucl. Phys.* **A540**, (1992) 501.
4. D. I. Bretton *et al.*, *Phys. Rev. Lett.* **68** (1992) 3000; C. Czapek *et al.*, *Phys. Rev. Lett.* **70** (1993) 17.
5. *Proceedings of the Second Tau Physics Workshop, Ohio State University, October (1992)*.
6. W. Marciano and A. Sirlin, BNL preprint (1993).
7. W. Marciano, *Phys. Rev.* **D45** (1992) R721.
8. W. Toki in these proceedings.
9. CLEO II, D. S. Akerib *et al.*, *Phys. Rev. Lett.* **69** (1992) 3610.
10. M. Peskin and T. Takeuchi, *Phys. Rev.* **D46** (1992) 381.
11. G. Degrassi, S. Franchiotti, and A. Sirlin, *Nucl. Phys.* **B351** (1991) 49.
12. W. Marciano and J. Rosner, *Phys. Rev. Lett.* **65** (1990) 2963.
13. G. Rädel in these Proceedings.
14. S. Ting in these Proceedings.
15. C. Baltay in these Proceedings.
16. Particle Data Tables, *Phys. Rev.* **D45** (1992) Part II.
17. R. Bernstein in these Proceedings.
18. R. Brock in these Proceedings.
19. J. Harton in these Proceedings.
20. S. Bertolini and A. Sirlin, *Nucl. Phys.* **B248** (1984) 589.
21. M. Noecker, B. Masterson and C. Wieman, *Phys. Rev. Lett.* **61** (1988) 310.
22. C. Wieman, Private Communication.
23. J. Sapirstein, Private Communication.

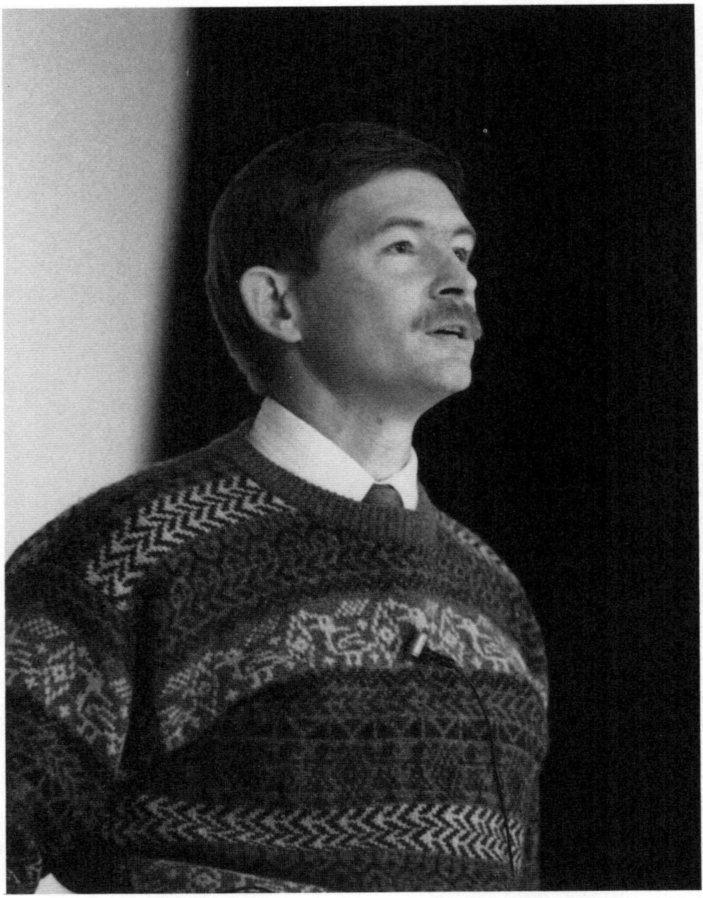

RECENT RESULTS IN CHARM PHYSICS

JOHN P. CUMALAT
Department of Physics, Campus Box 390
University of Colorado
Boulder, CO 80309, USA

ABSTRACT

Recent results in Charm Physics are reviewed. Major results include new semileptonic form factors for the D^+ and D_s^+, and a polarization measurement which confirms significant polarization in the $D^+ \to K^* l^+ \nu_l$ channel. A first measurement of the Cabibbo-suppressed decay $D^+ \to \pi^0 l^+ \nu_l$ was presented. Several charm lifetime measurements were presented and impressive new Charm Baryon results from the CLEO collaboration were reported.

1. Introduction

In the past 3 years since the Division of Particles and Fields meeting at Rice University in Houston, there has been dramatic progress in the field of Charm physics. CLEO have begun taking data with their improved γ and π^0 detector and has increased its luminosity a factor of five. In addition the Fermilab Fixed Target Program was completed in January, 1992 and new results are just beginning to become available.

While there were many new results on the production of charm particles, I have had to limit the scope of this paper to charm decays due to insufficient space. In addition, I have included no figures, but have summarized results in tables. For specific figures the reader should refer to the individual contributions.

The paper is organized as follows: semileptonics, lifetimes of charm particles, charm baryon decays, new charm meson results, future prospects, and a conclusion.

2. Semileptonic Decays of the D mesons

Semileptonic decays have played an important role in our understanding of strong and weak interactions. The semileptonic decays take place via the spectator graph and there is no interference between the final state hadrons and leptons. Hence, from our understanding of the weak interaction both the weak couplings and the hadronic portion of the matrix element may be studied.

First, the pseudoscalar decays of the $D^0 \to K^- l^+ \nu_l$ will be discussed. The full decay rate is given by

$$\frac{d\Gamma}{dE_K} = \frac{G_F^2}{4\pi^3} |V_{cs}|^2 |f_+(q^2)|^2 P_K \left(\frac{W_0 - E_K}{F_0}\right)^2 \left[\frac{1}{3} m_D P_K^2 + \frac{1}{3} m_l^2 \frac{P_K^2}{F_0} \right.$$
$$\left. + \frac{m_l^2}{8 m_D}(m_D^2 + m_K^2 + 2 m_D E_K) + \frac{1}{4} m_l^2 \frac{m_D^2 - m_K^2}{m_D} Re\left(\frac{f_-(q^2)}{f_+(q^2)}\right) + \frac{1}{4} m_l^2 F_0 \left|\frac{f_-(q^2)}{f_+(q^2)}\right|^2 \right],$$

where $W_0 = \frac{m_D^2 + m_K^2 - m_l^2}{2m_D}$, and $F_0 = W_0 - E_K + \frac{m_l^2}{m_D}$.

Generally all terms multiplied by m_l^2 are dropped leaving the total rate with respect to $E_K^{D^0 c.m.}$ given approximately as

$$\frac{d\Gamma}{dE_K} \simeq \frac{G_F^2}{12\pi^3} |V_{cs}|^2 |f_+(q^2)|^2 m_D P_K^3$$

with $f_+(q^2)$ assumed to have a pole dependence

$$f_+(q^2) = 1/(1 - q^2/m_{pole}^2).$$

At this conference experiment E687 presented new results[1] based on 40% of their muon data sample for the branching ratio $\frac{D^0 \to K^- \mu^+ \nu_\mu}{D^0 \to K^- \pi^+}$ and for the mass of the pole for $f_+(q^2)$. These new results together with existing measurements are presented in Table 1 along with a newly calculated world average. (The muon branching fraction has been multiplied by 1.017 before averaging with the electron branching fraction.) Theoretically the muon branching fraction is expected to be smaller by 1.7% than the electron branching fraction principally due to the reduced phase space.

Table 1. $D^0 \to K^- l\nu_l / D^0 \to K^- \pi^+$

Exp.	Mode	BR relative to $K^-\pi^+$	m_{pole}
E691[2]	$K^- e^+ \nu_e$	$0.90 \pm 0.07 \pm 0.11$	$2.1^{+0.4}_{-0.2} \pm 0.2$
CLEO[3]	$K^- e^+ \nu_e$	$0.91 \pm 0.06 \pm 0.06$	$2.1^{+0.4+0.3}_{-0.2-0.2}$
CLEO[3]	$K^- \mu^+ \nu_\mu$	$0.79 \pm 0.08 \pm 0.09$	
E687[1]	$K^- \mu^+ \nu_\mu$	$0.87 \pm 0.08 \pm 0.06$	$2.1^{+0.7+0.7}_{-0.3-0.3}$
MKIII[4]	$K^- e^+ \nu_e$		$1.8^{+0.5+0.3}_{-0.2-0.2}$
Average	$K^- l\nu_l$	0.88 ± 0.05	$2.02^{+0.29}_{-0.16}$

To average the information from Table 1 with other experiments, we need to multiply by the $D^0 \to K^-\pi^+$ branching fraction for which there is considerable uncertainty. In Table 2, two branching ratios are used to compute an overall average. Average 1 refers to using the Mark III branching fraction, while Average 2 refers to normalizing by the 1992 PDG value. It is important to continue to present the data as a comparison to the $D^0 \to K^-\pi^+$ branching fraction until an accurate absolute branching fraction becomes available. Also included in Table 2 are the branching ratios for $D \to K^* l\nu_l$.

In Table 2 the E653 branching fraction of $D^0 \to K^-\mu^+\nu_\mu$ is computed relative to the entire $D^0 \to \mu^+ X$ branching fraction. For the $D^0 \to K^{*0}\mu^+\nu_\mu$ channel, E653 uses two methods to determine the branching fraction. One method ratios the result to $D^0 \to K^-\pi^+\pi^+$ and the other method ratioes the channel to $D^0 \to K^-\mu^+\nu_\mu$ using measured D⁺ and D⁰ production cross sections. The second method is reported and flagged with an asterisk, but is not used in computing the average.

Table 2. $D^0 \to K^- l\nu_l$ Branching Fractions

Channel	Experiment	(%)	Comments	Rate(10^{10}sec^{-1})
$D^0 \to K^- l\nu_l$	Mark III[4]	3.4±0.5±0.4	Double D's	
	E653[5]	2.5±0.4±0.5	Muonic Rate	
	Average 1	3.70±0.49	4.2%	
	Average 2	3.21±0.23	3.65%	
	Result 1	3.33±0.33	4.2%	7.9±0.8
	Result 2	3.15±0.21	3.65%	7.5±0.5
$D^+ \to \overline{K}^0 e^+ \nu$	Mark III[6]	6.5±1.6±0.7	Double D's	
	E691[7]	6.1±0.9±1.6	$D^+ \to K^- \pi^+ \pi^+$	
	Average	6.3±1.3		5.8±1.2
$D \to \overline{K} l^+ \nu_l$	Average			7.2±0.5
$D^+ \to \overline{K}^{*0} e^+ \nu$	Mark III[6]	4.2±1.6	Double D's	
	E691[8]	4.4±0.4±0.8	$K^- \pi^+ \pi^+$	
	WA82[9]	5.6±1.6±0.9	$K^- \pi^+ \pi^+$	
	ARGUS[10]	4.2±0.6±1.0		
	E653*	3.25±0.71±0.75	$D^0 \to K^- \mu^+ \nu_\mu$	
	E653[12]	4.18±0.66±0.96	$K^- \pi^+ \pi^+$	
	E687[13]	4.8±.4±1.0	$K^- \pi^+ \pi^+$	
	Average	4.6±0.4		4.3±0.5
$D^0 \to K^{*-} e^+ \nu$	Mark III[6]	3.5±1.6	Double D's	
	CLEO[3]	1.7±0.8		
	ARGUS[10]	2.5±0.5±0.5		
	Average	2.3±0.5		5.4±1.2
$D \to K^* l^+ \nu_l$	Average			4.5±0.5

The semileptonic widths of the two D mesons are expected to be equal and they are to within errors. Thus, we can average the results to obtain Γ_K(Ave) = 7.2±0.5 × 10^{10}sec^{-1} for the pseudoscalar decay and Γ_{K^*}(Ave) = 4.5±0.5 × 10^{10}sec^{-1} for the vector decay. This will be addressed later, but for now it's only interesting to note that while both widths agree to within errors for both the D⁺ and the D⁰ mesons, it turns out that in both cases the D⁰ widths are larger than the D⁺ widths indicating a possible systematic error in the $D^+ \to K^- \pi^+ \pi^+$ or $D^0 \to K^- \pi^+$ branching fractions.

An important result presented at this conference was the first observation[14] of the Cabibbo-suppressed decay of the $D^+ \to \pi^0 l \nu_l$ decay channel by the CLEO collaboration. The signal is isolated by using $D^{*+} \to D^+ \pi^0$ and computing the pseudo mass difference $M_{diff} = M(\pi^0_{slow} \pi^0_{fast} l) - M(\pi^0_{fast} l)$. A fit to the mass difference yields 38±7 events. The channel is ratioed to $D^+ \to K^0_s l^+ \nu_l$ which is obtained in a similar technique. The result is $\Gamma(D^+ \to \pi^0 l^+ \nu_l)/\Gamma(D^+ \to \overline{K}^0 l^+ \nu_l) = (9.0 \pm 1.8 \pm 1.6)\%$. While this number may seem large, it is consistent with theoretical expectations due to the additional phase space available for the $D^+ \to \pi^0 l^+ \nu_l$ decay channel and to a small extent due to the lower pole mass. Using this result, one obtains

$$\left|\frac{V_{cd}}{V_{cs}}\right|^2 \left|\frac{f^\pi_+(0)}{f^K_+(0)}\right|^2 = 0.0452 \pm 0.0090 \pm 0.0080$$

which can be compared to a Mark III measurement[4] of

$$\left|\frac{V_{cd}}{V_{cs}}\right|^2 \left|\frac{f^\pi_+(0)}{f^K_+(0)}\right|^2 = 0.057^{+0.038}_{-0.015} \pm 0.005$$

Averaging these two measurements, adding the systematic and statistical errors in quadrature, and assuming that $\left|\frac{f^\pi_+(0)}{f^K_+(0)}\right| = 1$, we obtain $\left|\frac{V_{cd}}{V_{cs}}\right| = 0.222 \pm 0.022$.

Another result[15] on pseudoscalar decays was presented from the E653 collaboration on the decay channel $D^+_s \to (\eta, \eta')\mu^+ \nu_\mu$. The $\pi^+\pi^-$ mass is plotted and 29 events below a mass of 0.40 GeV/c² are seen. As the missing π^0's are not reconstructed, they are unable to distinquish between the η and η' production; however a search was made for 5 prong decays as a means of isolating the η'. The E653 collaboration obtains the following ratios with the conclusion that $D^+_s \to (\eta\mu^+\nu + \eta'\mu^+\nu)$ is unlikely to be dominated by $D^+_s \to \eta'\mu^+\nu$.

$$\frac{\Gamma(D^+_s \to (\eta\mu^+\nu_\mu + \eta'\mu^+\nu_\mu))}{D^+_s \to \phi\mu^+\nu_\mu} = 2.4 \pm 1.2 \quad and \quad \frac{\Gamma(D^+_s \to \eta'\mu^+\nu_\mu)}{D^+_s \to \phi\mu^+\nu_\mu} < 2.0$$

We now compare the exclusive semileptonic decay rates to the total inclusive decay rates. The information is presented in Table 3.

Table 3. Lifetimes, Branching Ratios, and Decay Rates of D mesons

Quantity	D^0	D^+
Lifetime $(10^{-13} s)$	4.20±0.08	10.66±0.23
$B(D \to Xe^+\nu_e)$ (%)	7.7±1.2	17.2±2.9
$\Gamma(D \to Xe^+\nu_e)(10^{11}s^{-1})$	1.83±0.29	1.61±0.27
$\Gamma(D \to \overline{K}e^+\nu_e)(10^{11}s^{-1})$	0.78±0.05	0.58±0.12
$\Gamma(D \to [\overline{K}+\overline{K}^*]e^+\nu_e)(10^{11}s^{-1})$	1.32±0.13	1.01±0.13
$\Gamma(D \to \pi^- e^+\nu_e)$ $(10^{11}s^{-1})$	0.09±0.02	0.05±0.03
$\Gamma(D \to [\overline{K}+\overline{K}^*+\pi]e^+\nu_e)$	1.41±0.13	1.06±0.13
$(\overline{K}+\overline{K}^*+\pi)/X$ ratio	0.77±0.14	0.66±0.14

In examining the last line of Table 3 it is clear that the exclusive rates are unable to account for all of the inclusive rates. Possible explanations for this shortfall are non-resonant $K^-\pi^+l^+\nu_l$ production, excited K* production, multiprong production, and Cabibbo-suppressed exclusive final states. The limit[8] on non-resonant $K^-\pi^+l^+\nu_l$ is quite small and could account for at most 10% of what is missing. Cabibbo-suppressed channels which are missing might account for 5% of the D^0 and 10% of the D^+.(The D^+ has additional Cabibbo-suppressed channels available such as $\eta\ l^+\nu, \eta'\ l^+\nu$, and $\omega\ l^+\nu$.) Hence at least 15% of inclusive semileptonics are not yet accounted for. The D^0 4-prong channels need to be investigated as well as channels with multineutrals such as $K^{*-}\pi^0 e^+\nu_e$, $\rho^-\overline{K}^0 e^+\nu_e$, and $\eta^0 K^- e^+\nu_e$. Again, perhaps one of the biggest uncertainites may be the absolute branching fractions of $D^0 \to K^-\pi^+$ and $D^+ \to K^-\pi^+\pi^+$.

Decays of D mesons to vector particles introduce Lorentz invariant products of momenta and spins. The decay width can be expressed in terms of 3 angles and $t \equiv M^2(\mu\nu)$. The angles are defined as θ_v which is the angle between $\vec{K}^-$ and $-\vec{D}$ in the rest frame of the $\overline{K^*}$; θ_μ which is the angle between $\vec{\mu}$ and $-\vec{D}$ in the rest frame of the $\mu\nu$; and χ which is the angle between the $l\nu$ and $\overline{K^*}$ planes in the D rest frame. E687 presented new results[13] on the form factors for the helicity amplitudes by first integrating over the χ variable. The width is then given as

$$\frac{d\Gamma}{dM_{K\pi}\ dt\ dcos\ \theta_v\ dcos\ \theta_\mu} \propto PS \times BW \times |\mathcal{M}|^2$$

where the phase space and Breit-Wigner terms are

$$PS \propto K\left(1-\frac{M_\mu^2}{t}\right) \quad and \quad BW = \frac{\Gamma M_{K^*}}{(M_{K\pi}^2 - M_{K^*}^2)^2 + M_{K^*}^2\Gamma^2}.$$

The matrix element is written in terms of helicity amplitudes as

$$|\mathcal{M}|^2 \propto t\left(1-\frac{M_\mu^2}{t}\right) \times \sin^2\theta_v\ \{(1+\cos\theta_\mu)^2\ |H_+(t)|^2\ +\ (1-\cos\theta_\mu)^2\ |H_-(t)|^2\}$$

$$+4\cos^2\theta_v \sin^2\theta_\mu\ |H_0(t)|^2 + \frac{M_\mu^2}{t}\ \{\text{mass terms}\}$$

Now as $M_l \to 0$ the helicity amplitudes become $H_\pm = \alpha\ A_1(t) \mp \beta\ V(t)$ and $H_o = \delta\ A_1(t) - \epsilon\ A_2(t)$ where α, β, δ, and ϵ are functions of t, $M_{K\pi}$, and K. Following the description of E691, definitions for R_V and R_2 are $R_V = \frac{V(0)}{A_1(0)}$ and $R_2 = \frac{A_2(0)}{A_1(0)}$, with the form factors assumed to be $F(t) = \frac{F(0)}{1-t/M_p^2}$. The pole masses are assumed to be $M_V = 2.1$, $M_{A_1} = 2.5$, and $M_{A_2} = 2.5$. Lastly, the polarization is found by

$$\frac{dN}{d\Omega} \propto 1 + \left(\frac{2\Gamma_\ell}{\Gamma_t}-1\right)\ \cos^2\theta_v \quad with \quad \frac{\Gamma_\ell}{\Gamma_t} = \frac{\int dt\ G(t)\ |H_o(t)|^2}{\int dt\ G(t)\ (|H_+(t)|^2 + |H_-(t)|^2)}$$

where it should be noted that $G(t)$ depends on M_ℓ.

In the past the $D \to K^*l\nu$ channel has been difficult to predict theoretically. The ratio of $\Gamma(\overline{K}^*l\nu)/\Gamma(\overline{K}l\nu)$ is 4σ from unity. The ratio of longitudinal to transverse widths, Γ_L/Γ_T, shows considerable polarization. Perhaps, the hardest to explain has been the lack of sufficient K* production. Recently, J.F. Amundson and

J.L. Rosner[16] have come up with a possible explanation which is as follows. Two main effects, perturbative QCD corrections and $\mathcal{O}(1/m_s)$ corrections, govern the decays of D mesons to $Kl\nu$ and $K^*l\nu$ final states. The authors argue that perturbative QCD corrections lead to an overall decrease of predicted rates, while $\mathcal{O}(1/m_s)$ effects tend to cancel the perturbative QCD corrections in the case of the $Kl\nu$ decay, but have minimal effect in the $K^*l\nu$ decay.

The new E687 results presented at this conference along with theoretical predictions are shown in Table 4. The predictions come from quark models of Altomari and Wolfenstein and from Korner and Schuler, lattice gauge models of LMS and BKS, and the QCD sum rule model of BBD. The E687 results confirm the large polarization values from E691 and E653 and substantially reduce the overall errors on the form factors. See reference 11 for further discussion of the various models.

Table 4. $\overline{K}^* e^+ \nu$ Results and Comparison to Theory

Experiment	Γ_L/Γ_T	$A_2(0)/A_1(0)$	$V(0)/A_1(0)$	$\Gamma(K^* e^+\nu)/\Gamma(K e^+\nu)$
Mark III	$0.5^{+1.0+0.1}_{-0.1-0.2}$			$0.8^{+0.36}_{-0.26}$
E691	1.8 ± 0.5	$0.0\pm0.5\pm0.2$	$2.0\pm0.6\pm0.3$	0.55 ± 0.14
CLEO				$0.51\pm0.18\pm0.06$
ARGUS				$0.55\pm0.08\pm0.10$
E653	$1.18\pm0.18\pm0.08$	$0.82\pm0.23\pm0.11$	$2.0\pm0.33\pm0.16$	
WA82	$0.6\pm0.3^{+0.3}_{-0.1}$			
E687	$1.48\pm0.14\pm0.11$	$0.48\pm0.14\pm0.11$	$1.46\pm0.24\pm0.18$	
Average	$1.30\pm.12$	0.55 ± 0.14	1.71 ± 0.22	0.57 ± 0.08
Theory				
WSB[17]	0.9	1.3	1.1	0.87
KSB[18]	1.2	1.0	1.0	0.9
ISGW[19]	1.1	1.0	1.4	1.14
AW[20]	1.2	0.8	1.9	1.34
LMS[21]	1.7 ± 0.6			1.1 ± 0.4
BKS[22]	1.2 ± 0.23	0.7 ± 0.3	2.0 ± 0.5	
BBD[23]	0.9 ± 0.1	1.2 ± 0.2	2.2 ± 0.2	0.6 ± 0.4

Finally, at this conference E653 presented the first measurement of the R_2 and R_v form factor ratios for the decay $D_s^+ \rightarrow \phi \mu^+ \nu$. E653 determines $R_2 = 2.1^{+0.8+0.1}_{-0.7-0.2}$ and $R_V = 2.5 \pm 1.1^{+0.3}_{-0.4}$.

3. Lifetimes of Charm Particles

The lifetimes of Charm Mesons and Charm Baryons have been reasonably well measured and have been found to vary by large factors from state to state. If the spectator picture was dominant, then the total widths of the different species of charm hadrons would be the same. By comparison of the lifetimes[24] and inclusive semileptonic branching ratios[25] of the D^+ and D^0 mesons, we find that

$$\frac{BR(D^+ \to l^+X)}{BR(D^0 \to l^+X)} \simeq \frac{\tau(D^+)}{\tau(D^0)},$$

$$\frac{BR(D^+ \to l^+X)}{BR(D^0 \to l^+X)} = 2.3^{+0.5+0.1}_{-0.4-0.1}, \text{ and } \frac{\tau(D^+)}{\tau(D^0)} = 2.54 \pm .07.$$

The ratios are in agreement. If we neglect small Cabibbo-suppressed semileptonic decays of the D^+, then isospin invariance predicts $\Gamma(D^+ \to l^+X) = \Gamma(D^0 \to l^+X)$. Hence, the difference in lifetimes is due to the hadronic decay sector and correctly predicting the lifetimes will be an important step in understanding the charm decays. Currently, two models predict the lifetimes of charm mesons and charm baryons. While the models agree on the charm meson lifetimes, they differ in the baryon sector. Guberina et al.[26] predict $\tau(\Omega_c^0) = \tau(\Xi_c^0) < \tau(\Lambda_c^+) < \tau(\Xi_c^+)$, whereas Voloshin and Shifman[27] predict $\tau(\Omega_c^0) < \tau(\Xi_c^0) < \tau(\Lambda_c^+) = \tau(\Xi_c^+)$ (each inequality represents a factor of about 1.5). These papers were published in 1986 and it is refreshing to learn that work[28] is continuing to improve the predictions. Both predictions use the spectator model with W-exchange and QCD light quark interference. At this conference E687 reported on a new D_s^+ lifetime measurement[29] of $\tau(D_s^+)$=0.47±0.02±0.01 picoseconds and new measurements[30] of the Λ_c^+ and the Ξ_c^+ lifetimes. The new baryon lifetimes are presented in Table 5 together with other precise measurements.

Table 5. High Statistics Charm Baryon Lifetime Measurements

Baryon	Experiment	Lifetime (ps)
Ξ_c^+	WA-62[31]	$0.48^{+0.21+0.20}_{-0.15-0.10}$
	NA-32[32]	$0.20^{+0.11}_{-0.06}$
	E400[33]	$0.40^{+0.18}_{-0.12}$
	E687[30]	$0.41^{+0.11}_{-0.08} \pm 0.02$
	New World Average	$0.36^{+0.08}_{-0.06}$
Λ_c^+	NA-14[34]	$0.18\pm0.03\pm0.03$
	NA-32[35]	$0.196^{+0.023}_{-0.020}$
	E687(88)[36]	$0.20\pm0.03\pm0.03$
	E691[37]	$0.22\pm0.03\pm0.02$
	E687(90+91)[30]	$0.215\pm0.016\pm0.008$
	New World Average	0.206 ± 0.012

Table 6 contains a summary of new world averages from this conference and includes for comparison the world averages from last year. Significant changes have occurred in the mean lifetimes of the D_s^+, Λ_c^+, and Ξ_c^+. While the mean values have all remained within the old world average errors, the trends are worth noting. All three world averages have increased. In fact, the lifetime of the D_s^+ relative to the D^0 is now

$$\frac{\tau(D_s^+)}{\tau(D^0)} = 1.100 \pm 0.045.$$

This is only a 2σ effect, but it is in the opposite direction from what one might expect and provides an excellent test for theoreticians.

Table 6. Charm Mean Lifetimes ($\times 10^{-13}$sec)

	D^+	D^0	D_s^+	Λ_c^+	Ξ_c^+	Ξ_c^0
Last Year	10.66±0.23	4.20±0.08	$4.50^{+0.30}_{-0.26}$	$1.91^{+0.15}_{-0.12}$	$3.0^{+1.0}_{-0.6}$	$0.82^{+0.59}_{-0.30}$
This Year	10.66±0.23	4.20±0.08	$4.62^{+0.18}_{-0.17}$	2.06±0.12	$3.60^{+0.8}_{-0.6}$	$0.82^{+0.59}_{-0.30}$

As the measurements have become more precise, we can now start to examine systematic effects. A curious test is to compare the two experiments at CERN, NA-14 and NA-32, with the two experiments at Fermilab, E691 and E687, which have the best errors on the charm particles. The summary is presented in Table 7. It is remarkable to note that every single measurement at CERN is less than the Fermilab measurements even though the experiments agree to within errors. Experiment NA-32 reports that its systematic errors are negligible and doesn't report any systematic error. Nevertheless, there is clearly a systematic effect between the laboratories and comparison with Table 6 demonstrates that the world average falls in between the numbers.

Table 7. Laboratory Comparison of Charm Mean Lifetimes ($\times 10^{-13}$sec)

Experiment	D^+	D^0	D_s^+	Λ_c^+	Ξ_c^+
NA-14	10.3±0.8±0.6	4.17±0.18±0.15	$3.3^{+1.2}_{-0.8}$±0.3	1.8±0.3±0.3	
NA-32	$10.5^{+0.77}_{-0.72}$	$3.88^{+0.23}_{-0.21}$	$4.69^{+1.02}_{-0.86}$	$1.96^{+0.23}_{-0.20}$	$2.0^{+1.1}_{-0.6}$
CERN	10.43±0.60	4.01±0.16	4.19±0.73	1.93±0.19	$2.0^{+1.1}_{-0.6}$
E691	10.90±0.30±0.25	4.22±0.08±0.10	4.7±0.4±0.2	2.2±0.3±0.2	
E687	10.75±0.40±0.18	4.24±0.11±0.07	4.7±0.2±0.1	2.15±0.16±0.08	$4.1^{+1.1}_{-0.8}$±0.2
Fermilab	10.83±0.29	4.23±0.09	4.70±0.20	2.16±0.17	$4.1^{+1.1}_{-0.8}$±0.2

4. New Charm Baryon Results

During the past year there have been several new charm baryon results. These new results[38,39] come almost entirely from the CLEO collaboration with their excellent γ and π^0 reconstruction capability. In particular, there have been two new W-exchange *only* decays of $\Lambda_c^+ \to \Sigma^+ K^+ K^-$ and $\Lambda_c^+ \to \Xi^0 K^+$ observed. The only previous evidence for W-exchange was in the $\Delta^{++}K^-$ structure seen in $pK^-\pi^+$ and in the $\Delta^{++}K^{*-}$ structure seen in $pK^-\pi^+\pi^0$. The observation of these channels are important as the W-exchange diagrams are expected to contribute significantly to Λ_c^+ decays as these diagrams are neither helicity nor color suppressed for baryons. It is the addition of these decays which give rise to the shorter lifetime of the Λ_c^+ relative to the charm mesons.

A summary of Λ_c^+ branching fractions relative to $\Lambda_c^+ \to pK^-\pi^+$ is presented in Table 8. The asterisks after the numbers indicate that the results have been obtained from reference 39. The inclusive lines are computed by this author using only the statistical errors. The line for inclusive Λ^0's includes the Σ^0 inclusive category.

Table 8. Λ_c^+ Branching Ratios Relative to $\Lambda_c^+ \to pK^-\pi^+$.

Λ_c^+ Decay Mode	BR/BR($pK^-\pi^+$)
$pK^-\pi^+$	1.0
$\Lambda^0\pi^+$	0.178±0.016±0.014
$\Lambda^0\pi^+\pi^0$	0.708±0.086±0.096
$\Lambda^0\pi^+\pi^-\pi^+$	0.501±0.052±0.040
$\Lambda^0K^0K^+$	0.17±0.05*
Ξ^0K^+	0.077±0.014±0.012
$\Sigma^0\pi^+$	0.236±0.027±0.019
$\Sigma^0\pi^+\pi^0$	0.38±0.09*
$\Sigma^0\pi^+\pi^-\pi^+$	0.144±0.036±0.011
$\Sigma^0 inclusive$	0.76±0.10
$\Lambda^0 inclusive$	2.32±0.15
$\Sigma^+\pi^+\pi^-$	0.56±0.07±0.06
$\Sigma^+K^+K^-$	0.076±0.014±0.011
$\Sigma^+\omega$	0.40±0.09±0.04
$\Sigma^+\pi^0$	0.17±0.03±0.02
$\Sigma(1385)^\pm\pi\pi$	0.51±0.12±0.11
$\Sigma(1385)^-\pi^+\pi^+$	0.21±0.07±0.05
$\Sigma(1385)^+\pi^+\pi^-$	0.30±0.09±0.07
$\Sigma^+ inclusive$	1.24±0.12

With so many decay modes of the Λ_c^+ now observed, we can start to examine the fraction of known Λ_c^+ decays and try to estimate what fraction of the decays are missing in Σ^- and neutron channels. First, we need the $pK^-\pi^+$ branching fraction. The Particle Data Group[24] reports a number of 3.2±0.7%, but the most recent number[41] by the CLEO group is 4.3±1.0±0.8%. For the purposes of this calculation

I will use the CLEO number. A previous Bubble Chamber Experiment[40] has measured the inclusive number of Λ^0's to be 27±9% and of $\Sigma^\pm$'s to be 10±5%. Using the Λ^0 inclusive number from the table and multiplying by 4.3% yields only 10% for $\Lambda_c^+ \to \Lambda X$. If we add in Ξ^0 and Ξ^- channels plus $\Lambda^0 l \nu_l$ semileptonic channels we obtain another 3%. We could generously add another 4% for channels with 2 π^0's in the final state and still we are at the low end of the Bubble Chamber Inclusive Numbers. It is not quite so bad for the Σ case where 5% of the decays have been observed and no decays involving a Σ^- have yet been observed.

Adding all decays we get between 25% and 35% of all decays identified. It seems rather unlikely that the rest of the decays are into modes containing neutrons. To this author the most likely situation is that the $\Lambda_c^+ \to pK^-\pi^+$ branching fraction is still too low.

The CLEO collaboration also reported[38] observations of new decay channels for the Charm-strange baryons. In addition E687 presented evidence[30] for the Charm-strange-strange Baryon, Ω_c^0. Table 9 summarizes the CLEO results and includes for reference previous observations of Charm-strange decay channels. Decay modes in Table 9 which are not referenced were new results reported by CLEO at this conference. Also included in this table are the results on the Ω_c^0.

Table 9. Summary of Ξ_c results

State	Decay Mode	Mass	Yield	Relative Branching Ratio
Ξ_c^0	$\Xi^-\pi^+$	2463.0±3.1	29.2±6.7	1.0
	$\Xi^-\pi^+\pi^0$	2468.2±2.9	45.0±9.5	3.5±1.1
	$\Xi^0\pi^+\pi^-$	2471.2±2.6	30.2±8.1	3.6±1.2
	pK^-K^{*0} [42]	2473.3±1.9	4	seen
	$\Xi^-\pi^+\pi^-\pi^+$ [43]	2472.1±2.7±1.6	36.2±9.1	$\simeq$ 3.3
Ξ_c^+	$\Xi^-\pi^+\pi^+$	2467.1±2.4	50.3±8.8	1.0
	$\Xi^0\pi^+\pi^0$	2469.9±4.6	24.5±7.6	3.2±1.0
	$\Xi^0\pi^+$	2470.6±3.0	15.7±4.9	0.61±0.23
	$\Lambda^0 K^-\pi^+\pi^+$ [44]	2460±25	82	seen
	$\Sigma^0 K^-\pi^+\pi^+$ [45]	2460±5±30	26	seen
	$\Sigma^+ K^-\pi^+$ [46]	2466.5±2.7±1.2	2	seen
Ω_c^0	$\Xi^- K^-\pi^+\pi^+$ [47]	2740±20	3	seen
	$\Omega^-\pi^+$ [30]	2706.3±3.0±5.0	9.6±3.7	seen
	$\Xi^- K^-\pi^+\pi^+$ [48]	2719.0±7.0±2.5	12.2±4.5	seen
	$\Omega^-\pi^+\pi^-\pi^+$ [49]	?	?	seen

5. New Charm Meson Results

During the past year there have been several new measurements of hadronic decays of D mesons. The principal results come from E691, CLEO, and E687.

E691 presented a Dalitz plot analysis[50] of D→ $K\pi\pi$ decays to measure the resonant substructure. The decays used were $D^0 \to K^-\pi^+\pi^0$, $D^0 \to \overline{K}^0\pi^+\pi^-$, and $D^+ \to K^-\pi^+\pi^+$. The results confirm the highly non-resonant nature of the $D^+ \to K^-\pi^+\pi^+$ decays. The individual resonant contributions are included in Table 10 along with measurements from Mark III[51] and E687[52]. While the theory predictions are not included in the Table 10, there are several models that address the D→ $K\pi\pi$ decays. Reference 50 compares the effective Lagrangian model[53] of Bauer, Stech, and Wirbel and the $1/N_C$ model of Lee[54]. As final state interactions can alter the predictions, it is difficult to distinguish one model over another.

Table 10. Dalitz Plot Results of D→ $K\pi\pi$

Final State	Decay Mode	E691 BR (%)	Mark III BR (%)	E687 BR (%)
$K^-\pi^+\pi^+$	$(K^-\pi^+\pi^+)_{NR}$	6.7±0.7±2.2	7.2±0.6±1.8	—
	$\overline{K}^*(892)^0\pi^+$	2.0±0.2±0.4	1.8±0.2±1.0	—
	$\overline{K}^*(1430)^0\pi^+$	3.0±0.4±0.2	—	—
	$\overline{K}^*(1680)^0\pi^+$	0.9±0.2±0.4	—	—
$K^-\pi^+\pi^0$	$(K^-\pi^+\pi^0)_{NR}$	0.41±0.04±0.18	1.2±0.2±0.6	—
	$\overline{K}^*(892)^0\pi^0$	2.4±0.4±0.4	2.6±0.3±0.7	—
	$\overline{K}^*(892)^-\pi^+$	2.8±0.5±0.4	4.9±0.7±1.5	—
	$K^-\rho(770)^+$	7.3±0.8±1.7	10.8±0.4±1.7	—
$\overline{K}^0\pi^+\pi^-$	$(\overline{K}^0\pi^+\pi^-)_{NR}$	1.4±0.13±0.22	2.1±0.3±0.7	2.1±0.5±0.3
	$\overline{K}^*(892)^-\pi^+$	3.9±0.9±1.0	5.3±0.4±1.0	6.0±0.8±0.5
	$\overline{K}^0\rho(770)^0$	1.2±0.3±0.2	0.8±0.1±0.5	1.3±0.4±0.2

The CLEO collaboration presented the first observation[55] of $D^+ \to \pi^+\pi^0$ with a yield of 28±7 events. Combining this observation with their own measurements of $D^0 \to \pi^+\pi^-$ and $D^0 \to \pi^0\pi^0$, they compare the $\Delta I = 1/2$ amplitude ($A_{1/2}$) to the $\Delta I = 3/2$ amplitude ($A_{3/2}$) and derive a ratio of the amplitudes $|\frac{A_{3/2}}{A_{1/2}}| = 0.7 \pm 0.2$ which shows no evidence for a suppression of $\Delta I = 3/2$ transitions in the D meson decays. (See reference 55 for further details.)

Another topic of interest was presented by CLEO[55] on the search for annihilation diagrams of the D_s^+ and the D^+. Thus far, the only evidence[56] for annihilation processes comes from the observation of non-resonant $D^+ \to \pi^+\pi^-\pi^+$ and $D_s^+ \to \pi^+\pi^-\pi^+$, and a recent publication[57] of $D_s^+ \to \phi K^+$. Preliminary values for the $D^+ \to \pi^+\pi^-\pi^+$ decay rates were presented by E687[58] at this conference.

CLEO reports on a search[55] to ϕK^+ for both D^+ and D_s^+ and normalizes the results to $\phi\pi^+$. The limits obtained by CLEO are consistent with the measurement of E691. CLEO also searched for $D_s^+ \to \omega\pi^+$ which is suppressed by G-parity. The results are presented in Table 11.

Table 11. Recent Annihilation Channel Results

Decay Mode	Yield	Branching Ratio (%)
$D^+ \to \phi K^+$ [57]	$4.5^{+2.4}_{-2.0}$	$0.033^{+0.018}_{-0.015} \pm 0.008$
$D^+ \to \phi K^+$ [55]	24 ± 16	< 0.052 (90% CL)
$D_s^+ \to \phi K^+$ [55]	16 ± 13	< 0.086 (90% CL)
$D_s^+ \to \omega K^+$ [55]	7 ± 10	< 0.33 (90% CL)

Finally, new data were presented on three of the L=1 Charmed meson states. Thus far only 5 of the predicted 12 states have been identified. E687 presented new results[59] on 3 P-wave states, $D^{**0}(2420)$, $D^{**0}(2460)$, and $D_s^{**+}(2533)$. The CLEO collaboration presented[55] a new decay mode for the $D_s^{**+}(2536)$ decaying to $D^{*0}K^+$ and measured a relative branching ratio to $D^{*+}K^0$ of 1.13 ± 0.30. CLEO also measured a flat helicity angle distribution for this state which supports a hypothesis that the spin and parity of the state is $J^P = 1^+$. A summary of results for the L=1 states is presented in Table 12.

Table 12. Summary of Reported P-wave cq mesons (MeV/c²)

Final State	Experiment	Mass(MeV/c²)	Width(MeV/c²)	Events
$D^+\pi^-$ (2460)	ARGUS[60]	$2455 \pm 3 \pm 5$	$15^{+13}_{-10}{}^{+5}_{-10}$	337 ± 100
	CLEO[61]	$2461 \pm 3 \pm 1$	$20^{+9}_{-12}{}^{+9}_{-10}$	440 ± 97
	E691[62]	$2459 \pm 3 \pm 2$	$20 \pm 10 \pm 5$	1427^{+42}_{-37}
	E687[59]	$2460 \pm 4 \pm ?$	$42 \pm 10 \pm ?$	501 ± 65
$D^{*+}\pi^-$ (2420)	ARGUS[63]	$2414 \pm 2 \pm 5$	$13 \pm 6^{+10}_{-5}$	171 ± 22
	CLEO[61]	$2428 \pm 3 \pm 2$	$23^{+8}_{-6}{}^{+10}_{-3}$	279 ± 34
	E687[59]	$2422 \pm 3 \pm ?$	$14 \pm 8 \pm ?$	201 ± 37
$D^{*+}K_s^0$, $D^{*0}K^+$ (2536)	ARGUS[64,65]	$2535.9 \pm 0.9 \pm 2.0$	< 4.6 (90%CL)	16 ± 4, 71 ± 17
	CLEO[61]	$2536.6 \pm 0.7 \pm 0.4$	< 2.5 (90%CL)	44 ± 8, 134 ± 22
	E687[59]	$2433 \pm 3 \pm ?$		25 ± 7

6. Future Prospects

Experiments with large charm data sets are just starting to present samples of their results. Fermilab experiment E687 presented many papers and results. Fermilab experiment E791 showed impressive results[66] from less than 15% of their data. It looks like E791 may fully reconstruct 200,000 charm decays and over 10,000 semileptonic decays. Fermilab experiment E789 presented[67] their first measurement of the D^0 lifetime and it looks like their experiment is functioning well. And finally CLEO presented remarkable Charm Baryon results. It seems likely that CLEO will fully map out the Charm Baryon masses and branching ratios.

7. Conclusions

The number of new results and topics covered is somewhat staggering. Most notable are new semileptonic results on form factors for all the D mesons and the first measurement of $D^+ \to \pi^0 l^+ \nu_l$. The lifetimes of the charm particles are becoming well measured and provide an important challenge to theory. Charm Baryon results from CLEO are very impressive. In addition the field is getting close to achieving samples which will allow Double Cabibbo Suppressed states to be studied. Notably missing from the conference were new measurements of $D^0 - \overline{D}^0$ mixing and new measurements or limits on fully leptonic decays.

8. Acknowledgements

I would like to acknowledge several individuals who sent me copies of their talks and papers prior to their presentations. In particular I would like to specially thank Jeff Appel, Doug Potter, Miland Purohit, Paul Karchin, Dan Kaplan, Bijan Nemati, Ron Sidwell, Alice Bean, Philip Baringer, and the E687 authors. I also like to thank Arne Freyberger for useful conversations of the $D^+ \to \pi^0 l^+ \nu_l$ analysis and Harry Cheung for helpful comments on the lifetime results. Finally I would like to thank Carlo Dallapiccola and Harry Cheung for a careful reading of this paper. This work was in part supported by the US Department of Energy account number DE-FG02-91-ER-40672.

8. References

1. Will E. Johns, (E687) The proceedings of this conference.
2. J.C. Anjos, et al., (E691) Phys. Rev. Lett. **62** (1989) 1587.
3. G. Crawford et al., (CLEO) Phys. Rev.**D44** (1991) 3394.
4. J. Adler, et al., (Mark III)Phys. Rev. Lett. **62** (1989) 1821.
5. K. Kodama, et al., (E653 Collaboration)Phys. Rev. Lett. **66** (1991) 1819.
6. Z. Bai, et al., (Mark III)Phys. Rev. Lett. **66** (1991) 1011.
7. J.C. Anjos, et al., (E691) Phys. Rev. Lett. **67** (1991) 1507.
8. J.C. Anjos, et al., (E691) Phys. Rev. Lett. **65** (1990) 2630.
9. M. Adamovich, et al., (WA82) Phys. Lett. **B268**(1991) 142.
10. ARGUS Collaboration, R.Wanke, diploma thesis, University of Hamburg, DESY Internal Report F15-91-06, November, 1991, and private communication

to S. Stone by H. Schroder.
11. S. Stone, Syracuse University Report No. HEPSY-1-92, to be published in *Heavy Flavors*, edited by A.J. Buras and H. Lindner, World Scientific, Singapore(1992)
12. K. Kodama, *et al.*, (E653 Collaboration) *Phys. Lett.* **B286** (1992), 187
13. R. Culbertson, (E687) The proceedings of this conference.
14. A. Bean, (CLEO) The proceedings of this conference.
15. D. Potter, (E653) The proceedings of this conference.
16. James F. Amundson and Jonathan L. Rosner, EFI-92-36, HEP-ph/9209263, September 21, 1992.
17. M. Wirbel, B. Stech, and M. Bauer, *Z. Phys.* **C29** (1985), 637.
18. J.G. Korner and G.A. Schuler, *Z. Phys.* **C38** (1988), 511; ibid, (erratum) **C41**, 1989, 690.
19. N. Isgur, D.Scora, B. Grinstein, and M.B. Wise, *Phys. Rev.* **D39** (1989), 799.
20. T. Altomari and L. Wolfenstein, *Phys. Rev.* **D37** (1988), 681.
21. V. Lubicz, G. Martinelli, M.S. McCarthy, and C.T. Sachrajda, "Semileptonic deays of D-mesons in Lattice QCD", (1992).
22. C.W. Bernard, A.X. El-Khadra, and A. Soni, Fermilab-PUB-91/242-T (1991).
23. P. Ball, V.M. Braun, and H.G. Dosh, Heidelberg Preprint HD-THEP-91-16, (1991).
24. Particle Data Group Review of Particle Properties, *Phys. Rev.* **D45** (1992), 1.
25. D. Hitlin, CALT-68-1472 and 1987 International Symposium on Lepton and Photon Interactions at High Energies, Hamburg.
26. B. Guberina *et al.*, *Z. Phys.* **C33** (1986), 297.
27. M.B. Voloshin and M.A. Shifman, *Sov. Phys. JETP* **64**(4), (1986) 698.
28. I.I. Bigi, (Notre Dame) The proceedings of this conference.
29. D. Pušeljić, (E687) The proceedings of this conference.
30. C. Dallapiccola, (E687) The proceedings of this conference.
31. S.F. Biagi, *et al.*, (WA62) *Phys. Lett.* **B150** (1985), 230.
32. S. Barlag, *et al.*, (NA32) *Phys. Lett.* **B233** (1989), 522.
33. P. Coteus, *et al.*, (E400) *Phys. Rev. Lett.* **59** (1987), 1530.
34. Alvarez, *et al.*, (NA14) *Z. Phys.* **C47** (1990), 539.
35. S. Barlag, *et al.*, (NA32) *Phys. Lett.* **B218** (1989), 374.
36. P.L. Frabetti, *et al.*, (E687) *Phys. Lett.* **B251** (1990), 639.
37. J.C. Anjos, *et al.*, (E691)*Phys. Rev. Lett.* **60** (1988), 1379.
38. B. Nemati, (CLEO) The proceedings of the conference.
39. J.G. Smith, (CLEO) "Recent τ and Charm Results from CLEO II", Wash-

ington APS meeting April, 1992.
40. K. Abe, et al. (SLAC Hybrid Facility)*Phys. Rev.* **D33** (1986), 1.
41. P. Avery, et al. (CLEO) *Phys. Rev.* **D43** (1991), 3599.
42. S. Barlag, et al. (NA-32) *Phys. Lett.* **B236** (1990), 495.
43. H. Albrecht, et al. (ARGUS) *Phys. Lett.* **B247** (1990), 121.
44. S. Biagi, et al. *Phys. Lett.* **150B** (1985), 230.
45. P. Coteus, et al. (E400) *Phys. Rev. Lett.* **59** (1987), 1530.
46. S. Barlag, et al. (NA-32) *Phys. Lett.* **B233** (1989), 522.
47. S. Biagi, et al. *Z. Phys.* **C28** (1985), 175.
48. H. Albrecht, et al. (ARGUS) DESY Preprint 92-052 (March, 1992).
49. J. Stiewe, (ARGUS) *Producion and decays from ARGUS*, XXVI Int. Conf. on High Energy Physics, Dallas, TX 6-12 August, 1992.
50. M.V. Purohit, (E691) The proceedings of the conference.
51. J. Adler, et al. (Mark III) *Phys. Lett.* **B196** (1987), 107.
52. P.L. Frabetti, et al. (E687) *Phys. Lett.* **B286** (1992), 195.
53. M. Bauer, B. Stech, and M. Wirbel, *Z. Phys.* **C34** (1987), 103.
54. D. Lee, *Phys. Lett.* **B275** (1992), 469 and erratum *Phys. Lett.* **B277** (1992), 52.
55. Philip Baringer, (CLEO) The proceedings of the conference.
56. J.C. Anjos, et al., (E691)*Phys. Rev. Lett.* **62** (1989), 125.
57. J.C. Anjos, et al., (E691)*Phys. Rev. Lett.* **69** (1992), 2892.
58. Guinyun Kim, (E687) The proceedings of the conference.
59. Shekhar Shukla, (E687) The proceedings of the conference.
60. H. Albrecht, et al., (ARGUS)*Phys. Lett.* **B221** (1989), 422.
61. P. Avery, et al., (CLEO)*Phys. Rev.* **D41** (1990), 774.
62. J.C. Anjos, et al., (E691)*Phys. Rev. Lett.* **62** (1989), 1717.
63. H. Albrecht, et al., (ARGUS)*Phys. Lett.* **B232** (1989), 398.
64. H. Albrecht, et al., (ARGUS)*Phys. Lett.* **B230** (1989), 162.
65. H. Albrecht, et al., (ARGUS) DESY Preprint 92-124, September, 1992.
66. R. Sidwell, (E791) The proceedings of the conference.
67. M. Schub, (E789) The proceedings of the conference.

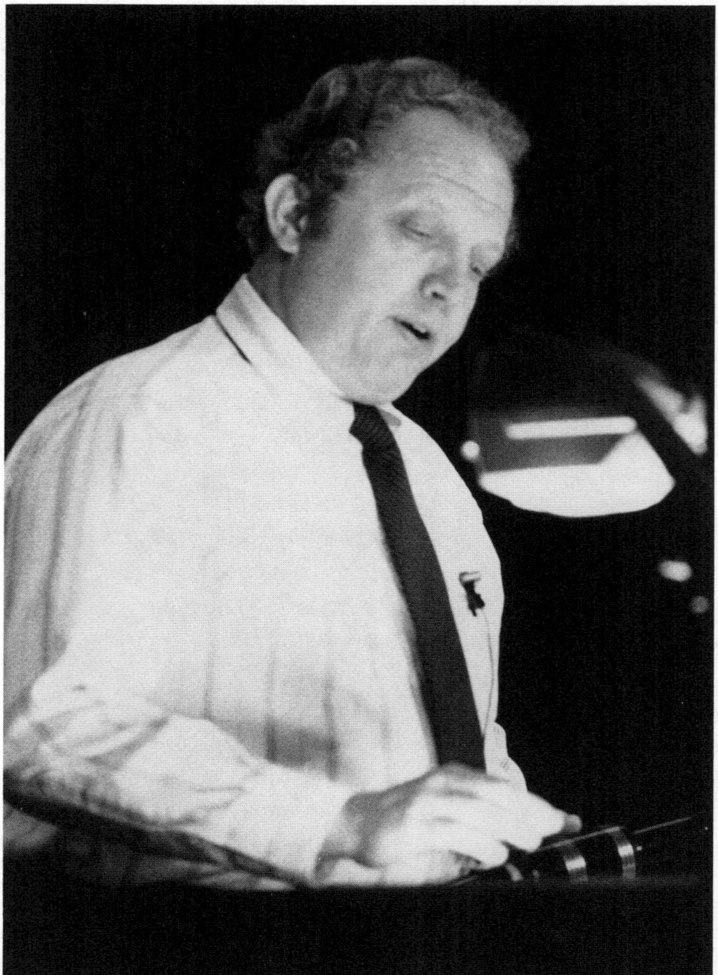

b PHYSICS

David G. Cassel
Laboratory of Nuclear Studies, Cornell University
Ithaca, NY 14853, USA

ABSTRACT

The report reviews the current status of the physics of the b quark with particular emphasis on weak decays. New results from ARGUS, CLEO, and the four LEP experiments have considerably enhanced our knowledge of this branch of b physics in the last year. LEP results include evidence for the B_s and Λ_b, significantly better measurements of the lifetimes of b hadrons, and new measurements of $B\bar{B}$ mixing. Important CLEO results include $B^0\bar{B}^0$ mixing, inclusive $b \to c\ell\nu$ decays, inclusive and exclusive $b \to u\ell\nu$ decays, searches for two-body decays of B mesons, and tests of theoretical models of B decay.

1. Introduction

The primary subject of this report is new experimental results[1] on the weak decays of hadrons containing b quarks. Currently, ARGUS, CLEO, and the LEP experiments dominate this field and many new measurements from these experiments have been described in the parallel sessions of this conference. A number of results on Υ physics and the production of b quarks are described in other reports at this meeting.

Research on b physics began at Fermilab 15 years ago with the discovery[2] of the Υ resonances. The discovery was soon confirmed at the DORIS storage ring at DESY and the focus of b quark studies shifted to e^+e^- storage rings. Most information about b quarks has come from CESR and DORIS, although the average lifetime of b hadrons was measured[3] at PEP and PETRA, and $B\bar{B}$ mixing was first observed[4] by UA1 at the SPS.

Fermilab is playing an increasingly important role in b physics. Results have been published[5,6] previously by CDF, and impressive new measurements and signals were exhibited[7] at this conference. Other new results presented at this meeting included an $\Upsilon(1S) \to e^+e^-$ signal from D0[8], and a $B \to J/\psi K(K^*)$ signal from the E672/E706 fixed target experiment[9]. The E653 Collaboration has previously reported[10] separate measurements of the lifetimes of charged and neutral B mesons.

At this conference the first results on b physics from the SLD experiment were described[11], and final conclusions on Υ spectroscopy and $\Upsilon(3S)$ decay from CUSB were also reported[12].

The LEP experiments have begun to play a major role in b physics, due to the precision vertex detectors installed in ALEPH, DELPHI, and OPAL for the 1991 LEP run and the large luminosity collected in that run. The CLEO II detector and record

CESR luminosities also provided major improvements in capability for studies of b physics. The ARGUS–CLEO and LEP programs are often complementary: ARGUS and CLEO run at the $\Upsilon(4S)$ which is just above the $B\bar{B}$ threshold, where only B^+B^- and $B^0\bar{B}^0$ pairs are produced. At LEP, B^-, B^0, B_s, and Λ_b are produced, without the tight correlation between the types of b hadrons produced in the hadronization. Measurements of b-hadron lifetimes are impossible at the $\Upsilon(4S)$ but are a major achievement of the LEP b-physics program. The $b\bar{b}$ data samples of these experiments is illustrated in Table 1.

Table 1: The principal data samples currently being used for reported results on b quark decay. The last column refers to the number of events available but not yet included in reported results.

		$b\bar{b}$ Events	
Experiment		Results Reported	Additional
ARGUS		200,000	–
CLEO 1.5		240,000	–
CLEO II		935,000	686,000
LEP	1990	35,000	–
LEP	1991	61,000	–
LEP	1992	–	163,000

2. Weak Decays of b Quarks

In the Standard Model (SM), (d', s', b') quarks decay to lighter quarks in the same generation via W^- emission. These (weak eigenstate) quarks are related to the mass eigenstates, (d, s, b), by the unitary Cabibbo-Kobayashi-Maskawa[13,14] (CKM) matrix V:

$$\begin{pmatrix} d' \\ s' \\ b' \end{pmatrix} = \begin{pmatrix} V_{ud} & V_{us} & V_{ub} \\ V_{cd} & V_{cs} & V_{cb} \\ V_{td} & V_{ts} & V_{tb} \end{pmatrix} \begin{pmatrix} d \\ s \\ b \end{pmatrix} \qquad (1)$$

The elements of this matrix give the effective couplings for decay of the d, s, and b quarks. In order for the SM to accommodate CP violation, all of the CKM matrix elements must be non-zero. Measurements of CKM matrix elements are described in the most recent Particle Data Group (PDG) summary[15] and other recent reports[16, 17]. Determination of V_{ub}, V_{cb}, V_{td}, and V_{ts} is a primary goal of studies of b quark decay. The first two are measured directly in B meson decay (Sections 5 and 6); the latter two are accessible through $B\bar{B}$ mixing (Section 7), and V_{ts} could also be studied via penguin diagrams in rare B decays.

Sensitivity of B decay to V_{cb} and V_{ub} is due to these couplings at the lower W^- vertex in the spectator diagram illustrated in Figure 1. In these decays, the other ($\bar{u}$, $\bar{d}$, or $\bar{s}$) quark in the B meson is a "spectator" because it does not couple to the W^-. This diagram dominates B decay; there is no evidence for the other possible contributions – annihilation diagrams in B^- decay or exchange diagrams in $\bar{B}^0$ decay.

When a c quark is produced in the decay of the b quark in B^- or $\bar{B}^0$ mesons, D, D^*, or D^{**} mesons usually appear[18,19] in the hadronization of the c quark and the spectator quark. Hadronization of the quarks at the upper W^- vertex can produce many different particles, leading to a large number of possible final states and small branching fractions for any one of them. Final states such as $J/\psi K(K^*)$ arise when a $\bar{c}s$ pair from the upper W^- vertex hadronize with the c quark from the lower W^- vertex and the spectator quark. High momentum leptons[1] (ℓ) are very useful tags for B decays because $B(b \to q\ell\nu)$ is relatively large ($\approx 10\%$) and leptons with large p_ℓ from other sources are very rare.

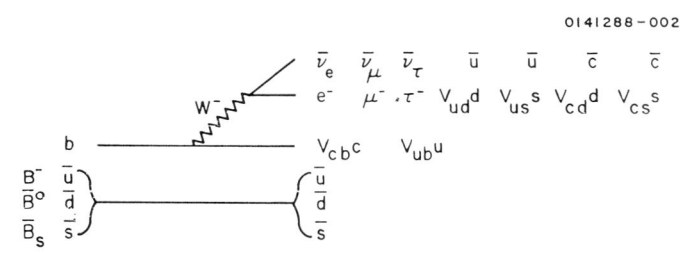

Figure 1: The spectator diagram for the decay of B^-, $\bar{B}^0$, and $\bar{B}_s$ mesons containing b quarks.

3. Evidence for the B_s and Λ_b

Previous evidence for the B_s and Λ_b listed[15] by the PDG is limited and has not been confirmed. There is now convincing and confirmed evidence from LEP experiments[20] for both B_s and Λ_b production in Z^0 decay.

Experiment	[%]	Ref.
ALEPH	$1.92 \pm 0.48 \pm 0.40$	[21]
DELPHI	$1.48 \pm 0.66 \pm 0.27$	[24]
OPAL	$1.39 \pm 0.39 \pm 0.34$	[26]
LEP Average	1.59 ± 0.42	

$B(b \to \bar{B}_s) \times B(\bar{B}_s \to D_s^+ X\ell\nu)$ [%]

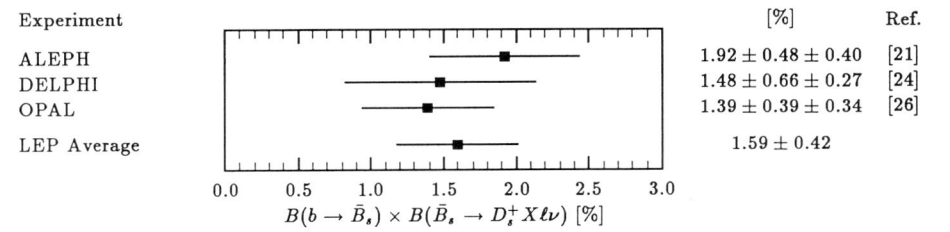

Figure 2: Summary of LEP measurements of $B(b \to \bar{B}_s) \times B(\bar{B}_s \to D_s^+ X\ell^-\nu)$. The common systematic error of each measurement due to the uncertainty in the D_s^+ branching fractions is 18% of the value.

Following experience with B^- and $\bar{B}^0$ decay, the decay $\bar{B}_s \to D_s^+ X\ell^- \bar{\nu}_\ell$ is a natural signature for B_s (see Figure 1). The D_s^+ arises from the hadronization of the c quark and the spectator $\bar{s}$ quark, either directly or from the decay of higher $D_s^{*(*)}$

---
[1] In this report, ℓ is used to refer to for either an e or a μ. When a branching fraction involves ℓ, (e.g., $B(b \to q\ell\nu)$) the branching fraction is the *average* of the e and μ branching fractions. In addition charge conjugate particles or decay modes are always implied.

states. ALEPH[21,22], DELPHI[23,24,25], and OPAL[26,27] have used the $D_s^+\ell^-$ signature to find B_s signals. ALEPH and OPAL reconstruct D_s^+ in the well-known $D_s^+ \to \phi\pi^+$ and $D_s^+ \to \bar{K}^{*0}K^+$ modes; DELPHI uses only the former mode (and only μ^- leptons). Significant right-sign lepton $(D_s^+\ell^-)$ signals are observed and there is no indication of a wrong-sign lepton $(D_s^+\ell^+)$ signal. The measurements of the product branching fraction $B(b \to \bar{B}_s) \times B(\bar{B}_s \to D_s^+ X\ell^-\nu)$ are illustrated in Figure 2. These were obtained using the PDG averages[15] for the D_s^+ branching fractions.[2]

The semileptonic decay $\Lambda_b \to \Lambda_c^+ X\ell^-\bar{\nu}_\ell$ is the corresponding signature for Λ_b. This decay arises from a spectator diagram analogous to Figure 1 with the ud diquark in the Λ_b taking the place of the spectator quark in the B meson. These semileptonic decays are detected by observing $\Lambda_c^+\ell^-$ correlations. Previous evidence (one step removed) for these decays came from studies of $\Lambda\ell$ correlations by ALEPH[28] and OPAL[29]. (The branching fraction[15] for $\Lambda_c^+ \to \Lambda X$ is about 30%.) More recently they reconstruct Λ_c^+'s in the $\Lambda_c^+ \to pK^-\pi^+$ mode and find significant signals with right-sign leptons $(\Lambda_c^+\ell^-)$ and no signal with wrong-sign leptons $(\Lambda_c^+\ell^+)$. The results (ALEPH[21,22,30] and OPAL[27,31]) for the product branching fraction, $B(b \to \Lambda_b) \times B(\Lambda_b \to \Lambda_c^+ X\ell^-\nu)$ are illustrated in Figure 3. These were obtained from the reported product branching fractions using $B(\Lambda_c^+ \to pK^-\pi^+) = (4.3 \pm 1.1)\%$, the average of ARGUS[32] and CLEO[33] measurements.

Experiment		[%]	Ref.
ALEPH		$1.50 \pm 0.35 \pm 0.40$	[28]
OPAL		$1.47 \pm 0.35 \pm 0.42$	[29]
LEP Average		1.48 ± 0.46	

$B(b \to \Lambda_b) \times B(\Lambda_b \to \Lambda_c^+ X\ell^-\nu)$ [%]

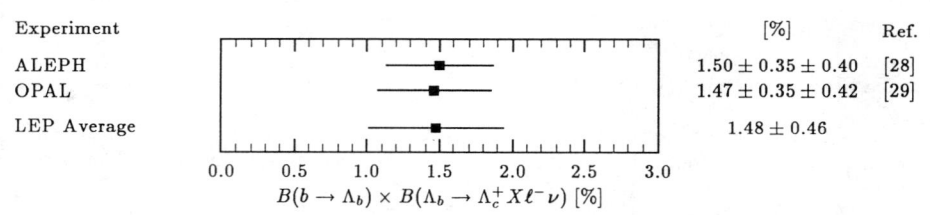

Figure 3: Summary of LEP measurements of $B(b \to \Lambda_b) \times B(\Lambda_b \to \Lambda_c^+ X\ell^-\nu)$. The common systematic error of the individual measurements due to the uncertainty in the $B(\Lambda_c^+ \to pK^-\pi^+)$ branching fraction is 26% of the value.

Since the B_s and Λ_b were detected in semileptonic decays, these results do not yield measurements of the masses. However, ALEPH and DELPHI have measured the B_s and Λ_b lifetimes; these are described along with other lifetime measurements in the next section.

4. b Hadron Lifetimes

The introduction of precision vertex detectors in ALEPH, DELPHI, and OPAL for the 1991 LEP run has led to qualitative improvements in measurements of lifetimes

---

[2] In the data summary figures, the error bars plotted for individual measurements generally do not include common systematic errors. These errors are included in the systematic (second) error in the number given and are included in the error bar for the average. Therefore, the error bars on individual points illustrate the scatter among the measurements, while the error bar on the average indicates the total uncertainty in the average. When this has been done the common systematic error is described in the figure caption.

of b hadrons. For example, in the ALEPH[34] detector the impact parameter[34] resolution improved from 140 µm to 25 µm. Most measurements of the average of the lifetimes of b hadrons are made using the impact parameter distribution of high p_t tracks (generally a lepton). The resulting lifetime, $\langle \tau_b \rangle$ is the average of the lifetimes of $\bar{B}^0$, B^-, B_s, and Λ_b, weighted by the product of the branching fractions for production and the semileptonic decay of each particle. The new measurements of this average lifetime from ALEPH[34], DELPHI[24,35], L3[36], and OPAL[37,38] are summarized in Figure 4. Each of these measurements is more precise than the most recent PDG average[3] (from 1990) which did not include any LEP measurements. Although each new measurement is in reasonable agreement with the 1990 PDG average, each is higher, and the average of these results is barely consistent with the previous average. I choose to use this LEP Average lifetime for the average B meson lifetime. The longer lifetime has a noticeable consequence, the value of $|V_{cb}|$ obtained from semileptonic B decay decreases (see Section 5).

Three other measurements of the average b hadron lifetime are included in Figure 4; ALEPH[39] and DELPHI[24] have measured the average lifetime by detecting J/ψ vertices and DELPHI[40] has used $D\ell$ events. Although these measurements agree with the impact parameter measurements within their substantially larger errors, they have not been included in the LEP Average. It is not clear that the weighting of the contributions of the individual particles are the same as the impact parameter weighting.

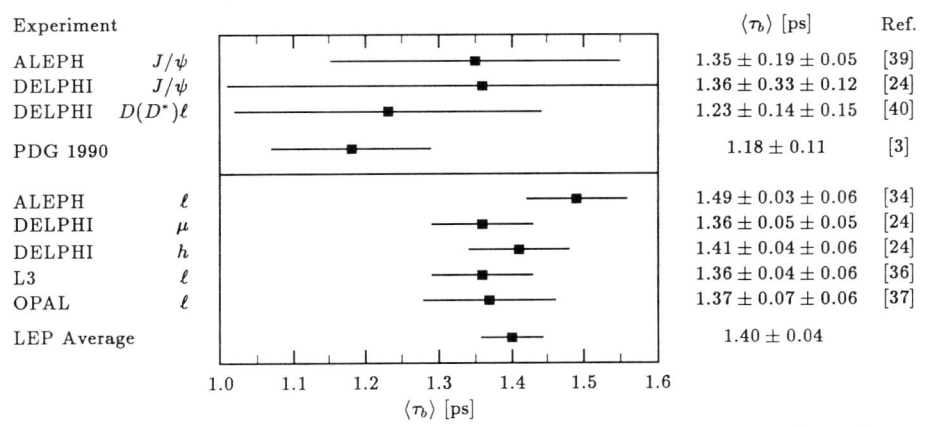

Experiment		$\langle \tau_b \rangle$ [ps]	Ref.
ALEPH	J/ψ	$1.35 \pm 0.19 \pm 0.05$	[39]
DELPHI	J/ψ	$1.36 \pm 0.33 \pm 0.12$	[24]
DELPHI	$D(D^*)\ell$	$1.23 \pm 0.14 \pm 0.15$	[40]
PDG 1990		1.18 ± 0.11	[3]
ALEPH	ℓ	$1.49 \pm 0.03 \pm 0.06$	[34]
DELPHI	μ	$1.36 \pm 0.05 \pm 0.05$	[24]
DELPHI	h	$1.41 \pm 0.04 \pm 0.06$	[24]
L3	ℓ	$1.36 \pm 0.04 \pm 0.06$	[36]
OPAL	ℓ	$1.37 \pm 0.07 \pm 0.06$	[37]
LEP Average		1.40 ± 0.04	

Figure 4: Summary of measurements of $\langle \tau_b \rangle$, the average lifetime of b hadrons. For each experiment the particle(s) used in the measurement are listed. Only the impact parameter measurements shown below PDG 1990 are used in the LEP Average. The common systematic error due to uncertainties in the fragmentation functions was estimated to 0.03 ps.

ALEPH[22,41] and DELPHI[40,42] have also made the first separate measurements of the B^- and $\bar{B}^0$ lifetimes (τ_- and τ_0). They use the same type of $D(D^*)\ell$ correlations used earlier by ARGUS[43] to measure the lifetime ratio, τ_-/τ_0. Considering only semileptonic decays to D and D^*, $B^- \to D^{(*)0}\ell^-\bar{\nu}_\ell$ and $\bar{B}^0 \to D^{(*)+}\ell^-\bar{\nu}_\ell$.

Since $D^{*0} \not\to D^+\pi^-$, D^+ can only come from $\bar{B}^0$. Furthermore, the D^0's that do not come from D^{*+} decay must come from B^- decay. These correlations are somewhat diluted by semileptonic B decays to D^{**} and non-resonant $D(D^*)n\pi$; correction for this dilution is the largest systematic error. The measurements of τ_- and τ_0 obtained using these correlations are illustrated in Figure 5; they are consistent with the measurements of the average lifetime $\langle \tau_b \rangle$.

ALEPH[41] and DELPHI[24] measurements of the B_s lifetime using $D_s^+\ell^-$ events are included in Figure 5. Their results[24,44] for the lifetime of b baryons, measured using $\Lambda\ell$ correlations, are also given in Figure 5.

All measurements of the lifetimes of b hadrons are consistent with $\langle \tau_b \rangle$, but all central values are somewhat lower than $\langle \tau_b \rangle$. Presumably this will be resolved as measurements of the individual lifetimes improve.

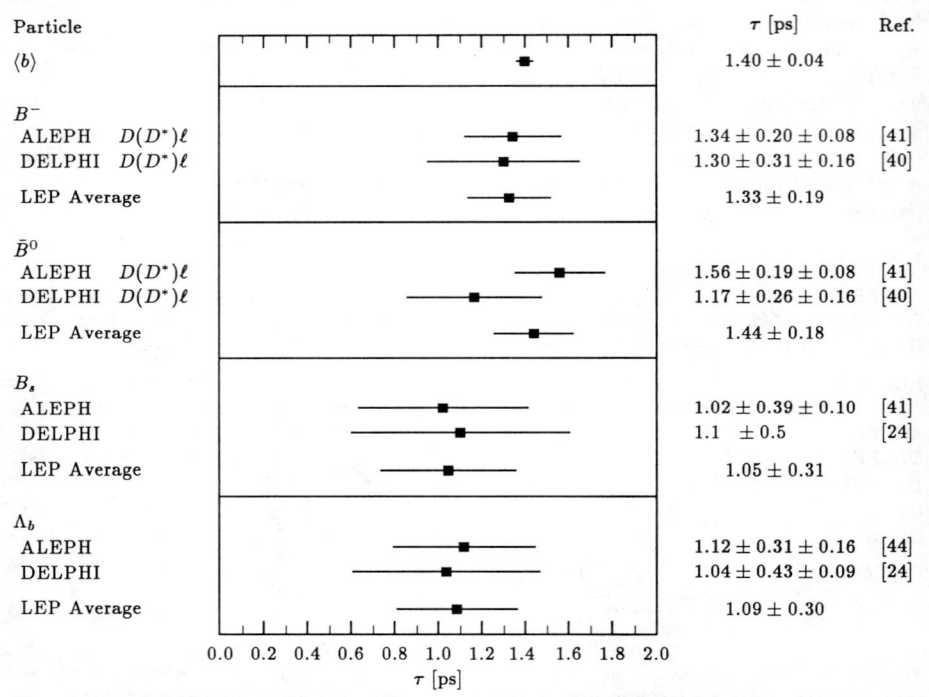

Particle		τ [ps]	Ref.
$\langle b \rangle$		1.40 ± 0.04	
B^-			
ALEPH $D(D^*)\ell$		$1.34 \pm 0.20 \pm 0.08$	[41]
DELPHI $D(D^*)\ell$		$1.30 \pm 0.31 \pm 0.16$	[40]
LEP Average		1.33 ± 0.19	
$\bar{B}^0$			
ALEPH $D(D^*)\ell$		$1.56 \pm 0.19 \pm 0.08$	[41]
DELPHI $D(D^*)\ell$		$1.17 \pm 0.26 \pm 0.16$	[40]
LEP Average		1.44 ± 0.18	
B_s			
ALEPH		$1.02 \pm 0.39 \pm 0.10$	[41]
DELPHI		1.1 ± 0.5	[24]
LEP Average		1.05 ± 0.31	
Λ_b			
ALEPH		$1.12 \pm 0.31 \pm 0.16$	[44]
DELPHI		$1.04 \pm 0.43 \pm 0.09$	[24]
LEP Average		1.09 ± 0.30	

Figure 5: Summary of measurements of the average lifetime of particles containing b quarks and the individual B^+, B^0, B_s, and Λ_b lifetimes. An estimated common systematic error of 0.07 ps was used in averaging these measurements.

The ratio of the lifetimes of the charged and neutral B mesons, τ_-/τ_0 is particularly interesting. Naive interpretation of the spectator diagram (Figure 1) suggests that the lifetimes of all B mesons should be the same. However, this naive expectation is violated dramatically in the case of D mesons, where[15] $\tau_{D^+} \approx 2.5 \tau_{D^0}$. This has been attributed primarily to a combination of interference and Pauli exclusion effects which reduce the D^+ hadronic width[45]. More recent work indicates that preasymptotic $(1/m_Q)$ QCD effects may play a significant role[46]. In any event, these effects are expected to be small for B mesons; suggesting that τ_-/τ_0 should be between 1.0 and 1.2. Most measurements of this lifetime ratio are indirect, depending on the assumption that the semileptonic widths of charged and neutral B mesons are the same. (Although the lifetimes of charged and neutral D mesons are very different, the semileptonic widths are equal, see Ref. [15].) ARGUS has used $D(D^*)\ell$ correlations[43] and the ratio of dilepton to single lepton rates[47] and CLEO has used $D(D^*)\ell$[18] and $B\ell$[48] correlations. The latter measurement is based on the reconstruction of approximately 850 B^- and 440 $\bar{B}^0$ candidates in nearly 80 decay modes. The ALEPH[41] and DELPHI[40] measurements of the individual lifetimes give direct measurements of this ratio. All of these measurements are included in Figure 6. The average of the ARGUS and CLEO measurements agrees well with the LEP average.

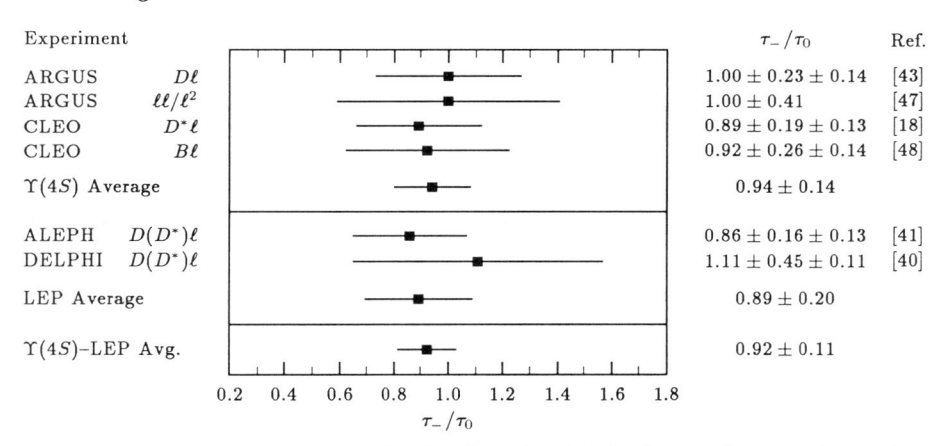

Experiment			τ_-/τ_0	Ref.
ARGUS	$D\ell$		$1.00 \pm 0.23 \pm 0.14$	[43]
ARGUS	$\ell\ell/\ell^2$		1.00 ± 0.41	[47]
CLEO	$D^*\ell$		$0.89 \pm 0.19 \pm 0.13$	[18]
CLEO	$B\ell$		$0.92 \pm 0.26 \pm 0.14$	[48]
$\Upsilon(4S)$ Average			0.94 ± 0.14	
ALEPH	$D(D^*)\ell$		$0.86 \pm 0.16 \pm 0.13$	[41]
DELPHI	$D(D^*)\ell$		$1.11 \pm 0.45 \pm 0.11$	[40]
LEP Average			0.89 ± 0.20	
$\Upsilon(4S)$-LEP Avg.			0.92 ± 0.11	

Figure 6: Summary of measurements of τ_-/τ_0, the ratio of the lifetimes of charged and neutral B mesons. In averaging the LEP measurements the common systematic error due to uncertainties in the primary D and D^* fractions was estimated to be 0.11

Two other measurements have not been included: DELPHI[24] finds $\tau_-/\tau_0 = 0.71 \pm 0.16 \pm 0.28$ based on the charge observed at the B decay vertex; this value may be sensitive to missing low-momentum particles. An E653[10] measurement, $\tau_-/\tau_0 = 4.74^{+3.61+0.99}_{-2.60-0.51}$, indicates that the lifetime ratio could be as large as it is in D mesons. This is so different from the other results and has such large errors that it is difficult to include it in the average.

The data in Figure 6 indicate that τ_-/τ_0 may be less than 1, whereas a value greater than 1 is expected from theory. This ratio is an test of these theoretical ideas, so more precise measurements are important. In addition, the ratio is an ingredient of a significant correction to dilepton measurements of $B^0\bar{B}^0$ mixing at the $\Upsilon(4S)$.

5. Measurements of $|V_{cb}|$

Semileptonic decays of B mesons can occur only through the spectator diagram, Figure 1, providing direct measurements of $|V_{cb}|$. However, theoretical models are required to extract $|V_{cb}|$ semileptonic decay data because the c or u quark that results from the b quark decay fragments with the spectator quark. The total semileptonic width $\Gamma(b \to q\ell\nu) = \Gamma(b \to c\ell\nu) + \Gamma(b \to u\ell\nu)$ for decay of a B meson is given by,

$$\Gamma(b \to q\ell\nu) = \frac{B(b \to q\ell\nu)}{\tau_B} = \gamma_c |V_{cb}|^2 + \gamma_u |V_{ub}|^2 \qquad (2)$$

where the two contributions represent the decay of the meson to final states with and without c quarks. The constants γ_c and γ_u must be obtained from a theoretical model, which introduces uncertainties into the measurement of branching fractions as well as $|V_{cb}|$. There are two basic kinds of models represented by:

- The ACCMM[49] free quark model with QCD corrections:
  This model starts with the the decay of a free b quark, adds QCD corrections, and models the binding of the quarks in the mesons with a Fermi momentum p_F. There is no description of the final states in this model. Several unknown parameters must be determined from the lepton momentum (p_ℓ) spectrum; the results are most sensitive to p_F and the mass of the c quark, m_c, and they are highly correlated in the fit[50]. The ACCMM model provides a good fit to the entire p_ℓ spectrum.

- The ISGW[51] form-factor model:
  This model describes the decay as the sum over exclusive channels; γ_c for the dominant dominant $b \to c\ell\nu$ decay is given by:

$$\gamma_c = \gamma_c(D\ell\nu) + \gamma_c(D^*\ell\nu) + \gamma_c(D^{**}\ell\nu) + \gamma_c(D(n\pi)\ell\nu) \qquad (3)$$

Form-factors for each of these channels are estimated in model calculations. The model indicates that the $D\ell\nu$ and $D^*\ell\nu$ channels dominate. In principle there are no parameters to be determined from the data in this model. However, CLEO[52] has observed that the model does not describe the shape of the lepton momentum spectrum well at low p_ℓ where the $D\ell\nu$ and $D^*\ell\nu$ contributions are small. If the $B \to D^{**}\ell\nu$ contribution is allowed to float in the fit, the best fit (with a satisfactory χ^2) occurs for a 32% $D^{**}\ell\nu$ contribution, compared to 11% predicted by the model.

The ARGUS and CLEO results for $B(b \to q\ell\nu)$ obtained from these models are illustrated in Figure 7. ARGUS and CLEO agree very well. However, there is obviously substantial model dependence which is comparable to the statistical and experimental systematic errors. The CLEO results for ISGW (11% $D^{**}\ell\nu$) and ISGW** (32% $D^{**}\ell\nu$) do not agree very well. Taking all of these uncertainties into account, CLEO[52] quotes a model-dependent "Final" result, $B(\bar{B} \to X\ell^-\bar{\nu}) = (10.8 \pm 0.2 \pm 0.4 \pm 0.4)\%$, where the third error is an estimate of the theoretical uncertainty.

Measurements of $B(b \to q\ell\nu)$ from the LEP experiments are also included in Figure 7. ALEPH[41,53] uses a global fit to single-lepton and dilepton yields,

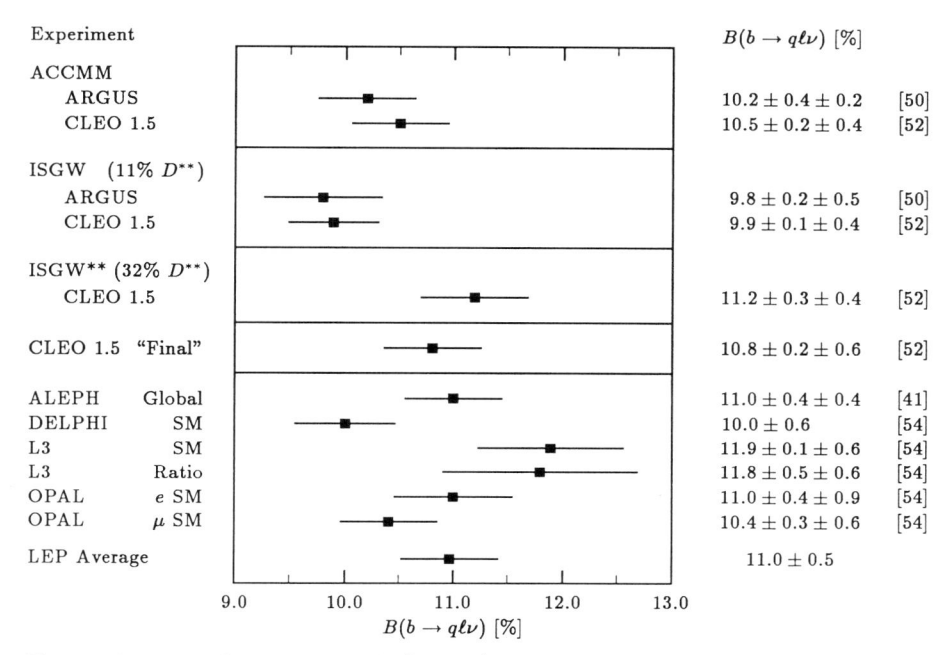

Experiment		$B(b \to q\ell\nu)$ [%]	
ACCMM			
ARGUS		$10.2 \pm 0.4 \pm 0.2$	[50]
CLEO 1.5		$10.5 \pm 0.2 \pm 0.4$	[52]
ISGW (11% D^{**})			
ARGUS		$9.8 \pm 0.2 \pm 0.5$	[50]
CLEO 1.5		$9.9 \pm 0.1 \pm 0.4$	[52]
ISGW** (32% D^{**})			
CLEO 1.5		$11.2 \pm 0.3 \pm 0.4$	[52]
CLEO 1.5 "Final"		$10.8 \pm 0.2 \pm 0.6$	[52]
ALEPH	Global	$11.0 \pm 0.4 \pm 0.4$	[41]
DELPHI	SM	10.0 ± 0.6	[54]
L3	SM	$11.9 \pm 0.1 \pm 0.6$	[54]
L3	Ratio	$11.8 \pm 0.5 \pm 0.6$	[54]
OPAL	e SM	$11.0 \pm 0.4 \pm 0.9$	[54]
OPAL	μ SM	$10.4 \pm 0.3 \pm 0.6$	[54]
LEP Average		11.0 ± 0.5	

Figure 7: Summary of measurements of $B(b \to q\ell\nu)$ from ARGUS, CLEO, and the LEP experiments. A common systematic error of 0.4% due to uncertainties in the lepton spectra was assigned to the LEP data. The CLEO "Final" error bars do not include this theoretical uncertainty.

L3[54,55] uses the ratio of dilepton to single-lepton yields, and DELPHI, L3, and OPAL compare[54] single-lepton yields from fits to the p_ℓ spectra to Standard Model predictions for the number of b quarks produced. These LEP measurements are not completely independent of the ARGUS and CLEO results because model parameters for the p_ℓ spectra used in the LEP experiments have been derived from the ARGUS and CLEO results. The agreement between LEP and $\Upsilon(4S)$ data indicates that the B^-, $\bar{B}^0$, and B_s semileptonic branching fractions are quite close.

It has been difficult for theory to accommodate gracefully the experimental values of the $b \to q\ell\nu$ branching fraction. Straight-forward spectator-model predictions[56] are between 12% and 15%. Non-spectator processes[57] can accommodate 10%–11%, as can preasymptotic QCD effects according to recent estimates[46].

To calculate $|V_{cb}|$ from $B(b \to q\ell\nu)$ the small ($\approx 0.2\%$) $b \to u\ell\nu$ contribution must be taken into account. ARGUS and the LEP experiments estimate this from measurements of $|V_{ub}/V_{cb}|$. CLEO uses $B(b \to c\ell\nu)$ obtained from the fit to the p_ℓ spectrum. For τ_B I have used LEP Average value, $\tau_B = 1.40 \pm 0.04$ ps with an additional estimated uncertainty of ± 0.14 ps since this value is quite different from the previous PDG[3] average. This results in a decrease in $|V_{cb}|$ compared to earlier estimates based on the smaller PDG-1990 value. The new values of $|V_{cb}|$, including one from the average of the LEP branching fractions, are illustrated in Figure 8.

These model dependent values of $|V_{cb}|$ are consistent with $|V_{cb}| = 0.042 \pm 0.005 \pm 0.005$, where the second error is an estimate of the model uncertainty. Substantial gain in precision will require more certain measurements of B meson lifetimes and elimination of the large model dependence.

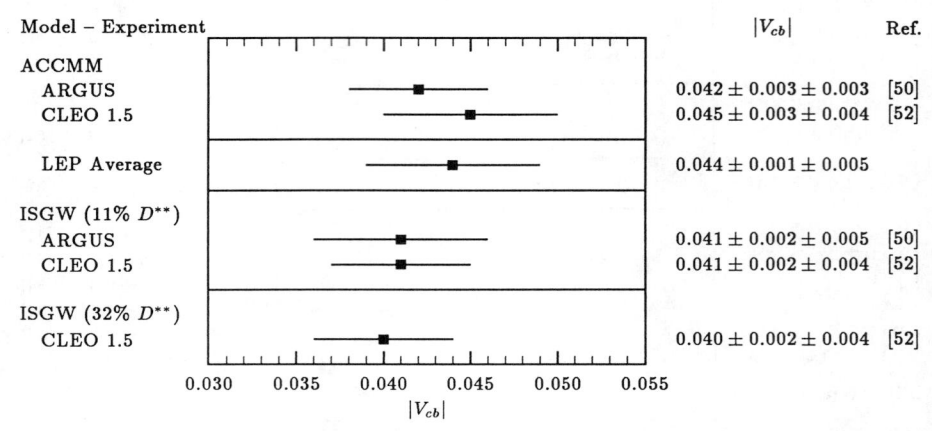

Model – Experiment	$|V_{cb}|$	Ref.
ACCMM		
ARGUS	$0.042 \pm 0.003 \pm 0.003$	[50]
CLEO 1.5	$0.045 \pm 0.003 \pm 0.004$	[52]
LEP Average	$0.044 \pm 0.001 \pm 0.005$	
ISGW (11% D^{**})		
ARGUS	$0.041 \pm 0.002 \pm 0.005$	[50]
CLEO 1.5	$0.041 \pm 0.002 \pm 0.004$	[52]
ISGW (32% D^{**})		
CLEO 1.5	$0.040 \pm 0.002 \pm 0.004$	[52]

Figure 8: Summary of measurements of $|V_{cb}|$ from the $\Upsilon(4S)$ and LEP experiments. The error bars and the systematic errors on the numbers include the uncertainty in τ_B and estimated theoretical uncertainties in γ_c.

In principle the model dependence can be eliminated by measuring the form factors. CLEO[58] has taken the first step in this direction. However, there are many form factors to determine (e.g., one is required for $\bar{B} \to D\ell^-\bar{\nu}_\ell$ but four others are necessary for $\bar{B} \to D^*\ell^-\bar{\nu}_\ell$) so this is indeed a very long program.

The best hope for measuring the form factors appears to be recent developments called Heavy Quark Effective Theory (HQET)[1,59]. HQET is based on the observation that in QCD the dynamics of the light quarks in a meson containing a heavy quark are nearly independent of the mass and spin direction of the heavy quark. This is analogous to the fact that the electronic structure of a hydrogen atom is nearly independent of the mass and spin direction of the proton. This symmetry in QCD implies relationships among the form factors in B meson decay. The five form factors for $D\ell\nu$ and $D^*\ell\nu$ final states can be written in terms of one function, $\xi(y)$ where $y = v \cdot v'$, and v and v' are the four-velocity vectors of the heavy quarks (b and c, respectively) before and after the weak decay. The function ξ is normalized absolutely at $v \cdot v' = 1$ to $\xi(1) = 1$. Moreover, although there are corrections of order $1/m_Q$ to this symmetry, these corrections vanish at $y = 1$, preserving the normalization.

ARGUS[60] has exploited this symmetry to measure $|V_{cb}|$ in a study of $\bar{B}^0 \to D^{*+}\ell^-\bar{\nu}_\ell$ decays. The data must be extrapolated $y = 1$ to determine $|V_{cb}|$ and ARGUS finds that the results are sensitive to the unknown shape of $\xi(y)$ near this point. They find $|V_{cb}| = 0.048 \pm 0.08 \pm 0.03 \pm 0.04$, where the last error comes from the scatter due to different assumptions about the shape of $\xi(y)$. (The ARGUS result has been rescaled to $\tau_B = 1.4$ ps, without including the uncertainties in τ_B.) This result is consistent with the model-dependent results from the inclusive p_ℓ spectrum and has comparable uncertainties. Much larger data samples will reduce the statistical error and the uncertainty due to the shape of $\xi(y)$, and can lead to substantial improvements in the precision of this method.

6. Measurements of $|V_{ub}/V_{cb}|$

Measurement of $|V_{ub}|$ has been a particularly difficult experimental challenge; the first signals were observed by CLEO and ARGUS little more than 2 years ago. These inclusive measurements involve the study the lepton momentum spectra from semileptonic B decay near and above the endpoint for $b \to c\ell\nu$ decays. ARGUS[61] used the p_ℓ range 2.3–2.6 GeV/c, while CLEO[62] used 2.4–2.6 GeV/c. In either case the p_ℓ spectrum in this region is dominated by fake leptons from continuum events. Both experiments use a number of reasonable cuts to reduce this background. ARGUS used cuts that were severe enough to essentially eliminate this background; CLEO used softer cuts and subtracted a smooth background. The resulting branching fractions, $\Delta B_{ub}(2.4, 2.6)$, for leptons in the momentum range 2.4–2.6 GeV/c are illustrated in Figure 9.

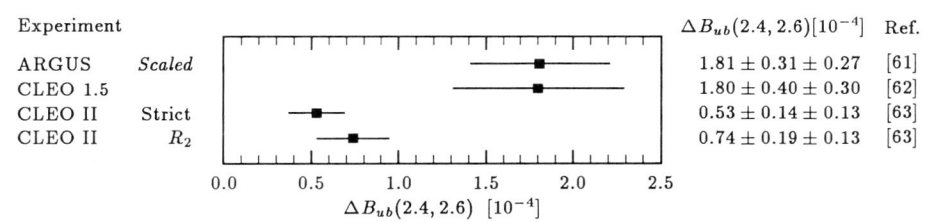

Experiment		$\Delta B_{ub}(2.4, 2.6)[10^{-4}]$	Ref.
ARGUS	Scaled	$1.81 \pm 0.31 \pm 0.27$	[61]
CLEO 1.5		$1.80 \pm 0.40 \pm 0.30$	[62]
CLEO II	Strict	$0.53 \pm 0.14 \pm 0.13$	[63]
CLEO II	R_2	$0.74 \pm 0.19 \pm 0.13$	[63]

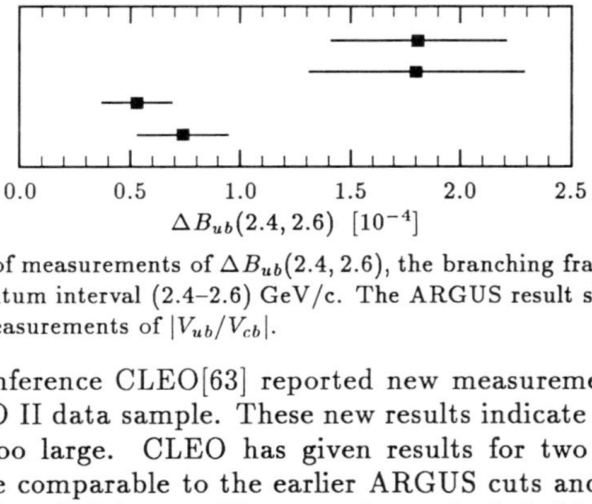

Figure 9: Summary of measurements of $\Delta B_{ub}(2.4, 2.6)$, the branching fraction for inclusive $b \to u\ell\nu$ decays in the momentum interval (2.4–2.6) GeV/c. The ARGUS result shown here has been scaled from the ARGUS measurements of $|V_{ub}/V_{cb}|$.

At this conference CLEO[63] reported new measurements from the substantially larger CLEO II data sample. These new results indicate that the earlier signals may have been too large. CLEO has given results for two different sets of cuts, "Strict" which are comparable to the earlier ARGUS cuts and "R_2" which are comparable to the earlier CLEO cuts. These results are included in Figure 9. The central values of the CLEO II branching fractions are about a factor of 3 smaller than those of the earlier results. A large amount of effort has been expended comparing old and new CLEO data and no explanation for this difference has been found.

The ratio $|V_{ub}/V_{cb}|$ can be obtained[62] from $\Delta B_{ub}(p)$ using

$$\left|\frac{V_{ub}}{V_{cb}}\right|^2 = \frac{\Delta B_{ub}(p)}{B(b \to c\ell\nu)} \frac{\gamma_c}{f_u(p)\gamma_u} \qquad (4)$$

where $f_u(p)$ is the fraction of the lepton momentum spectrum in the interval $(p) = $ (2.4–2.6) GeV/c. (ARGUS used a slightly different technique that involves the same uncertainties.) This quantity, as well as γ_u and γ_c must be obtained from theoretical models. The factor γ_u can be described as a sum over exclusive channels,

$$\gamma_u = \gamma_u(\pi\ell\nu) + \gamma_u((\rho,\omega)\ell\nu) + \gamma_u(\text{res } \ell\nu) + \gamma_u(\text{nonres } \ell\nu) \tag{5}$$

where the third term refers to the production of higher hadronic resonances and the fourth term describes non-resonant states. Estimates of all four terms are included in the ISGW[51] model, but the sum of these terms in the model are a factor of two below the free quark value of γ_u, implying a factor of two uncertainty in γ_u. Two other form-factor models, KS[64] and WSB[65] include only the first two terms but manage to saturate the free-quark value. The fraction $f_u(p)$ must also be estimated from the model and additional uncertainties are introduced by use of the models in the Monte Carlo calculations of efficiencies. These uncertainties introduce the large model dependence apparent in Figure 10. The data are most consistent with values of $|V_{ub}/V_{cb}|$ between about 0.05 and 0.15.

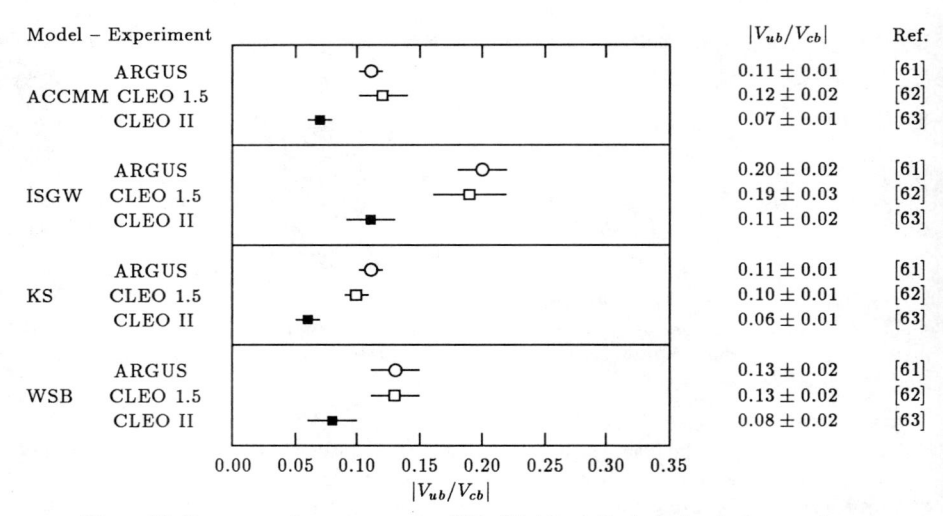

Model – Experiment			$|V_{ub}/V_{cb}|$	Ref.
ACCMM	ARGUS		0.11 ± 0.01	[61]
	CLEO 1.5		0.12 ± 0.02	[62]
	CLEO II		0.07 ± 0.01	[63]
ISGW	ARGUS		0.20 ± 0.02	[61]
	CLEO 1.5		0.19 ± 0.03	[62]
	CLEO II		0.11 ± 0.02	[63]
KS	ARGUS		0.11 ± 0.01	[61]
	CLEO 1.5		0.10 ± 0.01	[62]
	CLEO II		0.06 ± 0.01	[63]
WSB	ARGUS		0.13 ± 0.02	[61]
	CLEO 1.5		0.13 ± 0.02	[62]
	CLEO II		0.08 ± 0.02	[63]

Figure 10: Summary of measurements of $|V_{ub}/V_{cb}|$ from the inclusive lepton spectrum.

The model dependence of the measurements and the discrepancy between the CLEO II result and the earlier ARGUS and CLEO results are not very satisfactory. However, the most important question is whether or not V_{ub} is 0. The new CLEO II measurements of $\Delta B_{ub}(p)$ are more than 2.5 standard deviations away from 0, so we can be reasonably confident that V_{ub} is not 0, and it is possible for the Standard Model to accommodate CP violation.

Observation of exclusive $b \to u\ell\nu$ channels would be a much more satisfactory way to measure $|V_{ub}/V_{cb}|$. ARGUS[66] has reported preliminary evidence for a signal in the exclusive decay, $B^- \to \rho^0 \ell^- \bar{\nu}_\ell$. This is a natural search mode because the ρ^0 decays to charged pions and theoretical estimates suggest that branching fractions for decays to ρ's should be a factor of 3–5 higher than those for decays to π's. CLEO[67, 68] has searched for this mode and the additional modes, $B^- \to \omega \ell^- \bar{\nu}_\ell$ and $\bar{B}^0 \to \rho^+ \ell^- \bar{\nu}_\ell$. Isospin symmetry and simple quark models suggest that $B(\bar{B}^0 \to \rho^+ \ell^- \bar{\nu}_\ell) = 2B(B^- \to \rho^0 \ell^- \bar{\nu}_\ell) \approx 2B(B^- \to \omega \ell^- \bar{\nu}_\ell)$, so inclusion of these modes promises a substantial increase in sensitivity. CLEO does not find a signal in any of these modes or in the sum of all them. The ARGUS signal and CLEO upper limits are illustrated in Figure 11. The results depend on the semileptonic decay models; the ISGW[51], KS[64], and WSB[65] models have been used. Although the CLEO upper limits are about a factor of 3 below the ARGUS central value, the ARGUS errors are large enough that the result could be consistent with the CLEO upper limits.

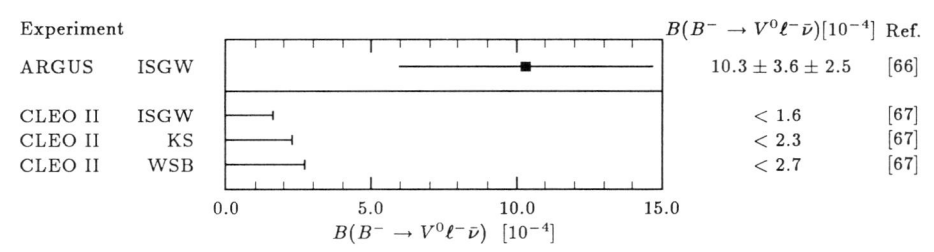

Experiment		$B(B^- \to V^0 \ell^- \bar{\nu})[10^{-4}]$	Ref.
ARGUS	ISGW	$10.3 \pm 3.6 \pm 2.5$	[66]
CLEO II	ISGW	< 1.6	[67]
CLEO II	KS	< 2.3	[67]
CLEO II	WSB	< 2.7	[67]

Figure 11: Summary of measurements of $B(B^- \to V^0 \ell^- \bar{\nu})$, the branching fraction for exclusive $b \to u\ell\nu$ decay to a neutral vector meson (V^0 represents either ρ^0 or ω). The ARGUS error bar includes both the statistical and systematic errors.

Estimation of $|V_{ub}/V_{cb}|$ from the data in Figure 11 requires τ_B and $|V_{cb}|$ in addition to theoretical models. I have rescaled the ARGUS and CLEO measurements using $\tau_B = 1.4$ ps and $|V_{cb}| = 0.042$ without including the uncertainties in these parameters. The results are presented in Figure 12. The CLEO upper limits from the exclusive search are consistent with the range 0.05–0.15 suggested by the inclusive data.

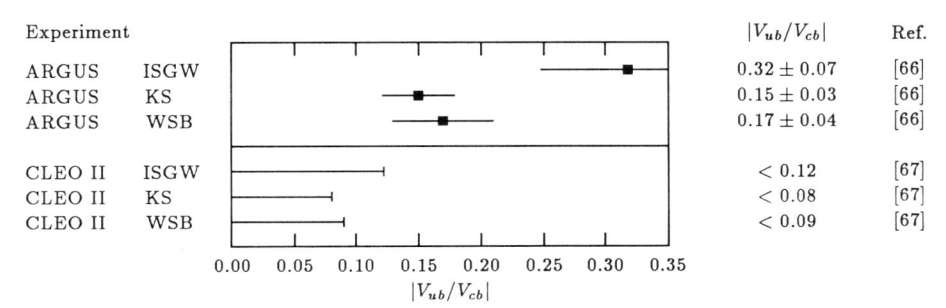

Experiment		$|V_{ub}/V_{cb}|$	Ref.
ARGUS	ISGW	0.32 ± 0.07	[66]
ARGUS	KS	0.15 ± 0.03	[66]
ARGUS	WSB	0.17 ± 0.04	[66]
CLEO II	ISGW	< 0.12	[67]
CLEO II	KS	< 0.08	[67]
CLEO II	WSB	< 0.09	[67]

Figure 12: Summary of measurements of $|V_{ub}/V_{cb}|$ from exclusive $B(B^- \to V^0 \ell^- \bar{\nu})$ decays.

7. Measurements of $B\bar{B}$ Mixing

Understanding $B\bar{B}$ mixing is important because this mixing[69]: probes understanding of loops involving W's and t quarks, can provide measurements of $|V_{td}|$ (from $B^0\bar{B}^0$ mixing) and $|V_{ts}|$ (from $B_s\bar{B}_s$ mixing), and leads to measurements of CP violation with the cleanest theoretical interpretation.

CKM matrix elements are related to measurements of $B\bar{B}$ mixing by[69],

$$x_{d(s)} \equiv \frac{\Delta M_{d(s)}}{\Gamma_{d(s)}} = A B_{B_{d(s)}} f_{B_{d(s)}}^2 m_t^2 |V_{td(s)}|^2 |V_{tb}|^2 \tag{6}$$

where $\Delta M_{d(s)}$, $\Gamma_{d(s)}$, $B_{B_{d(s)}}$, $f_{B_{d(s)}}^2$ are the mass difference, decay width, bag constant, and pseudoscalar decay constant for $B^0(B_s)$. The factor A is the product of reasonably well-known factors, but $B_{B_{d(s)}}$, $f_{B_{d(s)}}^2$, and the t-quark mass m_t are not well-known. These uncertainties lead to large uncertainties in determination of $|V_{td}|$ and $|V_{ts}|$ from mixing. However, mixing is the only source of direct information on these elements presently available. The ratio x is determined from the experimentally accessible quantity χ,

$$\chi \equiv \frac{\Gamma(B \to \bar{B} \to \ell^- X^+ \bar{\nu}_\ell)}{\Gamma(B \to \ell^+ X^- \nu_\ell) + \Gamma(B \to \bar{B} \to \ell^- X^+ \bar{\nu}_\ell)} = \frac{x^2}{2(1+x^2)}. \tag{7}$$

The relationship between χ and x comes from integration of the time-dependent rates for B and $\bar{B}$ decay[70]. Note that the relationship between χ and x implies $0 \leq \chi \leq 0.50$. Since the $\Upsilon(4S)$ can decay only to $B^0\bar{B}^0$ (and B^+B^-), ARGUS and CLEO measure χ_d; the LEP experiments measure the combination, $\chi_b = f_d \chi_d + f_s \chi_s$ of χ_d and χ_s from $B_s\bar{B}_s$ mixing. (The factors $f_{d(s)}$ are the fractions of $B^0(B_s)$ produced in the fragmentation of the b quark at LEP.)

Like-sign dileptons from the two B's is the principal signal for $B\bar{B}$ mixing. At the $\Upsilon(4S)$, $\chi_d = R_{\ell\ell}/\Lambda_0$, where $R_{\ell\ell}$ is

$$R_{\ell\ell} = \frac{N(\ell^\pm\ell^\pm)}{N(\ell^\pm\ell^\mp) + N(\ell^\pm\ell^\pm)}, \tag{8}$$

$N(\ell^\pm\ell^\pm)$ is the number of like-sign dilepton events, $N(\ell^\pm\ell^\mp)$ is the number of unlike-sign dilepton events,

$$\Lambda_0 = \frac{f_0 \tau_0^2}{f_0 \tau_0^2 + f_- \tau_-^2}, \tag{9}$$

and $f_-(f_0)$ are the branching fractions for $\Upsilon(4S) \to B^+B^-(B^0\bar{B}^0)$. The factor Λ_0 corrects the denominator of $R_{\ell\ell}$ for the number of charged B's in the unlike-sign lepton sample. This factor is a major systematic uncertainty in the dilepton results from the $\Upsilon(4S)$.

The dilepton results from ARGUS[71,72] and CLEO[48,73] are illustrated in Figure 13. I have recalculated these results using, $f_-/f_0 = 1.00 \pm 0.05$, a theoretical estimate[74] of f_-/f_0, and the $\Upsilon(4S)$-LEP Average of τ_-/τ_0 given in Figure 6.

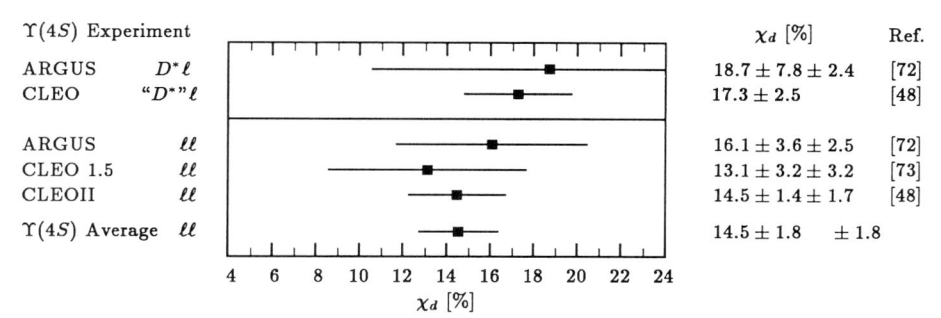

$\Upsilon(4S)$ Experiment		χ_d [%]	Ref.
ARGUS	$D^*\ell$	$18.7 \pm 7.8 \pm 2.4$	[72]
CLEO	"D^*"ℓ	17.3 ± 2.5	[48]
ARGUS	$\ell\ell$	$16.1 \pm 3.6 \pm 2.5$	[72]
CLEO 1.5	$\ell\ell$	$13.1 \pm 3.2 \pm 3.2$	[73]
CLEO II	$\ell\ell$	$14.5 \pm 1.4 \pm 1.7$	[48]
$\Upsilon(4S)$ Average	$\ell\ell$	$14.5 \pm 1.8 \quad \pm 1.8$	

Figure 13: Summary of measurements of $B^0\bar{B}^0$ mixing at the $\Upsilon(4S)$. The systematic errors in the $\ell\ell$ results do not include the uncertainties in Λ_0; these lead to the second error (1.8%) in the $\Upsilon(4S)$ average.

ARGUS[71,72] has also measured χ_d by reconstructing dilepton events containing $\bar{B}^0 \to D^{*+}\ell^-\bar{\nu}_\ell$ candidates. Since there are only neutral B events in this data sample, there is no correction for charged B events. The result is given in Figure 13 but has not been included in the average because there are only a few events and the error is quite large. CLEO[48] has measured χ_d using dilepton events in which $D^{*+}\ell^-$ candidates have been partially reconstructed by observing only the lepton and the slow pion from the $D^{*+} \to D^0\pi^+$ decay. This enriches the neutral B content of the dilepton sample, but a correction for charged B's is still required. The error in the result is comparable to the error in the CLEO II dilepton result, but the systematic errors are quite different. This result is not included in the average because the correlations between the CLEO result and the CLEO II $\ell\ell$ result have not yet been evaluated.

To estimate $|V_{td}|$ from χ_d, I have used $\sqrt{B_B}f_B = 180 \pm 50$ MeV and $m_t = 140 \pm 40$ GeV/c^2; these values and uncertainties are typical of current estimates. This gives, $|V_{td}| = 11.0^{+5.4}_{-3.1} \times 10^{-3}$ or $(6 \le |V_{td}| \le 20) \times 10^{-3}$ (90% CL). This range is comparable to the range $(3 \le |V_{td}| \le 18) \times 10^{-3}$ (90% CL) obtained[15] from 3-generation unitarity of the CKM matrix. The errors in $|V_{td}|$ are entirely dominated by the uncertainties in $\sqrt{B_B}f_B$ and m_t; measurement of m_t and better theoretical estimates[69,75] of $\sqrt{B_B}f_B$ will make it possible to replace unitarity limits on $|V_{td}|$ with measurements.

ALEPH[41,53], DELPHI[24], L3[76], and OPAL[77,31] have measured χ_b at LEP using dileptons; the results are given in Figure 14. In this case there is a different relationship, $R_{\ell\ell} = 2\chi_b(1-\chi_b)$, between $R_{\ell\ell}$ and χ_b, so knowledge of Λ_0 is not necessary. However, estimation of $|V_{ts}|$ by extracting χ_s from these data does require knowledge of f_d and f_s. DELPHI[24] has measured them and the results are consistent within large errors with typical values, $f_d = 0.38\pm0.05$ and $f_s = 0.15\pm0.05$, quoted from fragmentation models. (I have arbitrarily assigned an error of ±0.05 to both of these estimates.) The value of χ_s obtained from these values and the average values of χ_d and χ_b in Figures 13 and 14, is $\chi_s = (48.6 \pm 19.8)\%$. The large error is dominated by the uncertainty in f_s, but the contributions from χ_d and χ_b are

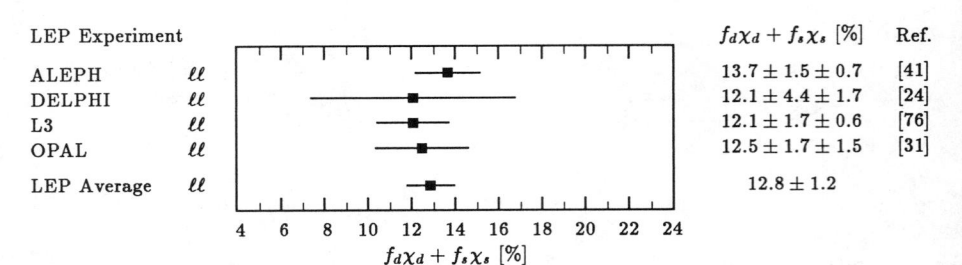

LEP Experiment		$f_d\chi_d + f_s\chi_s$ [%]	Ref.
ALEPH	$\ell\ell$	$13.7 \pm 1.5 \pm 0.7$	[41]
DELPHI	$\ell\ell$	$12.1 \pm 4.4 \pm 1.7$	[24]
L3	$\ell\ell$	$12.1 \pm 1.7 \pm 0.6$	[76]
OPAL	$\ell\ell$	$12.5 \pm 1.7 \pm 1.5$	[31]
LEP Average	$\ell\ell$	12.8 ± 1.2	

Figure 14: Summary of measurements of $B\bar{B}$ mixing at LEP. A common systematic error of 0.6% due to uncertainties in the b semileptonic branching fraction has been assumed.

comparable to each other and not negligible. The value of x_s is then $x_s = 5.9^{+\infty}_{-4.7}$. The infinite upper limit derives from the fact that the maximum value of χ_s is 50%. Due these uncertainties, measurement of χ_b does not yet yield useful information on $|V_{ts}|$.

8. Other Recent Progress in b Physics

This section includes short summaries of other recent progress in B meson decays. Most of these measurements were described in more detail in the parallel sessions of this conference.

The CLEO and ARGUS studies of the form factors in B decay also yield the first evidence that the structure of b quark decay is $V-A$. The evidence is derived from the angular distribution of the lepton in $\bar{B} \to D^*\ell^-\bar{\nu}_\ell$ decay. The sign of a forward-backward lepton asymmetry depends on whether the decay is $V-A$ or $V+A$. The CLEO[58] ($A_{FB} = 0.14 \pm 0.06 \pm 0.03$) and ARGUS[60] ($A_{FB} = 0.20 \pm 0.08 \pm 0.06$) results are consistent with the $V-A$ predictions from the ISGW[51], KS[64], and WSB[65] models, which lie between 0.13 and 0.15. CLEO derives model-dependent upper limits at 95% CL for $(V+A)/(V-A)$ of $< 19\%$ (ISGW), $< 30\%$ (KS), and $< 24\%$ (WSB).

ALEPH[20,78] has observed the decay $b \to q\tau\bar{\nu}_\tau$. In the Standard Model the branching fraction for this decay is expected[78] to be, $2.83 \pm 0.31\%$, although it could be much larger in some variations of the SM. The signature for $b \to q\tau\bar{\nu}_\tau$ events is the large missing energy due to the two missing neutrinos from the b and τ decay. These decays were detected by looking for $b\bar{b}$ events with a large missing energy and no high energy electrons or muons. After all cuts the missing energy spectrum agrees well with Monte Carlo calculations if a substantial contribution from $b \to q\tau\bar{\nu}_\tau$ at large missing energy is included. The data yield the branching fraction, $B(b \to q\tau\bar{\nu}_\tau) = (4.1 \pm 0.8 \pm 0.6)\%$, in excellent agreement with the SM prediction.

Rare two-body hadronic decays of B mesons such as, $B^0 \to \pi^+\pi^-$ and $B^0 \to \pi^+\rho^-$, are sensitive to V_{ub}. Two-body decays involving K mesons, such as $B^0 \to K^-\pi^+$ and $B^0 \to K^-\rho^+$, could provide information on the importance of penguin diagrams in B decay. All of these decays are important in understanding CP violation in the B meson system. The $\pi^+\pi^-$ mode can be used to measure an angle of the CKM unitarity triangle and interference between penguin and doubly Cabibbo-suppressed spectator decays could lead to observable direct CP violation in decays to $K^-\pi^+$ and $K^-\rho^+$. These decays and others like them have been the objects of intense searches by CLEO and ARGUS. The most recent results[79] from CLEO II, along with earlier ARGUS[80] and CLEO[81] results are presented in Table 2. These new upper limits are typically within a factor of 3 to 5 of theoretical estimates[82,83].

Table 2: Upper limits for some exclusive hadronic two-body decays.

Decay Mode	Upper Limit (90% CL)			Theoretical Estimates
	CLEO II [10^{-5}]	CLEO 1.5 [10^{-5}]	ARGUS [10^{-5}]	[10^{-5}]
$\bar{B}^0 \to \pi^+\pi^-$	4.8	9	13	2.0 [45]
$\bar{B}^0 \to K^-\pi^+$	5.6	9	18	1.1 [82]
$\bar{B}^0 \to \rho^-\pi^+$	20	–	52	6.0 [45]
$\bar{B}^0 \to K^-\rho^+$	11	–	–	0.2 [83]

CLEO[84] has also searched for $b \to u$ transitions by looking for two-body $\bar{B} \to D_s^- X$ decays where X is composed of only u and d quarks (except for $s\bar{s}$ mixing). In these decays, the D_s^- comes from the $\bar{c}s$ decay of the W^- in the spectator diagram (Figure 1). The search included the modes, $D_s^-\pi^+$, $D_s^-\rho^+$, $D_s^-a_1^+$, $D_s^-\pi^0$, $D_s^-\eta$, $D_s^-\rho^0$, $D_s^-\omega$, and $D_s^-a_1^0$. No signal was found in any of these modes or in the sums of the charged and neutral modes. The resulting upper limits are typically a factor of 3 better than upper limits previously reported by ARGUS[66].

Measurement of the branching fractions for $B^- \to \ell^-\bar{\nu}_\ell$ decays would provide a direct measurement of f_B (required to extract $|V_{td}|$ from $B^0\bar{B}^0$ mixing). These decays are very strongly helicity-suppressed if ℓ is either an e or a μ, so the decay $B^- \to \tau^-\bar{\nu}_\tau$ is the only real hope for this measurement. The branching fraction for this mode is about 4×10^{-5} for $f_B = 140$ MeV and $|V_{ub}| = 0.0042$. This mode is very difficult to detect because a τ decay must be found in an event containing a B meson. CLEO[85] has searched for this mode in a sample of approximately 1,400 fully reconstructed charged B mesons. The resulting upper limit is $B(B^- \to \ell^-\bar{\nu}_\ell) < 0.013$ (90% CL). Limits were also determined for the e and μ modes. These are the first limits on the branching fractions for any of these modes.

Many theoretical calculations in B decay are based on the hypothesis of factorization. In its simplest form, factorization requires that the hadrons from the two W^- vertices in the spectator diagram do not interact. CLEO[86] has made a number of significant tests of factorization and the spin symmetry of HQET and found good agreement with these hypotheses. In addition, a large polarization was measured in $B \to \psi K^*$ decay, demonstrating that this mode can be useful in measuring CP violation in B decay.

9. Conclusions

Our understanding of b physics has advanced significantly in the last year. The LEP experiments have made major progress in the measurement of the lifetimes of b hadrons and provided confirmed evidence for the existence of the B_s and Λ_b. ARGUS, CLEO, and LEP measurements of $|V_{cb}|$ from semileptonic B decay are now limited primarily by uncertainties in the theoretical models of these decays. ARGUS and CLEO have initiated programs to eliminate these uncertainties via measurements of form factors, including use of the HQET symmetry. A new CLEO measurement of $|V_{ub}|$ from the inclusive lepton spectrum indicates that it may be somewhat lower than indicated by earlier measurements. Searches for exclusive $b \to u\ell\nu$ decays at the level of sensitivity of the inclusive measurements of $|V_{ub}|$ have begun. CLEO searches for rare two-body hadronic B decays are now approaching the level of theoretical estimates. CLEO II and the LEP experiments have substantial additional data samples that have not yet been used in reported results, and they all will accumulate more data in the near future. The next few years promise to be equally exciting for b physics.

10. Acknowledgments

I am gratefully acknowledge the many contributions of my CLEO colleagues over our years of collaboration. J. Augustin, I. Brok, R. Clare, R. Kowalewski, H. Schröder, N. Stanton and M. Tuts have generously shared the results of their experiments prior to publication. Discussions with C.N. Brown, J. Dauwe, D. Kaplan, J.A. Mueller, and A.J. Slaughter concerning the b physics program at Fermilab have been very useful. P.S. Drell and S. Playfer have made helpful comments on particular aspects of this report. I especially appreciate many illuminating conversations with V. Sharma concerning the b physics programs of the LEP experiments.

11. References

1. Many of the topics discussed here are included in the review by P.S. Drell and J.R. Patterson Cornell Report No. CLNS 92/1177, to be published in the *Proceedings of the XXVI International Conference on High Energy Physics*, Dallas, TX, 1992.
2. S.W. Herb et al., *Phys. Rev. Lett.* **39** (1977) 252 and W.R. Innes et al., *Phys. Rev. Lett.* **39** (1977) 1240.
3. Particle Data Group, J.J. Hernandez et al., *Phys. Lett.* **B239** (1990) 1.
4. UA1 Collaboration, H.C. Albajar et al., *Phys. Lett.* **B186** (1987) 247.
5. CDF Collaboration, F. Abe et al., *Phys. Rev. Lett.* **67** (1991) 3351.
6. CDF Collaboration, F. Abe et al., *Phys. Rev. Lett.* **68** (1992) 3403 and **69** (1992) 3707.
7. CDF Collaboration, reported by A. Yagil at this conference.
8. D0 Collaboration, reported by R.J. Madaras at this conference.
9. Fermilab E672/E706 Collaboration, reported by J. Dauwe at this conference.

10. E653 Collaboration, K. Kodama et al., Ohio State University Report No. OHSTPY-HEP-E-92-019 (unpublished).
11. SLD Collaboration, reported by C. Baltay at this conference.
12. CUSB Collaboration, reported by U. Heintz and Q. Wu at this conference.
13. M. Kobayashi and T. Maskawa, *Prog. Theor. Phys.* **49** (1973) 652.
14. N. Cabibbo, *Phys. Rev. Lett.* **10** (1963) 531.
15. Particle Data Group, K. Hikasa et al., *Phys. Rev.* **D45** (1992) 1.
16. M. Schmidtler and K.R. Schubert, *Z. Phys.* **C53** (1992) 347.
17. G.R. Harris and J.L. Rosner, *Phys. Rev.* **D45** (1992) 946.
18. CLEO Collaboration, R. Fulton et al., *Phys. Rev.* **D43** (1991) 651.
19. CLEO Collaboration, D. Bortoletto et al., *Phys. Rev.* **D45** (1992) 21.
20. Also see the review by V. Sharma at this conference.
21. ALEPH Collaboration, D. Buskulic et al., *Phys. Lett.* **B294** (1992) 145.
22. ALEPH Collaboration reported by F. Weber at this conference.
23. DELPHI Collaboration, P. Abreu et al., *Phys. Lett.* **B289** (1992) 199.
24. DELPHI Collaboration, J-E. Augustin (private communication).
25. DELPHI Collaboration, reported by D. Vilanova at this conference.
26. OPAL Collaboration, P.D. Acton et al., *Phys. Lett.* **B295** (1992) 357.
27. OPAL Collaboration, reported by R. Mir at this conference.
28. ALEPH Collaboration, D. Decamp et al., *Phys. Lett.* **B278** (1992) 209.
29. OPAL Collaboration, P.D. Acton et al., *Phys. Lett.* **B281** (1992) 394.
30. ALEPH Collaboration reported by Y.S. Gao at this conference.
31. OPAL Collaboration, R. Kowalewski (private communication).
32. ARGUS Collaboration, H. Albrecht et al., *Phys. Lett.* **B210** (1990) 263
33. CLEO Collaboration, P. Avery et al., *Phys. Rev.* **D43** (1991) 3599.
34. ALEPH Collaboration, D. Buskulic et al., *Phys. Lett.* **B295** (1992) 174.
35. DELPHI Collaboration, reported by L. Diciaccio at this conference.
36. L3 Collaboration, reported by M. Pohl at the XXVI International Conference on High Energy Physics, Dallas, 1992 (unpublished) and by L. Taylor at this conference.
37. OPAL Collaboration, P.D. Acton et al., *Phys. Lett.* **B274** (1992) 513.
38. OPAL Collaboration, reported by J. Duboscq at this conference.
39. ALEPH Collaboration, D. Buskulic et al., *Phys. Lett.* **B295** (1992) 396.
40. DELPHI Collaboration, P. Abreu et al., CERN Report No. CERN-PPE/92-174 (unpublished).
41. ALEPH Collaboration, V. Sharma (private communication).
42. DELPHI Collaboration, reported by G. Maelhum at this conference.
43. ARGUS Collaboration, H. Albrecht et al., *Phys. Lett.* **B232** (1989) 554.

44. ALEPH Collaboration, D. Buskulic et al., CERN Report No. CERN-PPE/92-138 (unpublished).
45. M. Bauer, B. Stech, and M. Wirbel, Z. Phys. **C34** (1987) 103.
46. I.I. Bigi, N.G. Uraltsev, and A.I. Vainstein, Phys. Lett. **B293** (1992) 430 and the report by I.I. Bigi at this conference.
47. ARGUS Collaboration, H. Albrecht et al., DESY Report No. DESY 91-056 (unpublished).
48. CLEO Collaboration, reported by D.R. Perticone at this conference.
49. G. Altarelli et al., Nucl. Phys. **B208** (1982) 365.
50. ARGUS Collaboration, H. Albrecht et al., Phys. Lett. **B249** (1990) 359.
51. N. Isgur et al., Phys. Rev. Lett. **39** (1989) 799.
52. CLEO Collaboration, S. Henderson et al., Phys. Rev. **D45** (1992) 2212.
53. ALEPH Collaboration, reported by L. Bellantoni at this conference.
54. Reported by R. Clare at the XXVI International Conference on High Energy Physics, Dallas, 1992 (unpublished).
55. L3 Collaboration, reported by I. Brock at this conference.
56. A. Khodjamirian, S. Rudaz, and M.B. Voloshin, Phys. Lett. B **242**, 489 (1990).
57. G. Altarelli and S. Petrarca, Phys. Rev. Lett. B **261**, 303 (1991).
58. CLEO Collaboration, S. Sanghera et al., Cornell Report No. CLNS 92/1156, CLEO 92-5 (unpublished).
59. N. Isgur and M. Wise, Phys. Lett. **B232** (1989) 113 and **B237** (1990) 527.
60. ARGUS Collaboration, H. Albrecht et al., DESY Report No. DESY 92-146 (unpublished).
61. ARGUS Collaboration, H. Albrecht et al., Phys. Lett. **B234** (1990) 409 and **B255** (1991) 297.
62. CLEO Collaboration, R. Fulton et al., Phys. Rev. Lett. **64** (1990) 16.
63. CLEO Collaboration, reported by F. Muheim at this conference.
64. J.G. Körner and G.A. Schuler, Z. Phys. **C38** (1988) 511.
65. M. Wirbel, B. Stech and M. Bauer, Z. Phys. **C29** (1985) 637.
66. ARGUS Collaboration, H. Schröder (private communication).
67. CLEO Collaboration, A. Bean et al., Cornell Report No. CLNS 92/1174, CLEO 92-12 (unpublished).
68. CLEO Collaboration, reported by J.D. Richman at this conference.
69. For a comprehensive review and liteature survey, see A.J. Buras and M.K. Harlander, in *Heavy Flavors* edited by A.J. Buras and M. Lindner, (World Scientific, Singapore, 1992)
70. H. Schröder, in *B Decays*, edited by S. Stone, (World Scientific, Singapore).
71. ARGUS Collaboration, H. Albrecht et al., Phys. Lett. **B192** (1987) 245.
72. ARGUS Collaboration, H. Albrecht et al., Z. Phys. **C55** (1992) 357.

73. CLEO Collaboration, M. Artuso et al., *Phys. Rev. Lett.* **62** (1989) 2233.
74. G.P. Lepage,, *Phys. Rev.* **D42** (1990) 3251.
75. See the report on Lattice Guage Theory by S.R. Sharpe at this conference.
76. L3 Collaboration, B. Adeva et al., *Phys. Lett.* **B288** (1992) 395.
77. OPAL Collaboration, P.D. Acton et al., *Phys. Lett.* **B276** (1992) 379.
78. ALEPH Collaboration, D. Buskulic et al., CERN Report No. CERN-PPE/92-184 (unpublished).
79. CLEO Collaboration, reported by S.M. Playfer at this conference.
80. ARGUS Collaboration, H. Albrecht et al., *Phys. Lett.* **B223** (1989) 470 and **B254** (1991) 288.
81. CLEO Collaboration, D. Bortoletto et al., *Phys. Rev. Lett.* **62** (1989) 2436 and P. Avery et al., *Phys. Lett.* **B223** (1989) 470.
82. N.G. Deshpande and J. Trampetic, *Phys. Rev.* **D41** (1990) 895.
83. L-L. Chau et al., *Phys. Rev.* **D43** (1991) 2176.
84. CLEO Collaboration, reported by R.W. Stephens at this conference.
85. CLEO Collaboration, reported by D. Cinabro at this conference.
86. CLEO Collaboration, reported by S. Ball at this conference.

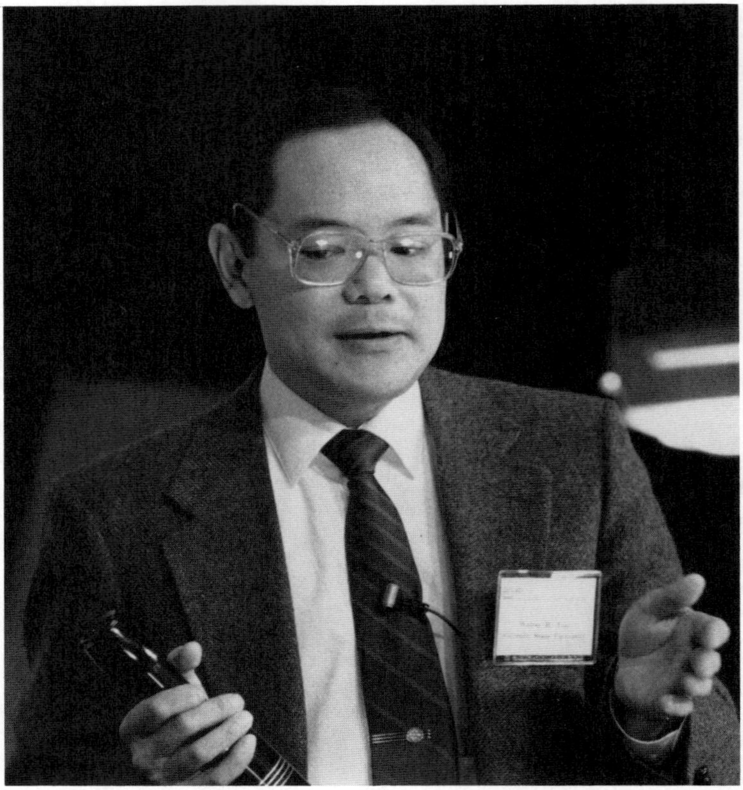

THE TAU OF PARTICLE PHYSICS

WALTER H. TOKI
Department of Physics, Colorado State University
Ft. Collins, CO 802523, USA

ABSTRACT

Tau lepton measurements from the DPF92 conference are reviewed. The latest summary of the mass, leptonic branching ratio and lifetime are 1777.0 ± .35 MeV, 17.80±.13%, and 294.3±3.5 fs, respectively. These results are used to determine the ratio of Tau/muon leptonic couplings to be $g_e/g_\mu = 1.004\pm.007$ and from the Tau electronic and muonic decay rates, electron /muon couplings are determined to be $g_e/g_\mu = .995\pm .0075$.

1.INTRODUCTION

The Tau of particle physics is the third and heaviest member of the family of charged leptons. First detected less than 20 years ago, it is now subject to precise measurements that test the Standard Model. Unlike the strongly interacting quarks of the eight fold path, the Tau interacts with only electroweak forces. This permits precise electroweak calculations and predictions from the Standard Model which can be tested in Tau decays. In addition, because it is more massive, the Tau is accessible to more decays than the electron and muon. This leads to more complexity, but also allows more ways in which to test the Standard Model.

In this paper Tau results presented in the DPF92 meeting are reviewed from talks by R. Kowalewski (OPAL), R. McNulty (DELPHI), P. Fisher (L3), M. Schmitt M. Walsh and J. Conway (ALEPH), G. Crawford and S. Henderson (CLEO), and L. Jones (BES), . Much of the material has been taken from the Tau-Lepton Workshop[1] at Ohio State in September 1992. The primary areas of this review to be covered are the measurements of the mass, branching ratios, lifetimes, and polarization. We begin with a very short synopsis of experimental issues, Tau physics and relevant formulas for Tau decays.

The experimental results on the Tau are from the LEP, CLEO, ARGUS and BES groups. The LEP data comes from the high statistics of $Z^\circ \to \tau\tau$ decays. The selected data samples from LEP are very clean with the Z° hadronic decays being easily separated. Also the LEP groups have new data taken with Silicon microvertex detectors. When coupled with the large Lorentz boost of the Tau's from Z° decays, the LEP groups are able to make precise Tau lifetime measurements. CLEO has superior statistics in numbers of produced Tau's and a CsI electromagnetic calorimeter for detection of neutral modes but they face more backgrounds in their Tau sample. The BES group operates in the Tau-Charm center of mass energy and uses this unique position to produce Tau pairs at threshold for precise Tau mass measurements.

The main focus of the experimental efforts in the last year have been in the Tau mass, lifetime and branching ratios. These lead to fundamental tests of the Tau leptonic coupling by making precise comparisons with the muon coupling. The high statistics data make many results systematics limited. This leads to subtle systematic biases when results are averaged from similar experiments with similar analyses.

2. TAU PHYSICS

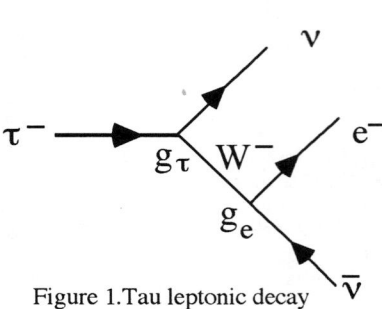

The Tau is a sequential lepton in the Standard Model and is expected to couple in identical manner as the muon and the electron. The lowest order Feynman diagram for the weak leptonic decay is shown in Figure 1. The reaction rate for a leptonic decay are calculable[2] as

$$\Gamma(\tau \to l\bar{v}_l v_\tau) = G_\tau G_e \frac{m_\tau^5}{192\pi^3} f(x) \delta_{EW} \delta_\gamma$$

where $G_\tau = \frac{\sqrt{2} g_\tau^2}{8 M_W^2}$ and $G_l = \frac{\sqrt{2} g_l^2}{8 M_W^2}$, and radiative corrections include

$$f(x) = 1 - 8x + 8x^3 - x^4 - 12 x^2 \ln x, \quad x = \frac{m_l^2}{m_\tau^2},$$

Figure 1. Tau leptonic decay

$\delta_{EW} = 1 + \frac{3}{5}\frac{m_l^2}{m_\tau^2}$ and $\delta_\gamma = 1 + \frac{\alpha(m_\tau)}{2\pi}\left(\frac{25}{4} - \pi^2\right)$. This leads to predictions when compared to muon decay of $\frac{\Gamma(\tau \to e\bar{v}_e v_\tau)}{\Gamma(\mu \to e\bar{v}_e v_\tau)} = \frac{g_\tau^2}{g_\mu^2}\frac{m_\tau^5}{m_\mu^5} \times 1.0004$. Thus coupling ratios predict,

$$\frac{g_\tau^2}{g_\mu^2} = \frac{m_\mu^5}{m_\tau^5}\frac{t_\mu}{t_\tau} B(\tau \to e\bar{v}_e v_\tau) \text{ and } \frac{g_e^2}{g_\mu^2} = \frac{B(\tau \to e\bar{v}_e v_\tau)}{B(\tau \to \mu\bar{v}_e v_\mu)} \times 0.97256$$

Using data from the 1992 Particle Data tables we obtain the following ratio,

$$\frac{g_\tau}{g_\mu} = \sqrt{\frac{t_\mu}{t_\tau}\frac{m_\mu^5}{m_\tau^5} B(\tau \to e v\bar{v})} = .972 \pm .012$$

and observe a 2 sigma discrepancy. This test of the coupling is expected to have little theoretical corrections.

3. TAU MASS

Measurements of the Tau mass have improved considerably in the last year. New measurements are from the ARGUS, BES and CLEO groups. From the BES group a special scan near Tau pair production threshold was performed to measure the mass. The ARGUS and CLEO groups have made new and improved measurements by fitting clever variables that are sensitive to the Tau mass and using their high statistics Tau data sample.

The BES group[3] has measured the Tau mass by measuring the e+e- production cross section of Tau pair production at threshold. The mass of the Tau is very close to the beam energy of the BEPC collider when they are produced at threshold. The precision of the Tau mass measurement depends largely on the calibration of the collider beam momentum. The BEPC collider momentum was checked by scanning the peak cross section of the J/ψ and the ψ' resonances which are accurately known. In order to maximize the sensitivity of the mass measurement for a given amount of integrated luminosity, a running scheme was devised analyzing the incoming data daily to detect ττ→με events and calculating a maximum likelihood prediction of a Tau mass. Using this updated Tau mass, a new beam energy was selected daily to maximize the sensitivity of the mass measurement. If the energy differed more than 2 MeV from the previous settings, the beam energy was readjusted. This data driven method converged very quickly as the run progressed to a e+e- center mass energy of twice the tau mass. The first results used ττ→με events (14 in total) to obtain $m_\tau = 1776.9^{+.4}_{-.5}$ MeV. In DPF92, a new result[4] was presented which includes additional modes ττ→eπ,ππ,μπ, and μμ events. The eπ events yielded a mass of $1776.9^{+.42}_{-.44}$ MeV and the ππ, μπ and μμ events yielded, $1776.8^{+.47}_{-.51}$ MeV. Combining all the results, a new preliminary BES mass for DPF92 is m_τ=1776.9±.3±.2 MeV.

The ARGUS group[5] has recently published a new Tau mass measure-ment using τ→a₁ν, where a₁→3π. This was fit to a pseudo mass assuming that the 3π momentum direction is the same as the unknown Tau direction. The pseudo mass variable is, $M_\tau^{*2} \equiv 2(E_{3\pi} - p_{3\pi})(E_{beam} - E_{3\pi}) + m_{3\pi}^2$. This pseudo mass distribution has the merit of being sensitive to the Tau mass. The ARGUS group obtains a Tau mass of m_τ =1776.3±2.4±1.4 MeV.

The CLEO group[6] used a completely different technique using the one prong versus one prong sample. Measuring the momenta of the two tracks and assuming for each event that the τ+τ- axis direction is consistent with a minimum tau mass another pseudo mass variable is obtained. Fitting this quantity they obtain a preliminary mass value of 1777.6±.9±1.5 MeV which includes an error for the Tau neutrino mass which is assumed to be zero. The Tau mass measurements are summarized in Figure 2. The world average including PDG92 is 1777.0±.35 MeV.

Fig. 2 Tau Mass measurements

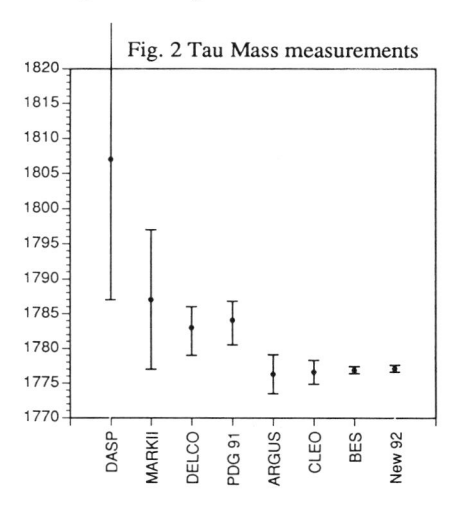

Table 1. CLEO Tau ν mass limits		
Mode	#events	m(ν) limit
5π±	44	110.5 MeV
3π±2π°	92	34.6 MeV
combine	132	36.7 MeV

CLEO also set an upper limit on the Tau neutrino mass. Using $\tau \to 5\pi^\pm \nu$ and $3\pi^\pm 2\pi^\circ \nu$ events, they fit an endpoint mass spectrum. They obtain a tau neutrino mass limit of <36.7 MeV listed in Table 1. Their limit is less stringent than the ARGUS value (<31 MeV), although they have 4 times the statistics in the $5\pi^\pm$ sample. This occurred because of this measurement largely depends on the mass of the highest mass event in the sample and the ARGUS result was lucky to have such events in their first set of 11 events.

4. TAU BRANCHING RATIOS

The Tau branching ratios have been measured for many years. There has been a lingering suspicion that the sum of the exclusive one prongs modes is less then the inclusive topological modes[7]. The rates from the 1990 PDG have been for the inclusive modes, $B(\tau \to 1$ charged track $+ X) = (86.1\pm.3)\%$ and for the inclusive modes $\Sigma B(1$ charged track exclusive) $\leq (80.2\pm 1.2)\%$. There are several possible reasons. These include undetected modes, new modes with neutrals, or possibly bad experimental results. Some solutions to this modest puzzle are to throw away old measurements or perhaps use only the best measurements. The best choice is to make new measurements, especially those with different systematics.

The ALEPH group has done an inclusive and exclusive mode measurement on the same data similar to the CELLO analysis[8] of PEP data. The CLEO group has measured neutral modes with better calorimetry and the leptonic branching ratio in an inclusive method.

The ALEPH group[9] using a consistent data set normalized by $Z^\circ \to e^+e^-$ and $\mu^+\mu^-$, they obtain the following results,

(1) topological BR's of $B_1=85.6\pm.4\pm.4$, $B_3=14.7\pm.2\pm.2$ and $B_5= 0.11\pm.03\pm.03$.
(2) a limit on undetected tau decays <1.1% at 95% CL by looking for undetected decays recoiling from a known Tau tag.
(3) Using their calorimeter to measure exclusive π°s (called exclusive modes in their analysis) and partially reconstructed π°s (called quasi-exclusive modes).

They obtain a summed rate of $100.9\pm.5\pm.4\pm.7$ where the last error is due to the normalization. Hence ALEPH concludes they observe no one prong deficit in their data within their errors. Their conclusion is similar to the CELLO results.

The CLEO group[10] has made an important measurement of the leptonic Tau branching ratio by measuring the exclusive mode $\tau\tau \to e^+e^- + X$. This was possible because CLEO has a large Tau sample. This measurement measures a rate which is proportional to the branching ratio squared and consequently the errors are halved since

$$B_e^2 = N_{ee} \frac{(1-f_e)}{\varepsilon \sigma_\tau L}$$

where N_{ee} is the normalization, f_e is the background fraction and ε is the detection efficiency. This is similar to an earlier Mark III analysis[11]. Normalizing with Bhabhas, CLEO measures, $B(\tau \to e\nu\nu)= 17.49\pm.14\pm.22\%$. This is the most precise single measurement to date. The errors are systematics limited from errors due to acceptance, luminosity and radiative corrections. This result differs from a recent CLEO publication[12] which used a different analysis and a different data sample to obtain $19.2\pm.4\pm.6\%$. In addition CLEO has measured Tau decays with reconstructed π°'s.

Table 2. LEPTONIC TAU BRANCHING RATIOS from LEP

Group	mode	BR	error(stat+sys)
ALEPH(89+90+91prem)	eνν	18.2±.3±.2	.36
	μνν	17.6±.2±.2	.28
OPAL(90+91)	eνν	17.5±.3±.3	.42
	μνν	16.8±.3±.3	.42
L3(90+91)	eνν	17.9±.4±.4	.56
	μνν	17.6±.4±.4	.56
DELPHI(90+91)	eνν	17.9±.5	.5
	μνν	17.6±.5	.5
CLEOII(92)	eνν	17.49±.14±.22	.26
ELECTRON SUMMARY	eνν	17.73±.17	
MUON SUMMARY	μνν	17.42±.20	
e + muon COMBINED	μνν+eνν	17.80±.13	

Table 3. Other Tau Branching ratio measurements

Mode	PDG92	CLEO Exclus.	ALEPH Exclus.	ALEPH Quasi-Exclus
eνν	17.94±.26	17.49±26	18.2±.36	
μνν	17.58±.27		17.6±.28	
hπ°	24.4±.6	24.83±.55	25.8±.5	24.4±.6
1h	12.7±.4		12.8±.28	
h2π°	9.0±.8	8.39±.43	8.8±.5	10.3±.6
h3π°		1.00±.14	1.8±.4	1.5±.4
h4π°		.15±.07(new)		
3h	8.4±.4		9.6±.28	
3hπ°			5.2±.2	5.2±3.6
sum			99.93±1.1*	100.9±.9
Σ1prong	82.0±1.2		84.94±.96*	
1prong	85.82±.25		85.6±.5	
3prong	14.06±.25		14.7±.28	
5prong	.111±.024		.11±.04	
SUM(1-3-5)	100.09		100.4±.6	

Numerous measurements have been presented at the DPF92 meeting and are summarized in Table 2 and 3..

From the results listed in the Tables 2 and 3 and plotted in Fig. 3, we note several trends. The in-dividual CLEO measurements with neutrals are 1-2 sigma lower then ALEPH measure-ments. A "CELLO-ALEPH" type analysis from CLEO might help to clarify the situation. All the LEP Tau leptonic BR values are higher than CLEO's. Using ALEPH, OPAL, L3, DELPHI and the new CLEO result, we obtain a $B_e = 17.80 \pm .13$ (including the B_μ)

5. TAU LIFETIMES

The Tau lifetime measurements have improved in the last year. There have been new analysis methods from ALEPH and the use of new Silicon microvertex detectors from ALEPH, DELPHI and OPAL. In Table 4 are the ratios of the vertex measurement resolution (x-y plane) normalized by theTau decay length in the lab frame. The LEP detectors with the large Tau boost from the Z° decay are able to measure the lifetimes most accurately. SLC with its very small collision point could also do well with high statistics data.

Table 4. Ratio of measurement error to tau decay length in the lab frame			
Expt.	ALEPH/DELPHI	OPAL	L3	CLEO
Lxy/γβct	.33	.6	1.3	2.3

The Tau lifetimes have been measured using several techiques. The main methods are listed in Table 5. The impact parameter is the projected closest distance of approach of the one prong track in the x-y plane to the beam line center. There is some subtlety in measuring the Tau lifetime because the production point and the tau direction are not directly measured and therefore this requires some monte carlo correction.[13] There has been some evidence that the old 3 prong measurements had bias toward longer lifetimes due to overlapping tracks in the same drift chamber cells near the vertex.[14] The new Silicon microvertex detector measurements from LEP should not have this problem. The various methods will have different dependences or bias. When results are combined using analyses that use the same data sets, there will be corrections for the correlated errors.

Table 5. Decay length measurement methods		
Name	Data	Method
Decay Length	1+3 prong	distance between 3 prong vertex and beam spot
Impact Parameter	1+3,1+1 prong	measure one prong signed impact parameter
Impact Parameter difference	1+1 prong	use difference of impact parameter. Reduces dependence upon Tau directions
Impact Parameter sum	1+1 prong	use sum of impact parameter. Reduces dependence upon beam smearing.

The summary of the measurements are listed in Table 6 and plotted in Fig.4. There is a trend of the data to lower lifetimes. The lifetime summary is 294.3±3.5 fs.

Fig. 3 Tau Leptonic Branching Ratios

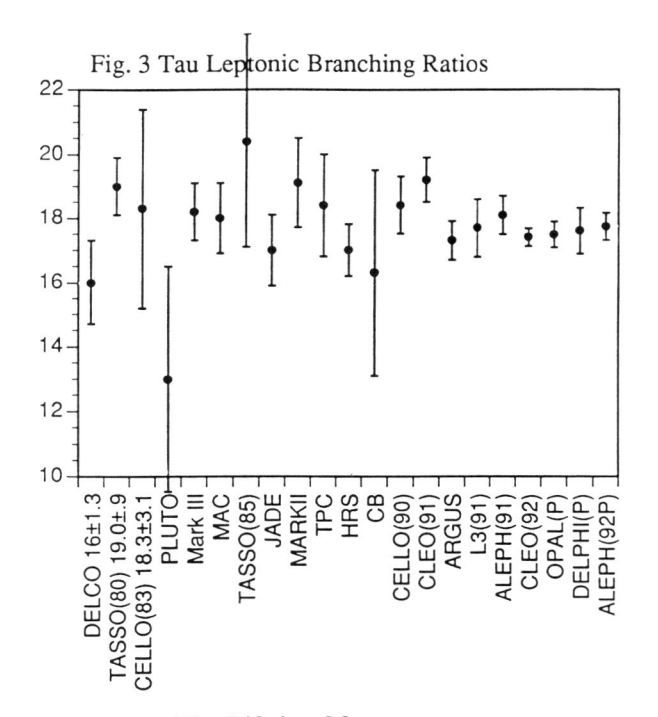

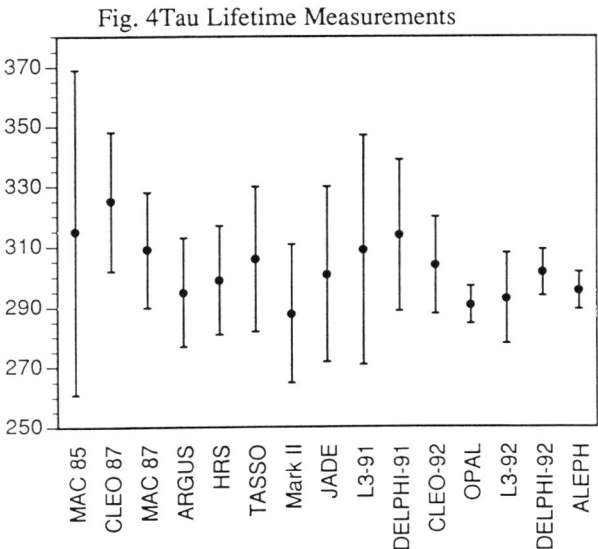

Fig. 4 Tau Lifetime Measurements

Table 6. Lifetime measurements reported at DPF92	
DELPHI(1pr,IPS,IPD)	301±7±4
DELPHI(3pr)	301±13±7
DELPHI(summary)[15]	301±7±4
OPAL(1pr)	295.5±6.9±4.
OPAL(3pr)	283.5±7.4±4.
OPAL(summary)[16]	290.0±6.0
Lifetime measurements from OSU, Tau Lepton Workshop	
ALEPH(89+90+91)	293.5±5.3±2.9
L3(91)	293±9±12
CLEO1.5	304±14±7

6. LEPTONIC COUPLING TESTS

The results of the previous sections can be considered in the Standard Model. From the ratio of the electronic and muonic decays of the Tau we can test the electron/muon coupling and obtain,

$$\frac{g_e}{g_\mu} = .995 \pm .0075$$

From the Tau lifetime, B_e (including B_μ) and the mass we obtain,

$$\frac{g_\tau}{g_\mu} = 1.004 \pm 0.007$$

Errors from lifetime, B_e and mass enter respectively as,

$$(.007 \text{ error})^2 = (.0059)^2 + (.0036)^2 + (.0005)^2$$

The largest error is from B_e. Previously, using data from the Particle Data Group, the errors were,

$$(.012 \text{ error})^2 = (.010)^2 + (.005)^2 + (.0044)^2$$

The results now show the $\tau-\mu$ coupling to agree to within <1 sigma and to a precision of 0.7%. This can be compared with other coupling tests shown in Table 7.

Table 7. Other tests of lepton universality			
Group	mode	coupling ratio	Value
Triumf[17]	$\pi \to e\nu, \mu\nu$	g_e/g_μ	0.997±.0023
SIN[18]	$\pi \to e\nu, \mu\nu$	g_e/g_μ	1.000±.002
CDF,UA1, UA2[19]	$W \to e\nu, \tau\nu$	g_τ/g_e	0.99±0.5

7. OTHER TAU MEASUREMENTS

Polarization measurements of the $e^+e^- \to Z^\circ \to \tau^+\tau^-$ have been measured at LEP. These measurements determine the couplings for the Tau and to some extent the electron.

The analyses are performed by fitting the energy of electron, muon, and pion channels and the angles in the rho channels. The polarization[20] is related to the couplings as

$$P_\tau(\cos\theta) \approx -\left[A_\tau - \left(\frac{2\cos\theta}{1+\cos^2\theta}\right)A_e\right]$$

where

$$A_L = \frac{2a_L v_L}{v_L^2 + a_L^2}$$

and v_L and a_L are the vector and axial vector coupling for lepton L. In the Standard Model the average of the polarization is related to the Weinberg angle as, $P \approx -2(1-\sin^2\theta_W)$. The results are summarized in Table 8. They agree well with the Weinberg angle obtained from the Z° mass and width.

Table 8. Polarization results from ee→Z° → ττ → π,e,μ and ρ channels

Group	$\langle P_\tau \rangle$	V/A(Tau)	$\sin^2\theta_W$
ALEPH[21]	-.143±.026	.066±.01	.2335±.0025
L3[22]	-.132±.026±.021	.069±.017	.2326±.0043
OPAL[16]	-.115±.046	.058±.023	.2356±.0058

8. SUMMARY

In summary there have been numerous improved Tau measurements. The mass of the Tau moved seven MeV down from the BES, ARGUS and CLEO measurements. The Tau lifetime moved down about ten fs from measurements from LEP with Silicon microstrip vertex detectors. The Branching ratio measurements on the Tau have new analyses. CLEO has made a new and improved Be exclusive measurement and detected neutral modes. ALEPH has done a "CELLO" type measurement and does not find a one prong problem within their statistics. The consistency between g_μ and g_τ is now at the one sigma level and hence at this time their appears to be no inconsistency.

In the future we look forward to more results from LEP, CLEO, ARGUS and BES. The higher statistics will shrink the statistical errors and really expose the systematic errors. This should drive the experimental efforts to really understand the subtle and common systematic errors. Hopefully more clever measurements with different systematics will come. This can sometimes lead to new and surprisingly different results from even the same experimental group. A significant improvement in Tau measurements could come from high statistics SLD data or a Tau/Charm factory.

To date, the Tau appears to follow the path of the Standard Model as well as the precision of current measurements allow. There appears to be little or no mysticism or rather mystery in the behavior of the Tau. In this regard, the Tau of particle physics and the tests of the Standard Model are a remarkable success story in our scientific comprehension of Nature.

9. REFERENCES

[1] 2nd Workshop on Tau Lepton Physics, Ohio State University, Columbus, Ohio, September 8-11,1992.
[2] W. Marciano, OSU talk and DPF92 talk.
[3] Z. Bai et al., Phys. Rev.Lett. **69**, 3021(1992).
[4] Lawrence Jones, BES talk in DPF92.
[5] H. Albrecht et al., Phys.Lett.**B292**,221(1992).
[6] S. Henderson, CLEO talk in DPF92.
[7] F. Gilman and S. Rhie, Phys. Rev. D31, 1066(1985) and see K. Hayes, Review of Particle Properties, Phys. Rev. **D45**, VI.19 (1992).
[8] H. Behrend et al., Z.Phys. **C46**, 537(1990)
[9] M. Walsh, ALEPH talk in DPF92.
[10] G. Crawford, CLEO talk in DPF92.
[11] J. Adler et al., Phys.Rev. Lett. **59**,1527 (1987).
[12] R. Ammar et al., Phys.Rev.**D45**,3976(1992).
[13] S. Wasserbaech, private conversation.
[14] C.K. Jung, Int. High Energy Physics Conf., Dallas, TX., August 1992.
[15] R. McNulty, DELPHI talk in DPF92.
[16] R. Kowalewski, OPAL talk in DPF92.
[17] D. Britton et al., Phys.Rev.Lett.**68**, 3000(1992).
[18] G. Czapek et al., Phys. Rev. Letts.**70**,17(1993).
[19] M. Rooney, OSU talk.
[20] K. Hagiwara et al., Phys.Lett.**B235**,198(1990).
[21] M. Schmitt, ALEHP talk in DPF92.
[22] P. Fisher, L3 talk in DPF92.

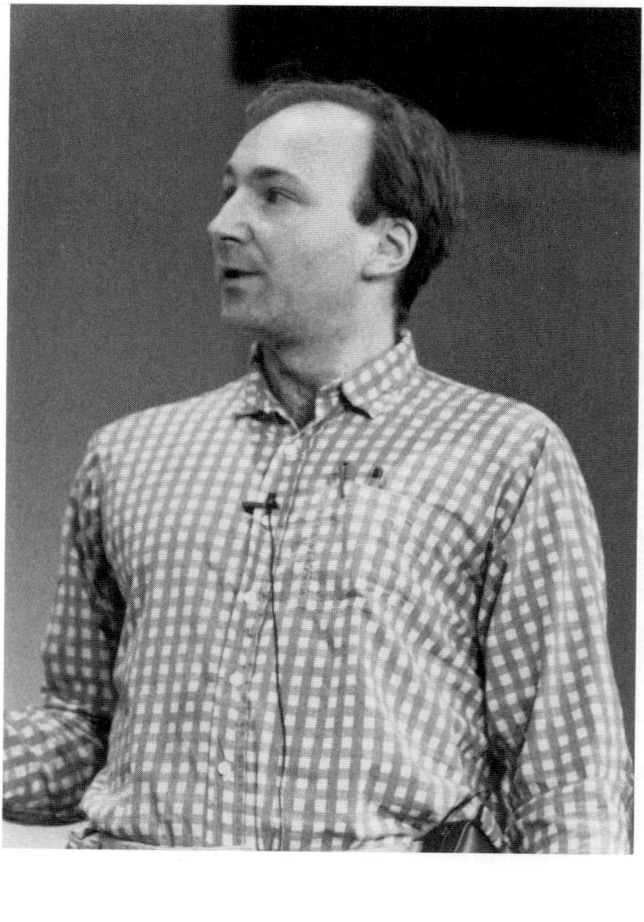

RECENT PROGRESS IN LATTICE QCD

STEPHEN R. SHARPE
*Physics Department, FM-15, University of Washington
Seattle, WA 98195, USA*

ABSTRACT

I give a brief overview of the status of lattice QCD, concentrating on topics relevant to phenomenology. I discuss the calculation of the light quark spectrum, the lattice prediction of $\alpha_{\overline{MS}}(M_Z)$, and the calculation of f_B.

1. INTRODUCTION

Lattice gauge theory has been somewhat out of the mainstream of particle physics for the past decade. It seems to me, however, that the field is now coming of age. It has certainly grown rapidly: roughly 300 people attended the recent *LATTICE '92* conference, compared to about 130 at *LATTICE '86*. That it has also matured is indicated by the breadth of the subjects being studied with lattice methods. These include the traditional—QCD spectrum and matrix elements; the more statistical mechanical—rigorous theorems on finite size scaling; the more abstract—random surfaces; and the exotic—finite temperature baryon number violation. More concrete evidence for maturation is that lattice results are becoming useful to the rest of the particle physics community. For example, in his summary of B-physics, David Cassel noted that the bounds on the elements of the CKM-matrix which follow from $B - \bar{B}$ mixing depend on the values of f_B and B_B, and that lattice results are now used as one of the estimates of these numbers. But perhaps the most important piece of evidence is that lattice studies are beginning to produce results with no unknown systematic errors. The best example is the calculation of the full QCD running coupling constant $\alpha_{\overline{MS}}$ by the Fermilab group [1]. As I discuss below, this number can be directly compared to experiment.

In summary, I would say that lattice studies are beginning to make themselves useful. The "beginning" in this claim is important—there is a very long way to go before we can calculate, say, the $K \to \pi\pi$ amplitudes from first principles. Thus this talk does not consist of results for a long list of matrix elements. Instead, I discuss a few topics in some detail. Because of lack of time, I concentrate entirely on results from lattice QCD (LQCD) which are relevant to phenomenology.

When thinking about the progress that has been made, it is useful to keep in mind the questions that one ultimately wishes to answer using LQCD:

1. Does QCD give rise to the observed spectrum of hadrons? Do these particles have the observed properties (charge radii, decay widths, etc)?

2. Does the same theory also describe the perturbative, high-energy jet physics?

3. What are the values of the hadronic matrix elements (f_B, B_K, etc.) which are needed to determine the poorly known elements of the CKM matrix?

4. What happens to QCD at finite temperature, and at finite density?

5. What are the properties of "exotic" states in the spectrum, e.g. glueballs?

6. What is the physics behind confinement and chiral symmetry breaking?

The last question is the hardest, and, while it is important to keep thinking about it, there have not been any breakthroughs. The other questions are being addressed using numerical simulations, complemented by a variety of analytic calculations. Most recent progress has concerned the first four questions, and I will discuss only the first three. For additional details see the reviews of Mackenzie (heavy quarks), Petersson (finite temperature), Sachrajda (weak matrix elements) and Ukawa (spectrum) at *LATTICE '92* [2].

To set the stage I begin with a brief summary of LQCD, eschewing as many details as possible. The action of QCD is the sum of a gauge term,

$$S_g = \frac{6}{g^2} \int_x \frac{1}{12} \sum_{\mu\nu} \text{Tr}(G_{\mu\nu} G_{\mu\nu}) , \qquad (1)$$

with $G_{\mu\nu}$ the gluon field strength, and a quark part

$$S_q = \int_x \sum_q \bar{q}(\gamma_\mu D_\mu + m_q)q , \quad D_\mu = \partial_\mu + iA_\mu .$$

These expressions are valid in Euclidean space, where numerical lattice calculations are almost always done. QCD is put on a hypercubic lattice by placing the quarks on the sites, and gauge fields on the links which join these sites, in such a way that gauge invariance is maintained. The derivative in D_μ can be discretized in many ways, leading to different types of lattice fermions. The most common choices are Wilson and staggered fermions. The coupling constant g has been absorbed in the gauge fields, and appears only as an overall factor in S_g. It is conventional (see Eq. 1) to use the combination $\beta = 6/g^2$ to specify g. In present simulations $\beta \sim 6$, so that $g^2 \sim 1$. The lattice spacing a is determined implicitly by the choice of g^2, as discussed below.

The prototypical quantity of interest is the two-point correlator, e.g.

$$C(t) = \left\langle \sum_{\vec{x}} [\bar{b}\gamma_0\gamma_5 d(t,\vec{x})] \, [\bar{d}\gamma_0\gamma_5 b(0)] \right\rangle$$

$$= \text{sign}(t) \, f_B^2 m_B e^{-m_B|t|} \left(1 + O(e^{-(m_{B'} - m_B)|t|})\right) . \qquad (2)$$

At large Euclidean time, t, one picks out the lightest state (here the B meson). The contribution of excited states (beginning with the B') is suppressed exponentially. Thus one can just read off the mass, m_B, while the amplitude of the exponential gives the decay constant (f_B) up to kinematical factors.

The expectation value in Eq. 2 indicates a functional integral over quarks, antiquarks and gluons weighted by $\exp(-S_g - S_q)$. Doing the quark and antiquark integrals, one obtains

$$C(t) = - \int [dA]\, e^{-S_g}\, [\Pi_q \det(\slashed{D} + m_q)] \sum_{\vec{x}} \text{Tr}[\gamma_0 \gamma_5 G_d(t, \vec{x}; 0) \gamma_0 \gamma_5 G_b(0; t, \vec{x})]\ . \tag{3}$$

Here $[dA]$ is shorthand for the functional integral over lattice gauge fields, and the G are quark propagators $G_q = (\slashed{D} + m_q)^{-1}$. The integral is normalized to give unity in the absence of the trace term. Diagrammatically, Eq. 3 can be written as

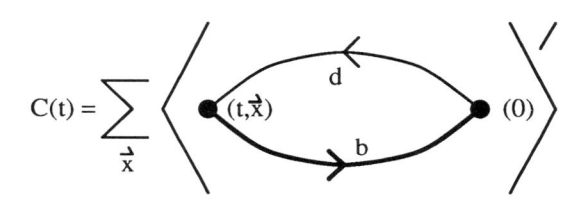

$$C(t) = \sum_{\vec{x}} \left\langle \bullet(t,\vec{x}) \xrightarrow{d}_{b} \bullet(0) \right\rangle$$

where the lines are quark propagators, and the primed expectation value includes the determinant.

To make the calculations numerically tractable, they must be done in a finite volume of $N_s^3 \times N_t$ points. The functional integral is then of large but finite dimension, and can be done by Monte-Carlo methods. Similarly, the propagators are obtained by inverting a finite matrix. Available computer speed and memory limits the number of sites in this four dimensional world. In fact, it is speed that limits present simulations: the bottleneck is the inclusion of $\det(\slashed{D} + m_q)$ in the measure. To make progress, many calculations use the "quenched" approximation in which the determinant in Eq. 3 is set equal to unity. This is equivalent to dropping all internal quark loops, so that there are only valence quarks. I discuss the consequences of this drastic approximation below.

It is important to realize that numerical LQCD calculations which do not use the quenched approximation become exact when the lattice spacing vanishes, the volume goes to infinity, and the statistical errors vanish. They are thus non-perturbative calculations from first principles, which have errors that can be systematically reduced. They are not "model" calculations. On the other hand, calculations in the quenched approximation are more similar to those in a model. Certain physics is being left out, and one does not know *a priori* how large an error is being made. As I will show, present calculations suggest that the error is small, at least for a range of quantities.

In the following three sections I discuss the spectrum, the calculation of $\alpha_{\overline{\text{MS}}}$, and that of f_B. I will focus mainly on quenched results since these are more extensive. I will only make some brief comments on results for "full QCD", i.e.

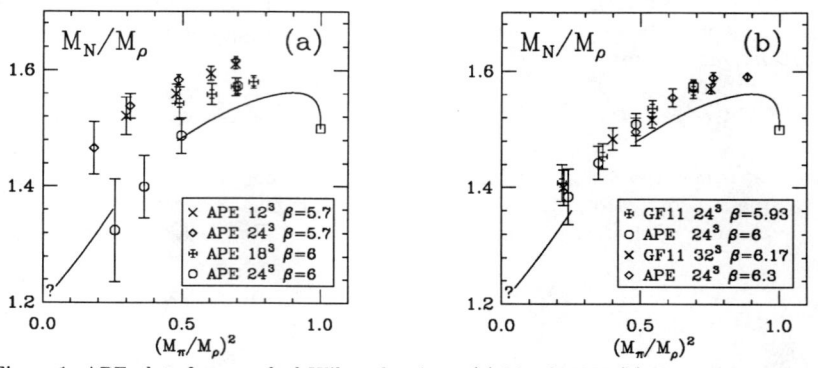

Figure 1: APE plots for quenched Wilson fermions: (a) March 1990 (b) November 1992

QCD including the determinant in the measure.

2. SPECTRUM

I begin by discussing the status of calculations of the spectrum of light hadrons. I concentrate on m_π, m_ρ and m_N (N refers to the nucleon), since these have the smallest errors. To give an idea of the rate of progress, I will compare with results from March 1990 [3]. The two and a half year interval since then is long enough to allow substantial changes. For example, computer power has increased as roughly $CPU \propto e^{\text{year}}$, so that, for a four dimensional theory such as QCD, the linear dimensions could have increased by a factor of $\sim e^{2.5/4} = 1.8$ in this period. In fact, the extra time has only partly been used in this way.

To display the data I follow the "APE" group and plot m_N/m_ρ versus $(m_\pi/m_\rho)^2$ (see Figs. 1). To understand the significance of these plots, recall the following. In a lattice calculation, we can dial the values of the quark masses. Ignoring for the moment the strange quark, and assuming degenerate up and down quarks, we then have a single light quark mass, m_l, at our disposal. Each value of m_l corresponds to a possible theory, each with different values for dimensionless mass ratios such as m_π^2/m_ρ^2, m_ρ/m_N, f_π/m_ρ, m_Δ/m_N, etc. We would like to fix m_l using one of these ratios, and then predict the others. In practice, it is technically very difficult to do a simulation with small enough m_l, and so we must extrapolate. The APE plot is one way of displaying how well this extrapolation agrees with the experimental masses. As m_l varies from $0 \to \infty$, m_π^2/m_ρ^2 varies monotonically from $0 \to 1$. Thus the theory maps out a curve in this plot, which we know must pass through the infinite mass point ($m_\pi = m_\rho = 2m_N/3$; shown by a square in the plots). The issue is whether this curve passes through the experimental point, indicated by a "?" on the plots.

The solid lines if Figs. 1 are the predictions of two phenomenological models. The curve for light quark masses uses chiral perturbation theory, with certain

Table 1: Parameters of lattices used to produce data shown in Fig. 1

Year	Ref.	β	a(fm)	π/a(GeV)	N_s	L(fm)	Lattices
1990	[4]	5.7	1/6	3.8	12,24	2,4	294,50
	[4]	6	1/10	6.3	18,24	1.8,2.4	104,33
1992	[7]	5.93	1/9	5.7	24	2.7	217
	[5]	6	1/10	6.3	24	2.4	78
	[7]	6.17	1/12	7.5	32	2.7	219
	[6]	6.3	1/16	10	24	1.5	128

assumptions, and is constrained to go through the physical point. The curve at heavier masses is based on a potential model. For more discussion see Ref. [3].

What do we expect for the lattice results? There will be corrections to physical quantities which vanish in the continuum limit as powers of a (up to logarithms, which I will ignore), e.g.

$$(m_N/m_\rho)_{\text{latt}} = (m_N/m_\rho)_{\text{cont}}[1 + a\Lambda + O(a^2)] \ . \tag{4}$$

Thus, for finite a, the lattice curve should not pass through the experimental point. Similarly, if the physical size of the lattice ($L = N_s a$) becomes too small the masses will be shifted from their infinite volume values. Thus, in addition to extrapolating in the quark mass, one must attempt to extrapolate both $a \to 0$ and $L \to \infty$.

What has happened in the last two years is that these extrapolations have become more reliable. I illustrate this with results using Wilson fermions in the quenched approximation (details of the data set are given in Table 1). Figure 1a shows the state-of-the-art in March 1990. The upper two sets of points are from a large lattice spacing ($a \approx 1/6$ fm) with two different lattice sizes ($L \approx 2$ and 4 fm). The results agree within errors, and I concluded that we knew the infinite volume curve for $a = 1/6$ fm with a precision of about 5%. This curve appeared *not* to pass through the physical point. The lower two sets of points are from a smaller lattice spacing ($a \approx 1/10$ fm). They suggested a downward shift in the data with decreasing lattice spacing, but it was difficult to draw definite conclusions given the large errors.

The present results are shown in Fig. 1b. To avoid clutter, I show only data with $a \leq 1/9$ fm.* These are all consistent with a single curve lying below that at $a = 1/6$ fm and close to the phenomenological predictions. The improvements in the results have come from using more lattices to approximate the functional integral, which reduces the statistical errors (see Table 1). Furthermore, the decrease in a has been compensated by an increase in N_s, so that (with the exception of the APE results at $\beta = 6.3$) the physical extent of the lattices exceeds $L = 2$ fm. The results at $\beta = 5.7$ imply that this is large enough to get within a few percent of the infinite volume results.

---
*The new results at $a = 1/6$ fm [7] confirm, with reduced errors, those in Fig. 1a.

The GF11 group have used their results at $a \approx 1/6, 1/9, 1/12\,\text{fm}$ to do an extrapolation both to physical quark masses and to $a = 0$ [7]. They find that, for a range of quantities, the results are consistent with their experimental values within $\sim 5\%$ errors. For example, $m_N/m_\rho = 1.284^{+0.071}_{-0.065}$ (cf 1.222 expt.) and $m_\Delta/m_\rho = 1.627^{+0.051}_{-0.092}$ (cf 1.604 expt.). It should be recalled that a few years ago the quenched results for m_N/m_ρ were thought to be larger than the experimental value, while $m_\Delta - m_N$ was smaller. What we have learned is that *both* the errors introduced by working in finite volume and at finite lattice spacing shift the curve in the APE plot upwards, so that one can easily be mislead by results on small lattices.

We seem, then, to know the spectrum of light hadrons in the quenched approximation fairly well, and it looks a lot like the observed spectrum. There is not, however, complete agreement on the numerical results. The QCDPAX collaboration, working at lattice spacings comparable to those in Fig. 1b, finds significantly larger values for m_N/m_ρ at smaller m_π^2/m_ρ^2 [10]. They suggest that the disagreement may be due to a contamination from excited states in the correlators (see Eq. 2). This disagreement will get cleared up in the next year or so. What is needed is operators which couple more strongly to the ground state, and less to excited states. There has been considerable improvement in such operators, for systems involving a heavy quark [11], but less so for light quark hadrons.

Let me assume that the results of Fig. 1b are correct, so that the quenched spectrum does agree with the experiment to within $\sim 5\%$. Does this imply that we can trust quenched calculations of other quantities to this accuracy? I do not think so. *A priori*, I would not have expected the quenched approximation to work so well, because it leaves out so much important physics. For example, the quenched rho cannot decay into two pions, unlike the physical rho, which might lead to a 10% underestimate of its mass [8]. Also, the pion cloud around the light hadrons is much different in the quenched approximation than in full QCD, which should shift m_ρ and m_N in different ways. While it is possible that these effects largely cancel for the spectrum, I see no reason for them to do so in other quantities. This argument can be made more concrete for the charge radii [9]. Futhermore, as I mention below, there are reasons to think that the approach to the chiral limit in the quenched approximation is singular.

My final remark on the quenched spectrum concerns the possibility of improving the approach to the continuum limit [12]. The gauge action is accurate to $O(a^2)$, but the Wilson fermion action has $O(a)$ corrections, as in Eq. 4. It is possible to systematically "improve" the fermion action so that the corrections are successively reduced by powers of $g^2/4\pi$. The idea is that by using a more complicated action one can work at a larger lattice spacing. The first results of this program are encouraging. Ref. [13] finds that an improved action shifts the results at $a = 1/6\,\text{fm}$ downwards so as to agree with those at $a \approx 1/10\,\text{fm}$, and that both agree with the "unimproved" results at $a \leq 1/9\,\text{fm}$ shown in Fig. 1b. Ref. [14] finds that the improved action makes no difference at a smaller lattice spacing, $a \approx 1/14\,\text{fm}$. All this suggests that it may be possible use lattice spacings as large as $1/6\,\text{fm}$ with an improved Wilson fermion action. Further evidence for this comes from lattice studies of charmonium [15, 16]. With staggered fermions, on the other hand, the prospects are less rosy. Although the corrections are of $O(a^2)$, and thus parametrically smaller than with Wilson fermions, they are in fact large at $a = 1/6$ fm [17].

Ultimately, we must repeat the calculation using full QCD. Much of the increase in computer time in the last few years has gone into simulations which include quark loops. Nevertheless, it is too early to discuss physical predictions, since it is not yet possible to reliably extrapolate $m_q \to 0$ or $a \to 0$. The limit $L \to \infty$ is, however, well understood and some interesting results have been obtained. The Kyoto-Tsukuba group finds good fits to the form $m = m_\infty(1 + c/L^3)$, and argue that this can be understood as due to the "squeezing" of the hadrons in the finite box [19].[†] The MILC collaboration finds that at $L = 2.7$ fm the finite volume effects are smaller than 2% [20]. Both these results are consistent with the finite volume effects observed in the quenched approximation [7].

3. $\alpha_{\overline{MS}}$ FROM THE LATTICE

It is straightforward, in principle, to extract $\alpha_{\overline{MS}}$ from lattice calculations:

1. Pick a value of $\beta = 6/g^2$.
2. Calculate a physically measurable quantity, e.g. m_ρ or f_π.
3. Compare lattice and physical values and extract a using, e.g.[‡]

$$(m_\rho)_{\text{latt}} = (m_\rho)_{\text{phys}} \times a \ (1 + O(a)) \ . \tag{5}$$

The $O(a)$ terms are not included when extracting a.

4. Convert from the lattice bare coupling constant $g^2(a)$ to $\alpha_{\overline{MS}}(q = \pi/a)$ using perturbation theory. The result can then be evolved to other scales, e.g. M_Z, using the renormalization group equation.

5. Repeat for a variety of values of β, and extrapolate to the continuum limit $a = 0$. In this way the $O(a)$ corrections in Eq. 5 are removed.

If this program were to be carried through, then the lattice result for $\alpha_{\overline{MS}}$ would allow absolute predictions of jet cross sections, $R(e^+e^-)$, etc. (modulo the effects of hadronization). If these predictions were successful, it would demonstrate that QCD could simultaneously explain widely disparate phenomena occurring over a large range of mass scales. While such success has not yet been achieved, there has been considerable progress in the last year or so. I will explain the two major problems, and the extent to which they have been resolved. I then discuss the present results.

3.1. Reliability of Perturbation Theory

The fourth step in the program requires that perturbation theory be valid at the scale of the lattice cut-off, which is roughly π/a in momentum space. On present

---
[†]This is not the asymptotic form: for large enough L the power law becomes an exponential [18].
[‡]The values for a quoted above were obtained in this way, using a variety of physical quantities.

lattices this ranges from 5 – 12 GeV (the values are given in Table 1). It turns out that these values are not large enough for perturbation theory in the bare coupling constant to be accurate, because there are large higher order corrections. These are exemplified by the relation needed in step 4 above [21]

$$\frac{1}{\alpha_{\overline{MS}}(\pi/a)} = \frac{1}{\alpha_{\text{latt}}(a)} - 3.880 + O(\alpha) ; \quad (\alpha = g^2/4\pi) . \tag{6}$$

Since $\alpha_{\text{latt}} \approx 1/13$, the first order correction is large, and higher order terms are likely to be important.

This problem has been understood by Lepage and Mackenzie [22]. The large corrections arise from fluctuations of the lattice gauge fields, and in particular from "tadpole" diagrams which are present on the lattice but absent in the continuum. The solution is to express perturbative results in terms of a "continuum-like" coupling constant, e.g. α_{MOM} or $\alpha_{\overline{MS}}$, with the scale $q \approx \pi/a$. When this is done the higher order coefficients are considerably reduced. This is similar to what happens in the continuum when one shifts from the MS to the $\overline{MS}$ scheme.

Having re-expressed all perturbative expressions in terms of, say, $\alpha_{\overline{MS}}$, there remains the problem of finding the value of this coupling in terms of α_{latt}, since Eq. 6 is not reliable. One has to use a non-perturbative definition of coupling constant which automatically sums up the large contributions, and which is related to $\alpha_{\overline{MS}}$ in a reliable way. One choice is [22]

$$\alpha_P = -\frac{3\ln\langle \text{Tr}\, U_P \rangle}{4\pi} ; \quad \frac{1}{\alpha_{\overline{MS}}(\pi/a)} = \frac{1}{\alpha_P} - 0.5 + O(\alpha) , \tag{7}$$

where U_P is the product of gauge links around an elementary square. One first determines α_P from the numerical value of $\text{Tr}\, U_P$, and then converts this to $\alpha_{\overline{MS}}$, which is then used in perturbative expressions. Lepage and Mackenzie find that the resulting numerical predictions of lattice perturbation theory work well for quantities (such as small Wilson loops) which are dominated by short-distance perturbative contributions. This is true for lattice spacings as large as 1/9 fm, and perhaps 1/6 fm. Thus the determination of $\alpha_{\overline{MS}}$ using Eq. 7 is reliable, with errors probably no larger than a few percent.

3.2. Errors Introduced by the Quenched Approximation

The dominant source of uncertainty in present calculations of $\alpha_{\overline{MS}}$ is the use of the quenched approximation. The problem is the lack of a "physical" quenched theory to use in the comparison of step 3 above. This shows up in two ways. First, the value of a depends on the quantity chosen in the comparison: using m_ρ gives one value, f_π another.[§] Second, the coupling constant that one obtains is for a theory with zero flavors, $\alpha_{\overline{MS}}^{(0)}$, and must somehow be related to the physical coupling constant $\alpha_{\overline{MS}}$. However, such a relationship involves non-perturbative physics, and so can only be determined by a calculation using full QCD! The best that we can hope for at present is a good estimate of the relationship between the couplings.

[§] Actually, since light hadron mass ratios are well reproduced by the quenched approximation, the variation of a is small for such quantities. This need not be true in general.

Table 2: Results for $\alpha_{\overline{MS}}$ in quenched and full QCD. Errors are statistical.

Quantity	Ref.	$\alpha_{\overline{MS}}^{(0)}(M_Z)$	$\alpha_{\overline{MS}}(M_Z)$
"Experiment"	[23]		0.1134(35)
$M_{1P} - M_{1S}$	[1]	0.0790(9)	0.105(4)
String tension	[24]	0.0796(3)	
String tension	[25]	0.0801(9)	

Recently, the FNAL group have made such an estimate for the coupling determined using the $1P - 1S$ splitting in charmonium [1]. The crucial simplifying feature is that charmonium is described reasonably well by a potential model, so one need only estimate the effects of quark loops on the potential itself. In outline, this is done as follows. Matching the lattice and continuum $1P-1S$ splittings makes the quenched and full QCD potentials similar at separations $R \sim 0.5\,\text{fm}$. The potentials will, however, differ at smaller separations. We understand this difference at small enough R, where the Coulomb term dominates, i.e. $V \propto -\alpha_{\overline{MS}}(1/R)/R$. In the quenched approximation α varies more rapidly with R because of the absence of fermion loops, which means that the quenched potential is steeper. Assuming that this is true all the way out to $0.5\,\text{fm}$, where the potentials match, implies that the quenched potential must lie below that for full QCD at short distances. It follows that $\alpha_{\overline{MS}} > \alpha_{\overline{MS}}^{(0)}$ at short distances. A quantitative estimate is given in Ref. [1].

Unfortunately, there is no such simple way of estimating the effects of the quenched approximation on the values of $\alpha_{\overline{MS}}^{(0)}$ extracted from the properties of light quark hadrons.

3.3. Results

Various physical quantities have been used to calculate $\alpha_{\overline{MS}}^{(0)}$, and I collect the most accurate results in Table 2. I also give the "experimental" number obtained from an average of various perturbative QCD fits to data [23]. I quote the coupling at the scale M_Z, to allows comparison with Fig. 1 of the 1992 Review of Particle Properties (RPP) [23]. The second row gives the results of the FNAL group, including the correction for quenching. The remaining results use the "string tension", σ. This is the coefficient of the linear term in the heavy quark-antiquark potential: $V(R) \to \sigma R$ for $R \to \infty$. All groups use the "improved" perturbation theory explained above. I have not shown results from light hadron masses as they are less accurate.

The results for $\alpha_{\overline{MS}}^{(0)}$ obtained using σ have the smallest statistical errors. Indeed, it is a triumph of LQCD that the linear term in the quenched potential is very well established, for it is this term that causes confinement. The difficulty is that σ is not a physical quantity. The "physical" value, $\sqrt{\sigma} = 0.44\,\text{GeV}$, is extracted from the potential needed to fit the $\bar{c}c$ and $\bar{b}b$ spectra. These systems do not, however, probe the region of the potential where the linear term dominates. Furthermore, at large R the full QCD potential flattens out due to quark-pair creation, while the quenched potential continues its linear rise. Thus the extracted value of σ is somewhat uncertain, and it is difficult to relate $\alpha_{\overline{MS}}^{(0)}$ obtained using σ to the full QCD coupling. Nevertheless, it seems to me possible to make a rough estimate, and it would certainly be interesting to try.

The lattice prediction for $\alpha_{\overline{MS}}$ is slightly less than 2σ below the RPP average. In his summary talk, Keith Ellis quoted an updated average, $\alpha_{\overline{MS}}(M_Z) = 0.119(4)$, which is almost 3σ higher than the lattice result. I think that this near agreement is a success of LQCD, and that it is too early to make anything out of the small discrepancy. For one thing, the dominant error in the lattice result is the uncertainty in the conversion from $\alpha_{\overline{MS}}^{(0)}$ to $\alpha_{\overline{MS}}$, and this might be underestimated. It is important to realize, however, that this uncertainty will be gradually reduced as simulations of full QCD improve.

I end this section with a general comment on the calculations. For the method to work, both non-perturbative and perturbative physics must be included *in a single lattice simulation*. At long distances the quarks are confined in hadrons, while at the scale of the lattice spacing their interactions must be described by perturbation theory. On a finite lattice, these two requirements pull in opposite directions. For example, if perturbation theory requires $a < 1/9$ fm, while finite volume effects require $L > 2.7$ fm (as may be true for light hadrons), the lattice must have $N_s \geq 30$, and so present lattices are barely large enough. This is another reason for using charmonium to determine $\alpha_{\overline{MS}}$. The $\bar{c}c$ states are smaller than light hadrons, and it turns out that $N_s = 24$ is large enough to reduce the finite volume errors below 1% [1].

Nevertheless, it would be nice to extend the range of scales so as to provide a detailed test of the dependence on a. To accomplish this with present resources requires the use of multiple lattices having a range of sizes. Lüscher *et al.* have proposed such a program, and done the calculation for SU(2) pure gauge theory [26].

4. The B-meson decay constant f_B

One of the most important numbers that LQCD can provide phenomenologists is f_B. Analyses of the constraints due to $\bar{K} - K$ and $\bar{B} - B$ mixing find (for $m_t \geq 140$ GeV) two types of solutions for CP-violation in the CKM-matrix (see, e.g. Ref. [27]). These are distinguished by whether f_B is "small" (100 – 150 MeV) or "large" (160 – 340 MeV). In the former case, CP-violation in $B \to K_S J/\psi$ is small; in the latter it is much larger. We would also like the lattice to resolve this ambiguity.

The calculation of f_B is also interesting as a testing ground for the "heavy quark effective theory" (HQET) [28]. The B-meson consists of heavy b quark, and a light quark (u or d). Imagine that we were free to vary the heavy quark mass, m_Q. The mass of the pseudoscalar meson (which I call m_P to distiguish it from the physical B meson mass, m_B), and its decay constant f_P, would depend upon m_Q.

As $m_Q \to \infty$ one can show that [29]

$$\phi_P = f_P\sqrt{m_P}\left[\frac{\alpha(m_P)}{\alpha(m_B)}\right]^{2/\beta_0} = \phi_\infty\left(1 + \frac{A}{m_P} + \frac{B}{m_P^2} + \ldots\right). \tag{8}$$

Here β_0 is the first term in the QCD β-function, and A and B are constants except for a weak logarithmic dependence on m_P. The issue for HQET is the size of the $1/m_P$ corrections at the B and D masses, for these might be indicative of the size of the corrections in other applications of HQET, e.g. $B \to D$ transitions.

It is important to realize that, while the $m_Q \to \infty$ limit simplifies the kinematics of the heavy quark, it does not simplify the dynamics of the light quark. In particular, the quenched approximation is no better in the heavy quark limit, nor is the dynamics more perturbative. Thus one needs a LQCD calculation here just as much as for light quark hadrons.

What we would like to do is map out the curve of ϕ_P versus $1/m_P$, and read off the values of f_B and f_D. Examples of present results are shown in Figs. 2, and in Table 3 I give the present numerical values for f_B and f_D. I also quote $f_B(\text{static}) = \phi_\infty/\sqrt{m_B}$, which is the value of f_B ignoring the $1/m_P$ corrections in Eq. 8. Unfortunately, the situation is less straightforward than the figures imply, and I will spend the remainder of this section explaining and evaluating these results.

There are three major causes of uncertainty in f_B. The first concerns the overall scale. To extract a result in physical units we need to know the lattice spacing. As discussed above, the value we obtain depends on the physical quantity that we use, particularly at finite lattice spacing. f_B is more sensitive to the uncertainty in a than are light hadron masses, since one is calculating $a^{3/2}\phi_P$ rather than am. To illustrate this sensitivity, I include in Table 3 results from Refs. [11, 32] using two different determination of a. For the other results, the uncertainty is about 15%. Ultimately, to remove this uncertainty one must repeat the calculation with full QCD.

The second problem concerns the isolation of the lightest state. In principle, calculating ϕ_P is straightforward. One simply studies the long time behavior of the two point function of the local axial current, Eq. 2, and reads off $f_P\sqrt{m_P}$. In practice, to obtain a signal it is necessary to use extended operators, which couple more strongly to the lightest state than the local current. This is particularly important at large m_Q. With a less than optimal operator there are likely to be systematic errors introduced by contamination from excited states. Indeed, there are disagreements between results using different operators. This is illustrated in Table 3 by the variation in $f_B(\text{static})$. It seems to me, however, that the operators of Ref. [34] are close to optimal, and that the discrepancies will go away as other groups optimize their operators.

The third and most difficult problem concerns putting very heavy quarks on the lattice. As the quark's mass increases, the ratio of its Compton wavelength to the lattice spacing, $1/(m_Q a)$, decreases. For $m_Q a > 1$, its propagation through the lattice will be severely affected by lattice artifacts. There are, however, no such difficulties for an infinitely massive quark, for such a quark remains at rest both

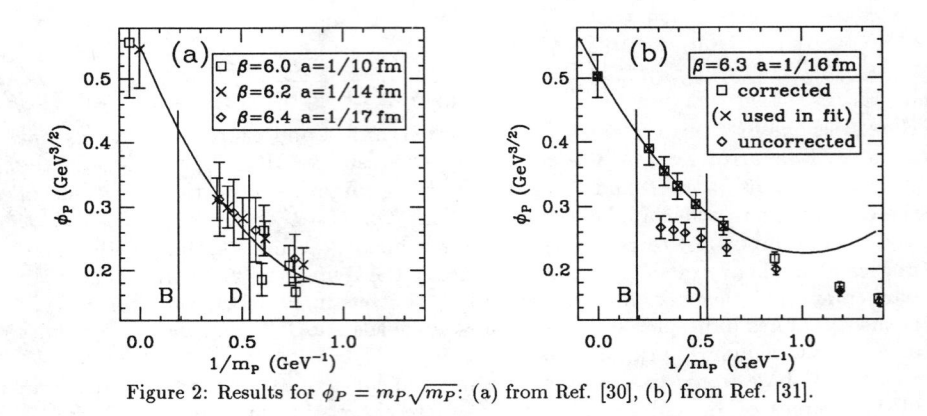

Figure 2: Results for $\phi_P = m_P\sqrt{m_P}$: (a) from Ref. [30], (b) from Ref. [31].

Table 3: Results for decays constants in the quenched approximation. The normalization is such that $f_\pi = 132\,\text{MeV}$. Only statistical errors are shown; systematic errors are discussed in the text.

Ref.	β	Scale from	f_B(static)(MeV)	f_B(MeV)	f_D(MeV)
[30]	6.0-6.4	f_π, m_ρ	310(25)	205(40)	210(15)
[33]	6.2	f_π		183(10)	198(5)
[31]	6.3	f_π	230(15)	187(10)	208(9)
[11]	5.9	$M(1P)-M(1S)$	319(11)		
		σ	265(10)		
[32]	5.74-6.26	σ	230(22)		
		m_ρ	256(78)		

in the continuum and on the lattice [29]. Thus it seems that we are forced to interpolate between $m_Q \sim 1/a$ and $m_Q = \infty$.

To illustrate the problems that this introduces, consider the situation about two years ago. The smallest lattice spacing was $a = 1/10\,\text{fm}$, so that $m_c a \approx 0.75$ and $m_b \approx 2.5$. Typical results are those represented by squares in Fig. 2a. The quark mass has been restricted to satisfy $m_Q a \leq 0.7$ to avoid large artifacts (an arbitrary but reasonable choice for an upper bound), and thus lie to the right of the D meson line. Clearly it is difficult to convincingly interpolate using Eq. 8: the variation in ϕ_P is so large that one cannot truncate the $1/M$ expansion. Nevertheless, if one assumes that the curvature is not too large, the fact that we know ϕ_∞ does allow a rough estimate of f_B.

There has been considerable progress in the last two years. The lattice spacing has been reduced to $1/17\,\text{fm}$, which allows one to use heavier quarks while keeping $m_Q a < 1$. This is illustrated by the remaining points in Fig. 2a, all of which have $m_Q a \leq 0.7$. These points can now be fit in a more reliable way to the asymptotic form of Eq. 8. The curve shows such a fit, the results from which are given in Table 3. Other groups, however, find results in apparent disagreement. For example. the "uncorrected" points in Fig. 2b should agree with those in 2a, but instead are lower. This disagreement is, I suspect, mainly due to inadequate isolation of the lightest B meson by one or both groups.

Another development has been the use an improved fermion action [33]. Since this has smaller $O(a)$ corrections, one should be able to work at larger values of $m_Q a$. I give the results in Table 3.

Despite these improvements, it would be much better if we could work at any value of $m_Q a$, and simply map out the entire curve. There is a dispute about whether this is possible, and I will attempt to give a summary of the arguments.

I begin by noting that the errors in ϕ_P do not keep growing as $m_Q a$ increases. This is because, if $m_Q \gg \Lambda_{\rm QCD}$, the quark is non-relativistic. Its dynamics can then be expanded in powers of $1/m_Q$ [35]

$$\mathcal{L} = \psi^\dagger \left[iD_0 + \frac{D_i^2}{2m_1} + c(g^2)\frac{\sigma_i B_i}{2m_2} + O(1/m_Q^2) \right] \psi \, , \tag{9}$$

where ψ is a two component field, and c is a perturbative coefficient. In the continuum, $m_1 = m_2 = m_Q$. The discrete rotational symmetries are sufficient to ensure that a heavy lattice quark will be described by the same Lagrangian, except that neither m_1 nor m_2 are equal to the bare lattice quark mass m_Q. Nevertheless, although the lattice heavy quarks have the wrong dynamics, this should only introduce errors of $O(\Lambda_{\rm QCD}/m_Q)$. Thus, if a is small enough that $m_Q a < 1$ when the quark becomes non-relativistic, the errors will be small for all $m_Q a$.

Strictly speaking, to bring the lattice Lagrangian into the form of Eq. 9, one must perform a wavefuction renormalization on the heavy field, which changes the normalization of the $\bar{b}u$ axial current. This has been calculated in perturbation theory keeping only the "tadpole" diagrams which are thought to be dominant [36]. The result is illustrated in Fig. 2b: upon renormalization the "uncorrected" points are shifted upwards into those labeled "corrected". With this modification, the curve for finite $m_Q a$ is guaranteed to pass through the ϕ_∞. Without it, the curve will bend over and eventually pass through the origin. In fact, the uncorrected points in Fig. 2b do appear to be flattening out at the smallest values of $1/m_P$, although those of Fig. 2a do not.

A second correction has also been applied in Fig. 2b. It is possible to partly account for the difference between m_1 and m_Q, by an appropriate shift to smaller $1/m_Q$. The size of this shift has been calculated keeping "tadpole" diagrams [36]. This correction ensures that the data approach ϕ_∞ with a slope which is linear in $1/m_P$. This slope will not, however, be correct since the $1/m_2$ term in Eq. 9 has the wrong normalization. Nevertheless, in contrast to the "uncorrected" points, the shifted points fit well to the form of Eq. 8. The fit is shown by the curve, and the resulting values for decay constants are given in Table 3.

The controversial issue is how to further modify the calculation so as to obtain the correct $1/m_P$ terms. Kronfeld, Lepage and Mackenzie have suggested a program for removing the error [36]. The idea is to add new terms to the lattice action, and to choose the parameters so that one obtains the correct Lagrangian at $O(1/m_Q)$. This is essentially a complicated way of putting non-relativistic QCD on the lattice [35]. The difficult question in both cases is how to fix the parameters.

Kronfeld *et al* propose that this can be done using perturbation theory. Maiani *et al.* argue, however, that non-perturbative contributions may be important [37]. Normally, such contributions are suppressed by powers of a, but here they are enhanced by factors $1/a$ due to linear divergences. (A clear explanation of this effect is given in Ref. [38].) The result is that, with parameters fixed using perturbation theory, there will be errors in ϕ_P which are of $O(\Lambda_{QCD}/m_Q)$, i.e. of the same size as the terms one is trying to calculate. The point of disagreement is whether these non-perturbative terms are large or small. If they are large, the only solution would be to fix parameters using non-perturbative normalization conditions. In general this would reduce predictive power.

Clearly more work is needed to resolve this dispute. One way to do this is to push the tests of perturbation theory [22] to the level at which non-perturbative terms show up.

It is fortunate, however, that this uncertainty has only a small effect on f_B and f_D. This is shown by the good agreement in Table 3 despite the different methods being used. The results favor the "large" solution for f_B. The only way this could change is if the systematic error due to the quenched approximation turns out to be large.

We can also estimate the size of the $O(1/M)$ corrections to the heavy quark limit. Taking the data of Ref. [31] as an example, they are $\sim 15\%$ for f_B, and $\sim 45\%$ for f_D. These numbers increase further if one uses the larger values of ϕ_∞ found by Ref. [11].

5. OUTLOOK

There are many interesting developments that I have not have had time or space to cover. One which impinges on much of the work discussed above concerns the accuracy of the quenched approximation [39]. In this approximation there are nine pseudo-Goldstone bosons, rather than the eight of QCD, the extra one being the η'. This means that quenched particles have an η' cloud, not present in full QCD. It turns out that this gives rise to singularities in the chiral limit, much as pion loops give singularities in the charge radii of pions and nucleons [9]. For example, the quark condensate diverges. The implications of these divergences are not yet clear. The most optimistic view is that the effects of η' loops are small as long as we work above a certain quark mass. This is supported by the absence of numerical evidence to date for the divergences.

Unfortunately, the quenched approximation is likely to be with us for a number of years. At present, the fastest computers simulating LQCD are running at $1-10$ GFlops. Even a TeraFlop machine, such as that proposed by the TeraFlop collaboration [40], will focus on quenched lattices. These will have $N_s \approx 100$, and should give definitive quenched results for a reasonable number of interesting quantities. The major problem with simulations of full QCD is that the CPU time scales as $m_\pi^{-10.5}$ with present algorithms. Clearly, it is crucial that effort go into improving these algorithms.

6. ACKNOWLEDGEMENTS

I thank Don Weingarten Jim Labrenz and Akira Ukawa for providing me with data, and Estia Eichten, Aida El-Khadra, Rajan Gupta, Brian Hill, Andreas Kronfeld, Jim Labrenz and Paul Mackenzie for discussions. This work was supported by the DOE under contract DE-FG09-91ER40614, and by an Alfred P. Sloan Fellowship.

7. REFERENCES

1. A. El-Khadra, G. Hockney, A. Kronfeld and P. Mackenzie, *Phys. Rev. Lett.* **69**, 729 (1992) ; and FERMILAB-CONF-92-299-T
2. Proceedings of the International Symposium on Lattice Field Theory, *"LATTICE 92"*, Amsterdam, The Netherlands, 1992, to be published
3. S. Sharpe, Proc. First Int. Symp. on *"Particles, Strings and Cosmology"*, Northeastern Univ., Boston, USA, March, 1990, Eds. P. Nath and S. Reucroft, p270
4. P. Bacilieri et al., *Nucl. Phys.* **B317** (1989) 509;
   S. Cabasino et al., Proceedings of the International Symposium on Lattice Field Theory, *"LATTICE 89"*, Capri, Italy, 1989, edited by N. Cabibbo et al., Nucl. Phys. B (**Proc. Suppl.**)17 (1990) 431
5. F. Butler, H. Chen, A. Vaccarino, J. Sexton and D. Weingarten, these proceedings; preprint hep-lat/9211051, to appear in Ref. [2]
6. S. Cabasino et al., *Phys. Lett.* **258B** (1991) 195
7. M. Guagnelli et al., *Nucl. Phys.* **B378** (1992) 616
8. Y. Iwasaki et al., preprint UTHEP-246, to appear in Ref. [2]
9. A. Duncan et al., preprint UCLA/92/TEP/40, to appear in Ref. [2]
10. P. Geiger and N. Isgur, *Phys. Rev.* **D41**, 1595 (1990)
11. D. Leinweber and T. Cohen, U. of MD Preprint 92-190
12. K. Symanzik, *Nucl. Phys.* **B226** (1983) 187; *ibid* 205
13. M.-P. Lombardo, G. Parisi and A. Vladikas, preprint ILL-(TH)-92-15
14. C.R. Allton et al., *Phys. Lett.* **284B** (1992) 377
15. A. El-Khadra, preprint FERMILAB-CONF-92/330-T, to appear in Ref. [2]
16. C.R. Allton et al., *Phys. Lett.* **292B** (1992) 408
17. S. Sharpe, Proceedings of the International Symposium on Lattice Field Theory, *"LATTICE 91"*, Tsukuba, Japan, 1991, edited by M. Fukugita et al., Nucl. Phys. B (**Proc. Suppl.**)26 (1992) 197

18. M. Fukugita et al., Phys. Rev. Lett. **68**, 761 (1992)
    M. Fukugita, et al., preprint KEK-TH-339
19. M. Lüscher, *Comm. Math. Phys.* **104**(1986)177
20. C. Bernard et al., preprint IUHET-233, to appear in Ref. [2]
21. A. Hasenfratz and P. Hasenfratz, Phys. Lett. **93B** (1980) 165
    R. Dashen and D. Gross, Phys. Rev. **D23**, 2340 (1981)
22. G.P. Lepage and P. Mackenzie, Proceedings of the International Symposium on Lattice Field Theory, *"LATTICE 90"*, Tallahassee, Florida, USA, 1990, edited by U. M. Heller et al., Nucl. Phys. B **(Proc. Suppl.)20** (1991) 173; preprint FERMILAB-PUB-19/355-T (9/92)
23. K. Hikasa et al., Phys. Rev. **D45**, S1 (1992)
24. G. Bali and K. Schilling, preprint WUB-92-29
25. S. Booth et al., preprint LTH 285
26. M. Lüscher et al., preprint DESY-92-096
27. M. Lusignoli et al., Nucl. Phys. **B369** (1992) 139
28. N. Isgur and M. Wise, Phys. Lett. **232B** (1989) 113; *ibid* **237B** (1990) 447
29. E. Eichten, Proceedings of the International Symposium on Lattice Field Theory, *"Field theory on the Lattice"*, Seillac, France, 1987, edited by A. Billoire et al., Nucl. Phys. B **(Proc. Suppl.)4** (1988) 170
30. C. Alexandrou et al., preprint CERN-TH 6692/92
31. A. Duncan, E. Eichten and H. Thacker in Ref. [2]
32. A. Abada et al., Nucl. Phys. **B376** (1992) 172
    C. Allton et al., Nucl. Phys. **B349** (1991) 598
33. C. Bernard, J. Labrenz and A. Soni, preprint UW/PT-92-21, in Ref. [2]
34. D.G. Richards, Edinburgh Preprint 92/518, to appear in Ref. [2]
35. G.P. Lepage and B. Thacker, Phys. Rev. **D43**, 196 (1991)
36. G.P. Lepage, Proceedings of the International Symposium on Lattice Field Theory, *"LATTICE 91"*, Tsukuba, Japan, 1991, edited by M. Fukugita et al., Nucl. Phys. B **(Proc. Suppl.)26** (1992) 45;
    A. Kronfeld, preprint FERMILAB-CONF-92/329-T, to appear in Ref. [2]
37. L. Maiani, G. Martinelli and C. Sachrajda, *Nucl. Phys.* **B368** (1992) 281
38. G. Martinelli, Proceedings of the International Symposium on Lattice Field Theory, *"LATTICE 91"*, Tsukuba, Japan, 1991, edited by M. Fukugita et al., Nucl. Phys. B **(Proc. Suppl.)26** (1992) 31
39. C. Bernard and M. Golterman, Phys. Rev. **D46**, 853 (1992) and in Ref. [2]
    S. Sharpe, Phys. Rev. **D46**, 3146 (1992) and in Ref. [2]
40. S. Aoki et al., Int. Jour. Mod. Phys. **C2** (1991) 829

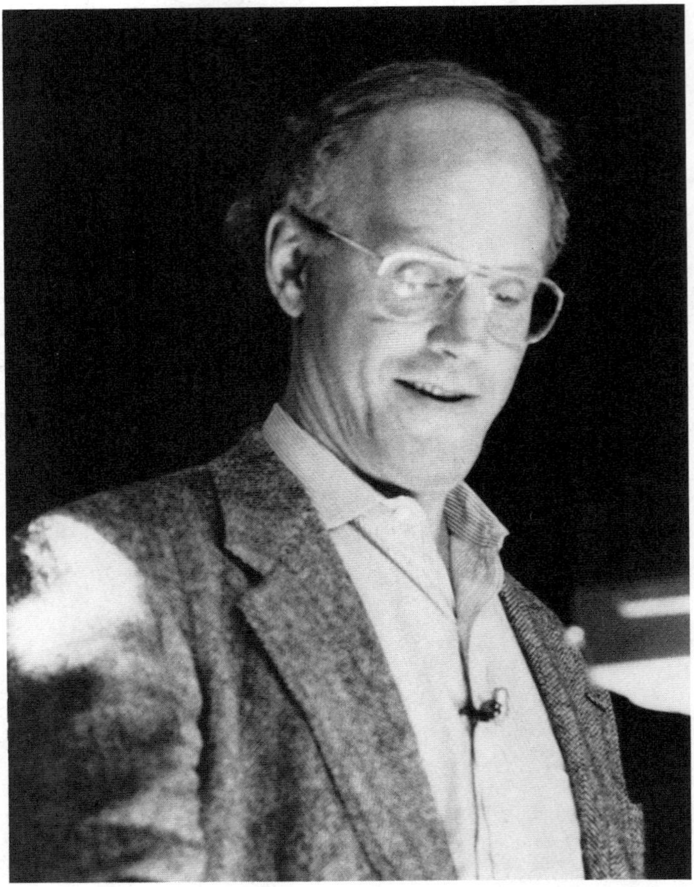

RECENT DEVELOPMENTS IN ABSTRACT THEORY

DAVID J. GROSS[1]

Departemnt of Physics, Princeton University
Princeton, N.J. 08544
and
Theoretical Physics Group, Lawrence Berkeley Laboratory
Berkeley, California 94720

ABSTRACT

In this talk current developments in quantum gravity, string theory and analytical approaches to QCD are reviewed.

1. Introduction

The original title of this talk was chosen by the organizers of this meeting. It referred to *formal theory*. I did not feel comfortable with the word formal to describe the physics I was assigned to review– string theory, quantum gravity, etc. A quick search through my thesaurus revealed why this was so. Synonymous with the word formal are the words artificial, awkward, dull, stiff, stilted, pompous, stodgy, stuffy and, perhaps foremost in the mind of the organizers, boring. Instead, I think a more appropriate term to designate this area of theoretical physics is *abstract theory*. The synonyms of abstract are conjectural, hypothetical, illustrative, general, ideal, symbolic and, most appropriately, theoretical.

I should remind my younger, more abstract, friends to take heart when arrows of scorn are flung their way by their more practical colleagues. Twenty years ago, in 1972, the abstract community was deep into such esoteric and impractical ideas as current algebra, non-Abelian gauge theories, the renormalization group and operator product expansions. These led, in 1973, to QCD and the completion of the standard model. Abstract theory turned rapidly into *practical* (doable, realistic and justifiable) theory producing high energy predictions and calculations of standard physics background that today are indispensable for the planning of current experiments. Most important, they led to our developing a qualitative, and in some cases quantitative, understanding of hadronic physics. The practitioners of abstract theory have much to be proud of.

In this talk I shall briefly review a few topics which fit into this category. I shall first survey the state of string theory. The last year has not been one of great developments in fundamental (theory of everything) string theory, so naturally many people in this field have turned to related problems. One of the most popular and interesting is the study of two-dimensional black holes, a topic I shall briefly address. There are renewed attempts to find new applications for strings–from the Ising model to turbulence. The possibility of representing QCD by means of an

---
[1]Supported by NSF Grant PHY90-21984 and by DOE contract DE-AC03-76SF00098.

effective string theory has been discussed anew this year. I shall briefly review some of my work on this subject. In addition there are other offshoots of string theory. For example, the recent matrix model developments have inspired Kazakov and Migdal to suggest a new approach to the large N limit of QCD. I shall briefly discuss this approach.

2. String Theory

It is important to remember that both the motivation for and the achievements of string theory stand undiminished. The main motivations for string theory stem from the success of the standard model and its inability to answer many of the questions that it raises, questions that can only be answered by further unification. This remarkable theory continues to be verified by experiment, and with increasing accuracy. The recent high precision experiments at LEP and SLAC have given support to the ability of experiment and theory to extrapolate the standard model by many orders of magnitude, have provided hints for supersymmetry and suggest a unification scale very close to the Planck scale. All of this bolsters the guess that the next significant threshold is the Planck scale, where the standard model gauge forces are unified with gravity. String theory remains the only viable theory which can pretend to accomplish this.

There are three significant achievements of string theory. First, string theory is a consistent logical extension of the conceptual structure of physics. Second, it produces a finite and consistent theory of quantum gravity. Finally, it contains all the ingredients needed for deriving the standard model and might describe the real world. These successes have only been strengthened in recent years.

String theory also makes many predictions. Unfortunately they refer to physics at the Planck scale, which is not directly observable. To connect to observable physics at a TeV we need to make much theoretical progress. The more we learn about string theory the more we are aware that our understanding of the theory is at a very primitive stage. We lack a deep comprehension of the conceptual framework of the theory, a non-perturbative formulation of the dynamics, an understanding of the underlying symmetry of the theory, the mechanism of symmetry breaking and much more. Some progress has been achieved in this direction. We seem to have a closed string field theory[1], which can at least reproduce perturbation theory. However, the goal of finding a true background independent formulation of the dynamics has not been realized, although in simple cases this can be done[2]. In the absence of true dynamical wisdom attempts to construct *string inspired* phenomenological models continues. This is very worthwhile, although it is not clear how sharp and definitive the predictions following from these models can be.

The spurt of activity generated by matrix models[3], which provided some exactly soluble toy string models has slowed during this year, even though important issues remain to be understood. The increased understanding of non-critical string theory has motivated a reexamination of some old ideas for applying string theory. These include the three dimensional Ising model[4], whose two-dimensional phase boundaries may have the dynamics of some string theory as well as QCD. These are examples of *applied string theory*, a worthy area of research especially in the absence of direct experimental clues for fundamental string theory or theoretical breakthroughs. Another fascinating offshoot of string theory is Polyakov's suggestion that two-dimensional turbulence related to a conformal field theory, which if true should allow for the calculation of scaling exponents of vorticity correlation functions[5].

3. Black Holes

One of the most active areas of abstract research this year was in the field of black holes. The ultimate fate of black holes is a subject of great conceptual interest. The discovery by Hawking, in 1975, that black holes emit radiation that has all the appearances of being thermal led him to conjecture that gravitational effects might force us to modify quantum mechanics. As matter falls into the black hole, featureless thermal radiation is emitted. The black hole shrinks and eventually disappears. Information, quantum coherence and baryon number have been lost down the hole. A initial pure state evolves into a mixed state with increase of entropy. The usual rules of quantum mechanics are replaced by something else, in which pure states can evolve into mixed states.

Is Hawking's conjecture this true? If information is lost then what replaces the unitary time evolution of quantum mechanics? Can such information non-preserving processes occur without having black holes? Can they be initiated by *virtual* black holes?

The possibility of having to modify quantum mechanics with an even less deterministic set of laws is distasteful to many (including me), and there have been many speculations that this is not what happens. Perhaps a *remnant* of the black hole is left behind, that embodies all the information of the state of matter that formed the black hole. This might not violate quantum mechanics but it would certainly entail some new physics, for such a remnant (=particle?) would have to be very strange. Since there are an infinite number of ways to form a black hole there would have to be an infinite density of remnant states. If so why are they not produced with infinite probability? If the black hole does disappear without leaving a remnant is it possible for all the information too emerge during the final stages of collapse? Again, this seems very difficult without major modifications of general relativity at larger than Planckian scales.

The problem of black hole evolution could very well represent the kind of paradox whose resolution leads to great advances in our understanding and to new physics. It has attracted the attention recently of many string theorists. Low energy string theory contains ordinary general relativity, but also always involves other fields, among the rest the dilaton and axion field. This has lead to a study of dilaton gravity, which turns out to have a very interesting spectrum of black hole solutions. Also perturbative string theory itself is governed by two-dimensional dilaton gravity–an interesting toy model of four dimensional general relativity (or dimensionally reduced four dimensional dilaton gravity).

The seminal paper in this field was that of Callan, Giddings, Harvey and Strominger[6], who considered such a two dimensional toy model, described by the Lagrangian,

$$S = \int d^2x \sqrt{g} \left[e^{-2\phi} \left(R + 4(\nabla\phi)^2 + \Lambda \right) + \sum_{i=1}^{N} (\nabla f_i)^2 \right], \tag{1}$$

where ϕ is the dilaton field, R the two dimensional intrinsic curvature, and f_i are N scalar fields.

This model has classical black hole solutions, whose quantum corrections, as the above authors noted, might be reliably calculated for large N. They studied the evolution of the black holes in this way, finding some signs of ordinary quantum mechanical time development. However, it turns out that the large N expansion breaks down in the presence of a black hole, and it breaks down before the singularity is reached. To understand the model it is therefore necessary to solve the theory exactly or by means of a more controllable approximation. This might be possible using conformal field theory[7].

Another possibility is to study the evolution of black holes within string theory itself, which also has classical solutions with black holes. Most interesting is the fact that there a two-dimensional models with black holes[8], which are closely related to the $c = 1$ two-dimensional models that can be solved with matrix model techniques[9]. If this correspondence can be firmly established one might find exactly soluble quantum mechanical black holes and discover whether unitary time evolution is possible.

4. Stringy QCD

It is an old idea that QCD might be represented as a string theory. This notion dates back even before the development of QCD. Indeed, string theory itself was stumbled on in an attempt to guess simple mathematical representations of strong interaction scattering amplitudes which embodied some of the features gleamed from the experiments of the 1960. Many of the properties of hadrons are understandable if we picture the hadrons as string-like flux tubes. This picture is consistent with linear confinement, with the remarkably linear Regge trajectories and with the approximate duality of hadronic scattering amplitudes.

Within QCD itself there is internal support for this idea. First, the $\frac{1}{N}$ expansion of weak coupling perturbation theory can be interpreted as corresponding to an expansion of an equivalent string theory in which the string coupling is given by $\frac{1}{N}$. This is the famous result of 't-Hooft's analysis of the $\frac{1}{N}$ expansion of perturbative QCD[10]. The same is true for any *matrix model*—i.e. a model invariant under $SU(N)$ or $U(N)$, in which the basic dynamical variable is a matrix in the adjoint representation of the group. The Feynman graphs in such a theory can be represented as triangulations of a two dimensional surface. 't-Hooft's principal result was that one can use $\frac{1}{N}$ to pick out the topology, *i.e.* the genus=number of handles, of the surface, since a diagram which corresponds to a genus G Riemann surface is weighted by $(\frac{1}{N})^{2G-2}$. The leading order in the expansion of the free energy in powers of $\frac{1}{N}$ is given by the planar graphs and is proportional to N^2.

Another bit of evidence comes from the strong coupling lattice formulation of the theory. The strong coupling expansion of the free energy can indeed be represented as a sum over surfaces [11]. Again there is a natural large N expansion which picks out definite topologies for these surfaces. This result is an existence proof for a string formulation of QCD. However, the weights of the surfaces are extremely complicated and it is not at all clear how to take the continuum limit.

From quite general considerations we expect that the large N limit of QCD is quite smooth, and should exhibit almost all of the qualitative features of theory. Thus an expansion in powers of $\frac{1}{3}$ or $(\frac{1}{3})^2$ might be quite good. The longstanding hope has been to find an equivalent (dual) description of QCD as some kind of string theory, which would be useful in to calculate properties of the theory in the infrared. QCD is a permanent part of the theoretical landscape and eventually we will have to develop analytic tools for dealing with the theory in the infra-red. Lattice techniques are useful but they have not yet lived up to their promise. Even if one manages to derive the hadronic spectrum numerically, to an accuracy of 10% or even 1%, we will not be truly satisfied unless we have some analytic understanding of the results. Also, lattice Monte-Carlo methods can only be used to answer a small set of questions. Many issues of great conceptual and practical interest–in particular the calculation of scattering amplitudes, are thus far beyond lattice control. Any progress in controlling QCD in an explicit analytic fashion would be of great conceptual value. It would also be of great practical aid to experimentalists, who must use rather ad-hoc and primitive models of QCD scattering amplitudes to estimate the backgrounds to interesting new physics.

The problems with this approach are many. First, if QCD is describable as a string theory it is not as simple a theory as that employed for critical strings. It appears to be easier to guess the string theory of everything than to guess the string theory of QCD. Most likely the weights of the surfaces that one would have to sum over will depend on the *extrinsic geometry* of the surface and not only its intrinsic geometry. We know very little about such string theories. Also there are reasons to believe that a string formulation would require many (perhaps an infinite) new degrees of freedom in addition to the coordinates of the string[*]. Finally, there is the important conceptual problem–how do strings manage to look like particles at short distances. The one thing we know for sure about QCD is that at large momentum transfer hadronic scattering amplitudes have canonical powerlike behavior in the momenta, up to calculable logarithmic corrections. String scattering, on the other hand, is remarkably soft. Critical string scattering amplitudes have, for large momentum transfer, Gaussian fall-off[12]. How do QCD strings avoid this? Recently there have been some interesting speculations regarding this problem[13], however it remains open.

Recently I have been studying two dimensional QCD as the perfect testing ground for the idea that a confining gauge theories might be equivalent to a string theory. Many features of QCD_2 are stringier in two than in four dimensions. For example, linear confinement is a perturbative feature which is exact at all distances. Most important is that the theory is exactly solvable. This is essentially because in two dimensions gluons have no physical, propagating degrees of freedom, there being no transverse dimensions. In fact QCD_2 is the next best thing to a topological field theory. The partition functions in this theory depends only on the *topology* of the manifold on which formulate the theory and on its total *area*. For this reason it is possible to solve the theory very easily and explicitly and to test the hypothesis that it is equivalent to a theory of maps of a two dimensional surface onto a two dimensional surface.

The partition function of QCD_2 on an arbitrary Euclidean manifold of genus G, $\mathcal{M}_G$, was calculated long ago[14]. It is given by,

$$Z_{\mathcal{M}_G} = \sum_R d_R^{2-2G} e^{-\frac{\lambda A}{N} C_2(R)}, \qquad (2)$$

where $\lambda = g^2 N$ is the appropriately normalized gauge coupling, A the area of the manifold and the sum runs over all representations of $SU(N)$, d_R ($C_2(R)$) is the dimension (quadratic Casimir) of the representation R. My conjecture is that the the free energy, $\mathcal{F} = \ln Z$, is equivalent to a closed string theory partition function with target space $\mathcal{M}_G$ where the string coupling is given by $\frac{1}{N}$ and the string tension by λ. Although I do not know how to formulate the precise string theory that reproduces Eq.(2), I do have much evidence that the conjecture is correct, based on properties of maps of two dimensional surfaces onto two dimensional surfaces[15].

To compare this result with a string theory we should expand Eq.(2) in powers of $\frac{1}{N}$ and try to identify the term $(\frac{1}{N})^{2g-2}$ with maps of a surface of genus g, $\mathcal{M}_g$, onto $\mathcal{M}_G$. Now all such maps can be *topologically* classified by the winding number n, which counts how many times the internal space wraps around $\mathcal{M}_G$. We can identify the winding number in Eq.(2) by looking for terms that behave as $e^{-n\lambda A}$ for large area. Now it is the case that given a target space manifold of genus G and a winding number n there is a minimum value that the genus of the internal space can take for smooth maps. Thus, we cannot smoothly map a sphere onto a torus, nor a genus two surface onto a genus two surface with winding number greater than one. In fact the following inequality must be satisfied,

$$2(g-1) \geq 2n(G-1) \qquad (3)$$

I have carried out the large N expansion of Eq.(2) and verified that this inequality is indeed satisfied to all orders[15]. This is a non-trivial test of the conjecture, it is hard to see how it would be true otherwise.

Even more suggestive is the fact that many of the terms in the $\frac{1}{N}$ expansion of Eq.(2) can be interpreted as counting the number of maps of $\mathcal{M}_g$ onto $\mathcal{M}_G$. Thus, the terms that saturate the inequality Eq.(3), covering maps, have weight (for $G > 1$),

$$Z_G \to \sum_{n=0}^{\infty} (\frac{1}{N})^{2n(G-1)} e^{-n\lambda A} \sum_{r=\text{rep of } S_n} [\frac{n!}{f_r}]^{2(G-1)}, \qquad (4)$$

where the second sum is over representations, r, of the symmetric group S_n, of dimension f_r. It can be shown that the coefficient of $(\frac{1}{N})^{2n(G-1)}e^{-n\lambda A}$ is precisely the number of topologically distinct (disconnected, since we have not taken the logarithm of $\mathcal{Z}_G$) covering maps of $\mathcal{M}_G$ by $\mathcal{M}_g$ [16].

What remains to be understood are the all the rational numbers that appear as coefficients of the powers of $e^{-\lambda A}$ and of $\frac{1}{N}$ in terms of the counting of maps of $\mathcal{M}_g$ onto $\mathcal{M}_G$. Some of these are understood[16], but not all. Once we can reconstruct the QCD partition function as a sum of maps it remains to construct a string action that reproduces these counting rules. Then we would like to extend the program to include Wilson loops and quarks into the theory. Finally we would like to generalize the string representation to four dimensions. Clearly, much remains to be done.

5. Induced QCD

QCD is hard to solve since it is a theory with no free, adjustable or small parameters. In pure QCD (no quarks) the only parameter we can adjust is the number of colors, N. Luckily, in the large N limit QCD simplifies enormously, and this limit remains the best hope to yield an exact or controllable treatment of the theory. We know that as $N = \infty$ only planar graphs survive. More generally we know that in terms of the appropriate variables the large N limit of gauge invariant observables is given, for $N = \infty$ by the *master field*, namely a solution of an appropriate classical equation of motion[17]. The large N limit is in the nature of a semi-classical expansion, with $\frac{1}{N}$ playing the role of Planck's constant. However all attempts, and there have been very many over the years, to find an appropriate equation for the master field have failed.

Recently Kazakov and Migdal proposed a soluble model, which although at first sight quite different than QCD might be equivalent to it. Their original model was simply the same as lattice QCD with adjoint scalar matter, but with no kinetic term for the gauge field. This is *induced QCD*[18], defined by

$$\mathcal{Z}_{KM} = \int \prod_{L,i} \mathcal{D}U_L \mathcal{D}\phi_i e^{-N\sum_i \text{Tr} U(\phi_i) + N \sum_{i,\mu=1...D} \text{Tr}(\phi_i U_\mu \phi_{i+\mu} U_\mu^\dagger)} \tag{5}$$

This theory is invariant under standard gauge transformations, $\phi_i \to V_i \phi_i V_i^\dagger, U_{i;\mu}^U \to V_i U_\mu V_{i+\mu}^\dagger$, which allow us to diagonalize the ϕ's. Becasue of the absence of the Wilson action induced QCD has the great advantage of being soluble, or at least reducible to a well defined master field equation. This is because the integral over the link matrices can be performed. This is the famous *Itzykson- Zuber* integral [19],

$$I(\phi, \chi) \equiv \int \mathcal{D}U e^{N \text{Tr}[\phi U \chi U^\dagger]} = \frac{\det[e^{N\phi_i \chi_j}]}{\Delta(\phi)\Delta(\chi)}, \tag{6}$$

where $\Delta(\phi) = \prod_{i<j}(\phi_i - \phi_j)$, with ϕ_i (χ_i) being the eigenvalues of the matrix ϕ (χ). This formula is very profound, underlies all the analysis of the $c = 1$ matrix model, and can be derived in many ways. One is the demonstration that the integral is given exactly by the WKB approximation, and the above formula is simply the sum over the $N!$ saddlepoints, at which the U's are permutation matrices.

Although soluble this model appears to be very far from QCD, since asymptotic freedom instructs us to set the lattice coupling to zero, not infinity, in the continuum limit. However, Kazakov and Migdal argued that even though there is no kinetic term for the gauge field, it could be *induced* at large distances[19]. They argued that if one integrates out the scalar mesons (even in the case of noninteracting scalars with $U(\Phi) = \frac{1}{2}m^2\Phi^2$), then at distances large compared to a, one would induce in four dimensions an effective gauge interaction,

$$S_{\text{eff}}(U) \sim \frac{N}{96\pi^2} \ln(\frac{1}{m^2 a^2}) \operatorname{Tr} F_{\mu\nu}^2 + \text{finite as } a \to 0. \tag{7}$$

This is simply the one loop vacuum graph for the scalars in a background gauge field, which is logarithmically divergent in four dimension. Now this looks very much like the ordinary Yang-Mills action, $\frac{1}{g^2(a)} \operatorname{tr} F_{\mu\nu}F^{\mu\nu}$, if we recall that asymptotic freedom tell us that $\frac{1}{g^2(a)} = \frac{11N}{48\pi^2} \ln(\frac{1}{M_g^2 a^2})$, where M_g is a mass scale for QCD, say the glueball mass. We can therefore identify these two (the fact that there are N^2 scalars is crucial, as is the sign of the effective action which is due to the non-asymptotic freedom of the scalars.) If we do so then we find that, $M_g^2 = m^{\frac{22}{11}} a^{\frac{1}{11}}$. Thus in the continuum limit the adjoint scalars become infinitely massive and decouple, but not before they have drive $\frac{1}{g^2}$ up, from zero at distance a to the large QCD value atdistance $\frac{1}{m}$, where $\frac{1}{M_g} >> \frac{1}{m} >> a$. The basic idea is that the infrared slavery of the scalars, at the size of the lattice spacing, produces an effective gauge theory at a larger scale (much larger than the inverse scalar mass), which then produces the usual asymptotically free fixed point theory.

There are many problems with this idea. For one the hard gluons are not absent and their contribution will overwhelm that of the scalars at short distances. Their asymptotic freedom is more powerful than the infrared slavery of scalars. Another issue is that the above theory possesses a much larger symmetry than the $SU(N)$ gauge symmetry of the usual lattice action. It is not difficult to see that, in D dimensions, it is invariant under $(D-1) \times (N-1)$ extra local $U(1)$-gauge symmetries. This is because the transformation $U_\mu(x) \to V_\mu^\dagger(x) U_\mu(x) V_\mu(x + \mu a)$, leaves the action invariant as long as $V_\mu(x)$ is a unitary matrix that commutes with $\Phi(x)$. If $V_\mu(x)$ were independent of μ then this would be the ordinary gauge invariance. Thus we have $D-1$ new gauge symmetries, which are of course isomorphic to the special unitary transformations that commute with Φ [20]. Thus $V_\mu(x) = D_\mu(x)\Omega(x)$, where $\Omega(x)$ is the unitary matrix that diagonalizes Φ and $D_\mu(x)$ is diagonal.

A subset of this symmetry is the, field independent, local Z_N symmetry, $U_\mu(x) \to Z_\mu U_\mu(x) Z_\mu^\dagger$, where Z_μ is an element of the center of the group. This symmetry alone prevents the Wilson loop from acquiring an expectation value. A Wilson loop contains different links, and thus $W(C) = \langle \prod_{L \in C} U_L \rangle \to (\prod_L Z_\mu) W(C) \Rightarrow W(C) = 0$. This symmetry must be broken if we are to recover the QCD fixed point from this formulation [21].

Finally, the simple Gaussian model is soluble and the answer is very simple[20]. How does one solve such a theory? In the large N limit the integral will be dominated by a translationally invariant saddlepoint for the density of eigenvalues of the matrices Φ_i, $\rho(z) \equiv \frac{1}{N}\sum_{a=1}^{N}\delta(z-\phi_a)$. Migdal has derived the master field equation for the saddlepoint, using the Schwinger-Dyson equations that are satisfied by $I(\phi,\chi)$ [22]. These are consequences of the fact that I satisfies $\text{tr}[(\frac{1}{N}\frac{\partial}{\partial\phi})^k]I = \text{tr}(\chi)^k I$. The net result is that one derives an equation for the function $F(z) \equiv \int dz \frac{\rho(\nu)}{z-\nu}$, whose imaginary part is $\text{Im}F(\nu) = -\pi\rho(\nu)$,

$$\text{Re}F(\lambda) = P\int \frac{d\nu}{2\pi i}\ln[\frac{\lambda - \frac{1}{2D}U'(\nu) - \frac{D-1}{D}\text{Re}F(\nu) + i\pi\rho(\nu)}{\lambda - \frac{1}{2D}U'(\nu) - \frac{D-1}{D}\text{Re}F(\nu) - i\pi\rho(\nu)}]. \tag{8}$$

This equation is much more complicated than the usual Riemann-Hilbert problem that one obtains for simple matrix models. It is sufficiently non-linear and complex that one might imagine that it describes QCD.

It turns out that when the potential is Gaussian then the density of eigenvalues is given by a semicircular distribution law[20]. This exact solution does not yield a sensible continuum limit and definitely shows that the model is *not* equivalent to QCD. However, there are interesting attempts to save the model and furthermore even if it does not yield a solution of QCD it might provide some interesting soluble matrix models which could yield new solutions of new string theories. Induced QCD is a matrix model and thus it corresponds to some kind of sum over surfaces. If we look at the Itzykson-Zuber integral we note that it could be expressed as,

$$I(\phi,\chi) = \exp[\frac{1}{2}\text{Tr}\,\phi^2\,\text{Tr}\,\chi^2 + a\,\text{Tr}\,\phi^4\,\text{Tr}\,\chi^4 + \frac{b}{N^2}(\text{Tr}\,\phi^2)^2(\text{Tr}\,\chi^2)^2 + \ldots]. \tag{9}$$

These terms will affect the structure of the large N expansion of the Feynman diagrams, and can be interpreted as yielding extra weights when the two-dimensional surfaces intersect[23]. Thus this model corresponds, perhaps, to some kind of string theory with weights that depend on the extrinsic geometry.

The simplest Gaussian model fails, but all hope is not lost. It is certainly possible to induce QCD if one introduces enough flavors of matter. The problem is that one then loses solubility. It might be that the self interactions of the scalars could be adjusted to drive the theory towards the asymptotically free fixed point. This hope has been pursued with great vigor by Migdal, who has also considered adding fermions, not too many so that the model remains soluble, so as to break the Z_N symmetry[24]. Time will tell whether this will succeed. Even if it does not these model might yield a new class of interesting soluble matrix models which could teach us something about new classes of strings, perhaps strings that depend on extrinsic geometry. For this reason alone it is worth studying these models.

6. Conclusions

Even though the last year has not been an exciting one for abstract theory, or for practical theory, or for experiment, we should not be pessimistic. We can hope for real progress in the near future in our understanding of QCD, black holes and even string theory.

References

1. B. Zweibach, IAS preprint, IASSNS-HEP-92/41 (1992).
2. E. Witten, IAS preprints IASSNS-HEP-92/53 and IASSNS-HEP-92/63.
3. D. Gross and A.Migdal, *Phys. Rev. Lett.* **64** (1990) 717; M. Douglas and S. Shenker, *Nucl. Phys.* **B335** (1990) 635 ; E. Brézin and V. Kazakov, *Phys. Lett.* **236B** (1990) 144.
4. A. Sedrakyan, *Phys. Lett.* **B260** (1991) 45; J. Distler, Princeton preprint, PUPT- (1992).
5. A. Polyakov, Princeton preprint PUPT- (1992).
6. C. Callan, S. Giddings, J. Harvey and A. Strominger, *Phys. Rev.* **D45** (1992) R1005.
7. A. Bilal and C. Callan, Princeton preprint, PUPT-1320 (1992); S. deAlwis, Boulder preprint COLO-HEP-280 and COLO-HEP-284 (1992).
8. E. Witten, *Phys. Rev.* **D44** (1991)314 .
9. S. Das, Tata preprint, TIFR-TH-92/62 (1992); A. Dhar, G. Mandal and S. Wadia, Tata preprint, TIFR-TH-92/63 (1992); J. Russo, Texas preprint, UTTG-27-92 (1992).
10. G. 't Hooft, *Nucl. Phys.* **B72** (1974) 461.
11. D. Weingarten, *Phys. Lett.* **B90** (1980) 285; V. Kazakov and I. Kostov, *Phys. Lett.* **B128** (1983) 316; I. Kostov *Phys. Lett.* **B138** (1984)191 ; *Nucl. Phys.* **B179**(1981) 283 ; K. O'Brien and J. Zuber, *Nucl. Phys.* **B253** (1985) 621.
12. D. Gross and P. Mende, *Physics Letters* **197B** (1987)129 .
13. J. Polchinski, *Phys. Rev. Lett* **68** (1992)1267 ; M. Green, QMW-91-24 (1991).
14. B. Rusakov, *Mod. Phys. Lett.* **A5** (1990)693.
15. D. Gross, Princeton preprint PUPT 1336, December 1992 .
16. D. Gross and W. Taylor, to be published.
17. L. Yaffe, *Rev. Mod. Phys.* **54** (1982) 407.
18. V. Kazakov, and A. Migdal, PUPT-1322, May 1992.
19. Harish-Chandra, *Amer. Jour. Math.* **79** (1957) 87; C. Itzykson and J. Zuber, *Jour. Math. Phys.* **21** (1980) 411; J. Duistermaat and G. Heckman, *Invent. Math.* **69** (1982)259.
20. D. Gross, *Phys. Lett.* **B293** (1992) 181.
21. I. Kogan, G. Semenoff and N. Weiss, UBCTP 92-022, June 1992.
22. A. Migdal, Princeton preprint PUPT-1323, June 1992.
23. S. Das, A. Dhar, A. Sengupta and S. Wadia, *Mod. Phys. Lett.* **A5** (1990) 1041; G. Korchemsky, UPRF-92-334 .
24. A. Migdal, PUPT-1332, LPTENS-92/23 , PUPT-1343 ; S. Khoklachev and Yu. Makeenko, ITEP-YM-7-92 (August 1992).

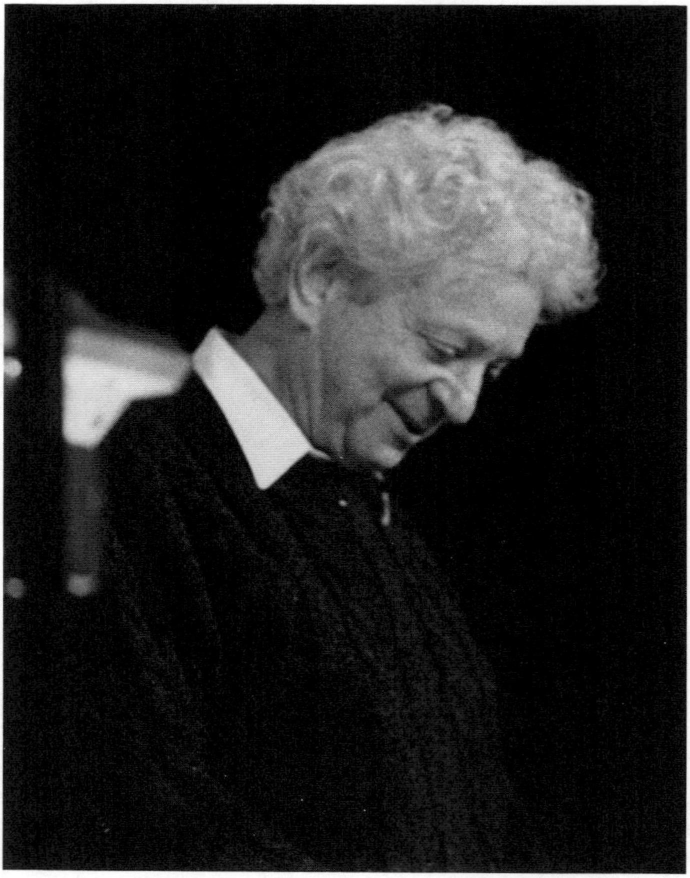

THE CONVENTIONAL VISIONARY TALK

LEON M. LEDERMAN
Department of Physics, Illinois Institute of Technology
Chicago, Illinois 60616

As you gather from the previous comments, the meeting is over. This talk is to speed you on your way to O'Hare or wherever you go. I was told to give a talk on vision. And as you all know, I always do what I am told. And, in fact, it so concerned me that I must give a talk on vision that I took my favorite source of all vision and stared at it for the last five days, missing all the meetings and all the good stuff. I couldn't bring it to a meeting because as everyone knows, visions are very bashful and wouldn't come to a meeting with lots of people. So I don't really know what happened at the meeting, but if the last talk was typical, well ...

Looking at the contents and getting a general idea by talking to people and stepping back a little bit to glimpse an overview of the meeting, one gets a feeling, perhaps naive, of amazement at the achievements of the field of particle physics over the past few years going back as far as you like. Of course, I'm speaking about the experimentalists and accelerator physicists. I suppose I have to acknowledge the help we do get from our able assistants, the theorists, who organize things, put things in bins vertically and horizontally. They really make it very easy to visualize and correlate the data.

Now, in particular, the thing that impressed me was the report we got about the CERN LEP experiments. Okay, there were four detectors and probably there's overkill. But still, 4 million Z^0's! That's pretty incredible, and so is the data. All these detectors seem to work. They are all extremely complex, state of the art for their time. The data is obviously incisive and constitutes a tremendous set of constraints on how we proceed beyond the standard model.

Incidentally, I have to have an obligatory standard model slide, cf. Table 1. I got this one from one of the summer students last year. They called it the substandard model. I think this was one of Drasko's senior high school students, so this gives you another point of view of the subject. In addition, of course, to the seminal work on the mass and the width of the Z^0, the constraints on other possibilities is impressive. I was, of course, amused by the glee with which CERN moved to preempt the discovery of the top by writing down the parameters of the top as obtained from top contributions to radiative corrections. In this way they have established the mass, and they leave it to the Tevatron to merely provide confirmation. That's fair enough. Also, they're beginning to make a serious impact on b physics.

Table 1. The Sub-Standard Model

QUARKS:

There are, as usual, six flavors of quarks. They are as follows:

Up		Vanilla
Down		Chocolate
Charm	*or, Alternately*	Strawberry
Strange		Spumoni
Top		Mint Chocolate-Chip
Bottom		Neapolitan

Because quarks interact with "color" forces, they can be said to have "color" properties. The six colors of quarks are fuschia, anti-fuschia, mauve, anti-mauve, puce, and anti-puce. Color neutrality is said to be "beige", since beige is possibly the most neutral and noncommittal color in existence. This can be easily seen in nature by the large number of bathrooms in the world that have been painted beige.

When you list the success, you have to give credit to the Directors. Directors rarely get enough credit. I've heard that Carlo Rubbia has taken recently to pacing the corridors of CERN with a large walking stick, a very thick one. And every once in awhile, when he sees someone he doesn't like, the story goes that he would beat them over the shoulders. This created a great deal of fear and one day, this is on good authority, he saw one of these graduate students rushing into an office. He said,

"Hey you, where are you going?"
"Is that your office?"
"No sir."
"Is that your friend's office?"
"No sir."
"Then why are you rushing into it?"

And the student decided to tell the truth and said, "I'm afraid of you." So Carlo said, "You're afraid of me?" and he started beating him, shouting, "You're supposed to love me. You're supposed to love me. You're not supposed to be afraid of me." Of course I don't believe one word of it. But seriously, Carlo and CERN deserve all the praise they are getting for the spectacular success of the LEP program.

Now the other thing that was notable was the Tevatron, another major player with its two detectors, D0 and CDF. The thing that's very impressive about the Tevatron is that it works. I think back on the years we were building the first superconducting thing with 1200 devices and gadgets of various kinds, dipoles, quadrupoles, all kinds of other coils and various kinds of boxes. If you live through the agonies of that kind of construction it is sort of amazing that here it is, 10 years later, and it is still working. Of course, when the DOE came to us in 1982 and asked us how long are these magnets going to last, we said about 10 years. So, I don't know, we may hear a crashing explosion any minute. But still, it's quite an achievement and in addition, the antiproton source is probably the most complicated assembly of accelerator gadgets ever to work. And it's clear that with the improvements that are under design, the antiproton source will give us a collider with more than 10^{31} luminosity over the next year. I think that's a good thing to look forward to.

The detectors are other things which had all these design, production and growing pains. One of the things that's interesting is that in the hadron business, as you get experience, you always want to change the detector. Take a detector like CDF, which in its original design spared very little expense in order to give it the best possible clout; nevertheless, you can upgrade it and make it still more powerful – and that's what's happening – as you can already see with the early data they're getting.

The D0 detector, as a turn on, has been enormously gratifying. In a short time and probably because of the competitive pressure, D0 is seeing data-taking at a very, very early stage in its experience. So from the point of view of keeping the U.S. somewhere near the lead in high-energy physics, the progress in these two detectors and in the machine have to be kept up to where they should be.

I haven't said anything about theoretical physics yet and I should really say something, especially after this very clear talk by Dave Gross. To put theory in its proper context, consider the standard thing which particle physics does. It builds a machine, it creates a beam of particles which hits a target, and it builds a particle detector. That's accelerator physics. And then we have non-accelerator physics where you don't need a beam. You do have a target and you look at that with a detector usually deep underground. There is another way to do it. You have a beam, cosmic rays and you don't need a target, but you have a detector. Or you do away with beam, target and detector. Then you are a theorist.

Well, what's been happening in our field? No one has found the free quark. Of course, people have stopped looking. No magnetic monopoles have shown up, although both quarks and monopoles were recorded at one time or another. No one has found a SUSY particle yet. The proton still hasn't decayed. To my knowledge, no one has claimed wimps or tachyons or cosmions or lepto-quarks or other wonders with similar euphonious names. The top quark hasn't been found yet. No one has claimed a second W or Z. Neutrinos can still have zero mass. No oscillations have been observed and for that matter, no double beta decay. No one has yet claimed the Higgs particle or the existence of the Higgs except Mrs. Higgs. No one has seen CP violation in B decay, although in the last fixed-target run, 137 billion $B^o \bar{B}^o$ pairs were made. Still we have no CP violation. No one has found structure inside the electron or the quark. For all we know, there may be ancient civilizations buried in there. The fifth force seems to have gone away. Cold fusion has emigrated to Japan. The 17 kilovolt neutrino is resting in peace. Cosmic-ray anomalies such as

Centauro and Cygnus anomalies have largely gone away, as far as I know.

At this meeting we had a report of something at 60 GeV from L3 which decays into 2 gammas. This may be related to the 17 kilovolt neutrino. It may be something you might call an "oops-Ting." It may be a very rational attempt to get the budget up at budget time. It may be a QED fluctuation or, it may be a real discovery. But it's interesting anyway to look at some of these other things. For example, if we look at the 17 kilovolt neutrino, there was a listing last year showing the different experiments with a remarkable accumulation of events at 17 kilovolts. In cold fusion we all remember the enormous number of confirming experiments that appeared shortly after cold fusion. The same thing happened with the 5th force. All kinds of people confirmed it, sometimes with a right sign, sometimes with a wrong sign.

There is an interesting sociology. Why is it that when you find something that turns out later not to have been there, it so often finds confirmation in the beginning? That's a Ph.D topic, but not in our field, I hope. Actually the 60 GeV effect was not claimed to be a discovery, and the report was given very responsibly. It said we need more data. And that's certainly true. It may be that there's something new there. It is useful for us to shake up our own view, both theoretical, but also experimental. Experimentalists must be reminded to look very hard at their data for new objects.

Looking at the vision ball very carefully, we take stock of what's going on in the accelerator business and its prospects. We see that the Cornell luminosity upgrade is going well, and they're on the road to what might be b factory, an asymmetric b factory. The SSC seems to be proceeding well. It had the political Perils of Pauline, of course, last year with Congress. And it probably will have more of these for the next year or so. If it survives another year it will probably be left alone, although you're never sure.

There's a very enthusiastic group of young people down there doing the designing. Of course, there are lots of worries in the design, technical worries, but that's to be expected. Detectors will be a problem because there's not enough money. How we are going to fund these 2 large detectors is a problem, and we must leave some money for new, innovative ideas. Here I make special note of Bj's imaginative proposal and advertise for collaborators. But we're pretty optimistic in the year, say 2003, plus or minus 2, this thing will begin to work. As we said, we expect that LEP will probably get us 10^7 Z^0's and then go on to look for W pair production, and then some of these other factories that Bj calls the "industrialization of physics" such as tau factories, charm factories, and phi factories may even get built.

As far as looking further ahead, the linear colliders seem to have a vigorous R&D program going on, rather worldwide. Are there any far out ideas in accelerator physics? None that have risen to call attention to themselves. In instrumentation there's a lot of progress, I think, an enormous number of ideas that have been materializing. It is appropriate for us to rejoice that George Charpak was awarded

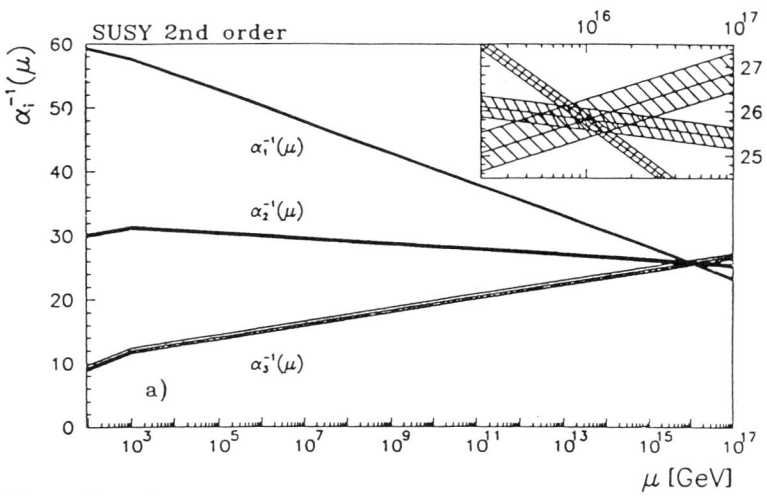

Fig. 1. Running coupling constants in the minimal SUSY model to 2nd order.

the Nobel Prize.

Now, let me say something about how things may play out in the far future. The vision ball says that particle physics will not solve all of its problems with the SSC. Very, very likely some of our problems must persist. This is the big virtue of having joined with the astronomers, since they help us see problems that are not going to be solved at the SSC. Then the question is, what is the next machine? Clearly there are just two candidates. That the SSC is the right machine, I think everything we've learned confirms that very nicely. We know we have to look at the 1 TeV mass scale.

Now let's look at the extrapolation of coupling constants. I don't know how universally accepted the graph of Ugo Amaldi in Fig. 1 is, which shows the need for something to appear somewhere to make grand unification a fact. It's a very elegant kind of a curve. It may not have anything to do with reality, but it's at least an indication that the 1 TeV mass scale is a crucial mass scale. If we were looking at the SSC parameters anew with all of the realism of having to design detectors, my guess is we might have redesigned it to make the energy 30 TeV instead of 20 TeV in order not to put such a burden on high luminosity which is very difficult. But that's a minor detail.

To go to the next machine, there are two candidates, the e^+e^- linear collider and the other candidate would be some sort of an extended circular SSC type machine, for example, the Eloisatron pushed by Nino Zichichi that just fits clearly with some comfort in Sicily. It is 200 TeV in the CM. Another machine was designed by a famous accelerator scientist, Bjorken, which was a 500 TeV on 500 TeV machine. The linear colliders have enormous technical problems, especially if you're trying to produce a machine of energy significantly higher in the CM than the SSC. The circular machines have a problem in that they're very costly, just scaling up the SSC.

Allowing for quantity discount, these circular machines are humongously expensive.

It seems to me that the way the thing might play out is sort of as follows: If I have it right, the linear collider mavens say that they can't really go to a machine which advances the energy say to 5 TeV on 5 TeV electrons. They have to start with something smaller, like a 200 GeV on 200 GeV.

These things are going to be pretty expensive and they're going to take some time. So a lot of it depends on estimating the future. For example, if money becomes more readily available then we can afford to try to build a linear collider demonstration model and start that up and begin to learn how that stuff works, beginning when SSC funding starts tapering off, maybe 1999 or the year 2000 or something like that. But if the SSC is hanging on by its fingernails financially, then clearly, if there's going to be another machine, aside from keeping up R&D, we have to decide what are the physics questions. Again, there are possibilities. By the year 2005 or 2007, somewhere around there with fair uncertainties, the SSC will have given us some results and again, there will be two possibilities. Either they'll see a mess but with suggested richness, in which case you want to clarify the data because the data's made with garbage cans hitting each other and then it would be profitable to get a modest energy linear collider that would have the virtue of point targets and that might well be in the 500 on 500 GeV range.

Or, on the other hand, the SSC might see clear signals e.g., there might be the first in a series of Higgs, or the clear beginnings of supersymmetric particles. Then you know we must go on and then you want to build a higher energy machine and sufficiently luminous machine.

Other issues may point to energy: What is the connection between quarks and leptons or what's the origin of mass spectrum of quarks or leptons or true origin of CP violation? Composite lists. We've seen little people inside the quark but we really don't know what their names are and so on. All kinds of things that might require this step to higher energy. We know how to go to higher energy, say 10 TeV on the constituent level. This is the circular route but it does require R&D, perhaps the high temperature superconductors will eventually support real magnets and so on. Maybe the two things will play out in a way that we don't really anticipate.

When I really look at that cloudy vision ball I want to talk for the last few minutes about a dark cloud that obscures the vision, and I want to share that dark cloud with you. You probably know about it. This is a cloud that not only affects particle physics but even some of these less deserving fields of science like solid state physics, chemistry, biology, all the sciences. Let me talk a little bit about that. We know that funding for science across the board has been pretty tight. We're competing against many claims on a budget that is in deficit.

The desire to "cut government spending" is strident. So that we've known about. We've known things are tight. It's very hard to do the kinds of things we would like to do in the style we would like to do them. More recently, there's been a squeezing down of opportunities. There's a job crisis which stems from different sources. Industry is getting out of science as far as I can tell, abandoning research. Defense cuts have also reduced the need for scientists there. The major research universities are all retrenching with hiring freezes and getting rid of departments, so that universities do not look like the rosy places they used to be. The state universities are so badly off that some of our colleagues who work there have developed so poor a credit rating that even their cash isn't accepted. Things aren't cheerful on that line.

There is a wave of anti-science that arises from time to time. It's ultimate source is fundamentalism of various kinds, but it also now has spread out so that you find people who normally should be responsible and intelligent are echoing some of the arguments about science. The general public never really understands science as we all know, but they used to trust science and trust universities, and that trust has been weakened by events that we all know about. We've been bothered in particle physics by excessive safety requirements, but all across the science front by excess regulation, by animal rights extremists, a general set of circumstances which makes life in science more complicated. And now, the most recent trend, is that we not only have all of these things to worry about, but we have to worry about our friends. Just in recent times we know that the National Science Foundation has impaneled a commission to look at the future of the NSF, and the instructions from the director look ominous. As far as I can see, it looks as if there's this wave of feeling that might be coming from the Congress (and I don't know where else) which says that science has to be useful. It has to be addressed to goals and George Brown, the most pro science congressman we've had for a long time who knows something about science, has written a committee's report and Op-Ed articles arguing the fact that we have to renegotiate the contract between science and government and that science must be directed toward "national goals." Funny, that is exactly where it is aimed, I thought!

If I want to caricature some of these statements it's that since 1946, we've given you guys hundreds and hundreds and billions and billions of dollars and what have we got from it? Our cities are in disarray, our economy is going down the drain, our environment is in bad shape. What have you done with all this money we've given you? But the mood, irrational as it may seem, is serious and echoed everywhere; e.g., the Office of Technology Assessment Report, and NIH is going in the same direction. There is, without any mistake, a real problem coming up as to how science will be changed, especially basic research, abstract research, useless research or some of this nice-words-research that we all think is important. It's amazing that some of these arguments are in fact echoed by people who should know better in the scientific community. This notion that we have to address specific goals has been around. It's not that any of us shouldn't do more in the way of applications, in the way of technology transfer. In fact, I think our record in that has been very good. But we're afraid that this trend will, in fact, eat into basic research in a very negative way. Because if you step back, this country spends 70 billion dollars on R&D, and the NSF is the one place in addition to a piece of the DOE where basic research is carried out, and that whole caboodle is a very small fraction of $70 billion. Pessimism is rampant among people in Washington who are wise and seem to know the score, so the question is what will we do about it? We can roll over, we can watch it, or we can be activists and see if we can do something about it.

Let me just wind up by telling you what a possible plan might be to address this issue. This comes from my stint as a president and chairman of the AAAS. It's a three year term, but in that term I got to understand some of these problems. What do we do? Well, it seems to me there are a lot of things you can do. You have to continue to educate Congressmen about the payoff of basic research, the role of research, the way research interacts between basic and applied. But it seems to me that something else has to be done more dramatic than that, and that is we have to go to the people who elect the Congressmen, namely the general public.

The gist of the plan will come to you because it will cost you. This was hammered out at a retreat that the AAAS sponsored outside of Washington last June to which we invited the Presidents, President-elects and the executive secretaries who are the corporate memory for the APS, the Chemical Society, the American Association Engineering Societies, Geophysical Union, etc. etc. We invited essentially the science and engineering societies that have as its total membership in science and engineering some 3 million members. We had about a 60% attendance and at this meeting we brought together experts in communication fields, media experts, the editor of Discover magazine, newspaper writers, television people in production and on-camera experts. We had two executives of large advertising firms and one guy who runs the largest public relations firm in the world. All involved in influencing peoples minds, if you like, which I think is what we have to do. What seems to be emerging from this, though it's by no means yet an official program, is a massive sustained program of trying to educate the general public on science.

The virtues of science, the limitations of science, the problems of science, the contributions of science to society conveyed in a sustained program which would involve all the means of communication you could find – mainly, of course, television – were discussed. There's a lot of science on television, but there's no science on network television, essentially zero. And that's where all the billions and billions of people are. It takes enormous effort to turn the dial all the way to public television and the wrists of people are not strong enough.

Anyway, that's the notion. Try to get on prime time television. That's a big effort. But it pays off. But don't leave anything out: magazines, Sunday supplements, Op-Ed articles, paid and unpaid, however you can do it, radio, whatever you can do in radio. Any other medium of communications.

We have an appointment with Kellogg's to get on cereal boxes, tell science stories on cereal boxes and shopping bags and McDonald place mats and so on. Leave no stone unturned. Skywriting, if any of you have an airplane, we'll try to use that. Anyway, that's the plan and it can backfire. I remember the story of Mr. Shapiro who was a self-made man. He was poor, but he built over his lifetime a very successful hardware store and then a series of stores and so on and started to manufacture things to put in the stores. He became very wealthy. He sent his son to Harvard to get an MBA. And at some point he told his son, this business is yours. It's thriving, it's successful, don't screw it up. I'm going on vacation. Six months later when the old man landed at the airport and drove into town, he saw a big billboard. And on this big billboard there was a big painting of Jesus on the cross and it said, "Shapiro's nails." This is to explain that you can go wrong. Not all public relations or public information can succeed. The idea of course is not to make mistakes, but to do it right.

The next step in this program is to meet again with the societies because this has to be done through the societies. The idea is that every society, already does some public relations: APS is doing this, the ACS does it a lot because chemical is a bad word, and they spend a substantial sum of money trying to make their case. The biomedical community has set up a not-for-profit corporation which is showing short videos and so on. But probably most of you in this room never saw any of these things, not the APS stuff, not the ACS stuff because it's all too small. If you add it all up, my guess is you need something like an order of magnitude more than that. The idea is not to sell the chemists, not to sell the physicists, but to bring them all together and sell science and its associated technology across the board.

Be prepared to do this for five years. And you'll begin to get effects earlier than that because you know if you go to a Congressman and make a case about something, he thanks you and his assistant takes notes and he says, we'll see what we can do. However, if he reads the same case in the Washington Post, that has a thousand times the clout. He knows that lots and lots of people are reading this and that's the way we might begin to have impact very quickly. So the next step is a meeting of a committee of the various societies that would then map out a specific plan with spending, with where to get the money, and then getting that back to the various societies and have their councils look at it and then we'll begin to see whether the word scientific community is an oxymoron or not or whether in the stress of these oncoming shadows, which I think are going to interfere with American science in a very serious way, whether we can do something about it.

Now, of course, we all put our hopes in the new administration. Incidentally, everything I say has not been checked with Clinton or Gore. Maybe the new administration will make things better, who knows? His philosophy of investment will confront deficit reduction. We can be optimistic about this, but we must do everything we can do in the way of trying to elevate the general public's interest in science. Why not have Science Night Line or LA Science? Did any of you ever see a movie in which the theorist rides off into the sunset with the girl in his saddle, or the girl rides off into the sunset with a theorist in her saddle? Can you name one service plaza named after a physicist? In the thousands and thousands of miles of highways connecting service plazas not one is named after a physicist. So you see we have a lot of things to do about the perception of scientists and science. And probably you'll soon be asked to check off your APS dues and add $10.00 a year but you know two or three of your friends who will be too cheap to give their $10.00; you'll have to give $30.00 to make up for it. I think with a budget like that and with good advice we can begin to do something that we should be doing anyway which is to educate the public about what science is like. Well, with that I think I'll stop. Thank you.

A. Electroweak including τ and W/Z Physics

Conveners: M. H. SHAEVITZ (Columbia U.)
J. L. ROSNER (U. of Chicago)
Liaison: R. RAJA (FNAL)

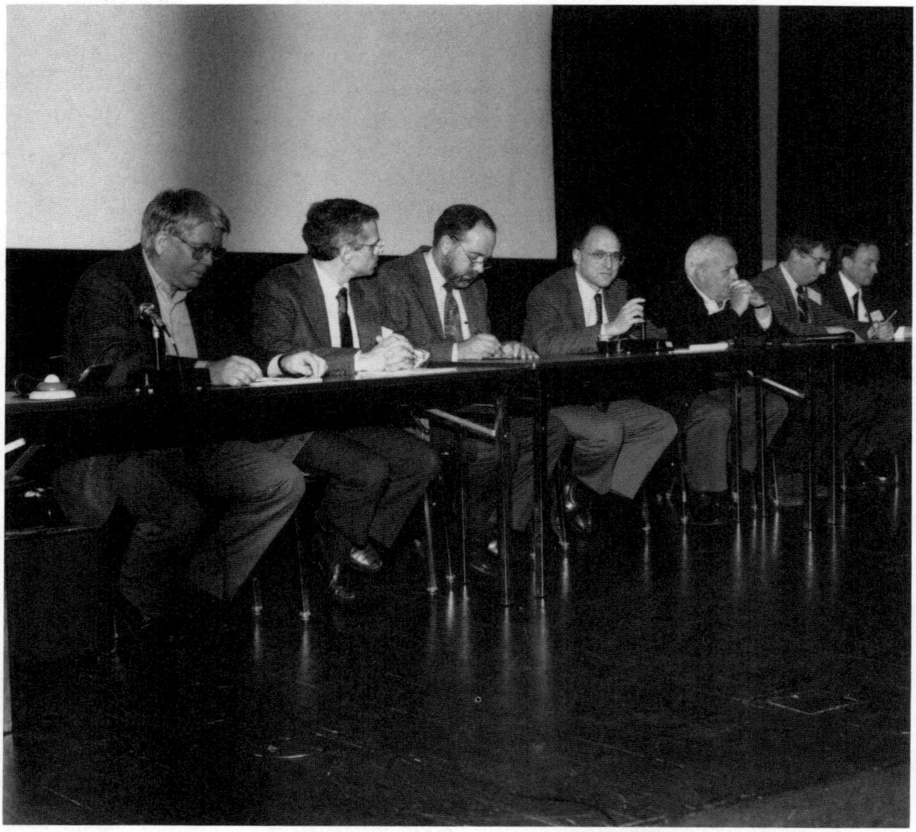

A PRECISE DETERMINATION OF g_τ/g_μ AND A MEASUREMENT OF THE TAU POLARIZATION IN Z^0 DECAYS

ROBERT V. KOWALEWSKI
*Physics Department, Carleton University,
Ottawa, K1S 5B6, Canada*

representing the

OPAL Collaboration

ABSTRACT

A sample of approximately 0.4 million Z^0 decays recorded with the OPAL detector at LEP during 1990 and 1991 has been used to measure the tau lifetime, branching ratios for several decay modes, and the final state polarization of taus produced in Z^0 decay. Combining the measured branching ratios into electrons and muons with the tau lifetime, the ratio of leptonic charged current couplings, g_τ/g_μ, is found to be 0.990 ± 0.013. The average tau polarization, measured in decays to e, μ, π, and ρ is -0.115 ± 0.046, which implies $\sin^2\bar{\theta}_W = 0.2356 \pm 0.0058$.

1. Event Selection

OPAL is a multipurpose, large solid angle, solenoidal detector at LEP, and is well described in Ref. [1]. The salient features are excellent charged particle tracking in the x-y plane (transverse to the beam direction, which defines z), adequate resolution on the track angle θ relative to the z direction, and electromagnetic calorimetry, hadronic calorimetry, and muon detection both in the barrel, outside an aluminum solenoidal coil, and in the endcaps.

The $\tau^+\tau^-$ event selection is based on the charged and neutral multiplicities, the visible energy, and the identification of muon tracks, and is described in detail in Ref. [2]. The number of charged tracks must be less than 8, the combined number of charged tracks and electromagnetic clusters must be less than 17. The visible energy must be above 18%, and the electromagnetic energy must be less than 80%, of the center-of-mass energy. Events identified as $Z^0 \to \mu^+\mu^-$ are rejected.

The thrust axis of the event must satisfy $|\cos\theta| < 0.90$ for the lifetime analysis and $|\cos\theta| < 0.68$ for the polarization and branching fraction analyses. These selection criteria result in a $\tau^+\tau^-$ sample of approximately 17400 events in the region $|\cos\theta| < 0.90$, and approximately 11400 events in the region $|\cos\theta| < 0.68$ in data collected by OPAL during 1990 and 1991. The non-tau backgrounds in the 1-prong and 3-prong samples are in the 1.0-1.5% range.

The Monte Carlo simulation of tau decay used in these analyses is provided by the KORALZ [3] program, and the response of the OPAL detector is simulated in detail with the OPAL implementation of GEANT [4].

2. Lifetime Determination

The lifetime analysis uses the same techniques as Ref. [5]. A brief description of the two techniques used follows.

2.1. Impact Parameter Analysis

The impact parameter is the distance of closest approach in the x-y plane between a charged track and the average intersection point of the LEP beams. This distance is signed using the thrust direction obtained from the charged tracks in the event: the impact parameter is positive if the track trajectory crosses the line passing through the beam spot parallel to the thrust direction downstream of the beam spot, and negative otherwise. This choice of sign produces a distribution whose mean is proportional to the tau lifetime. The mean of the impact parameter distribution is determined by tau decay kinematics and the tau lifetime, but is insensitive to detector resolution, since this merely broadens the distribution. The mean of the distribution is estimated using a trimmed mean [5], in which the highest and lowest 5% of the data are removed before taking the arithemtic mean of the remaining entries. This estimator is robust, and reduces uncertainties due to imperfect modelling of the detector response. A comparison of the mean values obtained from data and Monte Carlo impact parameter distributions is used to obtain the tau lifetime via

$$\tau_\tau = \frac{x_{data}}{x_{MC}} \tau_{MC}, \qquad (1)$$

where τ_{MC} is the generated value for the tau lifetime in the Monte Carlo, which was 303.5 fs in this analysis. Only 1-prong tau decays were used in this analysis to remain independent of the decay length analysis.

2.2. Decay Length Analysis

The classification of tau decays into 3-prongs takes place after the rejection of candidate photon conversions and K_S^0 decays. The 3-prong candidates are subjected to a vertex fit in x-y, and the candidates which survive a 1% cut on the vertex fit probability are input to a decay length fit. This decay length fit determines the best value for the x-y projection of the decay length using the 3-prong position and covariance matrix, the beam spot coordinates and spread, and a directional constraint from the charged track thrust axis. The 2-dimensional decay lengths are divided by $\sin\theta_{thrust}$ to determine the 3-dimensional flight distance. The decay lengths and errors for those candidates surviving a 1% probability cut are passed into a maximum likelihood fit for the average decay length.

2.3. Lifetime Results

The measured tau lifetimes in the 1-prong and 3-prong samples are

$$\tau_1 = 295.5 \pm 6.9 \pm 4.2 \text{ fs}$$
$$\tau_3 = 283.5 \pm 7.4 \pm 4.8 \text{ fs}$$

where the systematic errors are principally due to uncertainties in detector calibration (τ_3) and tau decay simulation (τ_1). Combining these results in quadrature yields a preliminary measurement of

$$\tau_\tau = 290.0 \pm 6.0 \text{ fs}$$

3. Branching Fraction Measurements

The 1-prong sample is searched for decays of the following types[6]: $\tau \to e\bar{\nu}\nu_\tau$, $\tau \to \mu\bar{\nu}\nu_\tau$, $\tau \to \pi(K)\nu_\tau$, and $\tau \to \rho\nu_\tau$. For each channel an efficiency is calculated and a background estimated using Monte Carlo information, cross-checked where possible with data (using, e.g., $Z^0 \to e^+e^-$ and $e^+e^- \to (e)e\gamma$ events for electron efficiency studies). The preliminary results for the branching fractions are

$$B(\tau \to e\bar{\nu}\nu_\tau) = 17.5 \pm 0.3 \pm 0.3\%,$$
$$B(\tau \to \mu\bar{\nu}\nu_\tau) = 16.8 \pm 0.3 \pm 0.3\%,$$
$$B(\tau \to \pi(K)\nu_\tau) = 12.2 \pm 0.3 \pm 0.4\%,$$
$$B(\tau \to \rho\nu_\tau) = 23.8 \pm 0.6 \pm 0.7\%,$$

where the first error is statistical and the second systematic. The systematic errors come principally from uncertainties in the selection efficiencies.

4. Determination of g_τ/g_μ

The ratio of leptonic couplings can be expressed as

$$\left(\frac{g_\tau}{g_\mu}\right)^2 = \frac{B(\tau \to e\bar{\nu}\nu_\tau)}{B(\mu \to e\bar{\nu}\nu_\mu)} \frac{\tau_\mu}{\tau_\tau} \left(\frac{m_\mu}{m_\tau}\right)^5 \quad (2)$$

The tau lifetime measurement and the measurements of $B(\tau \to e\bar{\nu}\nu_\tau)$ and $B(\tau \to \mu\bar{\nu}\nu_\tau)$ are combined[1] with the recently measured tau mass [7] and with the muon mass and lifetime [8] to yield $g_\tau/g_\mu = 0.990 \pm 0.013$

5. Tau Polarization Measurements

At the Z^0 peak, the Standard Model predicts a tau polarization of

$$P_\tau(\cos\theta) \simeq -\left(\lambda_\tau + \frac{2\cos\theta}{1+\cos^2\theta}\lambda_e\right) \quad (3)$$

where

$$\lambda_\ell = \frac{2v_\ell/a_\ell}{1+(v_\ell/a_\ell)^2}$$

with v_ℓ and a_ℓ being the vector and axial vector couplings for electrons or taus. This polarization leads to a distortion of the momentum spectra in $\tau \to e\bar{\nu}\nu_\tau$, $\tau \to \mu\bar{\nu}\nu_\tau$,

---
[1] We assume e-μ universality and divide $\tau \to \mu\bar{\nu}\nu_\tau$ by 0.973 to account for phase space effects before combining with $\tau \to e\bar{\nu}\nu_\tau$.

and $\tau \to \pi(K)\nu_\tau$ decays which is used to measure the polarization. The situation in $\tau \to \rho\nu_\tau$ decays is slightly more complicated, and it's more efficient to consider the decays angles relative to the boost direction of the ρ^- in the τ rest frame and of the π^- in the ρ^- rest frame. The analyses follow closely Ref. [6]. The preliminary results are:

$$\tau \to e\bar{\nu}\nu_\tau \quad : P_\tau = \quad +0.05 \pm 0.07 \pm 0.06\%,$$
$$\tau \to \mu\bar{\nu}\nu_\tau \quad : P_\tau = \quad -0.18 \pm 0.08 \pm 0.06\%,$$
$$\tau \to \pi(K)\nu_\tau \quad : P_\tau = \quad -0.09 \pm 0.06 \pm 0.05\%,$$
$$\tau \to \rho\nu_\tau \quad : P_\tau = \quad -0.18 \pm 0.06 \pm 0.05\%,$$

Combining these measurements yields an average polarization of -0.115 ± 0.046, from which the ratio of vector to axial vector couplings, v_τ/a_τ, is determined to be 0.058 ± 0.023, yielding $\sin^2 \bar{\theta}_W = 0.2356 \pm 0.0058$.

6. References

1. OPAL Collab., K. Ahmet et al., *Nucl. Inst. and Methods* **A305** (1991) 275.
2. OPAL Collab., M. Z. Akrawy et al., *Z. Phys.* **C52** (1991) 175.
3. S. Jadach et al., *Comput. Phys. Comm.* **66** (1991) 276.
4. OPAL Collab., J. Allison et al., *Nucl. Inst. and Methods* **A317** (1992) 47.
5. OPAL Collab., P. D. Acton et al., *Phys. Lett.* **B273** (1991) 355.
6. OPAL Collab., *Phys. Lett.* **B266** (1991) 201.
7. BES Collab., J.Z. Bai et al., *SLAC-PUB-5870 (1992)*, Submitted to Phys. Rev. Lett.
8. Particle Data Group, M. Aguilar-Benitez et al., *Phys. Rev.* **D45** (1992) 1.

TAU POLARIZATION IN ALEPH

MICHAEL SCHMITT [1]
University of Wisconsin
Madison, Wisconsin, 53706, USA

ABSTRACT

Preliminary results on the tau polarization measured by ALEPH using 18.8 pb^{-1} collected in 1990 and 1991 are presented. A new variable ω provides optimal sensitivity in the hadronic decay modes $\tau \to \rho\nu$ and $a_1\nu$. The sensitivity of leptonic decay modes $\tau \to e\nu\bar{\nu}$ and $\mu\nu\bar{\nu}$ is improved in a method based on the event acollinearity. These innovations, together with traditional analyses of the $e\nu\bar{\nu}$, $\mu\nu\bar{\nu}$, and $\pi\nu$ channels, yield a sensitive measurement of the variation of the tau polarization with the polar angle of the Z decay, thereby allowing a measurement of the electron couplings in addition to and independent from the tau couplings to the Z. The values ($\mathcal{A}_e = 0.123 \pm 0.031$ and $\mathcal{A}_\tau = 0.137 \pm 0.026$) support e-$\tau$ universality. The standard model parameter $\sin^2\theta_W^{\text{eff}} = 0.2335 \pm 0.0025$, measured to one percent.

1. Introduction

The Z couples to right- and left-handed fermions with different strengths, resulting in manifest parity violations in the process $e^+e^- \to \tau^+\tau^-$. In particular, the unpolarized beams at LEP produce polarized Z bosons (depending on the electron couplings to the Z: g_V^e and g_A^e), and the taus from the Z decay are polarized (depending on g_V^τ and g_A^τ). Both phenomena, which are independent, can be observed in the variation of the tau polarization with θ, the polar angle of the Z decay [1]:

$$P_\tau(\cos\theta) = -\frac{\mathcal{A}_\tau(1+\cos^2\theta) + \mathcal{A}_e(2\cos\theta)}{(1+\cos^2\theta) + \mathcal{A}_\tau\mathcal{A}_e(2\cos\theta)} \quad (1)$$

where $\mathcal{A}_\tau \equiv 2g_V^\tau g_A^\tau/((g_V^\tau)^2 + (g_A^\tau)^2)$, with a similar expression for $\mathcal{A}_e$. The comparison of $\mathcal{A}_\tau$ and $\mathcal{A}_e$ tests e-τ universality in the neutral weak currrent. In the Standard Model, $\mathcal{A}_\tau = \mathcal{A}_e$. Imposing this constraint leads to an accurate value for the electroweak mixing angle, $\sin^2\theta_W$, to be compared to measurements from the Z lineshape, or neutrino scattering.

2. Method

The kinematic distributions of the tau decay are sensitive to the longitudinal tau polarization. In the case of the decay $\tau \to \pi\nu$, the pion energy relates directly to the tau decay angle, because the pion is a scalar and the final state includes two particles only. [2] This channel is the most sensitive to the tau polarization. The leptonic channels $e\nu\bar{\nu}$ and $\mu\nu\bar{\nu}$ are less sensitive, because the final state consists of three fermions.

---
[1] Supported by the US Department of Energy, contract DE-AC02-76ER00881.
[2] Kaons and pions are not separated in this analysis.

The vector mesons in the channels $\tau \to \rho\nu$ and $a_1\nu$ absorb some of the spin information from the tau [2]. The sensitivity of these channels is regained, however, by considering the full differential decay density, which depends on the dynamics of the decay [3]. If $\vec{x}$ represents a complete set of kinematic quantities for the decay (three for $\rho\nu$, six for $a_1\nu$), then the decay density depends linearly on P_τ:

$$W(\vec{x}, P_\tau) \equiv \frac{1}{\Gamma}\frac{d\Gamma(\vec{x}, P_\tau)}{d\vec{x}} = h_0(\vec{x}) + P_\tau h_1(\vec{x}) \qquad (2)$$

where $h_0(\vec{x})$ and $h_1(\vec{x})$ are calculable kinematic functions which differ for each tau decay channel. It is not necessary to perform a multi-dimensional fit in order to extract P_τ, for optimal sensitivity is gained from the one-dimensional variable

$$\omega \equiv \left(\frac{1}{W}\frac{dW}{dP_\tau}\right)_{P_\tau=0} = \frac{W(\vec{x}, +1) - W(\vec{x}, -1)}{W(\vec{x}, +1) + W(\vec{x}, -1)} = \frac{h_1(\vec{x})}{h_0(\vec{x})}, \qquad (3)$$

which simply measures how much the density at $\vec{x}$ varies with P_τ.

In the cases $\tau \to e\nu\bar{\nu}$ and $\mu\nu\bar{\nu}$, the lepton energy and its angle with the event axis are not redundant since the lepton energy in the tau rest frame is not constant. The distribution of the event acollinearity ϵ provides additional information for measuring P_τ [4].

In the "energy method," a full Monte Carlo simulation is used to derive the expected contribution to the observed energy distribution from right- and left-handed taus, and from backgrounds. The energy variable is $E_{\text{daughter}}/E_{\text{beam}}$ for the $e\nu\bar{\nu}$, $\mu\nu\bar{\nu}$, and $\pi\nu$ channels, and ω for the $\rho\nu$ and $a_1\nu$ channels. The relative contribution from right- and left-handed taus determines the polarization; $P_\tau = (N_R - N_L)/(N_R + N_L)$. A binned maximum-likelihood fit gives N_R and N_L, under the constraint that the total number of expected events equals the number of observed events.

In the "acollinearity method," the observed acollinearity distributions are corrected for acceptance, background, resolution, and radiative effects, using the simulation. The corrected distribution is fit to a theoretical expression to determine P_τ.

3. Analysis Tools

The tau decays must be classified exclusively in order to retain statistical sensitivity and reduce systematic uncertainties. Efficient and exclusive particle identification is essential, and is achieved thanks to the many sources of information in the ALEPH detector [5]. Photon and π^0 reconstruction also is crucial, and is successful due to the fine transverse and longitudinal segmentation of the electromagnetic calorimeter.

4. Selection and Background Rejection

The event is divided into hemispheres based on the thrust axis. Each hemisphere is classified individually.

The decay channels $e\nu\bar{\nu}$ and $\mu\nu\bar{\nu}$ are selected by demanding an identified track accompanied by few photons; in the case of $\pi\nu$, no photons are allowed. Two

	decay channel				
item	$e\nu\bar{\nu}$	$\mu\nu\bar{\nu}$	$\pi\nu$	$\rho\nu$	$a_1\nu$
candidate hemispheres	3780	5492	3438	5232	2153
acceptance (%)	48	70	61	47	53
tau background (%)	1.9	1.3	7.0	6.2	6.2
non-tau background (%)	1.1	1.1	1.5	0.6	0.0

Table 1: Performance of channel classification and background rejection.

single photons consistent with a π^0 decay identify a $\rho\nu$ channel decay, or a single photon with at least 4 GeV with an identified pion track. The $\pi^\pm\pi^0$ invariant mass is restricted ($0.5 < M_{\pi\pi} < 1.2$ GeV) to reduce background and avoid poorly measured decays. Three prongs, none of them an electron, indicate an $a_1\nu$ channel decay, when there are no photons.

Non-tau events are rejected based on the characteristics of the recoil side. For example, contamination from Z→hadrons is reduced by restricting the track multiplicity and invariant mass of all tracks in a hemisphere. Lepton pair events are rejected based on their large visible energy. Two-photon events are rejected due to low visible energies and large acollinearities.

The absolute acceptance and background fractions are listed in table 1. Similar numbers pertain to the acollinearity method. The data logged in 1990 and 1991, corresponding to 18.8 pb^{-1}, contribute to this measurement.

5. Results and Conclusion

The preliminary results[3] are displayed in figure 1, and listed in table 2. Plot a shows the fits to the energy spectra for the lepton and pion channels. The distributions of ω are shown in plot b. Fitted distributions for the acollinearity method are shown in plot c.

Use of the variable ω improves the sensitivity of the $\rho\nu$ channel by approximately 5%, compared to a two-dimensional fit to the tau and rho decay angles. It improves the sensitivity of the $a_1\nu$ channel by a factor of two: the preliminary, projected statistical error for $P_\tau(\tau \to a_1\nu)$ is 0.06, which is better than both of the lepton channels.

Nine values for P_τ are obtained from the energy method fits restricted to nine regions of $\cos\theta$. These values are displayed in plot d. A fit to equation 1 gives $\mathcal{A}_\tau$ and $\mathcal{A}_e$ independently, and is represented by the dashed line. The values are listed in table 3, and support e-τ universality.[4] The value for $\mathcal{A}_{e-\tau}$ is listed, also, and the fit is represented by the solid line.

---

[3] The results presented here are based on the energy method applied to the channels $e\nu\bar{\nu}$, $\mu\nu\bar{\nu}$, $\pi\nu$, and $\rho\nu$.

[4] The values from the fit are corrected for photon exchange, the spread in center-of-mass enegies, and QED radiative effects.

decay channel	result
$e\nu\bar{\nu}$	$-0.161 \pm 0.089 \pm 0.045$
$\mu\nu\bar{\nu}$	$-0.153 \pm 0.068 \pm 0.029$
$\pi\nu$	$-0.149 \pm 0.032 \pm 0.019$
$\rho\nu$	$-0.127 \pm 0.032 \pm 0.030$

Table 2: Preliminary individual channel polarisation results. First error is statistical, second, systematic.

parameter	value
$\mathcal{A}_e$	$0.123 \pm 0.029 \pm 0.010$
$\mathcal{A}_\tau$	$0.137 \pm 0.022 \pm 0.014$
$\mathcal{A}_{e-\tau}$	$0.132 \pm 0.018 \pm 0.009$

Table 3: Polarisation parameters extracted from polar angle dependence. First error is statistical, second, systematic. These values are preliminary.

The universal Z coupling to charged fermions is calculated from $\mathcal{A}_{e-\tau}$, with the result

$$g_V^l/g_A^l = +0.066 \pm 0.010. \tag{4}$$

Using the definition $\sin^2\theta_W^{\text{eff}} = (1 - g_V^l/g_A^l)/4$ we obtain [6]

$$\sin^2\theta_W^{\text{eff}} = 0.2335 \pm 0.0025, \tag{5}$$

which nearly is a 1% measurement. [5]

REFERENCES

1. S. Jadach et al., *Z Physics at LEP I, CERN 89-08*, eds. G. Altarelli, et al., vol. 1, (1989) 235.
2. A. Rougé, *"Tau Decays as Polarization Analyzers,"* Proceedings of the Workshop on Tau Lepton Physics, 24-27 September 1990, eds. M. Davier and B. Jean-Marie, Orsay, France; A. Rougé, *Z. Phys.* **C48**, (1990) 75; K. Hagiwara et al., *Phys. Lett.* **B235**, (1990) 198.
3. A. Rougé et al., submitted to *Phys. Lett.*
4. R. Alemany et al., *Nucl. Phys.* **B379**, 3 (1992).
5. John Conway, presentation to this conference.
6. ALEPH Collaboration, to be published in *Z. Phys. C*.

---

[5] Addition of the $a_1\nu$ and the acollinearity results decrease the error on $\sin^2\theta_W$ by about 10%.

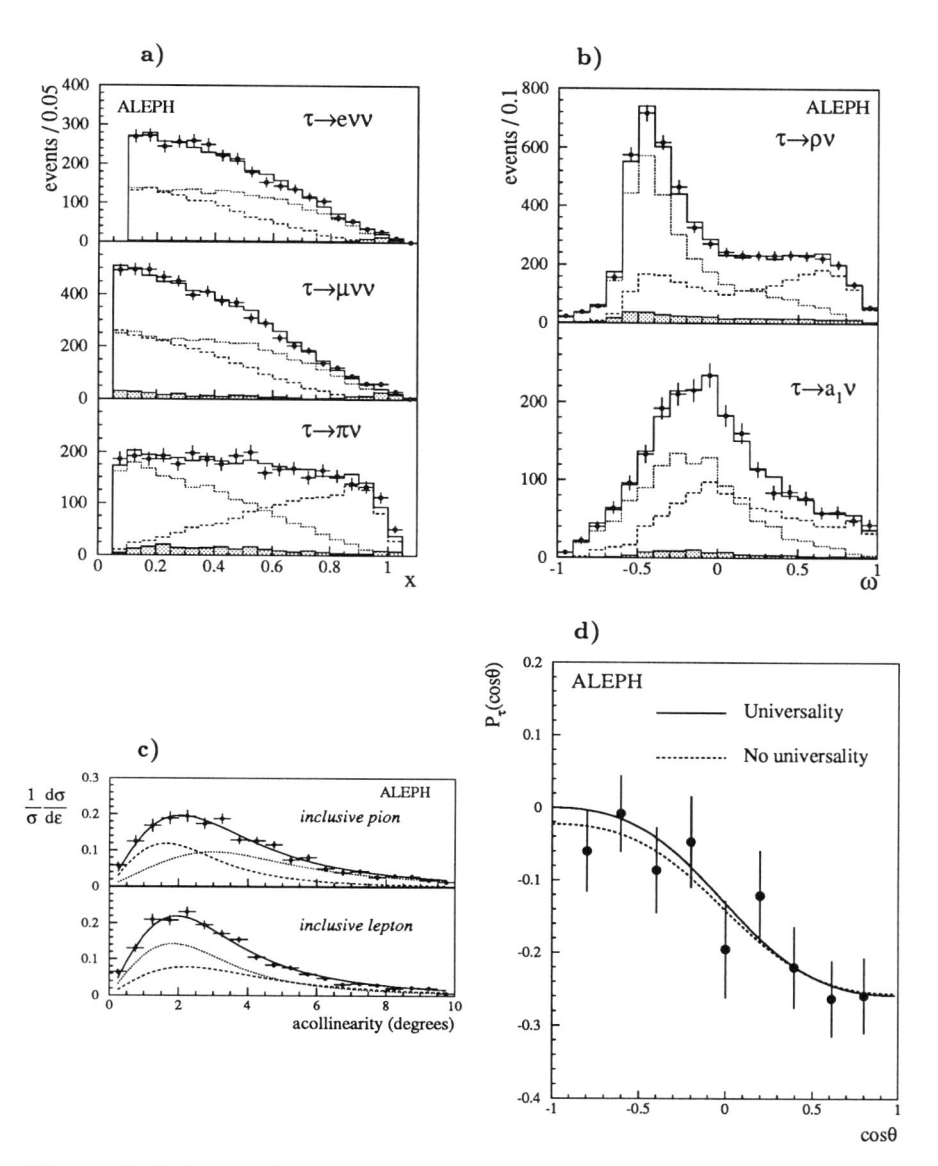

Figure 1: Preliminary results from the tau polarization measurement by ALEPH. Plot a shows the fits to the energy spectra for the $e\nu\bar{\nu}$, $\mu\nu\bar{\nu}$, and $\pi\nu$ channels; $x = E_{\text{daughter}}/E_{\text{beam}}$. Plot b shows the fits to the ω variable, defined in the text. The points represent the data; the dashed (dotted) histogram, the expected contribution from right- (left-)handed taus, the shaded histogram, from background. The solid line is the fit result, and is the sum of all contributions. Plot c shows the fits to the acollinearity distributions. Plot d shows the variation of P_τ with $\cos\theta$, as measured using the energy method. The solid line represents the fit assuming e-τ universality, and the dotted line, the fit relaxing this assumption.

A NEURAL NETWORK APPROACH
TO CHARGED PARTICLE IDENTIFICATION
IN LOW-MULTIPLICITY ALEPH EVENTS

JOHN S. CONWAY

Department of Physics, University of Wisconsin-Madison
Madison, Wisconsin 53711, USA

ABSTRACT

A feed-forward neural network trained with the backpropagation method, developed to identify electrons, muons, and pions in low-multiplicity ALEPH events such as tau pairs, obtains high efficiency and purity over a wide momentum range by using all available information from the tracking detectors, electromagnetic calorimeter, hadron calorimeter, and muon chambers. Evaluation of the systematic error of the neural network identification efficiency relies on particles identified via their kinematics. The small size of the systematic effects measured in this way allows application of the method to the ALEPH tau polarization measurement in such a way that the precision of the result remains statistically limited.

1. Introduction

Artificial neural networks have successfully addressed a number of problems in high energy physics [1], such as track finding and jet flavor tagging [2]. This note describes a feed-forward neural network which identifies electrons, muons and pions (hadrons in general) from low-multiplicity events based on information from the ALEPH tracking detectors, electromagnetic and hadronic calorimeters, and muon chambers.

2. Network Structure and Input

The ALEPH detector is described elsewhere [3]. The feedforward neural network for particle identification described here uses as input information from the tracking detectors (TPC and ITC), electromagnetic calorimeter (ECAL), hadron calorimeter (HCAL) and muon chambers for a given charged track, as discussed below. The network has 20 input quantities and two hidden layers each with 10 neurons. The output layer has three neurons, designated the e, μ, and π outputs, such that the desired output for an electron is (1,0,0), for a muon (0,1,0), and for a pion (0,0,1).

The method of "backpropagation," in which the derivatives of the error function with respect to changes in the weights and thresholds determine changes to be made in the weights and thresholds, accomplishes the task of "training" the network, here as implemented in JETNET 2.0 [4].

The training procedure uses tracks selected from 15 000 tau pair events, 3 000 mu pair events, and about 4 000 bhabha events. The tracks must have momentum greater than 200 MeV, a distance of closest approach to the beam axis of less than 20 cm, and a z value at the point of closest approach which within 40 cm of the interaction point. In addition, the tracks used for training must match with a Monte Carlo electron, muon, or pion. To avoid momentum-dependent bias, the training procedure selects randomly selected electrons and muons having momentum within 2.5 GeV of a randomly chosen pion. During the 10^8 training cycles, the JETNET learning parameter η decreases exponentially to damp oscillations.

In addition to the three neural network inputs of the charged track momentum $\cos\theta$, and ϕ, the dE/dx information for a track forms two more inputs. These two inputs, called R_e and R_π, take as their values the difference between the measured and expected dE/dx for the electron and pion mass hypotheses respectively, in units of standard deviations. Only the dE/dx electron and

track ID	$Z \to \tau^+\tau^-$			$Z \to e^+e^-$	$Z \to \mu^+\mu^-$
	e	μ	π	e	μ
e	98.3±0.1	-	2.5±0.1	98.2±0.1	-
μ	-	99.1±0.1	1.1±0.1	-	99.3±0.1
π	1.6±0.1	0.9±0.1	96.4±0.1	1.8±0.1	0.7±0.1

Table 1: Efficiency (in percent) for neural network particle identification method, for tracks with momentum above 3 GeV and $|\cos\theta| < 0.9$ from lepton pair events.

pion mass hypotheses respectively make useful distinctions between the various particle types given the small mass difference between muons and pions. The inputs R_e and R_π have values of 0 if fewer than 50 wire samples along a track exist.

The amount and spatial distribution of energy deposited in the ECAL distinguishes electrons, which shower electromagnetically, from pions, which either ionize minimally or shower hadronically in the ECAL. The neural network uses the four quantities E_{obj}/p, the ratio of the total ECAL object energy associated with a track to the track's momentum, and E_i^4/E_{obj}, i = 1, 2, 3, the ratios in each ECAL stack of the energy in the four towers nearest the extrapolated track to the total ECAL object energy. "Total ECAL object energy" here means the corrected cluster energy associated with the track. In addition, the fraction of a track's total trajectory in the ECAL region spent within 4.5 cm of a crack between modules makes a fifth ECAL input to the neural network.

The digital pattern of fired tubes in the HCAL discriminates muons from pions: muons leave a trail of one or two fired tubes in each layer, whereas hadronic showers from pions, leave a wider pattern of fired tubes. To quantify this pattern an algorithm makes connections between fired tubes in such a way as to build up "trees" whose properties charaterize the tube hit pattern. The network input consists of eight quantities: the number of trees associated to a track in a given domain, the length of the main tree, the energy associated to the tree, the sum of residuals for a fit of the main branch of the main tree by a parabola, called "residue", the "tortuosity" of the main tree, which measures the angular dispersion of the branches weighted by their energy, the ratio of energy to length for the main tree, the distance of the main tree to the track, and the angle between the main tree and the track.

Information from muon chamber hits in each layer of muon chambers forms two estimators used as input to the neural network. The estimators weight the quality of the nearest hit based on the distance d from the extrapolated hit and d_0, the estimated multiple scattering error, by taking as its value e^{-d/d_0}. Thus the value of the estimator lies in the range 0 to 1.

3. Performance and Systematic Errors

The identification efficiencies for the trained network appear in table 1, evaluated using tracks in lepton-pair Monte Carlo events. Figure 1 shows the behavior of the efficiencies as a function of momentum.

In applying this method to physical measurements such as the polarization of taus from Z decay, any discrepancy between the simulation of the network input quantities and their actual behavior leads to a systematic error. To estimate the magnitude of such errors one can select very pure samples of electrons, muons, and pions without making use of the network input information. Such "kinematically identified" particles include electrons and muons from electron- and muon-pair Z decays and two-photon events, and pions from rho decay from $\tau \to \rho\nu$ and $\tau \to a_1\nu$.

One can use kinematically identified particles either to study the quality of the agreement between the simulated and real network input quantities, and also to study whether the actual per-

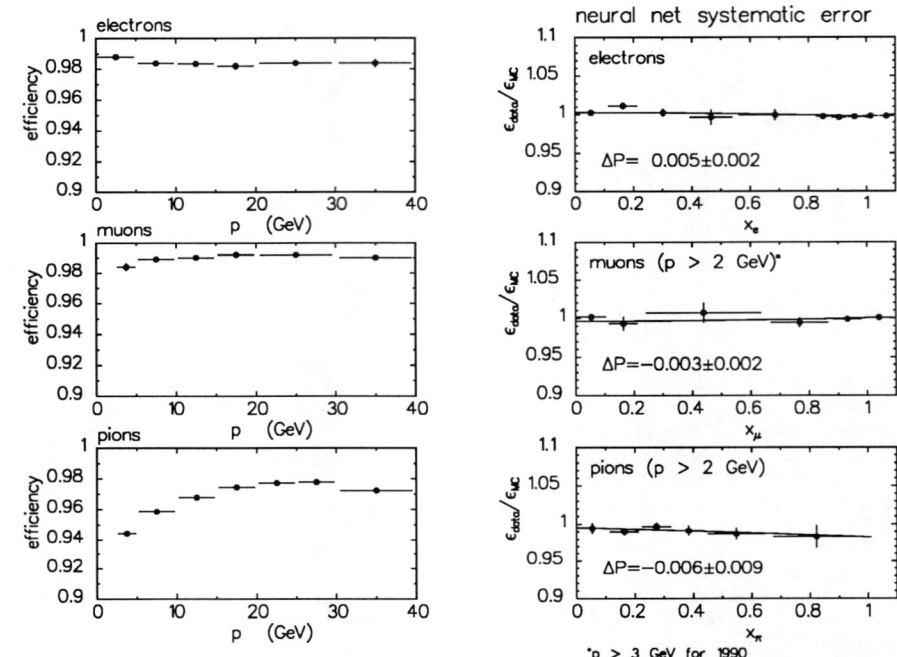

Figure 1: Neural network identification efficiency as a function of momentum (left) for electrons, muons, and pions with momentum greater than 2 GeV in Monte Carlo tau pair events, and ratio of data and Monte Carlo efficiency for kinematically identified tracks (right), indicating induced systematic error on tau polarization measurement.

formance of the neural network agrees with the simulation. Though discrepancies in the simulation exist, for example in the dE/dx and HCAL tube hit distributions, these do not ultimately greatly affect the final measurements.

In the case of tau polarization one can calculate the effect of the discrepancy on the measured tau polarization from the ratio of the efficiency for kinematically identitifed tracks in the real data to that in the Monte Carlo, shown in figure 1, with the result that in the electron, muon, and pion decay channels the systematic error on the polarization does not exceed 0.016, well within the statistical error of the measurements.

References

1. B. Humpert, Comp. Phys. Comm. 56, 299 (1990).
2. L. Bellantoni, et al., Nucl. Inst. Meth. A310, 618 (1991).
3. D. Decamp et al., Nucl. Inst. Meth. **A294**, 121 (1990).
4. L. Lönnblad et. al., Comp. Physics Comm. 70, 167 (1992).

TAU BRANCHING RATIOS IN ALEPH

Michael Walsh[1,2]
*Physics Department, University of Wisconsin,
1150 University Ave., Madison, Wisconsin 53706 U.S.A.*

ABSTRACT

Exclusive and topological branching ratios of the tau lepton have been measured by the ALEPH collaboration using data accumulated at LEP in 1989, 1990, and 1991.

1. Introduction

The sum of exclusive one-prong tau decay modes has in the past fallen short of the topological one-prong branching ratio by as many as four or five percentage points. Proposed explanations include new modes with photons not from π^0 (the known decay $\pi\pi^0\eta$ contributes only at the level of a few per mille[1]). Alternatively, higher branching ratios to the exclusive modes or a lower one-prong topological branching ratio could resolve the problem. Recent measurements from experiments performing both measurements, such as ALEPH[2], support changes in the branching ratios.

High selection efficiencies mean that most decays are selected and classified. We formulate a one-prong discrepancy hypothesis by classifying modes with photons with and without the requirement that the showers of photons from π^0 be separated, leading to "exclusive" and "quasi-exclusive" branching ratios. A comparison of the totals allows us to set a limit on modes with photons not from π^0. We also search for undetected decays of the tau.

2. Inclusive Selection and Normalization

Tau decays are classified either by the number of charged particles in the final state into one-, three-, and five-prong topological modes, or by particle identity and accompanying photons into exclusive modes. The central issues are the absolute normalization of the sample necessary to test the completeness of the measured branching ratios, and the quality of particle identification and photon reconstruction in the the data and in the simulation.

The normalization can be taken from any of the selections (topological, exclusive, quasi-exclusive), or independently from the measured luminosity and standard model tau cross section. We chose an absolute normalization from the ratio of leptonic to hadronic partial widths of the Z, measured by ALEPH using electron pairs and muon pairs. This normalization is precise and has no model dependence

---
[1] Representing the ALEPH collaboration
[2] Supported by the US Department of Energy, contract DE-AC02-76ER00881

| | wrong-charge topologies | |
element	data/MC ratio	main effects
11 → 12	1.04 ± 0.17	interactions, conversions
11 → 13	1.2 ± 0.6	interactions, conversions
13 → 11	1.3 ± 0.3	tracking
13 → 12	1.10 ± 0.07	tracking

Table 1: Systematic studies of efficiency matrix elements

beyond lepton universality in the weak neutral current. These redundant methods give us confidence in the overall normalization of the number of tau pairs.

There are 8538±89 produced tau pair events in the 1989-90 published data set, and 14193±95 events for the 1991 data set. The 1991 results are still preliminary, but have been combined with the published numbers in order to show the status of ALEPH's overall results.

Tau pair events are selected with 76.5±0.3% efficiency and 1.3±0.2% background. The efficiency is almost independent of the tau decay mode. This clean and unbiased sample is possible because of low backgrounds on the Z resonance, fine-grained electromagnetic calorimetry, and good track separation in the ALEPH detector.

3. Topological Branching Ratios

The method used to obtain the topological branching ratios employs an efficiency matrix to translate from the produced event topologies to the observed topologies. For instance, the probability for a one-prong on three-prong topology to be reconstructed as a one-on-two topology due to a lost track is recorded in the efficiency matrix element $\epsilon_{13 \to 12}$, determined from the Monte Carlo simulation.

Listing the number of events (subtracted for non-tau background) in each observed topology as a vector, we obtain a system of linear equations to be solved by a likelihood method for the vector of produced topologies. The same method is used for the quasi-exclusive branching ratios.

Systematic studies of the elements of the efficiency matrix have been done using wrong-charge topologies in the Monte Carlo simulation and in the data. The agreement is good, as shown in Table 1. Tracks are gained through nuclear interactions and photon conversions, and lost through track overlap and low momentum or low angle tracking limitations.

The preliminary 1991 results for the topological branching ratios (as combined with the published results) are listed in Table 2. The sum of the branching ratios is consistent with 100%, where the errors listed are statistical, systematic, and due to the absolute normalization as described above. A limit on the branching ratio of undetected decays of the tau lepton is set at <1.1% at the 95% confidence level (using the 1991 data only).

This limit can be improved by a direct search for undetected decays. We

topological mode	branching ratio
B_1	$85.6 \pm 0.4 \pm 0.3\%$
B_3	$14.7 \pm 0.2 \pm 0.2\%$
B_5	$0.11 \pm 0.03 \pm 0.03\%$
sum	$100.4 \pm 0.4 \pm 0.4 \pm 0.3\%$

Table 2: Preliminary topological branching ratios

select 10779 single tau decays. Looking at the opposite side of the event, we find six hemispheres with no tracks. In addition there are two hemispheres which do not have reconstructed tracks but which have hits in the Inner Tracking Chamber showing evidence of an unreconstructed track. The Monte Carlo prediction in these cases is for 4.5±1.0 hemispheres and 3.5±1.0 hemispheres, respectively. This is consistent with the observation. The observed events are explained as due to the endpoint of the kinematic range of tau decay to a low-momentum electron and ordinary neutrinos. A limit on tau decays to undetected modes is set at <0.11% at the 95% confidence level, which improves the limit from the absolutely normalized topological selection by an order of magnitude. This result can also be used to constrain the topological branching ratios to completeness with an uncertainty at the per mille level.

4. Quasi-Exclusive and Exclusive Results

Particle identification is done using a maximum likelihood method. Information on track ionization and shower development in the calorimeters allows a clean separation of electrons, muons, and charged hadrons (pions and kaons are not separated in this analysis). Photons are found as local maxima in electromagnetic calorimeter showers. They can be separated from other photons in the same shower, and from charged tracks striking the calorimeter as close as 4 cm. Additional cuts distinguish good photons from noise and hadronic shower fluctuations. Finally, 8% of good photons are reconstructed from conversion pairs in the tracking chambers.

The resulting photon spectra agree in the simulation and in the data. The reconstructed π^0 mass peaks also agree, and π^0s are accepted between 70 MeV and 210 MeV.

The main distinction between quasi-exclusive and exclusive modes lies in the requirement for fully reconstructed π^0s in the exclusive case; in the quasi-exclusive case, single electromagnetic showers are considered as possible π^0s with merged photon showers. This tends to occur for π^0s with momentum above 10 GeV/c.

The sum of the exclusive modes with photons, shown in Table 3, is consistent at the one-sigma level with the sum of the quasi-exclusive modes with photons, and allows us to place a limit on the total branching ratio of modes with photons not from π^0 at <2.8% at the 95% confidence level (using the 1991 data only). We find no evidence for a one-prong discrepancy from this source.

The ratio of the muonic to electronic branching ratios is 0.97±0.02±0.02,

	method	
mode	quasi-exclusive	exclusive
e	$18.2 \pm 0.3 \pm 0.2\%$	
μ	$17.6 \pm 0.2 \pm 0.2\%$	
h	$12.8 \pm 0.2 \pm 0.2\%$	
$h\pi^0$	$25.4 \pm 0.4 \pm 0.4\%$	$25.8 \pm 0.5\%$
$h2\pi^0$	$10.3 \pm 0.4 \pm 0.4\%$	$8.8 \pm 0.5\%$
$h3\pi^0$	$1.5 \pm 0.2 \pm 0.3\%$	$1.8 \pm 0.4\%$
$3h$	$9.6 \pm 0.2 \pm 0.2\%$	
$3h\pi^0$	$5.4 \pm 0.2 \pm 0.2\%$	$5.4 \pm 0.2\%$
sum, modes with γ	$42.6 \pm 0.4\%$	$41.8 \pm 0.6\%$
sum	$100.9 \pm 0.5 \pm 0.4 \pm 0.7\%$	

Table 3: Preliminiary quasi-exclusive and exclusive results

which agrees with the expectation of 0.973 for the case of lepton universality in the charged current.

There is a prediction[3] for the ratio of the rho and electron branching ratios of 1.32±0.05; the observed electron branching ratio leads to a predicted 24.0±1.0% rho branching ratio, which agrees at the one-sigma level with the uncorrected value for the $h\pi^0$ branching ratio of 25.4±0.6%, where no K^* subtraction has been done.

Lepton universality in the charged current also leads to a relation between the tau and muon lifetimes, using their masses and the leptonic branching ratio of the tau:

$$T_\tau = T_\mu \left(\frac{m_\mu}{m_\tau}\right)^5 B_\ell \qquad (1)$$

This predicts a tau lifetime of 296±4 fs, which agrees well with the value of 295±6 fs measured by ALEPH[4].

5. Conclusions

There is no evidence for tau lepton decay modes with photons not from π^0 beyond a few percent, or for undetected decay modes beyond a per mille. All measures of the branching ratios (topological, quasi-exclusive, and exclusive) have been absolutely normalized and show good agreement with completeness. Finally, the leptonic branching ratios obtained are consistent with the measured tau lifetime.

References

1. B.K.Heltsley, CLEO, at the SLAC Topical Conference, July 24, 1992.
2. D.Decamp *et al.*, ALEPH, Z. Phys. **C54**(1992) 211.
3. J.H.Kühn and A.Santamaría, Z. Phys. **C48**(1990) 445.
4. D.Buskulic *et al.*, ALEPH, to be published in Phys. Lett. Preprint CERN-PPE/92-186.

A MEASUREMENT OF τ POLARIZATION IN Z^0 DECAYS

PETER FISHER

The Henry A. Rowland Department of Physics and Astronomy, Johns Hopkins University
Baltimore, Maryland 21218, USA

for

THE L3 COLLABORATION

ABSTRACT

The polarization of τ leptons produced in $e^+e^- \to \tau^+\tau^-(\gamma)$ is measured using a sample of 8977 $\tau^+\tau^-$ pairs collected near the peak of the Z^0 resonance. A polarization of $-0.132 \pm 0.026(\text{stat.}) \pm 0.021(\text{syst.})$ is determined. This corresponds to a ratio of the vector to the axial-vector coupling constants of the τ lepton to the weak neutral current of $(g_V^\tau/g_A^\tau)_{\text{eff}} = 0.069 \pm 0.017$. This leads to a value of the effective $\sin^2\theta_W$ at the Z^0 resonance of $\sin^2\theta_{\text{eff}} = 0.2326 \pm 0.0043$.

1. Introduction

The measurement of the final state polarization of τ leptons produced by the process $e^+e^- \to Z^0 \to \tau^+\tau^-$ provides a sensitive measurement of the neutral current coupling constants which relatively independent of systematic errors in the beam energy and luminosity measurements. Here we describe the measurement of the P_τ using a data sample collected in 1991 and 1992 by the L3 detector at LEP. This data sample corresponds to 410 000 $Z^0 \to$ hadrons (17.6 pb^{-1}) and was collect at center of mass energies between 88.2 and 94.2 GeV with 80 % of the data collected at $\sqrt{s}$ = 91.222 GeV. A full report of this measurement and the L3 detector appears in [1].

2. Event Selection and Particle Identification

The procedures for the selection of electron, muon, pion, rho and a_1 decay modes are designed to be relatively independent of the energy of the τ decay products, in order to minimize the introduction of polarization biases. The preselection removes most of the cosmic ray, two photon and $Z^0 \to$ hadrons background. This is followed by the identification of electrons and μ's and rejection of $Z^0 \to e^+e^-(\gamma)$ and $\mu^+\mu^-(\gamma)$ events. The final data sample consists of events where at least one of the τ decays into one of the channels listed in the introduction. Selection efficiencies and backgrounds are calculated using Monte Carlo simulation of $Z^0 \to \tau^+\tau^-(\gamma)$, $e^+e^-(\gamma)$, $\mu^+\mu^-(\gamma)$, $Z^0 \to$ hadrons, and two photon reactions including full simulation of the L3 detector response. The same selection criteria are applied to data and Monte Carlo events and the number of selected decays for each channel is listed in Table 1.

Channel	Number Decays 1990	Number Decays 1991
$e^-\bar{\nu}_e\nu_\tau$	385	2016
$\mu^-\bar{\nu}_\mu\nu_\tau$	558	1844
$\pi^-(K^-)\nu_\tau$	220	1603
$\rho^-\nu_\tau$	503	3130
a_1	-	473

Table 1: Summary of the number of decays for each channel. The $\tau^- \to a_1^-\nu_\tau$ channel was not analysed in 1990.

The preselection selects 99.9% of $Z^0 \to$ hadrons events while rejecting less than 2% of the dilepton events. The data sample consists of 34203 events which includes more than 98% of each of the charged leptonic Z^0 decay modes and a background of 5% mainly from two photon interactions and $Z^0 \to$ hadrons. For the one-prong channels, each hemisphere with exactly one track and an associated Z-chamber hit is considered for selection. After preselection, individual selections are performed for each decay mode. The cuts for both the preselection and individual decay mode selections are described in detail in [1].

3. Measurement of $\mathcal{P}_\tau$

For each τ decay channel, $\mathcal{P}_\tau$ is measured by obtaining the linear combination of the $h = +1$ and $h = -1$ Monte Carlo distributions which best fits the data. For $\tau^- \to e^-\bar{\nu}_e\nu_\tau$, $\mu^-\bar{\nu}_\mu\nu_\tau$ and $\pi^-(K^-)\nu_\tau$, the energy distribution of the charged particle is used and the overall normalization and polarization are left as free parameters in a binned maximum likelihood fit. For $\tau^- \to \rho^-\nu_\tau$ and $a_1^-\nu_\tau$, multidimensional distributions are used. For each decay mode, the polarization of the background from other τ decays is varied simultaneously with the polarization for the decay mode being fit. The statistical error in each channel is verified by direct calculation from the functional form of the decay distributions after including the kinematics, efficiency corrections and detector resolution. The statistical errors due to limited Monte Carlo statistics are included in the calculation of the systematic errors. A breakdown of systematic errors for each channel is given in Table 2 and the result for each channel is given in Table 3.

4. Conclusions

The weighted mean of all five decay modes is

$$\mathcal{P}_\tau = -0.132 \pm 0.026(\text{stat.}) \pm 0.021(\text{syst.})$$

In calculating the average, statistical correlations in events where both hemispheres are used, as well as systematic correlations in the energy calibration of $\pi^\pm$'s in the

Channel	Selection	Background	Calibration	Radiative Corrections	Monte Carlo Statistics
$e^-\bar{\nu}_e\nu_\tau$	0.027	0.020	0.020	0.020	0.046
$\mu^-\bar{\nu}_\mu\nu_\tau$	0.020	0.020	0.020	0.010	0.046
$\pi^-(K^-)\nu_\tau$	0.017	0.009	0.013	0.005	0.021
$\rho^-\nu_\tau$	0.013	0.005	0.020	negl.	0.016
a_1	0.045	0.010	0.033	negl.	0.073

Table 2: Summary of systematic errors for all channels.

Channel	$\mathcal{P}_\tau$	Stat. Error	Syst. Error
$e^-\bar{\nu}_e\nu_\tau$	-0.127	0.097	0.062
$\mu^-\bar{\nu}_\mu\nu_\tau$	-0.020	0.101	0.055
$\pi^-(K^-)\nu_\tau$	-0.148	0.046	0.033
$\rho^-\nu_\tau$	-0.152	0.035	0.029
a_1	0.105	0.164	0.093

Table 3: Summary for $\mathcal{P}_\tau$ and errors for all channels.

$\pi^-(K^-)\nu_\tau$, $\rho^-\nu_\tau$ and $a_1^-\nu_\tau$ channels are taken into account. All other systematic errors are assumed to be uncorrelated and are added in quadrature.

Our measurement of $\mathcal{P}_\tau$ implies that parity is violated in the neutral current process $Z^0 \to \tau^+\tau^-(\gamma)$, as has been previously found in other neutral current processes.

Using the above value for $\mathcal{P}_\tau$ and applying a correction of 0.002 to account for initial state radiation and data collected off the Z^0 resonance, we obtain

$$\left(\frac{g_V^\tau}{g_A^\tau}\right)_{\text{eff}} = 0.069 \pm 0.017$$

which gives the effective weak mixing angle at the Z^0 resonance

$$\sin^2\theta_{\text{eff}} = 0.2326 \pm 0.0043.$$

This is consistent with other L3 measurements of the weak mixing angle from the study of the Z^0 lineshape and the forward backward asymmetries in the processes $Z^0 \to b\bar{b}$, $Z^0 \to e^+e^-(\gamma)$, $Z^0 \to \mu^+\mu^-(\gamma)$ and $Z^0 \to \tau^+\tau^-(\gamma)$ [1].

1. L3 Collaboration, O. Adriani *et al.*, "A Measurement of τ Polarization in Z^0 Decays", CERN-PPE/92-131, August 1992, submitted to *Phys. Lett.*

MEASUREMENTS OF THE TOPOLOGICAL BRANCHING FRACTIONS AND THE LIFETIME OF THE TAU LEPTON.

Ronan McNulty
*Dept. of Physics, University of Liverpool, Oxford Street
Liverpool, L69 3BX, England*

representing

THE DELPHI COLLABORATION

ABSTRACT

Using data collected by the DELPHI collaboration during 1991 measurements of the topological branching fractions and the lifetime of the tau lepton are presented. The former have been measured to be $B_1 = (84.08 \pm .59 \pm .45)\%, B_3 = (15.00 \pm .37 \pm .21)\%, B_5 = (0.31 \pm .11 \pm .07)\%$. The latter has been measured with four different techniques to obtain a combined result of 301 ± 7fs.

1. Introduction

Two properties of the tau lepton have recently given rise to some debate due to discrepancies between theoretical predictions and experimental measurements. The first is often referred to as 'The One Prong Problem' where it has been noted that the sum of the exclusive branching fractions into one charged particle does not equal the inclusive branching fraction. The second concerns the lifetime of the tau lepton which has disagreed with its predicted value by up to 3 sigma. Reviews of both subjects and possible explanations in terms of experimental systematics or new physics are to be found elsewhere [1]. In this talk I present results from the DELPHI collaboration on the Tau Topological Branching Ratios and the Tau Lifetime. These measurements have been made using the data taken in 1991.

1.1. DELPHI detector

DELPHI [2] is a 4π hermetic detector operating on the LEP e^+e^- collider. The barrel of the detector consists of tracking chambers and electromagnetic calorimeters placed in a 1.23T magnetic field outside which are hadronic calorimeters and muon chambers. Of particular importance for the analyses described here is the presence of a silicon Microvertex Detector close to the interaction region. It consists of 3 layers of single sided silicon strip detectors placed at average radii of 6.3, 9 and 11cm. Full details of this detector can be found elsewhere [3]. Here I mention four performance features which are of importance to the physics measurements to be described later.

- The efficiency for each of the three layers of the Microvertex Detector is greater than 95%.

- The two track separation is 50% at 100 μm. Less than 5% of 3-prong tau decays have tracks with a smaller separation.

- The association of Microvertex Detector hits to tracks reconstructed in the other subdetectors can be correctly performed better than 90% of the time provided two or more hits are present.

- The intrinsic resolution of the Microvertex Detector is 8 μm leading to an extrapolation precision at the interaction region of 21 μm.

The first three points are important in the measurement of the tau topological branching fraction. In addition the final point is essential to the lifetime measurement.

2. Measurement of the Tau Topological Branching Fractions

At its simplest level this problem is one of counting the number of decays of the two taus into the 1-1, 1-3, 1-5 and 3-3 topologies and from this deducing the branching fractions of a single tau into one, three and five prongs. Thus

$$N_{ij} = (2 - \delta_{ij})N_\tau B_i B_j \tag{1}$$

where N_{ij} is the number of events observed in the i-j topology, N_τ the total number of taus, δ_{ij} the Kronecker delta function and B_i the branching fraction for the tau into an i-prong.

The problem is complicated by 3 factors: firstly due to the migration from the topology i-j to the topology k-l;$(k, l = 0, 1, 2, 3, 4...)$; secondly due to the detection efficiency for a given channel; and thirdly due to background effects. This can be expressed through

$$N_{kl}^{COR} = \frac{N_{kl}^{OBS} - N_{kl}^{BACK}}{f_{kl}} \tag{2}$$

and

$$N_{kl}^{COR} = \sum_{ij} \mathcal{M}_{ijkl} N_{ij}^{TRUE} \tag{3}$$

where $N^{OBS}, N^{BACK}, N^{COR}, N^{TRUE}$ refer to the number of observed events, the estimated background, the corrected number of observed events and the true number in a given topology. f_{kl} is the efficiency for observation in the k-l decay and $\mathcal{M}_{ijkl}$ is the migration matrix which describes the probability of a true decay in the i-j topology being observed in the k-l topology.

2.1. Migration

Tracks are lost due to a number of factors such as the two track resolution of the detector, inefficiencies, dead regions, or errors in the pattern reconstruction. These effects are small and can be estimated from Monte Carlo. Tracks are gained primarily due to photons (from π^0s) which 99% of the time convert in material outside the beampipe and Microvertex Detector. Because of this fact, and due to the high efficiency, good two track resolution and low ambiguity of association for the Microvertex Detector, it can be used to veto the photon conversions. A track without any microvertex hits can be identified as a photon conversion and removed. This procedure considerably improves the topology recognition. Of the observed 1-3 topology only 70% are true 1-3, the remainder being true 1-1 with a conversion. After the veto is implemented 99% are true 1-3.

2.2. Fitting

The background, efficiency and migration matrices are determined from Monte Carlo calculations. In this way N_{ij}^{TRUE} is determined from N_{kl}^{OBS} (see Eqs. (2&3).) A maximum likelihood fit for the quantities B_1, B_3, B_5, N_τ is performed. Since there are three independent equations and 4 unknowns some extra information must be assumed. Using the obvious condition $B_1 + B_3 + B_5 = 1$ however, this leads to a correlation of .96 between B_1 and B_3. It is considered better to fix N_τ from the luminosity measurement (although this increases the statistical error somewhat.) The largest contribution to the systematic error comes from from knowledge of the selection efficiency and the background contributions. The result is

$$B_1 = (84.08 \pm .59 \pm .45)\%, B_3 = (15.00 \pm .37 \pm .21)\%, B_5 = (0.31 \pm .11 \pm .07)\%.$$

Throughout this paper the first quoted error is statistical, the second systematic.

3 Tau Lifetime

The lifetime of the tau lepton has been measured using its one prong decays and its three prong decays. Three methods have been used to extract maximum information from the one prong decays: firstly using the impact parameter of any single tau decay; secondly using the sum of the impact parameters of both taus produced back to back by the decaying Z^0; and thirdly using the difference of the impact parameters.

The impact parameter is defined as the distance of closest approach of a track to the interaction point. A non-zero impact parameter can be obtained in one of the following ways:

- Lifetime Effect: A secondary track when extrapolated to the primary interaction point will in general give a finite impact parameter due to the decay angle and the lifetime of the primary particle. The impact parameter δ is related to the lifetime of the particle t via

$$\delta = \beta \gamma c t \sin \psi \sin \theta \tag{4}$$

where ψ is the decay angle, θ the polar angle, c the speed of light, β and γ are relativistic factors.

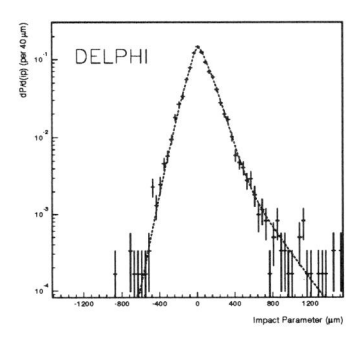

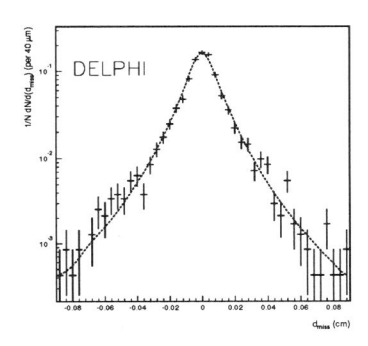

Figure 1: a) The lifetime signed impact parameter distribution; b) The Summed Impact Parameter Distribution; data points with the fitted lifetime superimposed.

- Resolution Effect: A track observed in the detector is not known to infinite precision and so on extrapolation back to its production point a finite impact parameter will be measured.

- Beam Effect: If the size of the interaction region is large then the actual production point is unknown. Choosing the centre of the beam as the point to measure the distance from will thus give a finite impact parameter.

3.1 One Prong Methods

3.1.1. Impact Parameter Method

The first technique used is the Impact Parameter Method. Tau decays are selected using a series of cuts which produce a sample of high purity ($> 98\%$). At least two Microvertex Detector hits are demanded on tracks. The impact parameter distribution is measured from the centre of the beamspot. It is signed positive or negative according to whether the extrapolated track intersects the event thrust axis on the same or opposite side of the beam. Resolution and beam effects are found by measuring the impact parameter distribution for electrons and muons (which have no lifetime effects. Monte Carlo calculations are made for different lifetimes and a maximum likelihood fit is made to extract the best value for the lifetime. The distribution of impact parameters with the best fit is shown in Figure 1(a).

The dominant systematics come from knowledge of the sample constitution and of the resolution. A value of $304 \pm 11 \pm 6\text{fs}$ is obtained.

3.1.2. Impact Parameter Sum

In the previous analysis the beam effect is on average twice as large as the lifetime effect so that the signal is extracted from a large background. By using *both* of the taus and summing the impact parameters the beam effect can be removed. The impact parameter is signed according to whether an observer sitting on the track sees the interaction point on her right or left. Thus the summed impact parameters are insensitive to the actual production point. In this case the lifetime distribution is symmetric and is convoluted only with resolution effects which can be calculated from the summed impact parameter distribution for electrons and muons. The result of the maximum likelihood fit is shown superimposed on the data in Figure 1(b).

As expected the statistical error on this determination is smaller, while the major systematic comes from knowledge of the resolution function. The value obtained is $301 \pm 9 \pm 6$fs.

3.1.3 Impact Parameter Difference

The third method takes the difference in the Impact Parameters. From Eq. (4) it is seen that

$$\delta_1 - \delta_2 = \gamma\beta c \sin\theta (t_1 \sin\psi_1 - t_2 \sin\psi_2) \qquad (6)$$

and so, averaged over many events

$$<\delta_1 - \delta_2> = \beta\gamma c\tau \sin\theta \Delta\psi \qquad (7)$$

where $\Delta\psi = \psi_1 - \psi_2 = \sin\psi_1 - \sin\psi_2$, true for small angles.

The error on the projected acoplanarity is small and that on the impact parameter difference is large (the beam size entering twice into the uncertainty), thus rendering the equation suitable to a least squares straight line fit.

Figure 2(a) shows the best straight line fit to the data where a 0.8% trim has been applied. Biases must also be taken into account, in particular a number of backgrounds for which $<\delta_1 - \delta_2> \approx 0$ irrespective of the projected acoplanarity. The major systematics come from the applied trim and the effect of the background contamination. The value obtained is $299 \pm 11 \pm 6$fs

3.1.4 Combined One prong measurements

The three measurements are combined together, due account being taken of the correlations between the methods, to give a result for the one prong measurements of $301 \pm 7 \pm 4$fs.

3.2 Three Prong Measurement

From the three tracks a common vertex for the decay point of the tau is reconstructed. The production point is taken as the centre of the beam spot and the flight distance measured, which in turn gives the lifetime via

$$t = \frac{d}{\beta\gamma c \sin\theta} \qquad (8)$$

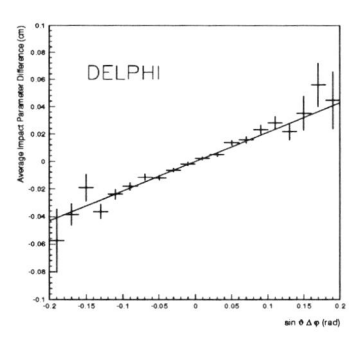

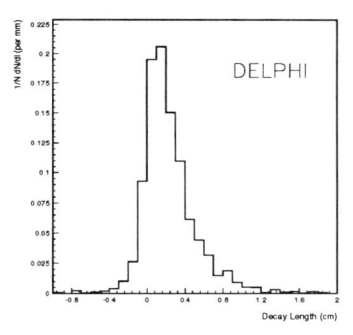

Figure 2: a) The correlation between impact parameter difference and the projected acoplanarity. b) The decay length distribution found by reconstructing the vertex for the three tracks in a tau decay.

where d is the distance travelled, and β, γ, c, θ are defined as before. The error on an event by event basis is also calculated and a maximum likelihood fit performed to obtain the best estimate of the mean lifetime. The decay length distribution is shown in Figure 2(b).

The dominant systematic comes from a few events where hadronic scattering occurs. The result for this method is $303 \pm 13 \pm 4$fs.

3.3 Final Tau Lifetime Result

When the 1-prong and 3-prong results are averaged together the final preliminary result for the tau lifetime obtained through analysis of the 1991 data collected by the DELPHI detector is 301 ± 7fs.

4. References

1. A. Pich CERN-TH 6489/92, CERN-TH 6237/91. Particle Data Group, M. Aguilar-Benitez et al.,*Phys. Rev.* **D45** (1992). Barish and Stroynowski *Phys. Rep.* **157** (1988) 1. W. J. Marciano BNL-46736. C. K. Jung SBHEP-92-1.
2. P. Aarnio et al., *Nucl. Instr. and Meth.* **A303** (1991) 233.
3. N. Bingefors et al., CERN-PPE/92-173

RECENT CLEO RESULTS ON TAU DECAYS

G. CRAWFORD[1]
Physics Department, The Ohio State University, 174 West 18th Ave.
Columbus, Ohio 43210, USA

ABSTRACT

We report on recent CLEO results in τ decays, including the observation of a new decay mode, $\tau^\pm \to 3h^\pm 2\pi^0 \nu_\tau$, and several precision measurements of one-prong decay modes. We discuss the implications of these measurements for testing the Standard Model and in resolving the "one-prong problem" in τ decays.

1. Introduction

Obtaining a consistent picture of τ decays remains a challenge to experimenters. In particular, the "one-prong problem,"[1,2] wherein the exclusive decays with one charged particle in the final state fail to saturate the inclusive rate, has persisted through many experiments and detector improvements. In this paper we present precision τ decay results from the CLEO II detector at the Cornell Electron Storage Ring (CESR) which address this problem. We also report observation of a new decay mode: $\tau^\pm \to 3h^\pm 2\pi^0 \nu_\tau$, where $h^\pm$ represents a charged hadron ($\pi^\pm$ or $K^\pm$).

CLEO II is a general purpose detector which is described in detail elsewhere.[3] For the analyses described in this work, its most important features are its hermiticity ($d\Omega = 0.95 \times 4\pi$) and a 7800 element CsI(Tl) calorimeter whose excellent energy resolution and fine segmentation permit reconstruction of decays containing multiple neutral particles. The dataset used in these analyses is obtained from e^+e^- collisions at a center-of-mass energy $E_{cm} \sim 10.6$ GeV, with an integrated luminosity of about 1.6 fb^{-1}, corresponding to 1.4×10^6 τ pairs produced.

2. Observation of $\tau \to 3h^\pm 2\pi^0 \nu_\tau$

Previous experiments have not been able to exclusively reconstruct 2 π^0's accompanying a 3-prong τ decay.[4] We only outline the analysis here, as it is described in detail elsewhere.[5] We select events with a 1-3 charged track topology and require exactly 4 photon candidates on the 3-prong side. The $2\pi^0$ signal is extracted from the $(3h^\pm + 4\gamma)$ events by a 2-dimensional fit to the $m_{\gamma\gamma}$ vs. $m_{\gamma\gamma}$ spectra, shown in Fig. 1. A clear peak is evident at the π^0 mass for both combinations. The significant background from hadronic $(e^+e^- \to q\bar{q})$ decays is calculated empirically from the data using 1-3 topology events which are kinematically inconsistent with τ pairs.

We normalize the branching fraction B($\tau \to 3h^\pm 2\pi^0 \nu_\tau$) to the inclusive 3-prong branching fraction (B$_3$) to minimize systematic errors. We find: $B_{3h2\pi^0}/B_3 = 0.038 \pm 0.004 \pm 0.006$, where the first error is statistical and the second systematic. The dominant component of the systematic error is the uncertainty in the relative efficiencies. Using $B_3 = (14.06 \pm 0.25)\%$[4] we obtain

$$B(\tau \to 3h^\pm 2\pi^0 \nu_\tau) = (0.54 \pm 0.05 \pm 0.08)\%, \qquad \text{PRELIMINARY}$$

where we have folded the uncertainty in B_3 into the systematic error.

---
[1] representing the CLEO Collaboration

Fig. 1. $m_{\gamma\gamma}$ vs. $m_{\gamma\gamma}$ for $(3h^{\pm} + 4\gamma)$ events.

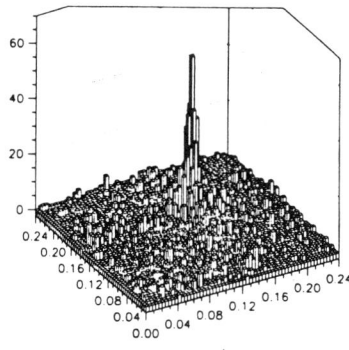

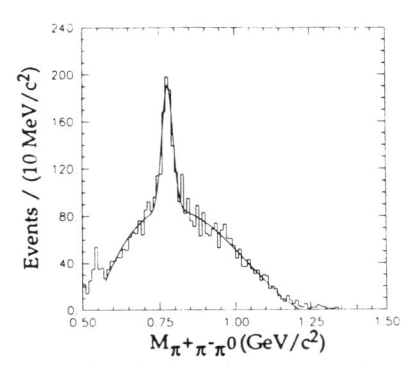

Fig. 2. $\pi^+\pi^-\pi^0$ invariant mass in $3\pi 2\pi^0$ events.

This is the first observation of this decay mode. The branching fraction is an order-of-magnitude larger than the $5\pi^{\pm}$ mode, which makes the $3h^{\pm}2\pi^0$ mode particularly attractive for studies of the tau neutrino mass.[6] This enhanced decay width may be due to significant resonant contributions to the $3\pi 2\pi^0$ state: a clean signal is observed at the ω mass in the $\pi^+\pi^-\pi^0$ channel, as shown in Fig. 2. The peak at the η mass is from the decay chain $\tau^{\pm} \to \pi^{\pm}\eta\pi^0\nu_{\tau}$, $\eta \to \pi^+\pi^-\pi^0$ [7].

3. Precision One-Prong Measurements

In this section we describe recent measurements from CLEO which relate to the one-prong deficit and other precision tests of the Standard Model. Here we only sketch the analyses and present the results; the reader is directed to the references for details.

3.1 Electronic Branching Fraction of the Tau

This analysis[8] uses di-electron events where both τ's decay to $e\bar{\nu}_e\nu_{\tau}$ and measures B_e^2 by normalizing to the total number of τ pairs produced; most errors are halved when extracting B_e. Significant QED and 2γ backgrounds (from radiative Bhabhas, $e^+e^- \to e^+e^-e^+e^-$ and $e^+e^- \to e^+e^-\tau^+\tau^-$) are highly suppressed by exploiting the hermiticity of the detector, since real τ pairs in this topology have 4 neutrinos in the final state, and hence substantial missing energy and momentum. The final result is:

$$B_e = (17.49 \pm 0.14 \pm 0.22)\%,$$

where the first error is statistical and the second systematic. The major contributions to the systematic error are from uncertainties in detector acceptance (0.84%); luminosity (0.75%); and radiative corrections to the theoretical τ pair cross-section (0.50%). This result is consistent with (and more precise than) the previous world average.[4]

Measurements of the leptonic branching fractions of the tau and its other basic properties (such as mass and lifetime) test the Standard Model assumption that the tau is a sequential lepton.[9] These comparisons indicate that the τ is indeed consistent with this hypothesis at $\leq 1\%$ precision.

3.2 Tau Decays with a Single π^0

A similar approach is used in this analysis[10], where we select events where both τ's decay to the $h\pi^0\nu_{\tau}$ final state and measure $B_{h\pi^0}^2$ by normalizing to the total number of τ pairs produced. Here the dominant background comes from other τ decays, specifically $\tau^{\pm} \to h^{\pm} \geq 2\pi^0\nu_{\tau}$, where one or more of the π^0's cannot be completely reconstructed. We reduce those backgrounds by employing the resolution of the calorimeter ($\sigma_{\gamma\gamma} \sim 7$ MeV) to completely reconstruct π^0's and reject extra neutral energy deposits. The result is

$$B_{h\pi^0} = (24.83 \pm 0.15 \pm 0.53)\%, \qquad \text{PRELIMINARY}$$

where the errors are as above. The principal sources of systematic error the same as in the B_e analysis but of slightly different magnitude: acceptance (1.7%); luminosity (0.8%); radiative corrections (0.8%). This result is also consistent with the world average[4] and of better precision. We have also measured the polarization of the $h\pi^0$ system (assuming $h = \pi$) and find it consistent with Standard Model expectations.

One can predict the ratio of $B_{\pi\pi^0}$ to B_e using $e^+e^- \to \pi^+\pi^-$ data and CVC.[2] One predicts $B_{\pi\pi^0}/B_e = 1.33 \pm 0.07$, where the error is due to uncertainties in the radiative corrections to the hadronic final state. Using only the CLEO II data, we measure[2] $B_{\pi\pi^0}/B_e = 1.39 \pm 0.03$ in good agreement with the prediction.

3.3 Tau Decays with a Multiple π^0's

To study multi-π^0 τ decays, we identify the decay of the recoiling ('tag') τ using leptonic ($e\nu\bar{\nu}$, $\mu\nu\bar{\nu}$) and 3-prong ($3h^\pm[\pi^0]\nu$) tags.[11] To minimize systematic errors here we normalize the multi-π^0 branching fractions to that of the single π^0 mode ($B_{h\pi^0}$). The segmentation of the calorimeter is used to exclusively reconstruct all π^0's in the decay and minimize backgrounds from hadronic events and other τ decay modes. We measure: $B_{h2\pi^0}/B_{h\pi^0} = 0.345 \pm 0.006 \pm 0.016$, $B_{h3\pi^0}/B_{h\pi^0} = 0.041 \pm 0.003 \pm 0.005$, and $B_{h4\pi^0}/B_{h\pi^0} = 0.006 \pm 0.002 \pm 0.002$, where the errors are as above. The primary source of systematic error is the uncertainty in the π^0 reconstruction efficiency. Using the "new" world average[12] $B_{h\pi^0} = (24.29 \pm 0.24)\%$ we conclude:

$$B_{h2\pi^0} = (8.39 \pm 0.15 \pm 0.40 \pm 0.08)\%,$$
$$B_{h3\pi^0} = (1.00 \pm 0.07 \pm 0.12 \pm 0.01)\%,$$
$$B_{h4\pi^0} = (0.15 \pm 0.04 \pm 0.05 \pm 0.002)\%,$$

where the final error is due to the uncertainty in $B_{h\pi^0}$.

These results are again consistent with and more precise than the world averages.[4] One can also relate the branching fraction $B_{\pi 3\pi^0}$ to B_e using $e^+e^- \to 4\pi$ data and CVC, as we did above for the $\pi\pi^0\nu_\tau$ final state. We find, using only the CLEO II data[3], $B_{\pi 3\pi^0}/B_e = 0.056 \pm 0.008$ consistent with the Standard Model expectation of $B_{\pi 3\pi^0}/B_e = 0.055 \pm 0.005$.

4. Summary

The precision one-prong branching fraction measurements described above are summarized in Table I. Previous world averages and recent results from ALEPH[13], which has measured all one-prong decay modes in both exclusive and quasi-exclusive analyses, are shown for comparison. One observes that both CLEO and ALEPH are are consistent with previous world averages but that CLEO results are consistently *lower* than ALEPH; this comparison is important since ALEPH resports *no* one-prong deficit in their analyses. In particular, the results for the $h2\pi^0$ mode are

---

[2] We subtract 0.5% from $B_{h\pi^0}$ to account for $\tau \to K^\pm \pi^0 \nu_\tau$ decays.
[3] Here we do not subtract for any Cabibbo-supressed modes, which comprise a few percent of $h3\pi^0$ decays.

intriguing since both CLEO and ALEPH exclusive analyses find a lower value than the ALEPH quasi-exclusive analysis, perhaps pointing out a systematic problem with one of the methods. Resolution of this discrepancy in particular and the one-prong problem in general is still an open question.

Decay Mode	PDG 92 [4] World Avg	CLEO II Exclusive	ALEPH 92 [13] Exclusive	ALEPH 92 [13] Quasi-Exclusive
$e^-\bar{\nu}_e\nu_\tau$	17.94 ± 0.27	17.49 ± 0.26	18.23 ± 0.37	18.20 ± 0.35
$h^-\pi^0\nu_\tau$	23.8 ± 0.8	24.83 ± 0.55	26.04 ± 0.85	25.50 ± 0.55
$h^-2\pi^0\nu_\tau$	9.0 ± 0.8	8.39 ± 0.43	8.69 ± 0.80	10.28 ± 0.56
$h^- > 2\pi^0\nu_\tau$	1.8 ± 0.5	1.15 ± 0.15	1.65 ± 0.90	1.51 ± 0.36

Table I. Comparison of CLEO II results presented in this paper with previous world averages and recent results from ALEPH using both a complete exclusive reconstruction and a "quasi-exclusive" reconstruction which only classifies all final states. Statistical and systematic errors have been added in quadrature.

5. Acknowledgments

I would like to thank Rich Galik, K.K. Gan, Brian Heltsley, Jon Urheim and Alan Weinstein in particular, and the intrepid τ analysis group in general, for many helpful discussions.

6. References

1. T. N. Truong, *Phys. Rev.* **D30** (1984) 1509.
2. F. J. Gilman and S. H. Rhie, *Phys. Rev.* **D31** (1985) 1066.
3. Y. Kubota et. al., *Nucl. Instrum. Methods* **A320**, (1992) 66.
4. Particle Data Group, *Phys. Rev.* **D45**, (1992) 1.
5. G. Crawford, *Proceedings of the 2nd Workshop on Tau Lepton Physics*, ed. K. K. Gan, World Scientific, Singapore, 1993.
6. See the contribution by S. Henderson in these Proceedings.
7. M. Artuso et. al., (CLEO) Cornell preprint CLNS 92/1159.
8. D. S. Akerib et. al., (CLEO) Cornell preprint CLNS 92/1163.
9. See for example the contribution by W. Marciano in these Proceedings.
10. B. K. Heltsley, "New CLEO Results in Tau Physics," Cornell preprint CLNS 92/1171, to appear in *Proceedings of the 1992 SLAC Summer Institute*.
11. M. Procario et. al., (CLEO) Cornell preprint CLNS 92/1165.
12. R. S. Galik, *Proceedings of the 2nd Workshop on Tau Lepton Physics*, ed. K. K. Gan, World Scientific, Singapore, 1993.
13. S. Snow (ALEPH), op. cit.; M. Walsh, these Proceedings.

A MEASUREMENT OF THE TAU LEPTON MASS AND A LIMIT ON THE TAU NEUTRINO MASS

STUART D. HENDERSON

High Energy Physics Laboratory, Harvard University, 42 Oxford St., Cambridge, MA, 02138

ABSTRACT

Using data from the CLEO-II detector at CESR, the tau lepton mass has been measured using a novel technique, yielding $1777.6 \pm 0.9 \pm 1.5^{+0.9}_{-0.0}$MeV/$c^2$, where the last uncertainty represents the increase in m_τ for a massive (35 MeV/c^2) neutrino. In addition, a limit on the tau neutrino mass, $M_{\nu_\tau} < 34.6$MeV/c^2 (95% CL), has been obtained from an endpoint analysis of the decay modes $\tau^\pm \to 5\pi^\pm \nu_\tau$ and $\tau^\pm \to 3\pi^\pm 2\pi^0 \nu_\tau$, where the accompanying $\tau^\mp$ decays leptonically.

1. Introduction

The standard model prediction for the tau mass[1] (based on measurements[2] of the electronic branching fraction and tau lifetime) lies 2.3 standard deviations below the present world average.[2] Indeed, recent measurements at BES[3] ($m_\tau = 1776.9 \pm 0.4 \pm 0.3$) and ARGUS[4] ($m_\tau = 1776.3 \pm 2.4 \pm 1.4$ MeV/c^2) indicate a smaller tau mass. We present the results of a novel technique to measure the tau lepton mass with CLEO-II.

Massive neutrinos have been invoked to explain a variety of outstanding problems in particle physics and astrophysics[5]. We present the results of an endpoint analysis of 5 pion final states yielding a limit on the tau neutrino mass.

2. The Tau Mass Measurement

For the two body decay $\tau^- \to h^- \nu_\tau$, where h^- is some hadronic system, the initial τ direction must lie on a cone of half angle θ_- about the hadron direction, given by $\cos\theta_- = (m_\nu^2 - m_\tau^2 - m_{h^-}^2 + 2E_\tau E_{h^-})/(2p_\tau p_{h^-})$. In the absence of initial state radiation, $\tau^+\tau^-$ pairs produced in e^+e^- annihilation are back-to-back and have $E_\tau = E_{beam}$. Therefore, in events in which both τ's decay hadronically, $\tau^+\tau^- \to h^+\bar\nu_\tau h^-\nu_\tau$, the true τ directions lie along the intersection of one cone (given by θ_-) and the parity inversion of the other cone (given by θ_+). Ordinarily, this occurs for two rays. If one imagines shrinking the tau mass, then the two angles θ_+, θ_- decrease and eventually the two cones just touch. This value of the tau mass is the *minimum kinematically allowed tau mass*, M_{min}, since further decrease would require the initial τ directions to no longer be back-to-back. At this point, all decay products lie in a plane and $\pi = \theta_+ + \theta_- + \theta$, where θ is the acolinearity between the two hadronic systems. Given this relation and the measured h^+, h^- momenta and energy, M_{min} may be calculated for the *event*. Monte-Carlo studies reveal that for a perfect detector the

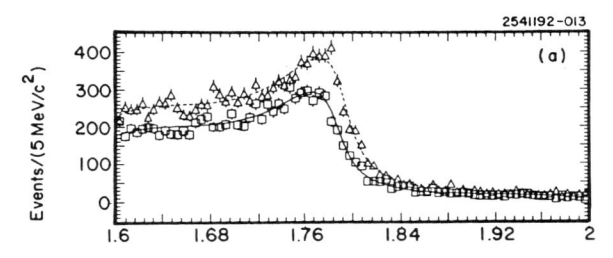

[Figure: Mmin distribution plot, y-axis "Events/(5 MeV/c²)" from 0 to 400, x-axis from 1.6 to 2, label "2541192-013", marker "(a)"]

Figure 1: The M_{min} distribution in the data (squares) is shown compared to a Monte-Carlo simulation (with arbitrary vertical scale) assuming $m_\tau = 1784.1$ MeV/c² (triangles). The fit functions for each have been superimposed. The data are best fit assuming $m_\tau = 1777.6$ MeV/c².

M_{min} distribution displays a pileup of events just below the tau mass, followed by a sharp edge and a very small high-mass tail.

The CLEO-II detector is described in detail in ref. 6. Events of the topology $\pi^\pm n\pi^0$ vs. $\pi^\mp m\pi^0$, where $n, m = 0, 1, 2$ are selected. At least one π^0 in the event is required. Tracks which have no associated π^0 must not be consistent with e or μ. Requirements on visible energy and transverse momentum are applied to suppress Bhabha and two-photon events. Events with excess electromagnetic energy greater than 100 MeV are rejected.

This analysis uses a total luminosity of 1.43 fb⁻¹ (1.31×10^6 $\tau^+\tau^-$ pairs) accumulated on the $\Upsilon(4S)$ resonance and the continuum nearby. The resulting M_{min} distribution is shown in figure 1, compared to a Monte-Carlo simulation assuming $m_\tau = 1784.1$ MeV/c². These distributions have been fit to a functional form consisting of an arctangent curve near the edge multipled by polynomials on either side. The functional form was determined from Monte-Carlo data, and only the overall normalization and position of the edge have been adjusted to fit the data. The data are best described assuming $m_\tau = 1777.6$ MeV/c².

The systematic error on m_τ is due to uncertainties in the calorimeter energy scale (± 1.2 MeV/c²), the momentum scale (± 0.8 MeV/c²), the beam energy scale (± 0.1 MeV/c²) and the fitting procedure (± 0.5 MeV/c²). The combined measurement yields $m_\tau = 1777.6 \pm 0.9 \pm 1.5^{+0.9}_{-0.0}$ MeV/c², where the errors are statistical, systematic, and due to the uncertainty introduced by a neutrino mass of 35 MeV/c². By requiring consistency between this measurement and that of BES at the 1.64 standard deviation level, we derive an upper limit on the tau neutrino mass of 71 MeV/c² (95%CL).

3. The Tau Neutrino Mass Limit

The τ neutrino mass limit has been obtained from an endpoint analysis of the decay modes $\tau \to 5\pi^\pm \nu_\tau$ and $\tau \to 3\pi^\pm 2\pi^0 \nu_\tau$. The accompanying $\tau^\mp$ is required to decay leptonically, so one track isolated by $\geq 90°$ is required to be identified as e or μ. Requirements on visible energy and transverse momentum are utilized to reject Bhabha and two-photon events. Events are required to have excess neutral energy less than 200 MeV in the tag hemisphere, and 400 MeV in the "X" hemisphere.

This analysis uses 1.59 fb^{-1} (1.46 × 10^6 $\tau^+\tau^-$ pairs) of data accumulated on the $\Upsilon(3S)$, $\Upsilon(4S)$ and continuum. The data have been fit using a maximum likelihood technique. For each event the likelihood is calculated, based on the measured 5π invariant mass, the estimated uncertainty in the measurement, the expected detection efficiency and the theoretical invariant mass distribution, which uses the spectral function from KORALB.[9] The data and results of the maximum likelihood fit are summarized and compared to other measurements in table 1. It bears emphasis that the data sample is substantially larger than in previous measurments, and that no events are observed above the tau mass. The quantity P_{mc} is the probability that upon repeating the measurement and accumulating an equal number of events, that the mass limit would be smaller than that which has been measured.

Background has been estimated to be well below one event in each mode studied, based on measurements derived from data as well as Monte-Carlo simulations. The systematic error on the measurement are due to uncertainties in the tau mass (0.5 MeV/c^2), mass scale (1.0 MeV/c^2), mass resolution (1.4 MeV/c^2), and spectral function (1.0 MeV/c^2). The tau neutrino mass limits including the contribution from systematic uncertainty are 110.5 MeV/c^2 ($e(\mu)5\pi^\pm$), and 34.6 MeV/c^2 ($e(\mu)3\pi^\pm 2\pi^0$).

4. References

1. W. Marciano, *Phys. Rev.* **D45**, (1992) R721.
2. Particle Data Group, *Phys. Rev.* **D45**, (1992) 1.
3. J. Bai, et. al., (BES), SLAC preprint SLAC-PUB-5870, (1992).
4. H. Albrecht, et. al., (ARGUS), DESY preprint DESY-92-086, (1992).
5. F. Boehm and P. Vogel, *Physics of Massive Neutrinos*, (Cambridge Univ. Press, 1987).
6. Y. Kubota, et. al., (CLEO), *Nucl. Inst. Meth.* **A320**, (1992) 66.
7. H. Albrecht, et. al., (ARGUS), *Phys. Lett.* **B202**, (1988) 149.
8. H. Albrecht, et. al., (ARGUS), 2nd Workshop on τ lepton Physics, Ohio State Univ., (1992)
9. S. Jadach and Z. Was, *Comput. Phys. Commun.* **64**, (1991) 267.

Table 1: Summary of results of the tau neutrino mass measurements

mode	events	Largest Mass (MeV/c^2)	95% CL Limit (MeV/c^2)	Peak (MeV/c^2)	$P_{mc}(\%)$
$e(\mu)5\pi^\pm$	44	1669 ± 5	110.4	$91.2^{+17.2}_{-19.3}$	96.7 ± 4.5
$e(\mu)3\pi^\pm 2\pi^0$	92	1747 ± 11	34.4	$5.5^{+23.1}_{-5.5}$	24.9 ± 1.7
5π total	136	1747 ± 11	36.7	$17.0^{+15.4}_{-17.0}$	44.2 ± 2.8
ARGUS (Ref. 7)	11	1775 ± 20	31	–	0.6 ± 0.3
ARGUS (Ref. 8)	20	1775 ± 20	31	–	2.0 ± 0.6

τ Mass Measurement from $e\mu$, $e\pi$ and
$(\mu\pi, \mu\mu, \pi\pi)$ Channels at BES/BEPC

Sheng Tian XUE
*Institute of High Energy Physics, Chinese Academy of Sciences
Beijing, 100039, China*

Representing the BES Collaboration

ABSTRACT

The mass of the τ lepton has been measured at the Beijing Electron Positron Collider using the Beijing Spectrometer to perform a search near threshold for $e^+e^- \to \tau^+\tau^-$. Following the analysis for $\tau^+\tau^-$ events with the $e\mu$ topology[1], as a subsequent analysis of our τ mass measurement, events from non-$e\mu$ channels, *i.e.*, with $e\pi$, $\mu\pi$, $\mu\mu$, and $\pi\pi$ topologies, have been analyzed. Using the events with these topologies, the τ mass values from each channel are given, and if the above channels are combined, the result is $m_\tau = 1776.9 \pm 0.3 \pm 0.2$ MeV/c^2.

1. Introduction

In our first paper on the τ mass measurement[1], the $\tau^+\tau^-$ events are identified in the $e\mu$ topology, by requiring that one τ decay via $\tau \to e\nu\bar{\nu}$, and the other via $\tau \to \mu\nu\bar{\nu}$. This article presents additional analyses of the τ mass, useful both for cross-checking and further improving the statistical errors, of events with non-$e\mu$ topologies, *i.e.* $e\pi$, $\mu\mu$, $\mu\pi$, and $\pi\pi$,

$$\begin{aligned} e^+e^- \to \tau^+ \quad & \tau^- \\ & \hookrightarrow e^-\bar{\nu}_e\nu_\tau, \mu^-\bar{\nu}_\mu\nu_\tau, \pi^-\nu_\tau \ . \\ \hookrightarrow e^+\nu_e\bar{\nu}_\tau, \mu^+\nu_\mu\bar{\nu}_\tau, \pi^+\bar{\nu}_\tau & \end{aligned} \quad (1)$$

Results from fits to the energy dependence of the $\tau^+\tau^-$ cross section the τ mass values are given for some of these channels, and from the analysis of the combined channels an overall τ mass is given.

The detector performance, search strategy, and fit method are described in our first paper on the τ mass measurement.[1] Here, the emphasis is on the event selection criteria, the background, and error analysis for the new non-$e\mu$ channels.

2. Event Selection Criteria

The event selection criteria were established based on studies of a sample of Monte Carlo τ lepton pairs and a data sample of 5 million J/ψ. The event selection for all of the non-$e\mu$ candidates requires exactly two oppositely charged tracks, and each track's point of closest approach to the intersection point to satisfy $|x| < 1.5$ cm, $|y| < 1.5$ cm, and $|z| < 15$ cm. In addition, there are individual event selection requirements for each event topology:

2.1. $e\pi$ Event Selection Criteria

The event selection for $e\pi$ candidates requires:[2] $5° < \theta_{acol} < 175°$, $10° < \theta_{acop} < 178°$, and $\theta_{acol} + \theta_{acop} > 50°$; no isolated photons;[3] one track identified as an electron having momentum between 250 MeV/c and the maximum for an electron from τ decay, and the other track identified as a pion having momentum consistent with a pion from $\tau \to \pi\nu_\tau$ decay, using a combination of calorimeter, dE/dx and time-of-flight information.

2.2. $(\mu\pi, \mu\mu, \pi\pi)$ Event Selection Criteria

The event selection for $(\mu\pi, \mu\mu, \pi\pi)$ candidates requires: $5° < \theta_{acol} < 175°$, $25° < \theta_{acop} < 178°$, and $\theta_{acol} + \theta_{acop} > 50°$; no isolated photons; each track having momentum between 550 MeV/c and the maximum for a muon from τ decay, identified as a muon or a pion, using a combination of calorimeter, dE/dx, time-of-flight and μ-counter information.

The numbers of events with different topologies passing the event selection criteria are listed in Table 1.

Table 1: A chronological summary of the $\tau^+\tau^-$ data

Scan Point	W/2 (MeV)	$\mathcal{L}$ (nb^{-1})	$N_{e\mu}$	$N_{e\pi}$	$N_{\mu\pi,\mu\mu,\pi\pi}$
1	1784.19	245.8	2	2	1
2	1780.99	247.7	1	0	1
3	1772.09	232.8	0	0	0
4	1776.57	322.5	0	0	0
5	1778.49	322.5	2	2	1
6	1775.95	296.9	0	0	0
7	1776.75	384.0	0	0	0
8	1776.98	360.8	1	1	0
9	1776.45	794.1	0	0	1
10	1776.62	1109.1	1	1	1
11	1799.51	499.7	5	5	4
12	1789.55	250.0	2	2	3

3. Efficiencies and Background Estimations

Monte Carlo simulations yield the detection efficiencies for each event selection criteria. Background rates are estimated by applying the same requirements to five million events from a dataset at the J/ψ energy. Using the total integrated luminosity of $\sim 5000\,\text{nb}^{-1}$ and an effective background cross section, the background for each topology in the entire $\tau^+\tau^-$ sample is estimated, as listed in Table 2.

Table 2: τ Mass from $\tau^+\tau^-$ Events with Different Topologies

Channel	$e\mu$	$e\pi$	$\mu\pi, \mu\mu, \pi\pi$	all
Number of selected events	14	13	12	39
Number of background events	0.12	0.09	0.24	0.45
Efficiency (%) from Monte Carlo	14.0	19.0		
Efficiency (%) from 2-dim fit	$14.1^{+4.7}_{-3.8}$	$21.0^{+7.3}_{-5.9}$		
$K = \sum_{i=1}^{n} \varepsilon_i B_i$ (%) from 2-dim fit			$0.715^{+0.268}_{-0.215}$	$2.43^{+0.47}_{-0.43}$
$M_\tau(\text{MeV}/c^2)$	$1776.94^{+0.38}_{-0.41}$	$1776.91^{+0.42}_{-0.44}$	$1776.78^{+0.47}_{-0.51}$	$1776.88^{+0.25}_{-0.26}$

4. τ Mass Determination and Error Estimations

4.1. Maximum Likelihood Fit of the τ Mass

The likelihood function used to estimate the τ mass incorporates the $\tau^+\tau^-$ cross section near threshold. The likelihood function is a product of Poisson distributions, one for each center-of-mass energy. At each point, the number of expected events N for each event topology, is given by: $N = [\varepsilon\, B\, \sigma(W, m_\tau) + \sigma_B]\, \mathcal{L}$. Here, ε is the detection efficiency, B is the product branching fraction for $\tau^+\tau^-$ to each event topology, $\mathcal{L}$ is the integrated luminosity, and σ_B is the effective background cross section estimated from the J/ψ data sample for each event topology.

In order to account for uncertainties in the efficiency ε, the branching fraction product and the luminosity, ε for a single channel, or K ($K = \sum_{i=1}^{n} \varepsilon_i B_i$) for n combined channels, is treated as a free parameter in a two-dimensional maximum-likelihood fit for m_τ and ε (or K) to the data of Table 1. Then the estimated m_τ and ε (or K) is obtained. The uncertainty in ε (or K) is equivalent to the uncertainty in the absolute normalization (since the background is small), and is treated as a source of systematic error. The τ mass as well as the statistical error in m_τ is determined from the one-parameter likelihood function with ε (or K) fixed to the value obtained from the two-dimensional fit, as listed in Table 2.

4.2. Systematic Error Estimations

Four independent sources of systematic error are considered: uncertainties in the product $\varepsilon\, B\, \mathcal{L}$, in the absolute beam energy scale, in the beam energy spread, and in the background.

The systematic uncertainty in ε B $\mathcal{L}$ is determined by fixing ε (or K) corresponding to $\pm 1\sigma$ variations obtained in the two-dimensional fit and fitting for m_τ, yielding changes in the mass of Δm_τ for each channel (or combined channels).

The energy scale and the beam energy spread and its variation with center-of-mass energy and beam current are determined from several scans of the J/ψ and $\psi(2S)$. The uncertainty in the absolute beam energy scale yields a systematic uncertainty of $\Delta m_\tau = \pm 0.09\,\mathrm{MeV}/c^2$. The uncertainty in center-of-mass energy spread is ± 0.08 MeV, yielding a systematic error $\Delta m_\tau = \pm 0.02\,\mathrm{MeV}/c^2$.

The systematic error due to the uncertainty in the background is estimated from the 1σ Poisson errors on the corresponding background estimates for each channel or combined channels.

Finally, these independent systematic errors are added in quadrature to yield a total systematic error Δm_τ.

5. Conclusions

From this analysis, the τ mass values for each channel or combined channels are determined to be:

$m_\tau = 1776.9 \pm 0.4^{+0.2}_{-0.3}$ MeV/c^2, for $e\pi$ channel;

$m_\tau = 1776.8 \pm 0.5 \pm 0.3$ MeV/c^2, for $(\mu\pi, \mu\mu, \pi\pi)$ channel;

$m_\tau = 1776.9 \pm 0.3 \pm 0.2$ MeV/c^2, for *all* channels (including $e\mu$) combined.

These results of m_τ from $e\pi$, $(\mu\pi, \mu\mu, \pi\pi)$ and *all* channels are preliminary. The results of m_τ from the different channels are consistent, and combining the channels yields an improved statistical error. Analyses on ee and $e\rho$ channels are in progress.

6. Acknowledgement

We would like to thank the BEPC staff and the Computer Center of IHEP for their outstanding efforts, and also Y.S.Tsai and J.M.Wu for helpful discussions about the $\tau^+\tau^-$ cross section near threshold.

7. References

1. J. Z. Bai et al., *Phys. Rev. Lett.* **69**, 3021 (1992).
2. Acoplanarity, θ_{acop}, is the angle between the planes spanned by the beam direction and the momentum vector of each track, respectively. Acollinearity, θ_{acol}, is the angle between the momentum vectors of the two tracks.
3. An isolated photon has an energy > 40 MeV and is separated from the nearest charged track by $> 14°$.

A MEASUREMENT OF $A_{FB}^{b\bar{b}}$ USING PROMPT LEPTONS AND OF $A_{FB}^{c\bar{c}}$ USING D* IN THE DELPHI EXPERIMENT AT LEP

L.Mirabito

IPN, Lyon, 43 Boulevard du 11 Novembre 69622 Villeurbanne, France

ABSTRACT

We have measured the Forward-Backward asymmetry of the process $e^+e^- \to Z \to b\bar{b}$ where b events were tagged by their semi-leptonic decays. 150,000 $q\bar{q}$ events were collected by DELPHI during the 1991 LEP run at $\sqrt{s} = M_Z$ and when they are combined with the 1990 result on muon asymmetry, we obtain:

$$A_{FB}^{b\bar{b}} = 12.6 \pm 2.9_{\text{stat.+syst.}} \pm 0.4_{\text{mixing}}$$

In a separate analysis, D* mesons with high $X_E = \frac{E_{D^*}}{E_{\text{beam}}}$ were used to measure $A_{FB}^{c\bar{c}}$. About 300 D* at high X_E were reconstructed from 187,000 hadronic events at the Z peak. The measured differential asymmetry corresponds to

$A_{FB}^{c\bar{c}} = 10.7 \pm 7.5_{\text{stat}} \pm 1.3_{\text{syst}}$ and $\sin^2\theta_{\text{eff}} = 0.221 \pm 0.017_{\text{stat}} \pm 0.003_{\text{syst}}$

1. Introduction

The angular distribution of the reaction $e^+e^- \to Z \to f\bar{f}$ can be expressed as:

$$\frac{d\sigma}{d\cos\theta_f} \propto (1 + \cos^2\theta_f + \frac{8}{3}A_{FB}^{ff}\cos\theta_f)$$

with $A_{FB}^{ff} = \frac{\sigma_F - \sigma_B}{\sigma_F + \sigma_B}$. To lowest order, A_{FB}^{ff} at $\sqrt{s} = M_Z$, is directly related to the vector and axial couplings of the fermion $A_{FB}^{ff} = \frac{3}{4}A_e A_f$, $A_i = \frac{a_i v_i}{a_i^2 + v_i^2}$. The higher order corrections of the couplings are large, so the measurement of asymmetries allows an accurate test of the Standard Model.

2. The $A_{FB}^{b\bar{b}}$ measurement using prompt leptons

2.1. Method

We used leptons at high P and high P_t from b semileptonic decays to tag b events. The jets are reconstructed using the JADE algorithm with a $y_{cut} = \frac{m_{ij}^2}{E_{vis}^2} = 0.01$ and the transverse momentum is calculted without including the lepton in the jet, which yields a better b purity at high P_t. The thrust direction oriented by the lepton jet direction is taken as the quark direction.

2.2. Hadronic events selection and leptons selection

Charged tracks are selected in the DELPHI apparatus [1] above 21.5° with good impact parameters and good momentum reconstruction. Only tracks with more than 200 MeV are kept. Neutral tracks are selected above 12° in the electromagnetic calorimeters (HPC, EMF) only, with an energy greater than 700 MeV. The hadronic selection requires at least 7 selected charged tracks and either $E^{\text{charged}} \geq 0.15\sqrt{s}$

or $E^{charged} + E^{Neutral} \geq 0.30\sqrt{s}$. Requiring good detector conditions, we select nearly 150,000 events at the Z° mass in the 1991 data with a Monte Carlo efficiency of $94.4 \pm 0.05_{stat}\%$ and with negligible $\tau^+\tau^-$ and $\gamma\gamma$ contaminations. Details of leptons selections are in reference [3]. The muon efficiency is evaluated to 78 ± 2 % in the barrel, with a pion misidentification probability of 0.8 ± 0.6 %. The efficiency for electrons, only selected in the barrel, is 58 ± 3 % with an hadron misidentification probability of 1.13 %. The efficiencies and contaminations were checked using γ conversions and K° decays.

2.3. Composition and fits

The following array gives purities and composition of our samples for 2 P_t cuts.

Type of process	Value of their asymmetry	Composition of the samples for $l = \mu$		for $l = e$	
		No cut	$P_{Tout} > 1.2$	No cut	$P_{Tout} > 1.2$
f_b : $b \to l^-$ $b \to \tau \to l^-$ $b \to \bar{c} \to l^-$ $b \to \bar{c} \to \tau^- \to l^-$	$A_{FB}^{b\bar{b},exp}$	32.3%	64.0%	37.6%	55.2%
f_{b+} : $\bar{b} \to \bar{c} \to l^-$ $\bar{b} \to \bar{c} \to \tau^- \to l^-$	$-A_{FB}^{b\bar{b},exp}$	13.6%	9.8%	9.9%	10.4%
f_c : $\bar{c} \to l^-$ $\bar{c} \to \tau^- \to l^-$	$-A_{FB}^{c\bar{c}}$	16.3%	8.8%	13.1%	10.6%
f_{Bkg} : Background	A_{FB}^{Bkg}	37.8%	17.4%	39.4%	23.8%

The observed asymmetry is then $A_{FB}^{obs} = \Sigma f_i . A_{FB}^i$. Assuming $A_{FB}^{c\bar{c}} = -0.88 A_{FB}^{b\bar{b}}$, where the -0.88 coefficient was evaluated by a Monte Carlo simulation, the experimental asymmetry with no mixing correction is $A_{FB}^{b\bar{b},exp} = \frac{A_{FB}^{obs} - f_{Bkg}A_{FB}^{Bkg}}{f_b - f_{b+} - 0.88 f_c}$. The evaluation of f_i's relies on Monte Carlo simulation and is sensitive to the fragmentation scheme adopted for c and b quark, and to the semileptonic branching ratios.

For both e and μ samples we used a χ^2 and a maximum likelihood fit. The χ^2 fit either of the local asymmetry $(A_{FB}^{obs}(i) = \frac{N^-(i) - N^+(i)}{N^-(i) + N^+(i)}$, for μ) or of the corrected angular distribution (for e, see figure 1) is used to check validity of the maximum likelihood fit at high P_t. We obtained:

$A_{FB}^{b\bar{b},exp}$ (μ : $P \geq 4$GeV, $P_t \geq 1.6$GeV) = 0.083 ± 0.039(stat) ± 0.011(syst)

$A_{FB}^{b\bar{b},exp}$ (e : $P \geq 4$GeV, $P_t \geq 1.2$GeV) = 0.099 ± 0.062(stat) ± 0.015(syst)

Systematics studies include variation of the fraction f_i, changes in fragmentation parametrisations and in fitting method. In the muon case, the main contribution comes from instabilities in the result when the jet reconstruction or the P_t definition are varied and is estimated to be 1 %.

The maximum likelihood fit is described in reference [2]. Without any P_t cut, (see figure 2 for stability) , we obtain:

$A_{FB}^{b\bar{b},exp}$ (μ : $P \geq 4$GeV) = 0.082 ± 0.030(stat) ± 0.011(syst)

$A_{FB}^{b\bar{b},exp}$ (e : $P \geq 4$GeV) = 0.092 ± 0.039(stat) ± 0.015(syst)

In this case again the main contribution to the systematic uncertainty comes from the instabilities in the reconstruction of jets.

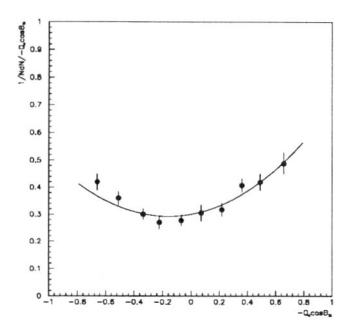

Figure 1: Fit of the polar angle distribution after background subtraction and efficiency correction.

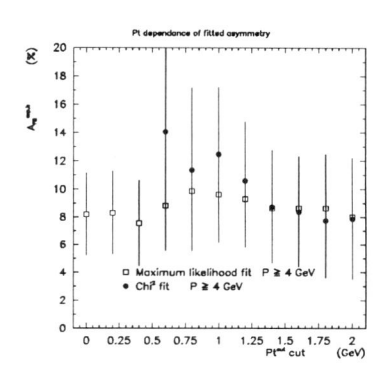

Figure 2: Pt dependances of $A_{FB}^{b\bar{b},exp}$ for various Pt cuts, and for χ^2 and likelihood fits.

2.4. Results and conclusion

Combining the 2 leptons samples and the 1990 result [4], we finally obtained: $A_{FB}^{b\bar{b},exp} = 0.094 \pm 0.021(stat + uncorr.syst) \pm 0.004(corr.syst)$ To obtain the final value of the $b\bar{b}$ forward backward asymmetry, we corrected the previous value for the mean $B^0_{s(d)}\overline{B}^0_{s(d)}$ mixing found at LEP : $\chi = 0.126 \pm 0.012$ [5], which yields :

$$A_{FB}^{b\bar{b}} = 0.126 \pm 0.029(stat + syst) \pm 0.004(mixing)$$

3. The $A_{FB}^{c\bar{c}}$ Measurement using high X_E D*

3.1. D* selection and sample

D*+ are tagged in the $D^0\pi^+$ decay mode, taking advantage of the small mass difference in the decay $\delta m = m_{D^*} - m_{D^0} \sim m_\pi$. D^0's are identified in 2 channels $D^0 \to K^+\pi^-$ and $D^0 \to K^+\pi^-\pi^0$.

We first select hadronic events with more than 5 charged tracks above 20° and above 500 MeV, and require a total charged energy above 0.12 $\sqrt{s}$. At peak, about 187,000 events are selected with an efficiency of 95 %. Main cuts for the D* selection are $1.5\text{GeV} \leq m_{K\pi} \leq 2.5\text{GeV}$, $P_{\pi^{soft}} \leq 4.5\text{GeV}$, and $\delta m \leq 200\text{MeV}$. Details of the selection can be found in reference [6]. In total 342 ± 26 D* with $X_E > 0.2$ from the 2 π mode and 249 ± 31 D* with $X_E > 0.3$ from the 3 π mode are reconstructed. From Monte Carlo, the efficiency for the first mode is $35 \pm 2\%$ and $31 \pm 3\%$ for the second.

3.2. Measurement of A_{FB}^{Obs}

We measure in each bin of $\cos\theta$, $A_{FB}(i)$ and then make a χ^2 fit over the whole range in θ. The respective contributions of D* and background are obtained by fitting the δm spectrum. Finally using 118 ± 18 D* with $X_E > 0.3$ from the 2 π mode and 115 ± 39 D* with $X_E > 0.4$ from the 3 π mode we measured an observed Forward Backward asymmetry:

$$A_{FB}^{obs} = 10.0 \pm 6.6_{stat} \pm 1_{syst} \%$$ with a $\chi^2 = 0.82$ for 7 degrees of freedom.

The 1 % systematic comes from a possible bias in the fit procedure.

3.1. Measurement of $\sin^2\theta_{eff}$ and final results

The observed asymmetry is $A_{FB}^{obs} = R_c A_{FB}^{c\bar{c}} + (1 - R_c) A_{FB}^{b\bar{b},mixed}$ with $A_{FB}^{b\bar{b},mixed} = (1 - 2\chi) A_{FB}^{b\bar{b}}$ and R_c the proportion of D* coming from c. R_c is evaluated with Monte Carlo simulation for the 2 D^o decay modes, the $B\bar{B}$ mixing parameter is calculated from χ_d measurement at lower energy and Monte Carlo predictions. Using the ZFITTER [7] program to account for QED and weak corrections, a fit of the differential asymmetry distribution yields:

$$\sin^2\theta_{eff} = 0.221 \pm 0.017_{stat} \pm 0.003_{syst}$$

Main contributions to the systematic uncertainty comes from the error on χ_d and on the rate of the process $\bar{b} \to W^+ \to c \to D^{*+}$. $A_{FB}^{c\bar{c}}$ is then calculated from this value of $\sin^2\theta_{eff}$ using ZFITTER:

$$A_{FB}^{c\bar{c}} = 10.7 \pm 7.5_{stat} \pm 1.3_{syst} \%$$

4. Conclusion

We report here on 2 preliminary results [2] [6] on heavy quarks asymmetries:

$A_{FB}^{b\bar{b}}$ (prompt leptons) = $12.6 \pm 2.9_{stat+syst} \pm 0.4_{mixing}\%$
$A_{FB}^{c\bar{c}}$ (D*) = $10.7 \pm 7.5_{stat} \pm 1.3_{syst}\%$

Accuracy on these results is in both cases dominated by the statistical uncertainty and will be largely improved by including 1992 DELPHI data.

5. References

1. DELPHI collaboration, P.Abreu et al , *NIM.* **A 303** (1991) 233.
2. DELPHI collaboration, *DELPHI note* 92-96 PHYS 207.
3. DELPHI collaboration, P.Abreu et al, CERN-PPE 92-79.
4. DELPHI collaboration, P.Abreu et al,*Phys. Lett.* **B 276** (1992) 536.
5. G. Smadja, *Contribution to the Physics in Collision Conference*, Boulder (Colorado) USA, June 1992.
6. DELPHI collaboration, M. Elsing, *DELPHI note* 92-51 PHYS 172.
7. D. Bardin et al, CERN-TH 6443/92.

ASYMMETRY AND MIXING IN $Z \to b\bar{b}$ AND $Z \to c\bar{c}$ DECAYS

DOUGLAS WRIGHT
Physics Department, Princeton University
Princeton, NJ 08544, USA

representing the
L3 COLLABORATION

ABSTRACT

Using data collected in 1990 and 1991 with the L3 detector at LEP, the forward-backward asymmetries of $Z \to b\bar{b}$ and $Z \to c\bar{c}$ events and the B^0-$\bar{B}^0$ mixing parameter were measured. Heavy quark events were selected by identifying electrons and muons coming from the semileptonic decay of the quarks. From a fit to the momentum spectra of the lepton pairs we determined the mixing parameter:
$$\chi = 0.121 \pm 0.017 \pm 0.006.$$
From an unbinned maximum likelihood fit to the single lepton and dilepton (p, p_T) spectra we determined the asymmetries:
$$A_{b\bar{b}} = 0.086 \pm 0.015 \pm 0.007$$
$$A_{c\bar{c}} = 0.083 \pm 0.038 \pm 0.027$$
at the effective center-of-mass energy $\sqrt{s} = 91.24$ GeV. Note that $A_{b\bar{b}}$ was corrected for mixing.

1. Introduction

The large number of events produced at the Z mass resonance at LEP provides a unique opportunity for making precision tests of the Standard Model. One such test is a determination of the weak mixing angle from the forward-backward asymmetry in $b\bar{b}$ pairs. By exploiting kinematic features of heavy quark fragmentation and semileptonic decay, an enriched sample of b events can be selected from hadronic Z decays.

Since the analysis was performed on inclusive final state b hadrons, the presence of B^0-$\bar{B}^0$ mixing reduced the experimentally observed asymmetry. The amount of mixing in our sample was determined by fitting the dilepton spectrum and this value was then used to correct the forward-backward asymmetry.

The data used in this analysis was composed of over 410,000 hadronic events collected with the L3 detector at LEP during the running periods of 1990 and 1991.

2. Lepton Identification

The L3 detector was designed to measure leptons and photons with high precision. A detailed description of the detector can be found elsewhere[1]; here the general features of lepton selection are discussed. The signature of an electron was a charged track that matched with a cluster in the electromagnetic calorimeter. The cluster was required to have a transverse shower profile consistent with profiles generated from an electron test beam. Candidates were rejected if there was energy in the hadronic calorimeter associated with the cluster. A muon was identified by requiring a high quality track reconstructed in the muon chambers that had a vertex consistent with the interaction region.

A good understanding of the amount of charge confusion in the lepton identification is important to both the measurement of the asymmetry and the mixing. Analysis of $Z \to \tau^+\tau^-$ data events indicated that charge confusion for electrons was $< 0.8 \pm 0.3\%$ and for muons was $< 0.2 \pm 0.2\%$.

3. Measurement of Asymmetry

An unbinned maximum likelihood fit to the single and dilepton data was performed to determine the observed forward-backward asymmetries of b and c quarks.[2] For each data event, the probability of observing an event with momenta (p, p_T) was calculated from the Monte Carlo lepton spectra. The results of the fit were:

$$A_{b\bar{b}}^{obs} = 0.066 \pm 0.011 \pm 0.004$$
$$A_{c\bar{c}} = 0.083 \pm 0.038 \pm 0.027.$$

Events in the high p_T region determined $A_{b\bar{b}}^{obs}$ while most of the sensitivity to $A_{c\bar{c}}$ came from low p_T muon events. The systematic error in $A_{b\bar{b}}^{obs}$ was dominated by the Monte Carlo statistics used to determine the probability functions. The background asymmetry was found to be consistent with zero from Monte Carlo studies; however, the uncertainty associated with this asymmetry made the largest contribution to the systematic error for $A_{c\bar{c}}$.

As a check on the likelihood fit, the asymmetry can be observed directly in the angular distribution of the data. Making a cut at $p_T > 1$ GeV to enhance the purity of b events, the angular distribution of the data was formed by subtracting the background and correcting for acceptance. Figure 1 shows this angular distribution with the result of the likelihood fit superimposed.

4. Measurement of Mixing

Evidence of B^0-$\bar{B}^0$ mixing in our data was observed as an excess of like sign dilepton events. To determine the mixing parameter χ, an unbinned maximum likelihood fit to the dilepton data was performed.[3] The joint probability of observing the leptons' momenta was assumed to factorize and the single lepton Monte Carlo was used to determine the probability functions. This reduced the systematic error associated with Monte Carlo statistics. The result of this fit was:

$$\chi = .121 \pm 0.017 \pm 0.006.$$

To check the factorization hypothesis, a term in the fit was introduced that could account for possible correlations between the lepton momenta. A fit to the data

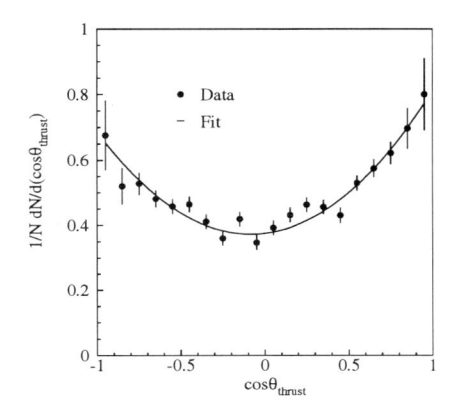

Figure 1: Acceptance corrected angular distribution with $p_T > 1$ GeV.

indicated that the correlation was compatible with zero. Independent analyses of the same data with a counting method and with a 4-dimensional fit to the momentum spectra were found to be in good agreement with the factorized fit.

5. Conclusion

Correcting the observed forward-backward asymmetry for mixing yielded:

$$A_{b\bar{b}} = 0.086 \pm 0.015 \pm 0.007.$$

A Standard Model fit to the asymmetry gave a determination of the effective weak mixing angle:

$$\sin^2\bar{\theta}_W = .2336 \pm 0.0029$$

at an effective center-of-mass energy of 91.24 GeV. This result is in excellent agreement with our previous measurement and with other LEP measurements of the weak mixing angle.

References

1. L3 Collab., B. Adeva et al., *Nucl. Inst. Meth.* **A289** (1990) 35.
2. L3 Collab., B. Adeva et al., *Phys. Lett.* **B288** (1992) 395.
3. L3 Collab., B. Adeva et al., CERN-PPE/92-121, 21 July 1992 to appear in *Phys. Lett.* (1992).

MEASUREMENTS OF $\Gamma(Z \to b\bar{b})$ AND $\Gamma(Z \to c\bar{c})$ AT LEP FROM OPAL

DEAN HINSHAW
Université de Montréal
Montréal, Quebec H3C 3J7, CANADA

ABSTRACT

I report on two measurements of the partial width of Z decays to quarks using data from the Opal detector at LEP. Using a sample of 673 charged D^*'s we performed a fit to the D^* energy spectrum and measured $\Gamma(Z \to c\bar{c}) = 327 \pm 53$ MeV/c^2. Using a 'mixed tag' method, whereby we combine information from a high p_t electron tag with that from an impact parameter tag, we measured $\Gamma(Z \to b\bar{b}) = 379 \pm 28$ MeV/c^2, independent of assumptions on b quark decay properties. The first measurement is an update of a previously published result, and the second measurement is preliminary. I also quote measurements of the average partial widths of Z to u-type and d-type quarks, based on a measurement of $\Gamma(Z \to q\bar{q}\gamma)$, also updated from a previous publication.

1. Introduction

The analyses presented here are based on data recorded with the Opal detector during the 1990 and 1991 data taking runs at LEP. The data set corresponds to $\sim$ 500K multihadronic events. A detailed description of the Opal detector can be found elsewhere[1]. The main components of the detector crucial to these analyses are the three drift chambers of the central detector, the electromagnetic barrel calorimeter and the silicon micro-vertex detector, which was only operational for the 1991 run.

2. Measurement of $\Gamma(Z \to c\bar{c})$

In this analysis we begin by selecting a sample of charge D^* candidates via the decay chain $D^{*+} \to D^0\pi^+, D^0 \to K^-\pi^+$ (charge conjugation is implied here and throughout this report). Cuts are made on $x_{D^*}(= 2E_{D^*}/E_{cm})$, the invariant mass of the D^0 candidate, the mass difference of the D^* and D^0 candidates, the dE/dx particle identification probability for the kaon candidate, and $\cos\theta^*$, where θ^* is the angle of the kaon direction in the rest frame of the D^0 with respect to the D^0 boost direction. The background is determined using the D^0 mass distribution for D^{*+} candidates where the $K\pi$ combination from the D^0 have the same charge. We find a total of 673 ± 33 D^{*+} canidates over a background of 446 ± 18. The efficiency for tagging D^{*+} was determined using a Monte Carlo sample of D^{*+}'s which decay into the searched for decay chain.

A fit is made to the x_{D^*} distribution in order to extract the value of $\Gamma(Z \to c\bar{c})$. The form of the fitting function is

$$f(x_{D^*}) = 2[F_b \cdot P_b \cdot d_b(x_{D^*}) + F_c \cdot P_c \cdot d_c(x_{D^*})] + b(x_{D^*})$$

where

$F_q = \Gamma(Z \to q\bar{q})/\Gamma(Z \to hadrons)$,
$P_q = BR(q \to D^*) \cdot BR(D^* \to D^0\pi \to \pi K\pi)$,
$d_q(x_{D^*})$ is a function describing the shape of the x_{D^*} distribution and
$b(x_{D^*})$ is a function describing the background distribution.

The shape for $d_c(x_{D^*})$ is taken to be the Peterson fragmentation function with x_{D^*} replacing z. The Peterson parameter ϵ_c is left as a free parameter as well as F_c. The other parameters are taken from Monte Carlo simulations or available experimental measurements. The function $b(x_{D^*})$ is parameterized from the data. An unbinned log-likelyhood fit is used to fit the function to the data. Systematic effects of the fit are studied due to uncertainties in the background, the efficiency, and the shape, rate and hardness of $b \to D^*$ production. The fit plus the systematic studies yield a final result of $\Gamma(Z \to c\bar{c}) = (327 \pm 32 \pm 42)$ MeV/c^2, where the first error is the combined statistical error and systematic error specific to this analysis, and the second error is the systematic error due to external sources.

3. Measurement of $\Gamma(Z \to b\bar{b})$

In this measurement we use two independent methods for tagging $Z \to b\bar{b}$ events. Both tags are done on a hemisphere basis, with the event divided by the plane perpendicular to the thrust axis. The first method uses a high p_t electron tag. The method of identifying electrons is described in detail elsewhere[2]. We tag hemispheres where an electron has $p > 4.0$ GeV/c and $p_t > 0.8$ GeV/c. The second method counts the number of tracks in the hemisphere which are significantly separated from the primary vertex. The impact parameter in the xy plane (d_0) of a track is signed with respect to the jet axis. For 1990 (1991) data, a hemisphere is tagged if two or more tracks have a value of d_0/σ_{d_0} greater than 1.5 (2.5). This last tagging method is referred to as the forward multiplicity tag. One can then count the number of tagged hemispheres and express the results in terms of the following 4 equations:

$$f_v = \epsilon_v \frac{\Gamma_{b\bar{b}}}{\Gamma_{had}} + \rho_v^c \frac{\Gamma_{c\bar{c}}}{\Gamma_{had}} + \rho_v^{uds}(1 - \frac{\Gamma_{b\bar{b}}}{\Gamma_{had}} - \frac{\Gamma_{c\bar{c}}}{\Gamma_{had}}),$$

$$f_l = \epsilon_l \frac{\Gamma_{b\bar{b}}}{\Gamma_{had}} + \Delta_c \frac{\Gamma_{c\bar{c}}}{\Gamma_{had}} + \Delta_{uds}(1 - \frac{\Gamma_{b\bar{b}}}{\Gamma_{had}} - \frac{\Gamma_{c\bar{c}}}{\Gamma_{had}}),$$

$$f_{vv} = \epsilon_v^2 \frac{\Gamma_{b\bar{b}}}{\Gamma_{had}} + (\rho_v^c)^2 \frac{\Gamma_{c\bar{c}}}{\Gamma_{had}} + (\rho_v^{uds})^2(1 - \frac{\Gamma_{b\bar{b}}}{\Gamma_{had}} - \frac{\Gamma_{c\bar{c}}}{\Gamma_{had}}),$$

$$\frac{f_{lv}}{2} = \epsilon_l\epsilon_v \frac{\Gamma_{b\bar{b}}}{\Gamma_{had}} + \rho_v^c\Delta_c \frac{\Gamma_{c\bar{c}}}{\Gamma_{had}} + \rho_v^{uds}\Delta_{uds}(1 - \frac{\Gamma_{b\bar{b}}}{\Gamma_{had}} - \frac{\Gamma_{c\bar{c}}}{\Gamma_{had}}),$$

where

- f_v is the fraction of hemispheres tagged by forward multiplicity,
- f_l is the fraction of hemispheres tagged by an electron,
- f_{vv} is the fraction of events with a forward multiplicity tag in both hemispheres,
- f_{lv} is the fraction of events with an electron tag in one hemisphere and a forward multiplicity tag in the other,
- ϵ_v is the efficiency to select a b quark hemisphere with the forward multiplicity tag,
- ϵ_l is the efficiency to select a b quark hemisphere with the electron tag,
- ρ_v^c is the probability to select a c quark hemisphere with the forward multiplicity tag,
- ρ_v^{uds} is the probability to select an u, d or s quark hemisphere with the forward multiplicity tag,
- Δ_c is the probability to select a c quark hemispheres by the electron tag, and
- Δ_{uds} is the probability to select an u, d or s quark hemispheres by the electron tag.

We choose to solve for $\Gamma_{b\bar{b}}/\Gamma_{had}$, ϵ_v, ϵ_l and ρ_v^c. The values of the remaining parameters are determined from the data itself, Monte Carlo simulations, and in the case of $\Gamma_{c\bar{c}}/\Gamma_{had}$, available experimental measurements. Because the equations imply integration over all variables on which the efficiencies are dependant, it is necessary to bin the results in $\cos\theta_{thrust}$. The equations are solved using a χ^2 method which allows one to solve for $\Gamma_{b\bar{b}}/\Gamma_{had}$ simultaneously over all kinematic subranges. Systematic errors are taken into account for uncertainties in all the input values to the equations. Systematics are also considered for dependance on the forward multiplicity cuts and jet multiplicity, and for azimuthal correlations. The final result is $\Gamma_{b\bar{b}}/\Gamma_{had} = 0.218 \pm 0.013(stat) \pm 0.010(syst)$, which corresponds to $\Gamma(Z \to b\bar{b}) = 379 \pm 28$ MeV/c.

4. Measurement of Γ_{u-type} and Γ_{d-type}

Opal has also performed a measurement of $\Gamma(Z \to q\bar{q}\gamma)$. Because the dependence on the elctroweak charges is different from that of $\Gamma(Z \to q\bar{q})$, one can use this measurement along with a measurement of the total hadronic width to determine values for the average partial widths to up-type and down-type quarks[3]. The final results for this analysis are $\Gamma_{u-type} = 242 \pm 46$ MeV/c and $\Gamma_{d-type} = 419 \pm 30$ MeV/c.

5. References

1. K. Ahmet et al., *Nucl. Instr. Meth.* **A305** (1991) 275;
   P. P. Allport et al., *The OPAL Silicon Microvertex Detector* (Submitted to Nucl. Instr. Meth.).
2. P. Acton et al., *Z. Phys.* **C55** (1992) 191.
3. P. Mättig and W. Zeuner, *Z. Phys.* **C52** (1991) 31.

THE FORWARD-BACKWARD ASYMMETRY OF QUARKS IN Z^0 DECAYS AT OPAL

Presented on behalf of the OPAL Collaboration by

P. S. WELLS

CERN, CH-1211 Geneva 23, SWITZERLAND

ABSTRACT

Measurements of the b asymmetry using a lepton tag, c asymmetry using a D* tag and the average charge asymmetry of hadronic Z^0 decays are presented.

1. Introduction

The differential cross section for fermion pair production in e^+e^- annihilation has the form: $1 + \cos^2\theta + (8/3)A_{FB}^f \cos\theta$, where θ is the angle between the directions of the incoming e^- and the outgoing particle. This form makes explicit the resulting forward-backward asymmetry, A_{FB}^f. The quark asymmetries are experimentally challenging, because the quark direction, and the distinction between q and $\bar{q}$, must be deduced from the final state particles. The OPAL experiment at LEP has collected about half a million hadronic Z^0 decays in 1990 and 1991. Preliminary measurements from b and c enriched samples and a published measurement of the average charge asymmetry of $Z^0 \to q\bar{q}$ are described here.

2. The b quark forward-backward asymmetry using a lepton tag

Their large mass, hard fragmentation and semileptonic decays allow b hadrons to be tagged by leptons with high momentum, p, and momentum component transverse to the associated jet, p_t. Electrons ($p > 2, p_t > 0.8\,\text{GeV}/c$) are identified by the track ionisation, dE/dx, the ratio of the electromagnetic energy deposited to the track momentum, and the electromagnetic shower shape[1]. Muons ($p > 4.5, p_t > 1\,\text{GeV}/c$), are identified by a positional match between the extrapolated track and a muon segment constructed from hits in the outer muon chambers. The quark direction is estimated from the thrust axis and lepton charge, Q. Writing $y = -Q\cos\theta_{\text{thrust}}$, the observed distribution is a sum over sources, s:

$$\frac{d\sigma}{dy} \propto \sum_s f_s \left(1 + y^2 + \frac{8}{3}A_{FB}^s\, y\right) \epsilon_s(|y|) \qquad (1)$$

where f_s is the fraction of each source, and ϵ_s the detection efficiency, which is a symmetric function of y. Contributions from b or c hadron decays (and their asymmetries) are: $b \to \ell^-$ (A_{FB}^b), $b \to c \to \ell^+$ ($-A_{FB}^b$), $b \to \bar{c} \to \ell^-$ (A_{FB}^b) and $c \to \ell^+$ ($-A_{FB}^c$). The direct b decay comprises 78% (77%) for e (μ) events, including 1% $b \to \tau^- \to \ell^-$, the cascade processes contribute 10% (7%), and the direct charm decay 6% (4%). The backgrounds from converted photons and misidentified hadrons have zero asymmetry, and form 6% (12%) of the e (μ) samples.

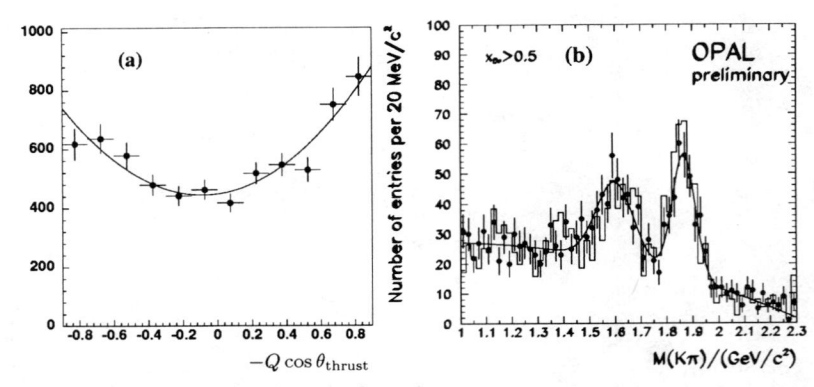

Figure 1: (a) The efficiency corrected $-Q\cos\theta_{\text{thrust}}$ distributions for muons. The curve is the fit result. (b) The $K^-\pi^+$ mass distribution for data (points) and Monte Carlo (histogram).

Because of the $\sqrt{s}$ dependence of the asymmetry, this measurement only uses data with $\sqrt{s} = M_Z$, (5167 e, 6074 μ candidates). For the muons, the fake and $c\bar{c}$ backgrounds are subtracted and the binned distribution is corrected for efficiency before fitting to the form of Eq.(1) for A^b_{FB} (see fig. 1(a)). For the electrons, ϵ_s has the same form for all sources to a good approximation. Using an event by event log-likelihood fit for A^b_{FB}, the symmetric efficiency then only adds a constant offset, and its exact form need not be known.

The branching ratios $Br(b \to \ell)$ and $Br(b \to c \to \ell^+)$ are derived from CLEO measurements[1]. The error from using different semileptonic decay models gives an anticorrelation between $Br(b \to \ell)$ and $Br(b \to c \to \ell^+)$, and therefore an increase in the systematic error as these sources have the opposite sign of asymmetry. The total error due to b semileptonic branching ratios with a self consistent treatment of the modelling uncertainties is $\pm 0.006(e), \pm 0.003(\mu)$. The dependence of the average electron identification efficiency on the source is uncertain, leading to an error via the f_s. The Standard Model prediction of $A^c_{FB} = 0.0542$ is used, with the range $0 < A^c_{FB} < 0.11$. The b and c fragmentation uncertainties, and detector resolution effects also contribute. The asymmetry must be corrected for the effect of $B^0\overline{B^0}$ mixing, which dilutes the observed asymmetry by $1/(1-2\chi)$, where χ is the average b mixing parameter[2]. Taking into account common errors, the combined result is:

$$A^b_{FB} = 0.099 \pm 0.018(stat) \pm 0.010(sys) \pm 0.006(mixing).$$

3. The c quark forward-backward asymmetry using a D* tag

Almost all D* mesons are produced in $b\bar{b}$ and $c\bar{c}$ events. In order to increase statistics for the asymmetry measurement, two decay modes are used: the standard decay[3,4], $D^{*+} \to D^0\pi^+ \to (K^-\pi^+)\pi^+$, and $D^{*+} \to D^0\pi^+ \to (K^-\pi^+\pi^0)\pi^+$, where the π^0 is undetected. The $K^-\pi^+$ mass spectrum is shown in fig. 1(b). The two D^0 decay modes are clear, as is the good agreement with the Monte Carlo simulation[5].

The energy of the D* divided by the beam energy, x_{D^*}, is used to separate $b\bar{b}$ and $c\bar{c}$ events. For the $(K^-\pi^+\pi^0)\pi^+$ mode, x_{D^*} is inferred from the slow π^+ from the D* decay, assuming the D^0 and π^+ are at rest in the D* rest frame. This method is tested with the $(K^-\pi^+)\pi^+$ mode and is reliable for $x_{D^*} < 0.9$.

The combinatorial background is estimated from events where the charged pions have opposite charge, and the efficiency of the D* identification as a function of x_{D^*} and $\cos\theta_{\text{thrust}}$ is taken from Monte Carlo[5]. To ensure a high purity (78%) of $c\bar{c}$ events, only those with $x_{D^*} > 0.5$ are used for the asymmetry measurement, resulting in samples of 515 (112, 167) events with $\sqrt{s} = M_Z$, ($\sqrt{s} < M_Z$, $\sqrt{s} > M_Z$). The thrust axis and D* charge are used to estimate the quark direction.

An event by event likelihood fit is used, with the fractions of each source a function of x_{D^*}. The effective $b\bar{b}$ asymmetry is derived from the lepton result above, taking into account the expected $B^0\overline{B^0}$ mixing for the predicted relative fractions of b hadrons. The dominant systematic errors arise from possible variations in background acceptance and asymmetry (± 0.018) and the measurement of x_{D^*} for the $(K^-\pi^+\pi^0)\pi^+$ mode (± 0.010), with small errors from the b and c fragmentation parameters, A_{FB}^b, and detector resolution effects. The final results are:

$$A_{FB}^c = 0.064 \pm 0.049(stat) \pm 0.022(sys) \quad \sqrt{s} = M_Z,$$
$$A_{FB}^c = -0.085 \pm 0.130(stat) \pm 0.032(sys) \quad 88.4\,\text{GeV} < \sqrt{s} < 90.3\,\text{GeV},$$
$$A_{FB}^c = 0.290 \pm 0.100(stat) \pm 0.032(sys) \quad 91.9\,\text{GeV} < \sqrt{s} < 93.8\,\text{GeV}.$$

4. The average forward-backward charge asymmetry of hadronic events

The average forward-backward charge asymmetry, A_{FB}^{had}, in hadronic Z^0 decays is measured within the context of the Standard Model[6]. A weight function method is used to estimate on a statistical basis the number of events in which the negative parton was in the forward direction in bins of $\cos\theta$. The contributions of up-type and down-type quarks partially cancel. Monte Carlo (MC) simulation provides the relationship between the leading tracks in an event and the quark charge. The dominant errors arise from the modelling of the quark fragmentation. The effective $\sin^2\overline{\theta_W}$ in the MC is tuned so that the MC asymmetry matches the data:

$$A_{FB}^{\text{had}} = 0.040 \pm 0.004(stat) \pm 0.006(sys) \pm 0.002(mixing)$$
$$\sin^2\overline{\theta_W} = 0.2321 \pm 0.0017(stat) \pm 0.0027(sys) \pm 0.0009(mixing)$$

References

1. OPAL Collab, CERN-PPE/91-38, to be published in *Z. Phys. C*
2. Talk by J. F. Kral in these procedings.
3. Talk by D. Hinshaw in these procedings.
4. OPAL Collab, *Phys. Lett.* **B262** (1991) 341.
5. J. Allison et al., *Nucl. Instr. Meth.* **A317** (1991) 47. OPAL Collab, *Z. Phys.* **C 47** (1990) 505. For lepton analyses Peterson fragmentation is used, instead of the default Lund Symmetric scheme.
6. OPAL Collab, CERN-PPE/91-119, submitted to *Phys. Lett.*.

A STUDY OF $\Gamma(b\bar{b})/\Gamma(had)$ AND $\Gamma(c\bar{c})/\Gamma(had)$ AND THE FORWARD–BACKWARD ASYMMETRY IN $Z^0 \to b\bar{b}$

Leo Bellantoni*
University of Wisconsin–Madison

ALEPH Collaboration

ABSTRACT

The yield of prompt leptons in 450,000 hadronic decays of the Z^0 recorded with the ALEPH detector at LEP has been analyzed to determine the rates of Z^0 decays into $b\bar{b}$ and $c\bar{c}$. These have been measured to be $\Gamma(b\bar{b})/\Gamma(had) = (21.1 \pm 0.7 \pm 0.8)\%$ and $\Gamma(c\bar{c})/\Gamma(had) = (17.0 \pm 1.0 \pm 2.2)\%$. From a sample of prompt leptons with a high momentum transverse to their jet, the forward–backward asymmetry in $Z^0 \to b\bar{b}$ has been measured to be $A^b_{FB} = (8.3 \pm 1.8 \pm 0.6)\%$.

1. Introduction

An important observable of the standard model is $\Gamma(b\bar{b})/\Gamma(had)$, because of diagrams diagrams with triangles at the $Z^0 b\bar{b}$ vertex involving the top quark. These diagrams occur only in $Z^0 \to b\bar{b}$, and cancel diagrams with top loops on the Z^0 propagator, which occur in all hadronic decays of the Z^0. Consequently, $\Gamma(b\bar{b})$ has little top mass dependence, but $\Gamma(b\bar{b})/\Gamma(had)$ does – and in the measurement of $\Gamma(b\bar{b})/\Gamma(had)$, there is a cancellation of many systematic errors. The partial width $Z^0 \to c\bar{c}$ is also precisely predicted[1]. Both $\Gamma(b\bar{b})/\Gamma(had)$ and $\Gamma(c\bar{c})/\Gamma(had)$ are relatively independent of M_H.

A second important quantity is the forward-backward asymmetry of $Z^0 \to b\bar{b}$, defined as

$$A^b_{FB} = \frac{\int_0^{+1} \frac{\partial \sigma}{\partial \cos(\theta)} d\cos(\theta) - \int_0^{-1} \frac{\partial \sigma}{\partial \cos(\theta)} d\cos(\theta)}{\int_{-1}^{+1} \frac{\partial \sigma}{\partial \cos(\theta)} d\cos(\theta)}$$

where the angle θ is zero when the produced b quark has the same direction as the incident e^-. This quantity is a sensitive measure of $\sin^2(\theta_W)$ in the standard model.

Beauty and charm are easily measured at LEP because b and c hadrons have the semileptonic decays $e\nu X$ and $\mu\nu X$. These decays produce leptons with a high momentum and a high momentum perpendicular ($P_\perp$) to the jets produced from the other decay products of the b and c quarks, and which are consequently easy to measure. The $P_\perp$ spectrum for $(b \to l)$ is harder than for $(c \to l)$ and $(b \to c \to l)$ because of the high mass of the b quark. The momentum spectra are also different for these three processes; the $(b \to l)$ spectrum is the hardest because of the high momentum of the primary b hadron, and the $(b \to c \to l)$ spectrum is the softest, due to the multibody cascade nature of this channel.

---
* Supported by the US Department of Energy, contract DE-AC02-76ER00881.

ALEPH is a large, general purpose detector which has been described in detail elsewhere[2]. Electrons are identified by matching a charged track to an energy deposits in the electromagnetic shower calorimeter. Muons are identified by matching a charged track to a pattern of hits in the hadron calorimeter and muon chambers[3].

2. Fit to determine $\Gamma(b\bar{b})/\Gamma(had)$ and $\Gamma(c\bar{c})/\Gamma(had)$

$\Gamma(b\bar{b})/\Gamma(had)$ and $\Gamma(c\bar{c})/\Gamma(had)$ are determined by fitting the P and $P_\perp$ spectra of the identified leptons simultaneously with the spectra of events with two leptons in them. In the fitting procedure, the values of $\mathrm{Br}(b \to l\nu X)$ and $\mathrm{Br}(c \to l\nu X)$ are allowed to float, along with the rate of B-$\bar{\mathrm{B}}$ mixing. More information about this procedure is available in another contribution[4]. From a sample of 18.6 pb^{-1} of data taken in 1990 and 1991, $\Gamma(b\bar{b})/\Gamma(had) = (21.1 \pm 0.7 \pm 0.8)\%$ and $\Gamma(c\bar{c})/\Gamma(had) = (17.0 \pm 1.0 \pm 2.2)\%$. The correlation between $\Gamma(b\bar{b})/\Gamma(had)$ and $\Gamma(c\bar{c})/\Gamma(had)$ is -26%.

3. Fit to determine A_{FB}^b

The measurement of A_{FB}^b requires distinguishing the b quark from the $\bar{b}$, and this is done by looking at the electric charge of the lepton produced in semileptonic b decay. The direction of the $b\bar{b}$ pair is taken to be the direction of the event's thrust axis. The scattering angle θ_a is defined by

$$\cos(\theta_a) = -(lepton\ charge)[\hat{e} \cdot \hat{T}]$$

where $\hat{e}$ is the initial direction of the electron beam, and $\hat{T}$ is the direction of that half of the thrust axis which is closest to the lepton. (If several leptons are detected in the event, the one of highest $P_\perp$ is used.)

The distribution of $\cos(\theta_a)$ is corrected for angle dependent detection efficiencies and fit to

$$1 + \cos^2(\theta_a) + (8/3)A_{FB}^{obs}\cos(\theta_a)$$

in the region $-0.9 < \cos(\theta_a) < +0.9$, with only the observed asymmetry A_{FB}^{obs} allowed to float. Table 1 gives A_{FB}^{obs} for four different beam energies. Figure 1 shows the fit to the asymmetry for data collected on the peak of the Z^0 resonance.

The asymmetry is measured using only leptons with P over 3 GeV and $P_\perp$ over 1 GeV. Table 2 lists the lepton source fractions for 1991 data.

The observed asymmetry is related to A_{FB}^b via

$$A_{FB}^{obs} = A_{FB}^b(f_{(b \to l)} + f_{(b \to (\bar{c}s) \to l)} + f_{(b \to \tau \to l)})(1 - 2\chi) \qquad (1)$$
$$+ A_{FB}^b(-f_{(b \to c \to l)})(1 - 2\chi) \qquad (2)$$
$$+ A_{FB}^c(-f_{(c \to l)}) \qquad (3)$$
$$+ A_{FB}^{bckgrnd}(+f_{bckgrnd}). \qquad (4)$$

Terms (1) and (2) are the asymmetry due to $b\bar{b}$ events. The process ($b \to c \to l$) produces leptons with a charge opposite to the ones created from ($b \to l$), and

C.O.M. energy	Raw Asymmetry	Statistical Error
$M_Z - 1$	0.047	0.038
M_Z	0.0456	0.0097
$M_Z + 0.8$	0.020	0.043
$M_Z + 1$	0.040	0.050

Table 1: A_{FB}^{obs} fit results (preliminary)

Process	Electrons	Muons
$(b \to l)$	0.841	0.776
$(b \to c \to l)$	0.063	0.061
$(b \to (\bar{c}s) \to l)$	0.010	0.010
$(b \to \tau \to l)$	0.010	0.014
$(c \to l)$	0.042	0.044
backgrounds	0.034	0.096

Table 2: Composition of leptons with $P > 3$ Gev, $P_\perp > 1$ GeV

so the contribution due to this process is subtracted. B-$\bar{\text{B}}$ mixing also dilutes the asymmetry by a factor of $(1 - 2\chi)$, where $\chi = 0.134 \pm 0.015$ from the fit of section 2 and a jet-charge based measurement[5]. Term (3) is the contribution due to $c\bar{c}$ events. A_{FB}^c is not measured, but instead taken from the standard model relation between A_{FB}^c and A_{FB}^b. The small background asymmetry $(1.1\pm2.5\%)$ is estimated from Monte Carlo simulations.

To interpret the results in Table 1, the off-peak measurements are corrected to values corresponding to data taken on-peak using the standard model prediction for the beam energy dependance of A_{FB}^b. This gives $A_{FB}^b(peak) = (8.3\pm1.8\pm0.6)\%$. The effective $\sin^2(\theta_W)$ is computed by applying corrections for QED effects in both the initial and final states, photon exchange diagrams, γ/Z^0 interference and final state gluon radiation. These corrections give a Born level value of $A_{FB}^{b(0)} = (8.8 \pm 1.9 \pm 0.6)\%$, which corresponds to $\sin^2(\theta_W)$ (eff.) $= 0.2343 \pm 0.0038$.

4. Acknowledgements

I am happy to thank Reisaburo Tanaka for the calculation of $\sin^2(\theta_W)$.

Source	Variation	ΔA_{FB}^b
$\chi = 0.134$	±0.015	0.0043
$Br(b \to l\nu X)$	10%	0.0024
$Br(b \to c \to l)$	10%	0.0007
$Br(b \to W \to \bar{c}s)$	50%	0.0011
$Br(c \to l\nu X)$	15%	0.0013
ϵ_b	1σ	0.0004
ϵ_c	1σ	0.0005
A_{FB}^{bkg}	1σ	0.0023
Bkg uncertainty	-	0.0014
Monte Carlo statistics	-	0.0004
Total		0.0059

Table 3: A_{FB}^b systematic errors (preliminary)

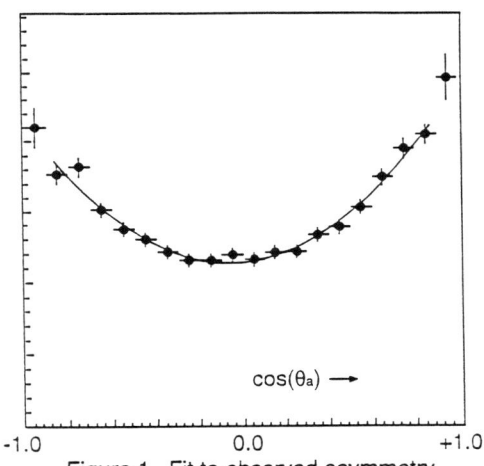

Figure 1. Fit to observed asymmetry

5. References

1. G. Altarelli, R. Kleiss, C. Verzegnassi, ed. *Z Physics at LEP1, Vol. 1, CERN 89-08*
2. ALEPH Collab., D. Decamp, *et al. Nucl. Instr. Meth.* **A294** (1990) 121
3. ALEPH Collab., D. Decamp, *et al. Phys. Lett.* **B244** (1990) 551
   ALEPH Collab., D. Decamp, *et al. Phys. Lett.* **B263** (1991) 325
4. L. Bellantoni for the ALEPH collaboration, Session C3, abstract 223 of these proceedings.
5. ALEPH Collab., D. Buskulic, D. Decamp, *et al. Phys. Lett.* **B284** (1992) 177

A PRELIMINARY MEASUREMENT OF $R_b = \dfrac{\Gamma(Z^0 \to b\bar{b})}{\Gamma(Z^0 \to \text{hadrons})}$ AT SLD*

THE SLD COLLABORATION
Represented By

D. SU

*Rutherford Appleton Laboratory
Chilton, Didcot, Oxon, England*

ABSTRACT

We present a preliminary measurement of R_b, the ratio of $\Gamma(Z^0 \to b\bar{b})$ relative to $\Gamma(Z^0 \to \text{Hadrons})$ using the silicon CCD-pixel vertex detector of the SLD at the SLAC Linear Collider (SLC). An impact parameter method and a displaced vertex method are applied to all charged tracks, to efficiently tag $Z^0 \to b\bar{b}$ events. From the impact (displaced vertex) approach we find $R_b = 0.231 \pm 0.012 \pm 0.026$ ($R_b = 0.213 \pm 0.011 \pm 0.029$), consistent with the standard model value.

1. Introduction

The branching fraction ratio R_b measures the sum of the squares of the vector and axial vector couplings of the b-quark to the Z^0. As the CKM parameter $V_{tb} \approx 1$ one anticipates large vertex and external radiative corrections ($\Delta V \propto (M_t/M_Z)^2$) for $M_t \gg M_Z$. R_b isolates the vertex corrections, as oblique corrections largely cancel in the ratio, being common to all fermions.[1] This is reflected in the weak dependence of R_b on $\sin^2\theta_W$, and on QCD corrections.[i] These insensitivity's to conventional rad. corrections make R_b an excellent variable in the search for new physics once M_t is known, and if $\delta R_b \sim 1\%$ can be obtained. We present herein preliminary results on the measurement of R_b from a sample of 11.6K Z^0 events (<e⁻ polarization> ≈ 22%) collected at $\sqrt{s} = 91.55$ GeV in the SLD at the SLC, using a CCD vertex detector. Z^0 events containing b-decays are tagged by two techniques; one similar to that used by MarkII,[2] namely the counting of *all* tracks with large impact parameters (b) to the interaction point (IP), and one that counts displaced vertices from b and c-quark decays directly. High efficiencies and purities are achieved as *both* hadrons and leptons are included in the tagging procedures.

2. Detector Description and Tracking Performance

For this analysis, only a subset of the elements of SLD are utilized; the central drift chamber (CDC)[3] covering 85% 4π sr, the CCD vertex detector (VXD)[4] covering 75% 4π sr, and the liquid argon calorimeter (LAC), covering 95% 4π sr.[5] The LAC is used in the SLD trigger. Charged tracks are reconstructed in the CDC and linked with

---

* Work supported in part by the U.S.Department of Energy Under Contract DE-AC03-76SF00515
[i] Oblique corrections renormalize the value of $\sin^2\theta_W$ (as characterized by $\Delta\rho$). The fractional change in Rb is less than 5% of any fractional change induced in $\sin^2\theta_W$. Similarly, a 10% change in α_s results in a 0.05% change in R_b.

pixel-clusters in the VXD. A combined fit using the Billior method[6] is performed, to properly account for multiple scattering as the track is extrapolated through the VXD material and the 25mm radius Be-beam pipe, into the IP. The angular errors of the CDC combined with local $<\delta\phi>$ and $<\delta Rz>$ of VXD clusters of 5μm and 8μm, respectively, lead to XY(plane $\perp$ to the e^+e^- beams) and Rz (plane containing the beam axis) impact resolutions of $(\alpha,\beta)_\phi$ = (13μm, 70μm) and $(\alpha,\beta)_{Rz}$ = (52μm, 70μm), respectively.[ii]

3. Beam Position

The beams of the SLC have RMS profiles averaged over our sample of $2 \otimes 2$ μm² in X and Y; while the luminous region in Z is ~650μm. Frequent beam-beam scans coupled with a feedback utilizing the pulse to pulse beamstrahlung monitor information is used to maintain the beams in collision and stabilize the IP position. The IP is *tracked* in SLD utilizing Z^0 events. A fit is performed for the X,Y IP position and error (σ_x, σ_y) using ~50 time ordered tracks of small b, from ~10 Z^0 events. Each sample spans ~0.5 hrs. to 3 hrs. for stability. The 447 measurements for the 1992 data run have $\sigma_x, \sigma_y \cong$ 10–15μm. The impact parameter of $\mu^+\mu^-$ & e^+e^- to the IP (Fig. 1) gives $<\sigma_{IP}> \approx$ 11μm after unfolding the single track impact resolution.

4. Detector and Event Selection

The SLD trigger is based on loose calorimetric criteria to eliminate primary beam related backgrounds; conventional $e^\pm$ and γ scattered from the beam pipe and masks, and upstream electroproduced muons, unique to SLC. The former are reduced by total energy and asymmetry cuts, while the latter are reduced utilizing the fine grained tower structure of the LAC and the pattern of energy deposition of the muons.

Hadronic Z^0 events are selected off-line for analysis from the sample of triggers. We require visible energy in tracks E_V>18 GeV and that the thrust axis lie within $|\cos(\theta_T)|$<0.71 where tracking is optimal. We require the number of tracks $N_{chrg} \geq 7$, eliminating 2γ and τ–pair events. Bad running periods and events with the number of CDC/VXD linked tracks<3 are rejected. We retain 4855 Z^0 events with an estimated background contamination <1%. Flavor dependence of the selection for b-quarks relative to all hadronic Z^0 events is found by Monte Carlo to be negligible within 1.000±0.007.

5. The Determination Of R_b

5.1 The Impact Technique

After event selection the set of CDC tracks having a VXD fit is further refined. We require that CDC tracks start at a radius r<0.4m, have N_{hit} >40 and have good fit quality (χ^2/df <5). Tracks originating from identified long lived vees and γ–conversions are eliminated. Tracks are extrapolated to the XY point of closest approach to the IP, and the 2-D impact parameter(b) and error (σ_b) are calculated. We require |b|<0.3cm and σ_b < 250 μm for tracks, equivalent to requiring momentum p $\gtrsim$ 0.5 GeV/c. All tracks are required to extrapolate to within 1cm of the average beam position in Z.

[ii] Here we parametrize the impact resolution function as : $\alpha \oplus \beta/P\sqrt{\sin^3\theta}$ where the sum is taken in quadrature.

The JADE algorithm[iii.] using charged tracks is used to reconstruct jets. Each track is assigned to the spatially nearest jet and a sign is attached to |b|. The +(-) convention is chosen for tracks crossing the jet axis in front (back) of the IP. A non-zero lifetime preferentially populates +|b|, while -|b| tracks reflects uncertainty in the jet direction and the tracking resolution. The normalized impact parameter (b_{norm}.) is formed from the signed b divided by σ_b in quadrature with σ_{IP} along the $\hat{b}$ direction.

The Monte Carlo (MC) simulation contains knowledge of resolution, geometry, efficiency and backgrounds, but unmodeled effects remain. These are associated with detailed CDC waveforms, models of drift velocity variation and residual misalignments and distortions. The MC is adjusted (as a function of p) to match tracking efficiency and resolution by removing 6% of the tracks and increasing σ_b to put b_{norm} in the data and the MC into agreement for $b_{norm} \leq 0$. Since -|b| tracks reflect resolution and not the lifetime effects of b- and c-quarks, this is an unbiased procedure for correcting the simulation of $b_{norm} \geq 0$ tracks. A similar correction is applied for Z impact in Sect. 5.2.

The first tagging technique for $b\bar{b}$ events utilizes the property that b-hadrons have a large decay length (~0.2cm) resulting in many large P_t tracks having large +|b|. We cut on the number of tracks ($\geq N_{sign.}$) in an event having $b_{norm} > 3$. Fig. 2 shows b_{norm} for MC and data, while Fig. 3 shows the tagging efficiency (ε_b) and purity (Π_b) vs. $N_{sign.}$. The standard model values for $\Gamma(Z^0 \to q\bar{q})$ are used to estimate the Π_b; however, only the ε values actually alter R_b. Choosing $N_{sign.}=3$, we tag 798 of 4855 events (Fig.5), resulting in $\varepsilon_b = 0.52$, $\varepsilon_c = 0.13$, $\varepsilon_{uds} = 0.04$, $\Pi_b=0.72$. and $R_b = 0.231\pm0.012$ (statistical error only).

5.2 I The Displaced Vertex Technique

The second technique is based on the observation that b-hadron decays results in more 2-prong vertices displaced from the IP, than decays in uds or c events. Pairs of tracks, each with p>0.3 GeV, |b| < 0.3cm, and |Z_0|< 1cm are combined to find candidate 2-prong vertices. The cut on |b| is effective in vee and $\gamma \to e^+e^-$ rejection. To reduce combinatorics of tracks from opposing jets, the opening angle of a pair must be less than 90^0 in the lab. A 3-D fit on each vertex must satisfy $\chi^2 < 5$. The decay length L (=l • $\mathbf{P_V}$ / |P_V|) from the IP to the fitted vertex must be < 2cm and >$6\sigma_L$ ($\sigma_L = \sigma_V \oplus \sigma_{IP}$, where σ_V is the flight distance fit error). The tag requires a minimum of vertices N_V to satisfy this cut. Fig. 4 shows ε_b, Π_b and ε_c, ε_{udsc} vs. N_V. For $N_V \geq 4$, (Fig. 6) we retain 774 of 4855 events with $\varepsilon_b = 0.58$, $\Pi_b=0.77$, $\varepsilon_c=0.11$, and $\varepsilon_{uds}=0.03$. An overlap of 469 events with the impact technique is observed. This analysis yields $R_b = 0.213\pm0.011$ (stat. error only).

6. Systematic Errors

Our preliminary estimates of systematic errors for the impact parameter and vertex techniques are shown in Table I. Detector errors are conservative estimates. The b-lifetime is varied from 1.2-1.5ps. The fragmentation has been studied with JETSET 6.3, using Peterson functions with ($<x_e>$, ε)=(0.494±0.025,0.06) and (0.700±0.021,0.006) for c and b-quarks respectively. Exclusive models of the decays of b and c hadrons have been adjusted to reflect present knowledge of their decays.[iv.] The $\Gamma(B \to D^0)/\Gamma(B \to D^+)$ ratio

---

[iii.] The parameter YCUT=0.02 is used for the jet discrimination.
[iv.] Models have been adjusted to reflect recent data presented from LEP, on fragmentation, CLEO, Argus

error was found to have a negligible effect. The value[7] of $\Gamma(Z^0 \to c\bar{c})/\Gamma(Z^0 \to \text{hadrons})$ = 0.17±0.03 is varied about its error, as was the D^+ fraction (±10%), therein. The charged track multiplicity of b decays = 5.52±0.25 was varied about its error. The measured values for R_b without radiative corrections are R_b = 0.231±0.012±0.026 (Impact method) and R_b = 0.213±0.011±0.029 (Vertex method), where the first error is statistical and the second systematic. These results are consistent with the prediction of $R_b \approx 0.22$ in the standard model.[8]

Table I. Systematic Errors (%)

SOURCE	IMPACT	VERTEX
Tracking Resolution	9.0	5.9
Tracking Efficiency	5.5	10.3
Beam Position	2.6	1.9
Subtotal	**10.9**	**12.0**
b-Lifetime	2.0	2.6
b-Fragmentation	0.5	0.7
b-Decay Properties	0.9	5.1
c-Fragmentation	0.5	1.7
$\Gamma(Z^0 \to c\bar{c})$	1.6	2.1
Subtotal	**2.8**	**6.4**
TOTAL	**11.2**	**13.7**

7. Conclusions

Tagging methods that exploit the small and stable SLC IP and the 3D information of the CCD-pixel vertex detector are found to be highly efficient for b-decays and to provide excellent background rejection against lighter quarks. These approaches systematically differ from conventional lepton tagging both in physics bias and the level required for detector modelling. The large systematic errors at present reflect our preliminary detector simulation and do not represent fundamental limits to the methods.

8. References

1. Boulware and Finnell, *Phys. Rev.* **D44** (1991) 2054, and references therein.
2. R.G.Jacobsen et. al., *PRL* **67** (1991) 3347.
3. SLD Design Report, *SLAC-REPORT* **273** (1984)
   W.B.Atwood et. al., *Nucl. Inst. Meth.* **A252**, (1986) 295.
4. See, M. Strauss, The SLD Collaboration, these Proceedings, for details of the performance of the silicon CCD vertex detector in the SLD.
5. D. Axen et. al., *SLAC-PUB* **5354**, (1992). To be published in *Nucl. Inst. Meth.*
6. P. Billior, *Nucl. Inst. Meth.* **225**, (1984) 352.
7. P. Kluit, "Heavy Flavor Physics at LEP", Lecture presented at the SLAC Summer Institute, (1992).
8. W.Hollik, *Fortschrift Phys.* **38** (1990) 165, and references therein.

on exclusive beauty decays and multiplicity, MARKIII and the Particle Data Group on charm decays and multiplicities. See J.Snyder,D. Su, R. Schindler, G. Punkar SLD B-Physics Internal Memo (10-15-92).

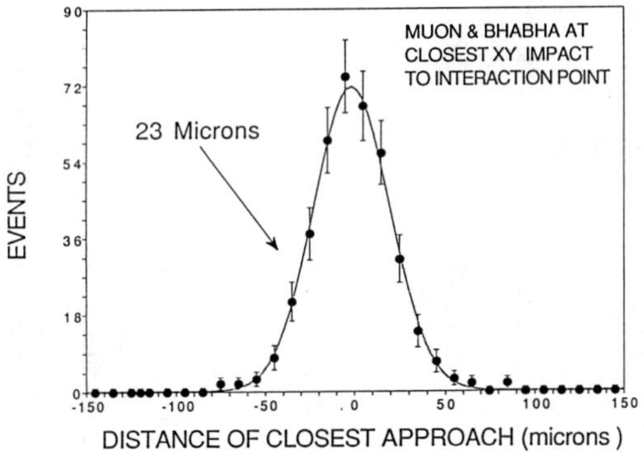

Figure 1. The XY impact parameter to the IP for tracks from muon-pair and Bhabha events.

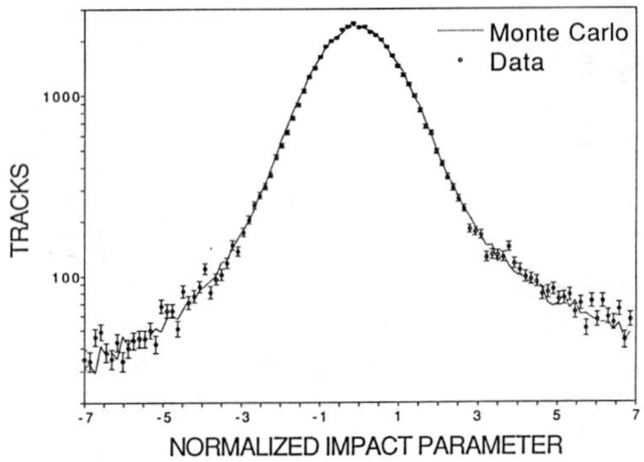

Figure 2. The signed and normalized impact parameter b_{norm} for all Z^0 candidate events.

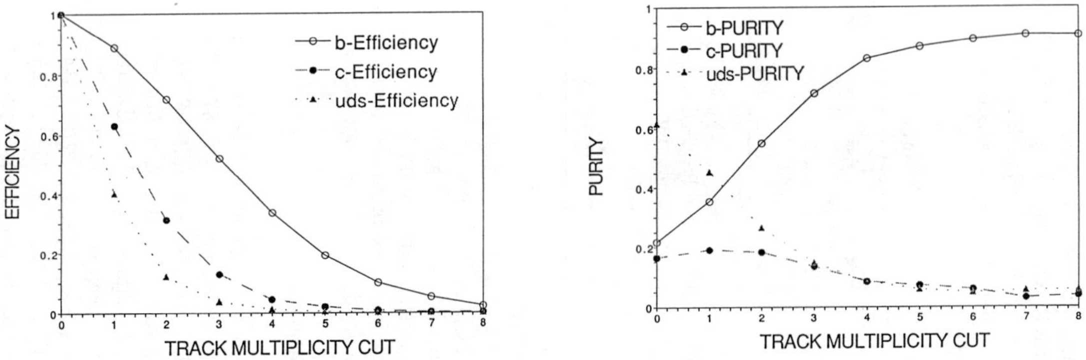

Figure 3. The impact tagging efficiency and purity as a function of the track multiplicity cut $\langle N_{sign} \rangle$ for $b_{norm}>3$ from MC.

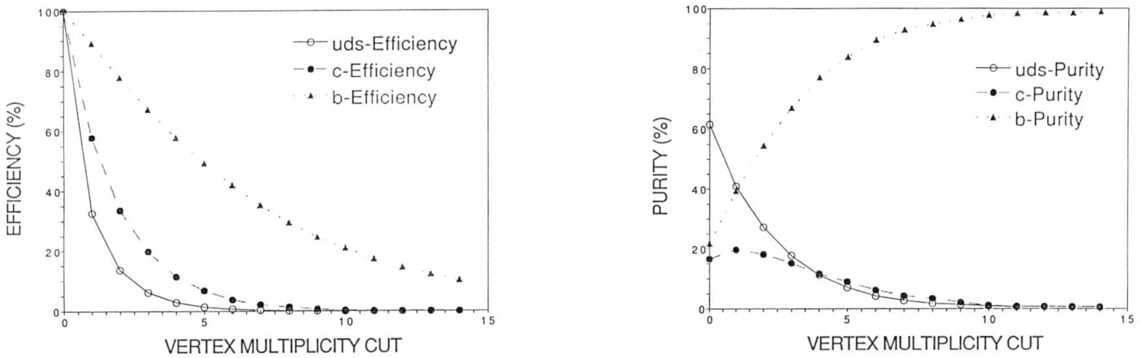

Figure 4. The vertex tagging efficiency and purity as a function of the vertex multiplicity cut (N_v) for $L/\sigma_L > 6$ from MC.

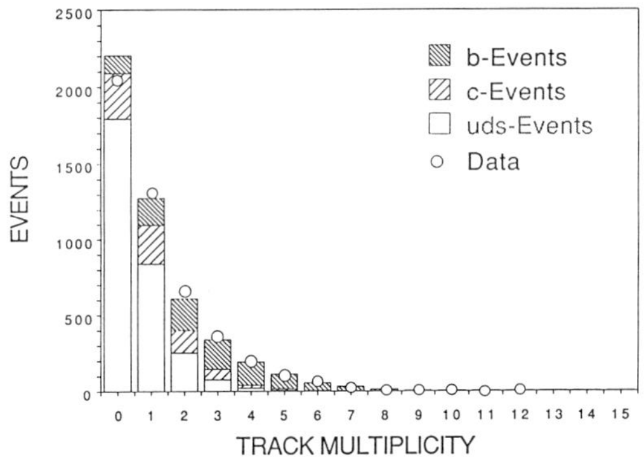

Figure 5. The distribution of track multiplicity (N_{sign}) for $b_{norm} > 3$ over the Z^0 sample.

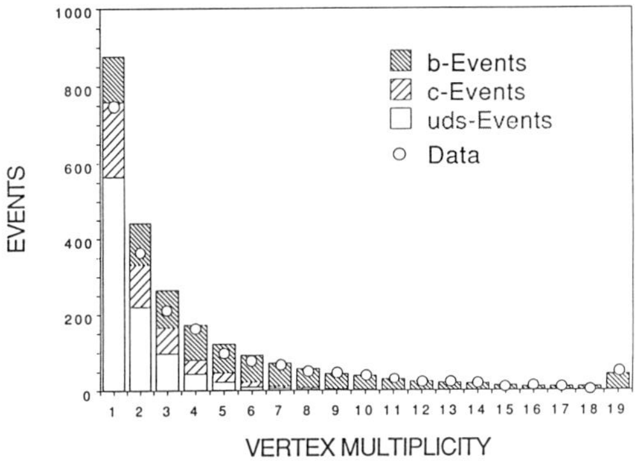

Figure 6. The distribution of vertex multiplicity (N_v) for $L/\sigma_L > 6$ over the Z^0 sample.

FIRST MEASUREMENT OF THE LEFT-RIGHT CROSS SECTION ASYMMETRY IN Z BOSON PRODUCTION AT $E_{CM} = 91.55$ GEV

THE SLD COLLABORATION
represented by
BRUCE A. SCHUMM
Physics Division
Lawrence Berkeley Laboratory, Berkeley, California 94720

ABSTRACT

The left-right cross section asymmetry for Z^0 boson production in e^+e^- annihilation (A_{LR}) has been measured at $E_{cm} = 91.55$ GeV with the SLD detector at the SLAC Linear Collider (SLC) using a longitudinally polarized electron beam. The electron polarization was continuously monitored with a Compton scattering polarimeter, and was typically 22%. We have accumulated a sample of $\sim 10,000$ Z^0 events. We find that $A_{LR} = 0.100 \pm 0.044 \pm 0.003$ where the first error is statistical and the second is systematic. From this measurement, we determine the weak mixing angle defined at the Z^0 boson pole to be $\sin^2 \theta_W^{\text{lept}} = 0.2378 \pm 0.0056$.

The left-right asymmetry is defined as

$$A_{LR} \equiv \frac{\sigma(e^+e_L^- \to Z^0) - \sigma(e^+e_R^- \to Z^0)}{\sigma(e^+e_L^- \to Z^0) + \sigma(e^+e_R^- \to Z^0)}, \tag{1}$$

where $\sigma(e^+e_L^- \to Z^0)$ and $\sigma(e^+e_R^- \to Z^0)$ are the production cross sections for Z^0 bosons with left-handed and right-handed electrons, respectively. Within the context of the Standard Model, this quantity is a sensitive function of the electroweak mixing parameter $\sin^2 \theta_W^{\text{lept}}$:

$$A_{LR} = \frac{2v_e a_e}{v_e^2 + a_e^2} = \frac{2\left[1 - 4\sin^2 \theta_W^{\text{lept}}\right]}{1 + \left[1 - 4\sin^2 \theta_W^{\text{lept}}\right]^2}, \tag{2}$$

where v_e and a_e are the vector and axial vector coupling constants of the Z^0 boson to the electron current. The left-right asymmetry has the following properties: it is sensitive to the initial state couplings and is insensitive to the final state couplings; it is sensitive to virtual electroweak corrections; it is insensitive to real radiative corrections; it is a weak function of center-of-mass energy, E_{cm}, near the Z^0 pole; and it is expected to be relatively large, in the range 0.10-0.15.

The SLC was designed to allow the production, acceleration, and collision of a spin-polarized electron beam with an unpolarized positron beam. Polarized e^- beams are produced by injecting the LINAC with electrons of $\sim 28\%$ polarization, produced by the illumination of a GaAs photocathode with circularly polarized laser light.[1] The electron helicity is randomized by changing the laser helicity on a cycle-by-cycle (120 Hz) basis. During the process of acceleration and transport, the beam suffers partial depolarization in the damping rings and arcs, arriving at the IP with a polarization of ~ 22%. The electron and positron beams are then transported to beam dumps, where the beam energies are continuously monitored by a pair of precision energy spectrometers.[2] The mean electron and positron energies were measured to be 45.71 GeV and 45.84 GeV, respectively, yielding a mean cms energy of $\langle E_{cm} \rangle = 91.55 \pm 0.04$ GeV.

Polarimetry is accomplished by passing the electron beam through a circularly polarized ($P = 93 \pm 2\%$) Nd:YAG laser beam of wavelength $\lambda = 532$ nm. In order to avoid systematic effects, the sign of the circular polarization is changed randomly on sequential laser pulses. Compton scattered electrons are then dispersed horizontally by a beamline dipole magnet ($p_\perp$ kick = 828 MeV) and exit the vacuum system through a thin window. Electrons in the energy interval 15-30 GeV are detected and momentum analyzed by a pair of redundant multichannel detectors (a Cherenkov detector and a proportional tube detector), which measure the asymmetry in the Compton scattering process for anti-parallel and parallel photon/electron beam helicities, as a function of transverse distance from the unscattered beam. The electron beam polarization is extracted from the overall normalization of the measured asymmetry function, which is given by the product of the laser and electron beam polarizations. Polarimeter data are logged continuously for intervals of 20,000 SLC cycles (~3 min) and written in summary form onto SLD data tapes.

To check for depolarization due to spin precession during the transport of the beam between the SLD and Compton IP's, we have run beams through the IP region with the SLD solenoid and intervening quadrupoles turned off. The stability of the beam trajectory under this change limits the change in polarization between the two IP's to be less than 0.1%.

Figure 1 shows the measurement of the asymmetry function in the Cherenkov detector, averaged over polarimeter data from the entire 1992 run. Also shown is the theoretical asymmetry curve; agreement between the measured and theoretical asymmetry function is quite good. We estimate the relative systematic error on the Compton Polarimeter measurement to be ±3%, dominated by the ±2% uncertainty in the laser circular polarization.

The absolute sign of the electron beam helicity is inferred from the sign of the Compton asymmetry, which is larger for parallel than anti-parallel spins. The absolute helicity of the laser polarization was determined with a quarter-wave plate for which the fast axis had been identified by several independent optical techniques.

The polarized e^+e^- collisions are measured by the SLD detector.[3] The Z^0 decay selection criteria used were based primarily on information from the projectively segmented Liquid Argon Calorimeter (LAC).[4] Z^0 candidates were required to have at least 20 GeV of visible energy deposited in the LAC, in each hemisphere a LAC tower (i.e., single electronics channel) of at least 500 MeV, and a normalized energy imbalance of less than 0.8. Wide-angle Bhabha's, which exhibit a different left-right asymmetry than other final states due to interference with the purely QED t-channel process, are removed by requiring that the sum of the two largest LAC towers in each hemisphere (4 towers total) contain less than 30 GeV (12 GeV) of deposited energy for θ greater than (less than) 15°. We estimate that the resulting sample contains ~ 0.5% wide-angle Bhabha's, and less than 1% single-beam and two-photon backgrounds. Neither of these contaminations has an appreciable effect on our determination of A_{LR}. After an additional requirement that there be a measurement of the beam polarization within 1 hour of each Z^0 event, the resulting sample contains 10224 Z^0 candidates, consisting of 5226 events produced with left-handed beam, and 4998 events produced with right-handed beam.

We have performed several checks to ensure that the beam conditions are left-right symmetric. We have binned beamstrahlung and beam deflection data according to left- and right-handed electron beam, and determined that the left-right luminosity asymmetry is less than 10^{-3}. A more direct, but statistically weaker, measurement of the luminosity asymmetry is given by the left-right asymmetry of 25615 small-angle Bhabha's identified by the silicon-tungsten luminosity monitoring system:[5] $A_{LR}^{Bhabha} = .002 \pm .006$. The left-right polarization asymmetry, measured with the entire sample of Polarimeter data, is $< 5 \cdot 10^{-3}$. We have also checked that the numbers of left-handed and right-handed pulses logged by the SLD data acquisition system are equal to within statistical errors.

With the luminosity and electron polarization left-right symmetric, and negligible event backgrounds, we calculate A_{LR} via the following simple expression:

$$A_{LR} = \frac{A_{meas}}{\mathcal{P}} = \frac{1}{\mathcal{P}} \cdot \left(\frac{N_L - N_R}{N_L + N_R} \right), \quad (3)$$

where $\mathcal{P}$ is the luminosity-weighted average polarization, and N_L and N_R are the total event counts produced by left- and right-handed electron beam, respectively. The luminosity weighted average polarization is given by

$$\mathcal{P} \equiv \frac{1}{N_Z} \sum_{i=1}^{N_Z} \mathcal{P}_i = 22.4 \pm 0.7\%, \quad (4)$$

where N_Z is the total number of Z^0 events, and $\mathcal{P}_i$ is the polarization that was measured when the ith event was logged. The uncertainty is dominated by the 3% relative systematic uncertainty on the polarimeter measurements. Combining this with the left- and right-handed event samples quoted above, we find that

$$A_{LR} = 0.100 \pm 0.044(\text{stat.}) \pm 0.003(\text{syst.}). \quad (5)$$

The small systematic error is dominated by the systematic error on the mean polarization. Based on formula (2), this yields a value of the electroweak mixing parameter

$$\sin^2 \theta_W^{\text{lept}} = 0.2378 \pm 0.0056(\text{stat.} + \text{sys.}). \quad (6)$$

This value includes a small (+.0003) correction to account for the effects of initial state radiation, and for the fact that the mean cms energy $\langle E_{cm} \rangle = 91.55\ GeV$ was slightly above the Z^0 peak. Both the value of A_{LR} and $\sin^2 \theta_W^{\text{lept}}$ quoted here are consistent with recent results from LEP experiments.

In the upcoming 1993 run, we anticipate an accumulated data sample of at least 50,000 events, with a mean electron polarization of 40%. With such a sample, we would measure A_{LR} to $\pm.011$, and $\sin^2 \theta_W^{\text{lept}}$ to $\pm.0014$. In addition, it may be possible to make use of the recent development of strained lattice cathodes to achieve source polarizations in excess of 80%,[6] further increasing the statistical power of the A_{LR} measurement.

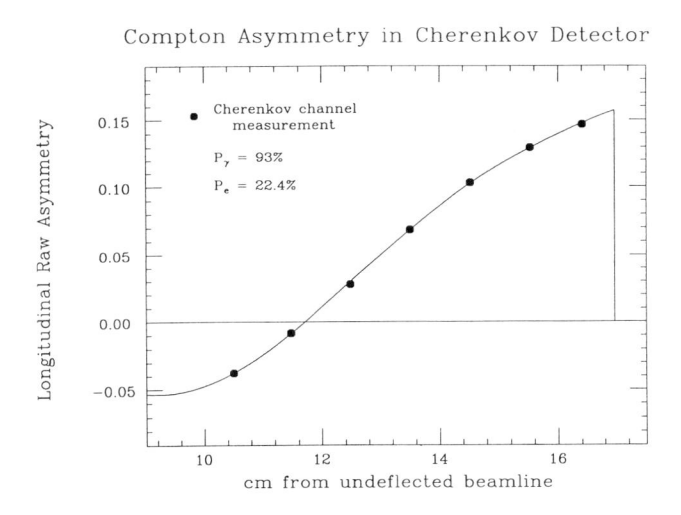

Figure 1: Comparison between theoretical asymmetry function and individual Cerenkov channel measurements (dots), averaged over the entire Polarimeter data set.

References

1. D. Schultz et al., SLAC-PUB-5768, 1992.
2. J. Kent et al., SLAC-PUB-4922, 1989.
3. The SLD Design Report, SLAC Report 273, 1984.
4. D. Axen et al., SLAC-PUB-5354, 1992 (to be published in Nucl. Instr. and Meth.).
5. S. C. Berridge et al., SLAC-PUB-5694, 1991 (to be published in IEEE Trans. Nucl. Sci.).
6. T. Maruyama et al., Phys. Rev. **B46**, 4261 (1992).

ELECTROWEAK MEASUREMENTS AND TOP QUARK MASS LIMITS

JONATHAN L. ROSNER

Enrico Fermi Institute and Department of Physics, University of Chicago
5640 S. Ellis Ave., Chicago, IL 60637, USA

ABSTRACT

The agreement of electroweak measurements with theory places limits on the masses of the top quark and the W boson. It is shown how these limits arise and what constraints various measurements (particularly a top quark mass determination) would provide on the theory. The degree to which present and future measurements can constrain the Higgs boson mass is examined.

1. Introduction

The unified description of weak and electromagnetic interactions has led to a series of predictions which are in accord with all present data, including recent measurements from e^+e^- collisions at the Z mass, $p\bar{p}$ collisions at high energies, deep inelastic scattering of neutrinos, and parity violation in atoms. This agreement is so good that it constrains higher-order effects, particularly that of the top quark mass. In the present paper we examine such constraints in the light of recent data, and extend the analysis of a recent review [1] to parameters S and T which describe effects of new physics [2].

2. Electroweak theory and radiative corrections

The electroweak theory replaces the Fermi coupling constant, $G_F = 1.16637 \pm 0.00002 \times 10^{-5}$ GeV^{-2}, by combinations of dimensionless couplings and masses:

$$\frac{G_F}{\sqrt{2}} = \frac{g^2}{8M_W^2} \quad , \quad \frac{G_F}{\sqrt{2}} = \frac{g^2 + g'^2}{8M_Z^2} \quad , \tag{1}$$

where (g, g') are the SU(2) and U(1) couplings. The electric charge e is related to g and g' by $e = g \sin\theta = g' \cos\theta$, so that

$$M_W^2 = \frac{\pi\alpha}{\sqrt{2}G_F \sin^2\theta} \quad , \quad M_Z^2 = \frac{\pi\alpha}{\sqrt{2}G_F \sin^2\theta \cos^2\theta} \quad . \tag{2}$$

The value of $M_Z = 91.187 \pm 0.007$ GeV [3] then can be used to predict the value of θ in the lowest-order theory, leading to a value of M_W.

The electromagnetic charge when probed at the scale of M_W or M_Z is slightly stronger than that at long distances as a result of vacuum polarization effects. The fine-structure constant, instead of being about 1/137, is about 1/128. This modification is crucial in obtaining a value of M_W from the above procedure which is close to the experimental average [4, 5].

The major effect of a top quark mass is a modification of the relation between G_F and M_Z:

$$\frac{G_F}{\sqrt{2}}\rho = \frac{g^2 + g'^2}{8M_Z^2} \quad , \quad \rho \simeq 1 + \frac{3G_F m_t^2}{8\pi^2 \sqrt{2}} \quad . \tag{3}$$

The quadratic dependence on m_t comes from the top quark's contribution to W and Z self-energy diagrams. No such quadratic dependence appears in the photon vacuum polarization because of electromagnetic gauge invariance. The relation for M_Z in terms of θ now becomes

$$M_Z^2 = \frac{\pi \alpha}{\sqrt{2} G_F \rho \sin^2\theta \cos^2\theta} \quad . \tag{4}$$

Higgs boson contributions to W and Z self-energies lead to an additional term

$$\Delta\rho = -\frac{3}{8\pi \cos^2\theta} \ln \frac{M_H}{M_W} \tag{5}$$

in ρ. Now, θ, M_W, and other electroweak observables depend on both m_t and M_H. This dependence, along with present bounds on M_W [4, 5], leads for $m_H < 1$ TeV to a crude upper limit of $m_t \leq 200$ GeV. The lower bound on m_t (95% c.l.) is 91 GeV [6]. A measurement of m_t to ± 5 GeV and m_W to ± 50 MeV will begin to distinguish among predictions for various Higgs masses.

Additional terms logarithmic in m_t lead to modifications of the relations written previously:

$$\frac{G_F}{\sqrt{2}} = (1 + \Delta Z_W)\frac{g^2}{8M_W^2} \quad , \quad \frac{G_F \rho}{\sqrt{2}} = (1 + \Delta Z_Z)\frac{g^2 + g'^2}{8M_Z^2} \quad , \tag{6}$$

where ΔZ_W and ΔZ_Z represent the effects of variation with momentum transfer between $q^2 = 0$ (where G_F is measured) and the W and Z poles (where coupling constants and masses are defined). They may be expressed in terms of quantities of order 1:

$$\Delta Z_W = \frac{\alpha S_W}{4 \sin^2\theta} \quad ; \quad \Delta Z_Z = \frac{\alpha S_Z}{4 \sin^2\theta \cos^2\theta} \quad , \tag{7}$$

Similarly, $\rho = 1 + \alpha T$ can be expressed in terms of a parameter T of order 1.

If one expands around nominal values of m_t and M_H, one finds [7]

$$T \simeq \frac{3}{16\pi \sin^2\theta}\left[\frac{m_t^2 - (140 \text{ GeV})^2}{M_W^2}\right] - \frac{3}{8\pi \cos^2\theta} \ln \frac{M_H}{100 \text{ GeV}} \quad , \tag{8}$$

$$S_W = \frac{1}{6\pi}\left[\ln \frac{M_H}{100 \text{ GeV}} - 2\ln \frac{m_t}{140 \text{ GeV}}\right] \quad , \quad S_Z = \frac{1}{6\pi}\left[\ln \frac{M_H}{100 \text{ GeV}} + 4\ln \frac{m_t}{140 \text{ GeV}}\right] \quad . \tag{9}$$

3. Electroweak observables and fits

The precise value of the Z^0 mass entails a value of $\sin^2\theta \equiv x_0 = 0.2323 \pm 0.0002 \pm 0.0005$ for $m_t = 140$ GeV, $M_H = 100$ GeV. We expand a set of electroweak obervables about this value; details are to be found in Ref. [1]. For example, we have [8]

$$\sin^2\theta - x_0 = \frac{\alpha}{1 - 2x_0}\left[\frac{1}{4}S_Z - x_0(1 - x_0)T\right] = (3.65 \times 10^{-3})S_Z - (2.61 \times 10^{-3})T \quad , \tag{10}$$

Table I: Electroweak observables incorporated into a fit to the standard electroweak theory.

Quantity	Reference	Experimental Value	Nominal Theory[a]	Expt. ÷ theory
Q_W (Cs)	b)	-71.04 ± 1.81	-73.20	0.970 ± 0.025
M_W(GeV)	c)	80.14 ± 0.27	$80.21^{b)}$	0.999 ± 0.003
N_ν [from $\Gamma(Z \to \nu\bar{\nu})$]	d)	3.04 ± 0.04	3	1.013 ± 0.013
$\Gamma(Z \to l^+l^-)$(MeV)	e)	83.52 ± 0.33	83.6	0.999 ± 0.004
$\Gamma(Z \to $ all$)$(MeV)	d)	2492 ± 7	2488 ± 6	1.001 ± 0.004
$\bar{x}$ (asymms., τ pol.)	d)	0.2324 ± 0.0011	0.2322	1.001 ± 0.005
$\bar{x}(q\bar{q}$ asymm.)	d)	0.2323 ± 0.0032	0.2322	1.000 ± 0.014
$\bar{x}(\bar{e}D)$	b)	0.224 ± 0.020	0.2322	0.965 ± 0.086
$\bar{x}(\bar{e}C)$	b)	0.20 ± 0.05	0.2322	0.86 ± 0.22
$\bar{x}\left[\sigma(\nu_\mu^{(-)})\right]$	f)	0.232 ± 0.009	0.2322	1.00 ± 0.04
M_W (MeV) from R_ν	g)	80.32 ± 0.32	80.21	1.001 ± 0.004
R_ρ	b)	0.387 ± 0.009	0.376	1.02 ± 0.02
$\bar{x}$ (A_{LR} at SLC)	h)	0.2378 ± 0.0056	0.2322	1.024 ± 0.024

[a] For $m_t = 140$ GeV, $M_H = 100$ GeV.
[b] As in Ref. [1].
[c] Raised from value in Ref. [1] as a result of new M_Z measurement [3].
[d] Ref. [3].
[e] F. Merritt, Seminar, Univ. of Chicago, April, 1992.
[f] New CHARM II value: Ref. [3] and G. Rädel, this conference.
[g] Based on CCFR value of $1 - (M_W/M_Z)^2 = 0.2242 \pm 0.0057$ [3].
[h] C. Baltay, this conference. Value not included in fit.

and corresponding other expressions for Z partial widths, neutral-current to charged-current ratios in deep inelastic neutrino scattering, and weak charges as measured in atomic parity violation. The data are summarized in Table I.

Based on the data in Table I, we obtain χ^2 for specific values of M_H as a function of m_t. The results are shown in Fig. 1. The minimum χ^2 values for $M_H = (100, 300, 1000)$ GeV are $(4.34, 4.33, 4.33)$, corresponding to $m_t = (144\pm16, 160\pm 15, 177\pm14)$ GeV. The lack of preference for any particular Higgs boson mass stands in contrast to other fits [9, 10] in which a slight (but not significant) tilt in favor of low Higgs mass occurs. This tilt has been traced to slightly different input values for the forward-backward asymmetry for b quark production and for the leptonic width of the Z.

A fit based on the degrees of freedom S and T of Ref. [2] was also performed. (Here we have assumed $S = S_W = S_Z$, as occurs when one has extra degenerate doublets.) The results are shown in Fig. 2.

The elongated nature of the ellipses illustrates the absence of any preference for a specific Higgs mass. One can change the Higgs mass without much penalty as long as the top quark mass changes in a compensating way. For $M_H < 1$ TeV (an approximate upper bound resulting from unitarity), we see from Fig. 2 that one can still only conclude $m_t < 200$ GeV, but with 90% confidence.

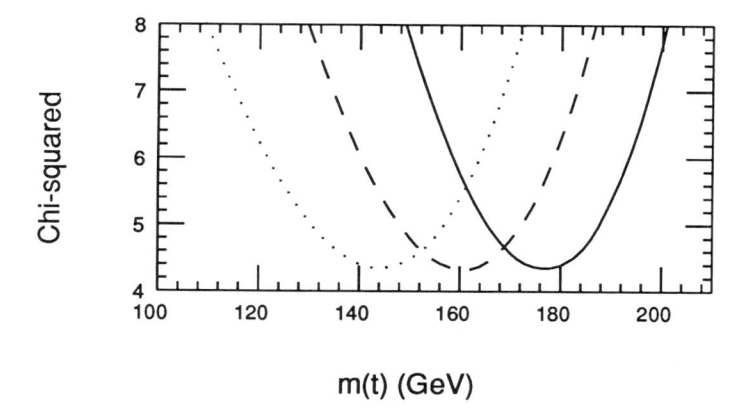

Figure 1: Values of χ^2 for fit to 12 electroweak observables. From left to right, the curves correspond to $M_H = 100$, 300, and 1000 GeV.

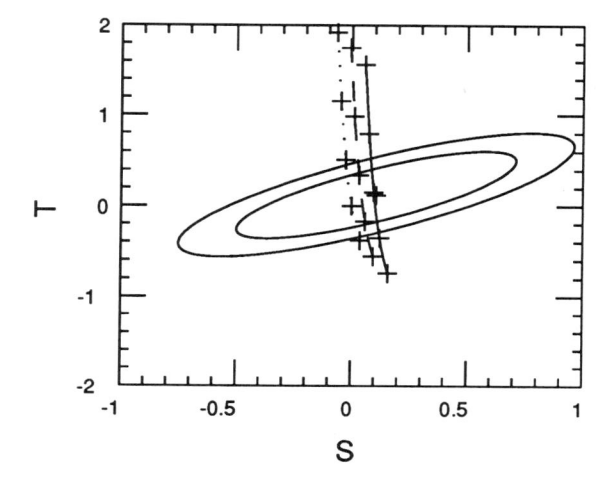

Figure 2: Fit to parameters S and T based on data of Table I. Plotted point corresponds to minimum χ^2; inner and outer ellipses correspond to 68% and 90% c.l. limits. Standard model curves correspond, from left to right, to $M_H = 100$, 300, and 1000 GeV. Ticks on these curves, from bottom to top, correspond to $m_t = 100$, 140, 180, 220, and 260 GeV.

4. Conclusions

We have shown that the top quark mass is limited by today's electroweak data to be less than about 200 GeV. Stronger limits are to be mistrusted. A plot in S and T shows no particular preference for any sign of S but implies $S < 1$ at the 90% confidence level. The discovery of the top quark and the measurement of its mass remain the highest priority for obtaining further information about the electroweak theory.

5. Acknowledgements

I thank Ugo Fano, Henry Frisch, John Harton, Chris Hill, John Huth, Bill Marciano, Jim Pilcher, Dorothea Schaile, and Jack Steinberger for helpful discussions. This work was supported in part by the United States Department of Energy under grant No. DE AC02 90ER40560.

6. References

1. J. L. Rosner, *Rev. Mod. Phys.* **64** (1992) 1151.
2. M. E. Peskin and T. Takeuchi, *Phys. Rev. Lett.* **65** (1990) 964; *Phys. Rev. D* **45** (1992) 381.
3. L. Rolandi, Rapporteur's talk at XXVI International Conference on High Energy Physics, Dallas, TX, August 1992.
4. CDF Collaboration, F. Abe *et al.*, *Phys. Rev. D* **43** (1991) 2070.
5. UA2 Collaboration, presented at DPF Meeting, Vancouver, Canada.
6. CDF Collaboration, F. Abe *et al.*, *Phys. Rev. Lett.* **68** (1992) 447.
7. D. C. Kennedy and P. Langacker, *Phys. Rev. Lett.* **65** (1990) 2967; **66** (1991) 395(E).
8. W. Marciano and J. L. Rosner, *Phys. Rev. Lett.* **65** (1990), 2963; **68** (1992) 898.
9. D. Schaile, *Z. Phys. C* **54** (1992) 387.
10. J. Harton, invited talk in Session A, this conference.

ELECTROWEAK SYMMETRY BREAKING
AT THE SSC AND LHC

JONATHAN A. BAGGER
Department of Physics and Astronomy
The Johns Hopkins University
Baltimore, MD 21218

In this talk we survey the SSC and LHC signals and backgrounds for the physics of electroweak symmetry breaking. We study the process $pp \to WWX$ and compute the rate for the "gold-plated" signals $W^{\pm} \to \ell^{\pm}\nu$ and $Z \to \ell^+\ell^-$ ($\ell = e, \mu$) for a wide variety of models. We use a forward jet tag and central jet veto to suppress the standard-model backgrounds. In this way we estimate the SSC and LHC sensitivities to the physics of electroweak symmetry breaking.

1. Introduction

In the standard model of particle physics, electroweak symmetry is broken by a the vacuum expectation value of a Higgs particle H, whose mass is expected to be less than a TeV. To date, however, there is still no experimental evidence – either direct or indirect – in favor of the Higgs.

One fact is certain: New physics is needed to break the electroweak symmetry. If one uses the known particles and computes the scattering amplitude for longitudinally-polarized W's, one finds that rate the diverges with energy, and that (perturbative) unitarity is violated below 2 TeV. New physics is necessary to unitarize the scattering amplitude.[1] In the standard model, the new physics is just the Higgs particle H.

In this talk we will look beyond the Higgs to study the SSC and LHC signals and backgrounds for a wide variety of models that break electroweak symmetry and unitarize the $W_L W_L$ scattering amplitude. Each of the models is completely consistent with all the data to date (including that from the Z). Together, they indicate the range of new physics that might be seen at the SSC or LHC.

2. The Models

At present, all we know about electroweak symmetry breaking is that $M_W \simeq M_Z \cos\theta$, which suggests that the underlying physics respects a global symmetry $G \supseteq SU(2)_L \times SU(2)_R$, spontaneously broken to $H \supseteq SU(2)_V$. In this talk we will examine a wide variety of models consistent with this "isospin" symmetry. The first major distinction is whether or not a given model is resonant in the $W_L W_L$ channel. If it is resonant, the model can be classified by the spin and isospin of the resonance. If it is not, the analysis is more subtle, and we shall see that all possibilities can be described in term of two parameters.

2.1. Spin-zero, Isospin-zero Resonances

1) *Standard Model.* The standard model is the prototype of a theory with a spin-zero, isospin-zero resonance. The $W_L W_L$ scattering amplitudes are unitarized by exchange of the Higgs particle H. The Higgs is contained in a complex scalar doublet, $\Phi = (v + H)\exp(2iw^a\tau^a/v)$, whose four components split into a triplet w^a and a singlet H under isospin.

The standard-model Higgs potential is invariant under an $SU(2)_L \times SU(2)_R$ symmetry. The vacuum expectation value $\langle \Phi \rangle = v$ breaks the symmetry to the diagonal $SU(2)$. In the perturbative limit, it also gives mass to the Higgs. For the purposes of this talk, we will take $M_H = 1$ TeV.

2) *O(2N).* This model attempts to describe the standard-model Higgs in the nonperturbative domain. In the perturbatively-coupled standard model, the mass of the Higgs is proportional to the square root of the scalar self-coupling λ. Heavy Higgs particles correspond to large values of λ. For $M_H \gtrsim 1$ TeV, naive perturbation theory breaks down.

One way to explore the nonperturbative regime is to exploit the isomorphism between $SU(2)_L \times SU(2)_R$ and $O(4)$. Using a large-N approximation, one can solve the $O(2N)$ model for all values of λ, to leading order in $1/N$. The resulting scattering amplitudes[2] can be parametrized by the scale Λ of the Landau pole. Large values of Λ correspond to small couplings λ and relatively light Higgs particles. In contrast, small values of Λ correspond to large λ and describe the nonperturbative regime. In this talk we will take $\Lambda = 3$ TeV.

2.2. Spin-one, Isospin-one Resonances

1) *Vector.* This model provides a relatively model-independent description of the techni-rho resonance that arises in most technicolor theories. One can use the time-honored techniques of chiral Lagrangians to construct the coupling between the techni-rho and the Goldstone bosons.[3,4] The basic fields are $\xi = \exp(iw^a\tau^a/v)$ and a vector ρ_μ, which transform nonlinearly under $SU(2)_L \times SU(2)_R$.

For the processes of interest, the effective Lagrangian depends on just two couplings, which we can take to be the mass and the width of the resonance. In what follows we will choose $M_\rho = 2.0$ TeV, $\Gamma_\rho = 700$ GeV and $M_\rho = 2.5$ TeV, $\Gamma_\rho = 1300$ GeV. These values preserves unitarity up to 3 TeV.

2.3. Nonresonant models

The final models we consider are nonresonant at SSC energies. In this case the new physics contributes to the effective Lagrangian in the form of higher-dimensional operators built from the Goldstone fields. To order p^4 in the energy expansion, there are only three operators that contribute to $W_L W_L$ scattering.[5] They are

$$\mathcal{L} = \frac{v^2}{4}\text{Tr}\,\partial_\mu\Sigma\partial_\mu\Sigma^\dagger + \frac{L_1}{16\pi^2}\left(\text{Tr}\,\partial_\mu\Sigma\partial_\mu\Sigma^\dagger\right)^2 + \frac{L_2}{16\pi^2}\left(\text{Tr}\,\partial_\mu\Sigma\partial_\nu\Sigma^\dagger\right)^2. \quad (1)$$

The coefficients L_1 and L_2 contain all information about the new physics.

Table 1. SSC cuts, tags and vetoes, by mode.

W^+W^- Basic cuts	Tag and Veto	ZZ Basic cuts	Tag only
$|y_\ell| < 2.0$	$E_{tag} > 3.0$ TeV	$|y_\ell| < 2.5$	$E_{tag} > 1.0$ TeV
$P_{T,\ell} > 100$ GeV	$3.0 < \eta_{tag} < 5.0$	$P_{T,\ell} > 40$ GeV	$3.0 < \eta_{tag} < 5.0$
$\Delta P_{T,\ell\ell} > 200$ GeV	$P_{T,tag} > 40$ GeV	$P_{T,Z} > \frac{1}{4}\sqrt{M_{ZZ}^2 - 4M_Z^2}$	$P_{T,tag} > 40$ GeV
$\cos\phi_{\ell\ell} < -0.8$	$P_{T,veto} > 60$ GeV	$M_{ZZ} > 500$ GeV	
$M_{\ell\ell} > 250$ GeV	$|\eta_{veto}| < 3.0$		
W^+Z Basic cuts	Tag and Veto	W^+W^+ Basic cuts	Veto only
$|y_\ell| < 2.5$	$E_{tag} > 2.0$ TeV	$|y_\ell| < 2.0$	$P_{T,veto} > 60$ GeV
$P_{T,\ell} > 40$ GeV	$3.0 < \eta_{tag} < 5.0$	$P_{T,\ell} > 100$ GeV	$|\eta_{veto}| < 3.0$
$P_{T,miss} > 75$ GeV	$P_{T,tag} > 40$ GeV	$\Delta P_{T,\ell\ell} > 200$ GeV	
$P_{T,Z} > \frac{1}{4}M_T^*$	$P_{T,veto} > 60$ GeV	$\cos\phi_{\ell\ell} < -0.8$	
$M_T > 500$ GeV	$|\eta_{veto}| < 3.0$	$M_{\ell\ell} > 250$ GeV	

* M_T is the cluster transverse mass.

The difficulty with this approach is that at SSC energies, the scattering amplitudes violate unitarity between 1 and 2 TeV. This is an indication that new physics is near, but not necessarily within the reach of the SSC. We choose to treat the uncertainties of unitarization in two ways:

1) *LET CG*. We take $L_1 = L_2 = 0$, and cut off the partial wave amplitudes when they saturate the unitarity bound.[1]

2) *Delay K*. We take $L_1 = -0.26$ and $L_2 = 0.23$, a choice that preserves unitarity up to 2 TeV. Beyond that scale, we unitarize the scattering amplitudes with a K-matrix.

3. Signal and Backgrounds

In the rest of this talk we will focus on SSC and LHC signals and backgrounds for the process $pp \to WWX$. We will concentrate on the "gold-plated" decays $W^\pm \to \ell^\pm \nu$ and $Z \to \ell^+\ell^-$, for $\ell = e, \mu$, in each of the final states W^+W^-, W^+Z, ZZ and W^+W^+.

We will take the signal to be the process $pp \to W_L W_L X$ because the longitudinal W's couple most strongly to the new physics. We will take $pp \to W_L W_T X$ and $pp \to W_T W_T X$ to be the background. These processes are dominated by diagrams that do not depend on the new physics, so we will represent the background by the standard model with a light Higgs (of mass 100 GeV). The difference between this and the true background is negligible at the energies we consider.

We will simplify our calculations by using the equivalence theorem, which lets us replace the longitudinal vector bosons by their corresponding would-be Goldstone bosons. We will also use the effective W approximation to connect the $W_L W_L$ subprocesses to the pp initial state.

Table 2. Event rates per SSC/LHC-year, assuming $m_t = 140$ GeV, $\sqrt{s} = 40/16$ TeV, and an annual luminosity of $10^4/10^5$ pb^{-1}.

W^+W^-	Bkgd.	SM 1.0	$O(2N)$	Vec 2.0	Vec 2.5	LET CG	Delay K
$M_{\ell\ell} > 0.25$	9.1/13	59/74	26/30	12/9.7	10/8.9	12/11	9.7/8.9
$M_{\ell\ell} > 0.5$	5.0/5.6	31/32	16/16	9.3/6.4	7.4/5.3	9.3/7.0	6.9/5.0
$M_{\ell\ell} > 1.0$	0.9/0.7	2.0/1.2	1.5/0.8	3.6/1.8	2.6/1.2	2.9/1.3	2.5/0.9
W^+Z	Bkgd.	SM 1.0	$O(2N)$	Vec 2.0	Vec 2.5	LET CG	Delay K
$M_T > 0.5$	2.5/2.3	1.3/1.0	1.5/1.1	9.6/4.8	6.2/3.2	5.4/3.1	5.5/2.9
$M_T > 1.0$	0.9/0.4	0.6/0.3	0.8/0.4	8.2/3.4	4.8/1.9	4.0/1.7	4.3/1.7
$M_T > 1.5$	0.3/0.1	0.2/0.1	0.3/0.1	5.9/2.1	3.4/1.1	2.5/0.8	2.9/0.9
ZZ	Bkgd.	SM 1.0	$O(2N)$	Vec 2.0	Vec 2.5	LET CG	Delay K
$M_{ZZ} > 0.5$	1.0/1.0	11/14	5.2/6.4	1.1/1.4	1.5/1.7	2.5/2.5	1.5/1.8
$M_{ZZ} > 1.0$	0.3/0.2	4.8/4.8	2.3/2.2	0.5/0.4	0.8/0.6	1.7/1.2	0.8/0.6
$M_{ZZ} > 1.5$	0.1/0.0	0.6/0.4	0.5/0.3	0.1/0.1	0.3/0.2	0.9/0.5	0.3/0.2
W^+W^+	Bkgd.	SM 1.0	$O(2N)$	Vec 2.0	Vec 2.5	LET CG	Delay K
$M_{\ell\ell} > 0.25$	3.5/6.0	6.4/9.6	7.1/10	7.8/12	11/16	25/27	15/16
$M_{\ell\ell} > 0.5$	1.9/2.1	3.8/4.6	4.5/5.2	4.5/6.0	7.2/8.8	20/18	11/9.6
$M_{\ell\ell} > 1.0$	0.3/0.3	0.7/0.5	1.1/0.7	0.6/0.5	1.5/1.2	8.3/4.9	5.3/2.6

In the W^+W^-, W^+Z and ZZ channels, the final states of interest are dominated by glue-glue and $q\bar{q}$ scattering. We suppress these contributions by requiring a tag on the forward jet[6] associated with an initial-state W. In the W^+W^-, W^+Z and W^+W^+ channels, there is a residual background from top decay that we suppress by requiring a central jet veto.[7] The combination of a forward jet tag and central jet veto is very effective in reducing the background in all charge channels.

The precise SSC cuts we use are summarized in Table 1. (The LHC cuts are the same except for the jet tags, which are $E_{jet} > 2.0$, 1.5, and 0.8 TeV in the W^+W^-, W^+Z, and ZZ channels, respectively.) In all channels, the dominant residual background is transverse electroweak, followed by $q\bar{q}$ annihilation and top decay.

Because we use the effective W approximation for our signal, we can only estimate the effects of the tag and veto. Therefore we have used the exact standard-model calculation with a 1 TeV Higgs to derive efficiencies for the tag and veto. These efficiencies are then applied to the effective W calculations to estimate the rate for each signal. The results for the signals and backgrounds are collected in Table 2.

4. Discussion

The results in Table 2 summarize the outcome of our study. As expected, the signal rates are largest in the resonant channels. Note, however, that the rates are all rather low. The events are clean, but the low rates will make it difficult to isolate high-mass resonances. We must be prepared for a high-luminosity program at the SSC and LHC.

A second conclusion from Table 2 is that all channels are necessary. For example, isospin-zero resonances give the best signal in the W^+W^- and ZZ channels, while isospin-one resonances dominate the W^+Z channel. The nonresonant models tend to show up in the W^+W^+ final state, so there is a complementarity between the different channels.[1]

A third conclusion is that we cannot cut corners. Accurate background studies are crucial if we hope to separate signal from background by simply counting rates. We must also try to measure all decay modes the W and Z, including $Z \to \nu\bar{\nu}$ and $W, Z \to jets$. Finally, we must work to optimize the cuts that are applied to each final state, with an eye to increasing the signal/background ratio without affecting the total rate. All these considerations indicate that if electroweak symmetry is dynamically broken, SSC and LHC studies of electroweak symmetry breaking might need a mature and long-term program before they give rise to fruitful results.

5. Acknowledgements

This work was supported in part by NSF grant PHY-90-96198. I would like to thank my collaborators V. Barger, K. Cheung, J. Gunion, T. Han, G. Ladinsky, R. Rosenfeld and C.-P. Yuan. I would also like to thank S. Dawson and G. Valencia for many conversations on the effective Lagrangian approach to electroweak symmetry breaking.

6. References

1. B.W. Lee, C. Quigg and H. Thacker, *Phys. Rev.* **D16** (1977) 1519; M. Chanowitz and M.K. Gaillard, *Nucl. Phys.* **B261** (1985) 379. See also M. Chanowitz, LBL preprint LBL-32938 (1992).
2. M. Einhorn, *Nucl. Phys.* **B246** (1984) 75.
3. S. Weinberg, *Phys. Rev.* **166** (1968) 1568; S. Coleman, J. Wess and B. Zumino, *Phys. Rev.* **177** (1969) 2239; 2247.
4. R. Casalbuoni, et al., *Phys. Lett.* **B249** (1990) 130; **B253** (1991) 275. See also M. Bando, T. Kugo and K. Yamawaki, *Phys. Rep.* **164** (1988) 217.
5. J. Gasser and H. Leutwyler, *Ann. Phys.* **158** (1984) 142; *Nucl. Phys.* **B250** (1985) 465.
6. R. Cahn, S. Ellis, R. Kleiss and W. Stirling, *Phys. Rev.* **D35** (1987) 1626; U. Baur and E. Glover, *Nucl. Phys.* **B347** (1990) 12; V. Barger, K. Cheung, T. Han and D. Zeppenfeld, *Phys. Rev.* **D44** (1991) 2701.
7. V. Barger, K. Cheung, T. Han and R. Phillips, *Phys. Rev.* **D42** (1990) 3052; D. Dicus, J. Gunion, L. Orr and R. Vega, *Nucl. Phys.* **B377** (1992) 31.

PROBING THE WEAK BOSON SECTOR IN $p\bar{p} \to Z\gamma$

U. BAUR
Physics Department, Florida State University
Tallahassee, FL 32306, U.S.A.

ABSTRACT

$Z\gamma$ production at the Tevatron is analysed for general $ZZ\gamma$ and $Z\gamma\gamma$ couplings. Deviations from the Standard Model gauge theory structure can be parametrized in terms of four $ZZ\gamma$ and four $Z\gamma\gamma$ form factors. The high energy behavior of these form factors is restricted by unitarity. Prospects for testing the self-interactions of Z bosons and photons at the Tevatron are explored.

1. Introduction

Experiments at the Tevatron $p\bar{p}$ collider are expected to collect data corresponding to an integrated luminosity of approximately 100 pb^{-1} in the 1992 – 1993 run, an increase of more than one order of magnitude in statistics over the data sample presently available. The significant increase in integrated luminosity will make it possible to probe previously untested sectors of the Standard Model (SM) of electroweak interactions, such as the vector boson self-interactions. Within the SM, at tree level, these self-interactions are completely fixed by the $SU(2) \times U(1)$ gauge theory structure of the model. Their observation is thus a crucial test of the model. Recently, the UA2 Collaboration[1] reported the first direct measurement of the $WW\gamma$ vertex in the reaction $p\bar{p} \to e^{\pm}\nu\gamma X$. Within rather large errors the UA2 result is consistent with SM expectations. More precise information can soon be expected from $W^{\pm}\gamma$ production in the ongoing Tevatron run[2].

Besides significantly improved bounds on the structure of the $WW\gamma$ vertex, the new Tevatron data will also offer the possibility to search for evidence of non-zero $ZZ\gamma$ and $Z\gamma\gamma$ couplings in $Z\gamma$ production. Here we study the capabilities of future Tevatron experiments to probe the $ZZ\gamma$ and $Z\gamma\gamma$ vertices via $Z\gamma$ production[3]. Four different anomalous couplings are allowed by electromagnetic gauge invariance and Lorentz invariance[4]. Their properties are summarized in Section 2. Our analysis is based on the calculation of helicity amplitudes for the complete processes $q\bar{q} \to Z\gamma \to \ell^+\ell^-\gamma$ and $q\bar{q} \to Z\gamma \to \bar{\nu}\nu\gamma$, where $\ell = e, \mu$. In case of the $\ell^+\ell^-\gamma$ final state, timelike virtual photon and radiative Z decay diagrams also contribute. Together with effects of the finite Z width, these are included fully in our calculation. In Section 3 we briefly discuss the signatures of anomalous $ZZ\gamma$ and $Z\gamma\gamma$ couplings at the Tevatron. Section 4 contains our conclusions.

2. $ZZ\gamma$ and $Z\gamma\gamma$ Couplings

Lorentz and electromagnetic gauge invariance restrict the tensor structure of the $Z\gamma V$, $V = \gamma, Z$ vertex sufficiently to allow just four free parameters, h_i^V, $i = 1\ldots 4$. The explicit form of the vertex function is given in Ref. 3. Due to Bose symmetry (electromagnetic gauge invariance), the $ZZ\gamma$ ($Z\gamma\gamma$) vertex function vanishes identically if both Z bosons (photons) are onshell.

The form factors h_i^V are dimensionless functions of the squared momenta of the three vector bosons. All couplings are C odd; h_1^V and h_2^V violate CP. Combinations of h_3^V (h_1^V) and h_4^V (h_2^V) correspond to the electric (magnetic) dipole and magnetic (electric) quadrupole transition moment. h_1^V (h_2^V) and h_3^V (h_4^V) receive contributions from operators of dimension ≥ 6 (≥ 8). Within the SM, at tree level, all couplings h_i^V vanish. At the one loop level, only the CP conserving couplings h_3^V and h_4^V are nonzero.

Tree level unitarity restricts the $ZZ\gamma$ and $Z\gamma\gamma$ couplings uniquely to their SM values at asymptotically high energies.[5] This implies that the $Z\gamma V$ couplings h_i^V have to be described by form factors which vanish at high energies, $\sqrt{\hat{s}}$. In the following we shall use generalized dipole form factors of the form

$$h_i^V(\hat{s}) = \frac{h_{i0}^V}{(1 + \hat{s}/\Lambda^2)^n} \qquad (1)$$

The values h_{i0}^V of the form factors at low energy are constrained by partial wave unitarity of the inelastic vector boson pair production amplitude in fermion antifermion annihilation at arbitrary center of mass energies.[3]

3. Signatures of Anomalous $ZZ\gamma$ and $Z\gamma\gamma$ Couplings at the Tevatron

The anomalous contributions to the $q\bar{q} \to Z\gamma$ helicity amplitudes grow like $(\sqrt{\hat{s}}/m_Z)^3$ for $h_{1,3}^V$, and $(\sqrt{\hat{s}}/m_Z)^5$ for $h_{2,4}^V$. If the Z boson decays into a pair of charged leptons, a typical signal for non-standard couplings will be a broad increase in the invariant mass distribution $d\sigma/dm_{\ell\ell\gamma}$ of the final state $\ell^+\ell^-\gamma$, system at large values of $m_{\ell\ell\gamma}$. This result is demonstrated in Fig. 1 which shows the $\ell\ell\gamma$ invariant mass distribution for the SM case, for $h_{30}^Z = 1$, and for $h_{40}^Z = 0.025$. The results for non-standard couplings are displayed for two form factor scales, $\Lambda = 0.5$ TeV and $\Lambda = 1$ TeV. p_T cuts of $p_{T\gamma} > 10$ GeV and $p_{T\ell} > 15$ GeV, pseudorapidity cuts of $|\eta_\gamma| < 3$ and $|\eta_\ell| < 3.5$, invariant mass cuts of $m_{\ell\ell} > 50$ GeV and $m_{\ell\ell\gamma} > 100$ GeV, and a charged lepton – photon separation cut of $\Delta R_{\ell\gamma} > 0.7$ are imposed. The curves of Fig. 1 have been obtained using the complete set of contributing tree level Feynman diagrams, which include timelike photon and final state bremsstrahlung graphs. Results for the CP violating couplings $h_{1,2}^Z$ are virtually identical to those obtained for the same values of $h_{3,4}^Z$. Anomalous $Z\gamma\gamma$ couplings give results very similar to those shown in Fig. 1.

If the Z boson produced in $q\bar{q} \to Z\gamma$ decays into neutrinos, the signal consists of a high p_T photon accompanied by a large amount of missing transverse

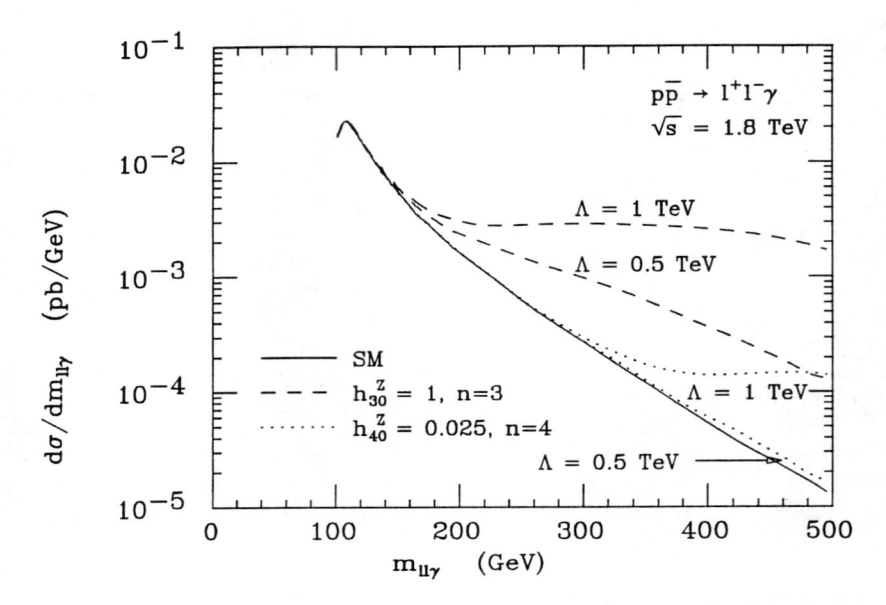

Fig. 1: Invariant mass distribution of the $\ell\ell\gamma$ system at the Tevatron for the SM, $h_{30}^Z = 1$ and $h_{40}^Z = 0.025$. Results for non-standard couplings are displayed for two choices of the form factor scale, $\Lambda = 0.5$ TeV and $\Lambda = 1$ TeV.

momentum, $\not{p}_T$. Since the neutrinos escape undetected, the final state invariant mass cannot be reconstructed, and the only distribution sensitive to non-standard $Z\gamma V$ couplings is the photon p_T spectrum. The effects of the anomalous couplings in $d\sigma/dp_{T\gamma}$ are qualitatively similar to those in the $\ell\ell\gamma$ invariant mass distribution. Compared to the charged lepton decay mode of the Z boson, the decay $Z \to \bar\nu\nu$ offers potential advantages. Due to the larger $Z \to \bar\nu\nu$ branching ratio, the differential cross section is about a factor 3 larger than that for $q\bar q \to e^+e^-\gamma$ and $q\bar q \to \mu^+\mu^-\gamma$ combined. Furthermore, final state bremsstrahlung and timelike virtual photon diagrams do not contribute for the $\bar\nu\nu\gamma$ final state. Potentially serious backgrounds from γj and dijet production can be controlled by cutting sufficiently hard on $p_{T\gamma}$.[3]

From Fig. 1 it is obvious that Tevatron experiments will be sensitive to anomalous $ZZ\gamma$ and $Z\gamma\gamma$ couplings. Sensitivity limits will, however, depend on the form factor scale and the power n in Eq. (1). The CP conserving couplings $h_{3,4}^V$ and the CP violating couplings $h_{1,2}^V$ do not interfere. Furthermore, $ZZ\gamma$ and $Z\gamma\gamma$ couplings interfere only marginally. Nonnegligible interference effects are found between h_1^V (h_3^V) and h_2^V (h_4^V), $V = Z, \gamma$. For an integrated luminosity of 100 pb^{-1}

Tevatron experiments should be able to reach 95% confidence level bounds of

$$\left|h_{1,3}^Z\right| = \pm 1.4 \;\; (\pm 0.52) \qquad \left|h_{2,4}^Z\right| = \pm 0.32 \;\; (\pm 0.05) \qquad (2)$$

for $\Lambda = 0.5$ TeV (1 TeV) in $p\bar{p} \to \ell^+\ell^-\gamma$. The power n in Eq. 1 was assumed to be $n = 3$ ($n = 4$) for $h_{1,3}^Z$ ($h_{2,4}^Z$). The corresponding limits for $Z\gamma\gamma$ couplings are about 5% weaker than those for the $ZZ\gamma$ couplings.

The unitarity bounds of h_{10}^V (h_{20}^V) and h_{30}^V (h_{40}^V) decrease like Λ^{-3} (Λ^{-5}).[3] If Λ becomes too large, no deviation from the SM will observable at the Tevatron. The maximum scale one can probe with 100 pb^{-1} at the 95% CL level turns out to be $\Lambda \approx 2.1$ TeV for $h_{1,3}^V$ with $n = 3$, and $\Lambda \approx 1.2$ TeV for $h_{2,4}^V$ with $n = 4$.

4. Conclusions

It is interesting to compare the sensitivity of hadron collider experiments with existing low energy limits on anomalous couplings and with the sensitivity to non-gauge theory $ZZ\gamma$ and $Z\gamma\gamma$ vertices accessible in e^+e^- collisions. Low energy experiments typically yield bounds of $\mathcal{O}(1-10)$. The limits obtained from present LEP data on non-standard contributions to $Z \to e^+e^-\gamma$ and $Z \to \nu\bar{\nu}\gamma$ are even weaker.[3] Bounds comparable to those from Tevatron experiments are, however, expected from LEP II. In view of our present poor knowledge of the self-interactions of Z bosons and photons, the direct measurement of the $Z\gamma V$ couplings h_i^V via $p\bar{p} \to \ell^+\ell^-\gamma$ and $p\bar{p} \to \gamma \not{p}_T$ at the Tevatron will constitute major progress and represent an important step towards a highly precise test of trilinear vector boson couplings at the LHC and SSC.

5. Acknowledgements

This research was supported by the U. S. Department of Energy under Contract No. DE-FG05-87ER40319.

6. References

1. J. Alitti et al. (UA2 Collaboration), *Phys. Lett.* **277B** (1992) 194.
2. U. Baur and E. L. Berger, *Phys. Rev.* **D41** (1990) 1476.
3. U. Baur and E. L. Berger, FSU-HEP-921030, ANL-HEP-PR-92-91, CERN-TH.6680/92 preprint (October 1992).
4. K. Hagiwara et al., *Nucl. Phys.* **B282** (1987) 253.
5. J. M. Cornwall, D. N. Levin and G. Tiktopoulos, *Phys. Rev. Lett.* **30** (1973) 1268; *Phys. Rev.* **D10** (1974) 1145; C. H. Llewellyn Smith, *Phys. Lett.* **46B** (1973) 233; S. D. Joglekar, *Ann. of Phys.* **83** (1974) 427.

PROBING THE $WW\gamma$ VERTEX IN $e^{\pm}p \to \nu\gamma X$

MICHAEL A. DONCHESKI
Physics Department, University of Wisconsin — Madison
Madison, Wisconsin 53706 USA

and

ULRICH BAUR
Physics Department, Florida State University
Tallahassee, Florida 32306 USA

ABSTRACT

We study the prospects of testing the $WW\gamma$ vertex in $e^-p \to \nu\gamma X$ and $e^+p \to \nu\gamma X$ at HERA and LEP/LHC. Destructive interference effects between the Standard Model and the anomalous contributions to the amplitude severely limit the sensitivity of both processes to non-standard $WW\gamma$ couplings. Sensitivity limits for the anomalous $WW\gamma$ couplings κ and λ at HERA and LEP/LHC are derived, taking into account experimental cuts and uncertainties, and the form factor behaviour of nonstandard couplings. These limits are found to be significantly weaker than those which can be expected from other collider processes within the next few years. At HERA, they are comparable to bounds obtained from S-matrix unitarity.

One of the prime targets for experiments at present and future colliders is the measurement of the $WW\gamma$ and WWZ couplings. In the Standard Model (SM) of electroweak interactions, these couplings are unambiguously fixed by the nonabelian nature of the $SU(2) \times U(1)$ gauge symmetry. In contrast to low energy and high precision experiments at the Z peak, collider experiments offer the possibility of a direct, and essentially model independent, measurement of the three vector boson vertices. A number of different collider processes which are sensitive to anomalous $WW\gamma$ and WWZ couplings have been studied (see *e.g.* Refs. [1] – [7]).

The UA2 Collaboration recently reported the first direct measurement of the $WW\gamma$ vertex in $p\bar{p} \to e^{\pm}\nu\gamma X$ [8]. A more precise measurement can soon be expected from Tevatron experiments. ep colliders such as HERA (30 GeV electrons/positrons on 820 GeV protons; $\sqrt{s} = 314$ GeV, $\mathcal{L} = 2 \cdot 10^{31} cm^{-2} s^{-1}$) or LEP/LHC (60 GeV electrons/positrons on 7.7 TeV protons; $\sqrt{s} = 1.36$ TeV, $\mathcal{L} = 2.8 \cdot 10^{32} cm^{-2} s^{-1}$[9]) also offer chances to test the $WW\gamma$ vertex. Single W boson production in ep collisions has been studied extensively in the past [4, 5]. The process $ep \to \nu\gamma X$ has only recently been investigated in Refs. [10] – [12].

Since the exchanged W couples to essentially massless quarks which effectively insures that $\partial_\mu W^\mu = 0$, the $WW\gamma$ vertex depends on four free parameters only, and can conveniently be described by the effective Lagrangian [2, 13]

$$\mathcal{L}_{WW\gamma} = -ie\left\{\left(W^{\dagger}_{\mu\nu}W^\mu A^\nu - W^{\dagger}_\mu A_\nu W^{\mu\nu}\right) + \kappa W^{\dagger}_\mu W_\nu F^{\mu\nu} + \frac{\lambda}{M_W^2}W^{\dagger}_{\lambda\mu}W^\mu_\nu A^{\nu\lambda}\right.$$

$$+ \tilde{\kappa} W_\mu^\dagger W_\nu \tilde{F}^{\mu\nu} + \frac{\tilde{\lambda}}{M_W^2} W_{\lambda\mu}^\dagger W_\nu^\mu \tilde{F}^{\nu\lambda} \bigg\}. \tag{1}$$

Here A^μ and W^μ are the photon and W^- fields, $W_{\mu\nu} = \partial_\mu W_\nu - \partial_\nu W_\mu$, $F_{\mu\nu} = \partial_\mu A_\nu - \partial_\nu A_\mu$, and $\tilde{F}_{\mu\nu} = \frac{1}{2}\epsilon_{\mu\nu\rho\sigma} F^{\rho\sigma}$. e is the charge of the proton, and M_W the mass of the W boson. The CP violating couplings $\tilde{\kappa}$ and $\tilde{\lambda}$ are constrained by the electric dipole moment of the neutron to be smaller than $\mathcal{O}(10^{-3})$[14] in magnitude. Subsequently we shall therefore concentrate on the anomalous couplings κ and λ.

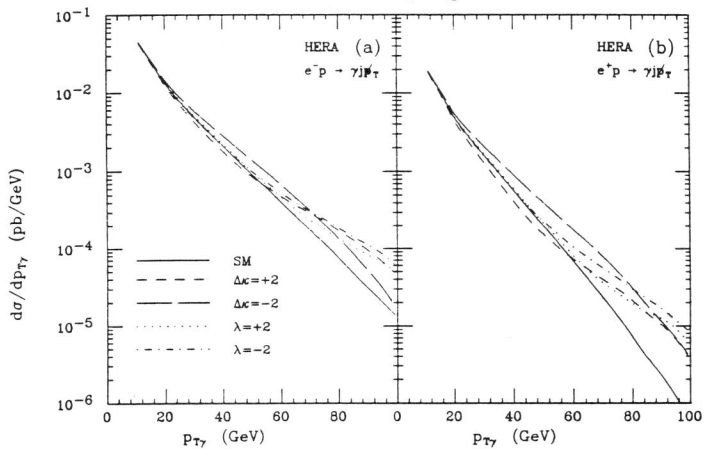

Figure 1 - Transverse momentum distribution of the photon in a) $e^- p \to \gamma j \not{p}_T$ and b) $e^+ p \to \gamma j \not{p}_T$ at HERA for the SM (solid line) and various anomalous values of κ and λ.

Tree level unitarity restricts the $WW\gamma$ couplings to their (SM) gauge theory values at asymptotically high energies [15, 16]. This implies that any deviation from the SM expectation has to be described by a form factor which vanishes when the absolute square of the four-momentum of either of the exchanged W bosons becomes large. Consequently, we shall include form factors

$$a(q_W^2, \bar{q}_W^2, 0) = a_0 \left[\left(1 - \frac{q_W^2}{\Lambda^2}\right) \left(1 - \frac{\bar{q}_W^2}{\Lambda^2}\right) \right]^{-n} \tag{2}$$

with $n = 1$ in all our calculations. The scale Λ in Eq. (2) represents the scale at which new physics becomes important in the weak boson sector, $e.g.$ due to a composite structure of the W boson. We shall use $\Lambda = 1$ TeV in our numerical simulations. In the limit $\Lambda \to \infty$, we find excellent agreement with both Refs. [11] and [10]. Further details of our calculation can be found in Ref. [12].

In Fig. 1, we show $p_{T\gamma}$ distributions at HERA, for various values of $\Delta\kappa$ and λ. The Feynman diagram involving the $WW\gamma$ vertex contains two W propagators and thus is suppressed with respect to the bremsstrahlung diagrams. Thus, at HERA, rather large anomalous couplings are necessary to produce significant deviations in $p_{T\gamma}$. This statement can be made quantitative by deriving those values of κ and

λ which would give a deviation from the SM at the 90% and 69% confidence level (CL) in the $p_{T\gamma}$ spectrum for an integrated luminosity of $\int \mathcal{L} dt = 10^3$ pb^{-1}. In order to derive realistic limits we allow for a normalization uncertainty of $\Delta \mathcal{N} = 30\%$. These 69% and 90% CL deviations are summarized in Table 1.

Finally, we compare the limits achievable in $e^{\pm}p \to \gamma j \not{p}_T$ with bounds from S-matrix unitarity and the sensitivity to non-gauge theory terms in the $WW\gamma$ vertex accessible in other present and future collider experiments. Bounds from S-matrix unitarity depend explicitly on the functional form and the scale Λ of the form factor. Varying only one coupling at a time, the following upper limits are obtained from unitarity for the form factor of Eq. (2) and $\Lambda \gg M_W$:

$$n=1 : \begin{cases} |\Delta\kappa| \lesssim 1.9 \text{ TeV}^2/\Lambda^2 \\ |\lambda| \lesssim 1.0 \text{ TeV}^2/\Lambda^2 \end{cases} \qquad n=2 : \begin{cases} |\Delta\kappa| \lesssim 7.6 \text{ TeV}^2/\Lambda^2 \\ |\lambda| \lesssim 4.0 \text{ TeV}^2/\Lambda^2 \end{cases} \qquad (3)$$

Comparing the bounds listed in Table 1 with Eq. (3), one observes that measuring the anomalous $WW\gamma$ couplings in either $e^-p \to \gamma j \not{p}_T$ or $e^+p \to \gamma j \not{p}_T$ at HERA will not significantly improve the limits from S-matrix unitarity.

$e^-p \to \gamma j \not{p}_T$

Coupling	C.L.	HERA	LEP/LHC
$\Delta\kappa$	90%	+2.2	+0.44
		−2.4	−0.54
	69%	+1.3	+0.25
		−1.4	−0.30
λ	90%	+2.8	+0.17
		−2.1	−0.12
	69%	+2.1	+0.12
		−1.3	−0.08

$e^+p \to \gamma j \not{p}_T$

Coupling	C.L.	HERA	LEP/LHC
$\Delta\kappa$	90%	+4.0	+0.53
		−2.2	−0.53
	69%	+3.0	+0.31
		−1.1	−0.30
λ	90%	+4.8	+0.21
		−3.8	−0.16
	69%	+3.1	+0.16
		−2.3	−0.10

Table 1: Sensitivities for the anomalous $WW\gamma$ couplings $\Delta\kappa$ and λ in $e^{\pm}p \to \gamma j \not{p}_T$ at HERA and LEP/LHC for an integrated luminosity of 1000 pb^{-1}. Only one coupling at a time is assumed to be different from the SM value.

Other processes can be used to probe the $WW\gamma$ vertex. eW production at ep colliders will provide useful limits. Currently, the UA2 Collaboration has measured κ and λ in the process $p\bar{p} \to e^{\pm}\nu\gamma X$ at the CERN $p\bar{p}$ collider, obtaining [8]

$$\kappa = 1^{+2.6}_{-2.2} \text{ (for } \lambda = 0) \qquad \lambda = 0^{+1.7}_{-1.8} \text{ (for } \kappa = 1). \qquad (4)$$

The errors in Eq. (4) are already within a factor of two of, or even better than those which can be expected from $e^{\pm}p \to \gamma j \not{p}_T$ with 1000 pb^{-1} at HERA. Moreover, they are expected to be reduced considerably in the near future with new Tevatron data. With an integrated luminosity of 100 pb^{-1}, $|\Delta\kappa|$ can be constrained to be less than 0.7 − 1.0 (1.1 − 1.5) at 69% (90%) CL in $p\bar{p} \to W^{\pm}\gamma$, whereas $|\lambda|$ can be measured to $|\lambda| < 0.25 - 0.30$ (0.40 − 0.50) [17]. An even more precise determination of the anomalous $WW\gamma$ couplings will be possible in $e^+e^- \to W^+W^-$ at LEP II where an accuracy of $|\Delta\kappa|, |\lambda| \approx 0.1 - 0.2$ is expected [2].

In summary, in the energy domain of HERA and LEP/LHC, we find sensitivity bounds for $e^\pm p \to \nu\gamma X$ which are significantly weaker than those which can be expected from $ep \to eWX$, $p\bar{p} \to e^\pm \nu\gamma X$, and $e^+e^- \to W^+W^-$ within the next few years. At HERA, the limits which can be achieved for κ and λ in $e^\pm p \to \nu\gamma X$ are similar to the bounds resulting from S-matrix unitarity.

This work was supported in part by the U. S. Department of Energy under Contract No. DE-AC02-76ER00881 and Contract No. DE-FG05-87ER40319, in part by the Texas National Research Laboratory Commission under Grant Nos. RGFY9173 and RGFY9273, and in part by the University of Wisconsin Research Committee with funds granted by the Wisconsin Alumni Research Foundation.

1. K. O. Mikaelian, *Phys. Rev.* **D17** (1978) 750; K. O. Mikaelian, M. A. Samuel and D. Sahdev, *Phys. Rev. Lett.* **43** (1979) 746; C. L. Bilchak, R. W. Brown and J. D. Stroughair, *Phys. Rev.* **D29** (1984) 375; J. Cortes, K. Hagiwara and F. Herzog, *Nucl. Phys.* **B278** (1986) 26; U. Baur and D. Zeppenfeld, *Nucl. Phys.* **B308** (1988) 127.

2. K. Hagiwara et al., *Nucl. Phys.* **B282** (1987) 253; D. Zeppenfeld, *Phys. Lett.* **183B** (1987) 380.

3. S. Willenbrock and D. Zeppenfeld, *Phys. Rev.* **D37** (1989) 1775; K. Hagiwara, J. Woodside and D. Zeppenfeld, *Phys. Rev.* **D41** (1990) 2113.

4. E. Gabrielli, *Mod. Phys. Lett.* **A1** (1986) 465; M. Böhm and A. Rosado, *Z. Phys.* **C42** (1989) 479.

5. U. Baur and D. Zeppenfeld, *Nucl. Phys.* **B325** (1989) 253.

6. E. Yehudai, *Phys. Rev.* **D41** (1990) 33; *Phys. Rev.* **D44** (1991) 3434; S. Y. Choi and F. Schrempp, *Phys. Lett.* **272B** (1991) 149.

7. E. N. Argyres et al., *Phys. Lett.* **B280** (1992) 324.

8. UA2 Collaboration, J. Alitti et al., *Phys. Lett.* **B277** (1992) 194.

9. The LHC Study Group, CERN Report No. 91-03, 1991 (unpublished).

10. S. Godfrey, Report No. OCIP 91-2 (unpublished).

11. T. Helbig and H. Spiesberger, *Nucl. Phys.* **B373** (1992) 73.

12. U. Baur and M. A. Doncheski, *Phys. Rev.* **D46** (1992) 1959.

13. K. Gaemers and G. Gounaris, *Z. Phys.* **C1** (1979) 259.

14. W. J. Marciano and A. Queijeiro, *Phys. Rev.* **D33** (1986) 3449; F. Boudjema, K. Hagiwara, C. Hamzaoui and K. Numata, *Phys. Rev.* **D43** (1991) 2223.

15. J. M. Cornwall, D. N. Levin and G. Tiktopoulos, *Phys. Rev. Lett.* **30** (1973) 1268; *Phys. Rev.* **D10** (1974) 1145; C. H. Llewellyn Smith, *Phys. Lett.* **46B** (1973) 233; S. D. Joglekar, *Ann. of Phys.* **83** (1974) 427.

16. U. Baur and D. Zeppenfeld, *Phys. Lett.* **201B** (1988) 383.

17. U. Baur and E. L. Berger, *Phys. Rev.* **D41** (1990) 1476.

CONSTRAINTS ON ANOMALOUS WWγ COUPLINGS FROM eγ COLLISIONS [1]

K. ANDREW PETERSON and STEPHEN GODFREY
*Department of Physics, Carleton University, 1125 Colonel By Drive
Ottawa, Ontario, Canada. K1S 5B6*

ABSTRACT

We study the potential for using eγ collisions produced by backscattered laser photons to investigate WWγ couplings. We present results for Next Linear Collider energies of 500 GeV and 1 TeV. We find that where statistics allow, off W mass shell results can be quite important, complementing on W mass shell results from this and other studies. It is shown that eγ colliders would prove quite valuable in the investigations of W-boson physics.

1. Introduction

The study of gauge boson interactions is still unexplored territory. To this point, our only glimpse of these interactions is via radiative loop corrections induced by these interactions at low energies. Although, high precision measurements give us some information on the gauge boson couplings, a direct test of them is still necessary. The first such direct test of triple gauge boson couplings will come at LEP200, where sufficient $\sqrt{s}$ energy exists for W pair production. However, the limited available phase space means precision tests of the three vector coupling will undoubtedly await the arrival of a 500 GeV to 1 TeV e^+e^- linear collider.

By limiting ourselves to e^+e^- collisions, we limit the information that can be obtained. W pair production can proceed through both γ and Z exchange, and one ends up probing both the WWZ and WWγ vertex simultaneously. A way to isolate one of these vertices is therefore needed. An eγ collider provides such a method. There exists two possible means of creating an eγ collider from a e^+e^- collider. The first possibility uses a combination of beamstrahlung photons and classical bremstrahlung[1, 2]. This possibility, however, suffers from its soft photon distribution. Hard photon distributions may be obtained through backscattering high intensity laser beams off the incoming electron beams [3]. It is this possibility that we will concentrate on.

To parametrize the WWγ vertex we use a common parametrization of the WWγ vertex that imposes C and P symmetries separately [4, 5]:

$$\mathcal{L} = -ie\left\{(W^\dagger_{\mu\nu}W^\mu A^\nu - W^\dagger_\mu A_\nu W^{\mu\nu}) + \kappa_\gamma W^\dagger_\mu W_\nu A^{\mu\nu} + \frac{\lambda_\gamma}{M_W^2}W^\dagger_{\lambda\mu}W^\mu_\nu A^{\nu\lambda}\right\}. \quad (1)$$

In the standard model, $\kappa_\gamma = 1$ and $\lambda_\gamma = 0$.

One may obtain model independent estimates of these anomalous couplings in the context of a chiral lagrangian framework [6], where one expects $\delta\kappa_V \sim O(10^{-2})$,

---
[1] talk presented by K. Andrew Peterson

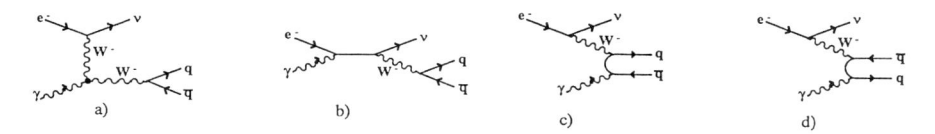

Figure 1: Feynman diagrams for the process $e\gamma \to \nu_e q\bar{q}'$

and $\lambda_V \sim O(10^{-4})$. Model specific calculations bear these estimates out [7]. What this implies is that unless there is some radical new physics, one must be able to measure these anomalous couplings to the percent level if one would like to see new physics. This paper will show that this percent level could be achieved at a $\sqrt{s} =$ 500 GeV or 1 TeV e^+e^- collider; the Next Linear Collider, operating in $e\gamma$ mode.

2. Calculations and Results

In previous papers of this nature[8, 9], calculations were performed using the process $e\gamma \to \nu_e W$, with the appropriate decay widths to the observed final states. This is a decent approximation to the actual process, since the greatest percentage of the cross section proceeds through a real W. However, we feel by making this approximation, possible valuable physics is lost. Although the off resonance cross sections are small, the deviations of non-standard model gauge couplings in these cross sections can be significant. We have therefore considered the processes $e\gamma \to \nu_e q\bar{q}'$, $e\gamma \to \nu_e \mu \bar{\nu}_\mu$, and $e\gamma \to \nu_e e \bar{\nu}_e$, which may proceed via the four diagrams of figure 1. The process, $e\gamma \to \nu_e e \bar{\nu}_e$ also proceeds through a Z exchange diagram not shown here. In what follows we will concentrate on the $q\bar{q}'$ modes.

Amplitudes for these processes were calculated using the CALKUL helicity technique. In the case of the anomalous magnetic moment, κ_γ, plus standard model terms, these amplitudes can be found in an earlier paper by Couture et al[10]. Monte Carlo integration techniques were then used to perform the phase space integrations and calculate the cross sections. The photon distributions are treated as structure functions, which are then integrated with the $e\gamma$ cross section to obtain our results. The exact forms of these photon distributions, along with the required parameters will be given in a longer paper [11].

Figures 2 and 3 display some of the relevant distributions of the $q\bar{q}'$ cross section for a $\sqrt{s}$ of 500 GeV and 1 TeV in the case of a backscattered photon. Displayed are the differential cross sections as functions of the the $q\bar{q}'$ invariant mass, $M_{q\bar{q}'}$, the transverse momentum of the reconstructed W, p_{TW}, and the angular distribution of the reconstructed W, θ_W. A beamline angular cut of 10° was made on the quark directions, as well as a 5 GeV cut on p_{TW}. For the p_T and angular distributions, we have also made a cut on $M_{q\bar{q}'}$ of $75 < M_{q\bar{q}'} < 85$.

From the invariant mass distribution we see that off W mass shell results can

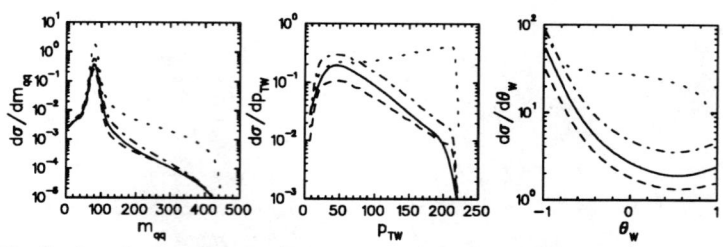

Figure 2: Distributions for 500 GeV $e\gamma$ collisions: Solid line is S.M., dashed-dotted is $\kappa = 1.5$, dashed line is $\kappa = 0.5$, and dotted line is $\lambda = 1.0$.

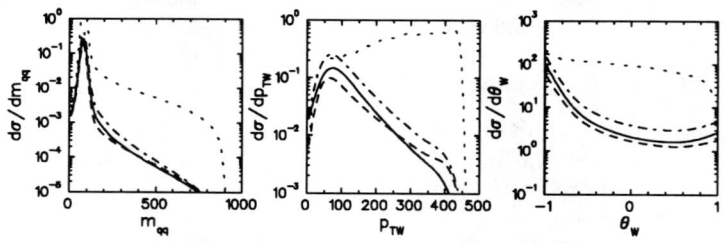

Figure 3: Distributions for 1 TeV $e\gamma$ collisions: Same legend as figure 2.

be particularly useful. Although the cross sections here are small, small deviations in either λ_γ and κ_γ can produce order of magnitude differences in the cross section. The p_T distribution also provides useful information. Here, especially in the high p_T regions, the non-standard model couplings deviate significantly from the standard model values. We will use a combination of p_T bins and angular distribution bins to provide our best constraints on the anomalous couplings.

To obtain constraints we consider the process $e\gamma \to \nu_e q \bar{q}'$ and assumed a integrated luminosity of 10 fb^{-1}. Our total cross sections at 500 GeV and 1 TeV are 16.7 pb and 18.9 pb respectively, so statistics should not be the limiting factor. We have assumed a systematic error of 5% on cross sections and a systematic error of 3% for ratios of cross sections. The total error is then taken to be the statistical and systematic error combined in quadrature. It should be emphasised that both the integrated luminosity and the systematic errors are conservative estimates. We expect that more realistic estimates of these variables will significantly improve our constraints.

Using the error in the standard model values as the error, we calculate the χ^2 values. Figure 4 a) is the resulting 95% confidence limits on κ_γ and λ_γ for a 500 GeV collider based on a 4 bin p_{TW} measurement and a 4 bin θ_W measurement. One sees that both κ_γ and λ_γ are constrained to 6%. Figure 4 b) repeats the above analysis for a 1 TeV collider. Figure 4 b) also includes the confidence level that is obtained through a measurement of the cross section with invariant mass, $M_{q\bar{q}'} > 600$ GeV. This is not included in the combined limits. One sees that here κ_γ is still constrained to 6% but λ_γ to 2%.

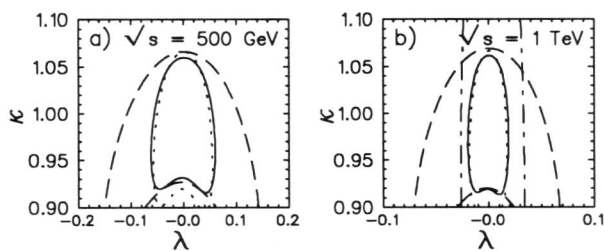

Figure 4: a) Limits on κ_γ and λ_γ at the 95% confidence level for a 500 GeV $e\gamma$ collider: Dashed line is limit based upon 4 θ_W bins, dotted line is based upon 4 p_{TW} bins, and solid line is the combined measurement. b) Same as a) except for 1 TeV $e\gamma$ collider: The additional vertical dash-dotted line is limit based upon cross-sectional measurement with $M_{q\bar{q}'} > 600$ GeV.

4. Conclusions

We see that an $e\gamma$ collider operating at either 500 GeV or 1 TeV can constrain the non-standard model gauge couplings κ_γ and λ_γ to the percent level. These constraints represent an improvement on similiar constraints from LEP and are comparable with those obtainable at SSC or LHC. We conclude that one would increase the knowledge of triple gauge boson couplings by running an e^+e^- accelerator in a backscattered laser $e\gamma$ mode.

5. Acknowledgements

The authors would like to thank Dean Karlen, F. Halzen, M.C. Gonzalez-Garcia for their helpful input. This work was supported in part by the Natural Sciences and Engineering Research Council of Canada.

6. References

1. R. Blankenbecler and S.D. Drell, *Phys. Rev. Lett.* **61** (1988) 2324.
2. O.J.P. Éboli *et al*, Universiy of Madison report, MAD/PH/701.
3. I.F. Ginzburg *et al.*, *Nucl. Inst. Meth.* **205** (1983), 47; **219** (1984), 5.
4. K. Hagiwara *et al*, *Nucl. Phys.* **B282** (1987) 253.
5. G.L. Kane, J. Vidal, and C.P. Yuan, *Phys. Rev.* **D39** (1989), 2617.
6. J. Bagger, S. Dawson, and G. Valencia, FERMILAB-PUB-92/75-T (1992);
7. G. Couture and J.N. Ng, *Z. Phys.* **C35** (1987), 65; G. Couture *et al*, *Phys. Rev.* **D36** (1987), 859; **D39** (1988), 860.
8. S.Y. Choi and F. Schremp, *Phys. Lett.* **B272** (1991), 149.
9. E. Yehudai, *Phys. Rev.* **D41** (1991), 33.
10. G. Couture, S. Godfrey and P. Kalyniak, *Phys. Lett.* **B218** (1989), 261; *Phys. Rev.* **D39** (1989), 3239; **D42** (1990), 1841.
11. S. Godfrey and K.A. Peterson, Carleton University report, OCIP/C-92-7.

ONE-LOOP CONSTRAINTS ON THE ELECTROWEAK TRIPLE GAUGE BOSON VERTEX

D. ZEPPENFELD and R. SZALAPSKI
Dept. of Physics, University of Wisconsin, Madison, WI 53706, USA

K. HAGIWARA
KEK, Tsukuba, Ibaraki 305, Japan

and

S. ISHIHARA
Department of Physics, University of Tokyo, Tokyo 113, Japan

ABSTRACT

Anomalous WWZ and $WW\gamma$ couplings affect observables in neutral and charged current interactions via 1-loop contributions. We analyse these effects in the framework of $SU(2) \times U(1)$ gauge-invariant effective interactions. Using a complete set of dimension six operators which involve the gauge fields and the Higgs doublet field Φ, all divergent contributions are absorbed into a renormalization of the parameters which contribute at tree level. Low energy constraints must assume absence of accidental cancellations. Resulting bounds are modest when compared to the sensitivity of vector boson pair production experiments at LEP II and at hadron supercolliders.

Since the commissioning of the LEP e^+e^- collider at CERN we have witnessed a dramatic confirmation of the predictions of the Standard Model (SM). At present, experiment and theory generally agree at the 1% level or better in the determination of the vector boson couplings to the various fermions. While this may rightly be considered a confirmation of the gauge boson nature of the W and the Z, the most direct consequence of the $SU(2) \times U(1)$ gauge symmetry, the nonabelian self-couplings of W, Z, and photon, remains poorly measured to date. Even if the underlying theory has an exact $SU(2) \times U(1)$ gauge symmetry, novel strong interactions in the gauge boson-Higgs sector may lead to substantial anomalous WWZ and $WW\gamma$ triple boson couplings. It is this scenario that is at the focus of this talk.

Restricting our attention to C and P even couplings, the most general WWV, $(V = Z, \gamma)$ vertex can be parameterized in terms of an effective Lagrangian[1]

$$\mathcal{L}_{eff}^{WWV} = -i\, g_{WWV}\left(g_1^V(W^\dagger_{\mu\nu}W^\mu - W^{\dagger\mu}W_{\mu\nu})V^\nu + \kappa_V W^\dagger_\mu W_\nu V^{\mu\nu} + \frac{\lambda_V}{m_W^2} W^\dagger_{\rho\mu}W^\mu{}_\nu V^{\nu\rho}\right), \quad (1)$$

with the overall normalization set by $g_{WW\gamma} = e$ and $g_{WWZ} = e\cot\theta_W$. Within the SM the couplings are given by $g_1^Z = g_1^\gamma = \kappa_Z = \kappa_\gamma = 1$, $\lambda_Z = \lambda_\gamma = 0$.

While the value of g_1^γ is fixed by electromagnetic gauge invariance (it is just the electric charge of the W^+) the other couplings have to be determined experimentally. Investigating $W\gamma$ production at the CERN collider, the UA2 collaboration has found[2]

$$\kappa_\gamma = 1^{+2.6}_{-2.2}, \qquad \lambda_\gamma = 0^{+1.7}_{-1.8} \qquad (2)$$

At LEP II one expects a sensitivity to deviations from the SM predictions of[3] $\Delta\kappa \approx \Delta\lambda \approx 0.1...0.2$, while the hadron supercolliders will push the precision of the λ_V measurements to the one percent level.[4]

Consider models with some novel strong interactions in the bosonic sector at an energy scale Λ, which may be of order 1 TeV. The low energy effects of this new physics can be described by an effective Lagrangian which contains the light degrees of freedom only. These we take to be the $SU(2)$ and hypercharge gauge fields W_μ^i and B_μ and a (possibly composite) Higgs doublet field Φ. This choice allows us to discuss Higgs mass effects and provides for decoupling of the new physics as $\Lambda \to \infty$. At low energies, only the lowest dimensional operators are relevant and we restrict our attention to dimension six operators. Due to the gauge symmetry of the underlying dynamics, these operators must be $SU(2) \times U(1)$ gauge invariant and a complete list can be found in Ref. 5. A general analysis of the twelve operators in the bosonic sector will be given in Ref. 6. Here it suffices to study the following seven,

$$\mathcal{L}_{eff} = \sum_{i=1}^{7} \frac{f_i}{\Lambda^2} \mathcal{O}_i = \frac{1}{\Lambda^2} \Big(f_\Phi^{(1)} (D_\mu\Phi)^\dagger \Phi \Phi^\dagger (D^\mu \Phi) + f_{BW} \Phi^\dagger \hat{B}_{\mu\nu} \hat{W}^{\mu\nu} \Phi$$
$$+ f_{DW} Tr([D_\mu,\hat{W}_{\nu\rho}][D^\mu,\hat{W}^{\nu\rho}]) - f_{DB} \frac{g'^2}{2}(\partial_\mu B_{\nu\rho})(\partial^\mu B^{\nu\rho}) \qquad (3)$$
$$+ f_B (D_\mu\Phi)^\dagger \hat{B}^{\mu\nu}(D_\nu\Phi) + f_W (D_\mu\Phi)^\dagger \hat{W}^{\mu\nu}(D_\nu\Phi) + f_{WWW} Tr[\hat{W}_{\mu\nu}\hat{W}^{\nu\rho}\hat{W}_\rho{}^\mu] \Big) ,$$

where $D_\mu = \partial_\mu + ig\frac{\sigma^i}{2}W_\mu^i + i\frac{g'}{2}B_\mu$ is the $SU(2) \times U(1)$ covariant derivative for the Higgs field, and the hatted field strengths are defined by $[D_\mu, D_\nu] = \hat{W}_{\mu\nu} + \hat{B}_{\mu\nu}$.

The last three operators, $\mathcal{O}_B$, $\mathcal{O}_W$, and $\mathcal{O}_{WWW}$, contribute to the WWV vertices at the tree level, as can be seen immediately by replacing the Higgs doublet field with its vacuum expectation value, $\Phi^\dagger \to (0, v/\sqrt{2})$. One finds

$$\kappa_Z = 1 + (f_W - s^2(f_B + f_W)) \frac{m_Z^2}{2\Lambda^2} , \qquad (4)$$

$$\kappa_\gamma = 1 + (f_B + f_W) \frac{m_W^2}{2\Lambda^2} , \qquad (5)$$

$$g_1^Z = 1 + f_W \frac{m_Z^2}{2\Lambda^2} = \kappa_Z + \frac{s^2}{c^2}(\kappa_\gamma - 1) , \qquad (6)$$

$$\lambda_\gamma = \lambda_Z = 3 g^2 \frac{m_W^2}{2\Lambda^2} f_{WWW} , \qquad (7)$$

with $s = \sin\theta_W$ and $c = \cos\theta_W$.

Here we concentrate on precision experiments which can be described by 4-fermion scattering amplitudes. Since the operators considered are purely bosonic, they give rise to oblique corrections only, and their effects can be analyzed in terms of the S, T, and U parameters of Peskin and Takeuchi[7] or in terms of the ϵ-parameters as defined in Ref. 8. The first four operators in Eq. (3) affect these observables at tree level already.[9] Their contribution to the ϵ_i is given by

$$\epsilon_1 = \alpha T = \epsilon_1^{SM}(m_t, m_H) - 2g^2 \frac{m_W^2}{\Lambda^2}(f_{DW} + \frac{s^4}{c^4}f_{DB}) - \frac{v^2}{2\Lambda^2}f_\Phi^{(1)} , \qquad (8)$$

$$\epsilon_2 = -\frac{\alpha}{s^2} U = \epsilon_2^{SM}(m_t, m_H) - 2g^2 \frac{m_W^2}{\Lambda^2} f_{DW} , \qquad (9)$$

$$\epsilon_3 = \frac{\alpha}{4s^2} S = \epsilon_3^{SM}(m_t, m_H) - 2g^2 \frac{m_W^2}{\Lambda^2}(f_{DW} + \frac{s^2}{c^2} f_{DB}) - \frac{m_W^2}{\Lambda^2} f_{BW} . \qquad (10)$$

The remaining three operators contribute at the 1-loop level only. In order to preserve gauge invariance at all stages of the calculation we have used dimensional regularization in order to identify the divergent contributions. Poles at $D = 2$ dimensions are identified with the Λ^2 divergencies which would arise in a momentum cutoff scheme, and poles at $D = 4$ are identified with logarithmic divergencies. One finds that all quadratic divergencies are absorbed into the renormalization of the SM parameters, which we take to be α, m_Z and G_F. The remaining logarithmic divergencies can be obsorbed completely into the renormalization of the tree level parameters f_{DW}, f_{DB}, f_{BW}, and $f_\Phi^{(1)}$, i.e. the leading effect of the anomalous three boson couplings is obtained by replacing the f_i in Eqs. (8)–(10) by the renormalized f_i^r:

$$f_{DW}^r = f_{DW} - \frac{1}{192\pi^2} f_W \log\frac{\Lambda^2}{\mu^2} , \qquad (11)$$

$$f_{DB}^r = f_{DB} - \frac{1}{192\pi^2} f_B \log\frac{\Lambda^2}{\mu^2} , \qquad (12)$$

$$f_{BW}^r = f_{BW} - \frac{\alpha}{32\pi s^2} \log\frac{\Lambda^2}{\mu^2} \left(f_B(\frac{20}{3} + \frac{7}{3c^2} + \frac{m_H^2}{m_W^2}) - f_W(4 + \frac{1}{c^2} - \frac{m_H^2}{m_W^2}) + 12g^2 f_{WWW} \right) (13)$$

$$f_\Phi^{(1)r} = f_\Phi^{(1)} + \frac{3\alpha}{8\pi c^2} \log\frac{\Lambda^2}{\mu^2} \left(f_B \frac{m_H^2}{v^2} + \frac{3m_W^2}{v^2}(f_B + f_W) \right) . \qquad (14)$$

After renormalization of the SM parameters and of the operators which contribute at tree level, the remaining corrections to four-fermion amplitudes are finite. This may be contrasted with previous work, where quadratically divergent contributions to observables like $\delta\rho = \epsilon_1$ were found.[10,11] The main difference in our analysis is the inclusion of the four operators $\mathcal{O}_{DW}$, $\mathcal{O}_{DB}$, $\mathcal{O}_{BW}$, and $\mathcal{O}_\Phi^{(1)}$, which contribute to four-fermion amplitudes at tree level already. The renormalization of these four operators absorbs the logarithmic divergencies. These $\log\frac{\Lambda^2}{\mu^2}$ terms describe the mixing of the seven operators between the new physics scale Λ and the weak boson mass scale $\mu = m_W$.

The quadratic divergencies observed in earlier work are cancelled by Higgs contributions to the vacuum polarization of the W and the Z: $SU(2) \times U(1)$ gauge invariance and the use of a linear realization for the symmetry breaking sector relates WWV anomalous couplings to anomalous Higgs-gauge boson interactions. Gauge invariance guarantees the cancellation of all quadratic divergencies between gauge boson and Higgs contributions.[12] A trace of the quadratic divergencies is preserved in the m_H^2 terms in the results of Eqs. (13),(14): the Higgs graphs give rise to $-\Lambda^2 + m_H^2 \log\Lambda$ terms. By including Higgs exchange we have therefore replaced quadratic divergencies by m_H^2 terms. In the limit $m_H \to \Lambda$ the quadratic divergencies are recovered.

Because the divergent effects of the anomalous triple gauge boson couplings can be absorbed into the renormalization of the tree level contributions, no direct measurement of the WWV couplings is possible with the present low energy data. Any bounds must *assume* the absence of cancellations between anomalous coupling contributions and the tree level operators, and therefore such bounds can be order of magnitude estimates only. Our analysis shows that even without such accidental cancellations deviations $\kappa_\gamma - 1 = 0.5$ or $\lambda = 0.5$ are clearly allowed by the data at 90% CL if the Higgs is relatively light.[6] These results strongly depend on the value of the top quark mass, and, because of the m_H^2 terms, there is a strong Higgs mass dependence as well. These ambiguities only highlight the fact that the low energy experiments cannot replace a direct measurement of the WWV couplings in vector boson pair production such as $e^+e^- \to W^+W^-$ at LEP II.

Acknowledgements

This research was supported by U. S. Dept. of Energy, by the Texas National Research Laboratory Commission, and by the University of Wisconsin Research Committee with funds granted by the Wisconsin Alumni Research Foundation.

References

1. K. Hagiwara *et al.*, Nucl. Phys. **B282** (1987) 253.
2. UA2 collaboration, J. Alitti *et al.*, Phys. Lett. **B277** (1992) 194.
3. G. Barbiellini *et al.*, in "Physics at LEP," ed. by J. Ellis and R. D. Peccei, report CERN 86-02, Vol. 2, p. 1; M. Davier *et al.*, ECFA Workshop on LEP 200, Aachen, CERN report CERN 87-08, Vol. I, p. 120.
4. See *e.g.* H. Kuijf *et al.*, ECFA Large Hadron Collider Workshop, Aachen, ed. by G. Jarlskog and D. Rein, CERN report CERN 90-10, Vol. II, p. 91; D. Zeppenfeld and S. S. D. Willenbrock, Phys. Rev. **D37** (1988) 1775.
5. W. Buchmüller and D. Wyler, Nucl. Phys. **B268** (1986) 621.
6. K. Hagiwara *et al.*, Phys. Lett. **B283** (1992) 353, and work in preparation.
7. M. E. Peskin and T. Takeuchi, Phys. Rev. Lett. **65** (1990) 964.
8. G. Altarelli and R. Barbieri, Phys. Lett. **B253** (1991) 161; G. Altarelli *et al.*, Nucl. Phys. **B369** (1992) 3; G. Altarelli, preprint CERN-TH.6525/92.
9. B. Grinstein and M. B. Wise, Phys. Lett. **B265** (1991) 326.
10. M. Suzuki, Phys. Lett. **B153** (1985) 289; H. Neufeld *et al.*, Phys. Lett. **B198** (1987) 563; J. J. van der Bij, Phys. Rev. **D35** (1987) 1088; J. A. Grifols *et al.*, Int. J. Mod. Phys. **A3** (1988) 225; G. L. Kane *et al.*, Phys. Rev. **D39** (1989) 2617.
11. A. Grau *et al.*, Phys. Lett. **166B** (1986) 233; J. A. Grifols *et al.*, Phys. Lett. **B197** (1987) 437; R. Alcorta *et al.*, Mod. Phys. Lett. **A2** (1987) 23.
12. A. de Rujula *et al.*, preprint CERN-TH. 6272/91 (1991).

RADIATIVE LEPTONIC EVENTS IN DELPHI

DELPHI Collaboration

presented by Jesús Marco
Centro de Estudios Avanzados de Física Moderna
Consejo Superior de Investigaciones Científicas y Universidad de Cantabria
Santander, 39005, Spain

DPF '92

ABSTRACT

The analysis of searches carried on dilepton events with energetic isolated photons or with a V, using the data collected in 1990 and 1991 (about 365,000 Z^0's) in the DELPHI detector at LEP, is described.

In the $\ell\ell V$ channel 28 events are found, 8 of them $\tau\tau$ V events, and the V mass distribution is in agreement with what expected from standard four fermion processes.

A total of 364 leptonic events with one isolated photon have been selected, and classified after lepton identification. Data is in good agreement with QED predictions for radiative corrections, showing universality. Improved limits on excited leptons decaying into a lepton and a photon have been obtained from the analysis of the invariant mass spectra.

Including '92 data for a total of about 1 M Z^0's, 30 $\ell\ell\gamma\gamma$ events have been selected. Number of events and invariant masses distributions are in agreement with QED higher order predictions. Two events, an $ee\gamma\gamma$ and a $\mu\mu\gamma\gamma$, show a high $\gamma\gamma$ mass of about 59 GeV/c^2.

1. Search for $\ell\ell V$ events

1.1. Introduction

$\ell\ell V$ events are characterized by a simple topology: a pair of charged leptons (e, μ or τ) plus a V (a pair of close particles with opposite charge : (ee), $(\mu\mu)$ or $(\pi\pi)$). The standard source for this type of events are four fermion processes.

1.2. Event selection and classification

Charged tracks should have $p > 0.2\ GeV/c$, $\theta > 25°$ and come from the interaction region. Only events with four or six tracks (to accept three prong τ decays) in at least two jets with charge balance and a total momentum above 15 GeV/c are accepted. Tau background is suppressed requesting an invariant mass above 2.5 GeV/c^2 for any triplet combination in four tracks events. On six tracks events, a τ like three prong combination is requested. Two track tangential at small distance with an invariant mass below 75 MeV are rejected as photon conversions. Hadronic background is removed by rejecting 2-2 track configurations. After defining the V candidate a final check is made asking for a quasi 3-body configuration.

Inelastic ($E_{TOT} < 65\ GeV/c$) four tracks events and six tracks events are classified as $\tau\tau V$ events. Track identification is used to divide the rest between eeV and $\mu\mu V$. The V is classified as a $(ee),(\mu\mu)$ or $(\pi\pi)$ pair using calorimetric and muon chambers information for energetic tracks, and the TPC dE/dx for low energy ones.

1.3. Results

A total of 28 candidate events have been found [1] and classified as shown in table 1, where the comparison with the expected number obtained using the Daverveldt [2] simulation is also given. There is agreement within the statistics. However small discrepancies are found in the $\tau\tau V$ channel, with an event with high V mass (around 17 GeV/c^2) and a low $\tau\tau$ mass ($26\ GeV/c^2$)

Table 1
Number of $\ell\ell V$ events found for each channel, and number of events expected from standard processes.

$V=$	(ee)	$(\mu\mu)$	$(\pi\pi)$	$(\mu\mu/\pi\pi)$	not id.	TOTAL	EXPECTED
eeV	2	5	0	3	1	11	9.9 ± 1.1
$\mu\mu V$	5	1	1	2	0	9	9.3 ± 0.9
$\tau\tau V$	3	3	1	1	0	8	$3.9 \pm 0.4\ (+1.5\pm0.5\ \tau\tau\ \text{bck})$

2. Leptonic events with energetic isolated photons

2.1. Introduction

Clean detector signatures are expected: two charged tracks (or four to cope with three prong τ decays) and one or more isolated photons, for the hard radiative corrections to Z^0 decay; one electron and a hard photon for the Compton channel. Higher order QED processes is the standard source of these events.

2.2. $\ell\ell\gamma$ events

Events with two acollinear ($10° < acol < 170°$) tracks, with $p > 2.5\ GeV/c$ and $\theta > 25°$) and an isolated photon ($E > 2\ GeV$, $\theta_\gamma > 25°$, $\theta_{iso} > 30°$) are selected. A three body kinematical fit using the measured directions of the particles is imposed, and used to recalculate their momenta and improve the $\ell\gamma$ invariant masses ($\sigma_{m(\ell\gamma)} \approx 250\ MeV/c^2$ for $ee\gamma$, $\mu\mu\gamma$ events, and about 2.5 GeV/c^2 for $\tau\tau\gamma$). Found events are classified as $ee\gamma$ (elastic, $E_{em}/p_{calc} > 0.7$), $\mu\mu\gamma$ (elastic and identified by muon chambers or calorimeters), or $\tau\tau\gamma$ (inelastic, $p_{meas}/p_{calc} < 0.5$). Table 2 shows the number of events selected [3] in each channel, and the number of expected events predicted by the simulation employing KORALZ as generator.

Table 2
Number of $\ell\ell\gamma$ events found for each channel, and number of events expected from standard processes.

Channel	Observed	Expected
$ee\gamma$	158	163 ± 13
$\mu\mu\gamma$	117	122 ± 10
$\tau\tau\gamma$	70	69 ± 6

2.3. $e\gamma$ events

An electron with $E_{em} > 2\ GeV$ and a photon with $E > 8\ GeV$ in the barrel region, giving an acolinearity greater than 5° are requested to select these events. The $(e\gamma)$ mass is computed using the $\theta_{e\gamma}$ angle and the center of mass energy assuming the spectator electron is aligned with the beam, so $|p_{z_{miss}}|/E_{miss} > 0.5$ is asked for to reduce ISR effects, obtaining a $\sigma_{m(e\gamma)} \approx 450\ MeV/c^2$. A total of 61 events are found, in agreement with the Compton simulation prediction of 66 events.

2.4. Limits on compositeness

Compositeness predicts the existence of excited leptons, ℓ^*, with high mass, decaying into normal leptons plus a photon. Couplings to gauge bosons depend on the energy scale of compositeness, Λ. At LEP I energy, excited leptons with masses up to 90 GeV/c^2 can be singly produced, with a cross section $\sigma(\ell^*\ell) \propto s/\Lambda^2$. Limits on Λ as a function of m_{ℓ^*} have been obtained by comparing the $m_{\ell\gamma}$ spectrum found in the data with the QED background and the expected signal from an excited lepton of a given mass, resulting in $\Lambda > 0.8\ TeV$ for $m_{\ell^*} < 85\ GeV/c^2$ [3].

2.5. $\ell\ell\gamma\gamma$ events

Events with two charged tracks and two photons ($E > 3\ GeV$) with an isolation angle greater than 15° are selected. A total of 22 events are found, in agreement with QED higher order prediction obtained employing the Stirling generator [4]: 10 $ee\gamma\gamma$ (9 expected), 6 $\mu\mu\gamma\gamma$ (7 predicted) , and 6 $\tau\tau\gamma\gamma$ (5 expected).

An update using the data collected in this year is currently in progress, preliminary results will be given in what follows.

Using a higher cut on the photon energy , $E_\gamma > 5\ GeV$, a total of 30 events are found in a total sample of about $1M Z^0$ events. Figure 1 shows the $m_{\gamma\gamma}$ spectrum and how it compares well with the simulation prediction.

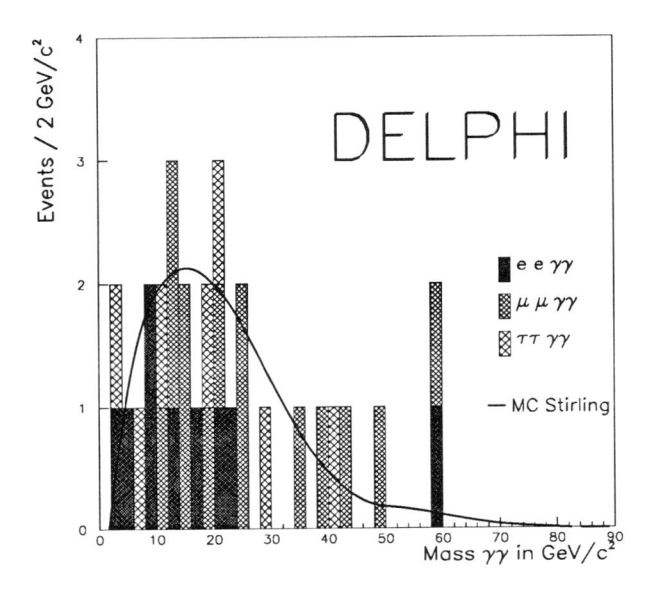

Figure 1: Distribution of $\gamma\gamma$ masses for the observed $\ell\ell\gamma\gamma$ events.

Comparing to the similar search made by L3 [5], two events are found with a mass above 50 GeV/c^2, both around 59 GeV/c^2: a $\mu\mu\gamma\gamma$ with a minimum photon isolation angle of 37° and an invariant mass of 59.0 ± 0.7 GeV/c^2, and an $ee\gamma\gamma$ with an isolation angle of 16° and an invariant mass of 58.4 ± 1.0 GeV/c^2.

Table 3
Kinematical variables measured for the two high $\gamma\gamma$ mass events

Event 1	P (GeV/c)	P_{fit} (GeV/c)	θ	ϕ	M_{inv} meas. (GeV/c^2)	M_{inv} fit (GeV/c^2)
μ_1	18.9	20.0	125°	116°	27.5	27.2
μ_2	11.4	10.6	27°	347°		
γ_1	34.1	33.6	62°	330°	58.9	59.0 ± 0.7
γ_2	26.6	27.1	120°	177°		
Event 2	P (GeV/c)	P_{fit} (GeV/c)	θ	ϕ	M_{inv} meas. (GeV/c^2)	M_{inv} fit (GeV/c^2)
e_1	15.6	22.7	64°	7.8°	5.6	6.7
e_2	4.7	4.5	70°	326°		
γ_1	46.4	43.8	121°	162°	61.4	58.4 ± 1.0
γ_2	20.9	20.3	58°	315°		

These mass values are obtained applying a kinematical four body fit that fixes the direction measured for each particle and the center of mass energy, and recalculates the momenta. These are then used to calculate the invariant masses, whose errors depend so on the measured angles for photons and tracks and on the kinematical event configuration, and are sensible to ISR. Typically the mass resolution varies between 0.5 and 1.0 GeV/c^2 for $ee\gamma\gamma$ or $\mu\mu\gamma\gamma$ events and is about 3 GeV/c^2 for $\tau\tau\gamma\gamma$.

With only two events of this type found in DELPHI, clearly compatible with an statistical fluctuation, more statistics are needed to clarify their origin. Also other related channels ($\nu\nu\gamma\gamma$, $qq\gamma\gamma$, $\gamma\gamma$) are being analyzed.

3. Conclusions

The $\ell\ell\nu$ channel has been studied and no anomalous behaviour with respect to standard four fermion processes has been found

Analysis of acollinear leptonic events with an energetic isolated photon shows a good agreement with QED expectation, providing limits on the couplings of excited leptons, and supporting universality.

Distributions for $\ell\ell\gamma\gamma$ events show a general good agreement with QED predictions. Preliminary analysis of '92 data finds two $\ell\ell\gamma\gamma$ events (a $\mu\mu\gamma\gamma$ and a $ee\gamma\gamma$) with high $\gamma\gamma$ masses, both around 59 GeV/c^2. More statistics are needed to clarify their origin.

5. Acknowledgements

I would like to thank Alfonso López and Francois Richard for their comments and indications while preparing this talk.

6. References

1. DELPHI Collaboration, *A Search for* $Z^0 \to \ell\ell\nu$, **XXVI International Conference in HEP, DALLAS** (1992).
2. F.A.Berends, P.Daverveldt and R.Kleiss, *Comp.Phys.Com.* **40** (1986) 271.
3. DELPHI Collaboration, *Leptonic Events with Energetic Isolated Photons in* Z^0 *Decays*, **XXVI International Conference in HEP, DALLAS** (1992).
4. W.J.Stirling, Z^0 *boson decay into a fermion-antifermion pair and an arbitrary number of hard photons*, **CERN-TH.6221** (1991)
5. L3 Collaboration, *High mass photon pairs in* $\ell^+\ell^-\gamma\gamma$ *events at LEP*, **CERN-PPE/92-152** (1992)

THE η_6 AND MASSIVE PHOTON PAIRS AT LEP

ALAN R. WHITE, IAN G. KNOWLES

High Energy Physics Division, Argonne National Laboratory, IL 60439

KYUNGSIK KANG

Physics Department, Brown University, Providence RI 02912

ABSTRACT

The η_6, a "heavy axion" associated with sextet quark electroweak symmetry breaking, may have been seen at LEP via its two-photon decay mode and also at TRISTAN via its hadronic decay modes.

1. Introduction

Dynamical electroweak symmetry breaking by a chiral condensate of *color sextet quarks*[1] has many attractive features, including the following.

i) Color plays the role of technicolor - the electroweak scale is a QCD scale.

ii) The symmetry breaking is that of a "minimal" Higgs sector - ensuring "$\rho = 1$".

iii) There is a resolution of the Strong CP problem via a unique "heavy axion" - the η_6 - that should be looked for instead of the Higgs.

iv) The necessary sextet quark sector may play a vital role within QCD giving, in particular, unitary Critical Pomeron scaling at high energy.

This last feature underlies the persistent advocacy of sextet symmetry breaking by one of us (ARW) for more than ten years. Nevertheless our understanding of the subtle dynamics of the sextet sector remains poor. Some existing, but unexplained, phenomena that may be "hints" of its existence include:

1) the strong production of W^+W^- and Z^0Z^0 pairs - UA1 (W + 2 jet) events,

2) composite operator contributions in the CDF inclusive jet cross-section,

3) the anomalous behaviour of the $\bar{p}p$ real part - as perhaps seen by UA4,

4) "exotic" Cosmic Ray events which suggest a new strong interaction scale.

About 3 years ago, we noted[2] that the Geminion and mini-Centauro exotic events could be explained as the diffractive production of a heavy particle and suggested this could be the η_6 (the estimated mass is now[3] ≥ 50 GeV). We linked the corresponding threshold to the UA4 result and proposed looking for the η_6, *via its two photon decay mode*, in hadronic diffractive interactions. Subsequently it was pointed out[4] that $Z^0 \to \eta_6 + \gamma$ could be observed (as a rare decay) at LEP.

2. Implications of LEP and TRISTAN Results

As reported at this meeting L3, DELPHI and perhaps ALEPH, have seen several events of the form $Z^0 \to l^+l^- + \gamma\gamma$ in each of which the mass of the $\gamma\gamma$ pair is close to 60 GeV. The lepton pairs are either muons or electrons. There are, as yet, no neutrino, quark, or τ pairs. While the kinematics of some of the events may be compatible with QED radiation, others look implausible explained this way. Therefore, the events suggest the existence of a massive "particle" with a mass of, perhaps, 59 GeV and a width of O(1) GeV. The first presumption would surely be that the new particle is radiated directly by the Z^0 with the lepton pair coming from an off-shell Z^{0*} (although we shall discuss another possibility later).

It is also very interesting to ask whether this "particle" has been seen at TRISTAN. In fact all three experiments saw a peak at 59.05 GeV. AMY obtained[5] a value of R more than 30% above the standard model value (although with a large error - giving at most a "2σ" effect). If this is produced by the same new particle that appears in the LEP events, we can infer both that it couples to e^+e^- and that it *has major hadronic decay modes*.

If the width were due to electroweak couplings to quark and lepton states, in analogy with the Z^0, then such decays would surely have already been seen at LEP. It seems more likely that high multiplicity hadron states are involved which would not be so easily identified at LEP, but clearly would be registered at TRISTAN. We emphasise therefore that

the existence of a massive particle with appreciable couplings to the weak bosons and non-trivial strong decays (not proportional to quark masses), strongly suggests electroweak symmetry breaking involves constituents that carry color.

Sextet quark symmetry breaking is an obvious candidate and an immediate question is whether the new particle could be the η_6? At first sight, as we discuss, the production rates involved appear to be calculable from the sextet quark triangle anomaly and are too low by orders of magnitude. However, as we shall also discuss, the Strong CP *(and C)* properties of the sextet quark sector are subtle and sextet quark Goldstone boson amplitudes violate CP. As a result there exist large "longitudinal" Z^0 and $W^\pm$ amplitudes which can not be calculated from the anomaly but could give large enough cross-sections at LEP and TRISTAN.

3. Color Sextet Symmetry Breaking and the η_6 Axion

A massless flavor doublet (U, D) of color sextet quarks with the usual quark quantum numbers (except that the role of quarks and antiquarks is interchanged) is first added to the Standard Model *with no scalar Higgs sector*. Within QCD, conventional chiral dynamics will break the sextet axial flavor symmetries spontaneously and produce four massless pseudoscalar mesons (Goldstone bosons), which we denote as $\pi_6^+, \pi_6^-, \pi_6^0$ and η_6. The π_6^+, π_6^-, and π_6^0 are "eaten" by the massless electroweak gauge bosons and respectively become the third components of the massive W^+, W^- and Z^0, giving $M_W \sim g\, F_{\pi_6}$ where F_{π_6} is *a QCD scale*. $F_{\pi_6} \sim 250 GeV$ is consistent with an elementary "Casimir Scaling" rule[1].

The η_6 is not involved in generating mass for the electroweak gauge bosons. Instead it is a "Peccei-Quinn axion" which produces Strong CP conservation in the triplet quark sector. Its mass is much higher than conventionally expected for an axion because of the intricate QCD dynamics of the sextet sector. The evolution of α_s is negligible above the electroweak (sextet) scale and there is an effective infra-red fixed-point controlling the dynamics. The absence of the infra-red growth of the gauge coupling implies that, in the sextet sector, confinement and chiral symmetry breaking involve instantons as an important "infra-red" effect. (There are no renormalons and instantons don't melt!). Each instanton interaction contains a factor[6] of cos $[\tilde{\theta} + <\eta_6>]$, where (in a conventional notation) $\tilde{\theta} = \theta + \det m_3$, and an axion potential of the form $V(\cos [\tilde{\theta} + <\eta_6>])$ is generated. Such a potential naturally retains the CP-conserving minimum at $\theta + <\eta_6> = 0$ while also giving an η_6 mass (the curvature at the minimum) of order the electroweak scale - say 60 GeV!

4. Anomaly Amplitudes and Longitudinal Couplings

If we assume that CP is conserved also in the sextet sector we obtain a set of amplitudes which are far too small to be compatible with the LEP events. In analogy with the chiral dynamics of the physical pion sector, $PCAC$ allows us to calculate[4] vertices for $\eta_6 \to \gamma\gamma$, $Z^0 \to \eta_6 + \gamma$ and $Z^0 \to \eta_6 + Z^{0*}$ directly from the sextet quark triangle anomaly. For $\eta_6 \to \gamma\gamma$ we obtain a very narrow width of 0.17 keV. (If the full experimental width is much larger then this would imply that a large fraction of the hadronic cross-section at LEP must involve the η_6!) For $Z^0 \to \eta_6 + \gamma$ we would predict one event in 20 million at LEP. While from $Z^0 \to \eta_6 + Z^{0*}$ we obtain a rate for $Z^0 \to \eta_6 + \mu^+\mu^-$ of 2 events in a billion. This is at least three orders of magnitude too small to explain the two photon events.

Note, however, that the η_6 acts as an axion *only in the low energy effective lagrangian for the triplet quark sector*. The full QCD lagrangian for the combined triplet and sextet sectors has no axion. Also to generate triplet quark (and lepton) masses, four-fermion (CP-violating) couplings must be added. As a consequence the "low-energy" effective lagrangian for QCD interactions of the η_6, π_6^+, π_6^-, and π_6^0 is *necessarily CP-violating*. In unitary gauge, it is the "longitudinal" (or scalar) components of the gauge boson fields i.e. $\partial^\mu Z_\mu^0$, $\partial^\mu W_\mu^+$ and $\partial^\mu W_\mu^-$, that inherit the interactions of the Goldstone bosons π_6^0, π_6^+ and π_6^- respectively. Therefore such interactions give large, CP-violating, couplings of the form $\eta_6 \partial^\mu Z_\mu^0 \partial^\mu Z_\mu^0$, $\eta_6 \partial^\mu W_\mu^+ \partial^\mu W_\mu^-$, $\eta_6 \partial^\mu Z_\mu^0 \partial^\mu W_\mu^+ \partial^\mu W_\mu^-$ ... etc..

5. η_6 Decay Modes

To compute electroweak amplitudes for the η_6, a first step would be to write an effective lagrangian for the (unitary gauge) longitudinal amplitudes we have just described, add the electroweak interaction, and compute to the lowest order in the electroweak couplings. This gives some immediate order of magnitude estimates.

First we note that $\eta_6 \to \gamma\gamma$ is given by a $\partial^\mu W_\mu$ loop which, because of the unitary gauge propagators, is dominated by large momenta. $\eta_6 \to l^+l^-$ is given by a similar loop but with one $\partial^\mu W_\mu$ propagator replaced by a neutrino propagator. Both amplitudes are $O(\alpha_{ew})$ but the photon amplitude should be significantly larger because of the additional unitary gauge boson propagator. The $\eta_6 \to e^+e^-$ vertex can potentially be large enough to allow the η_6 to be seen at TRISTAN.

Photon emission is generally favored by its coupling directly, to the Goldstone bosons involved, at large momentum. The $e^+e^- \to e^+e^- + \gamma\gamma\gamma$ event recorded by L3, in which the $\gamma\gamma\gamma$ mass is also close to 60 GeV., could involve an $\eta_6 \to \gamma\gamma\gamma$ decay.

Consider now the hadronic decay modes of the η_6. Perturbative gluon emission exposes the large sextet quark constituent mass ($\sim 400 GeV$) and so is very suppressed. We expect instanton interactions to be responsible for the dominant hadronic decays. The simplest possibility would be an isotropic distribution of five quarks and five antiquarks (one of each flavor), giving a high multiplicity hadron state with many (mini-) jets. (There is some, statistically insignificant, evidence in the published data on multiplicity distributions[5] that the increased cross-section at

TRISTAN is of this form.) At LEP, the combination of such a state with a hard lepton pair (i.e. $m_{l+l^-} \sim 20 - 30 GeV$), as in the two photon events, should be quite distinctive.

6. Lepton Pairs in the LEP Events

While it seems that the two-photon component of the LEP events can be straightforwardly associated with the decay of the η_6, the lepton pairs are not so simple. If the events are indeed produced by $Z^0 \to \eta_6 + Z^{0*} \to [\gamma\gamma] + [l^+l^-]$ then, because CP is not conserved, the Z^{0*} can be longitudinal and the initial vertex can be very large. However, the lepton vertex would then contain a factor m_l, giving *no neutrino pairs*, a negligible number of electron pairs, and an overwhelming number of τ pairs, compared to muon pairs! Since quark pairs carry color, QCD interactions with the initial vertex could reduce the corresponding amplitude for their production. Nevertheless, it seems unlikely that a simple mass dependence of the lepton vertex will correctly describe the experimental situation as more events appear.

There is, however, a further source of lepton pairs. The four-fermion sextet/lepton couplings, that provide masses in combination with the sextet condensate, will also provide a direct (short-distance) coupling of lepton pairs into (small) instanton interactions - without going via the electroweak interaction. That is *massive leptons* can be directly produced out of the sextet quark interaction by a mechanism that is *closely related to, but not identical to*, the mass-generation mechanism. Giving, in particular, $Z^0 \to \eta_6 + l^+l^-$ vertices. This mechanism will also produce lepton pairs out of very hard QCD interactions in hadron colliders.

7. Conclusions

The η_6 is a strong candidate for the new particle suggested both by the massive photon pairs seen at LEP and by TRISTAN data at the corresponding energy.

Unambiguous "discovery" of the η_6 could be a fundamental breakthrough in the problems of electroweak symmetry breaking and Strong CP conservation - at current accelerators!

It (and other signals of the sextet sector) should also be looked for in hadron colliders, in diffractive interactions and very high energy hard collisions.

References

1. W. J. Marciano, *Phys. Rev.* **D21** (1980) 2425; E. Braaten, A. R. White and C. R. Willcox, *Int. J. Mod. Phys.* **A1** (1986) 693.
2. K. Kang and A. R. White, *Phys. Rev.* **D42** (1990) 835.
3. T. Arizawa (and also S. Hasegawa) - Private communication.
4. T. Hatsuda and M. Umezawa, *Phys. Lett.* **B254** (1991) 493.
5. T. Kumita et al., *Phys. Rev.* **D42** (1990) 737, 1339.
6. B. Holdom, *Phys. Lett.* **B154** (1985) 316.

W AND Z DECAYS TO ELECTRONS IN DØ

Norman A. GRAF, for the DØ Collaboration
Brookhaven National Laboratory
Upton, Long Island, New York 11973

ABSTRACT

The DØ detector has been accumulating data at the Fermilab Tevatron at $\sqrt{s}=1.8$TeV for several months. In this paper we present the results of a preliminary analysis of W and Z vector boson decays into electrons based on $1.1 pb^{-1}$ of data collected from Aug. 26, 1992 through Nov. 2, 1992. The event characteristics, as well as the number of events detected, are in good agreement with expectations.

1. The DØ Detector

The DØ detector is composed of three major subsystems; the calorimeters, the central tracking and the muon systems. The electron analysis is based on the calorimetry and charged particle tracking.

The uranium-liquid argon calorimetry is designed with minimal cracks and uninstrumented regions and provides essentially hermetic coverage over the full range of pseudo-rapidity ($\eta \leq |4|$) and azimuthal angle (ϕ). The calorimeter read-out is arranged in pseudoprojective towers and is finely segmented in both longitudinal(4 electromagnetic(EM) plus 4-5 hadronic(HAD) layers) and transverse dimensions ($\sim 0.1 \times 0.1$ in η, ϕ; $\sim .05 \times .05$ at shower maximum in EM layer 3). The EM calorimeters represent approximately 20 radiation lengths of material and have an energy resolution of roughly $15\%/\sqrt{E}$; the energy resolution for hadrons is approximately $50\%/\sqrt{E}$.

The central tracking system contains a vertex drift chamber, a transition radiation detector, a central drift chamber and forward drift chambers. Tracks reconstructed in these chambers are used to differentiate electrons from photons and neutral hadrons.

2. Event Selection

The data sample was taken from the D0 Expressline which diverts selected triggers for immediate analysis. These events represent a subset of all triggers and are selected for their topical interest. In order to analyze the data in a timely fashion, and also to minimize the sources of systematic errors, the analysis was restricted to specific triggers. For the $W \to e\nu_e$ analysis, events were required to satisfy the following trigger: a Level 1 (hardware) EM trigger tower (0.2×0.2 in η, ϕ) was required to pass a transverse energy (E_T) threshold of

14GeV; the Level 2 (software) trigger subsequently required an EM cluster (passing shape cuts) with $E_T > 20$GeV and missing E_T also greater than 20GeV. The $Z \to e^+e^-$ analysis required two Level 1 EM trigger towers above 7GeV and two Level 2 EM clusters above 20GeV.

Offline electron candidates are identified using a nearest neighbor clustering of the EM calorimeter cells. Events selected were required to have an EM cluster with $E_T > 20$GeV with a ratio of cluster energy in the EM to total energy of $EM/Total > 90\%$. The cluster shape (transverse as well as longitudinal distributions) was required to agree with testbeam and Monte Carlo expectations. A χ^2 quantity calculated from the full covariance matrix of cluster elements was required to be less than 200. The clusters were further required to be isolated from the rest of the event, where we define the isolation quantity as the total energy within a cone of radius $R=\sqrt{\Delta\eta^2 + \Delta\phi^2} = 0.4$, minus the EM energy in a cone $R=0.2$, divided by the EM energy in a cone $R=0.2$. This quantity was required to be less than 0.1. In addition, a track was required to be found in the central tracking chambers and to point at the cluster. Tracks were accepted for which the angles between the track and cluster center were within $|\Delta\phi| < 0.05$ and $|\Delta\theta| < 0.07$ radians. Details of the trigger and electron identification are reported elsewhere.[1,2]

The W analysis required one good electron candidate with $E_T > 20$GeV and missing $E_T > 20$GeV. The Z analysis required at least one good electron, but relaxed the tracking requirement on the second EM candidate. Both clusters were required to have at least 20GeV E_T.

3. W and Z event characteristics

With the event selection criteria described in the previous section, we are left with 882 $W \to e\nu_e$ candidates and 72 $Z \to e^+e^-$ candidates. The W candidate transverse mass distribution (defined as $m_T^2 = 2E_T^e E_T^\nu (1 - cos(\phi^{e\nu}))$ is presented in Figure 1 and exhibits a sharp Jacobian edge in good agreement with Monte Carlo simulations. The invariant mass of the two electrons in the Z candidate sample is plotted in Figure 2, along with a Breit-Wigner fit to the distribution. The signal is very clean and sharply peaked; the fitted value of the mass is (86.0±0.6(statistical)±5% scale error). The scale error represents the systematic uncertainty in the transfer of absolute calibration from testbeam studies to the detector. It should be stressed that these are preliminary, uncorrected values.

4. W cross section

The production cross section times the branching ratio (σ_W^e)

for the process $\bar{p}p \to W + X$ where $W \to e\nu_e$ was derived from the following expression: $\sigma_W^e = (N_{candidates} - N_{background})/(\epsilon \cdot \int \mathcal{L}dt)$ The sources of background events which we have considered to date are: $W \to \tau^{\pm}\nu_e$ where $\tau \to e\nu_\tau\nu_e$ which is estimated from Monte Carlo simulations to comprise less than ~5% of the signal; additionally, background from QCD processes are estimated to be less than 1%, as are events arising from $Z \to e^+e^-$ where one of the electrons is "lost", thereby mimicking the neutrino. The efficiency for detecting $W \to e\nu_e$ events is estimated from Monte Carlo simulations as well as analysis of the collider data. The trigger efficiency (including geometrical acceptance) is estimated to be ~56%, and the cumulative effect of all the offline requirements reduces the overall efficiency for this analysis to $31 \pm 5\%$. The data represent $1.1pb^{-1}(\pm 15\%$ systematic), from which we obtain $\sigma_W^e = 2.3 \pm .5$ nb.

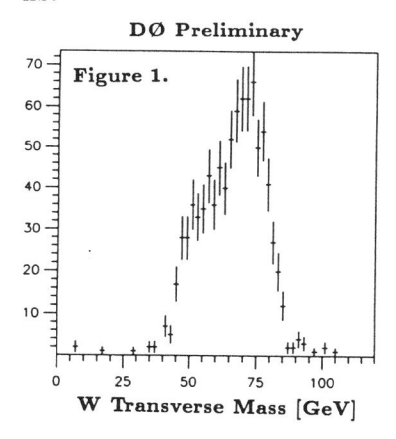

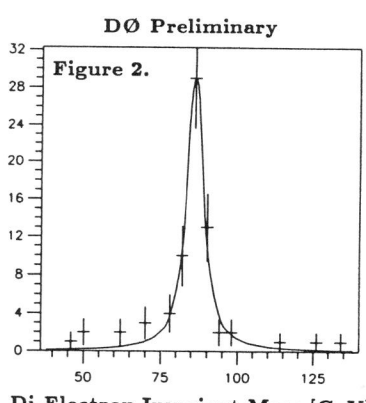

DØ Preliminary

Figure 1.

W Transverse Mass [GeV]

DØ Preliminary

Figure 2.

Di-Electron Invariant Mass [GeV]

5. Conclusions

Preliminary results on the event characteristics of the vector boson decays $W \to e\nu_e$ and $Z \to e^+e^-$ have been obtained using the newly commissioned DØ detector. The number of events detected, as well as the masses of the particles are in good agreement (within our current systematic errors) with published values.

6. References

1. J. Linnemann, Triggering the DØ detector, , *These proceedings*.
2. M. Narain, Electron Identification in DØ , *These proceedings*.

W AND Z DECAYS TO MUONS AT DØ

Darien R. Wood, for the DØ Collaboration
Fermilab, P.O. Box 500
Batavia, IL 60510, USA

ABSTRACT

The DØ collaboration has searched for the decays $W \to \mu\nu$ and $Z \to \mu\mu$ in $p\bar{p}$ collisions at $\sqrt{s} = 1.8$ TeV from the current Run 1a of the Tevatron collider. Based on 400–800 nb^{-1} of recent data, preliminary samples of W and Z candidates are presented. The production rates are compared to expectations.

1. The DØ Detector

Most of the properties of the DØ detector are described in the accompanying contribution on decays of W and Z to electrons.[1] For the present measurements, the muon system has central importance and it is described below in more detail.

1.1. Muon System

The DØ muon detection system[2] is divided into the wide angle muon system, which detects muons down to pseudorapidities of $|\eta| = 1.7$, and the small angle muon system which covers the far forward and backward regions ($1.7 < |\eta| < 3.4$). Only the wide angle system is used in this analysis.

The wide angle muon system is composed of three large iron toroidal magnets ($B \approx 2$ Tesla) and 11434 proportional drift tubes (PDTs). A typical muon from the interaction point passes through a total of ten planes of PDTs: four between the calorimeter and the toroids and two groups of three outside the toroids. Hadrons are effectively absorbed in the calorimeter and toroids (9-20 interaction lengths) and the muon momentum is determined by measuring the trajectory before and after the toroid. The PDTs are oriented so that the drift direction coincides with the bend direction, and this coordinate is measured using drift times. The other coordinate is measured with signal timing differences and a system of vernier cathode pads.[2] With a current precision of about 2.5 mm per tube in the drift view, the resolution achieved is about $(\delta p/p)^2 = (0.18)^2 + (0.01p)^2$. As the alignment and calibration are improved using additional accumulated muons, a precision of 0.5 mm is expected (based on test beam measurements) which corresponds to $(\delta p/p)^2 = (0.18)^2 + (0.002p)^2$.

1.2. Muon Triggers

The DØ trigger system is described in an accompanying contribution.[3] All muon triggers require a minimum bias signal from the level 0 counters in coincidence with one or more muon candidates from the coarse centroid trigger (level 1.0) and sometimes the fine centroid trigger (level 1.5) of the muon system. The centroids are based on groups of discriminator latches on the cathode pad signals and centroid combinations corresponding to roads from the interaction point are programmed into the trigger logic. The threshold for the level 1 trigger is about 5 GeV in p_T, and for level 1.5 about 7 GeV. For the data considered here, the single muon and dimuon triggers were operated without prescaling for $|\eta| < 1.0$ and $|\eta| < 1.7$ respectively.

The level 2 (software) trigger executes a slightly streamlined version of the offline muon reconstruction algorithm and makes cuts on muon track quality and p_T.

2. Offline Muon Identification

After the offline reconstruction, several standard requirements are made to identify a muon. A good fit is required in the bend view (residuals < 1.0 cm) and the non-bend view (residuals < 7 cm). The muon track must extrapolate to within 20 cm of the vertex reconstructed by the central tracking detectors, and it must match a track in the central detector. A fiducial cut is made on the amount of magnetized iron traversed: $\int B \cdot d\ell > 0.6$ GeV, where the units correspond to the lateral momentum kick of the field. The present efficiency of these cuts is estimated to be about 50% for muons satisfying the level 1 and level 1.5 trigger conditions.

3. $W \to \mu\nu$ Event Selection

W candidates are selected from a sample of 410 ± 60 nb^{-1} of single muon triggers ($|\eta| < 1.0$) taken in October 1992. The level 2 trigger required $p_T^\mu > 15$ GeV and vetoed events which were consistent with through-going cosmic rays. After standard offline muon identification and a tight cut on bend view quality (residuals < 0.4 cm), 161 events remain. This sample contains a combination of W's, QCD background, and cosmic rays.

The QCD background is reduced by requiring isolation in the calorimeter. An isolation variable is constructed by projecting the muon into the calorimeter and, at each layer in depth, adding all of the energy in a 5×5 array ($\Delta\phi\Delta\eta = 0.1 \times 0.1$ per cell) around the hit cell. An isolated muon is defined as one where the sum of energy in these cells is less than 1.5σ above the amount expected from the muon ionization alone. The residual QCD contribution is determined from the distribution of this isolation variable for events with a jet opposite the muon in phi. The efficiency is determined from a set of cosmic ray events which fall on top of minimum bias triggers. The isolation cut reduces the sample to 50 events, with an estimated QCD background of 10±5 events. The W kinematic cuts of $p_T^\mu > 20$ GeV and $p_T^\nu > 20$ GeV reduce the sample to 32 events and the QCD background estimate drops to 1±1 event.

A final cut, based on the muon drift time fit, rejects cosmic rays which are not synchronized to the beam crossing within 100 ns. Twenty-five events remain, with an estimated cosmic ray contribution of 5 ± 3 events. The transverse mass

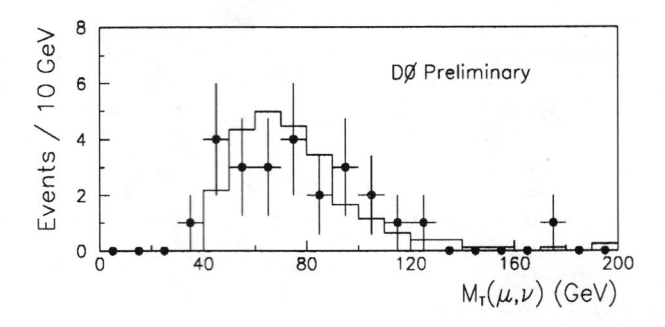

Figure 1: The transverse mass distribution of the final sample of $W \to \mu\nu$ candidates. The points are the data, while the histogram represents a Monte Carlo prediction based on $\sigma(p\bar{p} \to W+X)B(W \to \mu\nu) = 2$ nb.[4]

distribution for these events is shown in Fig. 1. The Monte Carlo curve is normalized to the expected signal of 22 ± 5 events (systematic error only) from $W \to \mu\nu$.

4. $Z \to \mu\mu$ Event Selection

The Z sample is selected from 770 ± 115 nb^{-1} of level 1 single muon ($|\eta| < 1.0$) and dimuon ($|\eta| < 1.7$) triggers. The level 2 trigger requires $p_T^{\mu_1} >10$ GeV and $p_T^{\mu_2} > 15$ GeV. Offline, the requirements are $p_T^{\mu_1} >15$ GeV and $p_T^{\mu_2} > 20$ GeV. If one of the muons is required to pass the standard offline cuts, eleven events remain: four like-sign pairs ($40< M_{\mu\mu} <50$ GeV) and seven $\mu^+\mu^-$ pairs ($50< M_{\mu\mu} <120$ GeV). Three events remain (all $\mu^+\mu^-$) when both muons are required to satisfy the standard cuts. About 4–9 events from Z decay are expected in this final sample.

5. Conclusions

Based on a small amount of data, DØ has detected signals for $W \to \mu\nu$ and $Z \to \mu\mu$ which are consistent with expectations. These results are preliminary and a large increase in integrated luminosity and significant improvements to muon identification are anticipated during the remainder of the present Tevatron run.

6. References

1. N. Graf, *W and Z Decays to Electrons at DØ*, these proceedings.
2. C. Brown, et al., *Nucl. Instrum. and Meth.* **A279** (1989) 331.
3. J.T. Linneman, *Triggering the DØ Detector*, these proceedings.
4. R. Hamberg, W.L. Van Neerven and T. Matsuura, *Nucl. Phys.* **B 359** (1991) 343.

AN ANALYSIS OF THE CDF MONOJET DATA

The CDF Collaboration*

Presented by Richard Markeloff
*Department of Physics, University of Wisconsin-Madison
Madison, WI 53706, USA*

ABSTRACT

An analysis is presented of events with a single jet and significant missing transverse energy selected from 4.7 pb^{-1} of $p\bar{p}$ data at $\sqrt{s} = 1800$ GeV. The goal is to identify events of the type $p\bar{p} \to Z^0 +$ jet; $Z^0 \to \nu\bar{\nu}$. Event selection and backgrounds are discussed. The number of observed monojet events is compared to the number of observed $Z^0 \to e^+e^-$ events in which the Z^0 is accompanied by a jet. We measure the number of light neutrino species to be $N_\nu = 2.2 \pm 1.5$ and we place an upper limit on the cross section for new physics of 8.3 pb^{-1} (95% C.L.).

1. Introduction

The missing energy technique can be applied to the analysis of $p\bar{p}$ collisions to observe the so-called "invisible" decays of the Z^0 boson into neutrinos, and to search for new physics that might produce a monojet signal.

The CDF detector is described in detail in Reference 1. We briefly mention the features of the detector most important to this study. Electromagnetic and hadronic calorimetery covered the region in polar angle $2° < \theta < 178°$ or $|\eta| < 4.2$, where η is pseudorapidity. The Central Tracking Chamber (CTC) covered the region $|\eta| < 1.1$ and measured charged particle trajectories and transverse momenta in an axial 1.5 T magnetic field. The Vertex Time Projection Chambers (VTPC) provided tracking information down to $\theta = 3.5°$ ($|\eta| < 3.5$). Muon coverage was also present in the region $|\eta| < 0.7$.

2. Data Sample and Event Selection

The data were collected with a trigger that required the missing transverse energy, $\rlap{/}{E}_t$, to be at least 25 GeV, and that the leading energy cluster (defined as the highest E_t cluster in the event) be in the region $|\eta| < 1.2$. The leading cluster was further required to have at least 8 GeV of energy deposited in the EM calorimeters. About 2.7×10^5 events came in on this trigger. We have measured the efficiency of the missing E_t trigger to be 89% for events that have $\rlap{/}{E}_t > 30$ GeV.

In the offline analysis, we applied the following cuts to the data sample:

- Timing information from the central hadron calorimeters was used to reject events that contained cosmic rays not in coincidence with a beam crossing.

---
*See Reference 3 for the author list.

- The $\not{E}_t$ was required to be at least 30 GeV.

- The quantity σ_{MET}, called the the "missing E_t significance" and defined as $\sigma_{\text{MET}} = \not{E}_t / \sqrt{\sum E_t}$ (where $\sum E_t$ is the scalar sum of E_t over all calorimeters), was required to be at least 2.4 GeV$^{\frac{1}{2}}$.

- We rejected events containing an energy cluster with $E_t > 5$ GeV within a 30° wedge opposite in azimuth to the leading cluster. This cut removed most of the background from dijet events in which one jet was poorly measured.

- There had to be one and only one energy cluster with $E_t > 15$ GeV.

- The scalar sum of the transverse momenta of the charged particles associated with the leading cluster had to be at least 10% of the E_t of the cluster. This cut eliminated most of the remaining cosmic ray and beam gas events.

- We required the leading cluster to have 0.1 < EM fraction < 0.85, where the EM fraction was defined as the ratio of the E_t in the EM calorimeters to the E_t in the hadronic calorimeters. Detector noise was removed by the lower bound on the EM fraction, and $W \to e\nu$ events were rejected by the upper bound.

- We required the event vertex to be within 60 cm of the center of the detector along the beam axis. This cut improved the hermeticity of the detector.

A sample of 510 monojet candidates survive the above cuts. However, a substantial portion of these events are of the type $W \to \ell\nu$, where the W is accompanied by a jet and the lepton was undetected. Some events are also $W \to \tau\nu$ where the τ decayed hadronically and was mistaken for a jet. We therefore applied further cuts to eliminate events with high-p_t muons or electrons and events containing narrow, low-multiplicity energy clusters that resemble τ decays. These W cuts rejected a total of 262 events. We next applied further cuts designed to reduce the background from cosmic rays, beam gas, and QCD dijets. These cuts were based on the characteristics of the leading cluster and the data from the CTC, and removed 22 events from the sample. We are left with a final data set consisting of 226 events.

Figure 1 shows the missing E_t distribution for the final monojet data set. Also shown is the expected $\not{E}_t$ spectrum of the $Z^0 \to \nu\bar{\nu}$ signal, from Monte Carlo simulations. Figure 1 shows that a large fraction of the monojet sample is background.

3. Background Estimates

In Table 1 we present a list of the possible sources of monojet backgrounds and the estimated contribution from each background source to the final data set.

To estimate the residual monojet backgrounds from vector boson decays, we relied on a Monte Carlo program based on the PAPAGENO[2] event generator. For the case of hadronic decays of W taus, we used a $W \to \tau\nu$ simulation based on 2664 $W \to e\nu$ events from the CDF data. For each real $W \to e\nu$ event, we replaced

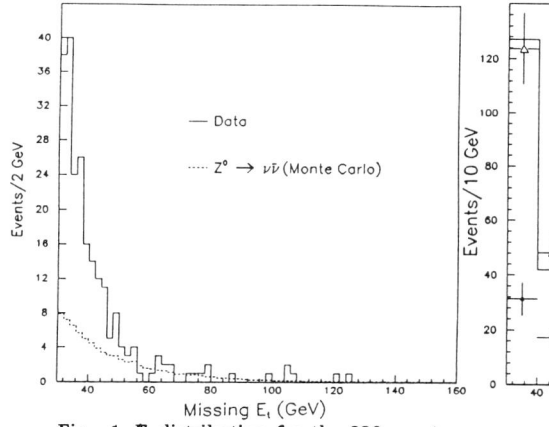

Fig. 1 E_t distribution for the 226 events that pass the monojet cuts. Also shown is the estimated E_t distribution for the expected $Z^0 \to \nu\bar{\nu}$ signal.

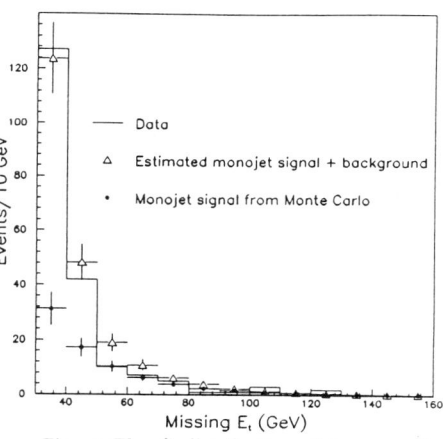

Fig. 2 The E_t distribution of the sum all estimated components of the monojet sample compared to the data, after events with energy clusters near calorimeter cracks have been removed.

the electron track and calorimeter cluster with a simulated τ lepton with the same momentum.

Information from the CTC and VTPC tracking detectors was used to estimate the residual background from QCD dijet events with one jet lost through calorimeter leakage. Multijet QCD background was estimated by examining the energy deposition in the calorimeter regions near known cracks, and by looking for correlations between the azimuthal coordinates of the missing E_t vector and any secondary energy clusters.

The CDF detector is unable to discriminate, on an event by event basis, between EM showers produced by single prompt photons and showers caused by multiple photons from decays of neutral mesons. For this reason we group these two sources of background together. Our methods for estimating direct photon and neutral hadron backgrounds are based on studies of both a sample of real CDF photon candidates[3] and Monte Carlo simulations.

4. Conclusions

Our total background estimate for the monojet data set is 177 ± 18 events. Subtracting this number from the 226 events in the data yields a $Z^0 \to \nu\bar{\nu}$ signal of 49 ± 24 events. This is consistent with our Monte Carlo prediction of 78 ± 15 events.

Figure 2 shows the E_t spectrum of the sum of the estimated components of the monojet sample and the spectrum observed in the data. Since we do not have

Table 1: The estimated contribution to the monojet sample from each source of background, and the estimated number of invisible Z^0 decays in the monojet sample.

Process	Estimated Number of Events
$p\bar{p} \to W^{\pm} + \text{jet}$; $W^{\pm} \to \ell^{\pm}\nu_\ell$	57 ± 11
$p\bar{p} \to W^{\pm}$; $W^{\pm} \to \tau^{\pm}\nu_\tau$; $\tau \to$ hadrons	26 ± 5
$p\bar{p} \to Z^0 + \text{jet}$; $Z^0 \to \ell^+\ell^-$	1 ± 0.2
QCD dijets	31 ± 11
Multijet events with ≥ 2 jets lost or mismeasured	18 ± 7
Multijet events with one jet lost or mismeasured	4 ± 4
Prompt photons and isolated neutral hadrons	31 ± 2
Cosmic rays and beam gas	9 ± 4
Total Background Estimate:	177 ± 18
Number of events in the final sample:	226
Extracted $Z^0 \to \nu\bar{\nu}$ Signal:	49 ± 23

knowledge of the E_t spectrum of the multijet QCD background, the data of Figure 2 do not include events with secondary energy clusters near known calorimeter crack regions. We also neglected the contributions to the monojet sample from multijet QCD events with one jet lost or mismeasured and from cosmic ray/beam gas backgrounds. The data set contains 198 events after events with clusters in crack regions are removed. The sum of the signal plus background estimates give a sample size of 217 ± 15 events.

We can test the size of the extracted $Z^0 \to \nu\bar{\nu}$ signal against the predictions of the Standard Model by comparing it to the number of $Z^0 \to e^+e^-$ events found in the CDF data[4] in which the Z^0 is accompanied by a jet. We measure the ratio of the branching fraction $BR(Z^0 \to \nu\bar{\nu})$ to $BR(Z^0 \to e^+e^-)$ to be equal to 4.4 ± 3.0. The Standard Model value for this ratio is 5.962 (assuming $N_\nu = 3$ and $\sin^2\theta_W = 0.23$). Expressing this result in terms of the number of light neutrino species, $N_\nu = 2.2 \pm 1.5$.

5.1. Limits on New Physics

Using the method described in Reference 5, we calculate an upper limit on the possible cross section for hitherto unknown processes that produce events with a single high-E_t jet ($E_t > 15$ GeV) with the jet in the central region ($|\eta| < 1.2$) and missing E_t greater than 30 GeV. This limit is $\sigma_{new} < 8.3$ pb (95% C.L.). The limit on the number of neutrino species is $N_\nu < 5$ at the 90% confidence level.

6. References

1. F. Abe et al., *Nucl. Inst. and Meth.* **A271** (1988) 387.
2. The author of the PAPAGENO event generator is Dr. Ian Hinchliffe. Current address: Lawrence Berkeley Laboratory, Berkeley CA 94720.
3. F. Abe et al., *Phys. Rev. Let.* **68** (1992) 2734.
4. F. Abe et al., *Phys. Rev. Let.* **67** (1991) 2937.
5. G. Zech, *Nucl. Inst. and Meth.* **A277** (1989) 608.

REVIEW OF ELECTROWEAK PROPERTIES
OF THE Z RESONANCE FROM LEP

JOHN L. HARTON[1]

Department of Physics, University of Wisconsin-Madison
Madison, WI 53706, USA

ABSTRACT

The four experiments at the LEP electron-positron collider (ALEPH, DELPHI, L3, and OPAL) have completed analysis on the first three years data, corresponding to about 18pb^{-1}, or one-half million Z decays, analyzed per experiment. Combined preliminary results on the lineshape and forward-backward asymmetries are presented. The results for the Z mass and width are 91.1869 ± 0.0072 GeV and 2.4916 ± 0.0070 GeV, respectively. The number of fermion families with neutrinos light enough to contribute to the Z width is 3.04 ± 0.04. Including in the analysis the LEP results on tau polarization leads to confirmation of lepton universality in the neutral currents and gives $g_V^l = -0.0353 \pm 0.0025$ and $g_A^l = -0.49947 \pm 0.00092$. Using additionally the LEP heavy quark forward-backward asymmetries and the results on α_s from event shape analysis at LEP yields a prediction of the top quark mass in the context of the Standard Model: $M_{TOP} = 153 \pm 32$ GeV. Combining the LEP results with measurements from $p\bar{p}$ colliders and neutrino scattering experiments the Standard Model predicts $M_{TOP} = 142 \pm 25$ GeV.

Introduction

The LEP experiments have published results on e^+e^- collisions at the Z resonance for data taken in 1989 and 1990, corresponding to about 7 pb^{-1} analyzed per experiment. This report contains these results, or re-analysis of those data, along with preliminary results on 1991 data (about 11 pb^{-1} per experiment) [1]. The 1992 run has just finished and no electroweak results from those data are yet available.

The lineshape for $e^+e^- \to f\bar{f}$, where f is fermion, is described by the LEP experiments [2] [3] in terms of three model independent parameters: the mass, width and peak cross section. The hadronic cross section dominates the determination of the Z mass and width; the peak hadronic cross gives information on the number of fermion families with light neutrinos. The cross sections for lepton production each allow the measurement of one additional parameter: a leptonic partial decay width of the Z. In terms of the vector and axial-vector couplings of the leptons to the Z, the leptonic decay widths [4] are proportional to $((g_V^l)^2 + (g_A^l)^2)$:

$$\Gamma(Z \to l^+l^-) = G_F M_Z^3 ((g_V^l)^2 + (g_A^l)^2)(1 + \frac{3\alpha}{4\pi})/(6\pi\sqrt{2}).$$

The forward-backward lepton charge asymmetries on the other hand are sensitive to the ratio of these couplings [5]. Each forward-backward asymmetry measures

---
[1]Supported by the US Department of Energy, contract DE-AC02-76ER00881.

A_{FB}^l, where $A_{FB}^l = 3A_e A_l/4$ and

$$A_l = 2g_V^l g_A^l/((g_V^l)^2 + (g_A^l)^2).$$

The average tau polarization, $\overline{P_\tau}$ measures A_τ while the tau polarization as a function of polar production angle, $P_\tau(cos\theta)$ yields A_e. Since the tau polarization yields a single power of the coupling ratio, the relative sign of the ratio is measured.

Together the leptonic partial widths, forward-backward asymmetries, and tau polarization measurements may be used to test universality in the neutral current couplings of the leptons to the Z.

The final LEP measurement used in this review is the forward-backward asymmetry of heavy quarks. This measurement is complicated by mixing of neutral B mesons and the signal is not a clean as those for the leptonic final states. Nevertheless the measurement may be interpreted in terms of the effective weak mixing angle $Sin^2(\Theta_W^{eff}(M_Z^2))$.

Event Selection and Systematic Errors

The hadronic and leptonic Z decays at LEP are cleanly selected by the experiments [1] due the hermicity of the detectors and the clear signals at LEP energies. Hadronic events are typically selected with better than 98% overall efficiency with the systematic uncertainty on the efficiency in the range 0.2-0.3%. Hadronic event selections exploit the high multiplicity and visible energy of $Z \to q\bar{q}$ events. Z decays to electrons and muons are characterized by two collinear leptons and very high visible energy. The electron channel contains typically 1% background from $Z \to \tau^+\tau^-$. Systematic selection efficiency uncertainties for the electron final state are typically 0.5%. Background in the muon channel from taus is usually well less than one percent with an additional few picobarn from cosmic ray muons (about 0.2% of the cross section at the Z peak). The systematic uncertainty on selection of $Z \to \mu^+\mu^-$ varies from 1% for L3 to 0.25% for OPAL, with ALEPH and DELPHI quoting 0.5% . Selection of $Z \to \tau^+\tau^-$ events is slightly more difficult. Background from hadronic Z decays is usually a percent or less, while the sum of backgrounds from the other leptons is 1-2%. The main systematic uncertainty in tau selection is the knowledge of the selection efficiency. The overall systematic uncertainties quoted are 0.8% for DELPHI and OPAL, 1% for L3, and 0.5% for ALEPH.

All the cross section measurements are normalized using the low-angle t-channel Bhabha scattering process. The BHLUMI Monte Carlo program [6] is now used to calculate an absolute cross section in a well defined region of a low-angle electromagenetic calorimeter. The experimental uncertainties on the acceptance regions systematically limit the four measurements of the hadronic peak cross section. These experimental uncertainties are decreasing as the detectors are better understood and are generally slightly lower for the 1991 data than for previous years. The preliminary uncertainties quoted for 1991 data are: 0.45% ALEPH, 0.5% DEPLHI, 0.7% L3. The OPAL uncertainty is 0.8% (1990 data). There is also a 0.3% theoretical uncertainty on the calculation which is common to the experiments and which systematically limits the combined measurement of σ_h^0. This systematic limitation appears also in the number of light neutrinos.

As the statistical and systematical precision of the LEP experiments continue to improve, so do the knowledge of the overall LEP center of mass energy and linearity of the LEP energy scale [7]. Still, the main uncertainty in the Z mass (± 6.3 MeV) comes from the LEP energy scale, and about half of the uncertainty in the Z width results from LEP systematic uncertainties. The LEP-induced uncertainty in Γ_Z is about 4.5 MeV.

Results on Cross sections and A_{FB}

Table 1 contains the results on the Z lineshape and forward-backward asymmetries reported by the experiments. The variables are a convenient way to parameterize the information because they are very uncorrelated. The largest correlation is about -20% between σ_h^0 and Γ_Z. R_l is the ratio of the hadronic partial decay width of the Z to the leptonic partial width. The experiments report a partial width and forward-backward asymmetry for each lepton and, assuming lepton universality, for a generic lepton. The results of combining these measurements, taking care with the common errors on M_Z, Γ_Z, and σ_h^0, are shown in table 2. As mentioned above, the only appreciable common errors are found in the mass, full width, and peak hadronic cross section. These common uncertainties appear again in the hadronic width and invisible width.

The number of neutrinos light enough to be present in Z decay is calculated using the formula

$$N_\nu \cdot \frac{\Gamma_{Z\to\nu\bar\nu}}{\Gamma_{Z\to ll}} = \sqrt{\frac{12\pi R_l}{M_Z^2 \sigma_h^0}} - R_l - 3.$$

The value for $\frac{\Gamma_{Z\to\nu\bar\nu}}{\Gamma_{Z\to ll}}$ is 1.993 [8] and is taken from the Standard Model. The combined LEP result is

$$N_\nu = 3.038 \pm 0.035.$$

Tau polarization and Combined Lepton Couplings

Another important electroweak effect measured at LEP is the tau polarization. The tau polarization measurements at LEP are made under the assumption of pure V-A couplings in tau decay. The measurements of average tau polarization from different tau decay modes generally agree within their errors, suggesting that no important deviation from pure V-A in the charged current is observed in the LEP data. The LEP results [9] on average tau polarization are summarized in table 3.

The tau polarization is a strong function of polar production angle given approximately by [5]

$$P_\tau(\cos\theta) = -\frac{A_\tau(1+\cos^2\theta) + A_e(2\cos\theta)}{(1+\cos^2\theta) + A_\tau A_e(2\cos\theta)}.$$

	ALEPH	DELPHI	L3	OPAL
M_Z[GeV]	91.187 ± 0.009	91.188 ± 0.010	91.196 ± 0.0095	91.180 ± 0.009
Γ_Z [GeV]	2.501 ± 0.012	2.488 ± 0.012	2.4950 ± 0.0110	2.483 ± 0.012
σ_h^0[nb]	41.60 ± 0.27	40.86 ± 0.28	40.95 ± 0.39	41.01 ± 0.41
R_l	20.78 ± 0.13	20.82 ± 0.16	20.93 ± 0.16	20.87 ± 0.13
A_{FB}^l [%]	1.54 ± 0.48	2.02 ± 0.59	2.64 ± 0.74	0.76 ± 0.48
R_e	20.69 ± 0.21	20.79 ± 0.28	21.24 ± 0.24	21.01 ± 0.26
R_μ	20.88 ± 0.20	20.92 ± 0.22	20.72 ± 0.27	20.65 ± 0.18
R_τ	20.77 ± 0.23	20.69 ± 0.30	20.63 ± 0.31	21.16 ± 0.25
A_{FB}^e [%]	1.40 ± 0.93	1.3 ± 1.3	1.7 ± 1.4	-0.2 ± 1.2
A_{FB}^μ [%]	0.74 ± 0.72	1.5 ± 0.8	3.1 ± 1.0	0.47 ± 0.76
A_{FB}^τ [%]	2.69 ± 0.82	3.3 ± 1.0	2.8 ± 1.6	1.65 ± 0.82

Table 1: Preliminary lineshape and A_{FB} results as reported by the LEP experiments. The errors are the full errors quoted by the experiments and contain some common errors, particularly in the M_z, Γ_Z, and σ_h^0. The common errors are separated in the LEP averages in see table 2.

M_Z[GeV]	91.1869	± 0.0034	± 0.0063
Γ_Z [GeV]	2.4916	± 0.0052	± 0.0045
σ_h^0[nb]	41.16	± 0.13	± 0.12
R_l	20.846	± 0.071	± negligible
A_{FB}^l [%]	1.54	± 0.27	± negligible
R_e	20.92	± 0.12	± negligible
R_μ	20.79	± 0.10	± negligible
R_τ	20.84	± 0.13	± negligible
A_{FB}^e [%]	1.03	± 0.58	± negligible
A_{FB}^μ [%]	1.20	± 0.41	± negligible
A_{FB}^τ [%]	2.46	± 0.48	± negligible
$\Gamma(Z \to$ hadrons) [GeV]	1.7371	± 0.0055	± 0.0038
$\Gamma_{INVISIBLE}$ [GeV]	0.5045	± 0.0047	± 0.0034
$\Gamma(Z \to l^+l^-)$ [MeV]	83.33	± 0.24	± 0.16
$\Gamma(Z \to e^+e^-)$ [MeV]	83.19	± 0.31	± 0.18
$\Gamma(Z \to \mu^+\mu^-)$ [MeV]	83.69	± 0.51	± 0.14
$\Gamma(Z \to \tau^+\tau^-)$ [MeV]	83.49	± 0.60	± 0.19

Table 2: Combined lineshape and A_{FB} results from LEP. The first error listed is the error from the experiments (containing each experiments statistical and non-common systematic uncertainty); the second error is the systematic error which is common to all four experiments. The full uncertainty on each parameter is the quadratic sum of the two uncertainties listed. The results above the double line are reintrepreted to obtain the partial widths.

	A_τ, Average polarization
ALEPH	0.134 ± 0.026
DELPHI	0.24 ± 0.07
L3	0.132 ± 0.033
OPAL	0.115 ± 0.046
LEP A_τ	0.138 ± 0.018
	A_e from $P_\tau(\cos\theta)$
ALEPH	0.120 ± 0.031
OPAL	0.23 ± 0.09
LEP A_e	0.132 ± 0.029

Table 3: LEP preliminary results on average tau polarization; yields a measure the tau couplings to the Z. The tau polarization as a function of polar production angle from LEP; the electron couplings to the Z are measured.

$g_V^e =$	-0.0356 ± 0.0044	$g_A^e =$	-.4990 ± 0.0011
$g_V^\mu =$	-0.028 ± 0.011	$g_A^\mu =$	-.5010 ± 0.0017
$g_V^\tau =$	-0.0379 ± 0.0043	$g_A^\tau =$	-.4998 ± 0.0019
$g_V^l =$	-0.0353 ± 0.0025	$g_A^l =$	-.49947 ± 0.00092

Table 4: LEP preliminary results on neutral current lepton couplings. Results are from a combined fit to LEP data on the leptonic partial decay widths of the Z, the forward-backward asymmetries, the average tau polarization, and the tau polarization dependence on polar production angle. The last line shows the result under the assumption of universality.

OPAL has measured the average tau polarization in the forward and backward hemispheres. ALEPH has measured P_τ in nine bins of polar angle. Both experiments determine the electron couplings ratio, or A_e; the results are in table 3.

The lepton couplings to the Z may be determined by combining the measurements of the leptonic partial decay widths, forward-backward asymmetries, and the tau polarization. Figure 1 shows the 68% confidence level contours for each lepton in the plane of g_V^l versus g_A^l. The axial-vector coupling is determined mostly from the partial width; the F-B asymmetry and tau polarization help determine the vector coupling. The uncertainties in the electron and tau couplings are smaller than those for the muon because the muons do not enter in the tau polarization measurement. Also shown in the figure is the contour obtained under the assumption of lepton universality in the neutral currents. Table 4 summarizes the results which confirm lepton universality.

Fits in the Context of the Standard Model.

The final two measurements from LEP included in this review are the heavy quark forward-backward asymmetry and the measurement of α_s from event shapes. The LEP result from the heavy quark A_{FB} is [10] $Sin(\theta_W^{eff}(M_Z^2)) = 0.2324 \pm 0.0020$.

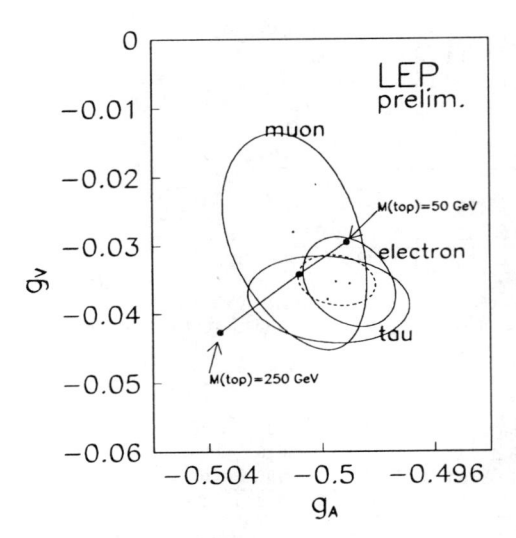

Figure 1: Preliminary results on lepton neutral current coupling to the Z from LEP. Contours are 68% C.L. for each lepton flavor. The dashed contour is the result assuming lepton universality. Also shown is the Standard Model [3] prediction for g_V versus g_A using the measured Z mass and top quark masses of 50, 150, and 250 GeV with the Higgs Mass set to 300 GeV.

Combining this with the cross sections, lepton A_{FB}'s, and tau polarization one can fit for the top quark mass and α_s in the context of the Standard Model [3]. The results are

$$M_{TOP} = 143^{+24+18}_{-30-20}$$

$$\alpha_s = 0.1337 \pm 0.088 \pm 0.019$$

where the central value and first error are evaluated with the Higgs mass set to 300 GeV. The second error reflects the change in the central value when re-doing the fit with the Higgs mass at 1000 GeV (upper error) or 60 GeV.

The LEP result on α_s from event shapes [10] is $\alpha_s = 0.120 \pm 0.006$. Including this in the fit results in a top mass estimate of

$$M_{TOP} = 153^{+22+17}_{-26-21}$$

where the first error again reflects the sensitivity of the experiments with the Higgs mass fixed at 300 GeV and the second error results from changing the Higgs mass (1000 and 60 GeV). Table 5 contains recent non-LEP results on the W mass and the W to Z mass ratio. When these are combined with the LEP results, the Standard

Experiment	quantity	result
CDF [11]	M_W	79.91 ± 0.39 GeV
UA2 [12]	M_W/M_Z	0.8813 ± 0.0041
CDHS [13]	$1-(M_W/M_Z)^2$	0.228 ± 0.006
CHARM [14]	$1-(M_W/M_Z)^2$	0.236 ± 0.006
CCFR [10]	$1-(M_W/M_Z)^2$	0.2242 ± 0.0064
FMMF [15]	$1-(M_W/M_Z)^2$	0.2342 ± 0.010

Table 5: Non-LEP results on the W mass and the W to Z mass ratio. These are combined with the LEP results to better estimate the top quark mass.

Model top quark mass estimate is

$$M_{TOP} = 142^{+17+17}_{-19-19}$$

with the same convention for Higgs mass as above.

There has been some discussion on the question of whether the present electroweak data are sensitive to the Higgs mass [10] [16]. This analysis agrees with [10] in that a small rise in the global χ^2 is seen for higher (fixed) Higgs masses. This analysis finds a χ^2 of about 24 for 27 DOF at $M_{HIGGS} = 60$ GeV rising linearly to about 27 at $M_{HIGGS} = 1000$ GeV. Most of the rise in χ^2 is coming from R_l and the heavy quark F-B asymmetry. The R_l value from the present data is about one standard deviation above the expectation from the Standard Model. If one artificially changes R_l by one sigma the increase in global χ^2 (from R_l) with Higgs mass disappears. Clearly more data are needed.

One can ask if LEP presently, or in the future, might be sensitive to the Higgs mass in the event that the top quark is found. Two fits have been done assuming that the top quark is found at the present preferred value of 142 GeV and that its mass is measured to ± 10 GeV. Additionally a penalty function has been included [17] to reflect the present limit [10] from direct searches for the Higgs. The first fit, using the above two constraints and the present LEP and non-LEP data, shows almost no sensitivity to M_{HIGGS}: the 68% confidence region in Higgs mass extends from the present direct search limit of 60 GeV to about 500 GeV. The second fit differs from the first in that the errors from LEP data have been reduced to reflect the gains expected by the end of LEP-I assuming a total of 2.5 million hadronic Z decays analyzed per experiment. The second fit shows only marginal improvement: the 68% confidence region extends from the direct search limit to about 300 GeV.

Acknowledgements

I would like to sincerely thank W. Chen of the University of Wisconsin-Madison for his help in preparing the presentation. I profited from conservation with other ALEPH collaborators including R. Tanaka, L. Rolandi, R. Jacobsen, and M. Martinez. Those who helped me gather and understand the results of the other LEP experiments included: D. Reid, R, Mount, I. Scott, S. Ganguli, M. Roney, J. Hobbs, T. Wyatt. I would also like to thank J. Rosner for interesting conversations and suggestions.

References

1. Aleph: Priv. comm. preliminary update of Z. Phys. C53 (1992) 20. Delphi: Priv. comm. preliminary update of Nucl. Phys. B367 (1991) 511. L3: Priv. comm. preliminary update of Z. Phys. C51 (1991) 179. OPAL: Priv. comm. preliminary update of Z. Phys. C52 (1991) 175.
2. F.A. Berends et al., in "Z Physics at LEP I" CERN 89-08, 1989. M. Martinez et al., Z. Phys. C 49 (1991) 645-655;
3. S. Jadach, M. Skrzypek, M. Martinez, CERN-PPE 92-04 (1992). D. Bardin et al., COMP. PHYS. COMM 59,(1990)303; D. Bardin et al., Z. Phys C44 (1989) 493; D. Bardin et al., Nucl. Phys. B351 (1991) 1; D. Bardin et al., Phys. Lett.B299 (1989) 405.
4. D.C. Kennedy, B.W. Lynn, Nucl. Phys. B322 (1989) 1. M. Consoli, W. Hollik in CERN Report 89-08 Vol I,7. W.J. Marciano, A. Sirlin Phys. Rev, Lett. 62 (1989) 163.
5. S. Jadach and Z Wąs et al., in "Z Physics at LEP I" CERN 89-08, 1989.
6. S. Jadach et al., CERN-TH 6230/91.
7. L. Arnaudon et al., CERN-PPE 92-125 submitted to the Conference on High Energy Physics, Dallas (1991).
8. PROGRAM ZSHAPE: F.A. Berends et al., Nucl. Phys. B297 (1988) 429. W. Beenakker and W. Hollik, ECFA workshop on LEP 200, CERN 87-08 p.185, ed. by A. Boehm and W. Hoogland; W. Hollik, DESY preprint 88-188.
9. Aleph: Priv. comm. preliminary results. Previous publication is Phys. Lett. B265 (1991) 430. Delphi: CERN-PPE/92-60. L3: CERN-PPE/92-132. OPAL: Priv. comm. preliminary results. Previous publication is Phys. Lett. B266 (1991) 201.
10. L. Rolandi, Review to appear in the proceedings of the Conference on High Energy Physics, Dallas 1991.
11. CDF: F. Abe et al., Phys. Rev. D43 (1991) 2070.
12. UA2: J. Alitti et al., Phys. Lett. B 276 (1992) 354.
13. CDHS: A. Blondel et al., Z. Phys. C45 (1990) 361.
14. CHARM: J. V. Allaby et al., Z. Phys. C36 (1987) 611.
15. FMMF: R. Brock talk given at this meeting.
16. J. Rosner, talk given at this meeting.
17. The penalty function is a one-sided Gaussian contriubtion to χ^2 for Higgs masses less than the limit from direct searches. The method used is due to M. Martinez of ALEPH.

MEASURING THE MASS OF THE Z BOSON AT LEP

Robert Jacobsen
CERN

ABSTRACT

In 1991, the mass of the Z boson was measured by the four LEP experiments. The LEP energy calibration was based on direct measurement of the beam energy via resonant depolarization and on precision magnetic measurements. A number of systematic effects were studied, including those due to asymmetric RF power, magnet aging and tidal forces. The systematic errors due to the remaining uncertainties were then estimated.

Any uncertainty in the energy of collision at LEP appears directly as a systematic error in the measurement of the Z boson mass and width. Methods first applied for the 1991 running[1] reduced this error significantly.

The beam energy is determined by the integral of the bending field seen by the particles. The magnetic field in the main ring dipoles was constantly monitored by the *Field Display*[2], an instrumented reference dipole wired in series with the ring dipoles. This provided the reference energy for each fill of the machine with a reproducibility of about 2.5×10^{-5}, although with considerably poorer absolute accuracy.

The *Resonant Depolarization* technique[3] precisely measures the beam energy under conditions similar to data-taking, and is therefore used to set the absolute scale. The energy can be determined with a precision of about 3×10^{-5} from the measured total angle of precession when a transversely polarized electron goes around LEP. A total of six measurements were made during four fills in 1991 with a variation of about 8×10^{-5}. The (-68±3.7) MeV mean difference between the field display reading and the depolarization measurement is used as a correction to the field display measurements for individual fills.

Several sources of variation have been identified. Measurements indicate the magnetic field varies with the magnet temperature causing an energy variation of $\Delta E/E = (1 \pm 0.25) \times 10^{-4}/°C$. A correction is applied based on the magnet temperature recorded in 8 magnets which together estimate the variation in average magnet temperature within ± 0.25 °C.

LEP's strong focusing makes the energy very sensitive to changes in circumference. Tidal motions of the underlying rock are expected to cause a small but noticeable energy variation. There is some evidence for this effect in the 1991 data (Figure 1) and experiments are planned to confirm the effect before the 1993 running, but no correction is as yet applied.

The energy loss per turn in LEP is 124 MeV at the Z peak. The beam particles regain this energy in RF cavities on either side of L3 and OPAL. The LEP design positioned the cavities such that the energy losses in the counter-rotating e^+ and e^-

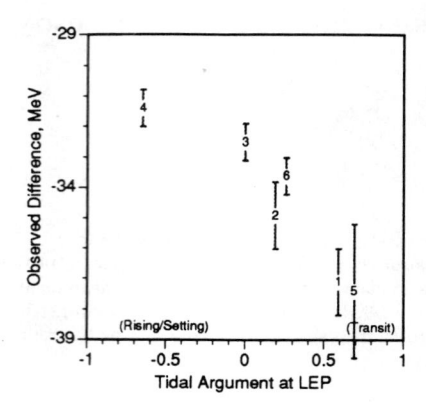

Figure 1: Evidence for effect of tides on LEP energy. The horizontal axis is the normalized magnitude of the tidal motion of the Earth, and vertical is the beam energy offset from the Field Display measured by depolarization. A slope of -3 MeV is predicted.

beams cancel, resulting in a constant center-of-mass collision energy. (Figure 2) A change in the RF frequency used during physics running was necessary, however, and effectively resulted in the RF particles arriving too early in the first cavity of each pair, and too late in the second. Both species regained more than half of the nominal energy loss before reaching the L3 and OPAL interaction points, and less than half after, so the center-of-mass energy in these points was approximately 13 MeV larger than in ALEPH and DELPHI. The value of this shift can be calculated, but depends to some extent on the RF power and phase distribution among the cavities. This results in a ±2 MeV error on the energy of a fill and a ±1 MeV error on the average over all fills.

The depolarization measurements were only available during the energy scan in the later half of run. Magnetic field stability before this was monitored using the *Flux Loop*, a closed loop of known area imbedded in the pole faces of the dipole magnets. Integrating the induced voltage while varying the magnet currents allows an absolute calibration of the field. Measurements were made before installation with a precision of ~10^{-4}, but the flux loop is insensitive to constant remnant fields and may have some variation with time. A 'step' was seen in the flux loop data just before the start of the energy scan. This may correspond to a change in the average temperature of the ring due a change to the magnet cooling system. The data taken on the Z peak before this step therefore have an additional 10 MeV beam energy error assigned.

Combining the uncertainty in the mean depolarization correction and residual uncertainties on the mean corrections for temperature and RF effects, the error on the absolute energy is determined to be $(\Delta E/E)^{abs} = 5.7 \times 10^{-5}$ at the 46.5 GeV

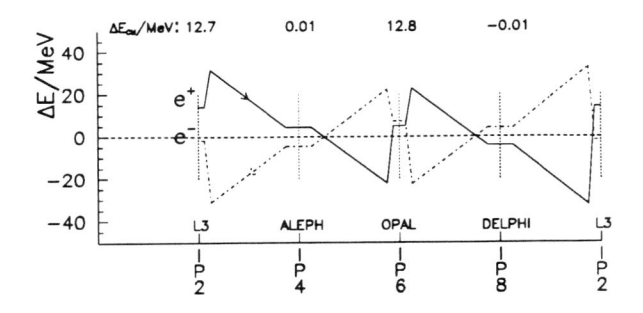

Figure 2: Typical beam energy variation at points around LEP. As discussed in the text, losses in the e$^+$ and e$^-$ beam cancel except at L3 and OPAL due to cavity positioning.

beam energy where all the depolarization measurements were made. Magnetic measurements and comparisons of proton calibrations[1] at 20 GeV and 45 GeV indicate that the magnetic field setting has a non-linearity error of $(\Delta E/E)^{lin} = (2.0 \pm 1.5) \times (93 - E_{cm}/\text{GeV})$. An additional random error of $(\Delta E/E)^{set} = 3 \times 10^{-5}$ was estimated to cover possible systematic setting errors at each energy. The variation in the depolarization can reliably be used as an estimate of the overall reproducibility of LEP settings. Combining the appropriate temperature and RF configuration uncertainties, the energy reproducibility from fill to fill is determined to be $(\Delta E/E)^{rep} = 10^{-4}$. The energy error for the n_i fills at each scan point i can then be written

$$\frac{\Delta E_i}{E_i} = \left(\frac{\Delta E}{E}\right)^{abs} \oplus \frac{1}{\sqrt{n_i}}\left(\frac{\Delta E}{E}\right)^{rep} \oplus \frac{(93 - E_i/\text{GeV})}{E_i}\Delta E^{lin} \oplus \left(\frac{\Delta E}{E}\right)^{set}.$$

When included in the experimental fits[4] for the parameters of the Z resonance, these result in systematic errors of approximately ±6.3 MeV on the 91.187 GeV mass of the Z, the dominant contribution to a total error of 7 MeV.

References

1. The Working Group on LEP energy, L. Arnaudon, *et al.*, "The Energy Calibration of LEP in 1991", *CERN-PPE/92-125, CERN-SL/92-37(DI)*
2. J. Billan, J. P. Gourber and K. N. Henrichsen, "Determination of the particle momentum in LEP from precise magnet measurements", 1991 Particle Accelerator Conference, San Francisco, CA May 1991
3. L. Arnaudon, *et al.*, *Physics Letters* **B 284** (1992) 431-439
4. J. Harton, this conference

LIMITS ON EXTRA Z BOSONS
FROM e^+e^- REACTIONS BELOW THE Z^0 POLE

BARRY L. HOWELL
Dept. of Physics, Purdue University
W. Lafayette, IN 47907 U.S.A.

ABSTRACT

From a chi-square fit of TRISTAN measurements for $e^+e^- \to \mu^+\mu^-$, $\tau^+\tau^-$, and $q\bar{q}$ reactions, limits on the existence of Z' bosons are derived, for the case of negligible Z^0-Z' mixing. We obtain $M_{Z'} > 150 \sim 260$ GeV for various Z's associated with E_6 models, and $M_{Z_1} > 462$ GeV for a Z_1 postulated with couplings identical to those of the Standard Model Z^0, at the 90% confidence level.

1. Introduction

While no deviation from Standard Model (SM) behavior has been observed in e^+e^- reactions up to LEP energies, the existence of Z' bosons with masses greater than ~ 100 GeV has not been ruled out if the Z^0-Z' mixing happens to be small[1]. For example Z's associated with E_6 extensions of the SM have been limited to $M_{Z'} > 400 \sim 500$ GeV if the mixing angle θ_{mix} is larger than ~ 0.02, but no limits are set if $\theta_{\text{mix}} = 0$. This is a consequence of the fact that LEP interactions are dominated by pure Z^0 exchange, so that a Z' is only detectable by shifts in the measured Z^0 mass and/or couplings.

By comparison, TRISTAN reactions are sensitive to Z' effects, even in the case of zero mixing[2]. This is illustrated in fig. 1, which shows the cross section, σ_{ll}, and forward backward asymmetry, A_{ll}, for lepton pairs, and the production rate for hadrons, R_{hadron}. Off the Z^0 pole, Z' exchange and the interference of Z'-Z^0 and Z'-γ make significant contributions to these processes. In this paper, bounds are presented for Z's, determined by fitting the TRISTAN data for σ_{ll}, A_{ll}, and R_{hadron}. We consider Z_ψ, Z_χ, Z_η, and Z_ν bosons associated with E_6 models[2], and an additional "SM-like" Z_1 boson having couplings equal to those of the observed Z^0.

2. Data Sample and Fit Procedure

The data for the fit corresponds to integrated luminosities of 74 pb^{-1}, 33 pb^{-1}, and 33 pb^{-1}, collected by the TOPAZ[3], VENUS[4], and AMY[5] experiments respectively. Correlations among individual points were taken into account by defining the chi-square to be

$$\chi^2 = \sum_{i,j} \Delta_i V_{ij}^{-1} \Delta_j + \left(\frac{M_{Z^0} - 91.175 \text{ GeV}}{0.021 \text{ GeV}}\right)^2 + \left(\frac{\Gamma_{Z^0} - 2.487 \text{ GeV}}{0.010 \text{ GeV}}\right)^2 + \left(\frac{\sin^2\theta_W - 0.2290}{0.0033}\right)^2,$$

where $\Delta_i = y_i^{data} - y_i^{theory}$ are the residuals for the measurements, and where V_{ij} is the error matrix. Diagonal elements V_{ii} are determined by summing the squares of all statistical, systematic point-to-point, and common normalization errors. Off-diagonal elements $V_{ij}, i \neq j$, are determined by the product of the common normalization errors for measurements i and j when they are correlated. For all three TRISTAN experiments, the normalization errors are dominated by uncertainties of $3 \sim 5\%$ associated with luminosity measurements. The fit parameters were M_{Z^0}, Γ_{Z^0}, $\sin^2 \theta_W$, and $M_{Z'}$, where the first three were constrained to fluctuate within ranges specified by other experiments[6]. QCD corrections to α_s at the three loop level, determined from the world-average value $\Lambda_{\overline{MS}} = 175$ MeV[7], were included in the calculation of $R_{hadrons}^{theory}$.

3. Results

The consistency of the data with the SM was verified by a fit with $M_{Z'}$ fixed at ∞. The results were $M_{Z^0}^{fit} = 91.176 \pm 0.019$ GeV, $\Gamma_{Z^0}^{fit} = 2.487 \pm 0.010$ GeV, and $\sin^2 \theta_W^{fit} = 0.2302 \pm 0.0030$, with $\chi_{min}^2/D.O.F = 63.76/77$ which suggest no disagreement of TRISTAN data with the SM constraints imposed. Conservative systematic error estimates may be the source of the small χ_{min}^2 value. Table 1 outlines the limits derived when various Z's are postulated. In all cases, large $M_{Z'}^{fit}$ values were preferred (> 10 TeV), suggesting no observable Z'. These limits exceed previous e^+e^- bounds[4] for a Z_1 and E_6-associated Z's by about $50 \sim 100$ GeV. They are, however, only at or below the bounds set by $p\bar{p}$ annihilation data[8]. TRISTAN experiments expect integrated luminosities of ~ 250 pb^{-1} by 1994, which will improve statistical precisions to $\sim 2\%$. With precise luminosity measurement ($\Delta L/L \simeq 1.5\%$ is expected for TOPAZ data collected since 1991), the sensitivity to Z' effects will be extended by > 100 GeV.

References

1. G. Altarelli et al., *Phys. Lett.* **B263** (1991) 459.
2. K. Hagiwara et al., *Phys. Rev.* **D41** (1990) 815 and references therein.
3. [TOPAZ] B. Howell et al., *Phys. Lett.* **B291** (1992) 206; I. Adachi et al., *Phys. Lett.* **B255** (1991) 613; I. Adachi et al., *Phys. Lett.* **B234** (1990) 525.
4. [VENUS] K. Abe et al., *Phys. Lett.* **B246** (1990) 297; K. Abe et al., *Z. Phys.* **C48** (1990) 13; K. Abe et al., *Phys. Lett.* **B234** (1990) 382; H. Yoshida et al., *Phys. Lett.* **B198** (1987) 570.
5. [AMY] T. Kumita et al., *Phys. Rev.* **D42** (1990) 1339; T. Mori et al., *Phys. Lett.* **B218** (1989) 499; A. Bacala et al., *Phys. Lett.* **B218** (1989) 112.
6. The LEP Collaborations, *Phys. Lett.* **B276** (1992) 247.
7. Particle Data Group, *Phys. Rev.* **D45** (1992) III.58.
8. [CDF] F. Abe et al., *Phys. Rev. Lett.* **D68** (1992) 1463.

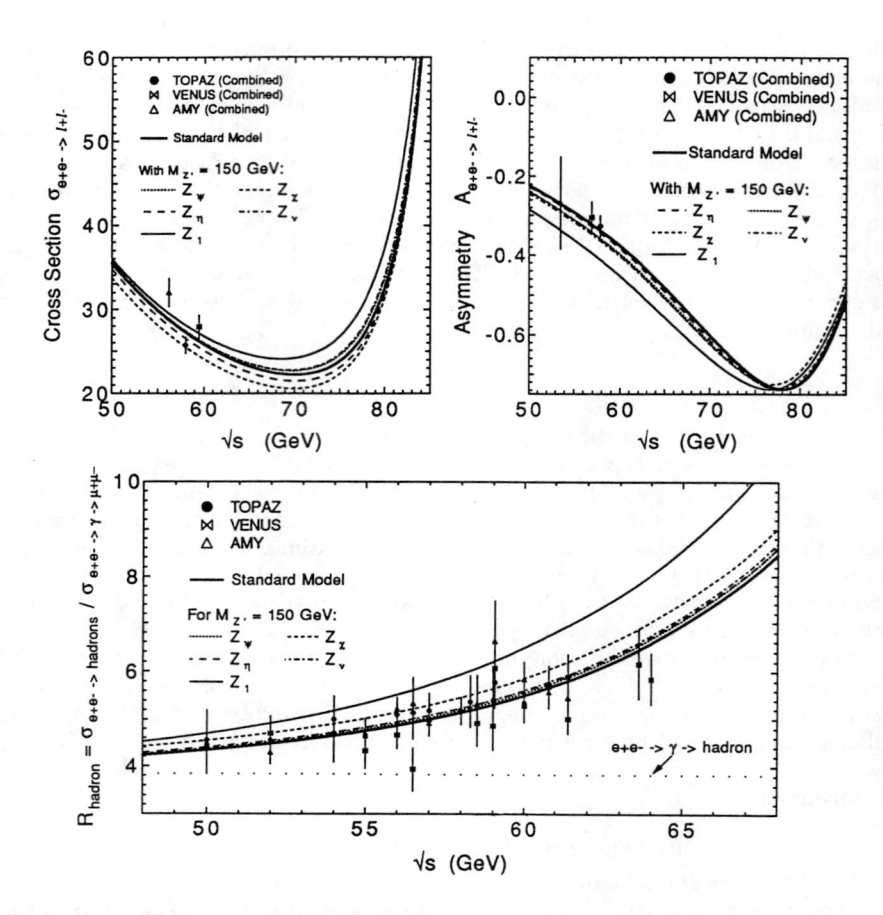

Figure 1: Sensitivity of TRISTAN e^+e^- measurements to the existence of various Z's ($M_{Z'}$ = 150 GeV assumed), as a function of energy. Some data points are combined for display purposes.

Table 1: Mass limits for various Z's determined by this analysis, with a comparison to previous e^+e^- and $p\bar{p}$ analyses.

Lower bound for $M_{Z'}$ (GeV)		Z_1	Z_ψ	Z_χ	Z_η	Z_ν
This analysis:	90% C.L.	> 462	> 163	> 257	> 150	> 195
	95% C.L.	> 401	> 146	> 230	> 133	> 173
VENUS e^+e^-	90% C.L.	> 426	> 105	> 231	> 125	—
CDF ($p\bar{p}$):	95% C.L.	> 412	> 320	> 340	> 340	—

MEASUREMENT OF THE WEAK MIXING ANGLE IN NEUTRINO-NUCLEON SCATTERING BY CCFR

R.H.Bernstein, F. Borcherding, M.J.Lamm, W.Marsh, K.W.B.Merritt, H.Schellman, D.D.Yovanovitch
Fermilab, Batavia IL 60510, USA

C.Arroyo, T.Bolton, C.Foudas, B.J.King, W.C.Lefmann, S.R.Mishra, M.H.Shaevitz, P.Z.Quintas, W.C.Leung, S.A.Rabinowitz, F.J.Sciulli, W.G.Seligman
Columbia University, New York, NY 10027

F.S.Merritt, M.J.Oreglia, B.A.Schumm
University of Chicago, Chicago IL 60637

A.Bodek, H.S.Budd, P. de Barbaro, W.K.Sakumoto
University of Rochester, Rochester, NY 14627

W.H. Smith, T. Kinnel, P.H. Sandler
University of Wisconsin, Madison, WI. 53706

ABSTRACT

We present the results of a preliminary determination of $\sin^2\theta_W$ from a study of νFe scattering in the Lab E detector at Fermilab. The analysis is based on a sample of 5×10^5 events with a mean neutrino energy of 166 GeV. Our result, $\sin^2\theta_W = 0.2242 \pm 0.0044_{\text{expt.}} \pm 0.0047_{\text{model}}$, is the highest energy high statistics determination of the weak mixing angle using neutrino data.

1. Introduction

The Standard Model of Electroweak Physics requires as input five parameters to describe high energy processes: α, G_F, M_Z, m_t, and m_H. The latter two enter into the calculations of low energy scattering processes such as $\sin^2\theta_W$ determined from νN scattering, via loop corrections to the W and Z self-energies. Comparisons of $\sin^2\theta_W$ determined through precision measurements of neutral current νN scattering to the value measured from the boson masses or asymmetries can be used to probe the radiative corrections to the Standard Model. Existing neutrino measurements of $\sin^2\theta_W$ already constrain the top mass to $m_t \approx 200$ GeV, a limit quite competitive with those attained by collider experiments.[1] Thus, considerable motivation exists to improve upon the determination of $\sin^2\theta_W$ in the neutrino sector.[2] We report herein on a new preliminary determination of $\sin^2\theta_W$ from Fermilab experiment E770 by the CCFRW collaboration.

2. Data Sample

The data were taken with the Lab E neutrino detector during the 1988 fixed target run of the Tevatron. The Lab E detector[3] consists of a 680 ton non-magnetized iron calorimeter followed by an iron toroid muon spectrometer. The toroid is not used in this analysis. The calorimeter consists of 84 planes of 3m×3m×10 cm steel absorber. Scintillation counters of the same transverse dimension sample the energy every 10cm ($0.6\lambda, 5.9X_0$) of steel, permitting a hadron energy resolution of $\frac{\Delta E}{E} = \frac{0.89}{\sqrt{E}}$. The scintillators also determine the event timing and establish the longitudinal vertex position. Transverse vertex position is provided by double planes of drift chambers placed at 20 cm intervals of steel; the x,y vertex resolution, using the chambers, is 5.0 cm.

Three essential quantities enter into the $\sin^2\theta_W$ analysis: the event length, the event radial vertex position, and the event energy.

The length is determined by counting the number of consecutive scintillation counter planes which see more than 0.25 of the energy deposit of a minimum-ionizing particle. Events with short length are predominantly neutral currents, whose length is set by the hadronic shower. The μ of charged-current events continues downstream, firing many consecutive counters. We simulate the ratio of the number of events with $L < 31$ counters (3.1 m of Fe) to the number of events with muons entering the toroid, and check against the sample of intermediate length events.

The event transverse vertex position is obtained from a weighted sum of drift chamber hits from the first two drift chamber planes downstream of the event vertex. To minimize the number of charged current events with $L < 31$ which exit the sides of the detector and to suppress electron neutrino background, we require the event radius to be less than 75.4 cm.

The event energy is defined as the sum of pulse heights from the first twenty counters in the event. We require events to have at least 30 GeV of visible energy. This cut insures that the calorimeter is being used well within its linear regime, guarantees 100% trigger efficiency, and strongly suppresses non-deep-inelastic processes and the cosmic ray background.

After all cuts, our event sample contains 1.51×10^5 short events, 2.93×10^5 toroid events, and 0.42×10^5 intermediate length events, with a mean visible energy of 100 GeV. This represents the highest energy high statistics neutral current neutrino measurement to date. The composition of short length events is approximately 60% ν_μ neutral current, 22% ν_μ charged current, 9% $\bar\nu_\mu$ neutral current, 1% $\bar\nu_\mu$ charged current, and 8% ν_e charged plus neutral current.

3. Analysis Technique

To determine the weak mixing angle, we attempt to reproduce the measured quantity $R_{30} \equiv \frac{N_{short}}{N_{toroid}}$ with a Monte Carlo using $\sin^2\theta_W$ as the sole free parameter. The Monte Carlo includes as ingredients the QCD corrected quark-parton model, a parameterization of the quadrupole-triplet neutrino beam, and a detailed description of the Lab E detector (previous $\sin^2\theta_W$ determinations have used a suitably corrected R_ν and then applied the Llewellyn-Smith formalism[4]).

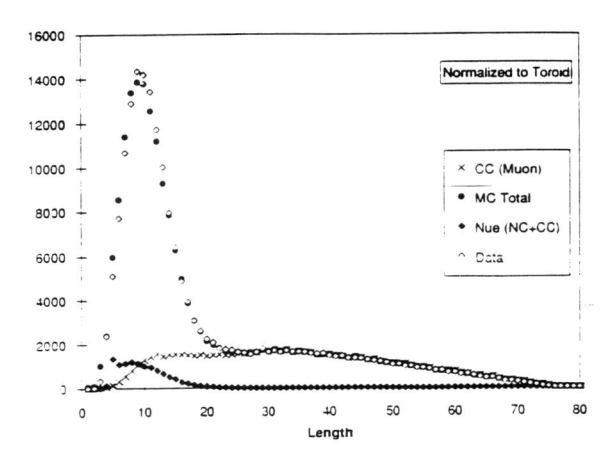

Figure 1: Event length for data (solid histogram) and Monte Carlo (dashed histogram) with $\sin^2 \theta_W^{uncorr.} = 0.2347$.

The parton distributions in our Monte Carlo are obtained directly from structure function measurements by the same experiment.[5] Charm production is modeled via the slow rescaling formalism in which charm threshold effects are parameterized using an effective charm mass, m_c. From an analysis of 6000 opposite sign dimuons from this experiment[6]: $m_c = 1.34 \pm 0.34$ GeV.

The dominant component of the neutrino flux arising from two body charged pion and kaon decays is directly measured in the experiment. A more serious issue is the electron neutrino flux. Since all ν_e interactions produce short length events, a mis-estimate of this component of the flux translates into a large error on $\sin^2 \theta_W$. There are two components to the ν_e flux. The first, originating from $K^+ \to \pi^0 e^+ \nu_e$ can be tightly constrained from $K_{\mu 2}$ decays, whose contribution from the flux can be separated from $\pi_{\mu 2}$ contribution by exploiting the well known energy-radius correlation. The second component of the ν_e flux is from $K_L^0 \to \pi^- e^+ \nu_e$; these decays contribute $\sim 17\%$ of the ν_e events. This source is important because the primary proton beam is targeted at 0 degrees relative to the Lab E detector to maximize total flux for charged current measurements. The K_L component cannot be constrained using $K_L^0 \to \pi^- \mu^+ \nu_\mu$ decays because the neutral $K_{\mu 3}$ decays are a small fraction of the charged $K_{\mu 2}$ decays. The K_L^0 component must instead be calculated using other experimental data on K_L^0 production.[7]. A check on the ν_e flux calculation can be obtained from the data itself by exploiting the different longitudinal energy distribution of charged current ν_e events compared to ν_μ neutral current events. The two independent calculations are consistent to within the errors of $\pm 4.6\%$ for the flux Monte Carlo and $\pm 6.8\%$ for the η_3 fits. Combining the two results, the estimated uncertainty for the ν_e flux is $\pm 3.8\%$.

5. Results

Our radiatively-corrected[9] value for $\sin^2 \theta_W$ is

$$\sin^2 \theta_W = 0.2248 \pm 0.0029_{stat} \pm 0.0033_{exp.sys} \pm 0.0044_{model} \qquad \text{(Preliminary)}$$

Combining the statistical and experimental systematics: $\sin^2 \theta_W = 0.2242 \pm 0.0044 \pm 0.0047$. This can be compared with the two highest precision existing measurements, $\sin^2 \theta_W = 0.228 \pm 0.005 \pm 0.005$ by CDHS and $\sin^2 \theta_W = 0.236 \pm 0.005 \pm 0.005$ by CHARM.[10] Our value is consistent with these two results, though slightly lower.

Our largest systematic error is due to uncertainties in charm production in the charged current sector. While the magnitude of this systematic error is not much less than previous analysis, we feel this contribution is under much better control. The 30 GeV visible energy cut that we impose lessens the influence of the charm threshold. More important however, we have measured all of the parameters of the slow rescaling model of charm production in the same experiment.

The largest experimental uncertainty is attributed to lack of knowledge of the ν_e flux, which is itself driven by the poorly constrained contribution of K_L^0 decays to the ν_e flux. Significant reduction of this error in this experiment can only be achieved through better understanding of K_L^0 production and decay in the quadtriplet beam; the prospects for this seem poor. Future experiments will remove these difficulties and significantly improve the error.[11]

1. D.C. Kennedy and P. Langacker, *Phys. Rev.* **D44** (1991) 1591; P. Langacker and M. Luo, *Phys. Rev.* **D44** (1991) 817; P. Langacker, M. Luo, and A. Mann, *Rev. Mod. Phys.* **64** (1992) 87.
2. W.J. Marciano and A. Sirlin, *Phys. Rev.* **D26** (1980) 2695; R.G. Stuart, *Z. Phys.* **C34** (1987) 445.
3. W.K. Sakumoto et al, *Nucl. Instr. Meth.* **A294** (1990) 179.
4. C.H. Llewellyn Smith, *Nucl. Phys.* **B228** (1983) 205.
5. P.Z. Quintas et al., Nevis Report 1457, Aug. 1991. Submitted to *Phys. Rev. Lett.*
6. M.H. Shaevitz, Nevis Report 1482, Sept. 1990; S.R. Rabinowitz et al., submitted to *Phys. Rev. Lett.*
7. P. Skubic et al., *Phys. Rev.* **D18** (1978) 3115.
8. R. Brun et al., CERN-DD/78/2, 1978.
9. A. De Rujula, R. Petronzio, and A. Savoy-Navarro, *Nucl. Phys.* **B154** (1979) 394.; A. Sirlin and W. J. Marciano, *Nucl. Phys.* **B189** (1981) 442.; we checked the results using D. Yu. Bardin and O. M. Fedorenko, *Sov. J. Nucl. Phys.* **B30** (1979) 418 and found agreement to ± 0.001 in $\sin^2 \theta_W$.
10. H. Abramowicz et al., *Phys. Rev. Lett.* **57** (1986) 298; J.V. Allaby et al., *Z. Phys.* **C36**, (1987) 611.
11. "Precision Electroweak Measurements with a Sign-Selected Beam", Fermilab Proposal P815, 1991.

NEUTRINO-ELECTRON SCATTERING WITH CHARM II RECENT RESULTS

CHARM II Collaboration

presented by

GABY RÄDEL

Deutsches Elektronen Synchroton, DESY, Notkestr.85, 2000 Hamburg 52, Germany

ABSTRACT

We are reporting on a determination of neutral current coupling constants from a study of differential cross sections of muon-(anti)neutrino electron scattering. The results were obtained with the CHARM-II detector which was exposed to the CERN wide band neutrino beam in the years 1987 to 1991. A total of about 3000 νe and 3000 $\bar{\nu} e$ scattering events were observed.

Idea and Realisation of the Experiment

For the study of higher order corrections it is of great interest to compare the very precise measurements of the electroweak parameters at the electron-positron collider LEP at CERN[1] at the Z-resonance with those performed at lower energy where processes occur by virtual Z exchange. Neutrino-electron scattering is perfectly suited for such a comparison, since the process is purely leptonic and, in terms of coupling constants, nearly equivalent to the annihilation of electrons and positrons into lepton pairs.

The aim of CHARM II is a precise measurement of electroweak parameters by studying the differential cross sections of muon-neutrino and muon-antineutrino scattering off electrons [2]. Several analyses were performed using different input information. So the electroweak mixing angle was determined from the final data sample in a most precise way from the ratio of the differential cross sections. The weak neutral coupling constants g_V and g_A were obtained from an absolut measurement of the cross sections and, for the first time, a model-independent determination of the shape of the y-distributions, together with a determination of the neutral current coupling constants was performed. The latter two measurements are based on data taken between 1987 – 1990, representing about 80% of the final statistics.

The CHARM II detector [3] consisted of a massive target calorimeter followed by a muon spectrometer. The detector was exposed to the horn focused wide band neutrino beam (WBB) at the CERN 450 GeV Super Proton Synchrotron (SPS). The signature of neutrino-electron scattering is a single, forward scattered electron producing an electromagnetic shower in the calorimeter. The variable $E_e \theta_e^2$, the product of electron energy and the square of the scattering angle, is kinematically constrained to values smaller than 1MeV. This fact is used to separate νe-scattering from the background of semileptonic events which has a broad distribution.

The energy resolution was found to be [4] $\Delta E_e/E_e = 0.09/\sqrt{E_e/\text{GeV}} + 0.11$. The angular resolution is equivalent to $\Delta\theta_e^{\text{proj}} \approx 17$ mrad/$\sqrt{E_e/\text{GeV}}$ in the energy range of our analysis.

The ratio of the neutrino and antineutrino fluxes was obtained with five different methods, which gave consistent results. Four of these were formed by event-rates of processes with a known cross section ratio for neutrinos and antineutrinos. The ratio of the muon fluxes in the shielding downstream of the decay region gave an independent measurement. The resulting precision in the flux ratio was 2.2%.

The absolute normalization of the neutrino flux was obtained from inclusive neutrino-nucleon scattering used as a monitor reaction with known cross section. The total uncertainty on the flux measurement was found to be 4.7% and 5.2% for the neutrino and antineutrino beam, respectively. The neutrino beam spectra and the relative flux of opposite helicity components were obtained from an analysis of charged current events with low momentum transfer. The electron-neutrino components were determined by Monte-Carlo methods.

The background consists of semileptonic neutrino reactions producing predominantly electromagnetic final states. The contributions are: coherent and diffractive neutrino production of single neutral pions in NC interactions [5], quasi-elastic neutrino-nucleon reactions of electron-neutrinos and, a small contribution due to inclusive neutrino reactions with a large electromagnetic component in the final state.

Analysis Method

The general form of the neutrino-electron scattering cross section can be written as [6]:

$$\frac{d\sigma}{dy} = \frac{G_F^2 m_e}{2\pi} E_\nu \sum_{i=1}^{3} A_i g_i \qquad (1)$$

where the g_i are different combinations of electroweak coupling constants:

$$g_1 = (g_V + g_A)^2, \quad g_2 = (g_V - g_A)^2, \quad g_3 = (2 + g_V + g_A)^2 \qquad (2)$$

where g_V and g_A are the vector and axial-vector coupling constants of the electron to the neutral current respectively.

The expressions A_i are given below for the four processes involved.

Process	A_1	A_2	A_3
$\nu_\mu e \to \nu_\mu e$	1	$(1-y)^2$	0
$\bar\nu_\mu e \to \bar\nu_\mu e$	$(1-y)^2$	1	0
$\nu_e e \to \nu_e e$	0	$(1-y)^2$	1
$\bar\nu_e e \to \bar\nu_e e$	0	1	$(1-y)^2$

The variable $y = (1 - \cos\theta^*)/2$ and θ^* is the scattering angle in the centre-of-mass system.

The four differential cross sections (1) depend on two parameters only, either on g_A and g_V, or using the Standard Model relation between the coupling constants and the electroweak mixing angle ($g_V = \rho(-1/2 + 2\sin^2\theta_W)$ and $g_A = -\rho/2$), on $\sin^2\theta_W$ and ρ, the relative coupling strength of the neutral current with respect to the charged current.

The measured event rate, e.g. in the neutrino beam is given by

$$dn^{\nu_e}/dy = \sum_{i=1}^{3} f_i^{\nu_e} g_i + \text{background} \qquad (3)$$

where the differential distributions $f_i^{\nu_e}$ contain all information about the neutrino flux and energy spectra, the cross section expressions A_i, and the experimental resolutions and acceptances. All these quantities are either known by calculation or are measured. The experimental data and the theoretical predictions are described as double differential distributions, $f_i^{\nu_e}$, in the kinematic variables E_e and $E_e\theta_e^2$. They discriminate between signal and background in the variable $E_e\theta_e^2$, and determine the background composition because of their different energy (E_e) distributions.

The theoretical prediction for neutrino-electron scattering was corrected for higher order QED effects [7]. The coupling constants determined from this fit are therefore effective values including, but not corrected for, higher order electroweak effects.

Determination of Weinberg Angle and Coupling Constants

A preliminary analysis using the full data sample taken in 1987 – 1991, was based on the measurement of the cross section ratio $R = \sigma(\nu_\mu e)/\sigma(\bar\nu_\mu e)$ and provides a precise determination of $\sin^2\theta_W$, where only the knowledge of the relative neutrino flux is necessary.

The $E_e\theta_e^2$ distributions of the selected events in the energy range $3-24\,\text{GeV}$ are shown in Fig. 1, together with the results of the best fit to the two-dimensional (E_e, $E_e\theta_e^2$) distributions. The fit was performed using (3) expressing g_V and g_A in terms of $\sin^2\theta_W$; ρ cancels in the ratio. The pronounced peaks at low $E_e\theta_e^2$ contain each nearly 3000 events. From these values a *preliminary* determination of $\sin^2\theta_W$ was deduced:

$$\sin^2\theta_W^{\nu_e} = 0.232 \pm 0.006_{\text{stat}} \pm 0.007_{\text{syst}}.$$

The inclusion of the knowledge on absolute ν-fluxes and experimental selection efficiencies makes it possible to determine simultaneously two electroweak parameters, e.g. g_V and g_A or $\sin^2\theta_W$ and ρ. Fits were performed according to (3) and using (2) for the coupling constants.

The fourfold ambiguity in the determination of g_V and g_A which is expected from the quadratic dependence of the cross sections on the couplings, is reduced to a two-fold one owing to the presence of ν_e and $\bar\nu_e$ components in the beam. About 10% of the ν_e events are induced by electron-neutrinos. The precision is sufficient to select two solutions. Results from $e^+e^- \to e^+e^-$ experiments [1] resolve

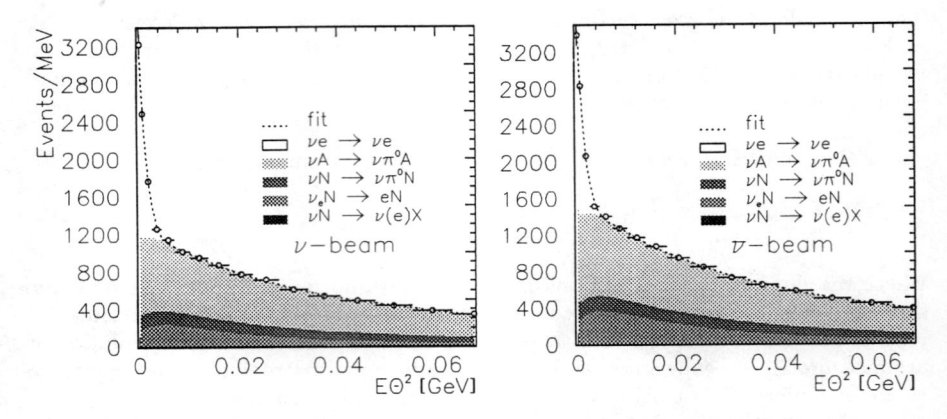

Figure 1: Experimental data and the result of the best fit: data are shown as circles and the fit results are displayed as a dashed line. Only the projections in $E_e\theta_e^2$ of the 2-dim. distributions are shown.

the remaining ambiguity. The systematic errors are dominated by uncertainties of the background determination, of the neutrino flux measurement and of the event selection efficiency.

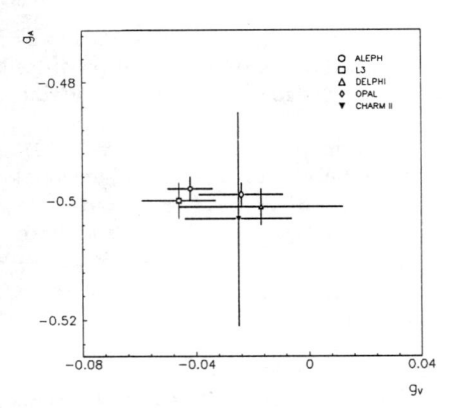

Figure 2: Comparison of results from νe scattering and from $e^+e^- \to e^+e^-$ annihilation at the Z^0 pole in the g_V-g_A plane [1]. The crosses show different experimental data points.

The results for the effective vector and axial-vector coupling constants from neutrino-electron scattering are: [1]

$$g_V^{\nu e} = -0.025 \pm 0.014_{stat} \pm 0.014_{syst}$$
$$g_A^{\nu e} = -0.503 \pm 0.007_{stat} \pm 0.016_{syst}$$

It is possible to compare this result directly with those obtained from a measurement of the partial width Γ_{ee} at the Z resonance and the forward-backward asymmetry A^{FB} at LEP (Fig. 2). The agreement of the measurement performed at $Q^2 \approx 0.01$ GeV^2 with those performed at $Q^2 = m_Z^2$ is remarkable.

Using the $\overline{MS}$ renormalisation scheme [10] we can correct our result for higher order electroweak effects. The net correction is negligible for $\sin^2\theta_W$ and amounts to -0.005 for ρ, with a theoretical uncertainty of ± 0.002 and ± 0.004, respectively,

---

[1] The fit can as well performed with $\sin^2\theta_W$ and the relative coupling strength ρ as free parameters. This yields $\sin^2\theta_W{}^{\nu e} = 0.237 \pm 0.007 \pm 0.007$ and $\rho^{\nu e} = 1.006 \pm 0.014 \pm 0.033$ as result.

induced by assuming a reasonable change of masses for the top quark and the Higgs boson.

Y-Distribution and Righthanded Coupling

The shape of the y-distribution of $\nu_\mu e$ and $\bar\nu_\mu e$ interactions was determined with a minimum of model dependence. No use was made of the knowledge of the relative normalization of the beams, and no assumption on the shape of the distribution was made other than assuming a smooth behaviour at the scale of the experimental resolution. To obtain the ν_μ and $\bar\nu_\mu$ y-distributions, a subtraction of electron-neutrino induced events was neccessary, introducing a small model dependence.

The differential cross sections $F(y) = d\sigma/dy$ were determined from the measured data with a procedure for regularized unfolding [8] which had already been applied to several similar problems in particle physics [9]. The analysis is based on the two-dimensional event distributions in the variables E_e and $E_e\theta_e^2$. Two different classes of background contribute. One is due to semileptonic processes, as already described above. Its contribution was evaluated from a fit of the four modelled background distributions to the measured $(E_e, E_e\theta_e^2)$ distributions in the region of 6 MeV $\leq E_e\theta_e^2 \leq$ 72 MeV, containing only background events, and extrapolating to the signal region below 4.5 MeV.

The second class of background consists of events produced by neutrinos of the wrong helicity or by electron-type neutrinos scattering on electrons. Their numbers cannot be determined in a model independent way, as the cross sections of these processes depend on $\sin^2\theta_W$. This dependence was found to be negligible compared to the statistical uncertainty. For the subtraction we used $\sin^2\theta_W = 0.2337$, which is the most recently published measurement of the four LEP collaborations [1]. The unfolded differential cross sections for $\nu_\mu e$ and $\bar\nu_\mu e$ scattering are shown in Figure 3. Only statistical errors are given. A fit of the Standard Model prediction to the measured points yields for the ratio of the squares of the neutral coupling constants:

$$g_R^2/g_L^2 = 0.60 \pm 0.19_{\text{stat}}, \qquad (4)$$

which confirms the existence of the right-handed coupling of the electron to the Z by three standard deviations. This result is entirely independent of the determination of the absolute cross section, and of cross section ratios and is hence independent of any assumed value for ρ. It compares well with an electroweak mixing angle $\sin^2\theta_W = 0.212 \pm 0.027_{\text{stat}} \pm 0.006_{\text{syst}}$, obtained from a direct fit to the shape of the two-dimensional distributions in E_e and $E_e\theta_e^2$ making use of equivalent assumptions. Compared to the statistical error, the systematic uncertainty is small. It is mainly due to the background evaluation.

This is the first measurement of the electroweak mixing angle using only the information from the shape of kinematical distributions from neutrino-electron data. It is in good agreement with our previous measurements [2].

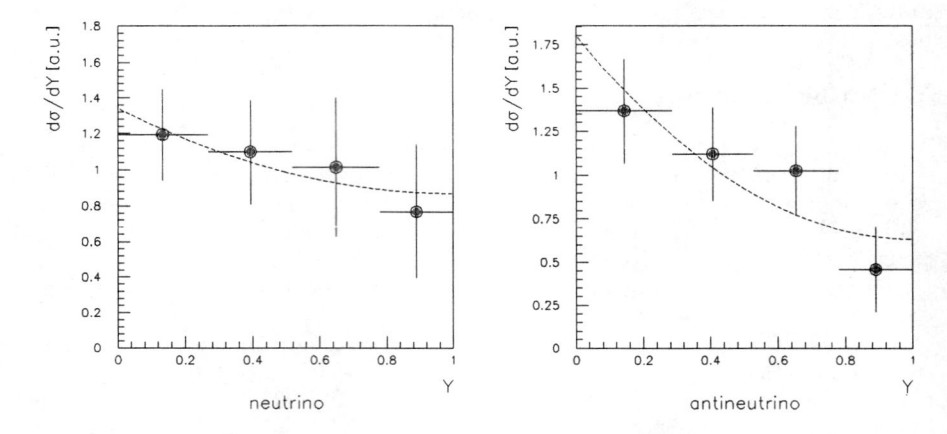

Figure 3: Unfolded differential cross sections for $\nu_\mu e$ scattering (left), and $\bar{\nu}_\mu e$ scattering (right) in arbitrary units. The line overlaid corresponds to the prediction of the Standard Model for a value of the electroweak mixing angle of $\sin^2 \theta_W = 0.212$.

In addition we can conclude that the values of $\sin^2 \theta_W$ we obtained with the different analyses of our data agree well. The small difference in the value of $\sin^2 \theta_W^{\nu_e}$ arises mainly from a more accurate new calculation of the beam spectra and from the additional event statistics.

References

1. The LEP collaborations: ALEPH, DELPHI, L3 and OPAL, *Phys. Lett.* **B276** (1992) 247.
2. CHARM II Collab., P. Vilain et al., *Phys. Lett.* **B281** (1992) 159.
3. CHARM II Collab., K. de Winter et al., *Nucl. Inst. & Meth.* **A278** (1989) 670.
4. CHARM II Collab., D. Geiregat et al., *Calibration and Performance of the CHARM-II Detector*, Nucl. Inst. & Meth. (in print).
5. A.A. Bel'kov and B.Z. Kopeliovich, *Yad. Fiz.* 46 (1987) 874.
6. G. t'Hooft, *Phys. Lett.* **B37** (1971) 195.
7. D.Yu. Bardin and V.A. Dokuchaeva, *Nucl. Phys.* **B246** (1984) 221; Preprint JINR E2-86-260 (1986).
   D.Yu. Bardin, NUFITTER, *a program to calculate electroweak radiative correction for neutrino-electron scattering*.
8. V. Blobel, *DESY* **84/118**, Hamburg 1984.
9. e.g.: CHARM Collab., J.V. Allaby et al., *Phys. Lett.* **B213** (1988) 554.
10. M. Consoli and W. Hollik, in *Report CERN* 89-08 (1989) 7.

A MEASUREMENT OF $\sin^2\theta_W$ FROM DEEP INELASTIC ν_μ-NUCLEON SCATTERING IN A FINE-GRAINED DETECTOR AT THE TEVATRON

RAYMOND BROCK
*Department of Physics & Astronomy, Michigan State University
East Lansing, MI 48824-1116, USA*

FOR THE FMMF COLLABORATION[a]

ABSTRACT

Neutral current and charged current deep inelastic ν_μ-nucleon scattering interactions were measured in the Lab C fine-grained neutrino detector at Fermilab with a ratio of 0.3075 ± 0.0041 *(stat.)* ± 0.0043 *(syst.)* above a hadronic shower energy cut of 10 GeV. From this, the electroweak mixing angle $\sin^2\theta_W$ was determined to be 0.2342 ± 0.0069 *(stat.)* ± 0.0073 *(syst.)* ± 0.0052 *(theor.)*. The analysis includes data from Fermilab E733 taken during the 1987/88 Tevatron Quadrupole-Triplet wide-band neutrino beam exposures.

1. Introduction

The precise measurement of the electroweak mixing angle $\sin^2\theta_W$ using deep inelastic neutrino-nucleon scattering is an important goal for current experimentation. The differing sensitivities of various $\sin^2\theta_W$-measuring methods to radiative corrections may permit constraints to be placed on other as-yet-unmeasured quantities such as the top quark mass, and to provide a check for the continued validity of the Standard Model after these quantities are eventually measured[1]. This is a report of preliminary results from Fermilab experiment E733 by the FMMF collaboration.

2. Apparatus & beam

The FMMF collaboration has performed such a measurement using data taken during the recent running of the Tevatron Quadrupole Triplet neutrino beam (QTB). The detector used was the fine-grained Flash Chamber–Proportional Tube neutrino detector in Laboratory C at FNAL. Details of this detector can be found elsewhere[2]. Briefly, it is a 300t (50t fiducial) digital flash-chamber calorimeter with fine sampling in both the transverse and longitudinal directions. The longitudinal sampling is 3% Λ and 22% X_o and the density is 1.35 g/cm^3. Typically, a minimum ionizing particle loses 3 MeV/cm of energy as it traverses the calorimeter which is 1900 cm long. Downstream of the calorimeter is an iron toroid spectrometer with a drift plane readout in four stations. Detailed features of the Tevatron QTB have been described elsewhere[3]. These data come from the 1987/88 fixed-target Tevatron run of 5×10^{17}

---
[a]FMMF is a collaboration of Fermilab, Michigan State University, MIT, and the University of Florida.

protons on target at 800 GeV/c. The restricted fiducial volume for this preliminary analysis results in 5×10^4 fully reconstructed CC events. The features of performing an experiment of this nature in the QTB relative to the more conventional Dichromatic beam include: an average interacting ν_μ energy of 150 GeV; reduced misidentification of charged current (CC) events; minimal sensitivity to kinematic cuts; reduced cosmic ray background; the presence of $\overline{\nu}_\mu$ in the ν_μ beam; an increased background from decays in the hadronic showers leading to increased misclassification of neutral current (NC) events; and an increased background from ν_e-induced events.

3. Analysis

The experiment depends solely on the pattern recognition of muons in the fine-grained detector. Muons are computer-recognized according to a definition which was specifically created in order to be reliably simulated. For these purposes a "μ" was a sequence of consecutive flash chamber hits in a narrow road from the vertex which had at least 1000 cm projected length in the downstream direction or 500 cm projected length for a track which left the side. The dominant systematic errors come from the uncertainties in this assignment. The analysis proceeded via the following general steps[b]. First, events were accepted according to their vertex position. The fiducial volume was restricted to a roughly cylindrical volume with a radius of 75 cm and a length of 1200 cm. Events were then classified into one of three categories[c]: CC, for events with a muon fit in the spectrometer; CC0, for events which contained a track which did not result in a fit; or NC, for events which contained no track satisfying the definition for "μ". The length of the shower was determined, and the energy deposited between the vertex and the shower end was measured. The muon energy deposition was subtracted from this using an algorithm determined in a variety of ways using data, "fake" muons, and GEANT Monte Carlo simulation. Events having $E_{hadron} > 10$ GeV were accepted. A background subtraction was made for cosmic rays, pile-up events, and events which were debris from upstream interactions. These subtractions were based on a physicist scan of 10% of the data.

The confusion matrix of CC events which were actually NC or *vice versa* was calculated in an enhanced 4-vector Monte Carlo program for deep inelastic neutrino scattering of all flavors expected in the QTB: ν_μ, $\overline{\nu}_\mu$, ν_e, and $\overline{\nu}_e$, where the latter two came from both charged and neutral K parents. The contributions from all neutrinos came from the Malensek parameterization[4] of the Atherton measurements[5] of secondary hadron production. The neutral K contribution came from a model used in E731 and NA31[6]. The 4-vector Monte Carlo CC event muons were run through a detector simulation. The result for each event was combined with the data definition of a "μ" to provide a classification for that event, simulating the possible misclassifications. The classification of simulated NC events used information from

---

[b] For a more detailed description, see G. J. Perkins, *A Measurement of the Ratio of Neutral Current to Charged Current Deep Inelastic Muon Neutrino Scattering Interactions in a Fine-Grained Neutrino Detector at FNAL* (Ph.D. Thesis, MSU, East Lansing, 1992).

[c] A further category was used in the analysis. N0 was the sum of NC and CC0.

two experimental sources. Each source served as a simulation of the production of
"μ" from hadronic showers due to decay muons and long, penetrating hadron tracks.
These sources were *(1)* the continuously available hadronic test beam which was
steered onto the front face of the detector between neutrino spills, and *(2)* the same-
sign and opposite-sign dimuon events in the ν data. Source *(1)* of hadronic shower
muons was only available in the upstream third of the calorimeter, and because the
details of this acceptance were crucial, was not the preferred method. The dimuon
events were used by ignoring the primary muon and treating the second "μ" as a
source of background to neutral current identification. The same-sign dimuon events
were used to estimate the charm contribution to the opposite-sign sample. A model
for charm production was used for this estimate, and a 25% uncertainty was assigned
for its subtraction. The two methods were compared in that region of the detector
which contained showers from the hadron beam and they agree well.

A 3-dimensional parameterization of the probability of NC misclassification
in our calorimeter as a function of longitudinal position, radial position, and hadron
shower energy, was put into the Monte Carlo. The physicist scan was used to determine that the muon algorithm failed 1.086±0.0118% of the time; this failure-correction
factor was applied in the Monte Carlo as well.

The determination of the number of NC and CC events originally produced
was made on the basis of the above corrections and subtractions. The result for
their ratio is $R_\nu = 0.3075 \pm 0.0041$ *(stat.)* ± 0.0043 *(syst.)*. Table 1 shows the data
reduction through all steps in the evaluation of the single measurable, R_ν. The
assignment of systematic errors resulted from controlled variation of the bounds of
assumed parameters. Table 2*a* shows these assignments and those due to the ranges
assumed for the K production model.

The extraction of the *derived quantity* $\sin^2\theta_W$ was done by making a variety of
increasingly complicated theoretical model assumptions and correlating the measured
R_ν with the prediction of those assumptions. Ultimately, the value of $\sin^2\theta_W$ includes
the following model inputs: the parton distributions of HMRS-BCDMS[7], box diagram
radiative corrections of Llewellyn-Smith and Wheater[8], full strange and charm sea, the
small non-isoscalarity for our calorimeter, and charm production as parameterized by
the naive slow-rescaling model with the m_c parameter assumed to be 1.3 GeV. Several
of the parameters of these model components were varied within reasonable bounds
to determine a "theoretical" uncertainty. Table 2*b* shows the uncertainty variation
due to these assumption variations, for a total theoretical uncertainty of ± 0.0052.
The extracted value is $\sin^2\theta_W = 0.2342 \pm 0.0069$ *(stat.)* ± 0.0073 *(syst.)*.

4. References

1. G. Altarelli, *Proceedings, Neutrino '90* (1990) 354.
2. F. E. Taylor *et al., IEEE Trans. Nucl. Sci. NS-27* (1980) 30; D. Bogert *et al.,
   IEEE Trans. Nucl. Sci. NS-29* (1982) 363.
3. L. Stutte, *N-Center Wide Band Neutrino Beam, Fermilab TM-1305.*

4. A. J. Malensek, *Fermilab Internal Note FN-341*, (12 Oct 1981).
5. H. W. Atherton, et al., *CERN Report 80-7*, (22 Aug 1980).
6. R. Bernstein, *E770 memo* dated 1 Feb 1990, unpublished.
7. P. N. Harriman et al., *Durham/Rutherford preprint DTP/90/04, RAL/90/007*, (Jan 1990).
8. J. F. Wheater and C. H. Llewellyn Smith, *Nucl. Phys.* **B208** (1982) 27–76; Errata, *Nucl. Phys.* **B226** (1983) 547.

Table 1: Sequence of Data Corrections in R_ν Derivation, 10 GeV E_H Cut

Status	NC	CC0	N0	CC−	CC+
Initial Data Events	18352 ±135	5669 ± 75	24021 ±155	42792 ±207	7630 ± 87
Δ Cosmics	− 85 ± 25	0 ± 0	− 85 ± 25	0 ± 0	0 ± 0
Δ Out-of-Time	− 62 ± 22	−108 ± 29	−170 ± 36	0 ± 0	0 ± 0
Δ Upstream	− 16 ± 11	0 ± 7	− 16 ± 13	− 16 ± 11	− 7 ± 7
Δ CC→NC→CC repr.	+161 ± 35	−153 ± 34	+ 8 ± 8	− 7 ± 7	− 1 ± 1
Subtotal	18351 ±144	5408 ± 88	23759 ±162	42770 ±207	7621 ± 88
Δ ν_e Events	−1304 ± 24	−204 ± 11	−1508 ± 22	− 12 ± 3	− 6 ± 2
Subtotal	17047 ±136	5204 ± 85	22251 ±153	42758 ±207	7615 ± 88
Δ N0 ↔ CC± conf.			−4792 ± 68	+4340 ± 58	+453 ± 36
Δ CC+ ↔ CC− conf.			0 ± 0	+137 ± 11	− 137 ± 11
Δ $\bar{\nu}_\mu$ N0 events			−2932 ±114	0 ± 0	0 ± 0
Corrected Events			14526 ±202	47235 ±237	7930 ± 99

Table 2: *(a)* Uncertainties in $R_\nu = 0.3075$ *(b)* Uncertainties in $\sin^2\theta_W = 0.2342$

Data statistical δR_ν	±0.0041
Systematic sources	
Acceptance, confusion, $\overline{\nu}$-corrections, etc.	±0.0025
MC statistics	±0.0018
E_H scale uncertainty	±0.0027
Subtotal	±0.0041
K-induced flux subtraction uncertainty, allowing for a ±5% change in K rate and a ± 25% change in K_L^0 rate	±0.0014
Total systematic δR_ν	**±0.0043**

Data statistical $\delta \sin^2\theta_W$	±0.0069
Systematic sources	
Acceptance, confusion, $\overline{\nu}$-corrections, E_H scale, MC statistics, etc.	±0.0068
δK-induced ν flux	±0.0024
Theoretical sources	
± 1/3 of radiative correction	±0.0027
± 0.3 GeV in m_c	±0.0042
± 10% in strange sea integral	±0.0011
± 50% in charm sea integral	±0.0010
± 10% in isoscalar correction	±0.0005
Total Theoretical $\delta \sin^2\theta_W$	**±0.0052**

B. Top and Higgs Physics

   Conveners: R. M. BARNETT (LBL)
              S. D. PROTOPOPESCU (BNL)
   Liaison: A. B. WICKLUND (ANL)

ASSOCIATED PRODUCTION OF W AND BOTTOM QUARK PAIRS IN HADRONIC COLLISIONS

MICHELANGELO L. MANGANO
INFN, Scuola Normale Superiore and
Dipartimento di Fisica dell' Universita', Pisa, Italy

ABSTRACT

We study the production of W and heavy quark pairs in hadronic collisions, using calculations performed with partonic level matrix elements and with shower Monte Carlo programs. We evaluate the effect of these processes on the detection of top quarks at the Fermilab Tevatron Collider. Relatively simple cuts will allow the selection of high-purity samples of top events with tagged b's.

New forthcoming data soon to be collected by the CDF and D0 experiments at the Fermilab hadron collider will hopefully provide us with the long-awaited discovery of the *top* quark. Current limits on its mass are set either by the lack of direct production ($m_t > 91$ GeV at the 95% C.L. [1]) or by the effects of a virtual *top* in the evaluation of electroweak radiative corrections to LEP observables and M_W. In this mass range a produced *top* will decay into a real W and a *bottom* quark, with the subsequent decay of the W into a lepton- or a quark-pair. Detecting the top will require a precise understanding of the possible sources of background to the selected decay channels. This will remain true even after the top will have been discovered and high purity samples will be required to study in detail properties such as its mass or the angular distributions of its decay products. It is to the understanding of some of these backgrounds that this study is devoted.

From the point of view of background, the two most promising alternatives are certainly the single and double leptonic decays. The two channels have complementary features. The dilepton channel is relatively background free, however it has a smaller branching ratio and does not allow for a precise reconstruction of either of the two t quarks. The single lepton has a higher branching ratio, making it preferable if m_t were very large. Furthermore it allows – at least in principle – for a precise reconstruction of one of the two t quarks. Unfortunately it has been known for some time that the background from the associated production of W and multi-jets [2, 3] is rather severe and has a large uncertainty in the overall calculated rate. With only a handful of events available it would probably not be possible to isolate distinct features which could unambiguously separate the signal from the background. One would have to rely just on some simple-minded event counting based on jet multiplicities, for example comparing the number of events with 3 or 4 jets above some assigned p_t threshold. Thus it would be preferable to rely on some stronger evidence that could uniquely discriminate the signal on an event by event basis rather than on a statistical one.

This stronger evidence will probably come from the direct tagging of one of the b quarks in the event via the reconstruction of its decay vertex. The probability that an event with a W – not coming from a t decay – has a b quark is expected to be very small, and therefore the background to the top substantially reduced. To which extent this is true, and how well we can determine the sources of backgrounds to b-tagging, is the subject of this presentation. A complete study can be found in ref. [4].

In the limit of hard and separated b's, the calculation of the $Wb\bar{b}+X$ matrix elements can be reliably performed in the massless limit. One can then use the massless matrix elements for production of $W+n$ jets found in references [2, 3]. It is in this limit that a preliminary assessment of the production rates for W's and associated tagged b's in $W+n$ jet events was made in reference [3]. The rates thus calculated make sense only if the b's are sufficiently hard and separated, in order to avoid collinear and infrared divergencies. In the case of a relatively light top (say around 100-120 GeV), however, the b's will be soft and in order not to loose too much signal one would not be able to afford requiring the b's to form stiff jets. The energy of the b's will be partly lost because of final state radiation and because of soft decay particles being swept away from the magnetic field, making the reconstruction of a clear jet very inefficient. An efficient top search would therefore aim at identifying one W via its leptonic decay and tagging just one b independently of its momentum and its position relative to other components of the event. It therefore becomes important to be able to control the rate of the background down to small values of the b momentum, as well as small separations, since it would be costly to tag the second b and require it to be hard or far away from the first one. This is true *regardless* of the requirement of the presence of additional 1 or 2 jets from the hadronic decay of the other W. Furthermore, in order to have a signal sample as big as possible, we want to understand how loose the cuts on the events can be kept, still guaranteeing the desired signal-to-noise ratio.

For all of these reasons we calculated the exact matrix element at tree level for $Wb\bar{b}$ production, taking into account all of the mass effects. The result of the calculation can be found in ref. [4]. This allows us to completely remove any p_t or separation cut on the final state b's.

We present the results for the inclusive $Wb\bar{b}$ production rates in $\bar{p}p$ collisions at the center of mass energy of 1.8 TeV in Table 1, where we selected different values of m_b, factorization scale and parton distributions to establish a range for the systematic theoretical uncertainty.

To be conservative, in the following comparisons with the signal we will include a K factor equal to 2, we will use m_b=4.5 GeV and $Q^2=M_{bb}^2$.

To account for the experimental selection criteria, we define the following set of cuts that we will impose on the generated events:

$$|\eta_e| < 1 \quad , \quad p_t^e > 20 \text{ GeV} \quad , \quad |\eta_b| < 1 \tag{1}$$

The cuts on the additional jets will be specified in the following. We will concentrate on the case of one family of leptons in the final state – say electrons – and will include

	$\sigma(Q^2 = M_{b\bar{b}}^2)$ pb		$\sigma(Q^2 = M_W^2 + p_{tW}^2)$ pb	
HMRSB	44	37	26	22
MTS2	48	40	27	23

Table 1: Total $Wb\bar{b}$ production rate in $\bar{p}p$ collisions at 1.8 TeV. The left and right columns for each choice of Q^2 correspond to the values m_b=4.5 and m_b=5 GeV, respectively.

the relative BR=1/9 in the following.

In Figure 1 we show the inclusive p_t distribution of the b and $\bar{b}$ quarks in events satisfying the cuts given in equation (1). For a comparison with the spectrum of the b's from top decay, we also superimpose the distributions in the case of m_t=120 GeV and 160 GeV (dashed lines). In the case of the heavier top, the background is at the level of 30%, and things get worse for even heavier top. To significantly

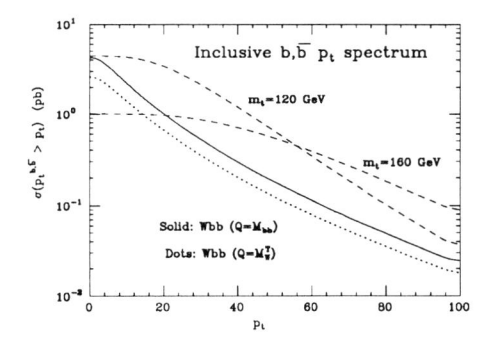

Figure 1: Inclusive p_t distribution of central b and $\bar{b}$ quarks: $Wb\bar{b}$ ($Q = M_{b\bar{b}}$) (solid line), $Wb\bar{b}$ ($Q = M_W^T$) (dotted line) and $t\bar{t}$ (m_t = 120 and 160 GeV, dashed histograms). Leptonic cuts, BR and K factor as described in the text.

improve the purity of the sample we have to impose additional cuts on the structure of the event. The right place to look for these further cuts is the residual hadronic activity of the top events, mostly given by the jets from the hadronic decay of the other W. In order to estimate the effect of additional cuts on the background we need a study of the process $\bar{p}p \to Wb\bar{b} +$ jets. The matrix elements for these processes, with the correct b mass effects included, are not available. Instead of calculating them exactly, we considered an alternative approach, namely the use of a shower MC. In our study we will use HERWIG, the MC developed by Marchesini and Webber [5]. We included the matrix elements used in the previous section into HERWIG (Version 5.4) and studied the structure of the final state after the perturbative evolution. We defined jets using a standard *cone* clustering algorithm with $R_{jet} = 0.7$ and applied the following cuts:

$$E_t > 20 \text{ GeV} \quad , \quad |\eta| < 2. \tag{2}$$

We plot in Fig. 2 the total cross section for events with at least two jets as a function of the b or $\bar{b}$ transverse momentum. As before, events with both b and $\bar{b}$ within the rapidity cut enter twice in the plot, in order to account for the probability of tagging either the b or the $\bar{b}$. We compare the $Wb\bar{b}$ background to the $t\bar{t}$ signal with m_t=120 and 160 GeV. Requiring the presence of at least two jets passing these cuts in a $t\bar{t}$ event is highly efficient, in particular for heavy top masses, while severely reduces the background. Even allowing for an additional factor of 2 uncertainty on the overall relative normalization of signal and background – possibly due to larger higher order corrections to the $Wb\bar{b}$ process – would leave a contamination smaller than 10% for values of m_t up to 160 GeV.

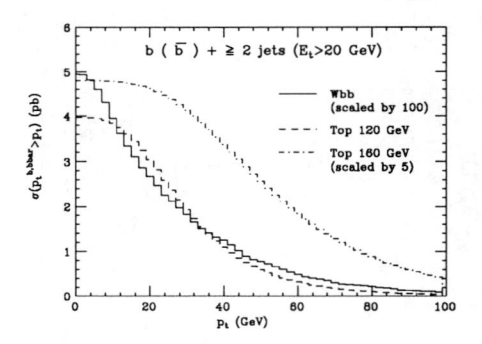

Figure 2: p_t distribution of b and $\bar{b}$ quarks in events with 2 or more jets, $E_t > 20$ GeV.

For higher top masses, when the production rate is very small, one should consider placing additional cuts. As an example we show in fig. 3 (left side) the same distribution displayed in fig.2, but with a higher jet E_t cut of 30 GeV. Here the background is compared with the signal from a 160, 180 and 200 GeV top. It is important to notice that in the case of the signal most of the events passing these cuts will have b quarks with $p_t > 20$ GeV, the threshold above which b-tagging becomes efficient. As an alternative cut to improve the purity of a sample of high-mass top events we can consider requiring the presence of at least 3 jets, although with a softer E_t of 20 GeV (Fig. 3, right side).

While the relative S/N ratio is better than the one achieved with the softer E_t cuts, the higher multiplicity selection is slightly less efficient on the signal in spite of the softer E_t requirement. This is because of the relatively wide η distribution of jets, extending well above our cut at $|\eta| = 2$. The figures show that it is always possible to raise the ratio S/N above the level of 10:1 without reducing the signal by more than 20%. Considering that the numbers in the previous plots are based on our most conservative estimate for the total background rate we claim that rather simple and highly efficient cuts can be imposed resulting in a highly pure sample of $t\bar{t}$ events, provided b-tagging can be applied. Cuts more suitable to the features of the experimental analysis can be applied in alternative, but the conclusions – which would depend in the details upon the specifics of the detector and of the jet definition – would not change qualitatively. Let us also add that at the inclusive level the cross section for production of $Wb\bar{b}$ is large enough to be clearly observable with the expected integrated luminosity of the forthcoming round of data taking (25 pb^{-1}). The observation of these events will help fixing more precisely the absolute rate.

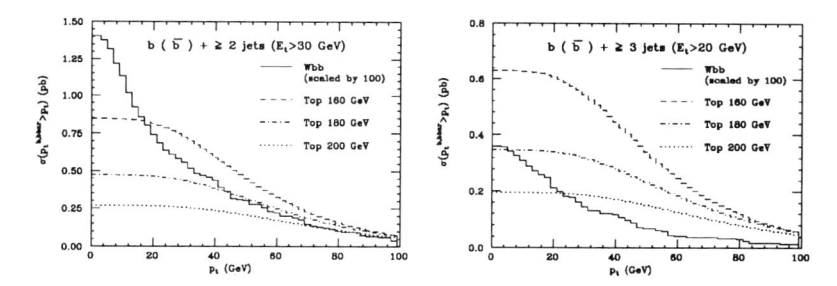

Figure 3: p_t distribution of b and $\bar{b}$ quarks in events with 2 or more jets, $E_t > 30$ GeV (left) and with 3 or more jets, $E_t > 20$ GeV (right).

References

[1] F. Abe et al., CDF Collab., *Phys. Rev.* **D45** (1992), 3921.

[2] F.A. Berends, W.T. Giele and H. Kuijf, *Nucl. Phys.* **B321** (1989), 39;
K. Hagiwara and D. Zeppenfeld, *Nucl. Phys.* **B313** (1989), 560;
F.A. Berends, W.T. Giele, R. Kleiss, H. Kuijf and W.J. Stirling, *Phys. Lett.* **224B** (1989), 237;
H. Baer, V. Barger and R.J.N. Phillips, *Phys. Lett.* **221B** (1989), 398;
W.T. Giele and W.J. Stirling, *Nucl. Phys.* **B343** (1990), 14.

[3] F.A. Berends, H. Kuijf, B. Tausk and W.T. Giele, *Nucl. Phys.* **B357** (1991), 32;
F.A. Berends, B. Tausk and W.T. Giele, FERMILAB-Pub-92/196-T (1992).

[4] M.L. Mangano, University of Pisa preprint, IFUP-TH 36/92 (1992).

[5] G. Marchesini and B.R. Webber, *Nucl. Phys.* **B310** (1988), 461.

TOP WIDTH EFFECTS IN SOFT GLUON RADIATION[1,2]

LYNNE H. ORR
Department of Physics, University of California
Davis, CA 95616, USA

YU.L. DOKSHITZER
Department of Theoretical Physics, University of Lund
Sölvegatan 14A, S-22362 Lund, Sweden

and

V.A. KHOZE and W.J. STIRLING
Department of Physics, University of Durham
Durham DH1 3LE, England

ABSTRACT

Soft gluons radiated in top quark production and decay can interfere in a way that is sensitive to the top width. We show how the width affects the gluon distribution in $e^+e^- \to t\bar{t}$ and discuss prospects for measuring Γ from gluons radiated near $t\bar{t}$ threshold.

1. Soft Gluon Radiation in $e^+e^- \to t\bar{t}$

Because the top quark is so heavy that it can decay to a real W and a b, it has a very large width: for large m_t, $\Gamma(t \to Wb) \approx (175 \text{ MeV})(m_t/m_W)^3$. Widths in the GeV range can give rise to interesting effects involving the interplay between the strong and weak interactions. For example, if top is heavy enough, it can decay before forming bound states, and there is not much resonant structure at the $t\bar{t}$ threshold, making it difficult to measure Γ. In this talk we consider the effect of the top width on soft gluon radiation in $e^+e^- \to t\bar{t}$, at arbitrary collision energies[1] and near $t\bar{t}$ threshold.[2] For complete discussions see Refs. 1 and 2.

Consider a gluon emitted in a $t\bar{t}$ event at an e^+e^- collider. Because of the top decays, the gluon can be radiated by the $t, \bar{t}, b,$ or $\bar{b}$. In the limit of soft gluons, the matrix element $\mathcal{M}$ factorizes and can be written as a product of the zeroth-order matrix element (with no gluon) and a term associated with the gluon emission. Schematically, we have $\mathcal{M} \sim \mathcal{M}^{(0)} J \cdot \epsilon$, where J^μ and ϵ_μ are the gluon current and polarization, respectively. We can then define a gluon emission probability density, which is just the differential cross section for radiating a gluon normalized to the zeroth-order cross section. It is given by

$$dN \equiv 1/\sigma_0 d\sigma_g = \frac{d\omega}{\omega} \frac{d\Omega}{4\pi} \frac{C_F \alpha_s}{\pi} \mathcal{R}, \qquad (1)$$

where ω and Ω denote the gluon energy and solid angle. $\mathcal{R}$ is obtained by integrating the absolute square of the current over the virtualities of the t and $\bar{t}$.

The important point is that the current can be decomposed in a gauge-invariant way into terms corresponding to order α_s corrections to $t\bar{t}$ production, to t decay, and to $\bar{t}$ decay. Therefore in $\mathcal{R}$ we can unambiguously identify each contribution:

---

[1] Work supported in part by the Texas National Research Laboratory Commission and the United Kingdom Science and Engineering Research Council.
[2] Presented by L.H. Orr.

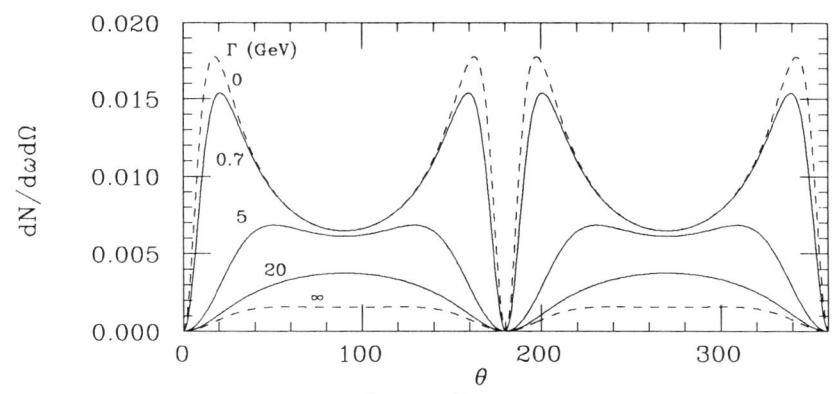

Figure 1: Soft gluon distribution in $e^+e^- \to t\bar{t}$ for c.m. energy 1 TeV, $m_t = 140$ GeV, $\omega = 5$ GeV and $\phi = 0°$. θ is the t-g angle; the t and $\bar{b}$ are at $0°$ and the $\bar{t}$ and b are at $180°$.

(production)^2, (t or $\bar{t}$ decay)^2, production–decay interference and decay–decay interference. The production and decay squared terms are independent of the width, but both interference terms have Γ dependence, including an overall factor of Γ^2.

2. Width Effects at High Energies

At high collision energies, the top width dependence arises from production–decay interference; the decay–decay interference is negligible. The production–decay interference is largest for large b-t angular separations, and is destructive, so that the effect of the width is to suppress the gluon radiation.

This is illustrated in Fig. 1, where we show the gluon emission probability as a function of the angle θ of the gluon with respect to the top quark. We vary the top width and take $m_t = 140$ GeV, $\omega = 5$ GeV, and center-of-mass energy 1 TeV. The t and $\bar{t}$ are produced back-to-back, and we have chosen a configuration in which the $t(\bar{t})$ decays to a backward $b(\bar{b})$. We see that for the SM case ($\Gamma = 0.7$ GeV) the peaks are suppressed compared to the case with no interference ($\Gamma = 0$) and as the width increases the peaks disappear altogether.

Now, energetic top quarks do not often decay to backward b's. If we take a slightly more likely b-t angle such as $90°$, we obtain similar sensitivity. However, in the most probable configuration — t and b collinear — there is almost no interference and therefore no sensitivity to the top width. Thus at high energies, the production–decay interference can be substantial, but the most sensitive configurations are the least likely to occur.

3. Width Effects Near $t\bar{t}$ Threshold

At lower energies, near the $t\bar{t}$ threshold, the total cross section is higher and the t's are produced nearly at rest, so that the relative orientations of the t and b momenta are irrelevant. We might expect, then, that top width effects could be more pronounced. On the other hand, if the t's are nearly at rest and only the b's can radiate, it is not obvious that the top width enters at all. Naively, one would

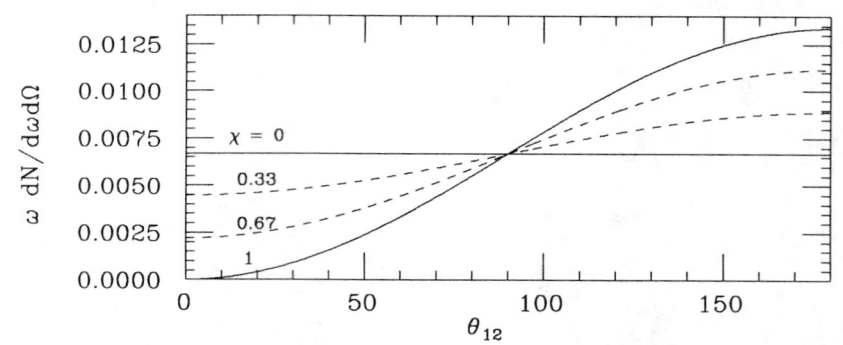

Figure 2: Soft gluon distribution in $e^+e^- \to t\bar{t}$ for $m_t = 140$ GeV, near $t\bar{t}$ threshold, with gluon perpendicular to $b\bar{b}$ plane; θ_{12} is the b–$\bar{b}$ angle.

expect the b's to radiate as if they were produced directly and the t's never existed.

That the top width *does* influence the radiation from the b's can be understood by considering the following extreme cases. As $\Gamma \to \infty$, the top lifetime becomes very short, the b and $\bar{b}$ appear almost instantaneously, and they radiate coherently, as though produced directly. In particular, gluons from the b and $\bar{b}$ interfere. In the other extreme, for $\Gamma \to 0$, top has a long lifetime and the b and $\bar{b}$ appear at very different times and therefore radiate independently, with no interference. Clearly, the top width controls the interference between gluons emitted by the b and $\bar{b}$.

The situation for finite width is between the two extremes. Let v be the b (or $\bar{b}$) velocity, $\theta_{1(2)}$ be the angle between the b ($\bar{b}$) and the gluon, and θ_{12} the angle between the b and $\bar{b}$. Then

$$\mathcal{R} = \frac{v^2 \sin^2 \theta_1}{(1 - v\cos\theta_1)^2} + \frac{v^2 \sin^2 \theta_2}{(1 - v\cos\theta_2)^2} + 2\chi \frac{v^2(\cos\theta_1 \cos\theta_2 - \cos\theta_{12})}{(1 - v\cos\theta_1)(1 - v\cos\theta_2)}, \quad (2)$$

where $\chi \equiv \frac{\Gamma^2}{\Gamma^2 + \omega^2}$. The interference is the term proportional to χ. Note that $0 \leq \chi \leq 1$ and $\chi = 0$ for $\Gamma = 0$ (independent emission) and $\chi = 1$ for $\Gamma = \infty$ (coherent emission). Thus a finite top width suppresses the interference compared to the naive expectation of full coherent emission. And from the form of χ we see that the radiation pattern exhibits maximum sensitivity to Γ when Γ is comparable to the gluon energy ω.

The width effects are discussed in detail in Ref. 2; here we give two examples. First consider gluons emitted perpendicular to the $b\bar{b}$ plane. Then $\theta_1 = \theta_2 = \pi/2$; $\mathcal{R}$ is simply proportional to $1 - \chi \cos\theta_{12}$ and χ regulates the θ_{12} dependence — see Fig. 2. Now for a 5 GeV gluon, a 140 GeV top quark with $\Gamma = 0.7$ GeV has $\chi \approx 0.02$, which means the distribution is much closer to the independent emission case ($\chi = 0$) than the coherent case we would naively expect – the interference is almost completely absent. If we could detect 1 GeV gluons, we would have $\chi \approx 0.3$ and the distribution would be very sensitive to the width. (Conversely, we would get the same sensitivity for more energetic gluons if the width were larger: $\chi \approx 0.3$ with gluon energy 5 GeV corresponds to $\Gamma \approx 3$ GeV.)

As a second example we show in Fig. 3 the gluon distribution integrated over

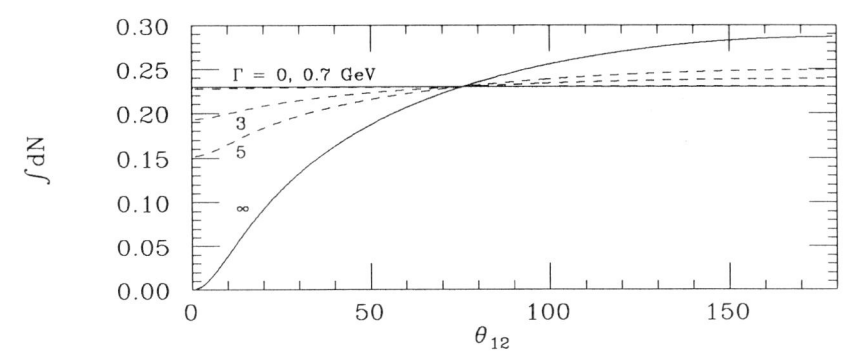

Figure 3: Soft gluon emission probablilty near $t\bar{t}$ threshold ($m_t = 140$ GeV) integrated over gluon angles and energies from 5 to 10 GeV.

the gluon solid angle (and in a slight nod to reality, integrated over gluon energies from 5 to 10 GeV). For independent emission the radiation probability does not depend on the angle between the b and $\bar{b}$, but in the coherent case the interference is destructive for small θ_{12} and constructive for large θ_{12}. Again, we see that the 140 GeV case is much closer to the independent than the expected coherent case, and that as the width reaches the few GeV range we become increasingly sensitive.

4. Discussion

Is looking at soft gluon radiation a useful method for measuring the top width, an alternative to studying the threshold structure[3] of the lowest order cross section? Each method has its disadvantages: The threshold structure is subject to large uncertainties due to beam energy spread; the soft gluon radiation is not, but it is a higher order process with a lower event rate. The two methods should be considered complementary, because the threshold cross section loses sensitivity with increasing width, but as we have seen, the gluon radiation pattern becomes *more* sensitive at larger Γ for accessible gluon energies. The bottom line is that for most of the expected top mass range, the threshold structure is probably better, but if m_t and Γ are large, examining soft gluons may be more useful.

In summary, we have seen that the top quark's large width gives rise to new effects from the interplay between the strong and weak interactions, and that the top width affects the distributions of soft gluons radiated in top events. At high collision energies, production–decay interference can suppress gluon radiation. Near the $t\bar{t}$ threshold, the effect of the width is to suppress the *interference* between gluons radiated by the b and $\bar{b}$, in contrast to the expectation of coherent radiation from the $b\bar{b}$ pair. Finally, if the width and gluon energy are comparable, the radiation pattern is quite sensitive to the value of Γ.

References

1. V.A. Khoze, W.J. Stirling and L.H. Orr, *Nucl. Phys.* **B378** (1992) 413.
2. Yu. L. Dokshitzer, V.A. Khoze, L.H. Orr, and W.J. Stirling, in preparation.
3. K. Fujii, KEK preprint 92-6 (1992) and references therein.

INFRARED CORRECTIONS TO THE TOP QUARK WIDTH

Pankaj Jain, Douglas W. McKay and Herman J. Munczek
Department of Physics and Astronomy
The University of Kansas
Lawrence, KS 66045-2151

ABSTRACT

We present a nonperturbative analysis of the top quark propagator using the Schwinger Dyson equation in the ladder approximation including both the electroweak as well as the infrared QCD effects. We find that the infrared effects are negligible only for top mass larger than about 250 GeV.

1. Introduction

The success of perturbative QCD is based on the fact that the QCD coupling gets smaller at large momentum. Therefore for any process for which the dominant contribution comes from the high momentum region, perturbative QCD should yield quantitatively reliable predictions. However for several interesting cases, perturbation theory fails to give reasonable results. For example, for the calculation of bound state masses the perturbative gluon propagator does not give correct results even for quark masses much larger then the typical scale of nonperturbative QCD. Presumably the infrared region gives a significant contribution in this case. Another important example is quark confinement. The fact that quarks are never observed as free particles suggests that the quark propagator is considerably different from the perturbative propagator and might receive significant contributions from the infrared region. This is supported by nonperturbative calculations, performed by choosing phenomenologically and theoretically motivated models for gluon propagator, which suggest that, independently of the mass of the quark, the dressed quark propagator is very different from the free propagator and in particular admits no mass pole, presumably a signal of confinement. Intuitively we can argue that, because of the large coupling, a quark has a large amplitude to exchange a soft gluon with itself which can in principle modify its singularity structure. This argument may not hold for the top quark because of its large decay rate into a W boson and a bottom quark. This suggests the possibility that the top quark might decay before exchanging a soft gluon with itself. If this were the case then the infrared region will be completely ignorable and perturbation theory becomes quantitatively reliable.

To get a rough idea of the mass of the top at which the infrared effects become negligible we compare the width of the top with the typical hadronic scale. If the width is much smaller than the scale of confinement then the top will have sufficient time to exchange a soft gluon. For a top quark of mass 150 GeV, its purely electroweak width at tree level is about 800 MeV. This is clearly comparable to the hadronic scale and we cannot rule out the possibility of significant infrared corrections. For the top quark of mass 250 GeV, however, the top width is larger than 4 GeV and the infrared effects should be completely negligible.

The top propagator can be calculated nonperturbatively by solving the Schwinger-Dyson (SD) equation [1],

$$S^{-1}(q) = S_0^{-1}(q) - i \int \frac{d^4k}{(2\pi)^4} \gamma_\mu S(k) \gamma_\nu G_{\mu\nu}(k-q) \quad (1)$$

We employ the ladder approximation for our calculation and choose phenomenologically and theoretically motivated models for the gluon propagator. We choose the Landau gauge for our calculation, in which case the gluon propagator has the form, $G_{\mu\nu}(k) = (g_{\mu\nu} - k_\mu k_\nu/k^2)G(k^2)$. We are interested in calculating the corrections to the top width due to the low momentum region and therefore need a model for $G(k^2)$ which might be qualitatively reliable in this region. There is some theoretical and phenomenological evidence that the gluon propagator has a $1/k^4$ behavior at small momentum. We therefore choose the following two models for $G(k^2)$, which represent a regularized form of the $1/k^4$ behavior.

$$G^a(k) = i\frac{4}{3}(2\pi)^4 \eta^2 \delta^4(k) \quad (2)$$

$$G^b(k) = \frac{8\pi a}{(k^2 - \epsilon^2)^2}. \quad (3)$$

The second model $G^b(k)$ leads to a linear potential, $V(r) = ar$, in the nonrelativistic limit as long as ϵ is small compared to the scale of confinement. We calculate the parameters in these potentials by fitting the light and heavy meson spectrum and decay constants [1], which give a range of values for these parameters.

2. Results and discussion

In this section we present the results for the top width obtained by choosing the two gluon propagator model given in Eqns. 2 and 3. Since we are only interested in getting a qualitative idea, the parameters in these potentials will be chosen within their range such that they give the smallest correction to the tree level calculation of width. For the potential G^a, this implies that $\eta = 450$ MeV and for G^b, we get a=(450 MeV)^2, $\epsilon = 150$ MeV. The numerical results are given in Table 1.

Table 1: Results for the top quark width Γ including infrared QCD corrections for the gluon propagator models given in Eqns. 2 and 3. Γ_0 is the top width at tree level.

m_t (GeV)	Γ_0 (GeV)	Γ (GeV) (model G^a)	Γ (GeV) (model G^b)
100	0.0922	0.0461	0.0715
150	0.80	0.40	0.61
190	2.0	1.44	1.85
234	4.0	3.79	3.91

Our results show that the low momentum region gives a negligible correction to the top width only if its mass is larger than about 250 GeV. For a top quark of mass 150 GeV, the infrared region can give a significant correction. These results follow the trend, as anticipated in the introduction, that as the width of the top gets much larger than the scale of confinement the infrared region becomes negligible. For comparison, perturbative QCD calculations gives about a 10% correction [2].

In conclusion, we have shown here that infrared effects can give significant contribution to the top width if the mass of the top quark is less than about 150 GeV. However once the mass gets larger than about 250 GeV, the infrared corrections are completely negligible. The magnitude of the corrections is dependent on the width of the top. The corrections get negligible only if the width is much larger than the scale of confinement.

3. Acknowledgements

We acknowledge useful discussions with John Ralston. This work was supported in part by the Department of Energy under grant No. DE-FG02-85-ER40214.

4. References

1. P. Jain, D.W. McKay and H.J. Munczek, submitted to Phys. Rev. D, rapid communications and references therein.
2. A. Denner and T. Sack, *Nucl. Phys.* **B 358**, 46 (1991); G. Eilam et al., *Phys. Rev. Lett.* **66**, 3105 (1991).

TOPONIUM PRODUCTION AT HADRON COLLIDERS[1]

J.H. Kühn and E. Mirkes
Institut für Theoretische Teilchenphysik,
Universität Karlsruhe, Kaiserstr. 12, Postfach 6980
7500 Karlsruhe 1, Germany

ABSTRACT

Toponium production at future hadron colliders is investigated. Perturbative QCD corrections to the production cross section for gluon fusion are calculated as well as the contributions from gluon-quark and quark-antiquark collisions to the total cross section. The dependence on the renormalization and factorization scales and on the choice of the parton distribution functions is explored. QCD corrections to the branching ratio of η_t into $\gamma\gamma$ are included and the two loop QCD potential is used to predict the wave function at the origin.

The production of heavy quarks at hadron colliders has received a lot of attention from the experimental as well as from the theoretical side. Recently it has been proposed in [1] to decrease the experimental error in the top mass determination significantly through the study of η_t in its $\gamma\gamma$ decay channel. Making use of the large luminosity of future hadron colliders, one should be able to overcome the tiny cross section multiplied by the small branching ratio into two photons. The excellent gamma energy resolution, originally developed for the search for a light Higgs boson, would in principle allow the measurement of the mass of the bound state at about 100 MeV accuracy. This would result in a determination of the top quark mass limited only by theoretical uncertainties. The estimates of [1] for the production and decay rate were based on the Born approximation and on fairly crude assumptions on the bound state wave function which was derived from a Coulomb potential neglecting QCD corrections. A more precise evaluation of the production rate is mandatory. In lowest order the reaction is induced by gluon-gluon fusion. QCD corrections have been calculated in [2,3]. They affect and indeed increase the rate in this channel by about 50%. Quark-gluon scattering and quark-antiquark annihilation into η_t enter at order α_s^3. The qg process increases the production cross section by about 8% whereas the effect of $q\bar{q}$ annihilation is negligible.

The production cross section for η_t with nonvanishing transverse momentum is infrared finite in the order considered here. The total cross section, however, exhibits singularities that have to be absorbed in appropriately choosen and defined parton distribution functions. A full NLO calculation requires the corresponding corrections for the physically interesting branching ratio. These are have been included in [2,3].

The bound state production cross section and the branching ratio of η_t into

---
[1] Supported by BMFT Contract 055KA94P,
presented by J.H. Kühn.

$\gamma\gamma$ depend (markedly!) on $R(0)^2$, the square of the bound state wave function at the origin and hence on the potential. The range of $R(0)$ compatible with the current knowledge of the perturbative two loop QCD potential and the present experimental results for Λ_{QCD} has been exploreded.

For the complete evaluation of NLO corrections for η_t production in gluon gluon fusion virtual corrections are required as well as corrections from real gluon radiation. In addition one needs the cross section for quark-antiquark annihilation into η_t+gluon and the (anti-)quark-gluon initiated reaction into η_t+quark. The hadronic cross section in NLO is then given by

$$\sigma^H(S) = \int dx_1 dx_2 f_a^{h_1}(x_1, Q_F^2) f_b^{h_2}(x_2, Q_F^2) \hat{\sigma}^{ab}(s = x_1 x_2 S, \alpha_s(\mu^2), \mu^2, Q_F^2) \quad (1)$$

where one sums over $a, b = q, \bar{q}, g$. $f_a^h(x, Q_F^2)$ is the probability density to find parton a with fraction x in hadron h if it is probed at scale Q_F^2 and $\hat{\sigma}^{ab}$ denotes the parton cross section for the process $a + b \to \eta_t + X$ from which collinear initial state singularities have been factorized out at a scale Q_F^2 and implicitly included in the scale-dependent parton densities $f_a^h(x, Q_F^2)$. The dependence on the renormalization and factorization scales μ_R and Q_F has been explored in [3]. In the following $\mu_R = Q_F = M$ will be adopted. For the gluon fusion the partonic cross section is (in the $\overline{MS}$ scheme) given by:

$$\hat{\sigma}^{gg} = \frac{1}{s} \frac{\pi^2}{3} \frac{R^2(0)}{M^3} \alpha_{\overline{MS}}^2(M^2) \Big\{ \delta(1-z)$$

$$+ \frac{\alpha_{\overline{MS}}(M^2)}{\pi} \Big\langle \delta(1-z) \Big(N_C \Big(1 + \frac{\pi^2}{12}\Big) + C_F \Big(\frac{\pi^2}{4} - 5\Big) - \frac{4}{3} T_f \ln(2) \Big) + N_C F(z) \Big\rangle \Big\} \quad (2)$$

where

$$F(z) = \Theta(1-z) \Big[\frac{11z^5 + 11z^4 + 13z^3 + 19z^2 + 6z - 12}{6z(1+z)^2}$$

$$+ 4\Big(\frac{1}{z} + z(1-z) - 2\Big) \ln(1-z) + 4\Big(\frac{\ln(1-z)}{1-z}\Big)_+$$

$$+ \Big(\frac{2(z^3 - 2z^2 - 3z - 2)(z^3 - z + 2)z \ln(z)}{(1+z)^3(1-z)} - 3\Big) \frac{1}{1-z} \Big] \quad (3)$$

For the gluon quark scattering and the quark antiquark annihilation the partonic cross sections can be found in [3]. Their contribution is typically small.

As stated in the introduction, the most important ingredients for the numerical evaluation are the wave function at the origin and the gluon distribution. The former are calculated for the two loop potential V_J. The results for the branching ratio of η_t into $\gamma\gamma$ are displayed in fig. 1 for the potentials with the $\Lambda_{\overline{MS}}^{(4)}$ values of 200 and 500 MeV, corresponding to $\alpha_{\overline{MS}}(M_Z) = 0.109$ and 0.127 (and corresponding to $\Lambda_{\overline{MS}}^{(5)} = 0.132$ and 0.366 MeV). This choice for $\Lambda_{\overline{MS}}^{(4)}$ covers well the present range $\alpha_{\overline{MS}}(M_Z) = 0.117 \pm 0.07$ derived from a global fit to the present data.

The magnitude of the QCD corrected cross section including all subprocesses is compared to the Born cross section in fig. 2 for $\sqrt{s}= 16$ and 40 TeV. The size of the corrections amounts to 40-50%. The final predictions for the cross section are shown in fig. 3a. The solid line corresponds to $V_J(\Lambda^{(4)}_{\overline{MS}} =300$ MeV), parton distribution functions of MT set B1 and α_s derived from $\Lambda^{(5)}_{\overline{MS}}$. The dashed and dotted curves enclose the range of predictions resulting from the dominant uncertainty in the potential and correspond to $V_J(\Lambda^{(4)}_{\overline{MS}} =500$ MeV) to $V_J(\Lambda^{(4)}_{\overline{MS}} =200$ MeV). The corresponding predictions for the cross section times the branching ratio into $\gamma\gamma$ are displayed in fig. 3b.

Evidendly, fairly optimistic assumptions are necessary to open even a narrow window for toponium discovery in the mass range of $m_t =90\text{-}110$ GeV. This is the consequence of the dominance single quark decays (SQD) and the small branching ratio into two photons. The situation improves dramatically, if new hypothetical quarks are considered with suppressed single quark decay. Examples are b' or isosinglet quarks with small mixing with ordinary d, s or b quarks. These would dominatly decay into gauge and Higgs bosons, leading to spectacular signatures.

1. G. Pancheri, J.-P. Revol and C. Rubbia, *Phys. Lett.* **B 277** (518) 1992
2. J.H. Kühn and E. Mirkes, Karlsruhe preprint TTP92-26, to appear in *Phys. Lett.* **B** (1992).
3. J.H. Kühn and E. Mirkes, Karlsruhe preprint TTP92-32.

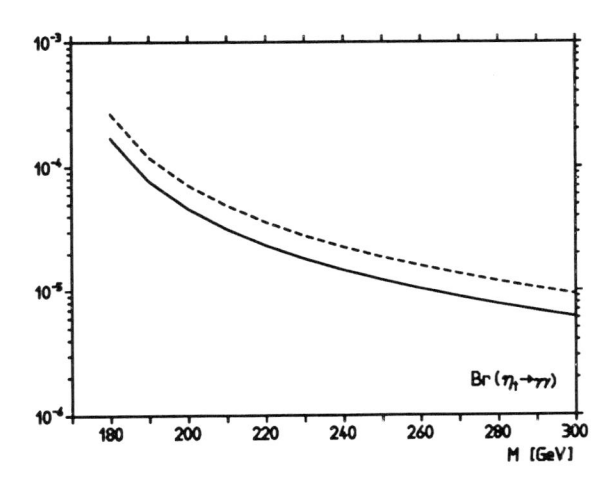

Figure 1: Predictions for the branching ratio of $\eta_t \to \gamma\gamma$ as functions of M for the potential V_J with $\Lambda^{(4)}_{\overline{MS}}=200$ (solid) and 500 MeV (dashed).

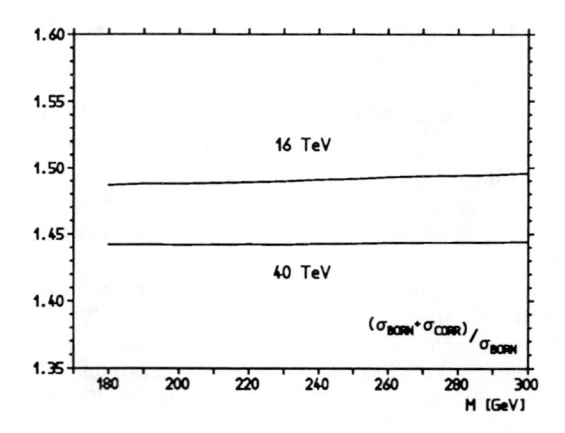

Figure 2: Ratio between the radiatively corrected cross section for $pp \to \eta_t + X$ and the lowest order result for $\sqrt{S}=16$ and 40 TeV.

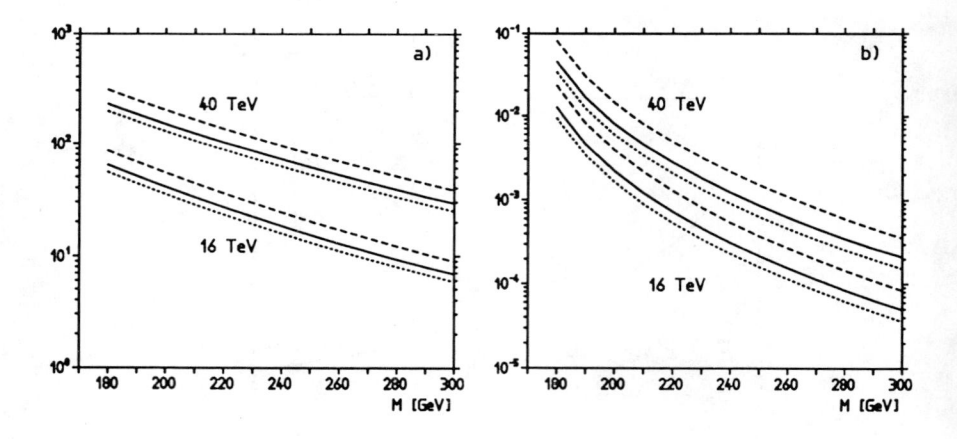

Figure 3: a) Cross section for η_t production including NLO corrections and (b) cross section multiplied by the two photon branching ratio at $\sqrt{S}=16$ and 40 TeV for the potential V_J with $\Lambda_{\overline{MS}}^{(4)}=300$ (solid), $\Lambda_{\overline{MS}}^{(4)}=200$ (dotted) and $\Lambda_{\overline{MS}}^{(4)}=500$ MeV (dashed).

TOPONIUM PRODUCTION AT HADRON COLLIDERS

AGNES GRAU
Physics Department, University of Granada
Granada, Spain

GIULIA PANCHERI
INFN, Laboratory Nazionali di Frascati, P.O.Box 13
00044 Frascati, Italy

ABSTRACT

The possibility of detecting top-antitop bound states at hadron colliders, LHC and SSC is discussed. It is shown that gluon-gluon fusion into a $J^{PC} = 0^{-+}$ state can give rise to a substantial number of events, if the toponium wave function at the origin is evaluated using a non-relativistic Coulomb type potential. In this approximation, for $m_{top} = 100 - 120\ GeV$ the decay width into two photons is $\approx 30 KeV$ and the signal $\eta_t \to \gamma\gamma$ is shown to be visible above the background from gluon-gluon fusion and $q - \bar{q}$ annihilation into two photons, both at LHC as well as at SSC, with present design luminosities.

1. Introduction

We present here a short study of the production of toponium states with $J^{PC} = 0^{-+}$ at hadron colliders and of their detection through the two photon decay mode [1]. The lower limits on the top mass established by the CDF Collaboration [2], i.e. $m_t \geq m_W + m_b$, have changed the bound state picture characteristic of charmonium and bottomium spectroscopy. The main decay channel for the top quark is now direct electroweak decay into a W-boson and a b-quark with a rate rapidly growing with the top mass and the bound state may not have time to form, except perhaps for top masses below 130-140 GeV. In which production process should one search for such loosely bound state? In the energy range $200 \div 260 GeV$, presently planned hadron colliders are good gluon factories with abundant production of all the states coupled to two gluons. Such is $J^{PC} = 0^{-+}$. On the contrary, the traditional avenue of discovery of charmonium at hadron colliders, i.e. the Drell-Yan process, favours production of spin triplet states with $J^{PC} = 1^{--}$, which proceeds mainly through $q\bar{q}$ annihilation, with rather low parton luminosities in this energy range. Considering that presently planned detectors for intermediate Higgs boson searches will investigate two gamma final states with optimal resolution, we suggest a search for the state 0^{-+} at hadron colliders into its two photon mode.

2. The Coulomb Case and Comparison with Potential Models

In this section we discuss the top-antitop bound states, using a Coulomb potential with QCD couplings and the non-relativistic Schroedinger equation to evaluate binding energies and the wave function at the origin. For a top quark with $m_t \geq m_W + m_b$, the total decay rate for a bound state is dominated by single quark decay into a W boson and a b- quark and we can estimate it to be $\approx 2\Gamma_t$. While the single quark decay width is fully determined from electroweak interactions, the splitting between the energy levels and the wave function at the origin depend upon the strength of the strong force between the quarks and their relative distance. For light quarks one can expect long range confining forces to be important, whereas for the top quark the Coulomb part of the potential, i.e. $V_Q = -\frac{4}{3}\frac{\alpha_s}{r}$, should be the dominant one. For the decay into two photons or two gluons, the following Born level expressions hold

$$\Gamma(\eta_t \to gg) = \frac{8}{3}\alpha_s^2 \frac{4\pi|\Psi(0)|^2}{m^2} \quad \text{and} \quad \Gamma(\eta_t \to \gamma\gamma) = 12e_t^4\alpha^2 \frac{4\pi|\Psi(0)|^2}{m^2} \quad (1)$$

where $|\Psi(0)|$ is the wave function at the origin and α_s is the strong coupling constant evaluated at $Q^2 \approx m_t^2$. In a non-relativistic hydrogen atom type model, with fixed $\alpha_s(Q^2)$, the wave-function at the origin is given by

$$|\Psi_{100}(0)|^2 = \frac{1}{\pi}\left(\frac{2}{3}m_Q\alpha_s\right)^3 \quad \text{with} \quad \alpha_s = \alpha_s(Q_s^2)$$

where m_Q is the mass of the heavy quark, and Q_s^2 is the appropriate scale to use for α_s in the wave function expression. In the non-relativistic model with a Coulomb potential, it can be estimated as follows :

$$Q^2 = -(\vec{p})^2, \quad \frac{p^2}{2m} = -E_b \quad \text{and} \quad \text{thus} \quad Q^2 = 2mE_b$$

Implementing reduced mass and finite width effects, one can write

$$Q_s^2 = m_Q\sqrt{E_b^2 + (\frac{\Gamma_{t\bar{t}}}{2})^2}$$

The above model for the energy splitting between the 1S and 2S state shows [1] that formation of the bound state in this model is possible for top quark masses less than 150 GeV, i.e. masses for which $\Delta E_{1S-2S} \leq \Gamma_{t\bar{t}}$.

The production cross-section at hadron colliders of a narrow 0^- resonance through gluon-gluon fusion can be written as

$$\sigma(pp \to \eta_t + X) = \frac{\pi^2}{8m^3}\Gamma(\eta_t \to gg)\left(\tau\frac{dL}{d\tau}\right)_{gg} \quad (2)$$

where $\tau\frac{dL}{d\tau}$ is the gluon-gluon differential luminosity with $\tau = m^2/s$. The observability of a possible signal depends upon the physics background from three processe, i.e. $q\bar{q} \to \gamma\gamma$, $gg \to \gamma\gamma$ and $qg \to q\gamma\gamma$. In the figures we show an evaluation of the cross-section (with kinematics cuts) for the the above background processes at LHC, and the differential cross-section for the process $pp \to \gamma\gamma + X$ at LHC and SSC, inclusive of the signal. In plotting the signal cross-section we have convoluted the natural width with an experimental resolution

$$\frac{\Delta E}{E} = \frac{0.02}{\sqrt{2}} \quad \text{with a constant term} \quad \frac{1}{2}\%$$

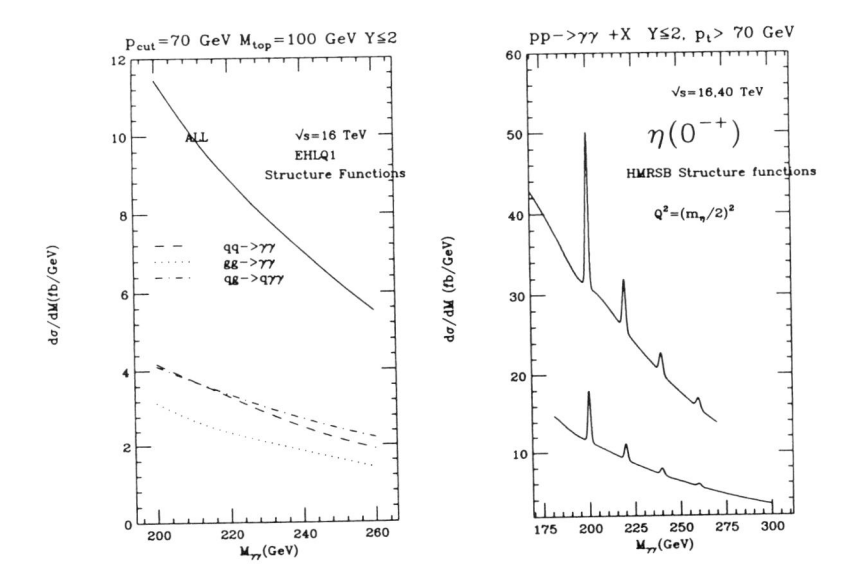

Figure 1: Two photon differential cross-sections: background at LHC (left), including toponium signal (right) at LHC and SSC . Kinematics cuts are included

The above estimates can be compared with those from a Coulombic-type potential, with a logarithmically softened singularity at the origin. In ref. [3], the wave function at the origin is calculated from potential models based on charmonium and bottomium spectroscopy and is estimated to be $\approx$ 30% lower than the one we have used. Since the overall signal is proportional to $|\Psi(0)|^4$, this results implies a reduction factor $4 \div 5$ relative to the estimate of ref [1]. Still, a high luminosity SSC option could detect toponium for the $m_t = 100$ GeV case. We have evaluated the statistical significance of the signal at SSC for two different SSC luminosities, $L_{SSC} = 10^{33}$ and 10^{34} $cm^2 sec^{-1}$, and for the two models. This calculation is shown in Table 1.

Table 1 : SSC $N_{sig}/\sqrt{N_{sign} + N_{bck}}$

Model	L	$m_t = 100 GeV$	$m_t = 110 GeV$	$m_t = 120 GeV$	$m_t = 130 GeV$
$PRR, ref.$[1]	10^{33}	9.7	4.3	2.1	1.2
$KM, ref.$[8]	10^{34}	6.5	2.3	1.2	0.5

3. References

1. G.Pancheri,J.-P. Revol and C.Rubbia, *Physics Letters* **B277** (1992) 518.
2. CDF Collaboration, F.Abe et al., *Phys Rev.Lett.* **64** (1990) 142,147; ibidem **68** (1992) 447.
3. J.H.Kuhn and Mirkes, TTP92-26, July 1992. To be published in Phys.Lett.B.

LARGE FLAVOR CHANGING NEUTRAL COUPLINGS OF THE TOP QUARK

GEORGE WEI-SHU HOU

Department of Physics, National Taiwan University
Taipei, Taiwan 10764, R.O.C.

ABSTRACT

The top quark, being the heaviest fermion, may possess large flavor changing couplings to neutral Higgs bosons (h^0). Such effects will not show up at low energies if $u_i u_j h^0$ couplings are proportional to $\sqrt{m_i m_j}$. The existing CDF bound on m_t may be evaded by the $t \to ch^0$ decay mode for the range $m_{h^0} < m_t < M_W$. This range can be fully covered by LEP II. For $m_{h^0} > m_t$, the $h^0 \to t\bar{c}$ mode dominates over $h^0 \to b\bar{b}$, and competes effectively with $h^0 \to t\bar{t}$, perhaps even against $h^0 \to W^+W^-$, ZZ modes. This may have implications on Higgs detection in the so-called "intermediate mass" region at supercolliders.

1. Introduction

Out of the four particles that are known to be very heavy, the top and the Higgs are *unusual*: their masses and properties are only described, not explained, in SM. We know so little about the Higgs sector because, as the "agent of mass", Higgs couplings are typically suppressed by particle masses, and their effects are negligible in low energy processes. On the other hand, indirect effects of the top quark are multiple. This is mainly due to the presumably large Yukawa coupling. At the same time, because the top is the heaviest fermion, we believe it should be sensitive to the Higgs sector.

The elusiveness of the top and Higgs may in fact reflect new physics. For example, with extra scalar doublets, the CDF bound may be circumvented by the $t \to bH^+$ process, while the LEP bound on m_{H^0} is weakened by having two channels, $Z \to Z^* h^0$ and $A^0 h^0$ (h^0 is the lighter neutral scalar, A^0 the pseudoscalar).

Since flavor changing neutral couplings (FCNC) of the top quark are *not* ruled out *experimentally*, here we would like to entertain the possibility of FCNC $t \to ch^0$ decay, where h^0 is now the generic, lightest neutral (pseudo)scalar. Clearly, if $t \to ch^0$ is substantial, the CDF bound can also be evaded. Is this at all possible?

2. Standard Expectations and Why

Within SM, because of GIM, FCNC of H^0 appear only at one-loop level, and[1] $BR(t \to cH^0) \lesssim 10^{-7}$, a feature that is retained in standard two Higgs models.

It is common knowledge that there are only two types of two Higgs doublet models (2HDM), but most people may have forgotten why. In 1977, impressed by the success of the GIM mechanism in eliminating FCNC, Glashow and Weinberg[2] wrote down the Natural Flavor Conservation (NFC) condition: *Flavor conservation* in the neutral sector should follow from the group structure and representation content of the theory, rather than by particular values taken on by the parameters. In 2HDM's, the fermion mass matrix is

$$M_{ij} = M_{ij}^{(1)} + M_{ij}^{(2)}, \qquad (1)$$

where $M_{ij}^{(k)} = \lambda_{ij}^{(k)} v_k/\sqrt{2}$ is due to the k-th doublet. In general, $M_{ij}^{(1)}$ and $M_{ij}^{(2)}$ are not simultaneously diagonalized with M_{ij}, hence, physical neutral Higgs bosons would have flavor changing couplings. This is in conflict with the NFC condition. The common way out is to assume that both u- and d-type quarks get mass from only one Higgs doublet (model I), or from different doublets (model II), resulting in two basic models. Model II is realized in minimal SUSY, however, in general, one needs to introduce discrete symmetries to enforce the NFC condition.

A remark on the practical side is in order. At the time when the 3rd generation was just emerging, nothing was known regarding quark mixing except that $V_{us} \sim 0.22$. Taking the KM matrix V to be arbitrary, the general d-s-h^0 coupling should be of order m_b/v, i.e. dominated by the largest mass eigenvalue. The observed K_L-K_S mass difference (Δm_K) would then imply[3] that $m_{h^0} > 100$ TeV! Thus, to work in 2HDM's that have normal (order v) physical Higgs boson masses, one *had* to adopt either model I or II. It was therefore quite prudent and rational.

3. Surprises in Flavor Sector since 1977

Although NFC was a good and well justified criterion in the 70's, as we move on to the "physics of the heavies", we should diligently question ourselves whether we have thrown out the baby with the bathwater.

The first surprise in flavor physics is in heavy fermions masses. Around 1977, m_τ and m_b were found around a few GeV, consistent with the pattern $m_f \ll M_W$, v. It was therefore widely expected that top was just around the corner, with mass of order 10-20 GeV. The Gestalt-switch came with the ARGUS discovery of large B^0-$\bar{B}^0$ mixing in 1987, leading people to believe that $m_t \gtrsim 50$ GeV.

The second surprise came in the KM matrix. In the way Kobayashi and Maskawa parametrized the 3 × 3 quark mixing matrix, followed by PDG up until mid-80's, the view was that the KM matrix should be "random", and any choice of the 3 Euler angles are equally fine, each expected to be of order the observed V_{us}. It therefore came as a surprise, especially around 1983, when the b hadrons turned out to be extremely long lived. Subsequent work showed that $|V_{ub}|^2 \ll |V_{cb}|^2 \ll |V_{us}|^2$, which is rather reminiscent of the mass hierarchies $m_u \ll m_c \ll m_t$ and $m_d \ll m_s \ll m_b$.

From the existence of mass and mixing hierarchies, and the fact that only m_t is of order v, it appears that Nature has chosen its parameters in a rather peculiar way (*Natural tuning* !), countering NFC. Do we have hope for large $BR(t \to ch^0)$?

4. Two Higgs Doublet Model Revisited

The mass and mixing hierarchies suggest that if

$$M_{ij} \sim \sqrt{m_i m_j}, \qquad (2)$$

where m_i corresponds to mass eigenvalues, then the two hierarchies can be qualitatively related, or even quantitatively *described*. The latter step is achieved by imposing additional zeros, such as in Fritzsch-type mass matrices, with subsequent developments that could accommodate heavy top.[4]

Generalizing to the two Higgs doublet case, Cheng and Sher argued[5] that, to avoid fine-tuned cancellations between Yukawa matrices, (1) and (2) imply that both $M_{ij}^{(1)}$ and $M_{ij}^{(2)}$ should be of the form (2), leading to the Yukawa couplings (even *after* diagonalization of mass matrix)

$$\lambda_{ij}^{(k)} = \Delta_{ij}^{(k)} \sqrt{m_i m_j}/v, \qquad (3)$$

where $\Delta_{ij}^{(k)}$ is of order unity. FCNC h^0 couplings are suppressed by external fermion masses! The earlier limit[3] of 100 TeV is now lowered by $\sqrt{m_d m_s}/m_b \sim 6 \times 10^{-3}$ to below 1 TeV, while for scalar h^0 it drops further by a factor[6] of $1/\sqrt{12}$ because of the pseudoscalar nature of K^0. Allowing further reductions in Δ_{ij}, one concludes that neutral Higgs bosons could have both FCNC *and* normal (order v) masses, *without* imposing NFC. This amounts to a third type of 2HDM, which I call model III.

We emphasize that we have NOT adopted the Fritzsch or any special mass matrix Ansatz here. Rather, one is taking a utilitarian point of view that (2) can account for the observed mass and mixing patterns. The generality of Yukawa couplings are retained in the "fudge" coefficients $\Delta_{ij}^{(k)}$. Aside from the statement of (3), the model is quite arbitrary, and it may be more appropriately called a scenario.

The features of models I/II and model III may be combined into a variant.[7] Low energy FCNC constraints come from d-type quarks and charged leptons (*e.g.* K^0-$\bar K^0$ and B^0-$\bar B^0$ mixings, $\mu \to e\gamma$, etc.), but the up quark sector is rather forgiving (*e.g.* D^0-$\bar D^0$ mixing). If one assumes the Cheng-Sher scenario, *i.e.* (3), to apply to u-type quarks only, but impose NFC on all other fermions, FCNC $u_i u_j h^0$ couplings may exist with practically no constraint on m_{h^0}. We shall call this model IV.

5. Tree Level $t \to ch^0$ and $h^0 \to t\bar c$ Decays

Due to the progressive nature of the FCNC couplings (3) with external fermion mass, the largest possible coupling is tch^0 within the standard fermion content. We may have $t \to ch^0$ and $h^0 \to t\bar c$ at *tree level* !

The FCNC Yukawa coupling is not much smaller than gauge couplings,

$$\sqrt{2}\lambda_{ct}/g = \sqrt{m_c m_t}/M_W \sim 0.1 - 0.2, \qquad (4)$$

for m_t between 50 and 200 GeV and $\Delta_{ct} = 1$. At first sight it appears that the $t \to ch^0$ process still cannot compete with the standard $t \to bW^{(*)}$ process because of (4). However, if the W is off-shell, *i.e.* for the mass region $m_{h^0} < m_t \lesssim M_W$ (recall that neutral Higgs bounds from LEP are weakened in 2HDM), the two body $t \to ch^0$ process may in fact dominate over the standard three body $t \to bW^*$ process. CDF cannot rule out the mass domain by the absence of isolated leptons plus missing p_T events! As $t \to ch^0$ would typically be followed by $h^0 \to b\bar b$, it would be rather difficult to see at hadronic colliders. One needs a true threshold machine, and LEP II can precisely cover this region. For $m_t \gtrsim M_W$, $t \to ch^0$ cannot dominate. However, $BR(t \to ch^0)$ would typically be at the per cent level, which is *very* interesting when compared to standard (SM or 2HDM) expectations[1] of order 10^{-7}. It should be detectable in $t\bar{t}$ production with standard $t \to bW$ as tag.

For the region $m_t < m_{h^0} \lesssim 2m_t$, in general $h^0 \to t\bar{c}$ is dominant over the standard $h^0 \to b\bar{b}$ mode, since $\sqrt{m_c m_t} > m_b$. If top decays via $t \to bW^{(*)}$, the event signature plus topology should be quite distinct, allowing Higgs detection in the so-called intermediate mass range, $M_W \lesssim m_{h^0} \lesssim 2M_W$, since the two mass ranges should have a good deal of overlap. For heavier h^0, the $h^0 \to t\bar{c}$ process competes well with $h^0 \to t\bar{t}$ until one is way above $2m_t$. It could even compete with $h^0 \to W^+W^-$, ZZ, since $h^0 WW$ and $h^0 ZZ$ couplings are diluted in multi-Higgs models. Thus, even for the mass range $m_{h^0} \gtrsim 2m_t$ or $2M_W$, $BR(h^0 \to t\bar{c})$ could still be appreciable.

6. Discussion and Summary

We do not go into details here. For further discussions, see ref. 7. We note in passing that, since model II is realized in SUSY models, if one finds evidence for model III and IV, one would as a by-product rule out minimal SUSY.

Let us summarize the highlights: NFC of Glashow and Weinberg can be replaced by $\lambda_{ij} \lesssim \sqrt{m_i m_j}/v$, which suppresses low energy FCNC (model III). Low energy constraints can be evaded completely if one assumes NFC for d-type quarks and charged leptons, but imposes the above relation for u-type quarks (model IV). No exotic fermions or bosons are added therefore GIM is preserved and Z couplings remain diagonal. All constraints, including quark mass and mixing patterns, are respected with minimal particle content for going beyond SM, but no new symmetry or parameter that was not already present in the standard model is added. The $t \to ch^0$ process could invalidate the CDF bound in case $m_{h^0} < m_t \lesssim M_W$, keeping in mind that the LEP bound on m_{H^0} is weakened. This gap, however, can be closed at LEP II. The $h^0 \to t\bar{c}$ mode is prominent in the region $m_t < m_{h^0} \lesssim 2m_t$ and may facilitate Higgs detection at supercolliders in the infamous intermediate mass region ($M_W \lesssim m_{h^0} \lesssim 2M_W$). Outside these ranges, FCNC t or h^0 decays could still be at or above the 10^{-3}-10^{-2} level and would still be extremely tantalizing.

FCNC processes may be quite commonplace at high energies afterall.

7. References

1. G. Eilam, J.L. Hewett and A. Soni, *Phys. Rev.* **D44** (1991) 1473.
2. S.L. Glashow and S. Weinberg, *Phys. Rev.* **D15** (1977) 1958.
3. B. McWilliams and L.F. Li, *Nucl. Phys.* **B179** (1981) 62; O. Shanker, *ibid.* **B206** (1982) 253.
4. X.G. He and W.S. Hou, *Phys. Rev.* **D41** (1990) 1517; S. Dimopoulos, L.J. Hall and S. Raby, *Phys. Rev. Lett.* **68** (1992) 1984.
5. T. P. Cheng and M. Sher, *Phys. Rev.* **D35** (1987) 3484.
6. M. Sher and Y. Yuan, *Phys. Rev.* **D44** (1991) 1461.
7. W. S. Hou, to appear in *Phys. Lett.* **B**.

THE UA2 SEARCH FOR H$^\pm$ FROM t-QUARK DECAY

J. INCANDELA
CDF Collaboration, Department of Physics, Fermilab
Batavia, Illinois 60510, USA

ABSTRACT

The decay chain t $\to$ H$^+$b, H$^+$ $\to$ $\tau\nu$, $\tau \to$ hadrons + $\bar{\nu}$ and its conjugate were probed by UA2 at the CERN $\bar{p}p$ collider by seeking an excess of τ's beyond that expected from W $\to \tau\nu$. No excess was observed and the above chain was excluded for various mass values and for B(H$^+ \to \tau\nu$) values of 0.5 and 1.0.[1]

The fine-tuning and hierarchy problems[2] of the standard model (SM) can be overcome by expanding the Higgs sector to include a higher symmetry such as SUSY. The simplest models which conform with experimental constraints are based upon combinations of Higgs singlets and doublets. Models with two doublets contain charged scalars, (H$^\pm$ with mass m$_H$), which can have important consequences for the discovery of the top quark since they would couple preferentially to a heavy top. For m$_t$ > m$_H$ the dominant decay modes of the H$^+$ would be H$^+ \to \tau\nu$ and H$^+ \to c\bar{s}$ with branching depending on particle masses and the ratio of vacuum expectations for the doublets, (tanβ = v$_2$/v$_1$). Furthermore, if m$_W$ > m$_t$ + m$_b$, the decay t $\to$ H$^+$ b does not have to compete with t $\to$ W$^+$ b. These final states were not considered in the SM top searches at $\bar{p}p$ colliders.[3-5] This leaves open the possibility that top could still be less massive than the W without contradicting the results of B$_o$ – $\bar{B}_o$ mixing.[6] For m$_t$ > m$_W$ + m$_b$ it is possible to simultaneously suppress both modes, rendering top undetectable at hadron colliders.[7]

In UA2 we have sought evidence for

$$t \to H^+b, \ H^+ \to \tau\nu, \ \tau \to \text{hadrons} + \bar{\nu} \tag{1}$$

for top produced via $\bar{q}q \to t\bar{t}$ or W $\to$ t$\bar{b}$. Our method has been to determine the numbers of e's and τ's in events with large missing momentum ($\not{p}_T$), to use the former and the assumption of e – τ universality to determine the number of τ's expected from W decay, and to compare this number to the number of τ's observed in the data. An excess would indicate new physics while no observed excess could exclude the H$^\pm$ hypothesis in some part of the parameter space.

To count the e's and τ's in the sample, we perform an analysis similar to that used in the UA2 measurement of e – τ universality.[8,9] However, in addition to studying events with only one cluster with E$_T$ above 10 GeV, we consider a second sample in which it is required that there be at least one additional cluster above 10 GeV (not opposite to the leading cluster in azimuth). The two samples are denoted "τ" and "τ + *jets*" respectively. The τ + *jets* sample contains fewer events and is not useful in a universality measurement but plays the dominant role in the study of t $\to$ H$^+$b.

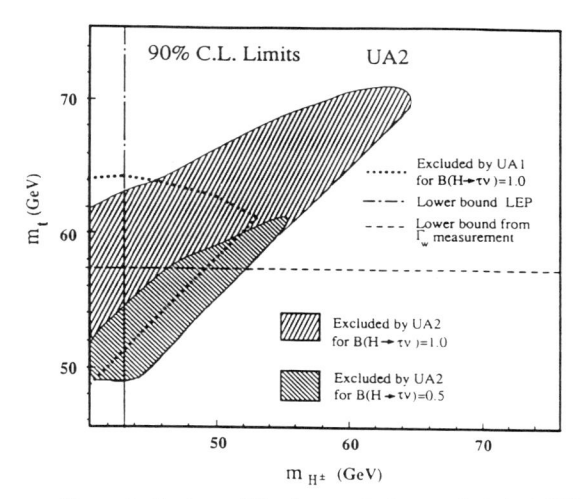

Figure 1: Regions of the (m_H, m_t) plane excluded at 90% CL

The data correspond to an integrated luminosity of 13.0 ± 0.8 pb^{-1}. For the 1988 and 1989 runs we used $p\!\!\!/_T$ triggers. In 1990 a dedicated level 1 "τ trigger" combined the $p\!\!\!/_T$ requirement with a veto of di-jet events and a veto of events with early veto counter hits (typical of beam-halo). At higher trigger levels, the $p\!\!\!/_T$ and opposite jet requirements were refined and τ candidates were sought on the basis of hadronicity (ξ) and profile (ρ), defined as: $\xi = E_{had}/E_{tot}$ and $\rho = (E_1 + E_2)/E_{tot}$ where E_{had} is the energy of the cluster contained in hadronic compartments, E_{tot} is the total cluster energy, and E_i is the energy of the ith leading energy cell in the cluster. For the final samples we required $p\!\!\!/_T$ > 20 GeV. The leading cluster was required to have $0.01 < \xi < 0.90$ and $E_T^1 > 17$ GeV, lie in the central calorimeter, and have at least one track in a 10° cone about the cluster axis.

For counting τ's in the sample, the numbers of events coming from halo, jets and e's are estimated and subtracted from the total. The jet subtraction is performed by exploiting the differences in the profile distributions for jets and τ's.[1,8] Corrections are made for efficiencies and contributions from other sources of electrons and hadronic τ decays (e.g. $Z \to \tau^+\tau^-$).

In determining our best estimate of $e - \tau$ universality, higher $p\!\!\!/_T$ and E_T^1 thresholds (25 and 20 GeV, respectively) and a threshold of 2.5 GeV for the cluster opposite the leading jet, were used. The result is

$$\frac{g_\tau^W}{g_e^W} = 1.02 \pm 0.04 \pm 0.04 \quad (2)$$

When using the thresholds of the charged Higgs analysis, we obtain a slightly less precise result of $0.99 \pm 0.06 \pm 0.04$, (and $1.04 \pm 0.18 \pm 0.05$ for the $\tau+jets$ sample). Thus no excess in τ events is observed. From the number of observed e's and the assumption

Table 1: Excess τ's in the τ and $\tau + jets$ samples

Sample	$W \to \tau\nu$	τ's Observed	Excess τ's
τ	$760 \pm 31 \pm 25$	$754 \pm 68 \pm 54$	$-6 \pm 75 \pm 60$
$\tau + jets$	$68 \pm 8 \pm 3$	$73 \pm 24 \pm 5$	$+5 \pm 25 \pm 6$

that the ratio of couplings of the e and τ to the W is unity we obtain estimates for the expected numbers of τ's from $W \to \tau\nu$. These are compared to the observed numbers in order to extract quantitative excesses as shown in Table 1.

It is possible to compare these numbers with expectations of the charged Higgs hypothesis. The PYTHIA[10] Monte Carlo (MC) was used for this purpose and included UA2 detector and underlying event simulations. Generations were done for 16 choices of m_H and m_t values in the ranges [44,66] GeV and [50,71.5] GeV, respectively. The number of τ's expected for each case was determined by applying analysis cuts and normalizing to the production cross-sections for top and the total integrated luminosity of 13 pb^{-1}. For τ's from $H^{\pm}$ there are contributions to the systematic uncertainties from theoretical, MC and experimental sources such as luminosity (± 6 %), top production (10 − 30 %), underlying event simulation (± 20%) and b-quark fragmentation (± 8 %).

Since the observed excesses are consistent with zero, we can ask whether (1) can be ruled out for some values of the relevant parameters. Levels of confidence for exclusion of (1) were calculated for two choices of $\tan\beta$. A region of the (m_H, m_t) plane exluded at 90 % CL is shown in Figure 1. For comparison, the regions excluded by UA1[11] are shown together with model independent lower bounds for m_t from hadron collider measurements of Γ_W and for m_H from LEP.[12−15]

References

1. UA2 Collaboration, J. ALitti et al.: Phys. Lett. B **280** (1992) 137
2. See for instance: L. Suskind, Phys. Rep. **104** (1984) 181
3. UA2 Collaboration, J. ALitti et al.: Z. Phys. C **46** (1990) 1
4. CDF Collaboration, F. ABE et al.: Phys. Rev. D **45** (1992) 3291
5. UA1 Collaboration, C.Albajar et al.: Z. Phys. C **48** (1990) 1
6. S.L. Glashow and E. Jenkins, Phys. Lett B **196** (1987) 233
7. V. Barger and R.J.N. Phillips, Phys. Rev. D **41** (1990) 884
8. UA2 Collaboration, J. Alitti et al.: Z. Phys. C **52** (1991) 209
9. UA2 Collaboration, J. Alitti et al.: Phys. Lett. B **276** (1992) 365
10. T. Sjostrand, Int. Journal of Mod. Phys. **3** (1988) 751
11. UA1 Collaboration, C. Albajar et al.: Phys. Lett. B **257** (1991) 459
12. ALEPH Collaboration, D. Decamp et al.: Phys. Lett. B **241** (1990) 623
13. DELPHI Collaboration, P. Abrew et al.: Phys. Lett. B **241** (1990) 449
14. L3 Collaboration, B. Adeva et al.: Phys. Lett. B **252** (1990) 511
15. OPAL Collaboration, M.Z. Akrawy et al.: Phys. Lett. B **242** (1990) 299

TOP QUARK SEARCH IN DØ FROM THE LEPTON + JETS MODE

Boaz KLIMA, for the DØ Collaboration
Fermi National Accelerator Laboratory
P.O. Box 500, Batavia Illinois 60510

ABSTRACT

The DØ collaboration has searched for Top quark production at $\sqrt{s}$ =1.8 TeV in $p\bar{p}$ collisions at Fermilab using a data sample corresponding to an integrated luminosity of 1.1 pb^{-1}, collected during the 1992 Tevatron run. We report the preliminary results of a search for $t\bar{t}$ production in which the Top quark decays to a W boson plus a b quark where one W decaying leptonically and the other decaying hadronically. Future prospects for extending the search for Top in the lepton plus jets channel are discussed.

1. Introduction

The Top quark is the only quark within the Standard Model (SM) which is yet to be observed. In $p\bar{p}$ collisions at Tevatron energies ($\sqrt{s}$ = 1.8 TeV) the dominant Top quark production process is the QCD creation of $t\bar{t}$ pairs. According to the SM each Top quark is expected to decay via the weak charged current into a b quark and a W boson, which can decay into leptons or light quarks. In this study we concentrated on the e+jets final state which has a branching ratio of 15%. The signature for these events is a high missing transverse energy, a high transverse momentum electron, and a few jets. Because of quark and gluon bremsstrahlung and the experimental definition of a jet the number of expected jets is not necessarily four. The physics processes which are the main background source for this channel are W+jets, QCD (mainly $b\bar{b}$), and $Z^0 \to e^+e^-$ where one electron was missed.

The detector, newly commissioned in the current run of the Fermilab Tevatron, is well-suited for identifying electrons and jets, and measuring the missing transverse energy of an event.[1]

2. Data Sample

The data used in this analysis were collected in September and October of this year (1992), after a 3 month commissioning period for the detector. The integrated luminosity was 1.1 pb^{-1}, representing less than 5% of the total expected for this collider run (Ia). The data were from that subset of triggers chosen to be analyzed immediately (Express Line) for topical physics results. A hardware trigger (Level 1) required at least one electro-magnetic (EM) trigger tower (0.2x0.2 in $\eta-\phi$ space) with $E_t > 14$ GeV. A software trigger (Level 2) required at least one EM cluster with $E_t >$20 GeV (with some electron cluster shape cuts) and missing $E_t >$ 20 GeV. There was no particular requirement about jets at the trigger level. The efficiency of these triggers (including geometric acceptance) is estimated to be 56%.

We have studied the trigger efficiency as a function of the number of associated jets and found that the efficiencies were similar, within our estimated errors, up to 4 associated jets per event.

Offline cuts were imposed to define $W \to e + \nu_e$ candidate sample. We required missing $E_t > 20$ GeV, one electron candidate with $p_t > 20$ GeV, and we imposed a few electron quality cuts (Details were reported elsewhere.[2]). Taking into account all the afforementioned online and offline cuts the final efficiency was 31%±5%. The number of events satisfying those criteria in that data sample was 882. Fig. 1 shows the transverse mass of those W candidates. We have estimated the contamination from $W \to \tau + \nu_\tau$ (where the τ decays into $e\nu_e\nu_\tau$) to be about 5%, from QCD events to be much less than 1%, and from Z^0 events (where one misidentifies one of the two electrons) to be much less than 1% (Details were reported elsewhere.[3]).

Fig. 2 shows the transverse mass of the W candidates for different number of associated jets. We used a fixed cone (R=0.5) jet finding algorithm with minimum E_T cutoff of 15GeV. The observed distributions are consistent with a full Monte Carlo simulation of W+jets events(Details were reported elsewhere.[4]).

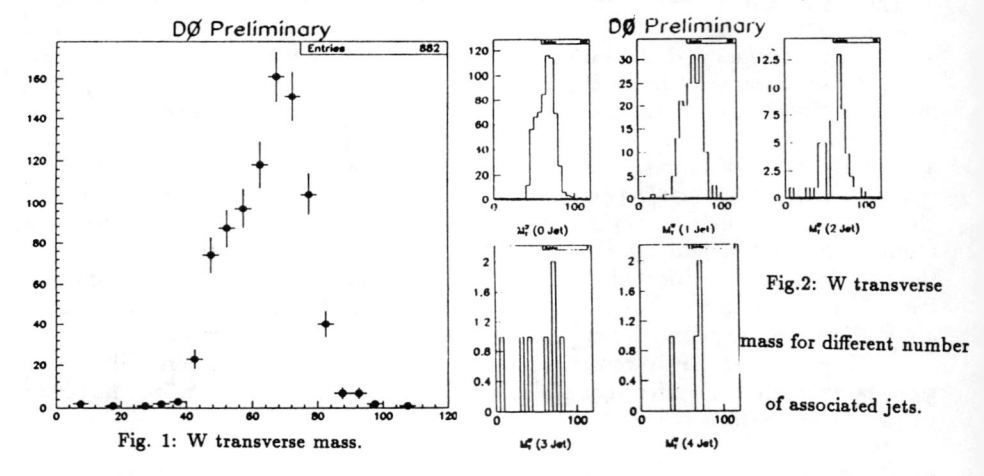

Fig. 1: W transverse mass.

Fig.2: W transverse mass for different number of associated jets.

3. Monte Carlo

We have generated Monte Carlo events based on a leading order theoretical prediction (encoded in the VECBOS generator) and put them through the full DØ detector simulation. We then compared the transverse momentum of W candidates in those Monte Carlo datasets with data normalizing the Monte Carlo sample to the same number of events, and the shapes agree well.

We also compared the number of events predicted by VECBOS (with ISAJET fragmentation) to the number of events observed in our data, and found a good agreement within the statistical errors. We varied the jet minimum E_t cutoff and found the following numbers of events:

E_T^{min}(jet) (in GeV)	W + 2 jets Data	W + 2 jets VECBOS	W + 3 jets Data	W + 3 jets VECBOS
15	35±6	29±2	5±2	3.5±0.4
20	17±4	17±2	1±1	0.3±0.1
25	8±3	9±1	0	0.05±0.05

4. Top to Electron + Jets

The analysis strategy depends on the integrated luminosity. We have generated 80 GeV Top Monte Carlo events, ran them through the DØ simulation programs, both for the detector (D0GEANT) and for the triggers, and processed them with the same reconstruction program (including offline cuts) as used for the data. The total cross section for Top events at $\sqrt{s}$ = 1.8 TeV in $\bar{p}p$ collisions was taken from Berends et al.[5] This estimated cross section is about 30% higher than previous calculations.[6]

We looked for W+3 jets events where the jets were found with the fixed cone algorithm (R=0.5), the E_T cut on the jets was 25GeV and their maximum pseudorapidity was 2.5. We observed no events which satisfied these criteria. A preliminary estimate of the uncertainties yields the following percentage errors: 1) Monte Carlo cross section - 30%, 2) Monte Carlo statistics - 8%, 3) Jet energy scale - 20%, 4) Luminosity - 15%, 5) Efficiency - 15%. In total the uncertainty was about 45%. Our Monte Carlo calculation for a Top mass of 80GeV predicted on average 2.6±1.2 events in the integrated luminosity of 1.1 pb^{-1}.

5. Conclusion

DØ has observed W → eν_e decays in events with different number of associated jets. The number of events predicted by VECBOS for different jet multiplicities in W events agrees well with the DØ data. A Monte Carlo study of 80GeV Top events predicts about 2.6±1.2 events in 1.1 pb^{-1} whereas no events were observed in the data. This analysis will certainly be improved with time and with the acquisition of significantly more data during the remainder of this collider run. We plan to better understand our detector and the data, to analyze other lepton+jets channels, and to apply sophisticated techniques for signal/background separation.

6. References

1. R. Madaras, Highlights from DØ , *These proceedings*.
2. M. Narain, Electron Identification in DØ , *These proceedings*.
3. N. Graf, W and Z Decays to Electrons in DØ , *These proceedings*.
4. J. Yu, W+Jet Production in DØ , *These proceedings*.
5. F. A. Berends, J. B. Tausk and W.T. Giele, *Fermilab-Pub-92/196-T*.
6. P. Nason, S. Dawson and R.K. Ellis, *Nucl. Phys. B303 (1988) 607*.

SEARCH FOR THE TOP QUARK IN DILEPTON EVENTS WITH DØ

Richard Partridge, for the DØ Collaboration
Physics Department, Brown University, Providence, RI 02912

ABSTRACT

Preliminary results are presented on a search by the DØ experiment for dilepton events consistent with top quark decay in $\bar{p}p$ collisions at $\sqrt{s} = 1.8$ TeV. These results are based on data taken in the first months of DØ operation at the Tevatron collider. No top quark candidates are found in this preliminary search.

1. Introduction

The top quark can be produced in $\bar{p}p$ collisions through both gluon fusion, $gg \to t\bar{t}$, and quark annihilation processes, $q\bar{q} \to t\bar{t}$. For a heavy top quark, the decay $t \to Wb$ will dominate and the final state can be classified according to the W decay modes. The dilepton channel results from both W bosons decaying leptonically.

The DØ detector[1] has demonstrated its ability to identify leptonic W decays in the $e\nu$ and $\mu\nu$ channels.[2,3] The top dilepton search proceeds in a manner similar to the W analyses with the additional requirement that a second lepton be identified in the event. In this paper, we present preliminary results on the ee and $e\mu$ dilepton channels from the first months of DØ operation. The $\mu\mu$ channel is also under study but will not be reported on here.

2. Search for Top in the Di-Electron Channel

The search for top in the ee channel is based on the DØ "express line" data sample, which contains events passing selected trigger conditions. The triggers used in the ee analysis require either two electron candidates or one electron candidate and missing transverse energy $\not{E}_T > 20$ GeV. The integrated luminosity of the sample is 924 ± 139 nb^{-1}.

Electron candidates are identified by finding calorimeter energy clusters with $> 90\%$ of the energy in the electromagnetic section of the calorimeter. Two electron candidates are required, each with $E_T > 15$ GeV, and at least one with a charged particle track match. Additional cuts on the isolation and shower profile of the electron candidates further discriminate against hadronic showers. Further detail on the electron identification algorithms can be found in Ref. 4.

Figure 1 shows a plot of the difference in azimuthal angle between the two electron candidates, $\Delta\phi(ee)$, versus $\not{E}_T$. A cluster of events is seen at large $\Delta\phi(ee)$ and small $\not{E}_T$. The di-electron mass distribution (Fig. 2) shows that many of these events are from $Z^0 \to e^+e^-$. This background is eliminated by requiring $\Delta\phi(ee) < 160°$ and $\not{E}_T > 20$ GeV, while Monte Carlo simulations show that 80% of top quark events satisfy these cuts. No events are found that pass the cuts.

3. Search for Top in the Electron-Muon Channel

The $e\mu$ analysis uses an express line data sample with an integrated luminosity of 873 ± 131 nb^{-1}. The trigger used for this analysis selects events with at least one electron candidate and at least one muon candidate. The electron selection criteria are identical to the ee analysis except that the E_T threshold is reduced to 8 GeV and a somewhat looser isolation cut is used. No track match is required for the electron candidate.

Muon candidates with $P_T > 8$ GeV are subjected to a number of selection criteria. Cosmic rays are eliminated by vetoing muons with a back-to-back track or a large impact parameter. Fiducial cuts restrict muon candidates to the trigger region, $|\eta| < 1.7$, and exclude muons near the gap between central and forward muon systems. The muon candidate is verified by requiring an energy deposit in the calorimeter and a matching track in the central tracking chambers. Events with multiple vertices are eliminated due to potential muon fitting errors with the present reconstruction software.

Six events pass the above selection criteria and are shown in Fig. 3. None of the events pass the kinematic cuts, $P_T(\mu) > 20$ GeV and $E_T(e) > 20$ GeV. Figure 4 shows the effect of the kinematic cuts on Monte Carlo events generated with an 80 GeV top mass.

4. Summary and Conclusions

A preliminary search for top candidates in the ee and $e\mu$ dilepton channels has been performed by the DØ experiment. No top candidates are found. Due to uncertainties in the detection efficiency for these channels, it is not possible to place a limit on the top quark mass at this time. Instead, the efficiency and expected number of events are estimated assuming a fixed top quark mass of 80 GeV.

Monte Carlo studies of the ee and $e\mu$ detection efficiencies yield $\epsilon_{ee} = 0.22$ and $\epsilon_{e\mu} = 0.075$, where the systematic errors are under study. These efficiencies are expected to increase as we include additional triggers and develop optimal selection criteria. The expected numbers of events for a top quark mass of 80 GeV are estimated to be $N_{ee} \approx 0.9$ and $N_{e\mu} \approx 0.6$ using a calculation of the cross section that includes $\mathcal{O}(\alpha_s^2)$ soft gluon corrections[5].

It should be noted that the present results are based on data taken in the first months of DØ operation; a significant increase in integrated luminosity is expected during the present collider run. A further increase in sensitivity is expected due to inclusion of the $\mu\mu$ channel, improvements in reconstruction and analysis software, inclusion of less restrictive triggers, optimal selection cuts, and improved understanding of backgrounds and efficiencies.

DØ Preliminary

Fig. 1: $\Delta\phi(ee)$ versus $\not{E}_T$ for ee events.

Fig. 2: ee invariant mass distribution.

Fig. 3: $P_T(\mu)$ versus $E_T(e)$ for $e\mu$ events

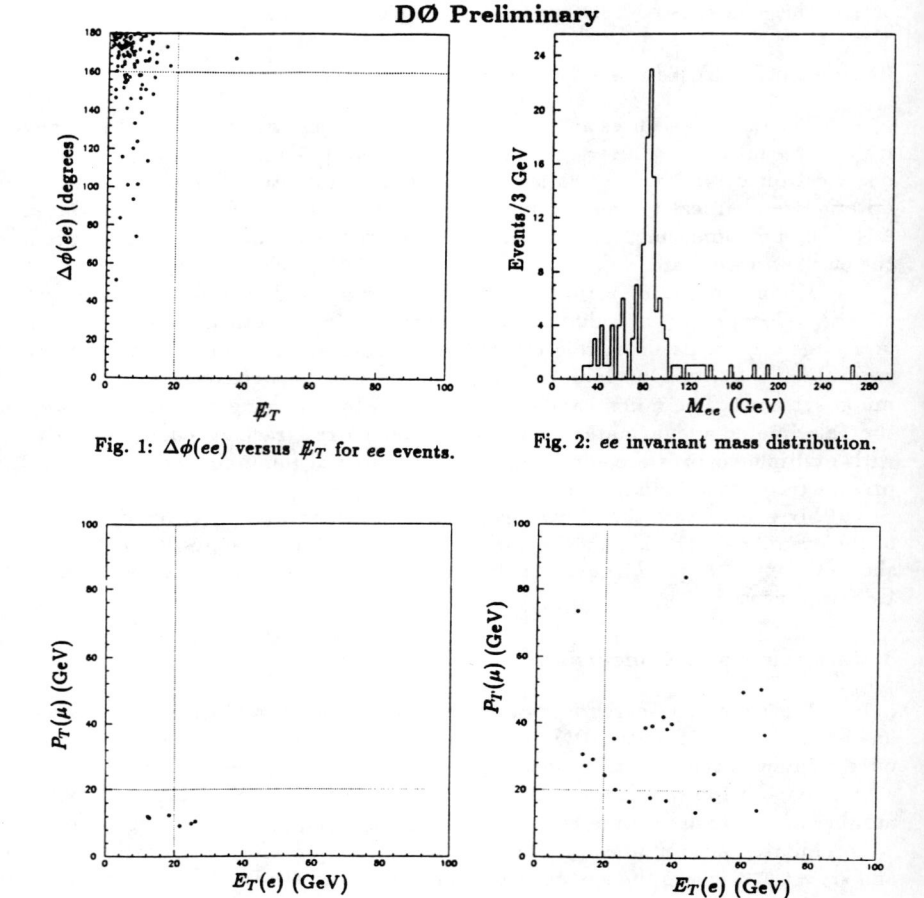

Fig. 4: $P_T(\mu)$ versus $E_T(e)$ for Monte Carlo $e\mu$ events with $m_t = 80$ GeV.

5. References

1. R. Madaras, *Highlights from DØ*, these proceedings.
2. N. Graf, *W and Z Decays to Electrons at DØ*, these proceedings.
3. D. Wood, *W and Z Decays to Muons at DØ*, these proceedings.
4. M. Narain, *Electron Identification in DØ*, these proceedings.
5. F.A. Berends, J.B. Tausk, and W.T. Giele, *Fermilab-Pub-92/196-T*.

Search for the Top Quark at CDF

N. M. Shaw
The CDF Collaboration
Purdue University, Dept. of Physics
W. Lafayette, IN 47907

ABSTRACT

We review prospects for top discovery in the current 1992 CDF run, focusing on the inclusive electron and muon channels. In the standard model, $\sim$ 37% of $t\bar{t}$ events contain a high P_T electron or muon. In particular, b tagging through soft leptons and secondary vertices are discussed. Expected signal to background and prospects for the current CDF 1992 run are given.

1. Introduction

1.1. Standard Model Top

At the Tevatron, Standard Model top quarks are expected to be pair produced in $p\bar{p} \to t\bar{t}$ through quark annihilation and gluon fusion. Total cross sections fall with increasing top mass, from $100 pb$ at $m(t) < 100 GeV/c^2$ to $1 pb$ above $200 GeV/c^2$.[1]

Standard Model top quark decays proceed through $t \to W^+ b$. The final state signatures follow from the W branching ratios. The dominant mode is $t\bar{t} \to$ 6 jets. However, this mode suffers from large backgrounds and will not be covered in this review. Considering only electrons and muons, approximately 37% of $t\bar{t}$ events contain at least one lepton and 5% contain at least two leptons from $W \to l\nu$. These high P_T inclusive lepton samples provide the most promising channels in which to search for the top.

1.2. Current CDF Top Limits

In previous CDF runs, several analyses using inclusive lepton channels were used. For the 1988-89 run, final states with ee, $\mu\mu$, and $e\mu$ were looked for. In addition, CDF has searched for a low-transverse-momentum muon as a tag of the b quark in events with a high P_T electron or muon and at least 2 jets. From a $4.1 pb^{-1}$ data sample, a lower limit of $m(t) > 91 GeV/c^2$ was set at the 95% confidence level.[2]

Additional constraints on the top mass can be placed from electroweak measurements. Using measurements of the W mass and assuming a Higgs mass of less than $1000 GeV/c^2$, an upper limit on m_{top} of approximately $225 GeV/c^2$ is obtained at 95% C.L. This implies that the relevant mass range for future Standard Model top searches is 91 to $\sim 225 GeV/c^2$.

2. CDF Detector for 1992

Between the 88-89 and 1992 runs, numerous upgrades have been made to the

CDF detector. Of particular interest are the upgraded muon system and the addition of a silicon tracking detector around the beampipe. Many other improvements were also made, including upgrades to the lepton triggers and improved electron systems.

The upgraded muon system consists of two parts. The Central Muon upgrade (CMP) adds a steel wall of over 2 hadronic absorption lengths and additional layers of muon chambers outside the previous Central Muon system (CMU). This increases the total number of absorption lengths to over 8 in the region $|\eta| < 0.4$. The Central Muon extension (CMX) provides muon identification in the region $0.63 < |\eta| < 0.9$.

The Silicon Vertex detector (SVX) consists of two barrels in the region $|z| < 26cm$.[3] There are four layers of single-sided silicon wafers per barrel, providing precision $r\phi$ tracking information. The layers are arranged from $r = 3$ to $8cm$. This covers a region out to $|\eta| < 1.9$ at the outermost layer. The impact parameter resolution of the device is better than $40\mu m$ for tracks with $P_T > 1 GeV/c$. Using preliminary alignment constants, we obtain an impact parameter resolution of $\sim 13\mu m$ for tracks with $P_T > 10 GeV/c$.

3. b Tagging

The high P_T lepton + jets channel, with its relatively high branching ratio, provides a good way to select $t\bar{t}$ events. However, W+jets background may prove troublesome for higher mass top. To reduce this background, b tagging can be used. For the 1992 CDF run, two methods of b tagging are being developed. The first utilizes the tracking information from the SVX, and tags the b through displaced tracks. The second is an extension of the soft lepton analysis used in the 88-89 run.

3.1. b Tagging with the SVX

With its precision tracking information, the SVX can be used to tag the decay products of long-lived particles, in particular b-flavored hadrons. These decay products can be tagged by their impact parameter (d) relative to the primary event vertex. We also use impact parameter significance (S_d), which is the impact parameter d divided by σ_d, the total error in d.

The S_d distribution for tracks which are daughters of b-flavored hadrons falls slowly with increasing S_d. In contrast, S_d is sharply peaked towards 0 for tracks which are not from b. The distributions from top MC with $m_{top} = 120 GeV/c^2$ are shown in figure 1.

Displaced tracks are selected by requiring a minimum d and/or S_d for each track. Minimum requirements on P_T are also made to reject very low momentum tracks which typically have poorer tracking resolution. Displaced tracks in an event are then grouped into candidate b jets by vertexing the tracks or by looking for correlations in $\eta\phi$ space. CDF has developed several such methods for b tagging. Since this is still a new device and a new type of analysis, these SVX b tagging algorithms are still under study. Three representative methods will be summarized here.

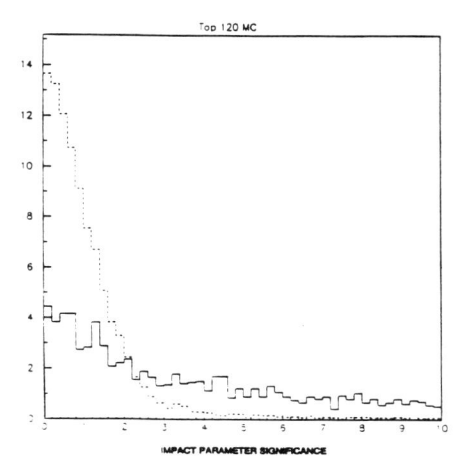

Figure 1: Impact Parameter Significance S_d for $m_{top} = 120 GeV/c^2$ Monte Carlo. Solid line is for tracks from b-flavored hadrons. Dashed line is for all other tracks. Distributions are normalised to equal area.

○ *$d\phi$ Clustering:* This method relies on the fact that tracks from a secondary vertex form a sinusoid in $d\phi$ space, where d is the signed impact parameter, and ϕ is the usual azimuthal angle in the transverse plane. This follows from simple geometric arguments. For forward boosted decays, we can approximate the relevant portion of the sinusoid with a straight line. Secondary vertices are then found by linking displaced tracks to straight lines in $d\phi$ space. Those with at least three tracks are tagged as b jet candidates.

○ *Jet Vertexing:* In this method, displaced tracks are assigned to jets if the track is within 25° of the jet axis. The displaced tracks in a given jet are then vertex constrained. Tracks which contribute more than 20 to the total χ^2 of the fit are discarded. The vertexing is then iterated. Jets with at least 2 surviving tracks are tagged as b jet candidates.

○ *Cone Tagging:* Cone tagging selects displaced tracks with some minimum P_T and S_d. A upper cut on d is also made, to reject very long-lived particles, such as K's. Displaced tracks within a cone of 0.4 are clustered together. Cones with at least three tracks are tagged as b jet candidates.

The event efficiencies for these b tagging methods rise with increasing top mass. For $m_{top} = 120 GeV/c^2$, efficiencies of about 23% are obtained. For $m_{top} = 160 GeV/c^2$, the efficiency rises to $\sim 33\%$. The expected background acceptance from W+jets is $\sim 0.7\%$ per event, where we have not included b tags due to real c and b quarks in W+jets events. These efficiencies include SVX acceptance, but do not include any kinematic or high P_T lepton cuts.

3.2. Kinematic Cuts

In addition to selecting a high P_T lepton and b tagging, kinematic cuts are needed to suppress the W+jets background. In particular, kinematic cuts should be extremely useful in reducing the $Wb\bar{b}$ background in the b tags.[4] We have studied many different variables, including jet counting, energy variables, such as ΣE_T and $\hat{s}$, and shape variables, such as sphericity and aplanarity. We find that jet counting seems to be as effective as any of the other methods, and has the advantage of being the simplest.

3.3. b Tagging with Soft Leptons

Another method of b tagging is to look for soft leptons from the processes $b \to l\nu X$ and $b \to cX \to l\nu X$. In every $t\bar{t}$ event, there will be two b and two c quarks. Using $Br(b \to lX) \sim 20\%$ and $Br(c \to lX) \sim 20\%$, where $l = e, \mu$, this means $\sim 57\%$ of all $t\bar{t}$ events will have at least one electron or muon from b or c. These leptons will have low P_T, with the spectrum peaked towards 0. CDF hopes to efficiently tag electrons and muons down to $P_T \sim 2 GeV/c$. Preliminary results give a low P_T lepton tag efficiency of $\sim 26\%$ per event for $m_{top} \geq 120 GeV/c^2$. The fake tag rate is on the order of 10^{-2} per track.

3.4. b Tag Observed Cross Sections

To illustrate the potential of these b tagging analyses, we use the following sets of cuts:

- an electron or muon with $P_T > 20 GeV/c$
- $\not{E}_T > 20 GeV$
- SVX or soft lepton tag:
  SVX tag: at least two jets with $E_T > 15 GeV$, at least one additional jet with $E_T > 10 GeV$, and an SVX b tag.
  Soft lepton tag: at least two jets with $E_T > 20 GeV$, at least one additional jet with $E_T > 10 GeV$, and an additional e or μ with $P_T > 2 GeV/c$.

In a data sample of $25 pb^{-1}$, the number of expected events using the SVX tag is ~ 13 for $m_{top} = 120 GeV$, falling to ~ 5 events for $m_{top} = 160 GeV$. The background from W+jets is ~ 2 events, which includes tags due to real c and b in the W+jets events. The expected number of top events using the soft lepton tag is comparable to that given by the SVX tag. However, the expected background for this mode is ~ 4 events. The expected observed cross sections for top and background are shown in figure 2.

4. Dilepton Analysis

The high P_T ee, $\mu\mu$, and $e\mu$ dilepton channels have a total branching fraction of only $\sim 5\%$, but has the advantage of low background rates. Based on the 88-89

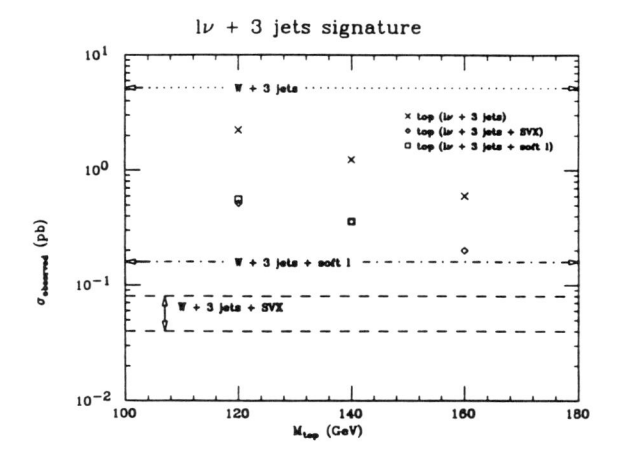

Figure 2: Expected observed cross sections for $t\bar{t}$ and W+jets using the high P_T lepton + 3 jets signature. The crosses are for top, before a b tag is applied. This should be compared to the dotted line for W+jets background. The diamonds are for top, after requiring an SVX b tag. The area bounded by the dashed lines is for W+jets+SVX. The squares are for top, after requiring a soft lepton b tag. The dot-dashed line is for W+jets+soft lepton.

analysis, we would expect about 64 top events for $m_{top} = 90 GeV$ in $25pb^{-1}$. A data sample of this size will allow CDF to look for top up to $\sim 130 GeV/c^2$ in the dilepton channels.[5] This is a conservative estimate, since CDF has a number of upgrades for the 1992 run, and the top selection efficiencies should rise slightly with increasing top mass. In addition, we can reduce the background to the dilepton analysis even further with kinematic cuts and/or b tagging.

5. Summary

CDF is working on a number of top search algorithms using dileptons and lepton + b tag. The SVX provides a powerful new selection method for tagging b jets, which complements the soft lepton tag algorithm. With $25pb^{-1}$ of data, these methods, and combinations these methods, will allow CDF to search for top up to masses of approximately 150 to $160 GeV/c^2$.

1. G. Altarelli *et al.*, *Nucl. Phys.* **B308**, 724 (1988); R. K. Ellis, *Fermilab-Pub-91/30T*; P. Nason *et al.*, *Nucl. Phys.* **B303**, 607 (1988).
2. F. Abe *et al.*, *Phys. Rev.* **D45**, 3921 (1992).
3. O. Schneider, contribution to these proceedings.
4. M. Mangano, contribution to these proceedings.
5. L. Song, contribution to these proceedings.

Top Search in the High P_T Dilepton Channel at CDF

Lingfeng Song
the CDF collaboration
Fermilab, Batavia, IL60510. USA

ABSTRACT

A standard model $t\bar{t}$ pair decays into high transverse momentum (P_T) dileptons (e or μ) with a branching ratio of 4/81. Top search in this channel has the advantage of a very clean signature and a low background rate, especially in the $e\mu$ channel. CDF has searched for top quark in this channel along with other decay channels during the 88/89 run, which had a total luminosity of 4.1 pb^{-1}. A lower top mass limit of 91 GeV was obtained. The current CDF data taking run is expected to yield a total luminosity of 25 pb^{-1}. In this talk, a summary of CDF's top search in this channel from the previous run as well as the current status at CDF will be presented.

1. Introduction

1.1. Top production and decay at the Tevatron energy

At $\sqrt{s} = 1.8$ TeV, the dominant process for top production is $p\bar{p} \to t\bar{t}$. In the Standard Model (SM), the top decay is mediated via weak charged current, i.e., $t \to Wb$. The current lower limit on the top mass is 91 GeV, obtained by the CDF collaboration during the 88/89 data taking run.[1] Therefore, the W produced in top decays are real. Based on the SM W decay branching ratios, one expects the total branching fraction for $t\bar{t}$ decays semileptonically to high P_T dileptons (e or μ) is 4/81. This does not include dileptons from $t \to \tau \to e$ or μ decays, which contributes to about 10% of the dilepton signal. Top search in the high P_T dilepton channels has many advantages. The high P_T isolated leptons are easily triggered and detected at a collider. The singals from W's and Z's will provide many important calibrations and efficiency factors. The background in this channel is relatively low and can be rejected with topology cuts. With enhanced B-tagging ability by introducing a silicon vertex detector for the 1992 run, CDF stands to improve the top signal in this channel much further.

1.2. The CDF detector for 1992 run

The CDF detector for the 88/89 run is well documented.[1] Here we just briefly describe the new and modified detector components. For the 1992-1993 run, two new muon system have been added. One overlaps with the existing central muon (CMU) system with a steel wall of 60cm thickness (about 2 interaction length λ). This brings the total materials for muons between pseudo-rapidity (η) 0.1 and 0.4 to about 7λ. Another muon system extends the coverage of CMU from $\eta = 0.63$ to 0.9. A silicon vertex detector (SVX) is first implemented at CDF. The SVX has 2 barrels, each with 4 layers of silicon strip detectors. The position resolution is studied to be

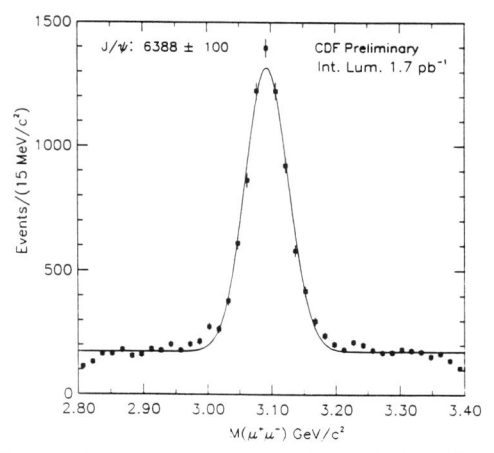

Figure 1: Low P_T dimuon invariant mass in the J/Ψ region

better than 12 microns. The SVX covers about 2/3 of the long interaction region. A new time projection vertex detector is also installed to replace the old detector. The end-plug calorimeter has been improved for better electron identification and triggering between $\eta = 1.1$ and 2.4. A new pre-shower detector is installed before the central calorimeter.

2. 1992 data (J/Ψ, W, Z)

The 1992-93 run is currently in progress. CDF has accumulated about 1.9 pb^{-1} as of writing. In this data sample, clean signals for J/Ψ, W and Z production has been studied. The J/Ψ acceptance is improved by a factor of 5 compare to the previous run, thanks to the lower trigger threshold and the new muon systems. A non-constraint low P_T di-muon invariant mass distribution in the J/Ψ mass region is shown in figure 1.

The W's and Z's are important not only for checking the working conditions of the detector, they are also very useful in determining the top detection efficiencies and for background studies. Figure 2 shows the W transverse mass and Z invariant mass distributions in both the electron and muon channels. The electron channel includes only the central calorimeters for the W's, while for Z's, the 2nd electrons can be in the plug. The muon tracks have been constrained to the colliding beam position in order to improve the momentum resolution. This is a preliminary result. No systematic corrections have been applied.

3. Detection efficiencies and background rejection

The detection efficiencies for high P_T leptons have been studied using the 88/89 data.[1] The over all efficiency for a 90 GeV top is about 0.8%. This means, if the top mass is 90 GeV ($\sigma = 150$ pb), 64 events will be expected in the high P_T

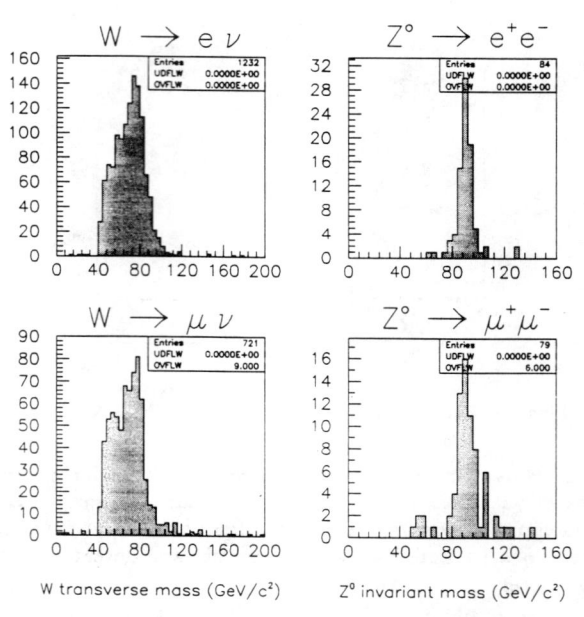

Figure 2: **W transverse mass and Z invariant mass distributions from 1992 data**

dilepton channel at CDF for an integrated luminosity of 25 pb^{-1}. The efficiency for higher top masses will be higher. The new CDF detector will also increase this efficiency factor. A conservative estimate based on this efficieny factor enables CDF to reach a top mass of about 130 GeV with 25 pb^{-1} in the dilepton channel.

4. Prospects for the 1992 run

For the current run, an integrated luminosity $\sim$ 25 pb^{-1} is expected. With the added B-tagging power by the SVX, some new search channels are available for $t\bar{t}$ decay to dileptons. One example is to look for an identified lepton, another high P_T track and a displaced vertex in the SVX. Since some leptons may fall into the inactive region of the detector or may just fail the lepton identification cuts, this search channel is expected to improve the acceptance for top decays into dileptons.

As accumulated luminosity rises, we are entering heavier top mass region, which leads to higher detection efficiencies. With 25 pb^{-1}, combining with all available searching channels, a 150 GeV top quark is within CDF's reach.

5. References

1. F. Abe et al. (the CDF Collaboration), *Phys. Rev.* **D45** (1992) 3921.

SEARCH FOR THE SM HIGGS AT LEP WITH THE L3 DETECTOR

Bing Zhou
Physics Department, Boston University
Boston, MA 02215, USA

Present the L3 Collaboration

ABSTRACT

Search for the Standard Model neutral Higgs is presented. Data collected with the L3 detector at LEP during 1990, 1991 and 1992 (untill Oct.), corresponding to 910,000 hadronic decays of the Z^0, were used in the analysis. At the 95% confidence level the Standard Model Higgs is excluded in the mass range $0 \geq M_{H^0} \geq 56.3$ GeV.

1. Introduction

1.1. The L3 Detector

The L3 detector[1] at the LEP e^+e^- collider covers 99% of 4π. The detector consists of a central tracking chamber, a high resolution electromagnetic calorimeter composed of BGO crystals with energy resolution of better than 1.5% for E > 2 GeV, a ring of scintillation counters, a uranium and brass hadron calorimeter with energy resolution of 10.2% at the Z^0 peak, and an accurate muon chamber system with momentum resolution of 2.5% for p = 45 GeV. These detectors are installed in a 12 m diameter magnet which provides a uniform field of 0.5 T along the beam direction.

1.2. Z^0 Collection at LEP with L3

L3 has collected large amount of data from Z^0 decays since fall 1989 as shown in the following table:

$Z^0 \to$	$q\bar{q}$	e^+e^-	$\mu^+\mu^-$	$\tau^+\tau^-$	Total
Events (89 - 91)	425k	16k	13k	10k	464k
Events (92, till Oct.)	565k	20k	17k	12k	614k

We report the search for the H^0 using the L3 data sample corresponding to 910,000 hadronic decays of the Z^0.

1.3. SM Higgs Production and Decays at LEP

At centre of mass energy near the Z^0 peak the main Higgs boson production mode is predicted to be through the Z^0 boson decay

$$e^+e^- \to Z^0 \to H^0 + Z^{0*} \to H^0 + f\bar{f}.$$

where fermion pairs from Z^{0*} are $\ell^+\ell^-$ pairs (Br=9%), $\nu\bar{\nu}$ pairs (Br=20%) and $q\bar{q}$ (Br=71%). In the search mass range that we are interested in, a Higgs boson decays mainly into $b\bar{b}$ (Br ~ 95%) in the Standard Model. The branch ratio of $H^0 \to \gamma\gamma$ is several order of magnitude lower. We list the major final states from $Z^0 \to H^0 Z^{0*}$ process and the LEP search status in the following table:

$H^0 \to$	$Z^{0*} \to$	Fraction (M_{H^0}=55 GeV)	Detection at LEP I
$q\bar{q}$	$\nu\bar{\nu}$	19.5%	high efficiency
$q\bar{q}$	e^+e^-	3.3%	high efficiency
$q\bar{q}$	$\mu^+\mu^-$	3.3%	high efficiency
$\tau^+\tau^-$	$\nu\bar{\nu}$	1.2%	low efficiency
$\tau^+\tau^-$	$q\bar{q}$	3.7%	very low eff.
$q\bar{q}$	$\tau^+\tau^-$	3.3%	very low eff.
$q\bar{q}$	$q\bar{q}$	65.8%	not used

It is clear that the final state '$q\bar{q}q\bar{q}$' has the largest branch ratio, however because of large QCD background, this channel has not been used at LEP for the SM Higgs search. We report on our search with clean signals in the $H^0\nu\bar{\nu}$, $H^0 e^+e^-$ and $H^0\mu^+\mu^-$ channels in the Higgs mass range from 30 GeV up to 70 GeV.

2. Search for the SM Higgs

We have previously reported on the searches for the Standard Higgs boson using the 1990+1991 data sample which corresponded to 408,000 hadronic decays of the Z^0[2], and excluded the SM Higgs in the mass range $0 < M_{H^0} < 52 GeV$ at the 95% C.L. With new data sample collected in 1992 (untill Oct.), which doubled the total data sample from 1990+1991, we have continued the search for the H^0.

2.1. $H^0\nu\bar{\nu}$ Event Selection

The $H^0\nu\bar{\nu}$ events are characterized by a large missing energy and momentum imbalance due to the undetected neutrinos from the Z^{0*} decay. However events with missing energy can also come from $\tau^+\tau^-$, 2γ process, and QCD background, where missing energies are due to neutrinos or particles escaped from the beam pipe. Large effort was made to separate the sources of the missing energies to distinguish the Higgs signals from the background based on the event topologies. The characteristic of the signal different from the background are: 1) Large low activity region due to $Z^{0*} \to \nu\bar{\nu}$; 2) Isolated missing energy (or undetected neutrinos); 3) Acollinear angle due to two jets from the Higgs decay receiving a Lorentz boost. The main criteria we used to select $H^0\nu\bar{\nu}$ event based on these features are:

- The energy imbalance transverse to the beam axis should be larger than 15%, and parallel to the beam axis should be less than 45% of the visible energy; the direction of the energy imbalance should be more than 0.4 rad away from the beam axis.

- $E_{90} < 10 GeV$ and $E_{60} < 3 GeV$, where E_{90} and E_{60} are the energies deposited in the cones with half opening angle of 90° and 60° respectively around two-jet back-side direction;

- $E_I < 1\ GeV$, where E_I is the energy deposited in a cone with a 20° half opening angle in the missing energy direction.

- Two-jet acollinear angle < 160° and acoplanar angle < 170°.

No data events pass our selection criteria.

2.2. $H^0\ell^+\ell^-$ Event Selection

The distinctive signature of the above process is the presence of two high energy well separated leptons (e^+e^- or $\mu^+\mu^-$) coming from the off-shell Z^{0*}, and isolated from the H^0 decay products. The main backgrounds with a similar signature are the four fermions process $e^+e^- \to \ell^+\ell^- q\bar{q}$ and the $Z^0 \to b\bar{b} \to \ell^+\ell^- X$ decay.

In addition to our previously selection criteria, we further required $H^0\ell^+\ell^-$ events satisfy the condition: $2m_{\ell\ell} + m_{recoil} > 80 GeV$ in order to reduce the four fermion background. Two $q\bar{q}e^+e^-$ events with m_{recoil} = 31.4±1.5 GeV and 67.6±0.7 GeV and one $q\bar{q}\mu^+\mu^-$ event with m_{recoil} = 70.4±0.7 GeV passed our selection cuts, which is consistent with predicted backgreound from four fermions.

2.3. Detection Efficiencies

The overall efficiency for the Higgs detection as a function of the H^0 mass is shown in the following table:

M_{H^0}(GeV)	30	40	50	55	60
$H^0\nu\bar{\nu}$ eff.(%)	29.5	52.8	57.7	51.8	46.2
$H^0e^+e^-$ eff.(%)	58.2	55.2	52.2	50.5	49.4
$H^0\mu^+\mu^-$ eff.(%)	61.8	64.8	64.2	59.6	57.4

The uncertainty in the selection efficiency has been studied in detail by changing the detector energy calibration and by using two different hadronisation models in the Monte Carlo. We found that the uncertainty level is below 1.5%.

3. New Results for the SM Higgs

Standard Model Higgs boson has been searched using the data collected with the L3 detector during 1990, 1991 and 1992, corresponding to 910,000 hadronic decays of the Z^0. We excluded the existance of the SM Higgs in the mass range $0 < M_{H^0} < 56.3$ GeV at the 95% confidence level.

4. Acknowledgements

I thank Drs D. Mao, A. Kunin, M. Pierim, J. Martin and L. Lista who contributed greatly to the L3 Higgs search analysis.

5. References

1. L3 Collaboration, B. Adeva *et al.*, *Nucl. Instr. and Meth.* **A289 (1990) 35**.
2. L3 Collaboration, CERN-PPE/92-40.

SEARCH FOR NON-MINIMAL HIGGS BOSONS FROM Z^0 DECAYS WITH THE L3 DETECTOR AT LEP[*]

A. SOPCZAK[†]

Department of Physics, University of California, San Diego
La Jolla, CA 92093-0319, U.S.A.

ABSTRACT

We report on a general search based on 408,000 hadronic Z^0 decays for neutral and charged Higgs bosons with no assumption that the Higgs sector consists of a single doublet as in the minimal Standard Model (MSM). No signal inconsistent with background is observed in any of the decay channels analyzed. From the results of direct searches, model independent limits on Higgs bremsstrahlung and on Higgs pair-production from the Z^0 are presented. We interpret the bremsstrahlung limits in the general two-doublet model. Z^0 lineshape measurements further restrict the parameter space available in the two-doublet model. Finally, the results are interpreted in the framework of the Minimal Supersymmetric extension of the Standard Model (MSSM).

In the Standard Model of electroweak interactions, the Higgs mechanism generates spontaneous breaking of the gauge symmetry and provides masses for the gauge bosons and charged fermions. A two-doublet extension of the MSM would have a richer Higgs particle spectrum and would add new phenomena to the Standard Model physics. The general theoretical background is summarized in [1]. Briefly, the Higgs sector of a two-doublet model contains 5 physical Higgs bosons: one neutral CP-odd scalar, A^0, two neutral CP-even scalars, H^0 and h^0, and two charged scalars, $H^{\pm}$. The masses of the Higgs bosons, the mixing angle α between the two neutral scalar Higgs fields and the ratio of the vacuum expectation values of the two Higgs doublets, $\tan\beta$, are free parameters. The Higgs production processes near the Z^0 resonance are: a) bremsstrahlung process ($Z^0 \to Z^{0*}h^0$ or $Z^0 \to Z^{0*}H^0$), b) neutral pair production ($Z^0 \to h^0A^0$ or $Z^0 \to H^0A^0$), and c) charged pair production ($Z^0 \to H^+H^-$).

A detailed presentation of this work is given in [2] and a comprehensive overview of Higgs searches at LEP is given in [3].

1. Constraints on Neutral Higgs Bosons of the Two-Doublet Higgs Model

The cross section for process (a) is proportional to $\sin^2(\beta - \alpha)$, while the cross section of process (b) is proportional to $\cos^2(\beta - \alpha)$. If for a set of parameters one process vanishes, the other dominates and the Higgs cannot escape detection.

1.1. Limit on $\sin^2(\beta - \alpha)$

Searches for Higgs boson bremsstrahlung in the mass range 0 to 60 GeV constrain the quantity $\sin^2(\beta - \alpha)$ of the two-doublet Higgs model. Besides the suppression of the Higgs production rate by $\sin^2(\beta - \alpha)$, the Higgs boson couplings to the up-and down-type fermions may be enhanced or suppressed compared to the predictions in the MSM. This relative enhancement factor depends on the unknown free parameters of the Higgs sector. A limit on $\sin^2(\beta - \alpha)$ is shown in Figure 1. The effects of changes in the selection efficiencies at production thresholds are clearly visible. The further structure in the exclusion contour is due to a few candidate events. Their number is in agreement with the expectations from four-fermion background.

1.2. Excluded Region in the (m_h, m_A) plane

---

[*]Talk given on behave of the L3 experiment.
[†]c/o CERN-PPE/L3, CH-1211 Geneva 23, Switzerland; E-mail: andre@cernvm.cern.ch

The limits on the contribution of pair-produced Higgs to Γ_Z give an upper limit on the quantity $\cos^2(\beta - \alpha)$. From our line-shape data, a limit on additional contributions to Γ_Z is set at 40 MeV. A mass pair (m_h, m_A) is excluded if the corresponding upper limit on $\sin^2(\beta - \alpha)$ from the bremsstrahlung process is lower than the lower limit coming from the pair production process. The selection efficiency for possible $h^0 \rightarrow A^0 A^0$ decays has been evaluated by dedicated searches. The reduction in the detection efficiency compared to the MSM Higgs search has been largely compensated. The small effect of the changed efficiencies are visible in the exclusion plots as discontinuities in the region where $h^0 \rightarrow A^0 A^0$ decays are allowed. The resulting exclusion plot is shown in Figure 2.

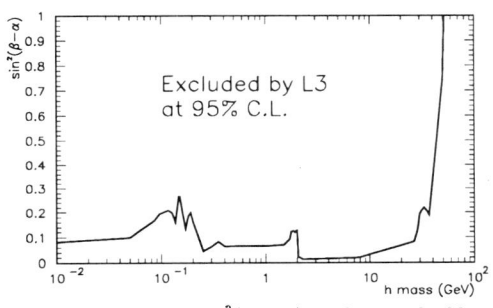

Figure 1: Limit on $\sin^2(\beta - \alpha)$ of the two-doublet Higgs model.

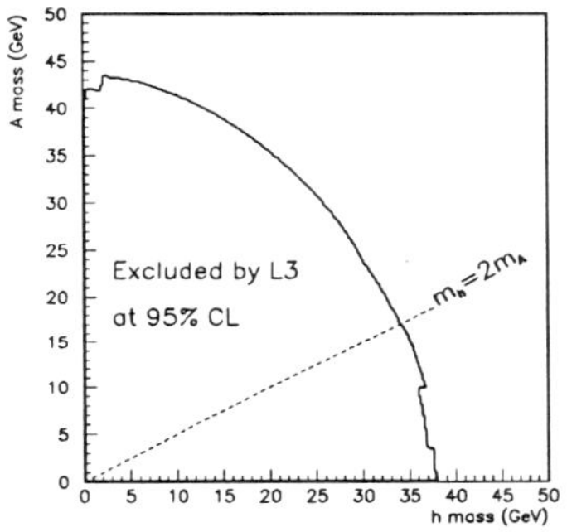

Figure 2: Exclusion in the (m_h, m_A) plane of the two-doublet Higgs model.

2. Search for Neutral Higgs Pair-Production

Signatures resulting from the following expected Higgs decay modes are investigated: $h^0/A^0 \rightarrow \tau^+\tau^-$, $h^0/A^0 \rightarrow b\bar{b}$, $h^0 \rightarrow A^0 A^0$. Searches for 4 jet, 6 jet, $\tau\tau$ jet jet and 4 τ signatures are performed. No signal has been observed in any of these channels. Figure 3 shows the excluded regions in the (m_h, m_A) plane for branching ratio limits on: $\Gamma(Z^0 \rightarrow h^0 A^0 \rightarrow \tau^+\tau^-\tau^+\tau^-)/\Gamma(Z^0 \rightarrow q\bar{q})$. The limits for the $Z^0 \rightarrow h^0 A^0 \rightarrow \tau^+\tau^- b\bar{b}$ process are shown in Figure 4 and the limits for the $Z^0 \rightarrow h^0 A^0 \rightarrow b\bar{b}b\bar{b}$ process are shown in Figure 5.

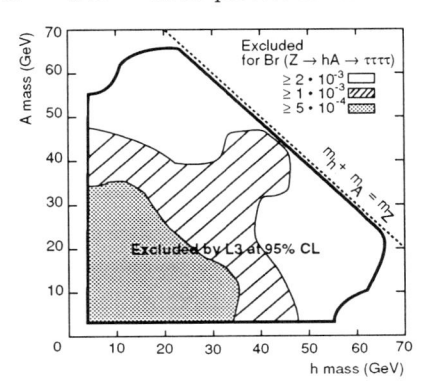

Figure 3: Regions of the (m_h, m_A) plane excluded at 95% CL for values of the branching ratio $\Gamma(Z^0 \rightarrow h^0 A^0 \rightarrow \tau^+\tau^-\tau^+\tau^-)/\Gamma(Z^0 \rightarrow q\bar{q})$ $\geq 5 \times 10^{-4}$ (dark region), 1×10^{-3} (hatched region) and 2×10^{-3} (region inside thick contour line).

The process $Z^0 \rightarrow h^0 A^0 \rightarrow A^0 A^0 A^0 \rightarrow b\bar{b}b\bar{b}b\bar{b}$ can dominate if $m_h > 2m_A$. The limit on the branching ratio in the mass range $18 \leq m_A \leq 27$ GeV and $m_h > 2m_A$ is given at 95% CL:

$$\frac{\Gamma(Z^0 \rightarrow b\bar{b}b\bar{b}b\bar{b})}{\Gamma(Z^0 \rightarrow q\bar{q})} \leq 9.4 \times 10^{-4}.$$

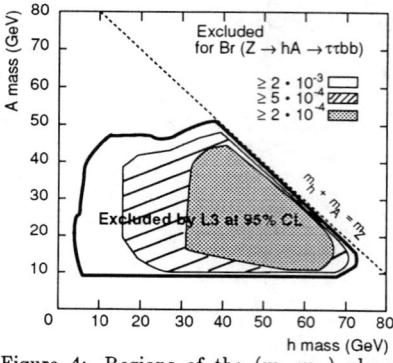

Figure 4: Regions of the (m_h, m_A) plane excluded at 95% CL for values of the branching ratio $\Gamma(Z^0 \to h^0 A^0 \to \tau^+\tau^- b\bar{b})/\Gamma(Z^0 \to q\bar{q}) \geq 2 \times 10^{-4}$ (dark region), 5×10^{-4} (hatched region) and 2×10^{-3} (region inside thick contour line). The analysis has been performed for $h^0 \to \tau^+\tau^-$ and $A^0 \to b\bar{b}$.

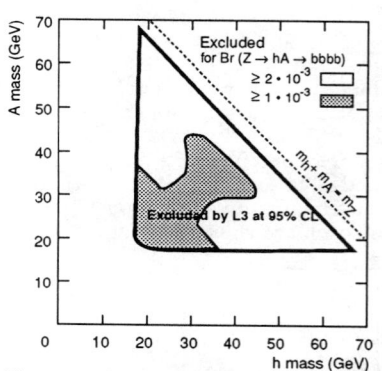

Figure 5: Regions of the (m_h, m_A) plane excluded at 95% CL for values of the branching ratio $\Gamma(Z^0 \to h^0 A^0 \to b\bar{b}b\bar{b})/\Gamma(Z^0 \to q\bar{q}) \geq 1 \times 10^{-3}$ (dark region), 2×10^{-3} (region inside thick contour line).

3. Search for Charged Higgs Pair-Production

The partial width for Z^0 decay into a charged Higgs pair depends only on the mass of the charged Higgs [1]. Searches for the three processes relevant at LEP-I are performed: $Z^0 \to H^+H^- \to \tau^+\nu\tau^-\nu$, $\tau\nu c\bar{s}$, $c\bar{s}\bar{c}s$.

No indication of a Higgs signal has been observed. The search in the hadronic decay channel is the most difficult one due to the irreducible $Z^0 \to q\bar{q}$ background. A lower Higgs mass limit of 41 GeV, independent of the Higgs branching ratio, is obtained. Figure 6 shows the 95% CL mass limit on charged Higgs bosons as a function of its leptonic branching ratio obtained from the search in the three channels.

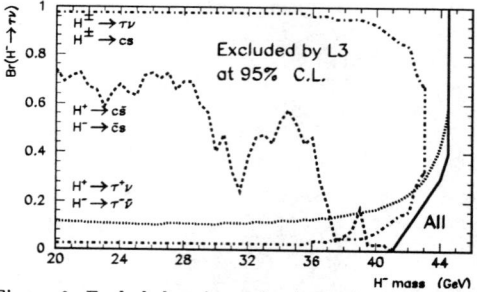

Figure 6: Excluded regions of pair-produced charged Higgs bosons as a function of the charged Higgs mass and the leptonic Higgs branching fraction. The thick contour line determines the combined mass limit.

4. Interpretation in the Minimal Supersymmetric Standard Model

The results obtained in the previous sections can be combined to set mass limits on the neutral Higgs bosons in the MSSM. The main implications of radiative corrections for the Higgs search can be extracted by making the following two assumptions [4]: a) it is assumed that all Supersymmetric partners are degenerate in mass and do not mix and b) only the leading top mass term in the radiative correction expression, m_{top}^4, is considered. Under the above assumptions, the radiative corrections to tree level calculations can be parameterized by a single dimensionless quantity, ϵ, for a given $m_{\rm top}$ and $m_{\rm stop}$: $\epsilon \equiv \frac{3\alpha_W}{2\pi} \frac{m_{\rm top}^4}{m_W^2 m_Z^2} \ln(\frac{m_{\rm stop}^2}{m_{\rm top}^2})$, where $\alpha_W = \alpha/\sin^2\theta_W$. The effects of radiative corrections on the expected Higgs signal are evaluated in the ranges: $90 < m_{\rm top} < 250$ GeV, $m_{\rm top} < m_{\rm stop} < 1000$ GeV. Within these ranges ϵ varies between 0 and 1.45. A range $1.0 < \tan\beta \le 50$ is chosen for this analysis. The effect of radiative corrections in the $(m_{\rm h}, m_{\rm A})$ plane is shown in Figure 7.

A given mass point in the $(m_{\rm h}, m_{\rm A})$ plane is excluded if, for any allowed value of ϵ, the model fails at least one of the searches for singly-or pair-production Higgs bosons, or if it fails the constraint from the Z^0 line-shape limit. Nearly the entire mass region in the $(m_{\rm h}, m_{\rm A})$ plane is excluded at 95% CL, independent of radiative corrections. Figure 8 shows the excluded regions.

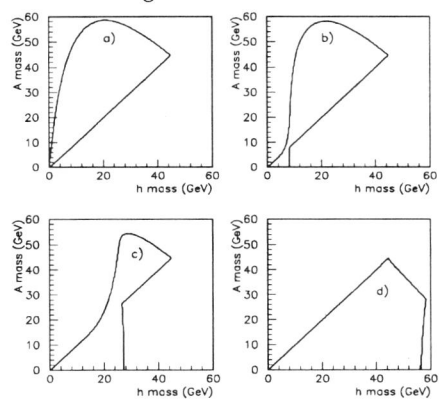

Figure 7: Region where more than 100 $Z^0 \to h^0 A^0$ events per 400,000 hadronic Z^0 decays are expected, including radiative corrections parameterized by ϵ. a) $\epsilon = 0.00$ b) $\epsilon = 0.01$ c) $\epsilon = 0.10$ d) $\epsilon = 1.00$.

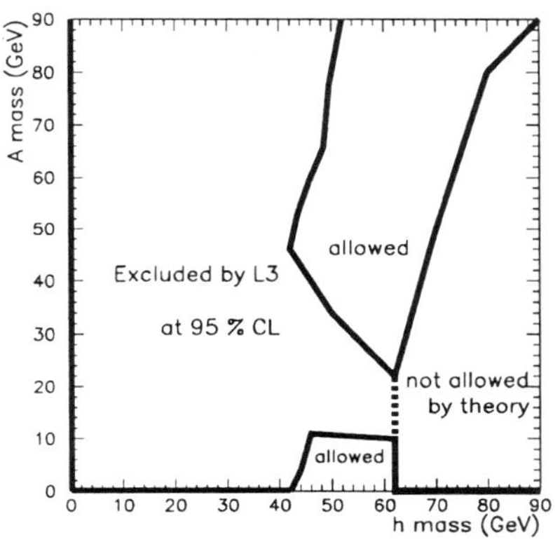

Figure 8: Excluded regions in the $(m_{\rm h}, m_{\rm A})$ plane at 95% CL in the MSSM, independent of radiative corrections.

References

1. S. Dawson, J.F. Gunion, H.E. Haber and G.L. Kane, "The Physics of the Higgs Bosons: Higgs Hunter's Guide" (Addison Wesley, Menlo Park, 1989).

2. A. Sopczak, "Search for Non-Minimal Higgs Bosons from Z^0 Decays with the L3 Detector at LEP", PhD Thesis, Univ. of Cal., San Diego, October 1992;
   L3 Collaboration, O. Adriani et al., "Search for Non-Minimal Higgs Bosons in Z^0 Decays", to be published by Z. Phys. C, CERN preprint CERN-PPE/92-163, September 1992;
   L3 Collaboration, O. Adriani et al., "Search for Non-Minimal Higgs Bosons in Z^0 Decays", to be published by Phys. Lett. B, CERN preprint CERN-PPE/92-140, August 1992.

3. A. Sopczak, Plenary talk "Higgs Search at LEP-I" given at the XV International Meeting on Elementary Particle Physics, Kazimierz, Poland, 25-29 May 1992, L3 note #1245, September 1992, to be published by World Scientific;
   A. Sopczak, "Search for Non-Minimal Higgs Bosons at LEP-I", L3 note #1230 and CERN preprint CERN-PPE/92-137, August 1992.

4. R. Barbieri and M. Frigeni, Phys. Lett. B **258** (1991) 395.

HINTS WITHIN THE STANDARD MODEL ON THE TOP-QUARK AND HIGGS-BOSON MASSES

ERNEST MA

Department of Physics, University of California
Riverside, California 92521, USA

ABSTRACT

If one or more otherwise divergent quantities in the standard model are actually finite, they may be indications of underlying dynamics. In particular, one-loop finiteness of the m_H renormalization is achieved if $m_t^2 \simeq m_H^2 = (2M_W^2 + M_Z^2)/3$.

1. Introduction

The standard model has a quadratic divergence proportional to

$$2\lambda + \frac{1}{2}g_1^2 + \frac{3}{2}g_2^2 - 4\sum_f \left(\frac{n_f}{3}\right) g_f^2, \tag{1}$$

where λ is the quartic scalar self-coupling, g_1 the U(1) gauge coupling, g_2 the SU(2) gauge coupling, and g_f the Yukawa couplings of the fermions f to the Higgs boson, with n_f the number of colors, i.e. 3 for quarks and 1 for leptons. This may very well be just an artifact of the regularization procedure and we can forget all about it after proper renormalization of all the physical quantities. Alternatively, we may take it seriously as a hint that new physics will come in at some energy scale higher than the electroweak scale of 10^2 GeV and make it finite. In a scenario involving supersymmetry, new particles will appear below 1 TeV or so and cancel the divergence associated with each term of the above expression. In a scenario without new particles up to an energy scale $\Lambda \gg 1$ TeV, it may be conjectured that whatever the underlying dynamics, it should be such that the above expression is suppressed, say of order $(10^2 \text{GeV}/\Lambda)^2$, which must then come about from the cancellation among the various couplings.

Attaching v^2 (square of the Higgs-boson vacuum expectation value) to (1) and setting it equal to zero, we obtain the well-known Veltman condition[1]

$$4m_t^2 \simeq 2M_W^2 + M_Z^2 + m_H^2, \tag{2}$$

where all other fermion masses have been dropped because their contributions are negligible. This condition is consistent with the present experimental data $M_Z = 91.175 \pm 0.021$ GeV, $M_W = 80.14 \pm 0.27$ GeV, $m_t > 91$ GeV, and $m_H > 60$ GeV.

2. A Closer Look

Since λ, g_1^2, g_2^2, and g_f^2 change as functions of q^2, and the expression (1) is not invariant under this change, the Veltman condition (2) should apply only at one unique mass scale. In the standard model, the presence of spontaneous symmetry breaking implies the existence of a tadpole diagram in which a physical Higgs boson ends up in a loop involving all the massive particles. This diagram is quadratically divergent and contributes to all self-masses. Hence the natural choice is $q^2 = m_H^2$.

3. Recent Conjectures

In addition to the condition (2), is there another hint within the standard model of a possible relationship among couplings? Perhaps a particular logarithmic divergence should be suppressed as well. This is the essence of 3 recent conjectures.

Osland and Wu[2] singled out the He^+e^- coupling and required its logarithmic divergence to be zero. This results in the condition

$$m_t^2 \simeq \frac{5}{2}M_Z^2 - M_W^2. \tag{3}$$

However it is not clear why this particular coupling should be chosen instead of some other, and once it is chosen, we must still define it at some q^2 because this logarithmic divergence cannot be zero at all mass scales.

Blumhofer and Stech[3] proposed to set the logarithmic divergence of the Higgs tadpole also to zero. This has the advantage of a well-defined q^2, *i.e.* m_H^2, but the procedure is gauge-dependent and therefore suspect. However, they argued that the choice $\xi = 0$ in the R_ξ gauge would correspond to a gauge-invariant physical quantity having to do with vacuum condensates. This then implies

$$4m_t^4 \simeq 2M_W^4 + M_Z^4 + \frac{1}{2}m_H^4. \tag{4}$$

Decker and Pestieau[4] chose the mass of the electron neutrino and required its logarithmic divergence to be zero, assuming of course that there is a right-handed singlet partner to the observed left-handed neutrino and they combine to allow a Dirac mass. This results in the following condition

$$4m_t^4 \simeq 2M_W^4 + M_Z^4 + \frac{1}{2}m_H^4 + \frac{1}{2}(m_e^2 - m_{\nu_e}^2)m_H^2, \tag{5}$$

which is almost identical to (4). Again it is not clear why this particular mass (which may not even exist) should be chosen instead of some other.

4. The Most Natural Choice

If a particular logarithmic divergence is to be chosen zero in addition to the Veltman condition, the most natural choice is clearly that of the Higgs-boson mass itself.[5] After all, it is uniquely defined at $q^2 = m_H^2$ as already assumed in (2). It is also gauge-independent. The resulting condition is

$$2m_t^2 \simeq 2M_W^2 + M_Z^2 - m_H^2, \tag{6}$$

which, when combined with (2), implies

$$m_t^2 \simeq m_H^2 = \frac{2}{3}M_W^2 + \frac{1}{3}M_Z^2. \tag{7}$$

If dimensional regularization is used to extract the quadratic divergence of the standard model, the residue of the pole at $d = 2$ depends also on d and the Dirac trace. To get the Veltman condition, we have to set both equal to 4. Perhaps we should[2] really use the value 2, then instead of (2), we find

$$6m_t^2 \simeq 2M_W^2 + M_Z^2 + 3m_H^2. \tag{8}$$

Remarkably, when combined with (6), the condition (7) is again obtained. Hence the proposed conjecture of one-loop finite m_H renormalization is independent of the regularization procedure for the quadratic divergence.

5. Conclusion

Numerically, the condition (7) implies

$$m_t \simeq 84 \text{ GeV } + \text{ higher} - \text{order corrections}, \tag{9}$$
$$m_H \simeq 84 \text{ GeV } + \text{ higher} - \text{order corrections}, \tag{10}$$

whereas present data require $m_t > 91$ GeV, and $m_H > 60$ GeV. Hence the above conjecture is on the verge of being ruled out. On the other hand, if either (2) or (6) turns out to be approximately satisfied, it may still be an indication of underlying dynamics.

It should be noted that the above conditions are all based on only one-loop contributions and there is no explicit reference to the mass scale Λ of new physics. The higher-order contributions, all defined at $q^2 = m_H^2$, are considered as small corrections, but they will depend on Λ logarithmically.

ACKNOWLEDGEMENT

This work was supported in part by the U. S. Department of Energy under Contract No. DE-AT03-87ER40327.

References

1. M. Veltman, *Acta Physica Polonica* **B12**, 437 (1981).
2. P. Osland and T. T. Wu, *Phys. Lett.* **B291**, 315 (1992); CERN Reports CERN-TH.6385/92, CERN-TH.6386/92, CERN-TH.6387/92.
3. A. Blumhofer and B. Stech, *Phys. Lett.* **B293**, 137 (1992).
4. R. Decker and J. Pestieau, Univ. of Karlruhe Report TTP/92-22 (Jun 1992).
5. E. Ma, Univ. of California, Riverside Report UCRHEP-T100 (Sep 1992).

TOP AND HIGGS MASSES IN A COMPOSITE BOSON MODEL

D.E. KAHANA
Physics Department, Kent State University
Kent, OH 44242, USA

and

S.H. KAHANA
Physics Department, Brookhaven National Laboratory
Upton, NY 11973, USA

ABSTRACT

The Standard model of electroweak interactions, with the gauge and Higgs bosons appearing as composites, is derived from a Nambu–Jona-Lasinio-type four-fermion interaction, which is assumed to be valid above a high scale μ. Simple relationships are found for the composite boson to top quark mass ratios and for the weak angle: $m_W^2 = 3/8 m_t^2$, $m_H^2 = 4 m_t^2$, and $\sin^2 \theta_W = 3/8$ as in grand unified theories. Assuming three generations and a 'desert' hypothesis, these relationships are evolved with the full renormalisation group down to present experimental energies, yielding predictions for the top quark and Higgs-boson masses, near 155 GeV for the former and near 140 GeV for the latter. In this fashion, fermion-antifermion condensates can be shown to yield a top mass consistent with that indicated from loop corrections for LEP data.

Recently Nambu[1] as well as Bardeen, Hill and Lindner[2] have suggested replacing the Higgs mechanism with dynamical symmetry breaking generated by four fermion interactions of the top quark. In fact the model for replacing the scalar sector is that of Nambu and Jona-Lasinio[3] (NJL) and one recovers the Higgs as a $t\bar{t}$ composite. Earlier authors[4,5,6,7,8] have also treated vector mesons as composites within the NJL framework, with perhaps the earliest suggestion being that of Bjorken[9] for a composite photon. Here[10] we attempt to generate the entire electroweak interaction from a specific current–current, baryon number conserving form of the four fermion interaction. The W, Z and Higgs bosons appear as coherent composites of all fermions, quarks and leptons, and not just of the top quark. The four fermion interaction is assumed to be valid above some high mass scale μ, and might perhaps be found as a low energy limit of some more basic theory, by eliminating non–fermionic degrees of freedom. The cutoff Λ, necessary in the non–renormalizable NJL may be viewed then as the proper scale for this more basic theory.

At the intermediate mass scale μ, $\Lambda \gg \mu \gg m_W$, simple asymptotic relations are obtained for the ratios of composite boson masses to the top mass and also for the weak angle θ_W. The theory is highly restrictive, specifying, under the assumption of a very massive top and three generations,

$$m_W^2(\mu) \approx (3/8)\, m_t^2(\mu) \tag{1}$$

and

$$\sin^2\theta_W(\mu) \approx 3/8 \tag{2}$$

the latter relation being reminiscent of grand unified models. The standard NJL result $m_H^2(\mu) \approx 4 m_t^2(\mu)$ is also present, following from a fine tuning which eliminates quadratic divergences in the scalar sector of the theory. The W to top mass ratio follows from a similar fine tuning in the vector sector which is, interestingly, equivalent to demanding a vanishing photon mass.

The scale μ at which these striking relations obtain does not represent new physics but simply a point below which the strong interactions cannot be ignored. Below the scale μ the effects of the extended SU(3)×SU(2)×U(1) are included through the usual renormalization–group equations. The mass and angle relations provide boundary conditions for the R-G evolution downwards to m_W, and lead to predictions for m_t/m_W and m_H/m_t at present experimental energies. There is a strong phenomenological hint that μ be near the GUT scale; this we think adds to the predictability of the model relative to theories based only on the scalar sector. We then find, for three generations, central values $m_t \approx 155$ GeV and $m_{\text{Higgs}} \approx 140$ GeV. Using the evolution of $\sin^2\theta_W$ to its known experimental value results in $\mu \approx 10^{13}$ GeV but a change to $\mu \approx 10^{15}$ little alters these mass predictions.

The model[10] is defined completely by the specific choice of Lagrangian

$$\begin{aligned}\mathcal{L} = \bar{\psi} i\gamma\cdot\partial\psi &- \frac{1}{2}[(\bar{\psi} G_S \psi)^2 - (\bar{\psi} G_S \tau\gamma_5\psi)^2] \\ &- \frac{1}{2} G_B^2 (\bar{\psi}\gamma_\mu Y\psi)^2 - \frac{1}{2} G_W^2 (\bar{\psi}\gamma_\mu \tau P_L \psi)^2\end{aligned} \tag{3}$$

with $\psi = [\psi_i]$, and $i = \{t_L, t_R, b_L, b_R, e_L e_R, \gamma_L\}$ for each included generation. G_B, G_W are universal vector couplings for the iso–scalar and iso–vector interactions respectively while P_L, Y, and τ are defined in the usual fashion. Breaking of weak isospin symmetry is introduced via the scalar coupling G_S, taken for simplicity to be diagonal. The choice in Eq.(3) is unique if the standard model for quark–boson interactions is to be recovered. The meson Lagrangian is obtained by constructing the effective potential through elimination of fermion degrees of freedom[10]. This corresponds also to treating the four fermion theory to leading order in the $1/N$ expansion.

The standard electroweak model follows, including fermion–boson couplings if two fine tunings are applied, the usual NJL scalar fine tuning[3] and a look–alike for the vector sector

$$n_g \frac{G_W^2 \beta^2}{\pi^4} \sum_i Q_i^2 \int d^4k \frac{1/2 k^2 + m_i^2}{(k^2 + m_i^2)^2} = 1 \tag{4}$$

with n_g the number of generations, $\beta = \sin\theta_W$, and Q_i, m_i the charge and mass of the i'th fermion. Both fine tunings provide connections between the dimensional NJL couplings and the cutoff in the form $G_{S,B,W}^2 \sim \frac{1}{\Lambda^2}$ for large Λ and after these are invoked only the usual dimensionless electroweak couplings survive.

The composite boson Lagrangian is generated directly from the effective potential, both kinetic and mass terms. Setting the photon mass term in the Lagrangian to zero produces Eq.(3) and yields the explicit relations Eq.(1) above between m_W, m_t and the symmetry breaking fermion masses. A straightforward diagonalization of the most divergent terms ($\sim \log \Lambda$) in the neutral vector meson sector in terms of the physical particles Z and the photon is responsible for the relationship $\sin^2 \theta_W(\mu) \approx 3/8$, independent of generation. Small corrections to these relations obtain because of non-vanishing lighter fermion masses and because of higher order electroweak interactions.

One might question the source of the simplicity of the mass relation and the unique value for $\sin^2 \theta_W$. One is dealing in the effective Lagrangian with the highest order terms, which are independent of the fermion masses. Therefore, given that our fermions fall into a $\bar{5} + 10$ representation of $SU(5)$, the results must reflect a symmetry consistent with this minimal GUT theory. The physics is however somewhat different: no direct baryon number breaking interactions are present and important constraints exist on the allowed boson masses.

Finally, we then assume the simple parameter relations are achieved at some mass scale μ near the GUT scale and hence in a region where strong and electroweak interactions are both weak. In detailed calculation only the Higgs self-coupling $\lambda(\mu) = 2g_t^2(\mu)$ is changing at all appreciably and we tested the stability of our results by allowing for a wide variation about the NJL relation $m_H^2 = 4m_t^2(\mu)$. We choose the scale μ so that $\sin^2 \theta_W$ evolves down to the experimental value 0.232. The choice of scale μ by this procedure may compensate for the vagueness in applying sharp boundary conditions. We find $\mu = 7.5 \times 10^{12}$ GeV for $\sin^2 \theta_W(m_W) = 0.232$. Evolving

$$\frac{m_t^2}{m_W^2} = \frac{2K_t}{\alpha^2} = \frac{8}{3} \qquad (5)$$

leads to

$$m_t(m_W) = 2.04 m_W = 155 \text{ GeV} \qquad (6)$$

which is altered by some 5% for a two orders of magnitude increase in μ. Using the single loop self-coupling to evolve the Higgs mass relation gives $m_H(m_W) = 137(128)$GeV for $\mu = 7.5 \times 10^{12}(7.5 \times 10^{14})$ GeV. A drastic change in mass ratio to $(m_H/m_t)^2 = 8$ moves the Higgs mass to 153 GeV/c, still a rather low value. For top masses in the region 100–150 GeV the evolution of the top mass from m_W to μ is rather flat. Thus the more rapidly evolving Higgs, essentially unimpeded by strong interactions, moves from barely bound (in terms of $t\bar{t}$) at μ to deeply bound at M_W.[2] These predictions are certainly consistent with constraints based on loop corrections and LEP data..

Introduction of a fourth generation is difficult. Assuming $m'_t = m'_b = m_t$ results in a top mass of 115 GeV, a barely altered Higgs and of course heavy 4th generation leptons. Such a possibility may be soon ruled out at Fermilab.

References

1. Y. Nambu, Fermi Institute Report No. 89-08, 1989 (unpublished)
2. W. Bardeen, C.T. Hill, and M. Lindner, *Phys. Rev.* **D41**, 1647 (1990)
3. Y. Nambu and G. Jona-Lasinio, *Phys. Rev.* **122**, 345 (1961)
4. H. Terazawa, Y. Chikashige, and K. Akama, *Phys. Rev.* **D15**, 480 (1977)
5. T. Eguchi, *Phys. Rev.* **D14**, 2755 (1976)
6. M. Bando, T. Kugo, and K. Yanawaki, *Phys. Rep.* **164**, 210 (1988)
7. M. Suzuki, *Phys. Rev.* **D37**, 210 (1988)
8. V.A. Miranski, M. Tanabashi, and K. Yamawaki, *Mod. Phys. Lett.* **A4**, 1043 (1989)
9. J.D. Bjorken, *Ann. Phys.* (NY) **24**, 174 (1963)
10. D.E. Kahana and S.H. Kahana, *Phys. Rev.* **D43**, 2361 (1991)

TWO-LOOP UNITARITY CONSTRAINTS ON THE HIGGS BOSON MASS[1]

L. DURAND, P. N. MAHER, and K. RIESSELMANN
Department of Physics, University of Wisconsin - Madison
Madison, Wisconsin 53706, USA

ABSTRACT

We have calculated the complete elastic $2 \to 2$ scattering matrix for the longitudinally polarized gauge bosons W_L^+, W_L^-, Z_L and the Higgs boson H to two loops in the limit $s \gg M_H^2 \gg M_W^2$. Using these amplitudes we have examined the breakdown of perturbation theory in an Argand diagram analysis of the diagonalized neutral elastic scattering matrix for the $J = 0$ partial wave. Introducing the running coupling λ_s we find that the perturbation series fails to converge to two loops unless $\lambda_s \lesssim 2.3$. Beyond this value the theory becomes effectively strongly interacting. Choosing a scale up to which the Standard Model is to be correct, we obtain upper limits on the mass of a weakly interacting Higgs boson. For a scale $\sqrt{s} = 5$ TeV (10^{16} GeV) the limit is $M_H \lesssim 380$ (155) GeV.

1. Introduction

One of the key particles of the Standard Model (SM) still eluding discovery is the Higgs boson H. Whereas experiments provide lower limits for its mass M_H, unitarity of scattering theory allows calculation of upper limits for M_H if a weakly interacting theory is assumed[1,2]. Denoting longitudinally polarized gauge bosons by W_L^+, W_L^-, and Z_L, we investigate $2 \to 2$ processes among the neutral pairs $W_L^+ W_L^-$, $Z_L Z_L$, HH, and $Z_L H$ for unitarity violation of the corresponding 4×4 S-matrix.

2. Calculation of S-Matrix

Using the equivalence theorem the scattering matrix $S(W_L^+, W_L^-, Z_L, H)$ is calculated by replacing the longitudinally polarized gauge bosons by scalar massless Goldstone bosons w^+, w^-, and z. Assuming $M_H \gg M_W$ the S-matrix is given by[3]

$$S(W_L^+, W_L^-, Z_L, H) = S(w^+, w^-, z, H) + \mathcal{O}(M_W/\sqrt{s}) + \mathcal{O}(g^2) \quad (1)$$

where g is the gauge coupling. Working in the high energy limit, $\sqrt{s} \gg M_H$, the calculation further simplifies as the 3-point coupling $i\lambda v$ of the Higgs sector results in scattering amplitudes of $\mathcal{O}(M_H/\sqrt{s})$ which we neglect. Consistent with this approach all particle lines in the scattering graphs can be taken massless. This leads to only three distinct 2-loop scattering graphs with all massless lines. For the on-mass-shell renormalization, however, all self-energy graphs with both 3- and 4-point couplings

---
[1] Talk presented by Kurt Riesselmann.

have to be calculated using the physical, non-zero Higgs mass and zero Goldstone boson masses. The counterterms can be fixed such that the tree-level relation $M_H^2 = 2\lambda v^2$ is preserved to all orders in λ and all tadpole graphs are completely cancelled[4]. We have calculated the finite contributions of the remaining 34 distinct 2-loop self-energy graphs[5].

3. Argand Diagram Analysis

We diagonalized the 4×4 S-matrix described above using two-particle eigenstates χ_i, $1 \leq i \leq 4$. Then the unitarity of the S-matrix can be written in terms of partial-wave amplitudes as

$$\left| a_J^{2\to 2,i} - \frac{i}{2} \right|^2 + \sum_{n>2}^{\infty} \left| a_J^{2\to n,i} \right|^2 = \frac{1}{4}, \quad 1 \leq i \leq 4, \quad (2)$$

where

$$a_J^{2\to 2,i} = \frac{1}{32\pi} \int_{-1}^{1} d\cos\theta \mathcal{M}^{2\to 2,i}(s,t,u) P_J(\cos\theta), \quad (3)$$

$\mathcal{M}^{2\to 2,i}$ being the Feynman amplitude of the scattering process $\chi_i \to \chi_i$. The neglect of the $2 \to n$ channels gives an inequality which limits the $2 \to 2$ amplitude to the interior of the usual unitarity circle. The energy dependence of the diagonalized amplitudes $a_J^{2\to 2,i}$ is absorbed into a running coupling[5]

$$\lambda_s(\frac{s}{M_H^2}) = \lambda \left[1 - \frac{12\lambda}{16\pi^2} \left(1 - \frac{13\lambda}{16\pi^2} \right) \left(\log(\frac{s}{M_H^2}) + \frac{25 - 3\sqrt{3}\pi}{12} \right) \right]^{-1} \quad (4)$$

and negligible anomalous dimension factors. This means $a_J^{2\to 2,i}(s, \lambda) \approx a_J^{2\to 2,i}(\lambda_s)$. The partial-wave projected diagonalized $2 \to 2$ amplitudes can then be plotted in an Argand diagram as a function of λ_s (Fig. 1). The violation of unitarity is obvious for

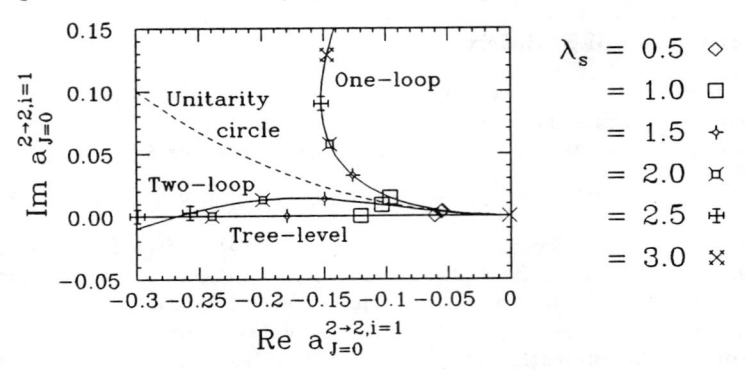

Figure 1: The Argand diagram for $a_{J=0}^{2\to 2,i=1}$. The amplitude is parametrized by λ_s.

large values of λ_s, especially as the imaginary part of $a_{J=0}^{2\to 2,i=1}$ becomes negative for

$\lambda_s \gtrsim 2.6$. A strong unitarity violation occurs despite the smallness of the amplitude.

4. Convergence of Perturbation Series

We have used several criteria to estimate how quickly the perturbation series converges for given λ_s, hence, to quantify the violations of unitarity evident in Fig. 1. The quantities we examined are

$$r_1 = \left|\frac{a^{(2)}}{a^{(0)} + a^{(1)}}\right|, \quad r_2 = \left|\frac{a^{(0)} + a^{(1)} + a^{(2)}}{a^{(0)} + a^{(1)}}\right|, \quad r_3 = \left|\frac{a^{(2)}}{a^{(1)}}\right|. \qquad (5)$$

where $a^{(m)}$ is the m-loop contribution to $a_J^{2 \to 2, i}$. For $J = 0$ we find that

$$r_1 \leq 1.0 \ (0.5) \text{ for } \lambda_s \lesssim 2.3 \ (1.8), \qquad (6)$$
$$r_2 \leq 2.0 \ (1.5) \text{ for } \lambda_s \lesssim 2.3 \ (1.9), \qquad (7)$$
$$r_3 \leq 1.0 \ (0.5) \text{ for } \lambda_s \lesssim 2.3 \ (1.2). \qquad (8)$$

Here we have given the strongest limit of any of the four amplitudes $a_{J=0}^{2\to 2,i}$. For $J \geq 1$ the restrictions are much less severe. However, the scattering amplitudes of the processes investigated come almost entirely from the $J = 0$ contribution. Thus the $J = 0$ restrictions given above are the ones indicating the onset of a strongly interacting theory.

5. Conclusions

Our calculation has shown that a too-heavy Higgs boson violates the unitarity of the S-matrix at two loops and severely inhibits the convergence of perturbation theory. This implies an upper bound on the Higgs mass in a weakly interacting SM. Taking $\lambda_s = 2.3$ in conjuction with Eq. (4) we obtain our bound on M_H. It depends on the choice of the energy scale up to which the SM is supposed to be correct. For a scale $\sqrt{s} = 5$ TeV (10^{16} GeV) the limit is $M_H \lesssim 380$ (155) GeV. These limits are almost identical to the limits found earlier in a one-loop calculation[2]. The results show the importance of questioning the validity of perturbative results involving a large Higgs mass.

6. References

1. B. W. Lee, C. Quigg, and H. B. Thacker, *Phys. Rev. Lett.* **38** (1977) 883; *Phys. Rev.* **D16** (1977) 1519.
2. Loyal Durand, James M. Johnson, and Jorge L. Lopez, *Phys. Rev. Lett.* **64** (1990) 1215; *Phys. Rev.* **D45** (1992) 3112.
3. J. Bagger and C. Schmidt, *Phys. Rev.* **D41** (1990) 264; H. Veltman, *Phys. Rev.* **D41** 2294 (1990).
4. J. C. Taylor, *Gauge Theories of Weak Interactions* (Cambridge University Press, Cambridge, 1976), Chapter 16.4.
5. Peter N. Maher, Loyal Durand, and Kurt Riesselmann, MAD/TH/92-1, 1992.

W, Z AND HIGGS SCATTERING AT SSC ENERGIES[*]

S. N. Gupta and James M. Johnson
Department of Physics, Wayne State University
Detroit, MI 48202, USA

and

Wayne W. Repko
Department of Physics and Astronomy, Michigan State University
East Lansing, MI 48824, USA

ABSTRACT

We examine the scattering of longitudinal W, Z and Higgs bosons in the Standard Model using the equivalent Goldstone-boson Lagrangian. Our calculations include the full one-loop scattering matrix between the states $W_L^+ W_L^-$, $Z_L Z_L$ and HH with no restrictions on the relative sizes of M_H and $\sqrt{s}$. In addition to deriving the perturbative eigen-amplitudes, we also obtain quite striking results by unitarizing the amplitudes with the use of the K-matrix and Padé techniques.

1. Introduction

There has been much recent interest in the scattering of longitudinal gauge bosons in the Standard Model. Theoretically, the symmetry breaking mechanism of the Electroweak theory is not well known, especially in the case of a strongly coupled symmetry breaking sector. Therefore it is natural to examine the most basic processes, such as the scattering of the longitudinal gauge bosons. Experimentally, the scattering of gauge bosons will be measured at future hadron colliders such as the SSC. For a sufficiently large Higgs mass, this process will be a main source for Higgs bosons. However, for large M_H and therefore strong coupling, the Feynman amplitudes violate unitarity and must be unitarized. The various unitarization methods must include all possible open channels, and at energies above $2M_H$ the HH channel must be included. Therefore the whole 3 × 3 matrix of amplitudes between the states $W_L^+ W_L^-$, $Z_L Z_L$ and HH must be calculated. Moreover, since we are interested in strong coupling, the tree amplitude will be insufficient, and we will need the amplitudes to at least one-loop.

2. Calculation

We performed this calculation with the aid of the Goldstone Boson Equivalence Theorem, which allows one to replace the longitudinal vector gauge bosons with the corresponding scalar goldstone bosons. Previously, the 3 × 3 scattering matrix has been calculated at the tree-level and the 2 × 2 submatrix of gauge boson

---
[*]Presented by James M. Johnson.

scattering to one-loop. The one-loop calculation of the HH channels is considerably more difficult because of the larger number of diagrams and their mathematical complexity. The complexity of diagrams increases with the number of massive internal propagators, and the new diagrams contained more of these. For example, of a total of six box diagrams in the entire calculation, five were new boxes needed for the HH channels. After adding the contributions of all of the diagrams, the amplitudes were then numerically integrated to yield the s-wave projections, shown in Figure 1.

3. Unitarization

Although the Feynman expansion is unitary as a whole, unitarity is violated order-by-order. This is especially noticeable at the Higgs pole, where the Feynman amplitude becomes infinite (see Figure 2a). One remedy is to add a finite width for the Higgs boson. However, this is an *ad hoc* solution which will not solve the problem of unitarity violation due to large coupling. In Figure 2b for a $M_H = 1000$ GeV, the absolute value of the Feynman amplitude is larger than one for all energies above the Higgs pole.

The solution is to consistently unitarize the amplitudes. We have considered two popular methods: the K-matrix and Padè unitarizations. If one starts with a Feynman expansion: $\mathbf{A}_1 + \mathbf{A}_2 + \ldots$, where $\mathbf{A}_1$ is the matrix of tree amplitudes and $\mathbf{A}_2$ is the matrix of one-loop corrections, then the K-matrix unitarization is given by $\Re(\mathbf{A}_1 + \mathbf{A}_2)[\mathbf{I} + i\Re(\mathbf{A}_1 + \mathbf{A}_2)]^{-1}$ and the Padé by $\mathbf{A}_1[\mathbf{A}_1 - \mathbf{A}_2]^{-1}\mathbf{A}_1$.

Since both techniques are given by matrix expressions, it is not surprising that the channels become mixed, and contributions of other channels can influence even the $W_L^+W_L^- \to W_L^+W_L^-$ scattering amplitude. Figure 2 shows the effects of these unitarizations on the Feynman amplitudes for this process. It is apparent that both techniques nicely unitarize the Higgs resonance, without the need to put in a width by hand. In the case of $M_H = 1000$ GeV, they both also reduce the large, unitarity violating amplitude above resonance. However, there are differences between them. In the case of $M_H = 500$ GeV, an additional resonance appears at $\sqrt{s} = 2800$ GeV in the Padé unitarization, but not for the K-matrix. For $M_H = 1000$ GeV the Padé amplitude also shows the effect of the HH threshold at $\sqrt{s} = 2000$ GeV, more so than for the K-matrix. How much physical significance to give to the interesting features from the Padé unitarization is unclear.

In Figure 3 we present cross-sections for $pp \to W_L^+W_L^- \to W_L^+W_L^-X$ at the SSC for the two unitarizations. For $M_H = 500$ GeV there is little difference at experimentally realizable energies, while for a larger Higgs mass there is a much larger difference between the unitarizations.

5. Acknowledgements

This work was supported in part by the U.S. Department of Energy under grant No. DE-FG02-85ER40209 and National Science Foundation grant 90-06117.

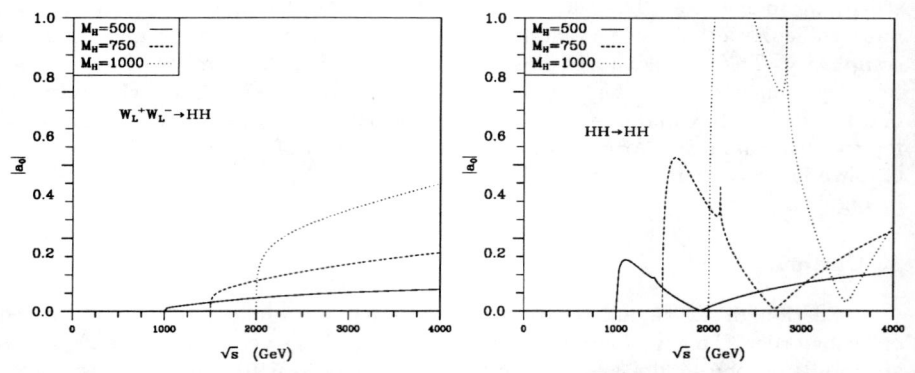

Figure 1: Absolute value of the s-wave Feynman amplitudes of $W_L^+ W_L^- \to HH$ and $HH \to HH$ scattering for $M_H = 500$, 750 and 1000 GeV.

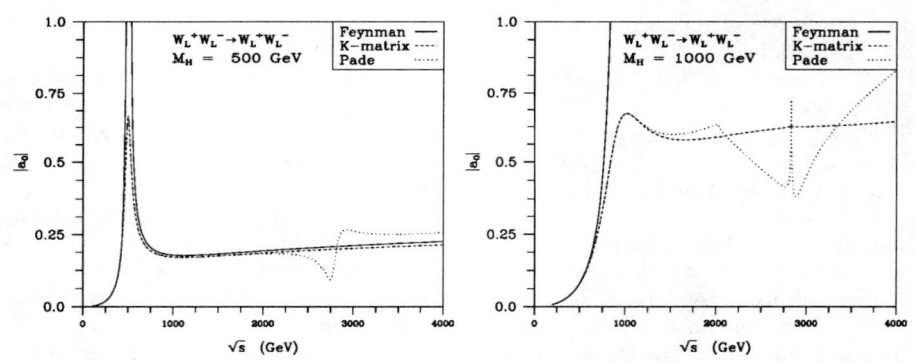

Figure 2: Comparison of the Feynman amplitude for $W_L^+ W_L^- \to W_L^+ W_L^-$ with the K-Matrix and Padé unitarized amplitudes. Results are shown for $M_H = 500$ and 1000 GeV.

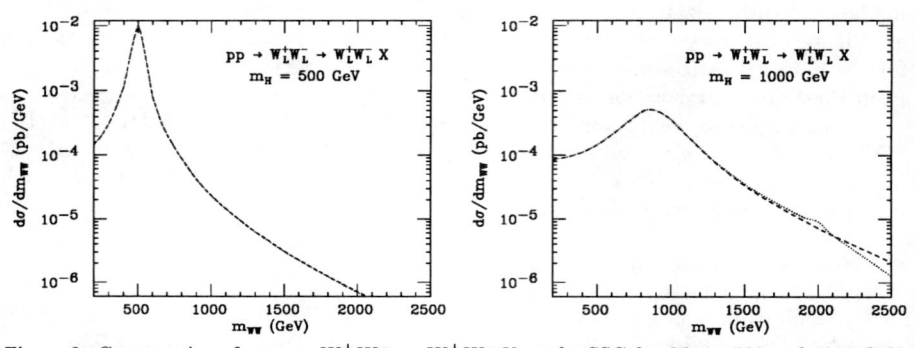

Figure 3: Cross-sections for $pp \to W_L^+ W_L^- \to W_L^+ W_L^- X$ at the SSC for $M_H = 500$ and 1000 GeV. The dashed line is the K-matrix unitarization and the dotted is the Padé unitarization.

QCD CORRECTIONS TO HIGGS BOSON PRODUCTION

SALLY DAWSON
Brookhaven National Laboratory
Upton, New York 11973

ABSTRACT

We discuss the $\mathcal{O}(\alpha_s)$ QCD radiative corrections to Higgs boson production in the limit in which the top quark is much heavier than the Higgs boson. The subleading corrections, of $\mathcal{O}(\alpha_s M_H^2/M_{\text{top}}^2)$, are presented for the decay $H \to \gamma\gamma$ and shown to be small.

1. Introduction

The search for the Higgs boson of the minimal standard model is one of the fundamental missions of future high energy colliders such as the SSC and the LHC. Over much of the interesting Higgs mass range, the dominant production mechanism is gluon fusion. If the Higgs boson is lighter than 160 GeV ($2M_W$), then it will decay predominantly to $b\bar{b}$ pairs. Due to the large QCD backgrounds to the $b\bar{b}$ decay mode, it will probably be necessary to search for the Higgs boson in this mass region through its rare decay modes, of which the decay $H \to \gamma\gamma$ has been discussed the most. The rates into modes such as $\gamma\gamma$ are small and hence knowledge of the QCD radiative corrections is essential for assessing the viability of the signal.

2. Gluon Fusion

The basic production mechanism is gluon fusion through a triangle diagram. The rate for this reaction is sensitive predominantly to the heavy quarks and has been known for some time.[1] It is also sensitive to new generations of heavy colored fermions, to the colored scalars of supersymmetric models and to any other new particles which couple to gluons and scalars. Because the Higgs-fermion coupling of the standard model is proportional to the fermion mass, a heavy fermion does not decouple when its mass is much heavier than the Higgs boson mass and so this decay provides a window for observing the consequences of new heavy particles. In the limit in which $M_{\text{top}} \gg M_H$, the rate can be found from the effective Lagrangian,[2]

$$\mathcal{L} = \frac{\beta_F}{g_s(1+\delta)} \frac{H}{2v} G^{a\mu\nu} G_{a\mu\nu} \quad , \tag{1}$$

where β_F contains only the contribution of heavy fermions to the QCD beta function. The factor of $(1+\delta) = 1 + 2\alpha_s/\pi$ results from the renormalization of the $Ht\bar{t}$ coupling. For $M_H < 2M_{\text{top}}$, the $M_{\text{top}} \to \infty$ limit is a reasonable approximation to the rate.

The radiative corrections to the process $gg \to HX$ can be performed in a straightforward manner using the effective Lagrangian of Eq. (1) and the results are given in Ref. 3. Numerically, they are well approximated by

$$\sigma(gg \to H) \sim \sigma_0(gg \to H)\left[1 + \frac{\alpha_s}{\pi}\left(\pi^2 + \frac{11}{2}\right)\right]. \tag{2}$$

For $\alpha_s = .2$ this gives an enhancement factor of 1.7. The results are of course also sensitive to the choice of renormalization scale and structure functions.

However we are not really interested in the region where $M_H \ll M_{\text{top}}$, but in the region where they have similar values. This is the so-called "intermediate mass" Higgs boson. It is thus of interest to compute the next contribution to the series, the terms of $\mathcal{O}(\alpha_s M_H^2/M_{\text{top}}^2)$, to assess the accuracy of the approximation. These terms cannot be computed using the effective Lagrangian, but rather require a direct evaluation of the relevant two loop graphs. We begin by computing the two-loop graphs contributing to the amplitude for $H \to \gamma\gamma$, which form a subset of those required for the computation of $gg \to H$.

3. $H \to \gamma\gamma$

We utilize the techniques of Hoogeveen[4] for evaluating two- loop graphs involving heavy fermions. This technique has also been successfully used to compute the 2– loop contribution to the ρ parameter from a heavy top quark.[5] Each graph gives a result of the form

$$\mathcal{A}_i^{\mu\nu} = \left(a_i g^{\mu\nu} k_1 \cdot k_2 + b_i k_1^\nu k_2^\mu + c_i k_1^\mu k_2^\nu\right), \tag{3}$$

where k_1^μ and k_2^ν are the external gluon momenta. Gauge invariance requires that

$$\sum_i a_i = -\sum_i b_i, \tag{4}$$

where the sum runs over all the diagrams (the c_i terms do not contribute for on-shell photons). This serves as a check of our result.

The denominators arising from the heavy-quark propagators can be expanded in powers of the external momentum. For example,

$$\frac{1}{(q-k_1)^2 - M_{\text{top}}^2} = \frac{1}{q^2 - M_{\text{top}}^2}\left(1 + \frac{2q \cdot k_1}{q^2 - M_{\text{top}}^2} + \ldots\right). \tag{5}$$

To obtain the terms of $\mathcal{O}(M_H^2/M_{\text{top}}^2)$ each denominator must be expanded up to terms containing two powers of k_1 and two powers of k_2. After contracting the amplitudes with various combinations of $g^{\mu\nu}$ and the external momenta and expanding the denominators as in Eq. (5) all the contributions have the form

$$\int \frac{d^n p}{(2\pi)^n} \int \frac{d^n q}{(2\pi)^n} \frac{(p \cdot q, p \cdot k_i, q \cdot k_i, \text{etc})}{(q^2 - M_{\text{top}}^2)^k (p^2 - M_{\text{top}}^2)^l (p-q)^2}. \tag{6}$$

Using the symmetries of the numerators the relevant integrals can be reduced to products of one-loop integrals plus integrals of symmetric form

$$B_{k,l} \equiv \int \frac{d^n p}{(2\pi)^n} \int \frac{d^n q}{(2\pi)^n} \frac{1}{(q^2 - M_{\text{top}}^2)^k (p^2 - M_{\text{top}}^2)^l (p-q)^2}. \tag{7}$$

Integrals of this form are tabulated as a power series in $1/M_{top}^2$ in Ref 4. and we can directly apply them here. Our final result for the fermion contribution to $H \to \gamma\gamma$ is then

$$\mathcal{A}_F^{\mu\nu} = \mathcal{A}_F \left(g^{\mu\nu} k_1 \cdot k_2 - k_1^\nu k_2^\mu \right)$$

with[6]

$$\mathcal{A}_F = -\left(\frac{2\alpha}{\pi v}\sum_i Q_i^2\right)\left\{1 + \frac{7}{120}\frac{M_H^2}{M_{top}^2} - \frac{\alpha_s}{\pi}\left(1 - \frac{61}{270}\frac{M_H^2}{M_{top}^2}\right)\right\} \qquad (8)$$

It is important to note that the QCD corrections are not just a rescaling of the lowest order result, but rather have a different dependence on M_H/M_{top}.

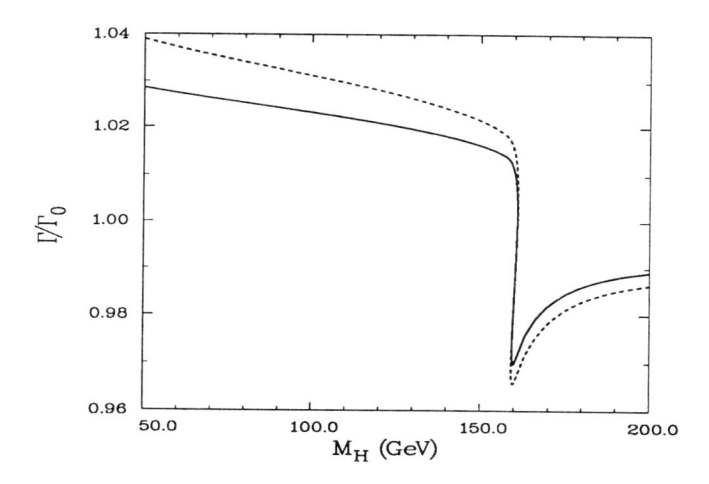

Fig. 1. Ratio of the $\mathcal{O}(\alpha_s M_H^2/M_{top}^2)$ result for the decay width for $H \to \gamma\gamma$ to the lowest order $M_{top} \to \infty$ limit.

The effect of the radiative corrections is shown in Fig. 1 for $M_{top} = 200\ GeV$ (solid line) and also for a degenerate doublet of $SU(2)$ quarks with $M = 400\ GeV$ (dotted line). This figure includes both top and W loops as can be clearly seen by the threshold at $2M_W$. The QCD corrections are well under control and are always less than 4%. Of course, in the standard model, the fermion loop contributions are dwarfed by the W boson loops which accounts for the insensitivity of the rate to the QCD corrections. In extensions of the standard model, however, this is not necessarily the case. In supersymmetric models, for example, it is straightforward to select parameters for which the fermion loop contribution is significantly enhanced relative to the W boson loops.

4. Conclusions

We have computed the $\mathcal{O}(\alpha_s M_H^2/M_{top}^2)$ contributions to the decay $H \to \gamma\gamma$ and have found them to be small. These corrections form a subset of those required for the $\mathcal{O}(\alpha_s M_H^2/M_{top}^2)$ computation of the rate for $gg \to gH$. This calculation is in progress.

5. Acknowledgements
This work has been done in collaboration with R. Kauffman.

6. References

1. F. Wilczek, *Phys. Rev. Lett.* **39** (1977) 1304; J. Ellis, M. K. Gaillard, D. V. Nanopoulos, and C. T. Nonopoulos, *Phys. Rev. Lett.* **40** (1978) 692; T. Rizzo, *Phys. Rev.* **D22** (1980) 178.
2. A. Vainshtein, M. Voloshin, V. Zakharov, and M. Shifman, *Sov. J. Nucl. Phys.* **30** (1979) 711.
3. S. Dawson, *Nucl. Phys.* **B359** (1991) 283; A. Djouadi, M. Spira, and P. Zerwas, *Phys. Lett.* **B264**(1991) 440.
4. F. Hoogevan, *Nucl. Phys.* **B59** (1985) 19.
5. J. van der Bij and M. Veltman, *Nucl. Phys.* **B231** (1984) 205.
6. S. Dawson and R. Kauffman, BNL-47927; A. Djouadi, M. Spira, J. van der Bij, and P. Zerwas, *Phys. Lett.* **B257** (1991) 187.

TOP QUARK AND CHARGED HIGGS MEASUREMENTS AT THE SSC

R. MICHAEL BARNETT
Physics Division, Lawrence Berkeley Laboratory
Berkeley, California 94720

ABSTRACT

Techniques for measuring the top quark mass at the SSC are discussed. If a charged Higgs exists and is lighter than the top quark, then it can be discovered in the decay of the top quark. Measurement of the mass of the charged Higgs is also analyzed.

1. Introduction

The mass of the top (t) quark is an important parameter in many analyses of the Standard Model and also enters into studies of new physics. It is therefore crucial to obtain an accurate measurement of its mass at the SSC and LHC. Top has a very large cross section at these energies and is frequently the largest background for new physics processes. There are simple extensions to the Standard Model involving additional Higgs doublets that lead to the existence of charged Higgs bosons ($H^{\pm}$). If $m(H^{\pm}) < m(\text{top})$, then the top quark will have branching ratios to $bH^{\pm}$ comparable to those to $bW^{\pm}$.

2. Measuring the Top Quark Mass

I will briefly review the three techniques developed by the SDC Collaboration[1] to measure the top quark mass. More attention will be given to the most accurate technique (reconstructing the mass from jets). The cleanest signature for t-quark production is expected to be the isolated high-p_T electron and muon that result from the semileptonic decays of both t quarks. The requirement of two different lepton species avoids backgrounds from Z^0 and Drell-Yan production. Candidate events are selected by requiring isolated electron and muon candidates of opposite charge, with $p_T > 20$ GeV and $|\eta| < 2.5$. This selection is expected to yield 10^6 events per SSC year for $M_{\text{top}} = 150$ GeV, and should be essentially free of background. Thus the analysis becomes a counting experiment, and we can use the observed number of candidate events to estimate the t-quark production cross section. Since the cross section falls as a function of t-quark mass, we can use the observed $t\bar{t}$ cross section to estimate the mass, assuming the Standard Model t-quark branching ratios into semileptonic final states. The uncertainty in this t mass measurement is dominated by the uncertainty in the predicted cross section and is estimated to be ±15 GeV.

A second method for measuring the t-quark mass relies on events with one isolated electron (from t decay) and one nonisolated muon of opposite sign (from the b-decay product of the same t quark).[1] We have studied this technique[1] for t-quark masses of 150 and 250 GeV. Muon candidates from the semileptonic b

decay are selected by requiring them to have $p_T > 20$ GeV. Nonisolated muons are selected by requiring at least 20 GeV of excess transverse energy in a cone of radius $R = 0.4$ around the muon direction. We reduce the background by requiring that $\Delta\phi(e\mu) < 80°$. Finally, we require $p_T(e\mu) > 100$ GeV to increase the sensitivity to the t-quark mass.

In one year of running at nominal SSC luminosity, we expect 70,000 and 17,000 events of this type for the two mass values. Adding all the uncertainties in quadrature, we expect to determine the t-quark mass with an uncertainty of ±4 GeV after a run of one year at the SSC design luminosity.

The t-quark mass can be measured directly[1,2] by reconstructing the three jets coming from its hadronic decay, $t \rightarrow bu\bar{d}$ or $bc\bar{s}$. In $pp \rightarrow t\bar{t}$ production, one can trigger on a lepton from the decay of one t quark into the modes $be\nu_e$ or $b\mu\nu_\mu$ and then examine the three jets from the hadronic decay of the other t quark. These events typically have a high-p_t charged lepton that is well-isolated from other energy flow in the event. The backgrounds to this signature are leptons from b quark decay, which tend to be nonisolated and to have lower p_t, and leptons from the decay of W bosons produced inclusively. These backgrounds can be reduced to a negligible level with the cuts described below.

We have studied[1] the capability of the SDC detector to measure the t-quark mass in this channel for the two cases $M_{top} = 150$ and 250 GeV. The events were simulated with ISAJET including the effects of finite calorimeter segmentation and nonlinear response as well as the magnetic field.

For this analysis, we require an isolated electron or muon with $p_T > 40$ GeV and $|\eta| < 2.5$, consistent with the expected inclusive lepton trigger threshold. To select events with a hadronic t quark decay, we require that at least three jets be reconstructed, each with measured $p_T > 30$ GeV in the opposite hemisphere from the lepton ($\Delta\phi > 90°$). One of these jets must be a b jet, within $|\eta| < 2$, which is tagged with a secondary vertex, see Figs. 1 and 2. Based on our studies, we estimate the efficiency for the b tag to be 30% for b jets with $p_T > 30$ GeV yielding a background rejection of order 100 to 1 against non-b jets. We require the two-jet invariant mass (the W) to be in the range 65 to 95 GeV. In order to reduce combinatoric background, we require the transverse momentum of the three-jet system to be large, which collimates the three jets, and separates them from other jets in the event. For the 150 and 250 GeV cases, we choose the minimum three-jet p_T to be 200 and 300 GeV, respectively, resulting in approximately 160,000 and 40,000 three-jet combinations (t candidates) per nominal SSC year, see Fig. 3. The three-jet invariant mass distributions are shown in Fig. 4 for the 150 GeV and 250 GeV cases. A large invariant mass peak for the t is evident and the combinatoric background is relatively small. The measured t invariant masses are 147.9 GeV and 243.6 GeV for the 150 (250) GeV true mass.

We expect the t-quark mass uncertainty to be dominated by systematic uncertainties, with the largest contribution coming from the uncertainty in the calorimeter energy scale. However, the W signal in the dijet channel in these final states can be used to calibrate the calorimeter mass scale. We conservatively estimate the remaining systematic uncertainty to be ~ 3 GeV, after taking into account possible differences in energy response for light quark and heavy quark jets.

3. Decay to Charged Higgs Bosons

If a charged Higgs boson is lighter than the t quark, then the branching ratio for the decay $t \to H^+ b$ could be comparable to that for $t \to W^+ b$. These branching fractions depend on the couplings of the two Higgs doublets to the quarks and leptons. We use a model predicted by minimal supersymmetry. The couplings of the charged Higgs bosons to fermions are entirely determined by the quark/lepton masses and by $\tan\beta = v_2/v_1$, where v_i are the vacuum expectation values of the Higgs fields. Therefore, $\tan\beta$ determines the branching fractions for $t \to bH^+$, $H^+ \to \tau\nu$, and $H^+ \to c\bar{s}$.

We have investigated two methods[1,2] for $H^\pm$ detection in $t\bar{t}$ events using several different values of M_{top} and $M_{H^\pm}$. The first involves a search for an excess of τ leptons. This technique is most effective when the branching ratio for $H^+ \to \tau\nu$ is large ($\tan\beta > 0.5$). The other method is to reconstruct the hadronic decays $H^+ \to c\bar{s}$. It is useful for $\tan\beta < 1.0$ where $t \to H^+ b$ and $H^+ \to c\bar{s}$ are both large. This is essentially identical to the technique described above for measuring the top mass.

In each case, events are triggered by requiring one t quark to decay via $t \to bW \to b\ell\nu$ yielding an isolated electron or muon (ℓ) with $p_T > 40$ GeV and $|\eta| < 2.5$. The events are also required to have at least one tagged b-quark jet with $p_T > 30$ GeV and $|\eta| < 2.0$. The efficiency for tagging the b-jets through secondary vertices is discussed above. The non-$t\bar{t}$ background coming from $Wb\bar{b}$, $Wc\bar{c}$, $Wc\bar{b}$, and $Wb\bar{c}$ final states and satisfying these criteria is small even before the $H^\pm$ signal criteria are implemented.

In Method 1, we search for ℓ-τ events (e.g., $t \to bW^+ \to b\ell^+\nu$, $\bar{t} \to [\bar{b}H^-$ or $\bar{b}W^-] \to \bar{b}\tau^-\nu$) in which the τ decays to a single $\pi^\pm$ (or $K^\pm$) with $p_T > 50$ GeV or with $p_T > 100$ GeV. The preference for H^+ to decay to $\tau\nu$ rather than $e\nu$ or $\mu\nu$ implies that an excess of ℓ-τ events over the universality prediction (for W^+) would be detected. Observation of a violation of universality consists of detecting the number of excess ℓ-τ events above the number predicted on the basis of universality. For the favorable case $\tan\beta \approx 1.2$, the excess due to the $t \to H^+ b$ decays over the universality prediction is more than a factor of four, and the number of events is large. Requiring five standard deviations above background, we conclude that after one year of SSC running we could detect the presence in top decays of the charged Higgs boson decaying to τ's for all $\tan\beta > 0.5$ in almost all cases studied.

The second method of detecting a charged Higgs boson in the decay of top quarks employs the decay $H^+ \to c\bar{s}$ and reconstructs the mass of the top and H^+ in the exactly the same manner as described above (in Sec. 2) for top and W^+. Due to lack of space I refer the reader to Ref. 2 for this technique and for more details about the technique using $H^+ \to \tau\nu$. I simply conclude that as long as $\tan\beta < 1$, reconstruction of a clearly distinguishable H^+ mass peak is generally quite straightforward, and an accurate measurement of $m(H^+)$ is possible.

4. Conclusions

I have described three techniques to measure the mass of the top quark at SSC (or LHC). I have also reported that discovery of the charged Higgs boson in top quark decays will be possible over the entire interesting range of parameter space. Overall, the techniques developed illustrate the importance of efficiently identifying b-quark jets and τ's.

5. Acknowledgements

This work has been done in collaboration with R. Cruz, J.F. Gunion, H.E. Haber, B. Hubbard, and members of the SDC Collaboration.

6. References

1. Solenoidal Detector Collaboration (SDC) Technical Design Report, SDC-92-201, SSCL-SR-1215 (1992).
2. R.M. Barnett, R. Cruz, J.F. Gunion, and B. Hubbard, report UCD-92-14, *Phys. Rev.* **D**, to be published.

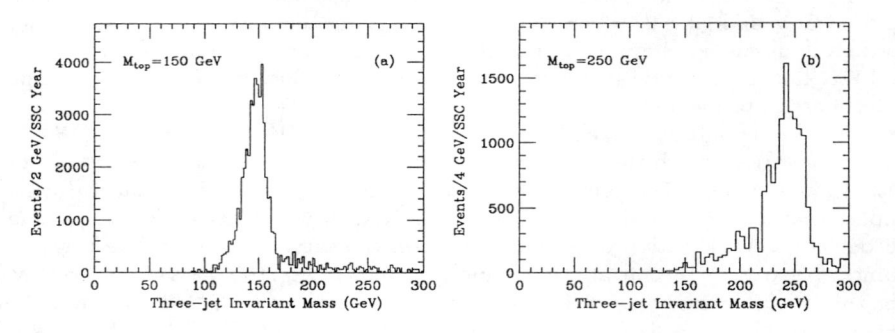

Fig. 4 – The three-jet invariant mass distribution, for (a) $M_{top} = 150$ GeV and (b) $M_{top} = 250$ GeV. In this plot the two-jet invariant mass is required to be consistent with the W mass $65 < M(2\text{-}jet) < 95$ GeV).

Fig. 1 – A typical $t\bar{t} \to b\mu^+\nu\bar{d} + \bar{b}e^-\nu$ event as it would appear in the SDC tracker. The actual size is about twice that shown. The t mass was taken to be 150 GeV. Reconstructed tracks were required to have $p_T > 2.5$ GeV and $|\eta| < 2.5$. ↪

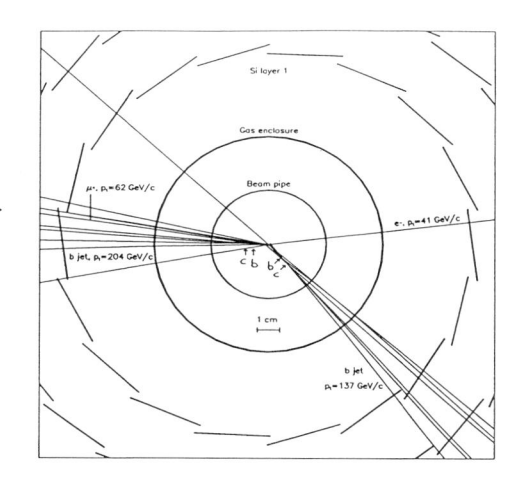

Fig. 2 – A blown up version of Fig. 1. ↪

Fig. 3 – A simulated typical $t\bar{t} \to bu\bar{d} + \bar{b}e^-\nu$ event as seen on a Lego plot. Note that one jet appears partially at $\phi \approx 0$ and partially at $\phi \approx 2\pi$. The t mass was taken to be 150 GeV. ↓

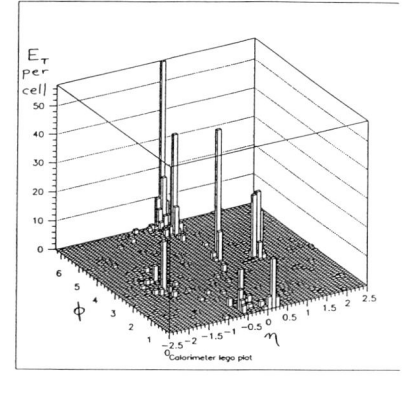

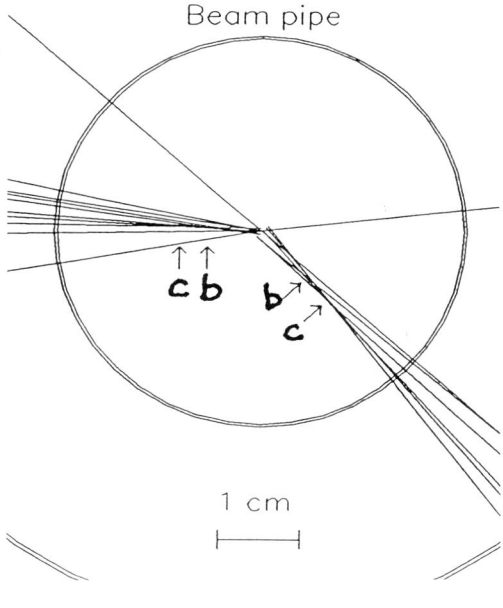

CONSTRAINTS ON THE CHARGED HIGGS SECTOR FROM B PHYSICS

J.L. HEWETT

High Energy Physics Division, Argonne National Laboratory
9700 S. Cass Ave., Argonne, IL 60439 USA

ABSTRACT

We present the bounds that can be obtained on the charged Higgs sector in two-Higgs-Doublet Models from measurements at LEP of the decay $B \to D\tau\nu$, and from searches by CLEO for the inclusive decay $b \to s\gamma$.

Many extensions of the Standard Model (SM) predict the existence of an enlarged Higgs sector beyond the minimal one-doublet version[1]. The simplest extensions are models with two-Higgs-Doublets (2HDM), which predict a physical spectrum of three neutral Higgs scalars, two of which are CP-even (h^0, H^0) while one is CP-odd (A^0), and two charged Higgs scalars ($H^\pm$). We consider two distinct 2HDM which naturally avoid tree-level flavor changing neutral currents. In Model I, one doublet (ϕ_2) provides masses for all fermions and the other doublet (ϕ_1) decouples from the fermion sector. In a second model (Model II), ϕ_2 gives mass to the up-type quarks, while the down-type quarks and charged leptons receive their masses from ϕ_1. Supersymmetry and many axion theories predict couplings of the type present in Model II. Each doublet obtains a vacuum expectation value (vev) v_i, subject only to the constraint that $v_1^2 + v_2^2 = v^2$, where v is the usual vev present in the SM. In a general 2HDM, the charged Higgs mass $m_{H^\pm}$ and the ratio of vevs, $v_2/v_1 \equiv \tan\beta$, are *a priori* free parameters, as are the masses of all the neutral Higgs fields. However, in supersymmetric models, mass relationships exist between the various Higgs scalars. At tree-level, in such models, only two parameters are required to fix the masses and couplings of the entire scalar sector, but once radiative corrections are included[2], the values of the top-quark and squark masses also need to be specified.

The strongest direct search limits on charged Higgs bosons are from LEP[3], with $m_{H^\pm} \gtrsim M_Z/2$. These charged scalars may also reveal themselves through contributions to a variety of low-energy processes. Previous analyses[4] of the $H^\pm$ contributions to processes such as $B^0 - \bar{B}^0$, $D^0 - \bar{D}^0$, and $K^0 - \bar{K}^0$ mixing have found the approximate bound $\tan\beta \gtrsim m_t/600\,\text{GeV}$. $H^\pm$ bosons may also mediate the tree-level decay[5] $B \to D\tau\nu$. In Model I, enhancements over the SM rate for this process only occur for values of $\tan\beta$ which violate the above bound from meson anti-meson mixing. However, enhancements are found in Model II for large values of $\tan\beta$. In Fig. 1 we show the ratio of $B(B \to D\tau\nu)$ in Model II to that of the SM as a function of $\tan\beta$, for various values of $m_{H^\pm}$. The solid horizontal line represents the 90% C.L. upper bound on this ratio as obtained by ALEPH[3]. We see that for some range of the parameters, the value of this ratio exceeds the experimental bound, and that very large values of $\tan\beta$ are thus excluded. For example, $\tan\beta \lesssim 60$ for $m_{H^\pm} = 100\,\text{GeV}$.

Next we examine the radiative b-quark decay $b \to s\gamma$. A 90% C.L. upper bound on the branching fraction for this mode, $B(b \to s\gamma) < 8.4 \times 10^{-4}$, has been obtained by the CLEO Collaboration[6] via an examination of the inclusive photon spectrum in B-meson decays. Recent detector refinements coupled with increasing integrated luminosity leads us to anticipate that either the current limit will be strengthened, or the decay may actually be observed in the near future. The transition $b \to s\gamma$ proceeds through electromagnetic penguin diagrams, which involve the top-quark, together with a $H^\pm$ or SM $W^\pm$ boson in the loop. At the W scale the coefficients of the operators which mediate this transition take the generic form[4, 7]

$$c_i(M_W) = A_W(m_t^2/M_W^2) + \lambda A_H^1(m_t^2/m_{H^\pm}^2) + \frac{1}{\tan^2\beta}A_H^2(m_t^2/m_{H^\pm}^2), \tag{1}$$

where $\lambda = -1/\tan^2\beta$, $+1$ in Models I and II, respectively, A_W corresponds to the SM amplitude, and $A_H^{1,2}$ represent the $H^\pm$ contributions; their analytic form is given for each contributing operator in Ref. 4,7. We employ the explicit form of the QCD corrections of Grinstein et al.[7], and use the 3-loop expression for α_s fitting the value of the QCD scale Λ to obtain consistency with measurements[3] of $\alpha_s(M_Z^2)$ at LEP.

Enhancements over the SM rate occur in Model I only for small values of $\tan\beta$. In Model II, large enhancements also appear for small values of $\tan\beta$, but more importantly, the branching fraction is found to *always* be larger than that of the SM. For certain ranges of the model parameters, the resulting value of $B(b \to s\gamma)$ exceeds the CLEO bound, and consistency with this limit thus excludes part of the $m_{H^\pm} - \tan\beta$ plane for a fixed value of m_t. This is shown in Fig. 2 for both models, where the excluded region lies to the left and beneath the curves. In Fig. 3a we present the branching fraction for Model II in the limit of large $\tan\beta$ as a function of m_t with $m_{H^\pm} = m_t - m_b$. If the actual value (or future upper bound) for the branching fraction were to lie below the solid curve, then the decay $t \to bH^\pm$ would be kinematically forbidden for a particular value of m_t. Here, we made use of the large $\tan\beta$ limit, since it minimizes the $H^\pm$ contributions to $b \to s\gamma$.

In the supersymmetric case, the bounds shown in Fig. 2b are more conventionally displayed as an allowed region in the $\tan\beta - m_A$ plane, where m_A is the mass of the CP-odd field. This is displayed in Fig. 3b for various values of m_t, where the radiative corrections to the SUSY mass relations have been employed assuming $M_{SUSY} = 1\,\text{TeV}$. For $m_t = 150\,\text{GeV}$, the excluded region is comparable to what can be explored by LEP I and II. We note that in supersymmetric theories, other super-particles can also contribute to the one-loop decay $b \to s\gamma$, and generally lead to a further enhancement in the rate[8].

In conclusion, we have shown that the decay $b \to s\gamma$ is by far the most restrictive process in constraining the parameters of the charged Higgs sector in 2HDM, yielding bounds which are stronger than those from other low-energy processes and from direct collider searches.

References

1. J.F. Gunion, H.E. Haber, G.L. Kane, and S. Dawson, *The Higgs Hunters Guide* (Addison-Wesley, Redwood City, CA, 1990).
2. See, for example, H. Haber and R. Hempfling, Phys. Rev. Lett. **66**, 1815 (1991), and Univ. of California Report SCIPP 91/33 (1992).
3. S.C.C. Ting, these Proceedings; L. Rolandi, (ALEPH Collaboration), talk presented at the *XXV International Conference on High Energy Physics*, Dallas, TX, August 1992.
4. V. Barger, J.L. Hewett, and R.J.N. Phillips, Phys. Rev. **D41**, 3421 (1990); A. Buras, et al., Nucl. Phys. **B337**, 284 (1990); J. Gunion and B. Grzadkowski, Phys. Lett. **B243**, 301 (1990).
5. P. Krawczyk and S. Pokorski, Phys. Rev. Lett. **60**, 182 (1988); B. Grzadkowski and W.-S. Hou, Phys. Lett. **B272**, 383 (1991).
6. M. Battle, et al., CLEO Collaboration, to appear in the *Proceedings of the joint Lepton-Photon and Europhysics International Conference on High Energy Physics*, Geneva, Switzerland, August, 1991.
7. B. Grinstein, R. Springer, and M. Wise, Nucl. Phys. **B339**, 269 (1990); T.G. Rizzo, Phys. Rev. **D38**, 820 (1988); W.-S. Hou and R.S. Willey, Phys. Lett. **B202**, 591 (1988); C.Q. Geng and J.N. Ng, Phys. Rev. **D38**, 2858 (1988).
8. S. Bertolini, et al., Nucl. Phys. **B294**, 321 (1987), and Nucl. Phys. **B353**, 591 (1991).

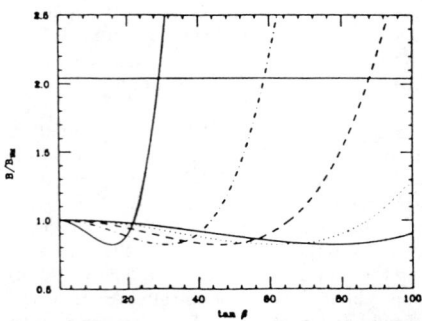

Fig. 1. The ratio of branching fractions for $B \to D\tau\nu$ in Model II to that of the SM. The solid horizontal line represents the ALEPH upper bound. From left to right the solid (dashed-dot, dashed, dotted, solid) curve represents $m_{H^\pm} = 50\,(100, 150, 200, 250)$ GeV.

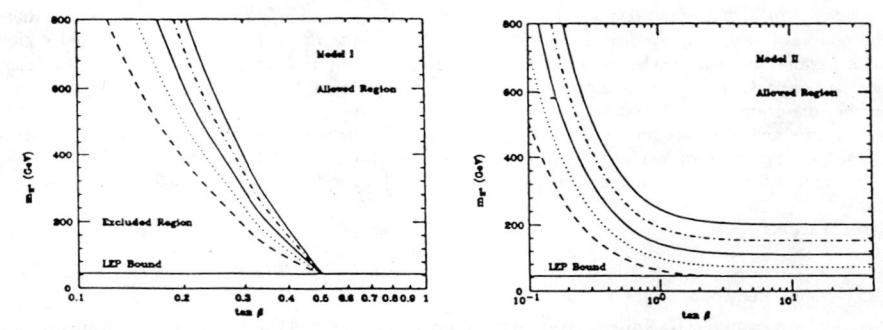

Fig. 2. The excluded regions in the $m_{H^\pm} - \tan\beta$ plane for various values of m_t, resulting from the present CLEO bound in (a) Model I and (b) Model II. In each case, from top to bottom, the solid (dashed dot, solid, dotted, and dashed) curve corresponds to $m_t = 210\,(180, 150, 120,$ and $90)$ GeV. The excluded region lies to the left and below each curve.

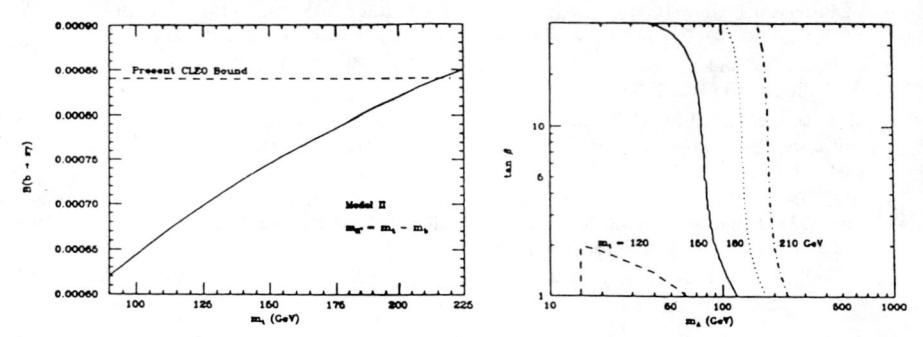

Fig. 3. (a) $B(b \to s\gamma)$ as a function of m_t, with $m_{H^\pm} = m_t - m_b$ in the large $\tan\beta$ limit in Model II. (b) The excluded region from the present CLEO limit in the $\tan\beta - m_A$ plane for various values of m_t as indicated.

C. Bottom, Charm and Strange Physics

Conveners: R. J. MORRISON (U. of C., Santa Barbara)
B. GRINSTEIN (SSCL)
Liaison: P. KASPER (FNAL)

SPECTROSCOPY FROM THE $\Upsilon(3S)$ STATE

U. HEINTZ[a], J. LEE-FRANZINI, D. M. J. LOVELOCK[b], M. NARAIN[c], R. D. SCHAMBERGER,
J. WILLINS[b], and C. YANAGISAWA
Physics Department, SUNY at Stony Brook, Stony Brook, NY 11794

and

Q. W. WU, P. FRANZINI, S. KANEKAL, and P. M. TUTS
Nevis Laboratories, Columbia University, P.O. Box 137, Irvington, NY 10533

ABSTRACT

Using the CUSB-II detector at CESR we have studied the Υ system. We present measurements of branching ratios for electric dipole transitions and of the masses, fine structure splittings, and the hadronic widths of the $\chi_b(2P)$ states.

We have used the $\Upsilon(3S)$ data sample of 288 pb^{-1}, collected 1985–1990 by the CUSB-II detector[1] at the Cornell Electron Storage Ring (CESR), to perform precision measurements of the Υ system. We have studied electric dipole (E1) transitions in the Υ system, both in the "inclusive" photon spectrum from hadronic $\Upsilon(3S)$ decays, as well as by reconstructing "exclusive" decay modes. Figure 1 shows the background subtracted inclusive photon spectrum from hadronic decays of the $\Upsilon(3S)$ [2,3]. A number of spectral lines due to transitions within the Υ system are visible. The three lines at 85–125 MeV are due to $\Upsilon(3S) \to \chi_b(2P_J)\gamma$. Events due to the E1 cascade $\Upsilon(3S) \to \chi_b\gamma \to \Upsilon\gamma\gamma$, followed by $\Upsilon \to \mu^+\mu^-$ or e^+e^-, can be completely reconstructed. Figure 2 shows the photon energy spectrum due to $\Upsilon(3S) \to \chi_b(2P_J)\gamma$ for these cascade events [2,4]. Fits to the spectra are shown superimposed on the figures. The photon energies (E_γ) from both spectra agree very well and the combined results are listed in table 1. The fitted number of events gives us the branching ratios for the observed processes, also listed in table 1. The first error is statistical, the second systematic. The branching ratios for the E1 decays of the $\chi_b(2P)$ states have been obtained by dividing the branching ratios for the cascades by those for $\Upsilon(3S) \to \chi_b(2P)\gamma$ from the inclusive photon spectrum.

From the total width of the $\Upsilon(3S)$[5] and the branching ratios we compute the rates (Γ_{E1}) of the transitions $\Upsilon(3S) \to \chi_b(2P_J)\gamma$. In table 2 they are compared with predictions of potential models [6–11]. The excellent agreement between experiment and theory indicates that potential models describe the spin independent features of the Υ system well. As the E1 rates are proportional to $(2J+1)$ this agreement

---

a present address: Columbia University, Nevis Laboratories, P. O. Box 137, Irvington, NY 10533
b present address: Medical Physics, Memorial Sloan-Kettering Cancer Center, 1275 York Av., New York, NY 10021
c present address: Fermilab, P. O. Box 500, MS 357, Batavia, IL 60510

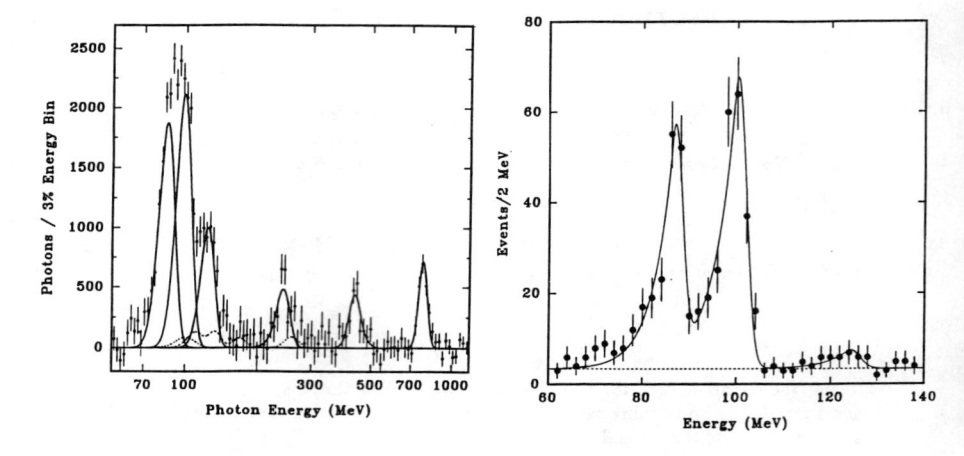

Figure 1. Background subtracted inclusive photon spectrum.

Figure 2. Photon spectrum from the transition $\Upsilon(3S)\to\chi_b(2P_J)\gamma$ in cascade events.

Table 1. Measured photon energies and branching ratios.

J	E_γ^*	$B(\Upsilon(3S) \to \chi_b(2P_J)\gamma$	$B(\chi_b(2P_J) \to \Upsilon(2S)\gamma$	$B(\chi_b(2P_J) \to \Upsilon(2S)\gamma$
2	(86.7±0.4) MeV	(11.1±0.5±0.4)%	(17.3±2.1±1.9)%	(7.0±1.0±0.6)%
1	(100.1±0.4) MeV	(11.5±0.5±0.5)%	(19.9±2.0±2.2)%	(8.0±0.9±0.7)%
0	(123.0±0.8) MeV	(6.0±0.4±0.6)%	(4.6±2.0±0.7)%	(0.9±0.6±0.1)%

* energy scale errors (0.9%) are not included

Table 2. E1 rates for the transitions $\Upsilon(3S)\to\chi_b(2P_J)\gamma$ in keV.

J	Γ_{E1} (keV)	GRR	MR	MB	KR	PF	LF
2	2.7±0.1±0.3	2.6	3.0	2.8	2.8	2.8	2.7
1	2.8±0.1±0.4	2.4	2.6	2.2	2.6	2.6	2.5
0	1.5±0.1±0.2	1.5	1.5	1.0	1.6	1.6	1.6

confirms the spin assignment for the $\chi_b(2P_J)$ states.

Using the photon energies and the mass of the $\Upsilon(3S)$[5] we obtain the center of gravity of the $\chi_b(2P)$ states, $\overline{M} = (10259.5 \pm 0.4 \pm 1.0)$ MeV, and the fine structure splittings $M_2 - M_1 = (13.5 \pm 0.4 \pm 0.5)$ MeV, and $M_1 - M_0 = (23.5 \pm 0.7 \pm 0.7)$ MeV. M_J is the mass of the $\chi_b(2P_J)$ state. The fine structure splitting can be parametrized in terms of the expectation values of the spin-orbit term (a) and the tensor term (b) in the spin-dependent Hamiltonian[12] . Our measurements for the parameters a and b and the fine structure ratio $R = (M_2 - M_1)/(M_1 - M_0)$ are listed in table 3 and compared to model calculations which differ in their assumptions about the interquark potential. The data confirms dominance of the spin-orbit over the tensor term, a common feature of all models. However, quantitatively the measurements do not agree well with the calculations. The measurement of $R_{\chi_b(2P)}$ is smaller than the previous measurement[5] of $R_{\chi_b(1P)}$, contrary to all model calculations.

Table 3. Fine structure parameters.

observable	experiment	GRR	MR	MB	PF	LF
a (MeV)	9.5±0.2±0.2	9.3	6.5	14.6	8.3	10.3
b (MeV)	2.3±0.1±0.1	1.9	2.1	4.2	1.6	1.9
$R_{\chi_b(2P)}$	0.584±0.024±0.02	0.67	0.42	0.48	0.71	0.70
$R_{\chi_b(1P)}$	0.66±0.05	0.64	0.42	0.45	0.70	0.67

The hadronic widths of the $\chi_b(2P_J)$ state can be infered from the measured branching fractions of the E1 decays of the $\chi_b(2P_J)$ states and potential model values of their rates. Using KR's potential model[9], we compute the hadronic widths listed in 4. These widths agree qualitatively with perturbative QCD calculations. The widths evaluated by KR[9] are also listed in table 4.

Table 4. Hadronic widths of $\chi_b(2P_J)$ states.

J	measured Γ_{had}	expected Γ_{had}
2	(89± 11±11) keV	153 keV
1	(65± 7±13) keV	51 keV
0	(343±118±58) keV	866 keV

I would like to thank all members of the CUSB collaboration for their contributions to this work. This work was supported by the National Science Foundation.

References

1. R. D. Schamberger et al., *Nucl. Instr. Meth.* **A309**, 450 (1991).
2. U. Heintz et al., *Phys. Rev.* **D46**, 1928 (1992).
3. M. Narain et al., *Phys. Rev. Lett.* **66**, 3113 (1991).
4. U. Heintz et al., *Phys. Rev. Lett.* **66**, 1563 (1991).
5. Particle Data Group, *Phys. Lett.* **239B** (1990).
6. Gupta, Radford and Repko (GRR), *Phys. Rev.* **D34**, 201 (1986).
7. P. Moxhay and J. L. Rosner (MR), *Phys. Rev.* **D28**, 1132 (1983).
8. R. McClary and N. Byers (MB), *Phys. Rev.* **D28**, 1692 (1983).
9. W. Kwong and J. L. Rosner (KR), *Phys. Rev.* **D38**, 279 (1988).
10. P. J. Franzini (PF), ENSLAPP-A-395/92 (submitted to *Physics Letters*).
11. L. P. Fulcher (LF), *Phys. Rev.* **D39**, 295 (1989).
12. J. L. Rosner, in *Experimental Meson Spectroscopy-1983*, ed. by S.J. Lindenbaum. AIP, New York, 461 (1984).

STUDY OF $\pi\pi$ TRANSITIONS FROM THE Υ(3S) STATE

Q. W. WU, P. FRANZINI, S. KANEKAL, AND P. M. TUTS
Physics Department, Columbia University
New York, New York 10027, USA

and

U. HEINTZ, J. LEE-FRANZINI, M. NARAIN
R. D. SCHAMBERGER, J. WILLINS, AND C. YANAGISAWA
Physics Department, SUNY at Stony Brook, Stony Brook, New York 11794

ABSTRACT

Using the CUSB-II detector, we have investigated the decay $\Upsilon(3S) \to \Upsilon(1S,2S)\pi\pi$, where the daughter state $\Upsilon(1S,2S)$ decays to a pair of leptons, we have measured the branching ratios and studied the property of the dipion system and compared it with predictions from theoretical models.

Hadronic transitions between heavy quarkonia ($c\bar{c}$ and $b\bar{b}$ bound states) have been studied extensively, both theoretically and experimentally. QCD describes the process as gluon emission from quark-antiquark bound states and then the hadronization of gluons dominantly into pions. The rates and di-pion system properties can be calculated with the multipole expansion of color fields of gluons. Here we present an analysis of $\pi\pi$ decays from Υ(3S) with a large data sample.

Data were collected by the CUSB-II detector at CESR[1]. This analysis is based on a data sample of 1.1 million produced Υ(3S) from 229 pb^{-1} of integrated luminosity. In addition we use Υ(1S) and continuum events from a 42 pb^{-1} and a 142 pb^{-1} integrated luminosity data sample respectively to study backgrounds. We study the decays in the exclusive mode, *i.e.* the daughter state Υ(1S) or Υ(2S) decays to lepton pairs, and thus we have four particles for $\pi^+\pi^-$ decays and six particles for $\pi^0\pi^0$ decays (each π^0 decays to two photons) in the detector, among them are 2 back-to-back leptons. The CUSB-II detector provides excellent identification of electrons and muons. An electron (photon) leaves all its energy in the calorimeter in the form of an electromagnetic shower, and a fast charged hadron (muon) leaves a uniform energy deposit pattern along its path, as would a minimum ionizing particle. A charged pion exhibits a variable energy deposition pattern in the calorimeter. So for leptons, we require two tracks in the drift chamber, collinear in azimuthal angle φ to within 15°. These two tracks must be associated with corresponding energy deposition patterns in the calorimeter. For charged pions, we require two tracks in the drift chamber and at least one pion must be observed in the calorimeter either as a track or a cluster. For neutral pions, we require 4 isolated clusters with energy greater than 15 MeV in the calorimeter. For half of the data analyzed here we had endcaps installed. For leptons that hit the endcaps we cannot distinguish between muons and electrons, we call these $ll\pi\pi$ events.

For events with charged pions, we then perform a kinematic fit based on the event information: φ and ϑ of all particles and energies of the pions and electrons. This yields a 2C fit for $\mu\mu\pi\pi$ and $ll\pi\pi$ events and a 4C fit for $ee\pi\pi$ events requiring energy-momentum conservation. Those events that passed the fit were classified as decays to $\Upsilon(1S)$ or $\Upsilon(2S)$ according to their di-lepton mass from the fit. We then refit these events with the additional constraint that the di-lepton mass be that of the $\Upsilon(1S)$ or $\Upsilon(2S)$. Only events with confidence levels greater than 1% are kept and then scanned by physicists. For events with neutral pions, we put a cut on the total energy of the four photons since its distribution shows two peaks corresponding to decays to $\Upsilon(2S)$ and $\Upsilon(1S)$.

The acceptance×efficiency is determined by MC study using the same analysis. It is sensitive to the lepton's angular distribution: from isotropic to $1 + \cos^2\vartheta_l$, where ϑ_l is the angle between the leptons and the beam axis in the $\Upsilon(1S, 2S)$ rest frame, the efficiency decreases by 16% for $\mu\mu\pi\pi$ and $ee\pi\pi$ and increases by 40% for $ll\pi\pi$. We choose the average and set the systematic error to be the difference between the average and either case. We also include detector tracking efficiency. Backgrounds are determined by scaling from $\Upsilon(1S)$ and continuum data. We list the total number of events found, and the branching ratios in table 1.

Table 1: Branching ratio result summary, we assume lepton universality and use $B_{\mu\mu}(\Upsilon(1S))=(2.48\pm0.06)\%$ and $B_{\mu\mu}(\Upsilon(2S))=(1.31\pm0.21)\%$ from Ref. 2.

mode	Number of events	Branching Ratios (%)
$\Upsilon(3S) \to \Upsilon(1S)\pi^+\pi^-$	451	$4.46 \pm 0.34 \pm 0.50$
$\Upsilon(3S) \to \Upsilon(1S)\pi^0\pi^0$	33	$2.2 \pm 0.4 \pm 0.3$
$\Upsilon(3S) \to \Upsilon(2S)\pi^+\pi^-$	138	$4.82 \pm 0.65 \pm 0.53$
$\Upsilon(3S) \to \Upsilon(2S)\pi^0\pi^0$	10	$1.7 \pm 0.5 \pm 0.2$

The reconstructed events were used to study the properties of the $\pi\pi$ system. The di-pion mass, $M_{\pi\pi}$, distribution is obtained after applying a bin-by-bin efficiency correction to the observed $M_{\pi\pi}$ spectrum. After efficiency correction the $M_{\pi\pi}$ spectrum exhibits a double-peaked shape which is different from other $\pi\pi$ decays in the $c\bar{c}$ and $b\bar{b}$ systems. We have compared the $M_{\pi\pi}$ spectrum with several theoretical models and find that none of them can describe the data. The Multipole Expansion method (ME) predicts a peak at large dipion masses[3] which agrees very well with experimental data for $\Upsilon(2S) \to \Upsilon(1S)\pi^+\pi^-$ and $\psi' \to J/\psi\ \pi^+\pi^-$ decays, however, it does not fit to our data, see Fig. 1. A four quark state Υ_1 consisting of $b\bar{b}q\bar{q}$ where q is a light quark has been proposed[4]. In this picture, the pion decay undergoes a chain of decays, $\Upsilon(3S) \to \Upsilon_1\pi, \Upsilon_1 \to \Upsilon(1S)\pi$. With the choice of $M_{\Upsilon_1}=10.213$ GeV/c^2 and width $\Gamma=10$ MeV/c^2, it can produce a double-peaked shape but with a different peak position, in addition, the accompanying monochromatic pions were not observed. Since the $\Upsilon(3S)$ is close to the open flavour threshold, it has been proposed that it might decay to a $B\bar{B}$ pair[5], $B\to B^*\pi$, $B^*\to B\pi$, $B\bar{B}\to\Upsilon(1S)$. By combining this Coupled

Channel (CC) effect and ME with a variable coefficient, we can make a reasonable fit, which shows that the CC effect must be of the same order of magnitude as ME to produce the double-peaked shape. A theoretical calculation incorporating CC with ME has been done recently[6], using the well measured $\psi' \to J/\psi \, \pi^+\pi^-$ data as input, it concludes that the CC effect is very small, and the low end of the $M_{\pi\pi}$ spectrum is improved slightly as compared with pure ME predictions. All these theoretical models predict similar shapes for $M_{\pi\pi}$ from $\Upsilon(3S) \to \Upsilon(2S)\pi^+\pi^-$.

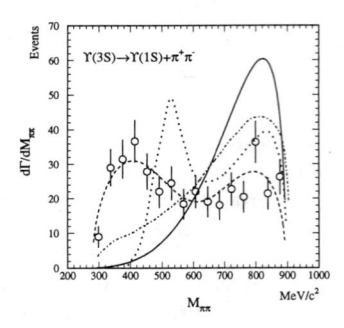

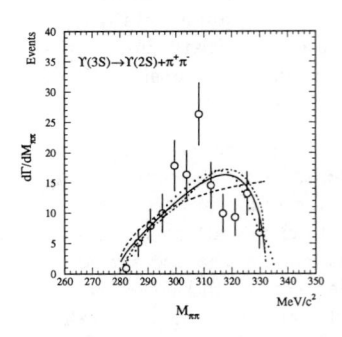

Figure 1: Di-pion mass spectrum for $\Upsilon(3S) \to \Upsilon(1S)\pi^+\pi^-$ and $\Upsilon(3S) \to \Upsilon(2S)\pi^+\pi^-$, the open-circle represents our measurements, the solid curves are the predictions from ME[3], the dotted-lines are predictions from four-quark states assumption[4], the dashed curves are the fit to the data points[5], the dashed-dotted lines are the result of ME+CC calculation[6]. All these curves have been normalized to the number of events observed.

We have also studied the angular distribution of the $\pi\pi$ system, and found that our result is consistent with the expectation that the di-pions are emitted in an S wave (isotropically) in $\Upsilon(3S)$ decays as suggested by ME.

In summary, we have measured the branching ratio of the $\pi\pi$ decay from $\Upsilon(3S)$. The di-pion mass $M_{\pi\pi}$ spectrum cannot be explained by the current theoretical models. We would like to thank CESR staff for providing excellent beam conditions. This work is supported in part by National Science Foundation.

1. R. D. Schamberger et al., *Nucl. Instr. Meth.* **A309** (1991) 450.
2. Particle Data Group, *Phys. Rev.* **D45** III (1992).
3. T. M. Yan, *Phys. Rev.* **D22** (1980) 1652; Y. P. Kuang and T. M. Yan, *Phys. Rev.* **D24** (1981) 2874.
4. M. B. Voloshin, *JETP Lett.* **37** (1983) 69; P. Bélanger, T. DeGrand and P. Moxhay, *Phys. Rev.* **D39** (1988) 257.
5. H. J. Lipkin and S. F. Tuan, *Phys. Lett.* **206B** (1988) 349; P. Moxhay, *Phys. Rev.* **D39** (1989) 3497.
6. Hong-Yi Zhou and Yu-Ping Kuang, *Phys. Rev.* **D44** (1991) 756.

PRECISION MEASUREMENTS OF CHARMONIUM STATES FORMED IN PROTON-ANTIPROTON ANNIHILATIONS

JAMES E. FAST
Department of Physics, University of California, Irvine
Irvine, California 92717, USA

(for the E760 Collaboration)

ABSTRACT

The E760 collaboration has studied the resonant production of charmonium states formed in proton-antiproton annihilations. Precision measurements of the mass and width of the χ_1 and χ_2 states have been made, as well as direct measurements of the J/ψ and ψ' widths. Evidence for the h_c ($^1P_1$) state has been seen near the χ_c center of gravity. The branching ratios of the η_c and χ_2 states to two photons have been measured.

1. Introduction

Fermilab experiment E760 uses an internal hydrogen gas-jet target in the Antiproton Accumulator ring to resonantly produce charmonium states in $\bar{p}p$ annihilations in order to make precise measurements of their masses, total widths, and branching ratios. In $\bar{p}p$ annihilation, all of the charmonium states can be produced directly, thus allowing measurements of their formation energies with the precision of the beam energy measurement, about 100 KeV in the center of mass. The narrow spread in the energy of the stochastically cooled beam, $(\sigma_{E_{cm}}/E_{cm}) \leq 2 \times 10^{-4}$, allows for direct measurement of the sub-MeV total widths typical of the low-lying charmonium states. A peak luminosity of $10^{31} cm^{-2} s^{-1}$ was achieved, providing the experiment with $\approx 1 \ pb^{-1}$ of data per week during the 1990-1991 fixed target run at Fermilab.

2. The Detector

The detector[1], shown in Fig.(1), is designed to efficiently distinguish electromagnetic decays of charmonium states from the large nonresonant hadronic background. The main body of the detector is cylindrically symmetric about the beam axis, covering the entire azimuth, ϕ, and the polar region $12° \leq \theta \leq 70°$. This portion of the detector consist of two sets of trigger hodoscopes, several layers of wire chambers, a threshold Čerenkov counter to tag electrons, and the lead glass central calorimeter. In addition, the region $2° \leq \theta \leq 12°$ is instrumented with a set of trigger hodoscopes, wire chambers, and a lead scintillator forward calorimeter. The hodoscopes, Čerenkov counter, and calorimeters provide signals for the experiments fast trigger logic[2].

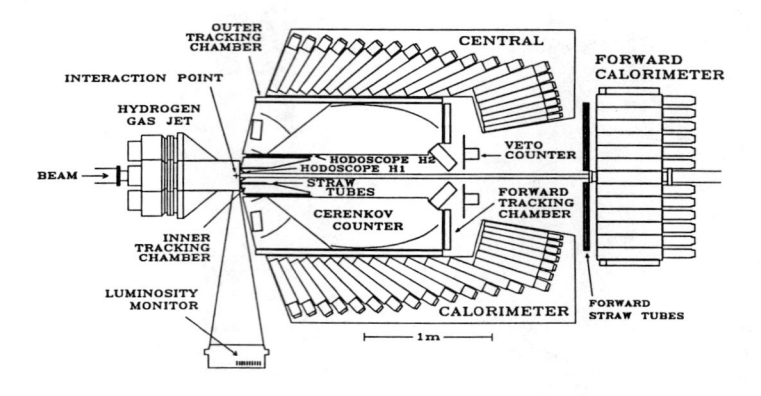

Figure 1: The E760 Detector

The luminosity is measured by counting elastically scattered protons at 86.5° (from the beam direction) in a 500μ thick silicon detector. The detector is sufficiently thick to stop the recoil protons, which can then be identified by the energy they deposit in the detector. The known elastic scattering cross section[3] is then used to extract the luminosity from the observed number of recoil protons.

3. Experimental Technique

The $\bar{p}$ beam is decelerated from the injection energy (9 GeV) to an energy just above the resonance of interest. Data are then collected at several points as the beam energy is stepped across the resonance in small intervals (200 KeV to 1 MeV steps). The rate of resonant production as a function of center of mass energy is given by the convolution of the Breit-Wigner shape of the resonance with the beam energy spectrum. With precise knowledge of the beam energy and energy distribution, the excitation curve can be de-convoluted and the resonance parameters (mass, width, and branching ratios) can be extracted.

3.1. Beam Energy Measurement

The $\bar{p}$ beam is unbunched during data taking, so it is possible to measure the beam Schottky noise spectrum[4], which provides a direct measurement of the beam frequency distribution to 1 part in 10^7. The orbit length is measured to 1 mm out of 474 m using a set of beam position monitors. From these measurements the $\bar{p}$ velocity, $\beta = Lf$, can be obtained, which is related to the center of mass energy by simple kinematical factors. This results in center of mass energy measurements accurate to $\approx$ 100 KeV.

4. Results

During the 1990-1991 Fermilab fixed target run the J/ψ (1^3S_1), ψ' (2^3S_1), χ_1 (1^3P_1), χ_2 (1^3P_2), h_c (1^1P_1), and η_c (1^1S_0) states were studied. A search for the η_c' (2^1S_0) was also made. In the case of the J/ψ and ψ', we have the first direct measurements of the total widths and a new measurement of the mass splitting[5]. For the χ_1 and χ_2, we have measured the masses, total widths, and $\bar{p}p$ branching ratios[1]. For the χ_2, we have also measured the branching ratio to $\gamma\gamma$[6]. We have evidence for the h_c resonance in the decay channel $J/\psi + \pi^0$ near the χ_c center of gravity[7]. The mass, total width, and branching ratio to $\gamma\gamma$ of the η_c have been measured[8]. For the η_c', no evidence of a signal was observed and limits have been placed on the product of branching ratios $BR(\eta_c' \to \bar{p}p)BR(\eta_c' \to \gamma\gamma)$ as a function of the η_c' mass and total width[8]. These results are summarized in the tables below.

Table 1: Resonance Mass and Total Width Results

Resonance	Mass (MeV/c^2)	Total Width (MeV)
J/ψ	3096.877 ± 0.006	$0.099 \pm 0.012 \pm 0.006$
ψ'	3686.0 ± 0.1 (input)	$0.306 \pm 0.036 \pm 0.016$
χ_1	$3510.53 \pm 0.04 \pm 0.12$	$0.88 \pm 0.11 \pm 0.08$
χ_2	$3556.15 \pm 0.07 \pm 0.12$	$1.98 \pm 0.17 \pm 0.07$
h_c	$3526.20 \pm 0.15 \pm 0.20$	< 1.1 (90% confidence)
η_c	$2989.9 \pm 2.2 \pm 0.4$	$15.6 \pm 6.9 \pm 6.4$

Table 2: Branching Ratio Results

Reaction	$BR_{in}BR_{out}$
$\bar{p}p \to J/\psi \to e^+e^-$	$(1.14^{+0.19}_{-0.14} \pm 0.06) \times 10^{-4}$
$\bar{p}p \to \psi' \to e^+e^- + X$	$(1.09^{+0.16}_{-0.14} \pm 0.05) \times 10^{-5}$
$\bar{p}p \to \chi_1 \to e^+e^- + \gamma$	$(1.47 \pm 0.21 \pm 0.20) \times 10^{-6}$
$\bar{p}p \to \chi_2 \to e^+e^- + \gamma$	$(0.84 \pm 0.09 \pm 0.07) \times 10^{-6}$
$\bar{p}p \to \chi_2 \to \gamma\gamma$	$(4.16 \pm 1.12 \pm 0.65) \times 10^{-7}$
$\bar{p}p \to \eta_c \to \gamma\gamma$	$(1.54 \pm 0.38 \pm 0.16) \times 10^{-8}$

5. Acknowledgements

We gratefully acknowledge the technical support from the collaborating institutions, the technical staff of Fermilab, and the Fermilab Accelerator Division, Antiproton Accumulator department.

6. References

1. T. A. Armstrong et al., *Nucl. Phys.* **B373** (1992) 35.
2. R. Ray et al., *Nucl. Instr. and Meth.* **A307** (1991) 254.
3. M. M. Block and R. N. Cahn, *Review of Modern Physics* **57**, No.2 (1985).
4. P. Bryant and S. Newman, *CERN Accelerator School*, (1984) CERN 84-15.
5. T. A. Armstrong et al., submitted to *Phys. Rev.* **D**.
6. T. A. Armstrong et al., submitted to *Phys. Rev. Lett.*
7. T. A. Armstrong et al., *Phys. Rev. Lett.* **69** (1992) 2337.
8. T. A. Armstrong et al., to be submitted to *Phys. Rev.* **D**.

QUARKONIUM AND POWER LAW POTENTIALS[1]

AARON K. GRANT and JONATHAN L. ROSNER
Enrico Fermi Institute and Department of Physics, University of Chicago
Chicago, IL, 60637

ABSTRACT

The spectra and decay rates of $c\bar{c}$ and $b\bar{b}$ levels are well described, for the most part, by a power-law potential of the form $V(r) = \lambda(r^\alpha - 1)/\alpha + $ const., where $\alpha \simeq 0$. The results of an up-to-date fit to the data on spin-averaged levels are presented. Results on electric dipole transitions in systems bound by power law potentials are also presented, with applications to the bottomonium system.

Charmonium ($c\bar{c}$) and bottomonium ($b\bar{b}$) systems provide a rich source of information on the interquark force at distances ranging from less than 0.1 fm to greater that 1 fm. At short distances our theoretical prejudices favor a potential which should act like a Coulomb potential $V(r) = \alpha_s(r)/r$, with α_s becoming smaller at shorter distances owing to the asymptotic freedom of QCD.[1] At long distances, there are both experimental and theoretical reasons[2] to believe that the interquark force in QCD becomes approximately distance-independent, corresponding to a linear potential $V(r) \sim r$. The $c\bar{c}$ and $b\bar{b}$ systems appear to lie in an intermediate range, where a power-law potential $V(r) \sim r^\alpha$ provides a convenient interpolating form[3] between the short-distance Coulomb-like and long-distance linear behavior.

An early fit to quarkonia spectra[4] found a power $\alpha \simeq 0.1$. Since then, data on P-wave levels have appeared,[5,6] and information on leptonic widths has improved. It is appropriate to update the earlier fit for a number of reasons. The power-law method can be of use in estimating properties of systems containing b and c quarks, and in interpolating between these cases to get estimates of $b\bar{c}$ properties. The power law method also gives an estimate of the mass difference between the b and c quarks, which can be of use in attempts[7] to extract the Cabibbo-Kobayashi-Maskawa matrix element V_{cb} from data on semi-leptonic b decays. One would also like to see if there is a consistent pattern of data signaling a departure from a single effective power at short distances, as one would expect from the short-distance behavior of QCD. Finally, power law potentials can be of use in explaining patterns of electric dipole transition rates in the $b\bar{b}$ system.

Since the power-law description does not give an adequate description of spin-dependent effects, we fit spin-averaged levels. For S waves, we use

$$M(S) = [M(^1S_0) + 3M(^3S_1)]/4 \quad , \tag{1}$$

a combination which eliminates hyperfine splittings. For P waves, we use

$$M(P) = \overline{M}(^3P) \equiv [M(^3P_0) + 3M(^3P_1) + 5M(^3P_2)]/9 \quad , \tag{2}$$

---
[1]Presented by Aaron K. Grant.

which eliminates spin-orbit and tensor force splittings. In the latter case we assume hyperfine effects are small. In the case of $b\bar{b}$ levels, the masses of the ^1S levels are not experimentally known. However, the hyperfine splitting can still be estimated[3] using information from the leptonic widths.

We obtain theoretical values for the masses and leptonic widths of the levels using non-relativistic quantum mechanics. We find the energies and wavefunctions of the radial Schrödinger equation by solving the dimensionless equation numerically and then rescaling the dimensionless quantities by appropriate powers of the mass and coupling constant.[3] We take $V(r) = \lambda(r^\alpha - 1)/\alpha + C$. Particle masses are then given by $M = E + 2m_Q$, where E is the binding energy and m_Q is the quark mass.

We present results from three fits. In each case we minimize χ^2, with the standard deviations for the energies set equal to 10 MeV, and the standard deviations for the leptonic widths set equal to the experimental errors. In the first fit, we consider the levels only. In this case, we find that the best fit is given by a potential $V(r) \sim r^{-0.045}$, and that the quark mass difference is $m_b - m_c = 3.19$ GeV. However, the fit gives little preference for quark masses, and in fact the best fit is given by $m_b, m_c \to \infty$. In the second fit, summarized in Table I, we remedy this by including the leptonic widths, which are given by the formula[8]

$$\Gamma(Q\bar{Q} \to e^+e^-) = \frac{16\pi e_Q^2 \alpha^2}{M^2}|\Psi(0)|^2 \left[1 - \frac{16\alpha_s(m_Q)}{3\pi}\right], \quad (3)$$

and where we use[9] $\alpha_s(m_b) = 0.189 \pm 0.008$, $\alpha_s(m_c) = 0.29 \pm 0.02$. In this case, we find

$$m_b = 5.24 \text{ GeV} \quad , \quad m_c = 1.86 \text{ GeV} \quad , \quad m_b - m_c = 3.38 \text{ GeV} \quad (4)$$

for the quark masses, while in the potential $V(r) = \lambda(r^\alpha - 1)/\alpha + C$, we have

$$\alpha = -0.14 \quad , \quad \lambda = 0.808 \quad , \quad C = -1.305 \text{ GeV} \quad . \quad (5)$$

We find that the fitted masses are correct to within 10 MeV or so, but the leptonic widths are off, typically, by 20 to 30 percent. In an attempt to remedy this, in the third fit, we include an *ad hoc* relativistic correction to the leptonic widths. We correct Eq. (3) by introducing a factor of the form $(1 + K\langle v^2/c^2\rangle)$, and treat K as a free parameter. In this case, we find $\alpha = -0.12$, $\lambda = 0.801$, and $C = -0.772$ GeV, while for the quark masses we have $m_b = 4.96$ GeV, $m_c = 1.56$ GeV, and $m_b - m_c = 3.40$ GeV. The constant K is found to be 1.25. The fitted quantities are given in Table I. The relativistic correction gives only a marginal improvement in the fit. In the fits to masses and leptonic widths, we find that m_b and m_c are not particularly well determined. However, the mass difference $m_b - m_c$ appears to be more stable, with a value around 3.39 GeV.

We can use the fitted potentials to estimate the centers of gravity of a few low-lying levels of $b\bar{c}$, $b\bar{s}$ and $c\bar{s}$ levels. For the $b\bar{c}$ system, we find

$$M_{b\bar{c}}(1S) = 6.304 \text{ GeV}, \quad M_{b\bar{c}}(2S) = 6.898 \text{ GeV}, \quad M_{b\bar{c}}(1P) = 6.764 \text{ GeV}, \quad (6)$$

while for the $b\bar{s}$ and $c\bar{s}$ levels, we have

$$M_{c\bar{s}}(1S) = 2.085 \text{ GeV}, \quad M_{c\bar{s}}(1P) = 2.509 \text{ GeV}, \quad M_{b\bar{s}}(1S) = 5.401 \text{ GeV}. \quad (7)$$

Table 1: J/ψ and Υ masses and leptonic widths

Particle	Mass (GeV)			Width (keV)		
	(Expt.)	(NR[a])	(RC[b])	(Expt.)	(NR[a])	(RC[b])
J/ψ(1S)	3.068	3.077	3.079	5.36±0.29	6.41±0.43	6.29±0.43
J/ψ(2S)	3.663	3.654	3.654	2.14±0.21	2.03±0.13	2.04±0.13
J/ψ(1P)	3.525	3.524	3.522	–	–	–
Υ(1S)	9.449	9.420	9.423	1.34±0.04	1.21±0.02	1.18±0.02
Υ(2S)	10.018	10.044	10.042	0.563±0.14	0.477±0.009	0.475±0.009
Υ(3S)	10.351	10.358	10.358	0.44±0.07	0.285±0.006	0.284±0.005
Υ(4S)	10.578	10.564	10.567	0.24±0.05	0.197±0.004	0.200±0.004
Υ(1P)	9.900	9.903	9.900	–	–	–
Υ(2P)	10.260	10.269	10.267	–	–	–
Υ(1D)	–	10.181	10.177	–	–	–
Υ(2D)	–	10.436	10.435	–	–	–

[a]No relativistic corrections   [b]With relativistic corrections

The experimental spin-averaged masses[10,11] of the $c\bar{s}$ states are 2.075 GeV for the 1S level, and 2.536 GeV for the 1P level. We have also estimated the 1S - 2S splitting in toponium. Taking m_t =130 GeV, we find the splitting to be roughly 0.8 GeV. We expect that this is a conservative lower bound, since the short-distance behavior of QCD (which will make this splitting larger) should be important in this case.

Power law potentials also offer some insight into the strengths of various E1 transitions in the $b\bar{b}$ system.[12] Experimentally,[10] we find that the 3S-1P transition is suppressed relative to the 3S-2P, and that the 2P-1S transition is suppressed relative to the 2P-2S. We can gain some insight into this by considering the the radial dipole matrix elements $\langle u_{n\ell}|r|u_{n'\ell\pm1}\rangle$, where n denotes the number of nodes in the radial wavefunction $u_{n\ell}$. We can approximately evaluate these matrix elements by considering the large ℓ limit. In this case, we expand the potential in the radial Schrödinger equation about the point the point $\bar{r} = \ell^{2/(2+\alpha)}$. The potential then has the form of a harmonic oscillator potential, plus anharmonic terms which we include perturbatively. For the dipole matrix elements, we find

$$\langle u_{n\ell}|r|u_{n\ell-1}\rangle = \ell^{2/(\alpha+2)}, \quad \langle u_{n\ell-1}|r|u_{n-1\ell}\rangle = \sqrt{n}\Psi_+(\alpha)\ell^{(2-\alpha)/(4+2\alpha)},$$

$$\langle u_{n-1\ell-1}|r|u_{n\ell}\rangle = \sqrt{n}\Psi_-(\alpha)\ell^{(2-\alpha)/(4+2\alpha)}, \quad \langle u_{0\ell}|r|u_{2\ell-1}\rangle = \Phi(\alpha)\ell^{-\alpha/(2+\alpha)}, \qquad (8)$$

where $\Psi_\pm$ and Φ are functions which depend only on α. We see from Eqs. (8) that transitions with $\Delta n = 0$ are dominant, and that the others are suppressed by a factor $\ell^{-\Delta n/2}$ in the limit of large ℓ. Furthermore, in the region of interest for quarkonium, $\alpha \simeq 0$, the coefficient Φ is quite small: $\Phi(0) \simeq -0.04$. This further suppresses the E1 rate for $\Delta n = 2$ transitions. Direct numerical calculations show that this is also the case for small ℓ: we find that the 3S-1P rate is dramatically suppressed relative to the 3S-2P rate. Consequently, it appears that the suppression of E1 transitions with nonzero Δn is a general property of power law potentials.

We can use the ratios of radial dipole matrix elements for certain transitions in the $b\bar{b}$ system to place limits on the power α. From the experimental data[6,10] we deduce the ratios

$$\frac{\langle 3S|r|1P\rangle}{\langle 3S|r|2P\rangle} = 0.016 \pm 0.004, \qquad \frac{\langle 2P|r|1S\rangle}{\langle 2P|r|2S\rangle} = 0.117 \pm 0.014. \qquad (9)$$

Computing these ratios numerically and comparing with experiment, we find that α is constrained to lie in the region $-0.2 < \alpha < 0$, consistent with what was found from the fit to levels and leptonic widths. Finally, we can estimate m_b using the rates of the 3S-1P, 3S-2P, and 2S-1P electric dipole transitions. Extracting the radial dipole matrix elements from the data, we find that the potential model favors a value $m_b \simeq 4.0 \pm 0.9$ GeV. This is smaller than expected, and in particular we find that the 2S-1P transition yields the surprisingly small value $m_b = 3.45 \pm 0.44$ GeV. This is an indication that either the potential model is inadequate for describing E1 rates, or that the $\Upsilon(2S)$ total width has been overestimated.

We thank Eric Rynes for collaboration on the results of Ref. 3. This work was supported in part by the United States Department of Energy through Grant No. DE FG02 90ER 40560.

1. D. J. Gross and F. Wilczek, Phys. Rev. D **8**, 3633 (1973); **9**, 980 (1973); H. D. Politzer, Phys. Rep. **14C**, 129 (1974)
2. Y. Nambu, Phys. Rev. D **10**, 4262 (1974).
3. A. K. Grant, J. L. Rosner and E. Rynes, Phys. Rev. D, to be published, and references therein.
4. A. Martin, Phys. Lett. **93B**, 338 (1980); **100B**, 511 (1981).
5. CUSB Collaboration, M. Narain et al., Phys. Rev. Lett. **66**, 3113 (1991) and earlier references therein; CLEO II Collaboration, R. Morrison et al., ibid. **67**, 1696 (1991) and earlier references therein (χ'_b states).
6. Crystal Ball Collaboration, W. Walk et al., Phys. Rev. D **34**, 2611 (1986), and earlier references therein (χ_b states).
7. J. L. Rosner, in *B Decays*, ed. by S. L. Stone (World Scientific, Singapore, 1992), p. 312.
8. V. A. Matveev, B. V. Struminskii, and A. N. Tavkhelidze, Dubna report P-2524, 1965 (unpublished); H. Pietschmann and W. Thirring, Phys. Lett. **21**, 713 (1966); R. Van Royen and V. F. Weisskopf, Nuovo Cim. **50A**, 617 (1967); **51A**, 583(E) (1967).
9. W. Kwong, P. B. Mackenzie, R. Rosenfeld, and J. L. Rosner, Phys. Rev. D **37**, 3210 (1988).
10. Particle Data Group, K. Hikasa et al., Phys. Rev. D **45**, S1 (1992), and references therein.
11. A. Asratyan et al., Zeit. Phys. C **40**, 483 (1988); ARGUS Collaboration, H. Albrecht et al., Phys. Lett. B **230**, 162 (1989); CLEO Collaboration, P. Avery et al., Phys. Rev. D **41**, 774 (1990).
12. A. K. Grant and J. L. Rosner, Phys. Rev. D **46**, 3862 (1992).

RETARDATION CORRECTIONS
TO THE QUARKONIUM SPECTRUM

N. Brambilla and G.M. Prosperi

Dipartimento di Fisica dell'Università di Milano and I.N.F.N.
Sezione di Milano, via Celoria 16, 20133 Milano, Italy

ABSTRACT

We reconsider the problem of the retardation corrections to the quarkonium spectrum due to some errors occurring in a preceding paper. We find that such corrections are too large ($\simeq 1 GeV$) and rule out the significance of the usual confining part I_{conf} of the BS kernel obtained by a simple "covariantization" of the instantaneous form suggested by the linear potential. On the contrary, once that I_{conf} is kept instantaneous, we find that the contribution coming from the one gluon exchange part of the kernel is in the right direction with respect to the potential results and improve the agreement of the hyperfine separation with the data.

The heavy quarkonium problem is usually treated in a potential framework. A theoretically well founded potential can be obtained in the context of the Wilson loop formalism and it is expressed as the sum of three terms; a static part $V_{stat} = \frac{4}{3}\frac{\alpha_s}{r} + C + \sigma r$ and two $O(\frac{1}{m^2})$ spin and velocity dependent ones, V_{sd} and V_{vd} [1], which involve the same parameters.

In principle the Bethe-Salpeter (BS) equation should be the most appropriate tool to treat the bound state problem in QCD and the potential should be reobtained in terms of the BS kernel (once that this is known) as a consequence of the so called instantaneous approximation. In practice only the perturbative part of the kernel can be immediately written down. Indeed in the Coulomb gauge and at the lowest order this takes the form

$$I_{pert} = \frac{4}{3}\alpha_s \frac{1}{2\pi^2}\left[-\frac{\gamma_0^{(1)}\gamma_0^{(2)}}{Q^2} - \frac{1}{t}\left(\gamma^{(1)} \cdot \gamma^{(2)} - (\gamma^{(1)} \cdot \hat{Q})(\gamma^{(2)} \cdot \hat{Q})\right)\right] \quad (1)$$

and reproduces correctly the whole part in α_s of the mentioned potential. Here $Q = q' - q$ denotes the tridimensional center of mass momentum transfer and $t = (\omega' - \omega)^2 - (q' - q)^2$ the corresponding quadridimensional invariant.

On the contrary, there is no means presently of obtaining the nonperturbative confinement part of the kernel consistently in a field-theoretical framework. In this situation an assumption frequently done is that of a purely scalar convolution kernel of the form [2]

$$I_{conf} = (2\pi)^3 \left(\frac{-\sigma}{\pi^2}\frac{1}{t^2}\right), \quad (2)$$

which reproduces the static potential σr in the instantaneous limit ($\omega = \omega' = 0$). This reproduces also the σ spin-dependent terms in V_{sd}, while additional $\frac{1}{m^2}$ terms are necessary to obtain even V_{vd} correctly. Once that (2) is assumed, the leading retardation correction to a pure potential treatment (i.e. the correction to the simple replacement $t \to -Q^2$ in (1) and in (2)) can be obtained as an additional contribution to the potential of the form[3]

$$\langle \mathbf{q}', \sigma_1' \sigma_2' | V_{\text{ret}}^{(1)} | \mathbf{q}, \sigma_1 \sigma_2 \rangle = -\frac{m^2}{(2\pi)^3 w(\mathbf{q}) w(\mathbf{q}')} \mathcal{R}e \int \frac{d^3 k}{(2\pi)^3} \frac{m^2}{w(\mathbf{k})^2}$$

$$\bar{u}_{\sigma_1'}^{(1)}(\mathbf{q}') \bar{u}_{\sigma_2'}^{(2)}(-\mathbf{q}') \Big\{ i \int \frac{d\omega_k}{2\pi} \Big[I_0(\mathbf{q}', \mathbf{k}) \frac{\Lambda_+^{(1)}(\mathbf{k}) \Lambda_-^{(2)}(-\mathbf{k})}{(\omega_k - \frac{\sqrt{s}}{2} + w(\mathbf{k}) - i0)(\omega_k + \frac{\sqrt{s}}{2} - w(\mathbf{k}) + i0)} I_1(\omega_k; \mathbf{k}, \mathbf{q}) +$$

$$+ \bar{I}_1(\omega_k; \mathbf{q}', \mathbf{k}) \frac{\Lambda_+^{(1)}(\mathbf{k}) \Lambda_+^{(2)}(-\mathbf{k})}{(\omega_k - \frac{\sqrt{s}}{2} + w(\mathbf{k}) - i0)(\omega_k + \frac{\sqrt{s}}{2} - w(\mathbf{k}) + i0)} I_0(\mathbf{k}, \mathbf{q}) \Big] +$$

$$+ I_0(\mathbf{q}', \mathbf{k}) \frac{\Lambda_-^{(1)}(-\mathbf{k}) \Lambda_-^{(2)}(\mathbf{k})}{\sqrt{s} + 2w(\mathbf{k})} I_0(\mathbf{k}, \mathbf{q}) \Big\} u_{\sigma_1}^{(1)}(\mathbf{q}) u_{\sigma_2}^{(2)}(-\mathbf{q}) \tag{3}$$

where $I_0(\mathbf{q}', \mathbf{q}) = I(0, \mathbf{q}'; 0\mathbf{q})$, $I_1(\omega; \mathbf{q}', \mathbf{q}) = I(0, \mathbf{q}'; \omega, \mathbf{q}) - I_0(\mathbf{q}', \mathbf{q})$ and $\bar{I}_1(\omega'; \mathbf{q}', \mathbf{q}) = I(\omega', \mathbf{q}'; 0, \mathbf{q}) - I_0(\mathbf{q}', \mathbf{q})$ and the prescription $\mathcal{R}e$ stays properly for *self adjoint part* of the following matrix element. Notice that only the confinement kernel (2) gives actually a contribution in the static limit to the above expression; adopted e.g. the regularization prescription

$$(\frac{1}{t^2})_{\text{reg}} = \frac{1}{2} \Big(\frac{\partial^2}{\partial \varepsilon^2} - \varepsilon \log \frac{\varepsilon}{\mu} \frac{\partial^3}{\partial \varepsilon^3} \Big) \frac{1}{t - \varepsilon^2 + i0} := D_\varepsilon^\mu \frac{1}{t - \varepsilon^2 + i0} \tag{4}$$

we can write $I_1(\omega'; \mathbf{q}', \mathbf{q}) = -(2\pi)^3 \frac{\sigma}{\pi^2} D_\varepsilon^\mu \Big(\frac{1}{\omega^2 - Q^2 - \varepsilon^2} + \frac{1}{Q^2 + \varepsilon^2} \Big)$. After various manipulations and using harmonic eigenfunctions in place of the exact nonrelativistic zero order ones, one can write

$$W_{nl}^{\text{ret}} = \langle \Phi_{nl} | V^{(1)} | \Phi_{nl} \rangle = 2 C_{nl} \int_0^\infty dk\, k \Big(\frac{W_{nl}^{(0)}}{2} - \frac{k^2}{2m} \Big) e^{-\lambda_{nl}^2 k^2} \int_0^\infty dp\, p\, e^{-\frac{\lambda_{nl}^2 p^2}{2}} \times$$

$$g_{nl}(p, k) D_\varepsilon^\mu \mathcal{P} \frac{1}{-\frac{W_{nl}^{(0)}}{2} + \frac{k^2}{2m} + \sqrt{p^2 + \varepsilon^2}} \frac{1}{p^2 + \varepsilon^2} = 2 C_{nl} D_\varepsilon^\mu I_{nl}(\varepsilon) \tag{5}$$

where $\mathcal{P}$ stands for the principal value prescription and g_{nl} are appropriate polynomials in k, p, $\sinh(kp\lambda^2)$ and $\cosh(kp\lambda^2)$.

In a preceding paper[3] we have applied (3) to the first three S states of the $c\bar{c}$ and $b\bar{b}$ systems. Unfortunately, due to a normalization error, the values of the constants C_{nl} as reported in[3] are wrong for a factor $-(2\pi)^{\frac{3}{2}}$. This fact, that changes by an order of magnitude the original results, and new calculations on the P states force to modify drastically the conclusions. The fact that the new corrections turn out larger than the level separations themselves makes the kernel (2) profoundly different from its instantaneous counterpart

$$I_{\text{conf}} = (2\pi)^3 \Big(-\frac{\sigma}{\pi^2} \frac{1}{Q^4} \Big) \tag{6}$$

which is strictly related to the linear potential. The surprising circumstance is clearly related to the highly singular character of kernel (2) and suggests that kernel (6) has to be preferred in its actual form in spite of the more aesthetic appearance of the preceding one. If (6) is adopted the only retardation effect comes from the second term in (1) and it is a spin-dependent one ($O(\frac{1}{m^2})$). On the S states this consists in a reduction in the singlet-triplet splitting as evaluated from the contact term in the pure potential and in the $c\bar{c}$ case it seems to be in the right direction.

Table 1: Static limit retardations corrections in MeV to $c\bar{c}$ and $b\bar{b}$ spectra for the following values of the parameters (in GeV) $m_b = 5.268, m_c = 1.913, \frac{4}{3}\alpha_s = 0.587, C = -0.707, \sigma = 0.146$ and for kernel (2) and $\xi = \ln\frac{\mu}{50}$

	$b\bar{b}$	$c\bar{c}$
1S	$-803 \pm 126 + 268\xi$ (-693)	$-976 \pm 94 + 425\xi$ (-1244)
2S	$-1071 \pm 94 + 520\xi$ (-1417)	$-520 \pm 126 + 2032\xi$ (-630)
3S	$-898 + 1181\xi$	$-2536 \pm 252 - 79\xi$
1P	$-1921 \pm 283 + 472\xi$ (-1984)	$-2520 \pm 121 + 882\xi$ (-2362)
2P	$-2366 + 936\xi$	$---$

Table 2: Purely potential triplet-singlet splitting and retardation corrections (in MeV) for values of the parameters as in Tab.1 and for kernel (1) and (6).

	$\frac{8\pi\kappa}{3m^2}\delta(\mathbf{r})$	W_{ret}^{SS}	Tot	EXP.
1S $c\bar{c}$	182	-44	136	116
2S $c\bar{c}$	102	-15	87	93
1S $b\bar{b}$	265	-29	236	$--$
2S $b\bar{b}$	89	-9	80	$--$

1. K. Wilson, *Phys. Rev.* **D10** (1974) 2445; E. Eichten and F. Feinberg, *Phys. Rev.* **D23** (1981) 2724; A.Barchielli, E. Montaldi and G.Prosperi, *Nucl. Phys.* **B296**(1988) 625; A. Barchielli, N. Brambilla and G. Prosperi, *Nuovo Cimento* **103A** (1990) 59.
2. e.g. R. McClary and N. Byers, *Phys.Rev.* **D28** (1983) 1692; M.G. Olsson and Miller *Phys. Rev* **D28** (1982) 674; D. Gromes, *Nucl. Phys.* **B131** (1977) 80.
3. N. Brambilla and G.M. Prosperi, *Phys. Rev.* **D46** (1992) 1096.

$q\bar{q}$ BOUND STATES IN THE BETHE-SALPETER FORMALISM

Pankaj Jain and Herman J. Munczek
Department of Physics and Astronomy
The University of Kansas
Lawrence, KS 66045-2151

ABSTRACT

We solve the Bethe-Salpeter equation in order to determine the spectrum of pseudoscalar and vector meson bound states for light as well as heavy quarks. The fermion propagators are obtained by solving the Schwinger-Dyson equation consistently with the Bethe-Salpeter equation, a procedure necessary for demonstrating the Goldstone nature of the pion in the chiral limit. Our results agree qualitatively and quantitatively with expectations both from current algebra for light quarks and from composite models for heavy quarks.

1. Introduction

There has been considerable theoretical study of the strongly interacting bound states. However most of the work is based on non-relativistic approximations to the bound state equations. This approach should be accurate if we consider the bound states which only involve heavy quarks, but is expected to fail for light mesons. In particular it does not take into account the fact that the light pseudoscalar mesons are almost Goldstone particles and that the light quark masses are mostly dynamical. Furthermore in most of the studies there is no clear connection between the constituent quark mass which is fed into the bound state equation and the current algebra mass. In order to correctly describe the light mesons it is necessary to go to a field theoretic framework. In the present paper we study the quark-antiquark bound states by solving the Bethe-Salpeter (BS) equation consistently with the Schwinger-Dyson (SD) equation for the quark propagator, in such a way that we get zero mass pseudoscalar states in the limit of zero bare quark masses. To simplify the problem we work in the ladder approximation. We employ for our calculations theoretically and phenomenologically motivated models for the gluon propagator.

The BS equation in the ladder approximation can be written as,

$$S_a^{-1}(q+\xi p)\chi(p,q)S_b^{-1}(q-(1-\xi)p) = -i\int \gamma_\mu \chi(p,k)\gamma_\nu G_{\mu\nu}(k-q)\frac{d^4k}{(2\pi)^4}, \qquad (1)$$

The quark propagators are determined by solving the SD equation, also in the ladder approximation,

$$S_a^{-1}(q) = \not{q} - \tilde{m}_a(\Lambda_c) + i\int \gamma_\mu S_a(k)\gamma_\nu G_{\mu\nu}(k-q)\frac{d^4k}{(2\pi)^4}, \qquad (2)$$

where Λ_c is the ultraviolet cutoff. The gluon propagator, $G_{\mu\nu}$, is modelled in terms of several parameters which can be fitted to experimental data. It is given in the

Landau gauge by $G_{\mu\nu}(k) = -(g_{\mu\nu} - k_\mu k_\nu/k^2)G(k^2)$ where,

$$G(k^2) = \frac{16\pi^2}{3}\left[\frac{d}{k^2 ln(x_0 + x)}\left(1 + b\frac{ln[ln(x_0 + x)]}{ln(x_0 + x)}\right) + (2\pi\eta)^2\delta^{(4)}(k) + a(1 - \omega k^2/k_0^2)e^{-k^2/k_0^2}\right],$$

and $x = k^2/\Lambda_{QCD}^2$. This model goes to the two loop form of the running coupling at large momentum and leads to an approximately harmonic oscillator potential in three dimensional configuration space, a form which is necessary to get the realistic spectrum of heavy mesons. The BS wave function for the pseudoscalar bound state can be expressed as,

$$\chi(p,q) = \gamma_5[\chi_0 + \slashed{p}\chi_1 + \slashed{q}\chi_2 + [\slashed{p},\slashed{q}]\chi_3] \quad (3)$$

with similar decomposition for other spin and parity states. The resulting BS equation is simplified by expanding the wave functions, χ_i in terms of Tschebyshev polynomials,

$$\chi_i\left(q^2, M_B^2, \cos\theta\right) = \sum_n \chi_i^{(n)}\left(q^2, M_B^2\right)T^{(n)}(\cos\theta), \quad (4)$$

where we have set $p^2 = -M_B^2$, the bound state mass squared. We keep only the leading order polynomial for our calculation. The contribution due to the dropped terms was estimated to be small. Details of the calculation for pseudoscalars are given in Ref. [1].

2. Results and discussion

Here we describe some qualitative and quantitative features of the results for pseudoscalar and vector mesons. The detailed numerical results for pseudoscalar mesons and the parameter choices are given in Ref. [1]. The mass functions for different quarks are displayed in Fig. 1. The asymptotic behavior of the mass functions and the wave functions agrees with the one found on the basis of operator-product-expansion considerations. For light mesons our results satisfy the Gell-Mann, Oakes and Renner relation, $M_{ab}^2 = [\bar{m}_a(\Lambda_c) + \bar{m}_b(\Lambda_c)] < q\bar{q}>_{ch}/f_{ch}^2$, where $\bar{m}$ is the bare mass of the quark defined in Eqn. 2 and the subscript ch means that the quantity is computed by using $\bar{m}(\Lambda_c) = 0$. Both $\bar{m}$ and the condensate $<q\bar{q}>_{ch}$ depends on the ultraviolet cutoff Λ_c but their product was found to be insensitive to Λ_c. For heavy quarks, the relationship between M_{ab} and $[m_a(0) + m_b(0)]$ is roughly linear, in agreement with nonrelativistic limit expectations.

We have also obtained preliminary results for vector mesons ground states. The overall fit was found to be better with parameters choices, a=-[32.9 MeV]$^{-2}$, η=270 MeV with the remaining parameters same as in Ref. 1. The results for pseudoscalar mesons were found to be within a few % of the ones given in [1]. The results for some of the vector mesons are as follows: m_ρ = 787 MeV (770 MeV), m_{K^*} = 978 MeV (892 MeV), m_ϕ = 1250 MeV (1019 MeV), m_{D^*} = 2075 MeV (2010 MeV), m_{B^*} = 5325 MeV (5324 MeV), $m_{J/\psi}$ = 3245 MeV (3097 MeV), m_Υ = 9500 MeV (9460 MeV). The numbers in parenthesis are the experimental results. These results were obtained by keeping only the dominant term in the invariant decomposition of the vector meson wave function. More complete results will be given in a forthcoming publication.

Finally we display our preliminary results for the electromagnetic and isospin splittings for pseudoscalar and vector mesons. Our results for the pseudoscalar mass splittings decrease significantly as we go from the Kaon to the B meson, in reasonable agreement with experiments. Quantitatively we find, $K^0 - K^+ = 4.02$ MeV (input), $D^+ - D^0 = 3.95$ MeV (4.77 MeV) $B^0 - B^+ = 1.0$ MeV (0.1 MeV). For the vector meson we do not get as strong a decrease as is displayed by the experiments. The results are as follows: $K^{*0} - K^{*+} = 11$ MeV (6.7 MeV), $D^{*+} - D^{*0} = 10.8$ MeV (2.9 MeV) $B^{*0} - B^{*+} = 7.4$ MeV (?) We are currently examining different models and calculating corrections to our result to determine if the agreement can be improved.

In conclusion, we have presented a covariant treatment of $q\bar{q}$ bound states which is applicable for both light and heavy mesons. Qualitatively our results are in good agreement with current algebra results for light quarks and nonrelativistic limit expectations for heavy quarks. Further tests of the approach described here, as well as parametrization of $\alpha_s(q^2)$, will be done by obtaining a more complete spectrum and by computing the electromagnetic and weak form factors of these mesons.

5. Acknowledgements

We thank Douglas W. McKay and John P. Ralston for useful discussions. This work was supported in part by the Department of Energy under grant No. DE-FG02-85-ER40214.

6. References

1. H.J. Munczek and P. Jain, *Phys. Rev.* D46 (1992) 438, and references therein.

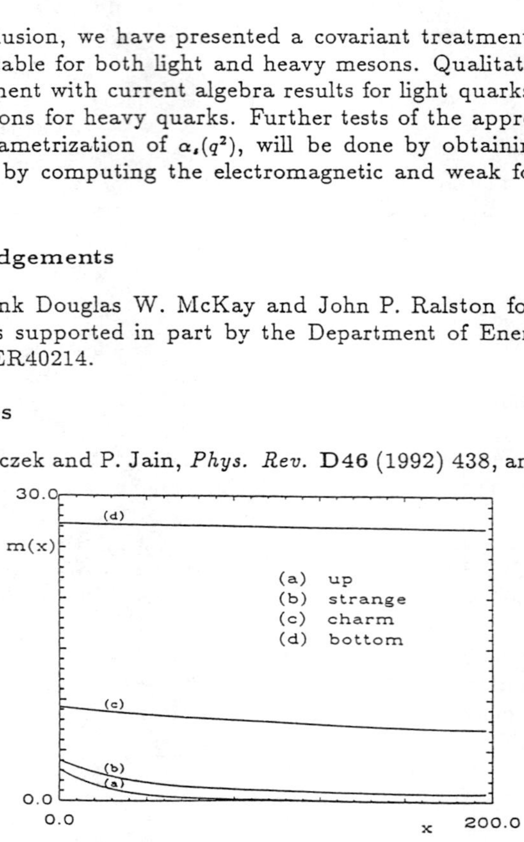

FIG. 1. Mass functions in units of Λ_{QCD} shown as functions of $x = q^2/(\Lambda_{QCD})^2$. Up and down quarks are assumed to be degenerate.

A COMPARISON OF SALPETER'S AND SCHRÖDINGER'S EQUATIONS IN HEAVY-LIGHT SYSTEMS

LEWIS P. FULCHER
Department of Physics and Astronomy
Bowling Green State University
Bowling Green, Ohio 43402

Using Salpeter's equation, eigenvalues for the Cornell potential are computed by diagonalizing the Hamiltonian operator in a complete set of basis functions. In each of the three cases studied, heavy-quark systems, heavy-light systems and the $s\bar{s}$ system, the Salpeter results agree with experiment better than those obtained with Schrödinger's equation.

I would like to motivate my interest in the spinless-Salpeter equation from two different points of view. The first of these is a calculation[1] of the leptonic widths, dipole transition rates, energies, and fine-structure splittings of charmonium and the upsilon system that was based on Richardson's potential and Schrödinger's equation. Whenever feasible in formulating this calculation, I have established contact with underlying concepts in quantum chromodynamics (QCD). In particular, I have addressed the following questions:

1. What is the role of the running coupling constant in determining those properties of heavy quarkonium systems that depend on the wave function near the origin?
2. Does the use of the full radiative one-loop expressions for the spin-dependent potentials lead to better agreement with experiment than the one-gluon-exchange potential?
3. If the sign of the ^1P energy relative to the $(^3P)_{cog}$ energy an indicator[2] of the applicability of perturbative QCD?
4. What is the experimental evidence[3] for a nonperturbative contribution to the quark-antiquark spin-orbit potential?

After addressing these issues in heavy-quark systems, it is natural to undertake their examination in a broader context that includes the B and D mesons. Because of the pioneering work of Godfrey and Isgur[4], it is apparent that one must consider a host of relativistic corrections, including the effects of a relativistic kinetic energy operator and several relativistic modifications of the potential energy operator. However, because of the surprising results of Gara et al.[5] and Lucha, Rupprecht and Schöberl[6] with the reduced Bethe-Salpeter equation, it is also apparent that much theoretical work will be required before we find a satisfactory means of treating relativistic quark-antiquark dynamics. Thus, it is very important to document whatever successes one can find in these systems. It is for this reason that we have undertaken a comparison of Schrödinger and Salpeter eigenvalues, to see if we can discover a signature of the relativistic kinetic energy operator. Our viewpoint is similar to that developed for heavy quarkonium systems by Jacobs, Olsson and Suchyta[7], in that we will allow the parameters to vary independently in both cases.

Our relativistic calculation is based on the spinless-Salpeter equation,

$$H \psi_n = E \psi_n; \quad H = \sqrt{m_1^2 + p^2} + \sqrt{m_2^2 + p^2} + V(r), \qquad (1)$$

where p denotes the momentum in the center of momentum frame and V is the Cornell potential,

$$V(r) = Ar - \kappa/r. \tag{2}$$

The string constant A and the Coulomb parameter κ of Eq. (2) are taken to be flavor independent. Since the kinetic energy operator of Eq. (1) is nonlocal, we determine the energy eigenvalues by diagonalizing the energy operator there in a complete set of basis functions. We have chosen the set,

$$R_{nl}(r) = N_{nl}\,\beta^{3/2}\,e^{-\beta r}\,L_n^{2l+2}(2\beta r), \qquad N_{nl}^2 = \frac{8(n!)}{\Gamma(n+2l+3)}, \tag{3}$$

where L_n^{2l+2} denotes an associated Laguerre polynomial[8].

With this basis we have found analytic expressions for both the linear and Coulomb parts of the Cornell potential for arbitrary l. For S states, these matrix elements are especially simple, that is,

$$\langle Ar \rangle_{nn'} = \frac{A}{2\beta}\left[(2n+3)\delta_{nn'} - \sqrt{n'(n'+2)}\,\delta_{n',n+1} - \sqrt{n(n+2)}\,\delta_{n',n-1}\right], \tag{4}$$

$$\langle \kappa/r \rangle_{nn'} = \kappa\beta\sqrt{\frac{(n+1)(n+2)}{(n'+1)(n'+2)}}, \qquad n \leq n'. \tag{5}$$

The matrix elements of the kinetic energy operator must be calculated in momentum space. Thus, one must calculate the Fourier transforms of the radial functions of Eq. (3). These can be expressed as Jacobi polynomials[9]. For S states, we have derived a simplified form of these polynomials,

$$g_{n0}(p) = \frac{4}{p}\sqrt{\frac{(n+2)(n+1)}{\pi\beta}}\sum_{k=0}^{n}\frac{n!\,(-2)^k}{(n-k)!\,k!}\,\frac{\cos^{k+2}\theta\,\sin(k+2)\theta}{(k+2)}, \tag{6}$$

where $\cos\theta = \beta/(\beta^2 + p^2)^{1/2}$.

Our results for the low-lying S and P states are given in Table I. There both the Schrödinger and the Salpeter results are compared with experiment and values for χ^2 are computed. For the Salpeter equation, our parameters are $m_b = 4.731$ GeV, $m_c = 1.321$ Gev, $A = 0.203$ GeV^2, $\kappa = 0.437$, $m_s = 0.366$ GeV and $m_u = 0.150$ GeV. No additive constant is required in the heavy quark sector. It is necessary to add constants to the charmed sector (-246 MeV) and the bottom sector (-214 MeV). The Schrödinger parameters are similar except that the two light quark masses are heavier (0.603 GeV, 0.325 GeV).

From the χ^2 values listed below the charmonium results, we infer that the Salpeter eigenvalues agree with experiment better than the Schrödinger eigenvalues for heavy quark systems. Thus, we agree with the conclusion of Jacobs, Olsson and Suchyta for these systems. From the second set of χ^2 values, it is clear that the Salpeter eigenvalues agree with experiment better than the Schrödinger eigenvalues in the charmed and bottom sectors. We have also found that the Salpeter eigenvalues are closer to experiment for the low-lying S and P states of the $s\bar{s}$ system.

REFERENCES

1. Lewis P. Fulcher, *Phys. Rev.* **D44** (1991) 2079; **D42** (1990) 2337.
2. T. Armstrong et al. (E760 Collaboration), to be published in *Phys. Rev. Lett.*
3. U. Heintz et al. (CUSB collaboration), *Phys. Rev.* **46** (1992) 1928.
4. S. Godfrey and N. Isgur, *Phys. Rev.* **D32** (1985) 189.
5. A Gara et al. *Phys. Rev.* **D42** (1990) 1651; **D40** (1989) 843.
6. W. Lucha, H. Rupprecht and F. Schöberl, *Phys. Rev.* **D46** (1992) 1088.
7. S. Jacobs, M. Olsson and C. Suchyta, *Phys. Rev.* **33** (1986) 3338.
8. E. Rainville, *Special Functions* (Macmillan, New York), 1960.
9. E. Weniger, *J. Math. Phys.* **26** (1985) 276.

TABLE I

Spin-averaged energies. The heavy quarkonium results were obtained with $\beta=2.0$ GeV and the diagonalization of a 9 by 9 matrix. The heavy-light results were obtained with $\beta=1.5$ Gev.

States	Schrödinger (MeV)	Salpeter (MeV)	Experiment (MeV)
Υ (1S)	9447	9449	9448 ± 5
Υ (2S)	10006	10000	10017 ± 5
Υ (3S)	10356	10352	10350 ± 5
Υ (1P)	9900	9901	9900 ± 1
Υ (2P)	10260	10263	10261 ± 1
$c\bar{c}$ (1S)	3068	3070	3068 ± 2
$c\bar{c}$ (2S)	3694	3670	3663 ± 5
$c\bar{c}$ (1P)	3498	3507	3525 ± 1
χ^2	775	344	
D(1S)	1973	1973	1973 ± 3
D(1P)	2474	2456	2437 ±10
D_S(1S)	2075	2076	2075 ± 2
D_S(1P)	2534	2545	2550 ±10
B(1S)	5313	5313	5313±10
B(1P)	5798	5779	
B_S(1S)	5383	5405	
B_S(1P)	5823	5859	
χ^2	16.3	4.1	

QCD STRUCTURE OF QUARKONIUM SPIN SPECTRA

F. Halzen, C. Olson, M. G. Olsson, and M. L. Stong
Department of Physics, University of Wisconsin, Madison
Madison, WI 53706, USA

ABSTRACT

We show that our QCD calculation [1] of the $^1P_1$ charmonium state can be incorporated into a global description of the fine and hyperfine structure of the charmonium and bottomonium systems. We find that the $\mathcal{O}(\alpha_s^2)$ perturbative QCD potential leads to a consistent description of all splittings. The results are used to predict the unmeasured bottomonium P-wave hyperfine splittings.

1. Calculation Scheme

For a given charm quark mass we fit to the spin-averaged charm and bottom spectra to obtain the corresponding potential parameters and bottom quark mass. We perform our calculation with two choices of m_c: 1.2 GeV and 1.8 GeV. Because the fitting process fixes m_b the lower(higher) charm quark mass implies a lower(higher) bottom quark mass. We treat the spin splittings as a perturbation to the static potential and ignore couplings to decay channels.

The wavefunctions are calculated via the Rayleigh-Ritz-Galerkin method with the Cornell potential [2] and the Indiana potential [3]. Perturbative QCD predicts the Fourier transform of the $Q\bar{Q}$ potential, which has been known to $\mathcal{O}(\alpha_s^2)$ for some time [4, 5, 6]. We find that the perturbative QCD expectation values are more straightforwardly evaluated in momentum space; however, the long range spin-orbit splitting is more easily calculated in coordinate space.

2. Hyperfine Splittings

The hyperfine potential $\Delta \tilde{H}_{hyp}$ is, in the $\overline{MS}$ scheme [4],

$$\Delta \tilde{H}_{hyp} = \mathbf{s}_1 \cdot \mathbf{s}_2 \frac{32\pi}{9m^2} \alpha_s \left\{ 1 + \frac{\alpha_s}{4\pi} \left[\left(-11 + \frac{2}{3} n_f \right) \ln\left(\frac{Q^2}{\mu^2}\right) + \frac{21}{2} \ln\left(\frac{Q^2}{m^2}\right) + \frac{23}{3} - \frac{10}{9} n_f - 3\ln 2 \right] \right\} \quad (1)$$

Here the momentum transfer $\mathbf{Q} = \frac{1}{2}(\mathbf{p}' - \mathbf{p})$. The quantities which depend only on the hyperfine splitting are

$$\begin{aligned} \Delta M_{hyp}^S &= M(n^3 S_1) - M(n^1 S_0) \,, \\ \Delta M_{hyp}^P &= M_{cog} - M(n^1 P_1) \,. \end{aligned} \quad (2)$$

where M_{cog} is the mass of the center of gravity of the triplet states. Figure 1 shows the $c\bar{c}$ 1S hyperfine splittings as a function of renormalization scale μ and various values of α_s. We make the choice $\mu = m_c$ for the renormalization scale, which results in small corrections to the tree-level. Note that for $m_c = 1.8$ GeV, the 1S and 2S states require different values of α_s. This lack of consistency would seem to favor lighter quark masses but could be eliminated by adjusting μ. Use of the Indiana potential in calculating the wavefunctions leads to small increases in the required α_s values. This is due to the less singular behavior of the Indiana potential at small r. Although the effect is small for $c\bar{c}$, it becomes significant for the $b\bar{b}$ S-wave states. The position-space wavefunctions for the P-waves vanish at the origin, leading to two significant simplifications. First, the behavior of the potential at the origin has little effect. Second, after performing the angular integrations the explicit μ-dependence which remained in the S-wave splittings does not remain in the P-wave,

$$\Delta M_{hyp}^P = -\frac{1}{(2\pi)^6}\frac{8\pi\alpha_s^2}{9m^2}\int dp'dp\tilde{\psi}(p')\tilde{\psi}(p)\left(-\frac{1}{2}+\frac{2}{3}n_f\right)$$
$$\times\left\{pp'\left(p^2+p'^2\right)+\frac{1}{4}\left(p^2-p'^2\right)^2\ln\left[\frac{(p-p')^2}{(p+p')^2}\right]\right\}. \quad (3)$$

This independence of renormalization scale makes the prediction of the P-wave splittings much less ambiguous than would otherwise be possible. Figure 2 shows ΔM_{hyp}^P for both light and heavy charm quark masses. For $\alpha_s = 0.3$, we find that $\Delta M_{hyp}^P = -1.0$ and -0.78 MeV for $m_c = 1.2$ and 1.8 GeV.

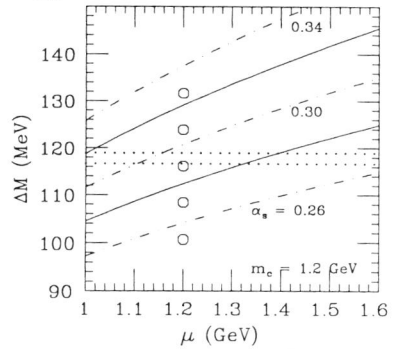

Fig. 1 - Hyperfine splitting, $\Delta M_{hyp}^S = M(J/\Psi) - M(\eta_c)$, in the charmonium 1S system, for three values of α_s. The large circles give the tree-level results for the same values of α_s. They have been placed at $\mu = m_c$ to demonstrate that the one-loop corrections are small for this choice of μ. The dotted horizontal lines indicate the experimental 1σ limits. [7]

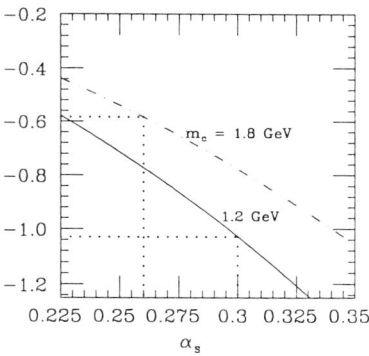

Fig. 2 - ΔM_{hyp}^P in charmonium 1P. The result is independent of μ. $\alpha_s = 0.3$ gives splittings of -1.0 and -0.78 MeV for $m_c = 1.2$ and 1.8 GeV, respectively. A recent experiment [8] gives $\Delta M_{hyp}^P = -0.93 \pm 0.23$.

3. Spin Orbit and Tensor Splittings

The fine structure involves the perturbative QCD result plus an additional spin-orbit term due to confinement. We take the perturbative terms again to be the $\mathcal{O}(\alpha_s^2)$ QCD result calculated in the $\overline{MS}$ scheme [4] and for the confinement contribution we assume that the confining potential is a pure Lorentz scalar [9]. Working with P-waves only, which are insensitive to the short-range behavior of the potential, we once again use the Cornell potential. We expect that the spin-orbit and tensor terms should have the same α_s value, as the two interactions have the same $\propto r^{-3}$ behavior when written in coordinate space. This is verified for low quark masses with the exception of the $b\bar{b}\, 2P$ splittings.

In contrast to the hyperfine case, the fine structure involves large corrections to the tree-level results. More specific conclusions are unwarranted given the magnitude of the one-loop effects. In particular the low ratio $R = (M_{\chi_2} - M_{\chi_1})/(M_{\chi_1} - M_{\chi_0})$ in the radial excitation of the χ_b found in recent CESR experiments [10] is still not explained. We point out that the tree-level predictions for spin-orbit and tensor splittings are considerably below the experimental measurements. In each case the one-loop correction is a significant improvement over the tree-level and, in fact, provides a reasonable representation of the data.

4. Conclusions

While the corrections to the spin-orbit and tensor splittings are large, the corrections to the hyperfine splittings are small and therefore allow reliable predictions of the unmeasured $b\bar{b}$ P-wave singlet states. Similar predictions of the S-wave states would be imprecise because of the strong dependence on the form of the potential near the origin. Our predictions are $\Delta M_{hyp}^P(1P) = -0.25 \pm 0.10\,\mathrm{MeV}$ and $\Delta M_{hyp}^P(2P) = -0.21 \pm 0.10\,\mathrm{MeV}$. The central values are obtained by the one-loop running from the hyperfine value of $\alpha_s(m_c)$ and the primary uncertainty is the variation in α_s. We find that QCD provides, at $\mathcal{O}(\alpha_s^2)$, a consistent description of all heavy $Q\bar{Q}$ spin splittings.

5. Acknowledgements

We would like to thank Don Lichtenberg and Kaoru Hagiwara for valuable discussions. This work was funded in part by the University of Wisconsin Research Committee with funds granted by the Wisconsin Alumni Research Foundation, and in part by the U.S. Department of Energy under Contract No. DE-AC02-76ER00881.

1. F. Halzen, C. Olson, M. G. Olsson, and M. L. Stong, *Phys.Lett.* **B283**, 379 (1992), F. Halzen *et al. et al.*, MAD/PH/706 (to be published *Phys. Rev. D.*).
2. S. Jacobs, M. G. Olsson, and C. Suchyta III, *Phys. Rev.* **D33**, 3338 (1986).
3. D. B. Lichtenberg, R. Roncaglia, J. G. Wills, E. Predazzi, and M. Rosso, *Z. Phys.* **C46**, 75 (1990).
4. J. Pantaleone, S.-H. H. Tye, and Y. J. Ng, *Phys. Rev.* **D33**, 777 (1986).
5. S. N. Gupta and S. F. Radford, *Phys. Rev.* **D24**, 2309 (1981); S. N. Gupta, S. F. Radford and W. W. Repko, *Phys.Rev.* **D26**, 3305 (1982); S. N. Gupta and S. F. Radford, *Phys. Rev.* **D25**, 2690 (1982).
6. W. Buchmüller, Y. J. Ng, and S.-H. H. Tye, *Phys. Rev.* **D24**, 3003 (1981).
7. Particle Data Group, *Phys. Rev.* **D45**, 1 (1992).
8. T. A. Armstrong *et al.*, *Phys. Rev. Lett.* (to be published).
9. T. Appelquist, R. M. Barnett, and K. D. Lane, *Ann. Rev. Nucl. Part. Sci.* **28** (1978) 387.
10. M. Narain *et al.*, *Phys. Rev. Lett.* **66**, 3113 (1991); R. Morrison *et al.*, *Phys. Rev. Lett.* **67**, 1696 (1991).

TWO STUDIES OF $\bar{B}^0 \to D^{*+}l\bar{\nu}$

K.W. EDWARDS
*Physics Department, Carleton University,
Ottawa, Ontario, K1S 5B6, Canada*
(For the ARGUS COLLABORATION)

ABSTRACT

Using the Argus detector at the e^+e^- storage ring, DORIS II at DESY, two studies of the exclusive semileptonic decay $\bar{B}^0 \to D^{*+}l\bar{\nu}$ have been performed. In the first the D^{*+} mesons are reconstructed in the decay chains $D^{*+} \to D^0\pi^+$ with $D^0 \to K^-\pi^+$ and $D^0 \to K^-\pi^+\pi^+\pi^-$. The branching ratio has been measured to be $(5.2 \pm 0.5 \pm 0.6)\%$. A significant rate for the decay $\bar{B} \to D^{**+}l\bar{\nu}$ has been observed. From an angular analysis the forward-backward asymmetry A_{FB} and the D^* polarization parameter α have been measured to be $A_{FB} = 0.20 \pm 0.08 \pm 0.06$ and $\alpha = 1.1 \pm 0.4 \pm 0.2$.

Using a partial D^{*+} reconstruction technique a much larger sample of events has been obtained and the branching ratio has been determined to be $(4.6 \pm 0.3 \pm 0.4)\%$. With this sample of tagged B^0 mesons, the branching ratio for inclusive semilepton decay $\bar{B}^0 \to Xl\bar{\nu}$ has been determined to be $(9.3 \pm 1.5 \pm 1.8)\%$. The lifetime ratio $\tau(B^+)/\tau(B^0)$ can be determined and has been found to be $1.1 \pm 0.3 \pm 0.4$. By comparing results with full and partial D^{*+} reconstruction the branching ratios for $D^0 \to K^-\pi^+$ and $D^0 \to K^-\pi^+\pi^+\pi^-$ have been found to be $(4.5 \pm 0.6 \pm 0.4)\%$ and $(7.9 \pm 1.5 \pm 0.9)\%$.

Semileptonic decays of B mesons are useful tools in determining $|V_{cb}|$ and for testing the Lorentz structure of the weak hadronic current. They are found to have relatively high branching ratios and low background. Signal is separated from background by means of the recoil mass distribution,

$$M_{rec}^2 = (E_{beam} - E_{D^{**}} - E_l)^2 - (\vec{P}_{D^*} + \vec{P}_l)^2 \qquad (Eq.1)$$

Since the B momentum is small at the 4S, the recoil mass is expected to be zero. In Figure 1, the possible contributions to the distributions have been obtained from Monte Carlo studies. The desired signal, peaking around $M^2_{rec} = 0_1$, is channel I. In channel II, $B \to D^{**}l\nu$, the presence of an extra π has shifted the peak to positive values of M^2_{rec}. Channel III results from D^{*+} and l being produced in different B decays and Channel IV from the continuum.

D^* mesons are reconstructed for $D^{*+} \to D^0\pi^+$, where $D^0 \to K^-\pi^+$ and $D^0 \to K^-\pi^+\pi^+\pi^-$. Fig.II shows the ($D^0\pi^+$) pairs for events containing negatively- charged leptons with momentum greater than 1 GeV/c, where the reconstructed D^0 mass lies within ±60 Mev/c^2 of the nominal D^0 mass. Fig.III shows the M^2_{rec} distributions for both D^0 decay channels. A fit to the expected distributions for channels I through IV gives the number of events shown in Table 1. Using the PDG branching ratios for the D^0 decays and the CLEO D^{*+} branching ratio gives Br($\bar{B}^0 \to D^*l\bar{\nu}$) = (5.2 ± 0.5 ± 0.6)%.

Table I has a significant number of D^{**}. In Fig.IV, the mass distribution of ($D^{**}\pi^-$) pairs is shown, with the events from $M^2_{rec}>0$ providing a signal and events with $M^2_{rec}<0$ providing the background. The fit to a function with peaks at 2420 and 2460 MeV/c^2 is consistent with the M^2_{rec} fit. In order to convert the observed number of D^{**} into a branching ratio, a theoretical model for the D^{**} is necessary. Using GISW[ ] Br($\bar{B}^0 \to D^{**+}l\bar{\nu}$) = (2.7 ± 0.5 ± 0.5)%, from BHKT[ ] Br($\bar{B}^0 \to D^{**+}l\bar{\nu}$) = (2.3 ± 0.6 ± 0.4)%. If the exclusive channels for D,D*, and D^{*+} are added, Br($\bar{B} \to$ D,D*,D$^{**}l\bar{\nu}$) = [(9.4 - 9.8) ± 1.0 ± 0.9]% in agreement with the observed total inclusive rate and the small contribution expected from b → u transitions.

The angular distribution of the lepton and the π relative to the direction of the D* (see Fig.V) provide information about the V-A nature of the W$^-$ decay and the polarization of the D*. Fig.VI shows the measured cosθ,cos θ*, M^2_{rec} and q^2 distributions, uncorrected in efficiency, and fit to the Monte Carlo distributions expected from channels I-IV. The contribution from channel II(D**) are shaded. The asymmetry in the lepton distribution gives A_{FB} = 0.20 ± 0.08 ± 0.06, while the π distribution gives the D* polarization α = 1.1 ± 0.4 ± 0.2.

Using the measured branching ratio and the B lifeline, the Kobayashi-Maskawa matrix element $|V_{cb}|$ can be determined with the aid of a theoretical model. Values in the range from 0.036 to 0.044 are obtained for $|V_{cb}|$ (see table). Heavy quark Effective Theory predicts that a fit to the q^2 spectrum determines one universal form factor. Fig.VII shows the measured dBr/dq^2 together with the fits with various choices of this form factor. These various choices produce values of $|V_{cb}|$ from 0.045 to 0.053 because of the strong dependence on the points near the end of the q^2 spectrum where there are few events.

Another approach to this problem relies on the fact that only about 6 MeV is available in the decay $D^{*+} \to D^0\pi^+$. The direction and magnitude of the D* momentum is closely related to that of the π. From a Monte Carlo simulation it is found that P_{D^*} = 8.23 P_π + 0.41 GeV/c. Events are selected by requiring a π with P<200 MeV/c together with an oppositely charged lepton with 1.4<p<2.5 GeV/c. This produces the M^2_{recoil} distribution in Fig.VIII. The shape of the background is represented well by the distribution of like charged lepton-pion pairs. After subtracting the background, the resulting distribution is fit by contributions from both D* and D** channels, resulting in N_{D^*} = 2693 ± 183 ± 105 and $N_{D^{**}}$ = 423 ± 138 ± 35 (Fig.IX). From a Monte Carlo stimulation using the IGSW model together with the CLEO Br[$D^{*+} \to D^0\pi^*$]. Br($\bar{B}^0 \to D^{*+}l\bar{\nu}$) = (4.6 ± 0.3 ± 0.4)%

is obtained, and is found to be stable against varying the pion cutoff from 150 to 300 MeV/c.

Comparing the number of fully reconstructed decays with the number of partially reconstructed decays yield the D^0 branching ratios,

$$Br(D^0 \to X) = \frac{N(\bar{B}^0 \to D^{*+}l^-\bar{\nu}, D^{*+} \to D^0\pi^+, D^0 \to X)}{N(\bar{B}^0 \to D^{*+}l^-\bar{\nu}, D^{*+} \to D^0\pi^+)} \frac{e_p}{e_f} \quad \text{(Eq.2)}$$

where ε_f and ε_p are the acceptances for full and partial reconstruction. $Br(D^0 \to K^-\pi^-) = (4.5 \pm 0.6 \pm 0.4)\%$, $Br(D^0 \to K\text{-}\pi^+\pi^+\pi^-) = (7.9 \pm 1.5 \pm 0.9)\%$.

An inclusive semileptonic branching ratio for neutral B mesons can be determined using the sample of B^0 tagged by their decay, $B^0 \to D^{*+}l^-\bar{\nu}$. Two samples of events are extracted: I) events containing at least one $l\pi^+$ with $|M^2_{rec}|<1 GeV^2/c^4$; II) events containing two leptons with $1.4<p<2.5$ GeV/c and with $\cos\theta_{ll}>-0.8$, and at least one $l\pi^+$ pair with $|M^2_{rec}|<1 GeV^2/c^4$.

The semileptonic branching ratios, Br^0_{Sl} and Br^+_{Sl} are obtained from,

$$N^0_I e_l Br^0_{Sl} + N^+_I e_l B^+_{Sl} = N_{II}, \quad Br^0_{Sl} + Br^+_{Sl} = 2Br_{Sl} \quad \text{(Eq.3)}$$

where N^0_I, N^+_I are the numbers of neutral and charged B mesons in the first sample, B_{Sl} is the average of the ARGUS and CLEO results using the IGSW model and ε_l is the efficiency. Then,

$$Br^0_{Sl} = \frac{\frac{N_{II}}{e_l N_I} - \eta Br_{Sl}}{1 - \eta}, \quad \eta = \frac{2N^+_I}{N_I} \quad \text{(Eq.4)}$$

From a Monte Carlo simulation N^+_I and N^0_I are determined, and $\eta = 0.337 \pm 0.046$. Using the IGSW model in a Monte Carlo simulation to determine the acceptance, $Br(\bar{B}^0 \to Xl\bar{\nu}) = 9.3 \pm 1.5 \pm 1.8\%$.

Then $\tau(B^+)/\tau(B^0) = Br^+_{Sl}/Br^0_{Sl} = 1.1 \pm 0.3 \pm 0.4$, where the systematic error includes uncertainties in efficiency determination and charged to neutral production rate.

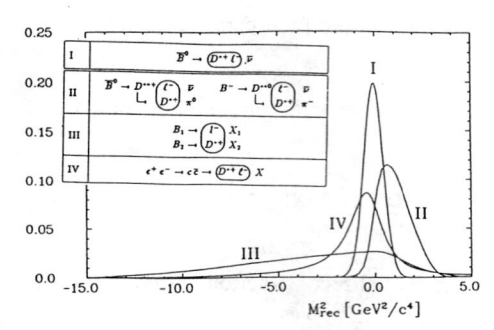

Fig.I The M^2_{rec} distribution expected for processes I to IV listed arbitrarily normalized to unit area.

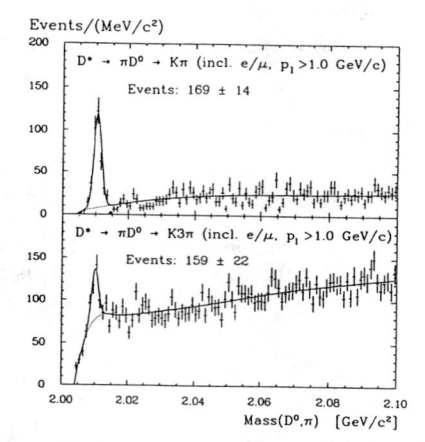

Fig.II Invariant mass of $(D^0\pi^+)$ combinations with (a)$D^0 \to K\pi^+\pi^+\pi^-$, for events containing either an e^- or μ^- with momentum larger than 1GeV/c^2. The difference between the nominal and the reconstructed D^0 mass was required to be less than 60 MeV.

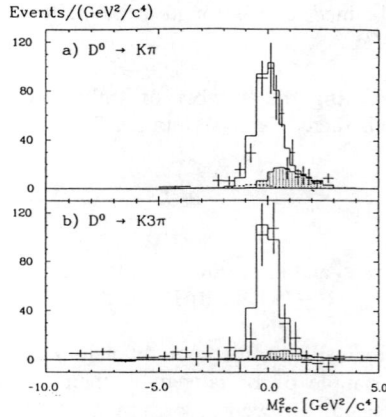

Result for:	Data: $K\pi$	$K3\pi$	$K\pi + K3\pi$
I	114±13±6	124±23±9	235±24±11
II	34± 9±2	21±13±4	63±15± 6
III	8± 4±5	14±10±6	16± 7± 8
IV	7± 4±1	6± 9±1	13± 7± 5
$\frac{N(D^{**}l)}{N(D^{*}l\bar\nu)}$	0.30±0.10±0.03	0.18±0.12±0.05	0.27±0.08±0.03
Br($\bar B^0 \to D^{*+}l^-\bar\nu$)	5.6±0.7±0.7	4.7±0.9±0.5	5.2±0.5±0.6
α	1.05±0.48±0.18	1.14±0.70±0.38	1.12±0.39±0.19
A_{FB}	0.14±0.10±0.06	0.27±0.12±0.06	0.20±0.08±0.06

Fig.III Measured M^2_{rec} distributions (points with error bars) for the two D^0 decay channels, fitted by a linear combination of the curves shown in Fig.I. The blank and shaded areas correspond to the rates for the signal process I and the feeddown process II, respectively. The continuum process (IV) is shown as dashed line.

i	type of D^{**}	Br($D_i^{**} \to D^*X$)	Br($\bar B^0 \to D_i^{**+}l^-\bar\nu$)/Br($\bar B^0 \to D^{*+}l^-\bar\nu$) GISW	ϵ^{**}_i GISW	BHKT
1	$D(1^1P_1)$	1	0.41	0.76	0.83
2	$D(1^3P_0)$	0	0.11	0.00	0.00
3	$D(1^3P_1)$	1	0.21	0.48	0.81
4	$D(1^3P_2)$	1/4 [17]	0.14	0.73	0.75
5	$D(2^1S_0)$	1	0.07	0.66	0.63
6	$D(2^3S_1)$	3/4	0.06	0.70	0.60

TABLE 3

Various branching ratios and relative efficiencies ϵ^{**}_i needed for the estimation of Br($\bar B \to D^{**+}l\bar\nu$)/Br($\bar B \to D^{*+}l\bar\nu$) from the visible ratio $N(D^{**}l)/N(D^*l)$.

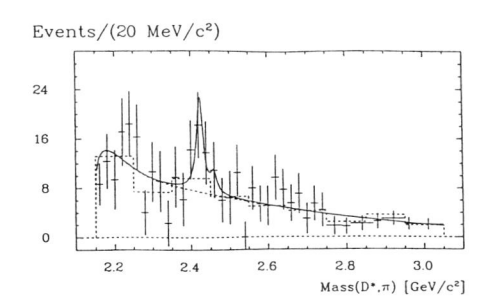

Events/(20 MeV/c²)

Fig.IV Measured distribution of the invariant (D*⁺π⁻) mass (points with error bars) obtained for $M^2_{rec}>0$. The dashed histogram was obtained for $M^2_{rec}<0$ and has been scaled to describe the combinatorial background in the distribution for $M^2_{rec}>0$. The dashed curve describes the background function fitted to the dashed histogram, whereas the solid line of the sum of the background function and two Breit-Wigner curves at masses of 2420 GeV/c² and 2460 GeV/c² fitted to the distribution with error bars.

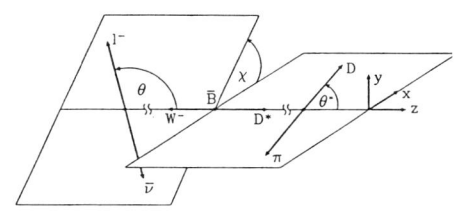

Fig.V D*⁺ rest frame and (l⁻ν̄) centre-of-mass system with the description of the angles θ, θ* and χ.

	ξ(y)	$|V_{cb}| \times 10^3$	ρ	χ^2/df
A	$1-\rho^2(y-1)$	$45 \pm 5 \pm 3$	$1.08 \pm 0.11 \pm 0.03$	5.1/6
B	$\frac{2}{y+1}\exp\left[-(2\rho^2-1)\frac{y-1}{y+1}\right]$	$53 \pm 8 \pm 3$	$1.52 \pm 0.21 \pm 0.10$	4.3/6
C	$\left(\frac{2}{y+1}\right)^{2\rho^2}$	$51 \pm 8 \pm 3$	$1.45 \pm 0.19 \pm 0.09$	4.3/6
D	$\exp[-\rho^2(y-1)]$	$50 \pm 8 \pm 2$	$1.37 \pm 0.19 \pm 0.08$	4.4/6

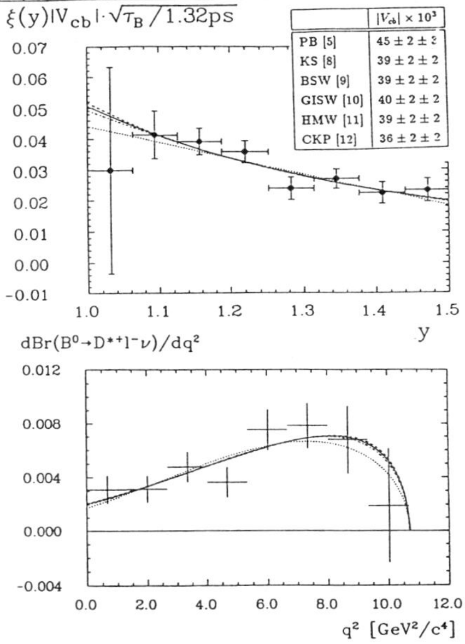

$\xi(y)|V_{cb}|\cdot\sqrt{\tau_B/1.32\text{ps}}$

	$|V_{cb}| \times 10^3$
PB [5]	$45 \pm 2 \pm 2$
KS [8]	$39 \pm 2 \pm 2$
BSW [9]	$39 \pm 2 \pm 2$
GISW [10]	$40 \pm 2 \pm 2$
HMW [11]	$39 \pm 2 \pm 2$
CKP [12]	$36 \pm 2 \pm 2$

$dBr(B^0 \to D^{*+}l^-\nu)/dq^2$

Fig.VII q²-distribution of the decay $\bar{B}^0 \to D^{*+}l^-\bar{\nu}$ corrected for background and efficiency. The four lines correspond to the fit of formula (8) and the four analytical expressions for the Isgur-Wise Function of Tab.5. The dotted line corresponds to $\xi(y)=1-\rho^2(y-1)$.

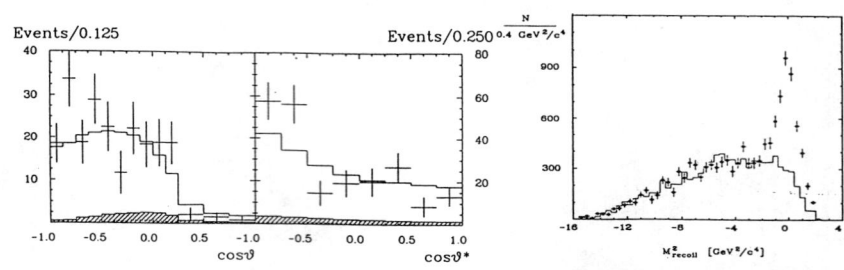

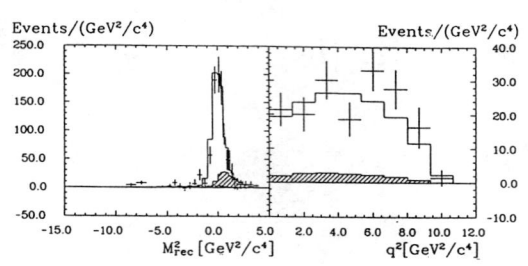

Fig.VI The measured $\cos\theta$, $\cos\theta^*$, M^2_{rec} and q^2 distributions, uncorrected for efficiency. The solid line histogram are the fitted sums of Monte Carlo distributions expected for the four processes 1-IV. The shaded histograms show the amount and shape of the background due to process $\bar{B} \to D^{**}(2420) l \bar{\nu}$.

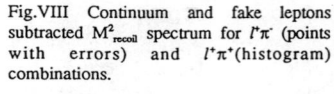

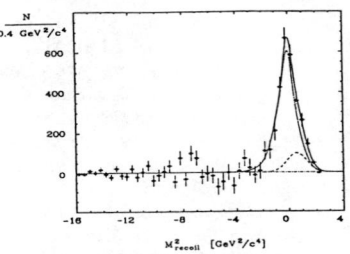

Fig.VIII Continuum and fake leptons subtracted M^2_{recoil} spectrum for $l^+\pi^-$ (points with errors) and $l^+\pi^+$ (histogram) combinations.

Fig.IX Background subtracted M^2_{recoil} spectrum. The curves show the results of the fit described in text.

HADRONIC B MESON DECAYS
TESTING FACTORIZATION AND HQET

STEVEN BALL
Dept. of Physics and Astronomy, University of Kansas
Lawrence, Kansas 66045, USA

ABSTRACT

Hadronic B decay results from 0.923 fb^{-1} $\Upsilon(4S)$ data taken with the CLEO II detector allow several important tests of predictions derived from factorization and Heavy Quark Effective Theory (HQET). We find excellent overall agreement with these predictions. An analysis of BSW model predictions is also given, yielding results in contrast to expectations from D decays. We also present a measurement of the polarization in the decay $B \to \psi K^*$, $\frac{\Gamma_L}{\Gamma} = 0.78 \pm 0.10 \pm 0.10$, which is of importance for future CP violation studies.

1. Predictions of Factorization and HQET

The tools that are presently essential for understanding hadronic B meson decays are factorization and Heavy Quark Effective Theory (HQET). Factorization assumes that final state hadrons do not interact with each other. As pointed out by several theorists [1, 2], this may be a good approximation for some 2-body B decays since a large energy release effectively removes decay products far apart before both full hadron final states are formed.

The recent formulation of HQET [3] relates many different final states in a model-independent way, since all transitions of the type $B \to DX$ and $B \to D^*X$ can be described with one universal form factor $\xi(v \cdot v')$ in the limit $m_b, m_c \to \infty$. This allow us to use semileptonic decay data to make predictions on hadronic decays. One example is:

$$R = \frac{\Gamma(\bar{B}^0 \to D^{*+}\pi^-)}{\frac{d\Gamma}{dQ^2}(B \to D^* l \, \nu)|_{Q^2=m_\pi^2}} = 6\pi^2 |V_{ud}|^2 f_\pi^2 \, |a_1|^2 = 1.2 \pm 0.2 \qquad (1)$$

A similar expression exists for $\bar{B}^0 \to D^{*+}\rho^-$. One may also relate decays to D and D^* mesons. In the low Q^2 regime, where the the simple 2-body modes lie, we expect (to lowest order) spin symmetry:

$$\Gamma(\bar{B}^0 \to D^+\pi^-) = \Gamma(\bar{B}^0 \to D^{*+}\pi^-)$$

and similarly for ρ^- modes. We can also make reasonably firm predictions for the polarization in the decay $\bar{B}^0 \to D^{*+}\rho^-$:

$$\frac{\Gamma_L}{\Gamma}(\bar{B}^0 \to D^{*+}\rho^-) = \frac{\Gamma_L}{\Gamma}(B \to D^* \, l \, \nu)|_{Q^2=m_\rho^2} \qquad (2)$$

which is from 85% to 88% [4, 5].

One important point concerning HQET is that the model dependence enters only as corrections of order $1/N_c$ or higher [6]. One model which makes predictions on a wide range of B decays is the Bauer, Stech, and Wirbel model (BSW [1]), which has two free parameters, a_1 and a_2. The "color-suppressed" a_2 amplitude is essentially a measure of their correction to the HQET limit, and gives rise to decays such as $\bar{B}^0 \to D^0\pi^0$ and $\bar{B}^0 \to \psi\bar{K}^0$. In light of future studies of CP violation in B decays, it is imperative to understand these decays.

2. CLEO II Results on B Decays

2.1. Exclusive Branching Ratios

The CLEO II detector [7] is well suited for reconstruction of hadronic B decays. We present results from a data sample of 0.923 fb^{-1}. In figure 1 are the mass distributions of neutral and charged B decays including 2, 3, and 4-body

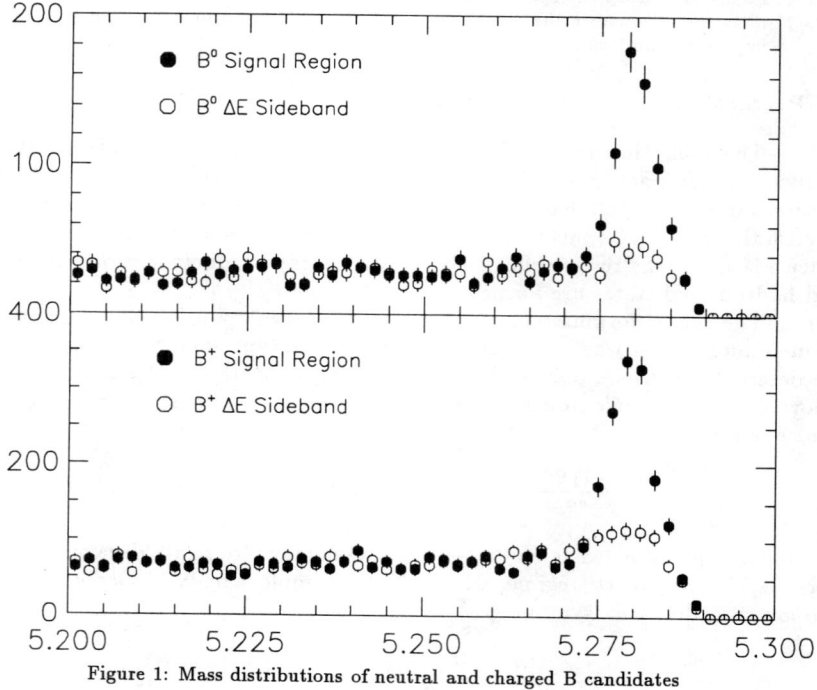

Figure 1: Mass distributions of neutral and charged B candidates

final states. Results on 12 exclusive branching ratios are given in table 1 along with CLEO 1.5 [8] and ARGUS [9] results and BSW model predictions [1] for comparison. While there is reasonable agreement [1] ,the CLEO II results are more precise.

Decay	CLEOII	CLEO 1.5	ARGUS	BSW
$B^- \to D^0\pi^-$	$0.40 \pm 0.03 \pm 0.09$	$0.50 \pm 0.07 \pm 0.09$	$0.20 \pm 0.08 \pm 0.06$	$0.265[a_1 + 1.23a_2]^2$
$B^- \to D^0\rho^-$	$1.02 \pm 0.11 \pm 0.29$		$1.3 \pm 0.4 \pm 0.4$	$0.622[a_1 + 0.66a_2]^2$
$B^- \to D^{*0}\pi^-$	$0.35 \pm 0.05 \pm 0.12$	$0.62 \pm 0.16 \pm 0.14$	$0.35 \pm 0.12 \pm 0.10$	$0.255[a_1 + 1.29a_2]^2$
$B^- \to D^{*0}\rho^-$	$1.14 \pm 0.16 \pm 0.37$		$0.9 \pm 0.5 \pm 0.4$	$0.703[a_1 + 0.74a_2]^2$
$B^- \to \psi K^-$	$0.10 \pm 0.02 \pm 0.01$	$0.09 \pm 0.02 \pm 0.02$	$0.08 \pm 0.04 \pm 0.01$	$1.819a_2^2$
$B^- \to \psi K^{*-}$	$0.18 \pm 0.06 \pm 0.03$	$0.15 \pm 0.11 \pm 0.04$	$0.19 \pm 0.13 \pm 0.06$	$2.932a_2^2$
$\bar{B}^0 \to D^+\pi^-$	$0.26 \pm 0.03 \pm 0.06$	$0.27 \pm 0.06 \pm 0.05$	$0.48 \pm 0.11 \pm 0.11$	$0.264a_1^2$
$\bar{B}^0 \to D^+\rho^-$	$0.71 \pm 0.10 \pm 0.21$		$0.9 \pm 0.5 \pm 0.3$	$0.621a_1^2$
$\bar{B}^0 \to D^{*+}\pi^-$	$0.27 \pm 0.04 \pm 0.06$	$0.32 \pm 0.08 \pm 0.06$	$0.23 \pm 0.07 \pm 0.05$	$0.254a_1^2$
$\bar{B}^0 \to D^{*+}\rho^-$	$0.73 \pm 0.10 \pm 0.16$	$1.5 \pm 0.6 \pm 0.9$	$0.57 \pm 0.24 \pm 0.24$	$0.702a_1^2$
$\bar{B}^0 \to \psi \bar{K}^0$	$0.10 \pm 0.04 \pm 0.02$	$0.07 \pm 0.04 \pm 0.02$	$0.09 \pm 0.07 \pm 0.02$	$1.817a_2^2$
$\bar{B}^0 \to \psi \bar{K}^{*0}$	$0.15 \pm 0.03 \pm 0.03$	$0.13 \pm 0.06 \pm 0.03$	$0.13 \pm 0.06 \pm 0.02$	$2.927a_2^2$

Table 1: Exclusive Branching Ratios

The measured values of R, defined by Eq.(1), for the decays $\bar{B}^0 \to D^{*+}\pi^-$ and $\bar{B}^0 \to D^{*+}\rho^-$ are $1.3 \pm 0.2 \pm 0.3$ and $3.2 \pm 0.4 \pm 0.7$ respectively. These agree entirely with the expected values of 1.2 ± 0.2 and 3.3 ± 0.6. We also see that the branching ratios for corresponding D and D^* modes are nearly equal, confirming the expectation of spin symmetry.

Using the model of BSW [1] we fit the parameters a_1 and a_2 using modes which are strictly a_1 or a_2 dependent. This yields $a_1 = 1.02 \pm 0.04 \pm 0.06$ and $a_2 = 0.23 \pm 0.01 \pm 0.01$. Using only the modes involving D mesons we fit the ratio a_2/a_1 and find $a_2/a_1 = 0.18 \pm 0.05 \pm 0.07$. What is remarkable is that good agreement is found with a relative positive sign, in contrast to what is needed to describe D meson decays [1]. This clearly needs to be better understood.

2.2. *Polarization of* $\bar{B}^0 \to D^{*+}\rho^-$ *and* $B \to \psi K^*$

We have measured the polarization of $\bar{B}^0 \to D^{*+}\rho^-$ followed by $D^{*+} \to D^0\pi^+$ and $\rho^- \to \pi^-\pi^0$. Shown in figure 2 are the decay angle distributions, where Θ_{D^*} is the angle between the D^0 in the D^{*+} frame and the direction of the D^{*+} in the $\bar{B}^0$ frame, and similarly for Θ_ρ. A joint maximum likelihood fit yields

$$\frac{\Gamma_L}{\Gamma}(\bar{B}^0 \to D^{*+}\rho^-) = 0.90 \pm 0.07 \pm 0.05$$

which agrees with the expected value, 85% – 88% [4, 5].

We have also measured the polarization in the decay $B \to \psi K^*$ followed by $\psi \to l^+l^-$ and $K^* \to K\pi$. Combining the exclusive modes $B^0 \to \psi K^{*0}$ and $B^+ \to \psi K^{*+}$, of which there are 39 virtually background-free, we find

$$\frac{\Gamma_L}{\Gamma}(B \to \psi K^*) = 0.78 \pm 0.10 \pm 0.10$$

Though there is no straightforward factorization prediction, it is nonetheless an important measurement for future CP violation studies. If this decay were 100%

---
[1] All branching ratios have been normalized to $B(D^0 \to K^-\pi^+) = (4.2 \pm 0.6)\%$, $B(D^+ \to K^-\pi^+\pi^+) = (9.1 \pm 1.1)\%$, $B(\psi \to l^+l^-) = (5.91 \pm 0.18)\%$ [10], and $B(D^{*0} \to D^0\pi^0) = (63.5 \pm 4.2)\%$, $B(D^{*+} \to D^0\pi^+) = (67.9 \pm 2.3)\%$ [11].

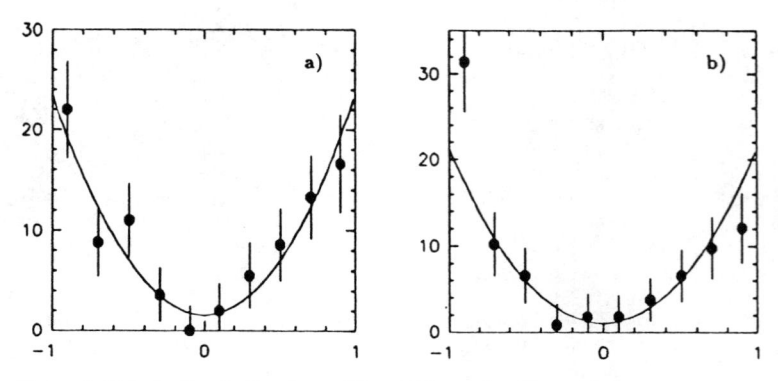

Figure 2: Polarization in the decay $\bar{B}^0 \to D^{*+}\rho^-$; a) $D^{*+} \to D^0\pi^+$, b) $\rho^- \to \pi^-\pi^0$

longitudally polarized ($\Gamma_L/\Gamma = 1$) then the decay $B^0 \to \psi K^{*0}$, $K^{*0} \to K_s^0\pi^0$ would be a CP positive eigenstate, and therefore quite useful for such a measurement. It is close to this limit.

3. Summary

Results on hadronic B decays measured with the CLEO II detector provide several important tests of factorization and HQET. We find excellent agreement with predictions for decay rates, spin symmetry, and polarization. The precision of the results is approaching an accuracy sufficient to also guide modeling corrections to the HQET limit, as demonstrated by an analysis of the BSW model predictions. We find that the polarization in the decay $B \to \psi K^*$, $\frac{\Gamma_L}{\Gamma} = 0.78 \pm 0.10 \pm 0.10$, may be strong enough to render this decay useful for future CP violation studies.

1. M. Bauer, B. Stech, and M. Wirbel, Z. Phys. **C29** (1985) 637; **C34** (1987) 103; **C42** (1989) 671.
2. J.D. Bjorken, SLAC-Report 378, 1990.
3. N.Isgur and M.B. Wise, Phys. Lett. **B232** (1989) 113; **B237** (1990) 527.
4. J. Rosner, Phys. Rev. **D42** (1990) 3732.
5. M. Neubert, Phys. Lett. **B264** (1991) 455.
6. C. Reader and N. Isgur, CEBAF-TH-91-23.
7. (CLEO), Nucl. Inst. and Meth. **A320** (1992) 66.
8. (CLEO), Phys. Rev. **D45** (1992) 21.
9. (ARGUS), Z. Phys. **C48** (1990) 543.
10. (Mark III), Phys. Lett. **B208** (1988) 89; Phys. Rev. Lett. **68** (1992) 282.
11. (CLEO), CLNS 92/1143, submitted to PRL.

NONPERTURBATIVE QCD EFFECTS IN WEAK NONLEPTONIC DECAYS

B.BLOK[a] and M.SHIFMAN[b],

[a] *ITP, Univ.of Calif.at Santa Barbara, Santa Barbara, CA 93106, U.S.A.*

[b] *Theoret.Physics Inst., Univ.of Minnesota, Minneapolis, MN 55455, U.S.A.*

ABSTRACT

QCD-based analysis of nonfactorizable parts of weak nonleptonic amplitudes is reported. Nonperturbative effects due to soft gluon exchange play a key role leading to the emergence of a dynamical rule of discarding $1/N_c$ corrections.

1. Introduction

The purpose of this talk is to review recent progress in calculating deviations from naive factorization in weak nonleptonic decays. We shall concentrate here on exclusive decays. (Inclusive decays are discussed elsewhere.) We shall show that the rule of discarding $1/N_c$ [1, 2, 3] has a dynamical origin, and is due to nonperturbative QCD effects. The key role is played by soft chromomagnetic gluon exchange. The resulting picture [4, 5] is rather versatile–not all transitions are alike in this respect. QCD effects lead to deviations from the naive factorization, specific for each channels. These deviations can be estimated in a model-independent way. In some channels the situation is close to the predictions of the $1/N_c$ rule , in others – to naive factorization. The degree of cancellation of the naive $1/N_c$- suppressed amplitudes is different for each channel, so we can call our approach a dynamical rule of discarding $1/N_c$.

2. The method

We shall describe our method using the decay $B^0 \to D^+\pi^-$ as an example. The reader is referred to ref. [4] for details. We are interested in the transitions induced by the color-octet times color-octet part of the weak Lagrangian $\mathcal{L} \sim (\bar{c}\Gamma^\mu t^a b)(\bar{d}\Gamma^\mu t^a u)$. In order to calculate the transition amplitude, we start with the correlator

$$\mathcal{A}^\beta = \int d^4x < D|T\{\mathcal{L}(x), A^\beta\}|\bar{B}> e^{iqx} \qquad (1)$$

where the axial current $A^\beta = \bar{u}\gamma^\beta\gamma^5 d$ annihilates the pion. Two key steps are made in order to calculate the latter correlator: we continue $\mathcal{A}^\beta$ into the Euclidean region $-q^2 \sim Q^2 \sim 1 \quad GeV^2$, and write in this region (borrowing some ideas from the QCD sum rule method [6]) a sum rule for the amplitude $M_{\text{n.f.}}$ governed by $\mathcal{L}$:

$$\mathcal{A}^\beta(Q^2) = M_{\text{n.f.}}\frac{f_\pi q^\beta}{q^2} + ... \qquad (2)$$

where +... denotes the contribution of higher resonances produced by the axial current. Second, we calculate $\mathcal{A}^\beta$ using the Operator Product Expansion. We immediately obtain

$$\mathcal{A}^\beta(Q^2) = -2i\frac{1}{8\pi^2}\frac{q^\alpha q^\beta}{q^2} <D|\bar{c}\Gamma^\mu t^a g\tilde{G}^a_{\alpha\mu}b|B> +... \qquad (3)$$

where +... denotes higher order power corrections and we retained only the kinematical structure proportional to q^β. Comparing the latter two equations and neglecting the dots we immediately obtain that the ratio of the nonfactorizable and $1/N_c$ naive factorizable parts of the amplitude is

$$r = -\frac{N_c m_{\sigma H}^2}{4\pi^2 f_\pi^2}. \qquad (4)$$

where $m_{\sigma H}$ parametrizes the matrix element in eq.(3). Note the key distinction from the standard QCD sum rule method: the matrix elements are taken between hadronic states, not between vacuum states. Using the methods of HQET [7] it is easy to get for $m_{\sigma H}^2 = \frac{3}{4}(m_{B^*}^2 - m_B^2)$.

It is instructive to emphasize the assumptions and approximations made in eq. (4). First, we neglected the corrections due to operators with higher dimensions, and contamination with higher resonances. Strictly speaking it is necessary to check that the corresponding window exists. This has not been done yet, although arguments in favor of smallness of the above corrections in a large class of transitions were given in ref. [4]. Second, and this is also important, we started from the theoretical limit where $M_B - M_D \ll \frac{1}{2}(M_B + M_D)$. Only in this limit the expansion in eq. (3) goes in dimensions, not twists. Moreover, in a number of cases the hadronic matrix element in eq. (3) reduces to the known quantity in this limit. Otherwise we would have to introduce an unknown function of recoil. Logarithmic corrections due to anomalous dimensions are also not included so far (although in the transitions considered in ref. [4] they seem to be unimportant). We refer to ref. [4] for the detailed discussion of the method and expected uncertainties. The expected accuracy for this particular channel is of order one.

Keeping in mind all these uncertainties—a vast field for future work— one can try to extend the method to other weak hadronic decays in a straightforward way. If the particle that splits away is not a pion, we do not get a simple $1/Q^2$ term in the OPE, but rather a more complicated function. Moreover, the higher power corrections can become more important. For example, for the $B \to DD$ decays we get the function $F(Q^2) = 1/Q^2 - \frac{m_c^2}{Q^4}\ln(\frac{Q^2+m_c^2}{m_c^2})$ as a coefficient in front of the operator $G_{\mu\nu}$, instead of $1/Q^2$. The relevant sum rule takes the form

$$\frac{m_{\sigma H}^2}{4\pi^2}F(Q^2) + ... = f_D\frac{M_{\text{n.f.}}}{Q^2 + m_D^2} + .. \qquad (5)$$

(where we once again neglected higher power corrections.) It works well for the Euclidean momenta $Q^2 \geq 1$ GeV^2.

The amplitudes of decays considered above were proportional to a_1 in the BSW language [1]. The amplitudes of decays proportional to a_2 contain an absolutely unknown formfactor, the matrix element $< B|\bar{b}\gamma^\nu g\tilde{G}_{\alpha\nu}u|\pi >$, which cannot be detemined using HQET. The sum rules for the decay $B^0 \to D^0\pi^0$ and other decays of the type "$B \to D$+light meson" in this group will be similar to the above, (with the function $F(Q^2)$ instead of $1/Q^2$) but will include this new formfactor. For the decay $B \to J/\psi K$ we have a new function $\tilde{F}(Q^2) = 2m_c^2 \int_{4m_c^2}^{\omega_c} \frac{ds}{(s+Q^2)\sqrt{s(s-4m^2)}}$ in the sum rule instead of F.

3. Decay Widths

Let us briefly discuss numerical aspects of our results. We shall concentrate on the values of r and the amplitudes a_1 and a_2 that can be directly compared with the experimental data.

For decays $B^0 \to D^+\pi^-$, $B^0 \to D^+\rho^-$ we get $r \sim -1.5$ and ~ -1 respectively. For $B^0 \to D^{*+}\pi^-$, $B^0 \to D^{*+}\rho^-$ we get $r' = r/3$ [4]. Taking here and below $c_1 \sim 1.12, c_2 \sim -0.26$, we obtain for these decays $a_1 \sim 1.16, 1.12, 1.08, 1.06$ respectively.

Consider now other decays using the same method. The discussion below is given for orientation only, keeping in mind that the effects unaccounted for in our analysis (see section 2) may be important for these decays. If we neglect these effects, we obtain for them once again the formulae similar to the one in eq. (3). Consider first the decays from the $B \to DD$ group. Their amplitudes are also proportional to a_1 and can be obtained using the sum rule sketched in section 2. We get for $B \to DD$ decays $r \sim -0.9\frac{m_{\sigma H}^2}{4\pi^2 f_D^2}$, where f_D is a leptonic decay constant taken to be ~ 170 MeV. We immediately see that $r \sim -0.8$. For $B \to D^*D^*$ decays using HQET we obtain $r \sim -0.9\frac{m_{\sigma H}^2}{12\pi^2 f_{D^*}^2} \sim -0.16$. For $B \to D^*D$ decays we get $r \sim -0.5$. For the corresponding a_1 factors in the amplitudes we find $a_1 \sim 1.1, 1.04, 1.07$ respectively. Note that our results for different channels lie between BSW [1] and naive factorization. The accuracy of these results is lower than for the previous group of decays, since we expect here the perturbative logs and higher corrections can play a bigger role.

Consider now the decays proportional to the factor a_2. Here we shall be extremely speculative, since the corresponding analysis is far from being completed. We shall only try to indicate what we expect for these decays at the moment, leaving more solid statements for the future investigation. The main difficulty here is that we do not know the key formfactor– $< B|\bar{b}g\tilde{G}_{\alpha\mu}\gamma^\mu u|\pi > P^\alpha$ (and the corresponding formfactor with the ρ-meson). We can try to roughly estimate these formfactors from our knowledge of the D meson decays using the symmetry between b and c. (Unfortunately, such estimates are very uncertain, though.) Let us completely ignore the recoil dependence in the formfactor $< B|\bar{b}g\tilde{G}_{\alpha\mu}\gamma^\mu u|\pi >$ (unlike $B^0 \to D^+\pi^-$ there is no justification for that) and parametrize $< B|\bar{b}g\tilde{G}_{\alpha\mu}\gamma^\mu u|\pi >$ by a number $m'^2_{\sigma H} \sim x m^2_{\sigma H}$, where x is an unknown constant. Then for the decays of the type $B^0 \to D^0\pi^0$ we obtain $r \sim -1.6x$, for $B^0 \to D^{*0}\pi^0$ we obtain $r \sim -0.8x$ (the difference between the values of r for decays to D and D^* is proportional to $f_D^2/f_{D^*}^2$. and we use

$f_D = 170$ MeV, $f_D^* = 220$ MeV). The value of x is not known, but the experimental data on D seem to indicate that it is below 0.4. If this is indeed the case for B decays, then the value of a_2 will be suppressed in comparison with the exact $1/N_c$ rule for this group of B decays, and can even be equal to zero for sufficiently small x. Such a suppression is favored by the recent experimental data [8]. Future calculations are needed to establish x, and at moment we cannot make any definite theoretical statement about this group of decays.

Finally, we note that the same calculation for $B \to J/\psi K$ leads to small r due to a big leptonic decay constant $F_{J/\psi} \sim 300$ MeV, $a_2 \sim 0.12$. However in this case there exist new difficult problems, due to a large recoil, an enhanced role of higher power corrections and higher twists and big continuum contribution (presumably absent for other modes). Moreover, hard gluons can play a significant role in this decay. (The sum rule from section 2 has no stability "window" in this case). Thus, we cannot exclude the possibility of the rule of discarding $1/N_c$ in this channel yet, neither can we confirm it.

We stress that the pattern of amplitudes $\propto a_2$ presented above is speculative and is nothing else than an educated guess. A lot of work, especially on the determination of chromomagnetic nondiagonal formfactors remains to be done.

4. Conclusion

We tried here to draw a general picture for deviations from the naive factorization in B decays stemming from nonperturbative QCD. A few aspects requiring further clarification are: higher power corrections, perturbative logs and – the most important – the nondiagonal magnetic formfactors must be determined. After all this is done the expected accuracy of our results may be 20-30%. We also considered $K \to \pi\pi$ and $K - \bar{K}$ mixing parameter (see ref. [5]).

Summarizing, the nonperturbative QCD effects (in particular, due to σH) play a key role in weak hadronic decays and can be responsible for the dynamical rule of discarding $1/N_c$. We now have a general method that allows one to estimate them with reasonable accuracy for B, and even for D and K.

6. References

1. M. Bauer, B. Stech and M. Wirbel, *Z. Phys.*, **C34** (1987) 103.
2. A.J. Buras, J.-M. Gerard and R. Rueckl, *Nucl. Phys.*, **B268** (1986) 16.
3. B. Blok and M. Shifman, *Sov. J. Nucl. Phys.*, **45** (1987) 135, 305, 522
4. B. Blok and M. Shifman, preprint NSF-ITP-92-76, *Nucl. Phys.*, in press
5. B. Blok and M. Shifman, *Phys.Lett.*, **B294** (1992) 417
6. M. Shifman, A. Vainshtein and V. Zakharov, *Nucl. Phys.* **B147** (1979) 338.
7. H. Georgi, *Phys.Lett.* **B240** (1990) 447; E. Eichten and B. Hill, *Phys.Lett.* **B234** (1990) 511; N. Isgur and M. Wise, Phys. Lett., **B232** (1989) 113.
8. T. Brower and M. Whitterell, private communication.

CALCULATING THE ISGUR-WISE FUNCTION ON THE LATTICE

Claude W. Bernard[a], Yue Shen[b,1] and Amarjit Soni[c]

[a] *Physics Department, Washington University, St. Louis, MO 63130, USA*
[b] *Physics Department, Boston University, Boston, MA 02215, USA*
[c] *Physics Department, Brookhaven National Laboratory, Upton, NY 11973, USA*

ABSTRACT

We calculate the Isgur-Wise function by measuring the heavy-heavy meson transition matrix element on the lattice. The standard Wilson action is used for both the heavy and light quarks. Our first numerical results are presented.

1. Method

Because of the new flavor and spin symmetries in the heavy quark effective field theory, the Isgur-Wise function ξ relevant to the $B \to D$ decay can be obtained also from the $D \to D$ elastic scattering matrix element [1]

$$< D_{v'} | \bar{c} \gamma_\nu c | D_v > = m_D C_{cc}(\mu) \xi(v \cdot v')(v + v')_\nu \;, \tag{1}$$

where

$$C_{cc}(\mu) = \left[\frac{\alpha_s(m_c)}{\alpha_s(\mu)} \right]^{a(v \cdot v')} \;, \tag{2}$$

and $a(v \cdot v')$ is a slowly varying function of $v \cdot v'$ and vanishes at $v = v'$. This of course requires that the D meson be sufficiently heavy for the onset of the heavy quark limit. Conventionally the elastic scattering matrix element can be parametrized as

$$< D_{v'} | V_\nu | D_v > = m_D f_+(q^2)(v + v')_\nu \;, \tag{3}$$

where $q^2 = (p' - p)^2$ is the momentum transfer between the initial and final states and V_ν is a vector current. Comparing this with Eq. (1) one finds the simple relation between f_+ and ξ

$$f_+ = C_{cc} \xi \;. \tag{4}$$

The lattice calculation method for f_+ has been well established [3, 4], and thus the result can be easily used to obtain ξ. For details we refer the reader to ref. [5].

2. Numerical Results

We use the standard Wilson action for quarks in the quenched limit. Both heavy and light quarks are treated as dynamical. We use data at $\beta = 6.0$ on $16^3 \times 39$ and $24^3 \times 39$ lattices. There are 19 configurations on the $16^3 \times 39$ lattice and 8 configurations on the $24^3 \times 39$ lattice. The hopping parameter for the heavy quark is set to $\kappa_Q = 0.118$ or $\kappa_Q = 0.135$. For the light quark we use $\kappa_q = 0.152 - 0.155$ and then extrapolate to the chiral limit $\kappa_{cr} \approx 0.157$. The techniques for measuring the two-point function and the three-point matrix elements are standard [3].

---
[1] Speaker at the conference

Table 1: The Isgur-Wise function. The heavy quark hopping parameter κ_Q and the lattice sizes are shown in the table.

	.118, $16^3 \times 39$		.118, $24^3 \times 39$		.135, $24^3 \times 39$	
$v \cdot v'$	1.0567(8)	1.1103(15)	1.0259(5)	1.0512(10)	1.0543(12)	1.1059(23)
ξ	1.00(4)	0.99(11)	0.974(20)	0.940(50)	0.952(20)	0.893(40)

Table 2: Comparison of the lattice calculation for the slope at $v \cdot v' = 1$ with various model calculations.

Lattice	[10]	[11]	[12]	[13]	[9, 8]
1.0(8)	1.6(4)	1.4(6)	1.05(20)	0.65(15)	$0.25 < \rho^2 < 1.42$

Comparing the measured f_0 value at $q^2 = 0$ ($f_0(0) = f_+(q^2 = 0)$) to the known continuum value $f_0(0) = 1$[1], we observed that the lattice artifacts are typically 20% – 40% at $\kappa_Q = 0.118$ and less than 10% at $\kappa_Q = 0.135$. We also measured the ratio f_-/f_+. We find the violation of Euclidean invariance [5] is typically 5% – 15% for $\kappa_Q = 0.118$ and 3% – 10% for $\kappa_Q = 0.135$. Note that the reduction of the lattice artifacts when κ_Q is changed from 0.118 to 0.135 agrees with our intuitive expectations. One may try to use the factors Z_V^{loc} and e^m to remove part of the $O(a)$ effects [5]. At $\beta = 6.0$ we get from perturbative calculation that $Z_V^{loc} \approx 0.7$ (using the shifted effective gauge coupling $\tilde{g}^2 \approx 1.7$ as suggested in ref. [6]). The factor e^m is about 2 for $\kappa_Q = .118$ and 1.5 for $\kappa_Q = .135$. Including both these factors the corrected $f_0(0)$ becomes 1 within errors. This is in agreement with other observations [7] that Z_V^{loc} and e^m factors seem to account for the largest part of the lattice artifacts.

We use the definition $\xi(v \cdot v') = f_+/f_0(0)$ and list the results in Table 1 [5]. We emphasize that this definition removes all momentum-independent $O(a)$ effects simultaneously, including both e^m and Z_V^{loc} factors. Note that in Eq. (4) there is a factor C_{cc} in the connection between f_+ and ξ. This factor comes from integrating out the QCD effects from the heavy quark scale down to a light scale μ. For the lattice calculation, however, μ is taken to be $O(1/a)$. Thus in our case $\mu \sim m_D \sim m_c$. Also $v \cdot v'$ is very close to one. So for practical purposes we can set $C_{cc} = 1$ according to Eq. (2).

We plot our results for the Isgur-Wise function in Fig. 1. For comparison we also plotted the theoretical bounds on the Isgur-Wise function. The top and bottom curves are the upper and lower bounds derived in ref. [8]. They are obtained using the dispersion relation for the two-point functions, with the requirements of unitarity and causality and with some assumptions on the analytic properties of the form factors. The curve in the middle is an upper bound on the Isgur-Wise function derived from current-algebraic sum rules [9]. This is a tighter upper bound. Our data obtained on the $24^3 \times 39$ lattice appear to be, within errors, inside of the upper bound of Bjorken [9] and the lower bound of de Rafael and Taron[8]. The data from the $16^3 \times 39$ lattice is consistant with the Bjorken upper bound within rather large errors.

Close to $v \cdot v' = 1$ the Isgur-Wise function can be parametrized as

$$\xi(v \cdot v') = 1 - \rho^2(v \cdot v' - 1) + O((v \cdot v' - 1)^2) \ . \tag{5}$$

If we calculate the slope using the data point closest to the $v \cdot v' = 1$ axis, we get $\rho^2 = 1.0(8)$. In Table 2 we list our result along with ρ^2 values estimated by other authors.

Note that the lattice meson mass we used is in the range of physical D meson.

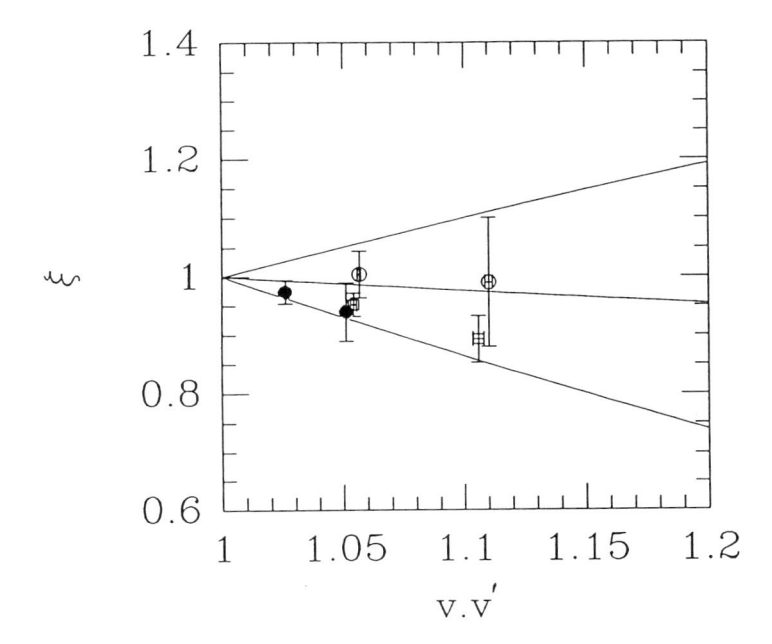

Figure 1: The Isgur-Wise function is plotted against $v \cdot v'$. The open circles represent data on the 16^3 lattice. The solid circles and squares represent data on the $24^3 \times 39$ lattice. The heavy quark hopping parameter is set at $\kappa_Q = 0.118$ (open and solid circles) and at $\kappa = 0.135$ (squares) while the light quark hopping parameters are extrapolated to the chiral limit $\kappa = \kappa_c \approx 0.157$.

Thus the $O(1/m_Q)$ correction may be quite significant. For a reliable calculation of the Isgur-Wise function we need to repeat this calculation for several different masses and then extrapolate to the infinite mass limit. For a check on the residual $O(a)$ effects we plan to repeat our calculation at $\beta = 6.3$.

Acknowledgement

This work was partially supported by the DOE grants DE2FG02-91ER40628, DE-FG02-91ER40676, DE-AC0276CH00016 and NSF contract PHY-9057173, and by funds from the Texas National Research Laboratory Commission under grant RGFY92B6.

1. For reviews, see M. Wise, CALT-68-1721, in the Proceedings of the Lake Louise Winter Institute, 1991 p.222; H. Georgi, preprint HUPT-91-A039, 1991.
2. P. Lepage, *Nucl. Phys.* **B (Proc. Suppl.) 26** (1992) 45.
3. C. W. Bernard, A. X. El-Khadra and A. Soni, *Phys. Rev.* **D43** (1991) 2140.
4. M. Crisafulli, G. Martinelli, V. Hill and C. Sachrajda, *Phys. Lett.* **B223** (1989) 90.
5. C. W. Bernard, Y. Shen and A. Soni, to be published in Lattice '92 proceedings, *Nucl. Phys.* **B (Proc. Suppl.)** (1993).
6. G. P. Lepage and P. B. Mackenzie, *Nucl. Phys.* **B (Proc. Suppl.) 20** (1991) 173.
7. C. W. Bernard, C. M. Heard, J. Labrenz and A. Soni, *Nucl. Phys.* **B (Proc. Suppl.) 26** (1992) 385. J. Labrenz, proceedings in Lattice '92.
8. E. de Rafael and J. Taron, *Phys. Lett.* **B282** (1992) 215.
9. J. D. Bjorken, SLAC report SLAC-PUB-5278 (1990).
10. J. L. Rosner, *Phys. Rev.* **D42**, (1990) 3732.
11. M. Neubert, *Phys. Lett.* **B264** (1991) 455.
12. H. Y. Jin, C. S. Huang and Y. B. Dai, AS-ITP-92-37.
13. B. Block and M. Shifman, preprint NSF-ITP-92-100, TPI-MINN-92-32/T, June 1992.

A STUDY OF EXCLUSIVE DECAYS OF B MESONS TO D_s MESONS AND PIONS

RANSOM W. STEPHENS
Department of Physics, University of Florida,
Gainesville, Florida 32611, USA

representing the

THE CLEO COLLABORATION

ABSTRACT

Using the 0.923 fb^{-1} of $\Upsilon(4S)$ data collected at the Cornell Electron Storage Ring by the CLEO II detector, we have studied the decays of B mesons to exclusive hadronic final states including a D_s meson and pions. These decays are dominated by the $b \to u$ transition. In particular, this paper describes preliminary results from decay channels including: $\overline{B}^0 \to D_s^- \pi^+$, $B^- \to D_s^- \pi^0$, $B^- \to D_s^- \eta$, $\overline{B}^0 \to D_s^- \rho^+$, $B^- \to D_s^- \rho^0$, $B^- \to D_s^- \omega$, $\overline{B}^0 \to D_s^- a_1^+$, and $B^- \to D_s^- a_1^0$.

The first observation of $b \to u$ transitions, and the first measurement of $|V_{ub}|$, were made by studying the lepton energy spectrum above the charm endpoint in inclusive semi-leptonic decays of B Mesons [1]. These inclusive techniques are difficult to model and do not involve direct observation of a decay involving the $b \to u$ transition. At this time, no clear, confirmed, exclusive $b \to u$ dominated process has been observed. In this contribution, we present an experimental study of exclusive reconstruction of $b \to u$ governed, hadronic, two-body B decays.

The most obvious hadronic mode is one like $B^0 \to \pi^+\pi^-$ where the virtual W^+ hadronizes into a π^+. In this paper we take a slightly different approach: we searched for exclusive two-body decays like $B^0 \to D_s^+\pi^-$. In these decays the W^+ fragments into a D_s^+ rather than a π^+. Since the coupling of a virtual W to a D_s is much stronger than its coupling to a π, by virtue of $(f_{D_s}/f_\pi)^2 \approx 4$, and since the form-factor may be bigger at the higher q^2 associated with the D_s, we expect the rate $B^0 \to D_s^+\pi^-$ to be more than three times the rate of $B^0 \to \pi^+\pi^-$.

Hence, with their greater rate and reasonable detector efficiency we expect the decays $\overline{B}^0 \to D_s^-\pi^+, D_s^-\rho^+, D_s^-a_1^+$ and $B^- \to D_s^-\pi^0, D_s^-\eta, D_s^-\rho^0, D_s^-\omega, D_s^-a_1^0$ to be good candidates for the first observation of exclusive, hadronic $b \to u$ transitions.

The CLEO II detector has been discussed elsewhere [2]. Of particular importance to this analysis is its fine tracking $((\delta p_\perp/p_\perp)^2 = (0.0011 p_\perp)^2 + (0.0067)^2)$, good particle identification (for tracks with $|p| < 1$ GeV), and excellent photon identification capabilities. In this analysis we have used 0.928 fm^{-1} of data taken on the $\Upsilon(4S)$ (almost a million B's) and 0.416 fm^{-1} 60 MeV below the $\Upsilon(4S)$, for continuum studies.

The dominant backgrounds of these channels is from the continuum, where $e^+e^- \to q\bar{q}$ rather than $e^+e^- \to \Upsilon(4S) \to B\bar{B}$, and misidentification of $D^\pm$ for $D_s^\pm$. There is also the possibility of background in the $\bar{B}^0$ modes from W-exchange.

The continuum background is suppressed by cutting out "jetty" events. This is done by requiring that the ratio of the 2nd to the 1st Fox-Wolfram parameters [3] be less than 0.3. According to Monte Carlo studies, this cut rejects 50% of the continuum background and retains 85% of the signal.

We performed a Monte Carlo study of the background from misidentification of $D^\pm$ for $D_s^\pm$. We found that simple particle identification constraints limited this background to less than 1 event per million B's (about the size of the data set under consideration) in the $B \to D_s\pi$ channels and less than half that in the other modes.

As for the W-exchange background, we expect the rates of these processes, $B^0 \to D_s^-K^+$ and $B^0 \to D_s^-K^{*+}$, to be of the same order of magnitude as the comparable channels: $\bar{B}^0 \to D_s^-\pi^+$ and $\bar{B}^0 \to D_s^-\rho^+$. We performed a Monte Carlo study of these processes and found that, if the processes had identical rates, then the ratio of the $b \to u$ to misidentified W-exchange in the data would be about three, in the former case, and about nineteen, in the latter.

We cover a bit more than 13% of the D_s branching fraction [4] in this study by using the modes : $D_s^\pm \to \phi\pi^\pm$ or $K^{*0}K^\pm \to K^+K^-\pi^\pm$ (3.9%), $D_s^\pm \to \phi\rho^\pm \to K^+K^-\pi^0\pi^\pm$ (4.0%), $D_s^\pm \to K_s^0 K$ (1.0%), $D_s^\pm \to \eta\rho^\pm \to \eta\pi^0\pi^\pm$ (we only use the $\eta \to \gamma\gamma$ mode in this analysis, 3.0%), $D_s^\pm \to \eta\pi^\pm$ (0.6%), and $D_s^\pm \to \phi\pi^+\pi^-\pi^\pm \to K^+K^-\pi^+\pi^-\pi^\pm$ (0.6%). Various cuts are used to clean the D_s channels, then candidates whose invariant mass is within 2.5σ of M_{D_s} are constrained to this nominal mass by a kinematic fit.

Of candidate B events, we require that they pass the cuts: $\Delta E = |E_{beam} - E_B| < 3\sigma$, where E_B is the B energy, σ is the standard error of E_B, and $|\cos\theta_B| < 0.81$ where θ_B is the polar angle of the B candidate. We combine the χ^2 values of the particle identification assignments and D_s fit to obtain an overall probability for the assumed final state and take that with the largest probability, if more than one B candidate, in a given D_s mode, passes the cuts. In this way, we allow at most one entry per D_s mode per event in the final B sample.

We have combined all the B^0 channels (except $B^0 \to D_s^+ a_1^-$ which is background dominated) and plotted their beam-constrained masses, $M^{beam}_{B \to D_s(n\pi)} = \sqrt{E^2_{beam} - p^2_B}$, in Fig. 1a, and similarly for the $B^\pm$ channels (leaving out the $B^+ \to D_s^+ a_1^0$ channel) in Fig. 1b.

There is no clear indication of a signal near the nominal B mass. The curves in Fig. 1 are a fit to the data including a smooth background shape and a Gaussian with a fixed mean of 5.2786 GeV and a fixed width of 2.8 MeV (the resolution of the beam-constrained mass). The fit to the B^0 plot, Fig 1a, yields -0.24 ± 2.28 events with a χ^2 per degree of freedom of 1.1; the fit to the $B^\pm$ plot, Fig. 1b, gives 0.17 ± 3.28 events

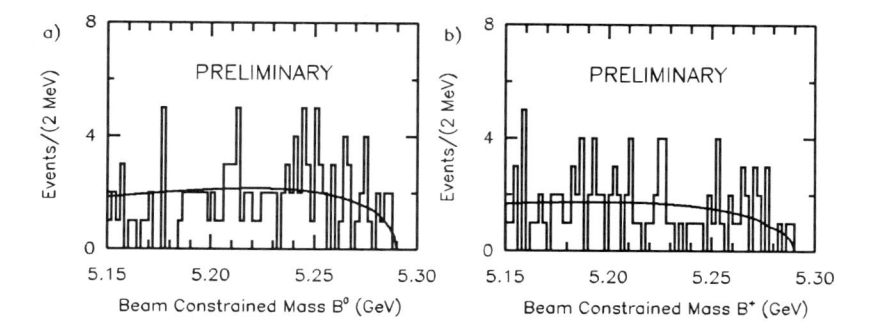

Figure 1. The beam constrained masses of a) neutral and, b) charged B candidates.

with a χ^2 per degree of freedom of 1.0. The results of the searches for each channel individually are given in Table 1 as 90% confidence level upper limits, the preliminary upper limits presented by ARGUS at the International Conference on Particle Physics, held at Dallas in August of 1992, are also given.

In the near future we will have results in all these modes with more data and with the $D_s{}^*$ channels as well as those discussed here.

Table 1. Summary of Results.

Decay Channel	CLEO (Preliminary) 90% U.L.	ARGUS (Preliminary) 90% U.L.
$B^0 \to D_s{}^+\pi^-$	4.7 $\times$ 10^{-4}	18 $\times$ 10^{-4}
$B^0 \to D_s{}^+\rho^-$	8.8 $\times$ 10^{-4}	28 $\times$ 10^{-4}
$B^0 \to D_s{}^+a_1{}^-$	36. $\times$ 10^{-4}	34 $\times$ 10^{-4}
$B^+ \to D_s{}^+\pi^0$	4.6 $\times$ 10^{-4}	16 $\times$ 10^{-4}
$B^+ \to D_s{}^+\eta$	4.0 $\times$ 10^{-4}	Not Available
$B^+ \to D_s{}^+\rho^0$	6.0 $\times$ 10^{-4}	35 $\times$ 10^{-4}
$B^+ \to D_s{}^+\omega$	8.5 $\times$ 10^{-4}	34 $\times$ 10^{-4}
$B^+ \to D_s{}^+a_1{}^0$	48. $\times$ 10^{-4}	39 $\times$ 10^{-4}

References

1. R. Fulton et al (CLEO), *Phys. Rev. Lett.* **64** (1990) 16; H. Albrecht et al. (ARGUS), *Phys. Lett.* **234B** (1990) 409; and, S. Henderson et al. (CLEO),*Phys. Rev.* **D45** (1992) 2212.
2. Y. Kubota et al. (CLEO), *Nucl. Instr. Meth.* **A320** (1992) 66.
3. G. Fox and S. Wolfram, *Phys. Rev. Lett.* **41** (1978) 1581.
4. K. Hikasa et al., (The Particle Data Group), *Phys. Rev.* **D45** (1992) S1.

## MEASUREMENTS OF b-FLAVOURED BARYONS AND STRANGE b-FLAVOURED MESONS PRODUCED IN Z^0 DECAYS AT LEP

RONEN MIR
Physics Department, Indiana University,
Bloomington, IN 47405, U.S.A

representing

THE OPAL COLLABORATION
CERN, 1211 Geneva 23, Switzerland

ABSTRACT

Evidence is presented for the production of b-flavoured baryons and the strange b-flavoured meson B_s^0 in hadronic Z^0 decays, recorded with the OPAL detector at LEP. The decays $\Lambda_b \to \Lambda \ell^- \bar{\nu} X$ (ℓ=e or ℓ=μ) and $\Lambda_b \to \Lambda_c^+ \ell^- \bar{\nu} X$ are observed, where the charmed baryon Λ_c^+ is reconstructed in the $pK^-\pi^+$ decay mode. The relevant product branching ratios are measured. Inclusive and semileptonic decays of the B_s^0 are studied, in which the strange charmed meson D_s^- is detected in the $\phi\pi^-$ and $K^{*0}K^-$ final states. A signal due to the decay $B_s^0 \to D_s^- \ell^+ \nu X$ is observed. The product branching ratio $f(\bar{b} \to B_s^0) \cdot B(B_s^0 \to D_s^- \ell^+ \nu X) \cdot B(D_s^- \to \phi\pi^-)$ is measured. An excess of inclusive D_s events is found beyond those expected from B^0 and B^+ decays and from the fragmentation of primary c quarks. This excess is consistent with the observation of the B_s^0 in the semileptonic decay. Searches are made for exclusive decays of the Λ_b and of the B_s^0.

1. Introduction

Decays of the Z^0 boson provide a copious source of B hadrons. The existence of b-flavoured baryons such as the Λ_b is predicted by the quark model[1]. The existence of the strange b-flavoured meson B_s^0 is indicated by the large mixing effect observed in the neutral B meson system[2]. The identification of the Λ_b and B_s^0 will allow measurements of their lifetimes, as well as $B_s^0 \bar{B}_s^0$ mixing.

The data reported here was collected with the OPAL[3] detector during the 1990 and 1991 LEP running periods, corresponding to approximately 470,000 hadronic Z^0 decays.

Evidence for the existence of B baryons, coming from $\Lambda \ell^-$ correlations (both charge conjugate states are implied throughout this paper) is presented. Observation of the decay $\Lambda_b \to \Lambda_c^+ \ell^- \bar{\nu} X$ is reported. Evidence for the existence of the B_s^0, coming from $D_s^- \ell^+$ correlations and inclusive D_s production, is presented. A search is made for the exclusive decays $\Lambda_b \to J/\psi \Lambda$ and $B_s^0 \to J/\psi \phi$.

2. Experimental Method.

Semileptonic decays of B baryons are expected to produce $\Lambda \ell^-$ pairs, but not $\Lambda \ell^+$ pairs, where ℓ=e or ℓ=μ. Similarly, semileptonic decays of the B_s^0 are expected to produce $D_s^- \ell^+$ pairs, but not $D_s^- \ell^-$ pairs. The lepton ℓ is characterized by large momenta (p) and large transverse momenta (p_T) relative to the B hadron direction.

The branching ratio for $B_s^0 \to D_s^- X$ is expected to be large[4]. Thus an excess of inclusive D_s^- production above the backgrounds from B^+, B^0 decays and c quark fragmentation, is expected.

In order to select charm and lepton candidates we require:
- Electrons to be identified by the ionization energy loss measured in the jet chamber, and by the electromagnetic calorimeter and presampler.
- Muons to be identified by associating central detector tracks to track segments in the muon detector, and by ionization energy loss measurements.
- The Λ baryon to be reconstructed via its $\Lambda \to p\pi^-$ decay.
- The Λ_c^+ baryon to be reconstructed via its $\Lambda_c^+ \to pK^-\pi^+$ decay.
- The strange charmed meson D_s^- to be reconstructed via the decays $D_s^- \to \phi\pi^-$ and $D_s^- \to K^{*o}K^-$. The ϕ is detected in the K^+K^- mode and the K^{*o} in the $K^+\pi^-$ mode.

Following the selection of charm and lepton candidates, the charm mass peaks are fitted to obtain the number of produced events. The backgrounds are estimated and subtracted. From the resulting excess a product branching ratio for $f(b \to B$ hadron)·(the appropriate branching ratios) is calculated, where $f(b \to B$ hadron) is the B hadron production rate per b quark in Z^0 decays. The Standard Model value of 0.217 for $\Gamma_{b\bar{b}}/\Gamma_{had}$ is assumed[5]. Results given in this paper are quoted with a statistical error first, followed by a systematic error, unless otherwise stated.

3. Results

3.1. Evidence for Λ_b Production[6].

Events containing $p\pi^-$ and a lepton with high p and p_T are selected. The $p\pi^-$ invariant mass distributions for $p\pi^- \ell^-$ and $p\pi^- \ell^+$ combinations are shown in Figures 1a and 1b. Clear excess in the $p\pi^- \ell^-$ combination is observed. The background processes contributing to this excess are calculated and found to be small. The quantity $f(b \to \Lambda_b) \cdot B(\Lambda_b \to \Lambda \ell^- \bar{\nu} X)$ is measured. The numerical results are summarized in Table 1.

3.2. Observation of $\Lambda_b \to \Lambda_c^+ \ell^- \bar{\nu} X$

The decay $\Lambda_b \to \Lambda_c^+ \ell^- \bar{\nu} X$ is expected to dominate the semileptonic Λ_b decays, while semileptonic decays of other b-flavoured baryons are not expected to form the final state $\Lambda_c^+ \ell^- \bar{\nu} X$. Events containing $pK^-\pi^+$ and a lepton with high p and p_T are selected. The $pK^-\pi^+$ invariant mass distributions for $pK^-\pi^+ \ell^-$ and $pK^-\pi^+ \ell^+$ combinations are shown in Figures 1c and 1d. A Λ_c^+ signal is observed in the $pK^-\pi^+ \ell^-$ combination. The background processes contributing to these excess are calculated and found to be small.

The quantity $f(b\to\Lambda_b)\cdot B(\Lambda_b\to\Lambda_c^+\ \ell^-\bar{\nu} X)$ is measured, where we assume $B(\Lambda_c^+\to pK^-\pi^+)=(4.3\pm1.0)\%$[7]. The numerical results are summarized in Table 1.

Table 1. Results on Λ_b and B_s^0 production from OPAL

Evidence for	Process	Excess Events	Product BR (x10^{-3})
Λ_b	$\Lambda\ell^-$ correlations	$55.0\pm9.0\pm^{0.3}_{3.1}$	$2.9\pm0.5\pm0.7$
Λ_b	$\Lambda_b\to\Lambda_c^+\ \ell^-\bar{\nu} X$	$22.0\pm5.6\pm0.9$	$1.5\pm0.35\pm0.26$
B_s^0	$D_s^-\ell^+$ correlations	$18.3\pm5.2\pm0.9$	$0.39\pm0.11\pm0.08$
B_s^0	Inclusive D_s	147 ± 48	$5.9\pm1.9\pm1.1$

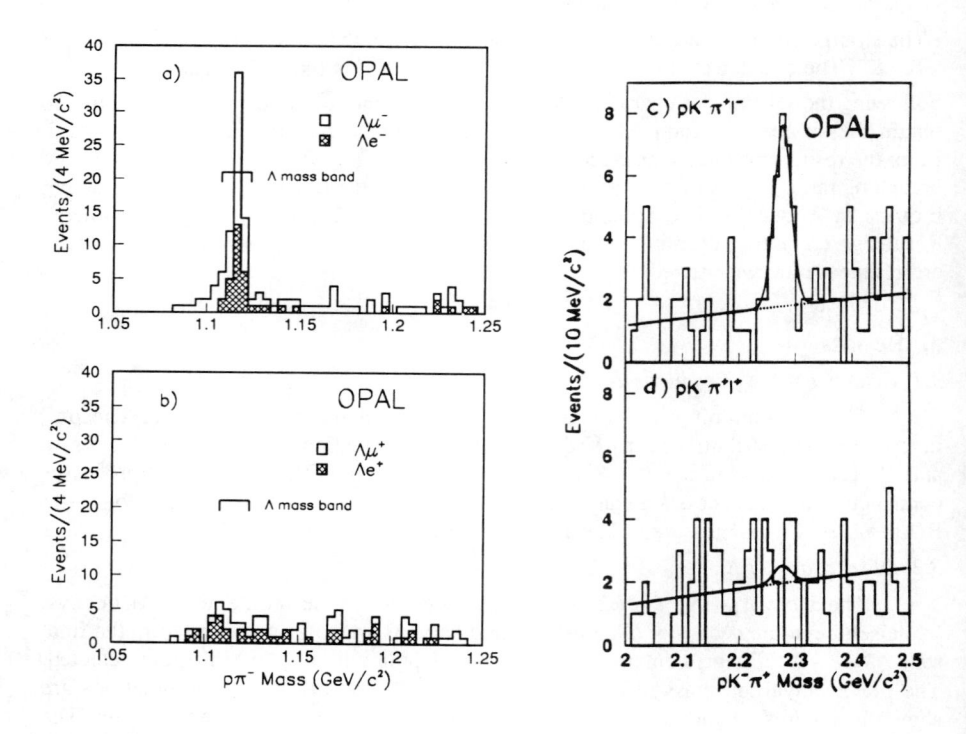

Figure 1. Evidence for Λ_b production

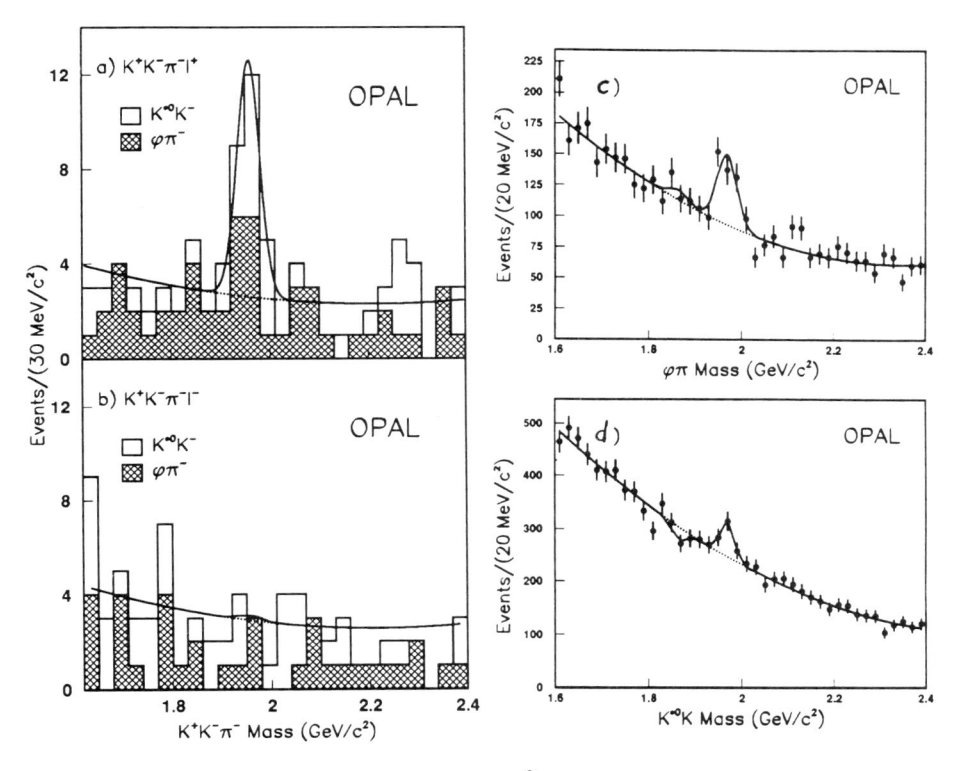

Figure 2. Evidence for B_s^0 production

3.3. Evidence for $B_s^0 \to D_s^- \ell^+ \nu X$[8].

Events containing $\phi\pi^-$ or $K^{*o}K^-$, and a lepton with high p and p_T are selected. The $K^+K^-\pi^-$ invariant mass distributions for $K^+K^-\pi^-\ell^+$ and for $K^+K^-\pi^-\ell^-$ combinations are shown in Figures 2a and 2b. An enhancement in the $K^+K^-\pi^-\ell^+$ combinations at the D_s^- mass is seen. The background processes contributing to these excess are calculated and found to be small. The quantity $f(\bar{b}\to B_s^0)\cdot B(B_s^0\to D_s^-\ell^+\nu X)\cdot B(D_s^-\to\phi\pi^-)$ is measured, where we use the ratio $B(D_s^-\to K^{*o}K^-)/B(D_s^-\to\phi\pi^-)$ to average the two modes.

3.4. Study of inclusive D_s^- production[8].

Events containing $\phi\pi^-$ or $K^{*o}K^-$ are selected. The $K^+K^-\pi^-$ invariant mass distributions for the two D_s^- decay modes are shown in Figure 2c and 2d. The fits to these distributions yield a total of 282±43±15 D_s^- events. The background contributions from c quark fragmentation, and from B^+ and B^0 decays are estimated to contribute 135±44 events. The excess quoted in Table 1 is attributed to $B_s^0\to D_s^- X$ decays, where the errors are combined. The quantity $f(\bar{b}\to B_s^0)\cdot B(B_s^0\to D_s^- X)\cdot B(D_s^-\to\phi\pi^-)$ is measured.

3.5. Search for exclusive Λ_b and B_s^0 decays.

The decays $\Lambda_b \to J/\psi\, \Lambda$ and $B_s^0 \to J/\psi\, \phi$ provide clean channels in which to search for the Λ_b and B_s^0 directly. The J/ψ is reconstructed in the $\mu^+\mu^-$ and e^+e^- decay channels. Approximately 120 J/ψ events are observed over a background of 22 events. No J/ψ Λ candidates are found, giving $f(b \to \Lambda_b) \cdot B(\Lambda_b \to J/\psi\, \Lambda) < 0.23\%$ at 90% CL. One J/ψ φ candidate is found, with an invariant mass of 5.36 GeV/c², yielding $f(\bar{b} \to B_s^0) \cdot B(B_s^0 \to J/\psi\, \phi) < 0.22\%$ at 90% CL.

4. Discussion.

From the measurements above we can estimate $f(b \to B$ hadron), assuming the semileptonic branching ratio of the B hadron to be 11%[9]. The results are quoted in Table 2.

Table 2. Results on $f(b \to B$ hadron) from OPAL

Process	$f(b \to B$ hadron)	Result (%)
$\Lambda_b \to \Lambda_c^+ \ell^- \bar{\nu} X$	$f(b \to \Lambda_b)$	13.3±3.2±3.1
$D_s^- \ell^+$ correlations	$f(\bar{b} \to B_s^0)$	12.7±3.6±2.3

During 1992 OPAL has collected 750,000 more hadronic Z° decays. We are currently analyzing these events. We expect to be able to measure the lifetimes of the Λ_b and B_s^0. Future running at the Z° will offer us the opportunity to measure $B_s^0 \bar{B}_s^0$ mixing.

5. Acknowledgments.

It is a pleasure to thank my colleagues from OPAL, the CERN SL Division (LEP), and the organizers of this stimulating conference.

6. References

1. See for example, S. Capstick and N. Isgur, *Phys. Rev.* **D 34** (1986) 2809; N. Isgur and M.B. Wise, *Phys. Rev. Lett.* **66** (1991) 1130.
2. The average mixing in the neutral B meson system is large, indicating the production of the B_s^0.
3. OPAL Collaboration, K. Ahmet et al., *Nucl. Instrum. and Meth.* **A 305** (1991) 275.
4. M.Suzuki, *Phys. Rev.* **D 31** (1985) 1158; LBL Preprint LBL-18796. $B(B_s^0 \to D_s^- X)$ is predicted to be $0.86^{+0.08}_{-0.13}$.
5. D. Bardin et al., CERN-TH.6443/92 (1992) (unpublished).
6. OPAL Collaboration, P.D. Acton et al., *Phys. Lett.* **B 281** (1992) 394.
7. CLEO Collaboration, G Crawford et al., *Phys. Rev.* **D 45** (1992) 752.
8. OPAL Collaboration, P.D. Acton et al., *Phys. Lett.* **B 295** (1992) 357.
9. Particle Data Group, K. Hikasa et al., *Phys. Rev.* **D 45** (1992) I.1. The average semileptonic branching ratio of B hadrons at LEP is compatible with 11%.

EVIDENCE FOR Λ_b BARYON IN Z DECAYS

Yong-Sheng GAO [1]
Physics Dept. University of Wisconsin-Madison
Madison, WI 53706
ALEPH Collaboration

ABSTRACT

Evidence for Λ_b baryon production at LEP using ALEPH data is reported. In 450,000 hadronic Z decays recorded with the ALEPH detector at LEP, the yields of $\Lambda\ell^-$ and $\Lambda_c^+\ell^-$ combinations have been measured, providing the first evidence for Λ_b baryons in Z decays and measurement of Λ_b semileptonic decay rate. The product branching ratios have been measured to be:

$$\text{Br}(b \longrightarrow \Lambda_b) \cdot \text{Br}(\Lambda_b \longrightarrow \Lambda_c^+ x\ell^-\bar{\nu}) \cdot \text{Br}(\Lambda_c^+ \longrightarrow \Lambda x) = (0.70 \pm 0.10 \pm 0.18)\%$$

$$\text{Br}(b \longrightarrow \Lambda_b) \cdot \text{Br}(\Lambda_b \longrightarrow \Lambda_c^+ x\ell^-\bar{\nu}) = 0.030 \pm 0.007 \pm 0.009$$

1. INTRODUCTION

Not much information on b baryons exists. Z decays at LEP provide an abundant source of a variety of b hadrons with a large boost. It is of clear interest to measure the production and decay properties of b baryons.

The Λ_b is expected to be the lightest [1,2] and most copiously produced b baryon. In this paper, evidence for Λ_b produced in Z decays via reconstruction of its semileptonic decay products is reported. The semileptonice decay of Λ_b studied in this paper is $\Lambda_b \longrightarrow \Lambda_c^+ x\ell^-\bar{\nu}$ where $\Lambda_c^+ \longrightarrow \Lambda x$ and $\Lambda_c^+ \longrightarrow pk^-\pi^+$ with the reconstruction of the high momentum lepton and a Λ ($\Lambda \longrightarrow p\pi^-$) or Λ_c^+ ($\Lambda_c^+ \longrightarrow pk^-\pi^+$). The correlations $\Lambda\ell^-$ and $\Lambda_c^+\ell^-$ as opposed to $\Lambda\ell^+$ and $\Lambda_c^+\ell^+$ are distinctive signatures of semileptonic b baryon decay. Throughout this paper the generic b baryon is referred to as Λ_b and charge conjugation is always implied.

2. $\Lambda\ell$ CORRELATION IN SEMILEPTONIC Λ_b DECAY

The technique described in this paper takes advantage of the large decay rate of Λ_c^+ to Λ [3,4]. Due to the kinematics of its decay, in the laboratory frame, the decay $\Lambda \longrightarrow p\pi^-$ can be unambiguously differentiated from its antiparticle decay $\overline{\Lambda} \longrightarrow \bar{p}\pi^+$. Hence an observable correlation exists between the charge of the lepton from the semileptonic decay of Λ_b and the charge of the decay products of the Λ from the subsequent decay of Λ_c^+. Therefore, the signature of the semileptonic decay of Λ_b is the presence of a $\Lambda\ell^-$ or $\overline{\Lambda}\ell^+$ pair on the same side of an event. As a result of the high momentum of the b hadrons and their relatively large mass, the decay

---
[1] Supported by the US Department of Energy, contract DE-AC02-76ER00881.

products of the semileptonic decays of b hadrons emerge with high momenta and high transverse momenta ($P_\perp$) with respect to the jet direction. These features can be used to distinguish the $\Lambda\ell^-$ combinations from Λ_b decay from different possible sources of background.

There are five possible sources of $\Lambda\ell$ combinations on the same side of a hadronic Z decay. They can be classified on the basis of the resulting charge correlation between the Λ and the lepton:

$$\Lambda_b \longrightarrow \Lambda_c^+ x\ell^-\bar{\nu}, \quad \Lambda_c^+ \longrightarrow \Lambda x \quad (1)$$
$$\overline{B} \longrightarrow \Lambda_c^+ x\ell^-\bar{\nu}, \quad \Lambda_c^+ \longrightarrow \Lambda x \quad (2)$$
$$b \longrightarrow \Lambda_c^+ x, \quad \Lambda_c^+ \longrightarrow \Lambda\ell^+ x \quad (3)$$
$$c \longrightarrow \Lambda_c^+ x, \quad \Lambda_c^+ \longrightarrow \Lambda\ell^+ x \quad (4)$$
$$\text{Accidental combinations.} \quad (5)$$

Process (1) and (2) lead to $\Lambda\ell^-$ combinations, while processes (3) and (4) are sources of $\Lambda\ell^+$ combinations. In addition, Λ baryons are produced copiously in the process of hadronization of quarks. Sometimes such a Λ can pair up with a prompt lepton (e.g., from semileptonic decays of heavy flavours) or a misidentified hadron (fake lepton) and produce a $\Lambda\ell$ combination. Process (5) listed above refers to this possibility. If there is no dominant correlation between the Λ and the lepton charge from this process, the $\Lambda\ell^-$ and $\Lambda\ell^+$ pairs are expected to be observed with equal rates [5].

These five processes have characteristic kinematic features. The $P_\perp$ of the lepton from process (1) is on average relatively large compared with (2), (3) and (4), so we can get rid of the $\Lambda\ell$ combinations from processes (2) - (4) by applying a cut on $P_\perp$ of the lepton [5]. The rate and the momentum spectrum of the Λ produced during hadronization of heavy quarks has not been measured at LEP energies. Therefore, the contribution of $\Lambda\ell^-$ from process (5) must be estimated from data. A measurement of the level of accidental combinations in the $\Lambda\ell^-$ yield can be obtained from the yield of the $\Lambda\ell^+$ sample, provided the $\Lambda_c^+ \longrightarrow \Lambda\ell^+ x\bar{\nu}$ contribution is removed. This can be achieved by requiring the lepton to have more than 5 GeV/c of momentum and $P_\perp$ greater than 1.0 GeV/c. This eliminates more than 95% of all $\Lambda\ell^+$ combinations from processes (3) and (4), leaving process (5) as the largest source of $\Lambda\ell^+$ combinations. Therefore, any excess of the $\Lambda\ell^-$ over the $\Lambda\ell^+$ yield is evidence for semileptonic decays of b baryons.

To obtain a sample of leptons enriched in b content, lepton candidates are required to have at least 5 GeV of momentum and a transverse meomentum $P_\perp$, with respect to the associated jet, of at least 1 GeV. The Λ candidates are identified by their decay $\Lambda \longrightarrow p\pi^-$ and are required to have at least 3 GeV of momentum and to have a decay length of at least 5 cm with respect to the average fill-by-fill beam centroid. Lepton and Λ candidates are required to be within 45 degrees of each other.

The yields of $\Lambda\ell^-$ and $\Lambda\ell^+$, after the above selection cuts, are shown in Figure 1, where the $p\pi^-$ invariant mass is plotted. The two mass distributions are fitted simultaneously to a single Gaussian representing the signal and a second order polynomial to parameterize the shape of the combinatoric background. The fitted signals consist of 170 ± 16 $\Lambda\ell^-$ combinations and 53 ± 9 $\Lambda\ell^+$ combinations, implying an excess of 117 ± 18 $\Lambda\ell^-$ combinations.

Contributions from background processes are small. Less than 7 $\Lambda\ell^-$ are expected from process (2) and the contribution to the $\Lambda\ell^+$ sample of processes (3) and (4) is estimated to be 5 ± 5 combinations, which is added as a correction to the observed excess. The ratio of $\Lambda\ell^-$ to $\Lambda\ell^+$ accidental combinations is taken to be 1.0 ± 0.4. These considerations together imply a b baryon signal of $122 \pm 18(stat)^{+22}_{-23}(syst)$ events.

Using JETSET 6.3 Monte Carlo simulation, a reconstruction efficiency for the process $\Lambda_b \longrightarrow \Lambda_c^+ x \ell^- \bar{\nu}$ where $\Lambda_c^+ \longrightarrow \Lambda x$ of 9.0 ± 1.6 ± 1.0 % was obtained. Assuming the Standard Model value for the partial width of $Z^\circ \longrightarrow b\bar{b}$, applying the above corrections yields a product branching ratio:

$$\text{Br}(b \longrightarrow \Lambda_b) \cdot \text{Br}(\Lambda_b \longrightarrow \Lambda_c^+ x \ell^- \bar{\nu}) = 0.030 \pm 0.007 \pm 0.009$$

3. $\Lambda_c \ell$ CORRELATION IN SEMILEPTONIC Λ_b DECAY

In the previous analysis only the Λ from the decay of the charm baryon and the lepton from the b baryon decay were reconstructed. In the following analysis a more direct study of the Λ_b semileptonic decay with a completely reconstructed Λ_c^+ is reported [6].

The five possible sources of $\Lambda_c^+ \ell^-$ combinations in Z decays are:

$\Lambda_b \longrightarrow \Lambda_c^+ x \ell^- \bar{\nu}$ (6)
$\overline{B} \longrightarrow \Lambda_c^+ x \ell^- \bar{\nu}$ (7)
$\overline{B} \longrightarrow \Lambda_c^+ D_s^+ x,$ $D_s^+ \longrightarrow x \ell^- \bar{\nu}$ (8)
$\Lambda_b \longrightarrow \Lambda_c^+ D_s^+,$ $D_s^+ \longrightarrow x \ell^- \bar{\nu}$ (9)
Accidental combinations. (10)

No experimental evidence exists for processes (7) and (8). The rates for the processes (7), (8) and (9) are estimated to be less than 0.32%, 0.1% and 1.2% respectively.

The Λ_c^+ candidates were identified in this analysis via the decay $\Lambda_c^+ \longrightarrow p k^- \pi^+$. To suppress the combinatorial background, the proton, kaon and pion candidates, with the appropriate charge combination, were required to have momenta greater than 4, 2 and 1 GeV, respectively. The specific ionization in the TPC of the proton candidate was required to be inconsistent (2 standard deviations) with that expected for a pion of similar momentum. The kaon candidate was required to have its specific ionization within 3 deviations of the expectation for a kaon when ionization information was available for the track. The three tracks were fitted to a common vertex in three dimensions, which was required to be in front of the average fill-by-fill beam spot. Surviving Λ_c^+ canadidates with momenta greater than 8.0 GeV were then paired with identified leptons with momenta greater than 3 GeV and within 45° of the Λ_c^+ direction. The momentum of the $\Lambda_c^+ \ell$ system was required to be greater than 20 GeV and the mass of this system was required to exceed 3.5 GeV. From a JETSET 7.2 based simulation, less than 1.2 $\Lambda_c^+ \ell^-$ were expected from processes (7) - (9) in the data sample.

The invariant-mass distribution of the $pk^-\pi^+$ candidates for the surviving $\Lambda_c^+\ell^-$ combinations is displayed in Fig 2(a). A fit to this mass distribution using a Gaussian to parameterize the signal and a flat background yielded 21.0 ± 5.0 events. The contribution of the accidental combinations to this sample was estimated to be 0.4 ± 0.3. The observed Λ_c^+ mass of 2.283 ± 0.002 and resolution of 0.008 ± 0.001 GeV are consistent with the expectation. The $pk^-\pi^+$ invariant-mass distribution for the "wrong-sign" $\Lambda_c^+\ell^+$ is shown in Fig 2(b).

From a simulation of the three-body decay $\Lambda_b \longrightarrow \Lambda_c^+ x \ell^- \bar{\nu}$ using JETSET prescription, a reconstruction efficiency for this process of $8.0 \pm 1.0 \pm 1.0$ % was obtained. Using the measured partial width of the process $Z \longrightarrow b\bar{b}$, the measured rate [3] $\mathrm{Br}(\Lambda_c^+ \longrightarrow pk^-\pi^+) = 4.3 \pm 1.1$ % and the efficiency quoted above, a product branching ratio of $\mathrm{Br}(b \longrightarrow \Lambda_b) \cdot \mathrm{Br}(\Lambda_b \longrightarrow \Lambda_c^+ x l^- \bar{\nu}) = 0.030 \pm 0.007 \pm 0.009$ was obtained. This result is consistent with the previous measurement assuming that the Λ_b is the dominantly produced b baryon at the Z resonance.

4. CONCLUSION

In 450,000 hadronic Z decays recorded with the ALEPH detector at LEP, the yields of $\Lambda\ell^-$ and $\Lambda_c^+\ell^-$ combinations have been measured, providing evidence for the semileptonic decay of Λ_b baryon.

An excess of 117 ± 18 $\Lambda\ell^-$ combinations is observed, giving the first evidence of Λ_b baryon in Z decays. The product branching ratio for semileptonic Λ_b decay is:

$$\mathrm{Br}(b \longrightarrow \Lambda_b) \cdot \mathrm{Br}(\Lambda_b \longrightarrow \Lambda_c^+ x \ell^- \bar{\nu}) \cdot \mathrm{Br}(\Lambda_c^+ \longrightarrow \Lambda x) = (0.70 \pm 0.10 \pm 0.18)\%$$

21.0 ± 5.0 $\Lambda_c^+\ell^-$ combinations were observed in the $\Lambda_c^+ \longrightarrow pk^-\pi^+$ channel. This is the first observation of semileptonic Λ_b decay with exclusively reconstructed charm baryons. The product pranching ratio for semileptonic Λ_b decay is:

$$\mathrm{Br}(b \longrightarrow \Lambda_b) \cdot \mathrm{Br}(\Lambda_b \longrightarrow \Lambda_c^+ x \ell^- \bar{\nu}) = 0.030 \pm 0.007 \pm 0.009$$

5. References

1. A. Martin and J. M. Ricard, *Phys. Let.* **B185** (1987) 426.
2. W. Kwong and J. Rosner, *Phys. Rev.* **D44** (1991) 212.
3. G. Crawford et al., (CLEO Collab.), *Phys. Rev.* **D45** (1992) 752.
4. Particle Data Group, J.J. Hernandez et al., Review of particle properties, *Phys. Let.* **B239** (1990) VIII. 129.
5. D. Decamp et al. (ALEPH Collab.), *Phys. Let.* **B278** (1992) 209.
6. D. Decamp et al. (ALEPH Collab.) Preprint no. CERN PPE-92-73

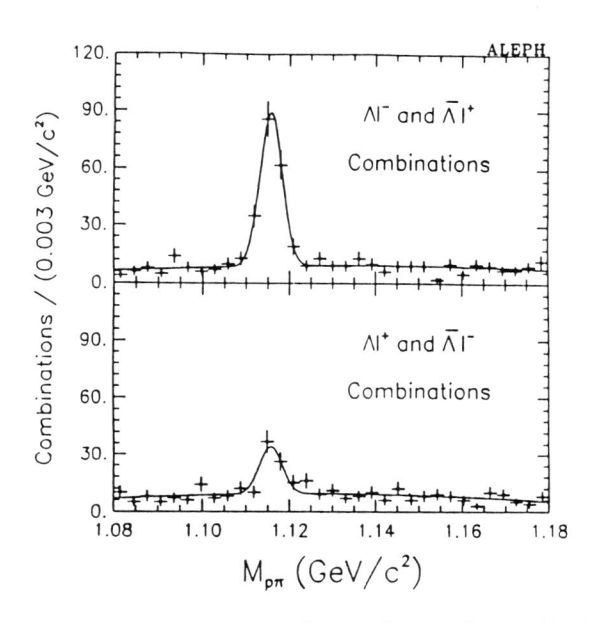

Figure 1: The $p\pi$ invariant mass distribution of the $\Lambda\ell^-$ and $\Lambda\ell^+$ combinations.

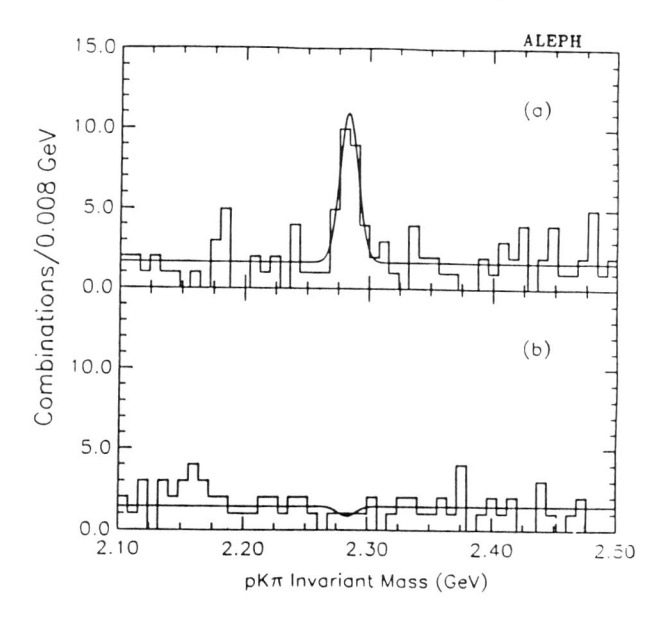

Figure 2: The invariant mass spectrum of the $pk^-\pi^+$ for (a) for the "right sign" $\Lambda_c^+\ell^-$ and (b) for the "wrong sign" $\Lambda_c^+\ell^+$ combinations.

EVIDENCE FOR THE B_S MESON
AND MEASUREMENT OF THE B_S AND Λ_b LIFETIMES

F. V. WEBER

Physics Department, University of Wisconsin–Madison
Madison, WI U.S.A.
ALEPH collaboration

ABSTRACT

In 450,000 hadronic Z decays recorded with the ALEPH detector at LEP, the yield of $D_S^- \ell^+$ combinations is measured. 16.0 ± 4.3 $D_S^- \ell^+$ combinations are observed in the $D_S^- \to \phi\pi^-$ channel and 17.0 ± 4.5 combinations are observed in the $D_S^- \to K^{*0} K^-$ channel, providing evidence for B_S and measurement of the product branching ratio $Br(\bar{b} \to B_S) \cdot Br(B_S \to D_S^- X \ell^+ \nu) = 0.040 \pm 0.011 \, ^{+0.010}_{-0.012}$. The B_S lifetime is measured to be $1.02^{+0.46}_{-0.31} \pm 0.10$ ps from a fit to the decay length distribution of the $D_S^- \ell^+$ combinations.

Semileptonic b baryon decay is identified using the decay chain $\Lambda_b \to \Lambda_c X \ell^- \nu$, $\Lambda_c \to \Lambda X$, $\Lambda \to p\pi^-$. Fitting to the impact parameters of the leptons in the $\Lambda \ell^-$ sample provides the first measurement of the b baryon lifetime: $\tau_{\Lambda_b} = 1.12^{+0.32}_{-0.29}(stat) \pm 0.16(syst)$ ps.

1. Introduction

This note reports on the observation of the semileptonic decays of the B_S meson and the Λ_b baryon, and the measurement of the B_S and Λ_b lifetimes. These analyses are based on 450,000 hadronic Z decays collected with the ALEPH detector at LEP. For a subset of the data sample, the ALEPH silicon microvertex detector (VDET) was installed and operational.

2. B_S Signal and Lifetime

2.1. Evidence for B_S

The details of the isolation of the signal for B_S decay are given in [1]. The B_S meson is identified using its semileptonic decay $B_S \to D_S^- \ell^+ \nu X$, where the D_S^- is reconstructed in its $\phi\pi^-$ and $K^{*0} K^-$ decay modes. The ϕ is identified via its decay to $K^+ K^-$, while the K^{*0} is reconstructed in its $K^+ \pi^-$ decay mode. The possible sources of $D_S^- \ell^+$ combinations in Z decays are: 1) $B_S \to D_S^- \ell^+ \nu X$, 2) $\overline{B} \to D_S^- DX$, $D \to X\ell^+ \nu$, 3) $B \to D_S^- {}^uK" W^{*+}, W^{*+} \to \ell^+ \nu$, 4) Accidental Combinations. Backgrounds 2 and 3 are expected to make small contributions to the $D_S^- \ell^+$ sample, as both have branching ratios of the order of 2% or less and can be further reduced with kinematic cuts. The contribution from process 4 can be estimated from the data and is similarly small.

The most important cuts in the reconstruction of the D_S^- candidates are as follows: the ϕ and K^{*0} candidates are required to have at least 5.0 GeV of

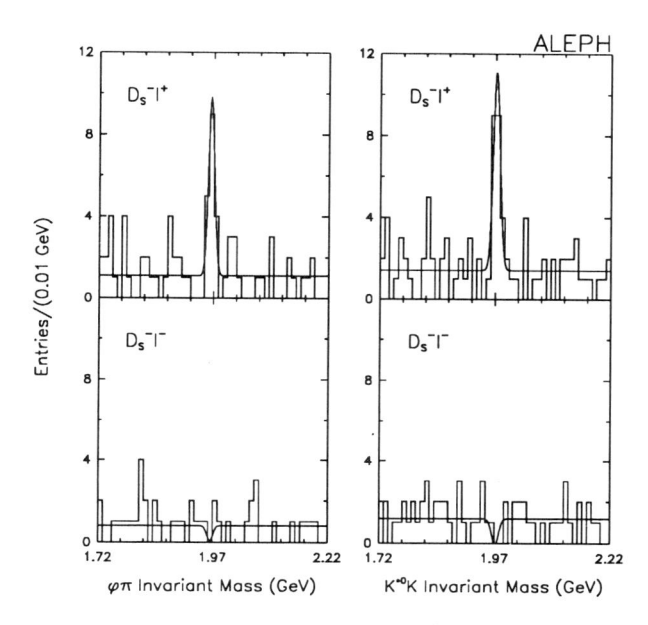

Figure 1: The invariant mass distributions of the $\phi\pi^-$ and $K^{*0}K^-$ tracks in $D_S^-\ell^+$ events. The peaks in the right sign combinations are evidence for B_S semileptonic decay; the absence of signals in the wrong sign combinations suggests no significant contribution from accidental $D_S^-\ell^+$ combinations.

momentum, and the measured $\frac{dE}{dX}$ of the K and π tracks, when available, is required to be within two standard deviations of the hypothesis. The ϕ candidates within ±0.009 GeV of the nominal ϕ mass are combined with π^- candidates with at least 3.0 GeV of momentum to construct D_S^- candidates. Similarly, K^{*0} candidates within ±0.05 GeV of the K^{*0} mass are combined with K^- candidates which are required to be compatible with the $\frac{dE}{dX}$ hypothesis within two standard deviations, and to have at least 3.0 GeV of momentum.

To identify B_S semileptonic decay, D_S^- candidates with at least 8.0 GeV of momentum are combined with electron and muon candidates within 45 degrees having at least 3.0 GeV of momentum. The invariant mass of the $D_S^-\ell^+$ system is required to be greater than 3.0 GeV. In 1991 data, the improved vertex resolution with the silicon microvertex detector allows further reduction of combinatoric background with the requirement that the fitted D_S^- vertex in the $K^{*0}K^-$ decay mode is displaced by 0.08 cm transverse to the beam direction from the beam spot. The resulting D_S^- invariant mass distributions are shown in Fig. 1, consisting of 16.0 ± 4.3 $D_S^-\ell^+$ combinations in the $\phi\pi^-$ decay mode, and 17.0 ± 4.5 in the $K^{*0}K^-$ decay mode. To calculate the number of $D_S^-\ell^+$ combinations from semileptonic decay of B_S, the remaining contributions of the background processes must be subtracted. In the $\phi\pi^-$ sample, the contributions are estimated to be 1.8 ± 0.6 $D_S^-\ell^+$ from process 2, less than 2.0 ± 0.6 from process 3 (90% C.L.), and 0.53 ± 0.30 from process 4. In the $K^{*0}K^-$ sample are an estimated 1.6 ± 0.6 $D_S^-\ell^+$ from process 2, less than 1.8 ± 0.6 from process 3 (90% C.L.), and 0.45 ± 0.25 from process 4; in addition, reflections from decays of $B \to D^-X\ell^+\nu, D^- \to K^{*0}\pi^-$ contribute 1.8 ± 2.4 more background "$D_S^-\ell^+$" combinations. The $D_S^-\ell^+$ combinations coming from semileptonic B_S decays are thus measured to be $13.7 \pm 4.4^{+0.0}_{-2.0}$ in $\phi\pi^-$, and $13.1 \pm 5.5^{+0.0}_{-1.8}$ in $K^{*0}K^-$. Using efficiencies from simulation, these yields are combined to measure $Br(\bar{b} \to B_S) \cdot Br(B_S \to D_S^-X\ell^+\nu) = 0.040 \pm 0.011 \,^{+0.010}_{-0.012}$.

2.2. Event Selection for B_S Lifetime Analysis

To perform the fit for the B_S lifetime, only 1991 data is used, as the precision tracking of the VDET is needed for vertex reconstruction. The lepton and at least 2 out of the 3 D_S^- daughter tracks are required to have at least 2 coordinates in the inner tracking chamber and at least one $r\phi$ or z coordinate in the VDET. The requirements on the position of the D_S^- vertex are dropped to avoid lifetime bias. Finally, both the D_S^- and B_S vertices are required to have a χ^2 of less than 50. These additional requirements leave 15 events within ± 0.016 MeV of the D_S^- mass from the distributions in Fig. 1 for use in the lifetime fit.

2.3. B_S Decay Length and Proper Time

The method used to extract the B_S lifetime follows closely the B^0 and B^+ lifetime analyses reported in these proceedings [4]. The D_S^- vertex is reconstructed using its 3 daughter tracks, and a D_S^- "track" is constructed, which is then combined with the lepton to form the B_S decay vertex. The primary vertex is reconstructed on an event-by-event basis to a precision of 70 microns in x and z, and 10 microns in y. The B_S decay length resolution obtained is typically 250 microns.

To extract the lifetime of the B_S meson, the B_S proper time $t = \frac{\delta}{\beta\gamma c}$ is required. Since there is always a missing neutrino in semileptonic decays, the B_S momentum is not known exactly, and the shape of the correction factor $\kappa = \frac{p_{D_S\ell}}{p_{B_S}}$ is estimated from simulation. The expected decay length distribution of B_S events is then given by the convolution of an exponential (from the B_S lifetime) with a gaussian resolution function and the κ distribution. The shape of the decay length distribution expected from the background processes is taken from the sidebands of the D_S^- invariant mass peak (for combinatoric background), or from Monte Carlo simulation (processes 2 and 3).

2.4. B_S Lifetime

The composition of the sample is estimated to be 74% from B_S, 8% from $\bar{B} \to D_S^-DX$, $D \to X\ell^+\nu$, and 18% from combinatoric background. A contribution of up to 5% is allowed from $B \to D_S^-$ "K" $\ell + \nu$ as a systematic error. An unbinned maximum likelihood fit is performed to the reconstructed decay lengths of the $D_S^-\ell^+$ events, yielding $\tau_{B_S} = 1.02^{+0.46}_{-0.31}$ ps, and is shown in Fig. 2a.

The largest sources of systematic error in this measurement are the knowl-

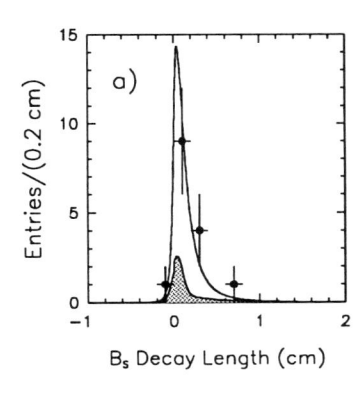

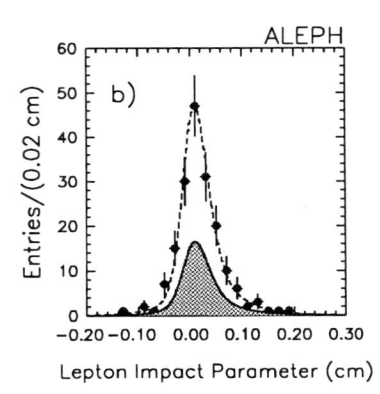

Figure 2: a) The decay length distribution of $D_S^- \ell^+$ events. Overlaid is the result of the unbinned maximum likelihood fit for the B_S lifetime. b) Lepton impact parameter distribution for the $\Lambda \ell^-$ sample, together with the result of the unbinned maximum likelihood fit. The shaded regions indicate the background contributions in the samples.

edge of the $D_S^- \ell^+$ sample composition (0.075 ps), the uncertainty in the parameterization of the vertex resolution (0.04 ps), and the parameterization of the shapes of the background decay length distributions (0.03 ps). The possible contribution of the process $B \to D_S^- "K" \ell + \nu$ to the B_S lifetime is estimated to be 0.036 ps. The total systematic error is estimated to be ±0.10 ps.

3. Λ_b Lifetime

3.1. Evidence for Λ_b

The details of isolating a sample of Λ_b baryons with $\Lambda \ell^-$ correlations are outlined elsewhere in these proceedings [2]. In addition to the cuts described there, some additional requirements are added to ensure high track quality for the leptons used in the Λ_b lifetime fit. At least 6 TPC hits and 2 ITC hits are required to be associated to each track, and the χ^2/d.o.f. of the track fit is required to be less than 4. These cuts leave 178 $\Lambda \ell^-$ candidates within a ±5 MeV window around the Λ mass, to be used in the lifetime fit.

3.2. Lifetime Measurement with Lepton Impact Parameter

The details of the lifetime fit can be found in [3]. The impact parameter of the leptons in the $\Lambda \ell^-$ sample is used to extract the Λ_b lifetime. An expected impact parameter distribution is constructed for leptons from Λ_b as the convolution of a "Physics Function", taken from simulation, describing the shape of the distribution one would obtain with a perfect detector (without resolution effects), with a "Resolution Function", obtained from the data, parameterizing the tails in the impact parameter resolution. From the difference in the yields of $\Lambda\ell^-$ and $\Lambda\ell^+$ combinations, a purity of 57% is estimated for leptons from Λ_b decay in the $\Lambda\ell^-$ sample. The remainder of the $\Lambda\ell^-$ combinations come from a real or fake lepton combined with a Λ from fragmentation or from combinatoric background. In either case, the Λ has no physical connection to the lepton, and hence the shape of the impact parameter distribution of leptons from the background in the $\Lambda\ell^-$ sample is identical to that of the inclusive lepton sample after application of the p and $p_\perp$ requirements used for the $\Lambda\ell^-$ selection.

3.3. Λ_b Lifetime Result

The impact parameter distribution of the leptons in the $\Lambda\ell^-$ sample is shown in Fig. 2b, with the result of the unbinned maximum likelihood fit shown superimposed. The contribution from the background sources is indicated by the shaded region, and is taken from the inclusive lepton distribution, scaled to the appropriate fraction of the $\Lambda\ell^-$ sample and held fixed during the fit. The fitted value of the Λ_b lifetime is $\tau_{\Lambda_b} = 1.12^{+0.32}_{-0.29}$ ps.

The largest contributions to the systematic uncertainty are from the statistics of the Λ_b Physics Function (0.09 ps), from the determination of the Resolution Function (0.07 ps), from the assumption that the background leptons have the same shape as the corresponding inclusive distribution (0.06 ps), and from the estimation of the lepton source fractions (0.05 ps). The total systematic uncertainty due to all considered sources is estimated to be 0.16 ps.

4. Conclusions

In 450,000 Z^0 decays collected with the ALEPH detector in 1990 and 1991, $D_S^-\ell^+$ correlations are used to measure the product branching ratio $Br(\bar{b} \to B_S) \cdot Br(B_S \to D_S^- X \ell^+ \nu) = 0.040 \pm 0.011~^{+0.010}_{-0.012}$. From a subsample of these events collected in 1991, the B_S lifetime is measured to be $\tau_{B_S} = 1.02^{+0.46}_{-0.31} \pm 0.10$ ps. The Λ_b lifetime is measured in a sample of events containing $\Lambda\ell^-$ correlations to be $\tau_{\Lambda_b} = 1.12^{+0.32}_{-0.29} \pm 0.16$ ps.

5. References

1. D. Decamp *et. al.* (ALEPH Collab.), "Observation of the Semileptonic Decays of B_S and Λ_b Hadrons at LEP", CERN–PPE–92–73, 4 May 1992, to be published in Phys. Lett. B.
2. Y.-S. Gao, "Evidence for Λ_b Baryon in Z Decays," these proceedings.
3. D. Buskulic *et. al.* (ALEPH Collab.), "A Measurement of the b Baryon Lifetime", CERN–PPE–92–138, 12 August 1992, to be published in Phys. Lett. B.
4. F. V. Weber, "A Measurement of the B^0 and B^+ Meson Lifetimes," these proceedings.

PRODUCTION OF B_s^0 AND Λ_b PRODUCTION IN Z^0 HADRONIC DECAYS

Didier VILANOVA
CE-Saclay, DAPNIA/SPP
91191 Gif-sur-Yvette CEDEX, FRANCE

On behalf of the DELPHI Collaboration

ABSTRACT

Evidence for B_s^0 and Λ_b production in Z^0 hadronic decays is given using D_s-lepton, φ-lepton correlations, inclusive D_s production and Λ-lepton correlations in the LEP data collected by the DELPHI experiment. Measurements of the corresponding production rates and lifetimes are given as well as the probabilty f_s for a heavy quark to hadronize into a strange meson.

The basic principle of the following analyses is to enrich the data sample selecting jets with a large p_t lepton or a charm signature. On the other hand, the excellent performances of the microvertex detector (VD) allow B hadrons lifetime measurements in spite of their shortness ($\approx$ 1 ps). Four different analyses are summarized herein, viz. studies of D_s-lepton correlations, D_s inclusive production and φ-lepton correlations in which evidence for B_s^0 production can be shown, and Λ-lepton correlations due to Λ_b production. A full description of the DELPHI detector can be found in [1].

Several processes, all from B decays, can contribute to the production of $l^{\pm}D_s^{\mp}X$ final state, with a lepton and a D_s in the same jet. However, according to Monte Carlo simulations, the distribution of p_t, the transverse momentum of the lepton with respect to the jet axis, strongly depends on the decay chain. For example, with $p_t > 1.2$ GeV/c, more than 90 % of the events are expected to originate from B_s^0 semileptonic decays. For this analysis, 270 000 Z^0 decays have been used. Only tracks with a muon in the same hemisphere, hits in the VD and a momentum greater than 2 GeV/c were kept. The D_s was reconstructed in its $\varphi\pi$ and $K^{*0}K$ modes. Details on different cuts can be found in ref. [2] A clear signal of D_s can be seen in fig. 1; it corresponds to a number of events $N_{D_s} = 7.5^{+3.3}_{-2.6}$. After subtraction of the eventual reflection of the D^0 in its $KK\pi$ decay mode, corrections for acceptance an efficiencies, the following production rate has been found :

$$P(Z^0 \to b \text{ or } \overline{b} \to B_s^0 \to D_s\mu\nu X, D_s \to \varphi\pi) = (18 \pm 8) \times 10^{-5}.$$

A comparison of the candidate decay length distribution with the corresponding distribution of the B → D⁰lX sample yielded the ratio : $\tau(B_s^0)/\tau(B) = 0.8 \pm 0.4$.

The main sources of φ correlated with a lepton in the same jet are the B_s^0 decay into $D_s l\nu$ followed by $D_s \to \varphi\pi$, the direct D_s production from c hadronization and non-strange B decays into D and D_s. All those processes are related to f_s and can be discriminated by their different p_t distibutions. The background consists essentially in "fake"leptons. Starting from 243 000 hadronic Z^0 decays, keeping only tracks with hits in the VD and a momentum greater than 2.5 GeV/c, a signal of 51 ± 11 events with a φ decaying into KK and a muon in the same jet has been found. Among them, 22 ± 6 had a p_t greater than 1 GeV/c. A fit of the p_t distribution gave $f_s = 0.20 \pm 0.12(\text{stat.}) \pm 0.08(\text{syst.})$.

In order to evaluate B_s^0 lifetime, muons and electrons have been used. To improve the signal, only events with a p_t greater than 1 GeV/c have been selected. The measurement of the distance of the K-K-lepton secondary pseudo-vertex to the interaction point and an empirical evaluation of the B momentum from the φ-lepton one allow to histogram the B proper time distribution, wich has been fitted, taking into account the background evaluated outside the φ mass signal (fig. 2). The final result is : $\tau(B_s^0) = 1.24^{+0.61}_{-0.52}(\text{stat.}) \pm 0.20(\text{syst.})$ ps. More details on this study will be found in [3].

According to the Lund simulation, the branching fraction $\text{Br}(B_s^0 \to D_s X)$ is equal to 70 %, and then, the D_s can be used as a B_s^0 production signature. Other sources of D_s are the decays of the non-strange B's and the direct production from c quark hadronisation. Although the total rates of those processes are expected to be roughly equal, the separation of direct D_s from cascade ones can be performed using their transverse momentum, expected to be higher in B decays. Starting from 243 000 hadronic Z^0 decays, D_s have been reconstructed in their $\varphi\pi$ mode, using KK mass combinations in the φ mass range; the complete description of cuts is in ref. [3]. To reduce direct charm contribution, only D_s with an energy less than $E_{beam}/2$ have been select. A clear signal of D_s can be seen on fig. 3, corresponding to 58 ± 12 events After subtracting direct D_s contribution and correcting for acceptance and efficiencies, the following rate has been obtained :

$$\text{Br}(b \to D_s X) \times \text{Br}(D_s \to \varphi\pi) = (8.31 \pm 2.05(\text{stat.}) \pm 1.21(\text{syst.}))10^{-3} \ .$$

This rate is larger than the one observed at the $\Upsilon(4S)$, viz. $(3.06\pm0.47)10^{-3}$ [4], and this excess of D_s can be interpreted as due to B_s^0 production. The probability f_s is then equal to $f_s = 0.29 \pm 0.10(\text{stat.}) \pm 0.10(\text{syst.})$.

The B lifetime was evaluated using a smaller sample of candidates, selected with a more stringent cut on φ mass with $p_t > 0.5 \text{GeV}/c$. The proper time distribution is the result of the convolution of the D_s flight length distribution with the resolution function and was scaled to take into account the B boost. Since it has been previously determined that there is $(67 \pm 10)\%$ of B_s^0 in the sample, the B_s^0 lifetime is : $\tau(B_s^0) = 0.75^{+0.52}_{-0.33}$(stat.) $\pm$ 0.24(syst.) ps. More details of this study can be found in [3]. Combining the three previous measurements of B_s^0 lifetime, the following is obtained : $\tau(B_s^0) = 1.0 \pm 0.9$ ps.

The Λ_b baryon is expected to decay semi-leptonically into final states containing a Λ_c, which can decay itself into ΛX. The presence of a pair Λl^- or $\overline{\Lambda} l^+$ in the same jet is then a good signature of B_s^0 production. 365 000 hadronic events have been used for the present study. Only events containing a lepton (e or μ) with a momentum greater than 3 GeV/c and a Λ reconstructed in the pπ mode have been selected. To eliminate the direct production of Λ's, a momentum greater than 4 GeV/c was demanded. The reconstruction efficiency was evaluated to be (16.2$\pm$2.4)%, and 527$\pm$29 Λ's were selected. To get rid of B-meson decays into $\Lambda_c X$, direct Λ_c semi-leptonic decays and fake leptons, only events with a lepton p_t greater than 1 GeV/c were selected. Other cuts are described in ref. [5]. The comparison of right and wrong sign mass distribution shows an excess of 30 $\pm$ 10 events (fig. 4), attributed to Λ_b decays. The expected background is very weak and was included in the systematic errors. After corrections for acceptances and efficiencies, the following rate for Λ_b production was estimated :

$$f(b \to \Lambda_b) \times Br(\Lambda_b \to \Lambda l\nu X) = (0.41 \pm 0.13(\text{stat.}) \pm 0.09(\text{syst.}))\% \text{ per lepton flavour.}$$

The Λ_b proper time distribution has been obtained in recontructing a pseudo-secondary vertex with the lepton, the Λ and another opposite sign particle in the jet with $p > 0.6$ GeV/c and hits in the VD, supposed to come from the Λ_b decay. The Λ_b momentum has been computed by the "residual energy" method (see ref [5]). The proper time distribution of the 18 decays successfully reconstructed among 37 $\Lambda\mu$ combinations has been fitted, taking into account the background from B mesons, and gave : $\tau(\Lambda_b) = 1.04^{+0.48}_{-0.38}$(stat.) $\pm$ 0.09(syst.) ps.

References

1. P. Abreu et al., (DELPHI Collaboration) *Nucl. Instrum. Methods* **A 303** (1991), 233.
2. P. Abreu et al., (DELPHI Collaboration) *Phys. Lett.* **B289** (1992), 199.
3. DELPHI Collaboration "B_s^0 tagging at LEP energies using D_s and φ meson", paper submitted to the XXVI International Conference on High Energy Physics, DALLAS, Texas, USA (1992).
4. CLEO Collaboration D. Bartoletto et al., *Phys. Rev. Lett.* **64** (1990), 2117.
5. DELPHI Collaboration " Measurement of Λ_b production and lifetime in Z^0 hadronic decays", paper submitted to the XXVI International Conference on High Energy Physics, DALLAS, Texas, USA (1992).

Figure captions

- Fig. 1 : Mass distribution for $\varphi\pi$ and K^{*0} candidates, accompanied, in the same jet, by a muon of opposite sign with p_t greater than 1.2 GeV/c.

- Fig. 2 : Measured proper time distribution of $\varphi - l$ events. The curve is the result of the likelihood fit. The shaded area corresponds to the background distribution. In the inset is plotted the invariant mass distribution of the φ candidates used for the lifetime measurement.

- Fig. 3 : Invariant mass distribution of the $\varphi\pi$ candidates.

- Fig. 4 : Distribution of $p\pi$ invariant mass for $\Lambda - l$ correlations. a) right combinations; b) wrong sign combinations. The dashed area corresponds to Λ-electron combinations.

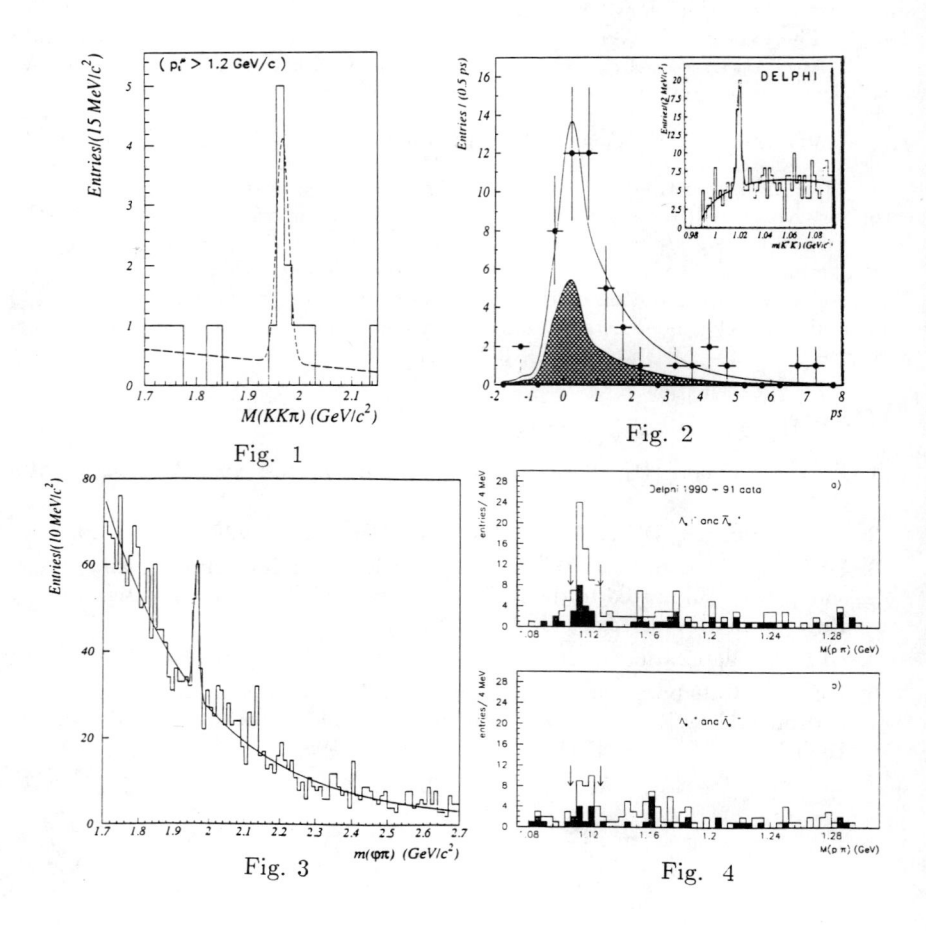

Fig. 1

Fig. 2

Fig. 3

Fig. 4

LIFETIMES OF CHARGED AND NEUTRAL B HADRONS PRODUCED IN Z^0 DECAYS

Gunnar Maehlum
Institute of Physics, University of Oslo, pob. 1048 Blindern
N-0316 Oslo, Norway
Representing the DELPHI Collaboration

ABSTRACT

The lifetimes of neutral and charged B hadrons have been measured using the DELPHI detector at LEP. Higly enriched samples of b-hadrons are obtained by identifying the p_t lepton from the semileptonic b decay in correlation with a reconstructed D meson or by uniquely reconstructing the secondary vertex from the b decay. The proper times are determined using the measured decay length of the b-hadron.

1. Motivation

We have now measurements of the mean lifetimes of b-hadrons with a precision better than 5%. Four different species of b-hadrons have been observed, the $\bar{B}^0$, B^-, B^0_s and Λ_b. If differences in the lifetimes between the various b-hadrons exist the concept of a "mean" b lifetime is not valid since the decay length distribution is not described by a single exponential.

The lifetimes of hadrons in the charmed sector are known to be different: $\tau(D^+)/\tau(D^0) = 2.5 \pm 0.1$ This can be understood qualitatively in terms of interference effects in non-leptonic decay modes. For the decay mode $D \to K\pi$ there are two diagrams leading to similar final states. In the case of D^+ the two final states are identical, $\bar{K}^0\pi^+$, whereas for D^0 there are the two states $K^+\pi^-$ and $\bar{K}^0\pi^0$. Destructive interference between the two graphs in D^+ decay is the main cause of the lifetime difference. This interference is not possible in the D^0 decay since the final states are distinguishable.

The spectator diagram is believed to dominate in the decays of b-hadrons due to the larger mass of the b quark thus leading to similar lifetimes of the different b-hadrons.

This paper presents direct lifetime measurements on samples enriched in B^0 and B^+ content. The silicon microstrip vertex detector installed in DELPHI allows precise decay vertex determination with a precision in the order of $100\mu m$ in the plane transverse to the beam direction. The proper time of the decays are determined from the decay distances combined with an estimate of the b-hadron energy.

2. D-lepton Correlations[1]

From figure 1 it can be seen that neutral B mesons decay semileptonic to a charged $D^{(*)}$ (where $D^{(*)}$ is either a D^{*+} or a D^+). Similarly charged B mesons decay semileptonic to neutral D mesons. The weak decay of the D meson is such that the charged kaon must have the same charge as the lepton from the $B \to Dl\nu$ transition. This correlation is then used to determine the charge of the decaying B meson.

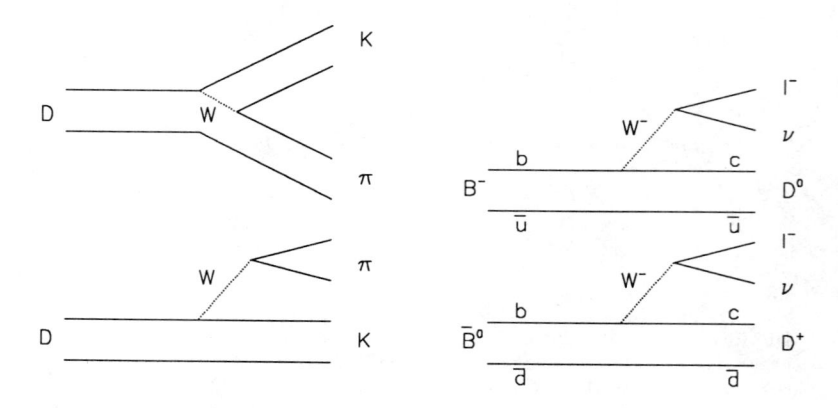

Figure 1: Left: Internal conversion (upper) and spectator (lower) diagrams in nonleptonic D decays. Right: B$^+$ (upper) and B^0 (lower) semileptonic decay diagrams.

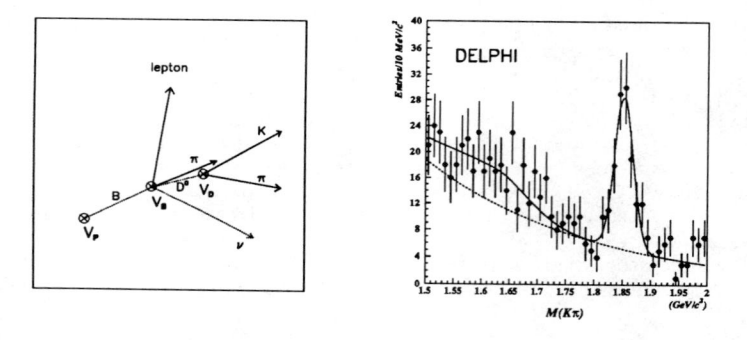

Figure 2: Left: Vertex geometry. Right: D^0 signal in the Kπ channel.

Figure 2 shows the vertex geometry. The D meson are reconstructed by first identifying an electron or a muon with a momentum of at least 3 GeV/c and a high tranverse momentum p_t with respect to the jet axis. Kπ vertices, V_D, are searched for using only tracks in the same hemisphere as the lepton. The D^0 candidates are extrapolated to search for a vertex, V_b, with the identified lepton. The decay length is the distance from the primary vertex V_p to V_b.

Evidence for charmed mesons in multihadronic events with an identified lepton is shown in figure 2. A total of 92±14 D$^0 \to$ K$^-\pi^+$ candidates, 35±8 D$^+ \to$ K$^-\pi^+\pi^+$ candidates, 30±6 D$^{*+} \to$ (K$^-\pi^+$)π^+ candidates and 31±10 D$^{*+} \to$ (K$^-\pi^+\pi^+\pi^-$)π^+ candi-

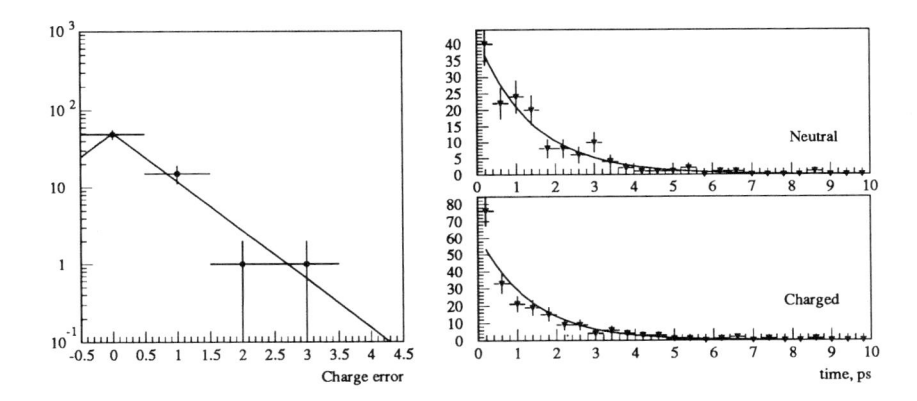

Figure 3: Left: Charge measurement precision. Right: Proper time distributions

dates were found. The lifetimes were determined using an event by event maximum likelihood fit.

The results of the fit are, in picoseconds:

$\bar{B} \to D^0 l^- X$ $1.27^{+0.22}_{-0.18}(stat) \pm 0.15(syst)$
$\bar{B} \to D^+ l^- X$ $1.18^{+0.39}_{-0.027}(stat) \pm 0.15(syst)$
$\bar{B} \to D^{*+} l^- X$ $1.19^{+0.25}_{-0.19}(stat) \pm 0.15(syst)$

The simple charge correlation is however complicated by production of higher spin D resonances (D^{**}) or nonresonant $D^{(*)} + n \cdot \pi$. The D^{**} charge is mixed into the $D^{(*)}$ and pion charges reducing the B-D charge correlation. Recent measurements by ARGUS and CLEO indicate that these contributions might be as large as 40% of the semileptonic branching ratios. The lifetimes of B^0 and B^+ thus were extracted after unfolding this effect using a model for D^{**} production and measured branching ratios. The results are in table 1.

3. Vertex Charge[2]

The idea is to separate all the charged particles in a jet into two unique vertices, one from the primary Z^0 decay and one from the b decay. The finite decay length of the D meson produced in the b decay can be neglected compared to the longer b decay distance. The charge of the decaying b-hadron is reconstructed by simply adding up the charges of the particles assigned to the b vertex.

First a primary vertex is formed constrained by the beam spot. The $P(\chi^2)$ of the vertex fit was requred to be less than 1%. Jets which formed a satisfactory single vertex were thus not considered further. Then all the tracks in a jet were divided into two groups and all possible permutations of tracks were tried in a fit to a primary and a secondary vertex. The jet were retained only if the combined $P(\chi^2)$ for the primary and secondary vertex were larger than 10% and there were no other combination with a $P(\chi^2)$ larger than 10%.

Hadron	D-lepton (ps)	Vertex charge (ps)
B^+	$1.30^{+0.33}_{-0.29} \pm 0.15 \pm 0.05$	$1.42 \pm 0.10 \pm 0.17 \pm 0.12$
B^0	$1.17^{+0.29}_{-0.23} \pm 0.15 \pm 0.05$	$1.39 \pm 0.16 \pm 0.10^{+0.23}_{-0.45}$
$\tau(B^+)/\tau(B^0)$	$1.11^{+0.51}_{-0.39} \pm 0.05 \pm 0.10$	$1.02 \pm 0.14 \pm 0.11^{+0.26}_{-0.16}$

Table 1: B^0 and B^+ lifetime results, the first error is statistical, the second experimental systematic and the third is the constribution from D^{**} production in the case of Dl correlation and contribution from the composition in the case of vertex charge.

The charge measurement is about 80% correct with misidentification rates of 10% for $\Delta Q = \pm 1$ and 1% for $\Delta Q = \pm 2$, figure 3, determined from the rate of doubly charged vertices and cross checked with Monte Carlo.
An event by event maximum likelihood fit gives the results (in ps):

$$\tau_{charged} = 1.32 \pm 0.13(\text{stat}) \pm 0.15(\text{syst})$$
$$\tau_{neutral} = 1.47 \pm 0.17(\text{stat}) \pm 0.15(\text{syst})$$
$$\tau_+/\tau_0 = 0.91 \pm 0.17(\text{stat}) \pm 0.09(\text{syst})$$

This result is obtained by measuring the *excess decay length* from the minimum visible decay length obtained from data for each event. This results are consistent with a fit using an average acceptance function obtained from Monte Carlo.
The neutral verices originates from the decay of B^0, B_s^0 and Λ_b, while the charged vertices mainly stem from B^+ with a possible small contribution from Σ_b^+ baryons. To extract the B^0 and B^+ lifetimes the charge misidentification were unfolded and the production rates of B_s^0 and Λ_b were modeled. The lifetimes of the latter were taken from recent LEP measurements. The results are in table 1.

4. Conclusions

Within errors the lifetimes of B^0 and B^+ are equal and no such effect as seen in the charm sector is observed.

5. Acknowledgemests

I thank D. Bloch, W. Murray for explanations and plots.

6. References

1. DELPHI Collaboration, *A Measurement of B Meson production and Lifetime Using Dl Events in Z^0 decays*, CERN-PPE/92-174, contributed paper.
2. DELPHI Collaboration, *A measurement of the mean lifetimes of neutral and charged b-hadrons*, contributed paper.

A MEASUREMENT OF THE B^0 AND B^+ MESON LIFETIMES

F. V. WEBER
Physics Department, University of Wisconsin–Madison
Madison, WI U.S.A.
ALEPH collaboration

ABSTRACT

In a sample of 260,000 hadronic Z^0 decays collected with the ALEPH detector at LEP, B^0 and B^+ mesons are identified by their semileptonic decays including a D or D^* meson. The decay length of the B meson is reconstructed using the silicon microvertex detector. From a fit to the proper time distributions and the yields of $D\ell$ and $D^*\ell$ combinations, preliminary values of the exclusive B meson lifetimes are measured to be $\tau_0 = 1.56^{+0.20}_{-0.18}(stat)^{+0.09}_{-0.06}(syst)$ ps, $\tau_+ = 1.34^{+0.21}_{-0.19}(stat)^{+0.10}_{-0.06}(syst)$ ps, $\frac{\tau_+}{\tau_0} = 0.86^{+0.18}_{-0.14}(stat)^{+0.14}_{-0.11}(syst)$.

1. Introduction

This note reports on the measurement of the B^0 and B^+ lifetimes performed using data collected with the ALEPH detector at LEP in 1991. The signal is identified via $D^{*+}\ell^-$ and $D^0\ell^-$ correlations, and the B decay vertex is reconstructed using the ALEPH silicon microvertex detector (VDET). The lifetime of the B^0 and B^+ mesons is extracted with a maximum likelihood fit to the reconstructed proper time distributions of the $D^{*+}\ell^-$ and $D^0\ell^-$ samples.

2. Event Selection

Samples of B^0 and B^+ are identified using $D^{*+}\ell^-$ and $D^0\ell^-$ correlations. $D^{*+}\ell^-$ correlations can arise from the decay $\overline{B^0} \to D^{*+}\ell^-\overline{\nu}$, where the D^{*+} is reconstructed via its decay $D^{*+} \to D^0\pi^+, D^0 \to K^-\pi^+$ or $D^0 \to K^-\pi^+\pi^-\pi^+$. Thus, events containing $D^{*+}\ell^-$ combinations should be enriched in B^0 content (throughout this report, charge conjugate states are implied). To obtain a sample containing B^+, $D^0\ell^-$ correlations are used to identify decays of the form $B^- \to D^{*0}\ell^-\overline{\nu}, D^{*0} \to D^0 X$, or $B^- \to D^0\ell^-\overline{\nu}$, where the D^0 is reconstructed in its $K^-\pi^+$ mode only, as the signal-to-noise ratio in the $K^-\pi^+\pi^-\pi^+$ channel is too low for lifetime analysis. Since $D^0\ell^-$ combinations are also produced in the previously described B^0 decay, the $D^0\ell^-$ sample will contain a mixture of B^0 and B^+. A complication arises due to decays of the form $B \to D^{**}\ell\overline{\nu}, D^{**} \to D^*\pi$, as these introduce significant uncertainty on the fractions of B^0 and B^+ in the $D^{*+}\ell^-$ and $D^0\ell^-$ samples.

The most important cuts in the identification of the $D^{*+}\ell^-$ events are as follows. For a D^{*+} candidate, the mass difference between the D^{*+} and the D^0 is required to be within 1.5 MeV of the known value, the D^0 momentum in its $K^-\pi^+$ ($K^-\pi^+\pi^-\pi^+$) decay mode is required to be at least 5 (10) GeV, and at least two of the D^0 daughter tracks are required to have VDET hits in both the $r\phi$ and z views. The D^0

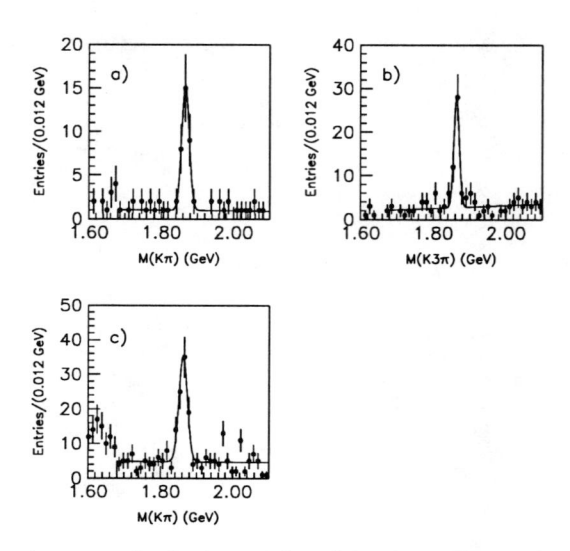

Figure 1: The invariant mass distributions of the D^0 daughter tracks in a)$D^{*+}\ell^-$,$D^0 \to K^+\pi^-$, b)$D^{*+}\ell^-$,$D^0 \to K^+\pi^-\pi^+\pi^-$, and c)$D^0\ell^-$,$D^0 \to K^+\pi^-$. Overlaid are the results of the gaussian (signal) + 1st order polynomial (background) fits.

vertex fit is required to have a χ^2 probability of at least 1%, and the $\frac{dE}{dx}$ of the kaon track is required to be within two standard deviations of the hypothesis. Lepton identification has been described in [1]; identified electron and muon candidates with momentum of at least 3 GeV and at least one VDET hit in $r\phi$ and z are paired with identified D^{*+} to form the $D^{*+}\ell^-$ samples, and the invariant mass of the $D^{*+}\ell^-$ combination is required to be at least 3 GeV. The results are shown in Fig. 1a-b, where the $K^-\pi^+$ and $K^-\pi^+\pi^-\pi^+$ invariant mass is plotted, showing peaks at the D^0 mass. In the $K^-\pi^+$ ($K^-\pi^+\pi^-\pi^+$) sample, there are 31±6 (41±7) events, with a signal-to-background ratio of 9:1 (5:1).

In the $D^0\ell^-$ sample, the minimum D^0 momentum was 8 GeV, the kaon (pion) momentum is required to be at least 2 (1.5) GeV, and a two standard deviation cut is imposed on the measured $\frac{dE}{dx}$ for both the kaon and pion tracks. To ensure independence of the $D^{*+}\ell^-$ and $D^0\ell^-$ samples, $D^0\ell^-$ combinations are rejected if already present in the $D^{*+}\ell^-$ sample. The remaining cuts are as for the $D^{*+}\ell^-$ sample, yielding the $K^-\pi^+$ invariant mass distribution shown in Fig. 1c, with 71±10 entries in the D^0 peak, and a signal-to-noise ratio of 4:1.

3. Sample Composition and Event Ratio Constraint

To extract a B^0 and B^+ lifetime, the fraction of B^0 and B^+ in the $D^0\ell^-$ and

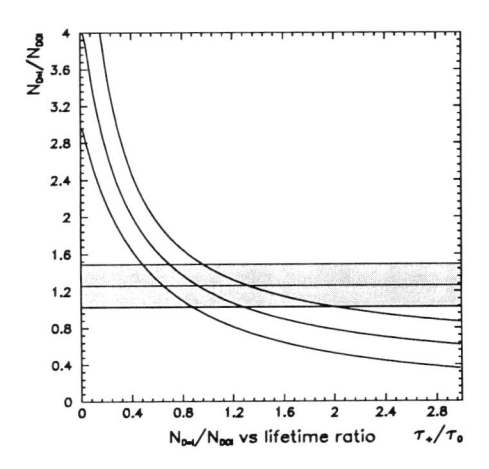

Figure 2: The expected ratio of $D^{*+}\ell^-$ events to $D^0\ell^-$ events as a function of $\frac{\tau_\pm}{\tau_0}$, with $\pm 1\sigma$ (stat+syst) contours shown. Shaded region is observed ratio of 1.26 ± 0.24(stat); intersection of the two curves occurs at $\frac{\tau_\pm}{\tau_0} = 0.95$. Graph is used as a constraint in lifetime fit.

$D^{*+}\ell^-$ samples is calculated. Branching ratio measurements for B^0 decays to $D^{*-}\ell^+\nu$ and $D^-\ell^+\nu$ are taken from experiments at the $\Upsilon(4S)$ [2]. Assuming that corresponding semileptonic partial widths are equal in B decay, e.g., $\Gamma(\overline{B^0} \to D^{*+}\ell^-\overline{\nu}) = \Gamma(B^- \to D^{*0}\ell^-\overline{\nu})$, B^+ branching ratios can be related to their B^0 counterparts via $BR = \Gamma/\tau$. The branching ratio of $B \to D^{**}\ell\overline{\nu}$ is taken as the difference between inclusive and exclusive semileptonic branching ratio measurements at the $\Upsilon(4S)$. From this information, two results can be obtained. First, the fractions of B^0 (f_0) and B^+ (f_+) in the $D^{*+}\ell^-$ and $D^0\ell^-$ samples can be calculated, and depend only on measured quantities and $\frac{\tau_\pm}{\tau_0}$. Second, a prediction can be obtained for the observed ratio of $D^{*+}\ell^-$ events to $D^0\ell^-$ events, R_{exp}. From this information alone, the observed ratio of $D^{*+}\ell^-$ to $D^{*+}\ell^-$ events, $R_{obs} = 1.26 \pm 0.24$, predicts a value of $\frac{\tau_\pm}{\tau_0}$ of $0.95^{+0.37}_{-0.25}$, as shown in Fig. 2. This is used as a constraint in the fit for the B^0 and B^+ lifetimes. The large experimental uncertainty in the branching ratio of $B \to D^{**}\ell\overline{\nu}$, and in the quantum numbers of the D^{**} states produced, introduce significant uncertainties in the calculation of f_0, f_+, and R_{exp}, and constitute the largest contribution to the systematic errors on τ_+ and τ_0.

4. B^0 and B^+ Lifetimes

To extract the B^0 and B^+ lifetimes from the $D^{*+}\ell^-$ and $D^0\ell^-$ samples, a fit is performed to the proper decay times reconstructed for the B mesons in these events, making a cut at two standard deviations around the nominal D^0 mass.

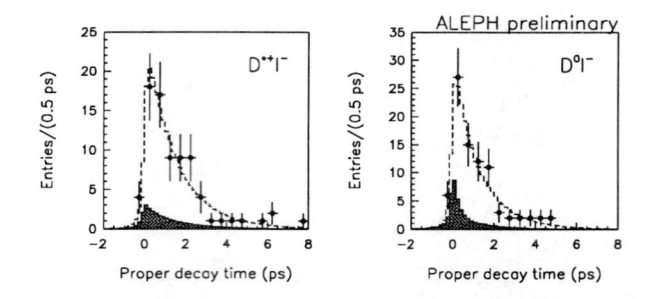

Figure 3: The reconstructed proper times of the $D^{*+}\ell^-$ and $D^0\ell^-$ events, combining the $K^-\pi^+$ and $K^-\pi^+\pi^-\pi^+$ modes in the $D^{*+}\ell^-$ sample. Overlaid is the result of the lifetime fit. The shaded regions represent the background contributions.

The decay length of the B meson is reconstructed in three dimensions. The D^0 decay point is reconstructed first from its daughter tracks, then a D^0 "track" is constructed using the vertex and the momentum sum of the daughter tracks. This D^0 track is then combined with the lepton track to form the B meson decay point. The interaction point is reconstructed on an event-by-event basis to a precision of roughly $70 \times 10 \times 70$ μm, and the B meson decay length resolution is typically 300 μm. The average decay length of B mesons in the ALEPH detector is ~ 2.4 mm.

The B decay lengths reconstructed are converted to an estimated proper time using $\tau = \delta/\beta\gamma c$, where $\beta\gamma$ is calculated from the $D^{*+}\ell^-$ or $D^0\ell^-$ tracks. Since the energy associated with the neutrino in these events is lost, an uncertainty on the boost of the B is introduced. This uncertainty is modelled using Monte Carlo simulation to predict the shape of the distribution of $(\beta\gamma)_{D\ell}/(\beta\gamma)_B$, referred to as the correction factor κ. The expected proper time distribution reconstructed from B decays is thus the convolution of an exponential (for the B lifetime) with a gaussian (for experimental resolution) and the κ distribution. The expected proper time distribution for events from the combinatoric background under the D^0 mass peaks is taken from the sidebands of the D^0 invariant mass distribution, excluding D^0 candidates with masses below 1.68 GeV to avoid $D^0 \to K^-\pi^+\pi^0$. The shape of the background contribution is fixed in the lifetime fit, and is scaled to the appropriate fraction of the total number of events as calculated from the fits to the invariant mass distributions in Fig. 1.

A simultaneous, unbinned, maximum likelihood fit is performed to the reconstructed proper time distributions in the $D^{*+}\ell^-$ and $D^0\ell^-$ samples, including the constraint using R_{exp} mentioned in the previous section. The results are $\tau_{B^0} = 1.56^{+0.20}_{-0.18}$ ps, $\tau_{B^+} = 1.34^{+0.21}_{-0.19}$ ps, $\tau_+/\tau_0 = 0.86^{+0.18}_{-0.14}$, from the fit shown in Fig. 3. The systematic uncertainties considered are listed in Table 1. They are entirely dominated by the uncertainty on the fractions of B^0 and B^+ in the samples induced by lack of exper-

Table 1: Contributions to the systematic uncertainty on the B^0 and B^+ lifetimes, and $\frac{\tau_+}{\tau_0}$. Values for τ_{B^0} and τ_{B^+} are in picoseconds.

Contribution	$\Delta(\tau_{B^0})$	$\Delta(\tau_{B^0})$	$\Delta(\frac{\tau_+}{\tau_0})$
$B \to D^{**} \ell \bar{\nu}$, other BR	$^{+0.09}_{-0.06}$	$^{+0.09}_{-0.06}$	$^{+0.14}_{-0.11}$
Background shape and fraction	± 0.01	± 0.01	$^{+0.02}_{-0.01}$
κ, Boost Correction	$^{+0.03}_{-0.02}$	$^{+0.03}_{-0.02}$	$^{+0.00}_{-0.01}$
Decay Length Resolution	< 0.01	± 0.01	± 0.01
TOTAL	$^{+0.09}_{-0.06}$	$^{+0.10}_{-0.06}$	$^{+0.14}_{-0.11}$

imental knowledge of $B \to D^{**} \ell \bar{\nu}$.

4. Conclusions

In 260,000 Z^0 decays collected with the ALEPH detector in 1991 $D^{*+} \ell^-$ and $D^0 \ell^-$ correlations have been used to measure the B^0 and B^+ lifetimes. The preliminary results obtained are

$$\tau_{B^0} = 1.56^{+0.20}_{-0.18}(stat)\ ^{+0.09}_{-0.06}(syst)\ ps,$$

$$\tau_{B^+} = 1.34^{+0.21}_{-0.19}(stat)\ ^{+0.10}_{-0.06}(syst)\ ps,$$

$$\tau_+/\tau_0 = 0.86^{+0.18}_{-0.14}(stat)\ ^{+0.14}_{-0.11}(syst).$$

5. References

1. D. Decamp et. al. (ALEPH Collab.), Phys. Lett. **B 263** (1991) 325.
2. Exclusive semileptonic branching ratio measurements are taken from:
   D. Bortoletto, et. al., (CLEO Collab.), Phys. Rev. Lett. **63**, (1989) 1667,
   R. Fulton et. al., (CLEO Collab.), Phys. Rev. **D 43**, (1991) 651,
   Yu. Zaitsev, "Selected Results on B Meson Decays", presented at the XXVI International Conference on High Energy Physics, August 1992, Dallas, U.S.A.
   H. Albrecht et. al., (ARGUS Collab.), preprint DESY 92–039, February 1992.
   Inclusive B^0 semileptonic branching ratio is from:
   S. Henderson et. al., (CLEO Collab.), Phys. Rev. **D 45**, (1992) 2212.

MEASUREMENT OF THE AVERAGE B HADRON LIFETIME USING THE L3 DETECTOR AT LEP

LUCAS TAYLOR
Department of Physics, Northeastern University
110 Forsyth Street, Boston, MA 02115, U.S.A.

ABSTRACT

The average b-hadron lifetime, $\langle \tau_b \rangle$, has been measured using the L3 detector at LEP, running at $\sqrt{s} \approx M_Z$. A b-enriched sample was obtained from 300 000 hadronic Z decays collected in 1991 by tagging electrons and muons from semileptonic b-hadron decays. The preliminary 1991 L3 result, from a fit to the electron and muon impact parameter distributions, is $\langle \tau_b \rangle = (1.36 \pm 0.04^{(\text{stat})} \pm 0.05^{(\text{syst})}) ps$.

1. Introduction

Electroweak theory predicts the b-quark semileptonic partial decay width in terms of G_F, the b-quark mass (m_b), phase-space and QCD correction terms (f_c and f_u) and the Cabibbo-Kobayashi-Maskawa (CKM) matrix elements V_{cb} and V_{ub}:

$$\Gamma(b \to \ell) \equiv \frac{\text{BR}(b \to \ell)}{\langle \tau_b \rangle} = \left(\frac{G_F^2 m_b^5}{192\pi^3}\right)(f_c V_{cb}^2 + f_u V_{ub}^2) \tag{1}$$

Thus, given the semileptonic branching fraction, $\langle \tau_b \rangle$ constrains V_{cb} and V_{ub}.

2. Data sample

The L3 detector[1] has a tracking wire-chamber (TEC), a BGO crystal electromagnetic calorimeter, a Uranium-PWC Hadron calorimeter and a precise muon spectrometer. All are contained within a uniform magnetic field of 0.5T.

An enriched b-sample was obtained from the 1991 sample of $\approx$ 300 000 hadronic events by tagging leptons ($e^\pm$ and $\mu^\pm$) from the semileptonic decays of b-hadrons. The inclusive muon selection required a well measured track in the muon spectrometer, originating from the primary vertex and matched with a TEC track. Electron candidates consisted of a TEC track matched in energy and position with a narrow (electromagnetic) energy cluster in the BGO. Leptons from b-decays have high momentum, due to the hard fragmentation, and high momentum transverse to the neighbouring jet, due to the high b-quark mass. To enrich the b-sample, muons and electrons were required to have momentum greater than 4GeV/c and 3GeV/c respectively, and transverse momentum greater than 1GeV/c.

The JETSET 7.3 Monte Carlo[2] was used to generate hadronic Z decays, which were then passed through a full simulation of the L3 detector based on the GEANT[3] and GHEISHA[4] programs. Table 1 summarises the inclusive lepton samples, where the composition was estimated from Monte Carlo. Both the prompt and cascade components are sensitive to $\langle \tau_b \rangle$. The category "other sources" includes hadronic punchthrough and π/K decays (for the muon sample) and misidentified hadrons and photon conversions (for the electron sample).

Table 1: Summary of the inclusive lepton samples.

Purity	Muons	Electrons
Prompt $b \rightarrow \ell$	72.5%	82.3%
Cascade $b \rightarrow c, \tau, J/\psi, \bar{c} \rightarrow \ell$	10.8%	7.7%
$c \rightarrow \ell$	6.7%	2.5%
Other sources	10.0%	7.5%
Efficiency $b \rightarrow \ell$	21.0%	15.8%
No. of lepton candidates	3705	2336

3. Average b-lifetime measurement

The impact parameter, δ, is the perpendicular distance of the lepton track from the beam centroid, signed negative (positive) if the lepton intersects the jet before (after) the vertex. To obtain $\langle \tau_b \rangle$ the δ-distribution of the lepton tracks was fitted with the weighted sum of the δ-distributions for the four components of the b-sample. The background was estimated from the data by selecting tracks which passed all the selection criteria but which failed the lepton identification cuts. For the prompt, cascade and charm distributions we used the Monte Carlo distributions (with jet axis errors only) convoluted with a resolution function, obtained from the background sample by requiring that the plane of the lepton and jet be largely in the z direction and that δ be negative. These requirements minimise lifetime biases due to hadrons from c-, b-, K_S^0 and Λ decays.

The results of the binned log-likelihood fits to the lepton δ-distributions, with $\langle \tau_b \rangle$ as the only free parameter, are shown in figure 1. The contributions to the systematic errors are shown in table 2. The results obtained from the muon and

Table 2: Systematic errors in the $\langle \tau_b \rangle$ measurement (ps).

Source of error	Muons	Electrons
b fragmentation	0.010	0.010
Hadronic background shape	0.007	0.005
Charm lifetime	0.010	0.010
Sample composition	0.013	0.017
Monte-Carlo δ distributions	0.032	0.032
Tracking and beam spot errors	0.050	0.040
Total	0.063	0.056

electron samples are $\langle \tau_b \rangle = (1.362 \pm 0.053^{(\text{stat})} \pm 0.063^{(\text{syst})})ps$ and $\langle \tau_b \rangle = (1.355 \pm 0.054^{(\text{stat})} \pm 0.056^{(\text{syst})})ps$ respectively. These values have been combined allowing for correlations in the systematic errors. The preliminary L3 result for the average b-hadron lifetime

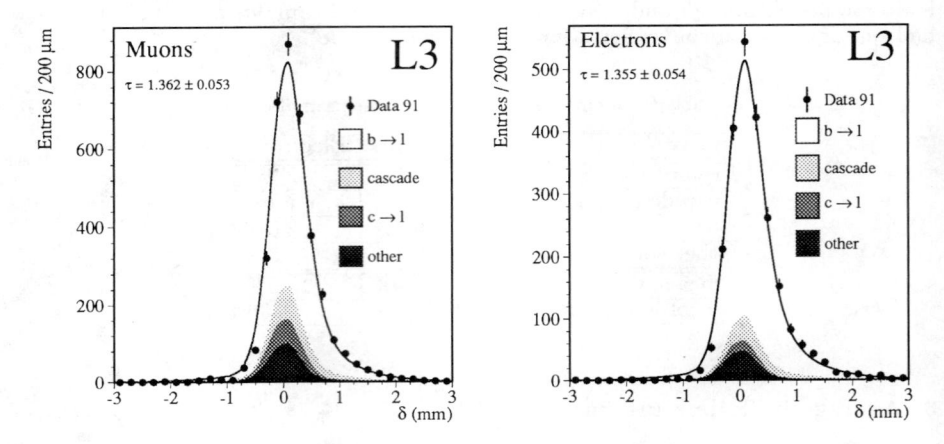

Figure 1: Fits to muon and electron impact parameter distributions.

from the 1991 data sample is $\langle \tau_b \rangle = (1.36 \pm 0.04^{(\text{stat})} \pm 0.05^{(\text{syst})})ps$, in good agreement with the L3 value for 1990 data[5] of $\langle \tau_b \rangle = (1.32 \pm 0.08^{(\text{stat})} \pm 0.09^{(\text{syst})})ps$.

4. Acknowledgements

I would like to thank my L3 colleagues, in particular David McNally, for all their help and advice. This work was supported in part by the National Science Foundation.

5. References

1. B. Adeva *et al.*, *Nucl. Instrum. Methods* **A289** (1990) 35.
2. T. Sjöstrand and M. Bengtsson, *Comp. Phys. Comm.* **43** (1987) 367.
   T. Sjöstrand in "Z Physics at LEP", *CERN report* **89-08**, (1989) 143.
3. R. Brun *et al.*, "GEANT 3", *CERN report* **DD/EE/84-1** (1984).
4. H. Fesefeldt, *RWTH Aachen report* **PITHA 85/02** (1985).
5. B. Adeva *et al.*, *Phys. Lett.* **B270** (1991) 111.

A PRECISE MEASUREMENT OF THE AVERAGE B HADRON LIFETIME WITH THE OPAL DETECTOR AT LEP

J. E. DUBOSCQ
CERN, PPE DIVISION
CH1211 GENEVE 23, SWITZERLAND
representing
The OPAL Collaboration at LEP

ABSTRACT

The 1990 OPAL measurement of the average lifetime of the B hadrons produced in $e^+ e^-$ annihilation near $E_{cm} = M_Z$ is reviewed. The lifetime is determined from a fit to the distribution of the impact parameters of high momentum leptons to be $<\tau_b> = 1.37 \pm 0.07 \pm 0.06$. Prospects for the coming years are discussed.

1. The Importance of the Average B Lifetime

An important goal of B physics is the measurement of the CKM quark mixing matrix elements V_{cb} and V_{ub}. Spectator diagrams are believed to dominate in B decays (herein B hadron refers to the B^0, B^+, B_S, and Λ_b) and the lifetimes of the different species are thought to be equal to within 10%. The B inclusive semileptonic branching ratio relates the lifetime to the CKM matrix elements. We present a measurement of the average B lifetime made at the OPAL experiment on the LEP storage ring, using 6.6 pb^{-1} of data recorded during 1990 at or near the Z^0 resonance. This lifetime was first measured at PEP and PETRA[2] and we will use the impact parameter method first used by the MARK II collaboration.

2. Method and Data Selection

2.1 The Impact Parameter

The impact parameter of the lepton in semileptonic B decays relative to the B creation point is an estimator of the lifetime: the average impact parameter is a monotonically increasing function of lifetime. The B lifetime is measured by using the impact parameter distribution of the muons and electrons in semileptonic B decays along with detector resolution functions. The impact parameter used is that of the tracks projected onto a plane transverse to the beam direction, relative to the average beam spot.

2.2. Event Selection

We chose to work with 2 jet events, well contained within the barrel, starting from the 150,000 hadronic Z^0 events collected in 1990. More details about the cut selection may be found in Ref.[3], while the detector is described in Ref.[4]

As B 's are created at an average energy of 33 GeV, requiring a minimum momentum cut on the daughter electron of 4.5 GeV preferentially selects semileptonic

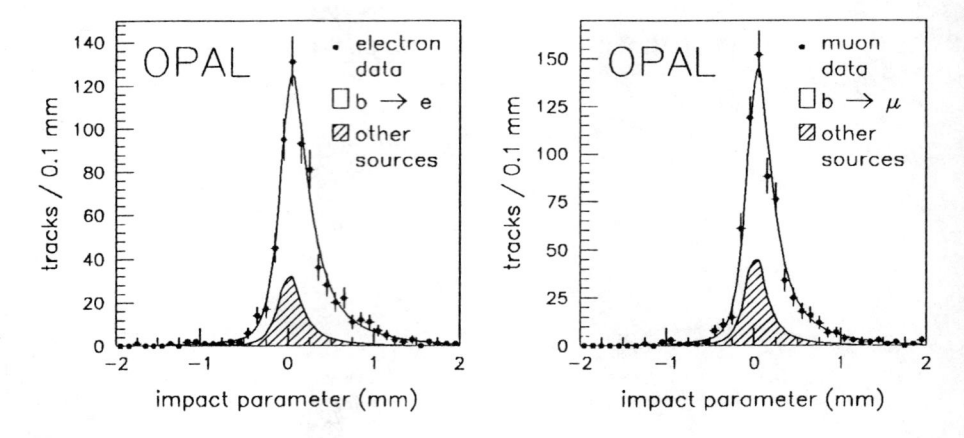

Figure 1: Distribution of the impact parameters for electron and muon candidates. The curves are the result of a maximum likelihood fit for τ_b. The shaded area shows the contribution from all sources other than leptons produced in the semileptonic decays of B hadrons.

decays from primary events. The energy available to the electron in a semileptonic B decay can be quite large and we simply require that the lepton have a minimum transverse momentum (P_t) of 1.5 GeV relative to the jet associated with the B. The chosen jet, reconstructed with the JADE algorithm,[5] is the one whose momentum dotted with the lepton's is positive. If the lepton passes on the same side of the production point as the jet, the impact parameter is positive. Otherwise it is negative. In events with the lepton associated to the correct jet, and given perfect resolution, the impact parameter would always be positive. The negative impact parameter sample serves as a resolution and background estimator. The resulting impact parameter distribution for the 689 muon candidate and 665 electron candidates is shown in Fig 1.

Events can come from five source: direct leptons from B decays (72.6% of μ's, 78.5% of e's), leptons from charm or τ decays from B 's (9.3%, 8.8%), leptons from direct charm decays (6.0%, 5.5%), misidentification of hadrons as leptons (8.3%, 6.9%) and muons from decays in flight of pions or kaons (3.8%) or Dalitz decays and photon conversions for electrons (0.3%). The population distribution given is determined in each case from Monte Carlo, except for the electron hadronic background which is found directly from the data. Fits show good agreement between the total distribution and the data.[3]

3. The Lifetime Fit

In order to extract the lifetime of the B, we maximize a product likelihood over all events encompassing the sum of impact parameter distributions weighted by the population fractions given above. We are left with a likelihood function whose only free parameter is the B lifetime. The fit, as shown in Fig 1, yields a lifetime of $1.37 \pm 0.07 \pm 0.06$ ps for the combined electron and muon subsamples.

4. Systematic Errors

The dominant systematic error in the electron sample is due to the electron identification efficiency and contributes 0.04 ps to the uncertainty. In the muon case it is the finite statistics used in estimating the underlying physics distribution (0.04 ps). The dominant common systematic error is the uncertainty in the resolution of the impact parameter (0.04 ps) followed by the uncertainty of all the involved branching ratios (0.02 ps). These errors and others are discussed in Ref.[3]

5. Future Prospects

We are currently analyzing the data collected during 1991, which includes a total of of 350 K hadronic decays of the Z^0. We expect all statistics limited numbers to be better measured by a factor of almost two. With this improvement, our measurement will be limited almost solely by the systematic errors enumerated above. All sources of these errors are being reviewed. In particular, we will be increasing the range of the Peterson fragmentation parameter involved in b hadronization. We are also examining more closely the decay models we use for B and D decays. These two sources of systematics will cause an increase in their associated error, and perhaps a change in momentum cuts. Our errors due to Monte Carlo statistics will decrease, while the inclusion of neutral particles in the jet finding algorithm will help in the correct signing of the impact parameter. The 1992 sample will include some 650 K Z^0's, for a total of well over 1,000,000 Z^0 hadronic decays over the years 1990 to 1992, making the measurement limited only by systematic errors. However, 1993 will bring the introduction of a double sided microvertex detector, including 3 dimensional event reconstruction, and hopefully many more Z^0 hadronic decays. These two improvements bring great promise to the improved measurement of the average and individual B lifetimes.

6. Conclusion

We have presented the average B lifetime of $1.37 \pm 0.07 \pm 0.06$ ps derived from 6.6 pb^{-1} collected at the OPAL detector at LEP in 1990. We have given our understanding of the systematic errors associated with this measurement, as well as our hopes for increased statistics and better understood systematic errors in the coming years. The installation of the new microvertex detector in 1993 will without a doubt decrease backgrounds substantially.

7. Acknowlegements

I would like to thank R. Kowalewski and D. Denis for their help in preparing this talk.

8. References

1. J. H. Kühn, P. M. Zerwas, *Z Physics at LEP 1*, CERN89-08, volume 1, 21 September 1989, p. 267.
2. MARK-II Collab., A. Lockyer et al., *Phys. Rev. Lett.* **51** (1983) 1316;
   MARK-II Collab., R. A. Ong et al., *Phys. Rev. Lett.* **62** (1989) 1236;
   MAC Collab., W. Ash et al., *Phys. Rev. Lett.* **58** (1987) 640;
   HRS Collab., J. M. Brom et al., *Phys. Lett.* **B195** (1987) 301.
3. OPAL Collab, P.D. Acton et al.,*Phys. Lett.***B274** (1992) 513.
4. OPAL Collab., K. Ahmet et al., *Nucl. Inst. and Methods* **A305** (1991) 275-319.
5. JADE Collab., W. Bartel et al., *Z. Phys.* **C33** (1986) 23;
   JADE Collab., S. Bethke et al., *Phys. Lett.* **B213** (1988) 235;
   OPAL Collab., M. Z. Akrawy et al., *Phys. Lett.* **B235** (1989) 389.

INCLUSIVE MEASUREMENT OF THE AVERAGE B-HADRON LIFETIME WITH THE DELPHI DETECTOR

LUCIA DI CIACCIO

University of ROMA II and INFN (Tor Vergata)
Via della Ricerca Scientifica, I-00173 ROMA
On behalf of the DELPHI Collaboration

ABSTRACT

The average lifetime of B-hadrons τ_B was measured with the DELPHI detector at LEP using the impact parameter distributions of samples of high p_t muons and of high p_t charged tracks. This analysis based on the data collected in 1991 ($\approx$ 9.5 pb^{-1}) has profited from the higher statistics and from the improved performance of the upgraded silicon microvertex. The preliminary results are : $\tau_B = (1.36 \pm 0.05(stat) \pm 0.05(syst))$ ps (muon sample) and $\tau_B = (1.41 \pm 0.04(stat) \pm 0.06(syst))$ ps (inclusive sample) giving a combined value of $\tau_B = (1.39 \pm 0.06)$ ps. The 1990 and 1991 combined result is $\tau_B = (1.38 \pm 0.05)$ ps.

1. Introduction

In the Standard Model, hadrons containing b quarks decay by flavour changing weak transitions. The "spectator model", which is believed to give an adequate description of these decays, predicts that the B-hadron lifetimes are all equal and correspond to the b quark lifetime. Measuring τ_B constraints the quark mixing matrix elements $|V_{ub}|$ and $|V_{cb}|$ [1].

Measurements of τ_B are competitive at LEP compared to previous measurements due to the fact that B-hadron production is abundant at the Z pole ($\approx$ 6 nb at LEP, $\approx$ 0.01 nb at PETRA) and the charm background is reduced by about a factor 4. Moreover, since at LEP particles are produced with higher momentum, the impact parameter of B-hadron decay products is less dependent on momentum, the tracks are less affected by multiple scattering, and very high purity samples can be obtained. Further advantages are that the LEP beam overlap region is small ($\sigma_x \approx 150~\mu m$, $\sigma_y \leq 10~\mu m$), and very good tracking resolution has been achieved with the use of microvertex detectors.

The Delphi [2] microvertex detector [3] is made of 3 layers of capacitatively coupled silicon microstrip detectors. The strips are parallel to the z direction and allow the reconstruction of the $R\phi$ coordinate with measured intrinsic resolution $\sigma_{intr} \sim 6~\mu m$. The alignment resolution is $\sigma_{align} \sim 5~\mu m$. The tracking resolution as measured from the muon miss distance in $Z \to \mu^+\mu^-$ events is $\sigma_{asym} \sim 30~\mu m$.

2. Impact parameter calculation

The average τ_B is extracted from the signed impact parameter (δ) distribution of charged tracks. δ is defined as the distance of closest approach between the track projected on the $R\phi$ plane and the Z production point. The jet axis is used to estimate the B-hadron direction. The impact parameter of a track is positive if the jet intersects the track after having passed through the primary vertex, and negative in the opposite case. Primary tracks have δ equal to 0 while secondary tracks have always a positive δ ($\langle\delta\rangle \propto c * \langle\tau_{parent}\rangle$ at high momenta). The following experimental uncertainties broaden the original δ distribution and populate the negative part: the Z production point uncertainty, the tracking resolution, how well the jet direction represents the B-hadron direction and the jet resolution.

The average beam overlap region (measured with $\sim$ 15 μm resolution in x and $\sim$ 8 μm in y) or the reconstructed event vertex obtained with a constrained fit has been taken as the Z production point.

The contribution to the impact parameter resolution coming from tracking errors has been measured on data to be $\sqrt{(69/p_{R\phi})^2 + 24^2}$ μm ($p_{R\phi}(GeV)$ is the track momentum projected on the $R\phi$ plane) and agrees well with Monte Carlo expectations [3].

The difference $\Delta\phi$ between the ϕ of the jet and that of b quark has been studied with Monte Carlo events. Jets reconstructed with the JADE algorithm have been found to give a good description of the quark directions. The $\Delta\phi$ distribution has an average value of about 0 and a r.m.s. $\sim$ 65 mrad. The jet resolution measured from the $R\phi$ projected acoplanarity in 2 jet events has been found to have a r.m.s. of 69 mrad and agrees well with Monte Carlo expectations.

3. B-hadron lifetime measurements

Two analysis have been performed [4] : the first uses only identified muon candidates, the second considers all charged tracks.

The first sample is enriched in semileptonic B-hadron decays by requiring a high momentum (p) and a high transverse momentum (p_t) with respect to the jet axis. The enrichment criteria exploits the facts that b quarks fragment hard and that they are heavy.

The second analysis includes all B-hadron decays, so it allows higher statistics. But since it has little b enrichment better tracking resolution is needed in order to observe a clear signal from B hadron decays in the shape of the δ distribution. The Delphi resolution using microvertex and primary vertex fitting makes this measurement possible.

After hadronic event selection the tracks are required to have p above 3 GeV and p_t above 1 GeV in the μ sample and above 0.8 GeV in the inclusive sample (the p_t cut is optimized in the first analysis to select b events in the second to minimize the mis-signing errors). In addition track quality cuts have been applied and for the muon analysis muon identification is required.

About 3800 tracks are left in the muon analysis of which about 61 % are from b events. The result is extracted by fitting the measured δ distribution with an unbinned maximum likehood fit as the sum of 5 components : μ from B-hadron decays, μ from cascade B-hadron decays, μ from C-hadron decays, μ from π and

K decays and μ from misidentified hadrons. The fractions of these 5 components have been estimated by fitting the p and pt experimental spectra to the Monte Carlo spectra. The expected δ distributions of μ from the first 3 components have been obtained from the convolution of the Monte Carlo physics functions (without detector effects) with a resolution function measured on data. The expected δ distribution of μ from π and K decays is taken from Monte Carlo simulation and that of misidentified hadrons from data. The preliminary result is $\tau_B = (1.36 \pm 0.05(stat) \pm 0.05(syst))$ ps. The breakdown of the systematic errors is shown in Table 1.

There are about 35000 tracks left in the inclusive sample of which 27 % are from b events. The result is obtained by fitting the measured δ distribution as the sum of 3 components: tracks from b events, from c events and from u, d, s events. The expected δ distributions of these components are obtained from the convolution of the physics functions with a resolution function measured on data and multiplied by correction factors taken from Monte Carlo simulation, which account for the different δ resolution of the different quarks (due to different primary vertex reconstruction resolutions). The preliminary result is $\tau_B = (1.41 \pm 0.04 \pm 0.06)$ ps. The breakdown of the systematic errors is shown in Table 2.

Table 1: Systematic errors on τ_B for the μ sample.

Source	$\Delta \tau_B (ps)$
Physics functions	0.03
Muon sample composition	0.02
Resolution function	0.02
Decay Backgr.	0.02
Average τ_c	0.02
Hadronic Backgr.	0.01
Fragm. effect on δ	0.01
Total	0.05

Table 2: Systematic errors on τ_B for the inclusive sample.

Source of error	$\Delta \tau_B (ps)$
Resolution function	0.02
Wrong-sign	0.02
Clusterization	0.02
b-fragmentation	0.02
B-baryons	0.01
τ_C	0.03
Hadron p_t	0.02
Total error	0.06

4. Conclusions

The two analysis described here give compatible results within experimental errors. The combined (preliminary) result is : $\tau_B = (1.39 \pm 0.06)$ ps. The 1990 and 1991 combined result is $\tau_B = (1.38 \pm 0.05)$ ps.

More data and improved δ resolution will decrease the statistical error. The systematic error depends weakly on the statistics and the resolution. On the other hand for small $|Vub|$ the relative uncertainty on $|V_{cb}|$ can be expressed by

$$\Delta |V_{cb}|^2 / |Vcb|^2 \sim \Delta \tau_B / \tau_B + \Delta Br_{sl} / Br_{sl} + \Delta (f_c m_b^5)/(f_c m_b^5)$$

The first term is ~ 3 % (LEP average from the 1992 Dallas Conference), the second term (the relative uncertainty on the b semileptonic branching fraction) is ~ 5 % (LEP average from the 1992 Dallas Conference), while the third term (the relative uncertainty on the product of the QCD and phase space correction factors) is estimated to be ≈ 12 % and is at the present the dominant term.

6. References

1. A. Ali, *B-Decays - Introduction*, **DESY 91–137**, p. 23., published in 'B Decays' World Scientific Publishers, Singapore (editor S.Stone)
2. DELPHI Collab., P. Aarnio et al., *Nucl. Instrument. Methods* **A 303** (1991) 233 .
3. N. Bingefors et al., *The DELPHI Microvertex Detector*, **CERN-PPE/92-173**
4. DELPHI Collab., *Refined Measurement of The Average Lifetime of B Hadrons using high p_t muons*, and
Inclusive Measurement of the average lifetime of B-hadrons produced at the Z peak
(Contributions to the 1992 HEP Dallas Conference)

MEASUREMENT OF THE b SEMILEPTONIC BRANCHING RATIO AND $\Gamma_{b\bar{b}}$ WITH L3

IAN C. BROCK
Physics Dept., Carnegie Mellon University
Pittsburgh, PA 15213, USA

ABSTRACT

The semileptonic branching ratio for b-hadrons has been measured using the L3 detector. Assuming the Standard Model value for $\Gamma_{b\bar{b}}$, we find $\text{Br}(b\to\ell) = 0.119 \pm 0.001$ (stat) $\pm$ 0.006 (sys). Using the ratio of the number of dilepton to the number of single lepton events we obtain $\text{Br}(b\to\ell) = 0.118 \pm 0.005$ (stat) $\pm$ 0.006 (sys), almost independent of $\Gamma_{b\bar{b}}$.

The rate of b-quark production from decays of the Z is accurately predicted in the Standard Model. It is of especial interest because the decay width depends only weakly on the top quark mass. In this analysis b-quark events are tagged by using the fact that the b-quark is heavy and that its semileptonic branching ratio is fairly large ($\approx 10\%$). The leptons can be produced with a high transverse momentum (p_T) with respect to the b-quark direction, and they have high momentum. Backgrounds from cascade decays (b $\to$ c $\to$ ℓ) and other sources tend to have lower lepton momentum and transverse momentum.

The L3 detector has been described in detail elsewhere[1]. A short description of the selection criteria for electrons and muons in $b\bar{b}$ events is given. Muons are identified as tracks in the muon chambers with a segment in at least 2 out of the 3 chamber layers. The track must be consistent with coming from the vertex, and have a momentum greater than 4 GeV. If a p_T cut of 1 GeV is applied the efficiency for finding a prompt b $\to$ μ decay is 42.5% with a purity of 70.5%. Electrons are selected by requiring a cluster with more than 3 GeV in the BGO electromagnetic calorimeter, which matches with a track in the central tracking chamber, and which is consistent with being from an electromagnetic shower. With a p_T cut of 1 GeV the efficiency for finding a prompt b $\to$ e decay is 23.3% with a purity of 79.8%.

The data sample used in this analysis was taken during 1990 and 1991 and contains 410000 hadronic events corresponding to an integrated luminosity of 17.6 pb^{-1}. We observe 20937 inclusive muon events and 5443 inclusive electron events and a total of 1944 inclusive dilepton events.

In the absence of background, the number of single lepton events that we observe is given by:

$$\frac{N_\ell}{N_{\text{had}}} \propto \frac{\Gamma_{b\bar{b}}}{\Gamma_{\text{had}}} 2\text{Br}(b\to\ell)(1 - \text{Br}(b\to\ell)) \qquad (1)$$

The number of dilepton events is given by:

$$\frac{N_{\ell\ell}}{N_{\text{had}}} \propto \frac{\Gamma_{b\bar{b}}}{\Gamma_{\text{had}}} \text{Br}(b\to\ell)^2 \qquad (2)$$

We use two methods to extract the semileptonic branching ratio:

- **Standard Model Fit:** We can invert Eq. (1) to get an expression for Br(b→ℓ) in terms of the number of single lepton events and $\Gamma_{b\bar{b}}$.

- **Ratio Fit:** If we divide Eq. (2) by Eq. (1) we can eliminate $\Gamma_{b\bar{b}}$ and get an expression for Br(b→ℓ) in terms of the ratio of the number of dileptons to the number of single leptons.

These formulae are complicated by the presence of background. The background due to cascade decays includes $\Gamma_{b\bar{b}}$, whereas direct charm production does not. However, the ratio method still only depends very weakly on $\Gamma_{b\bar{b}}$.

The composition of the event sample and the efficiency for finding leptons from each channel are determined using Monte Carlo[2]. In order to do this accurately, it is important that the lepton momentum and transverse momentum spectra from the Monte Carlo and the data agree. We can check whether the Monte Carlo provides a good description of semileptonic decays by comparing the momentum spectrum for B mesons generated at the $\Upsilon(4S)$ with those published by ARGUS and CLEO[3] (Fig. 1a). At high lepton momenta the JETSET spectrum clearly disagrees with the data. This version of the Monte Carlo contains only B meson decays to D and D* mesons. If we also include 32% D** mesons, as suggested by results from CLEO and ARGUS, then we obtain the Monte Carlo spectrum shown in Fig. 1b which is in much better agreement with the data.

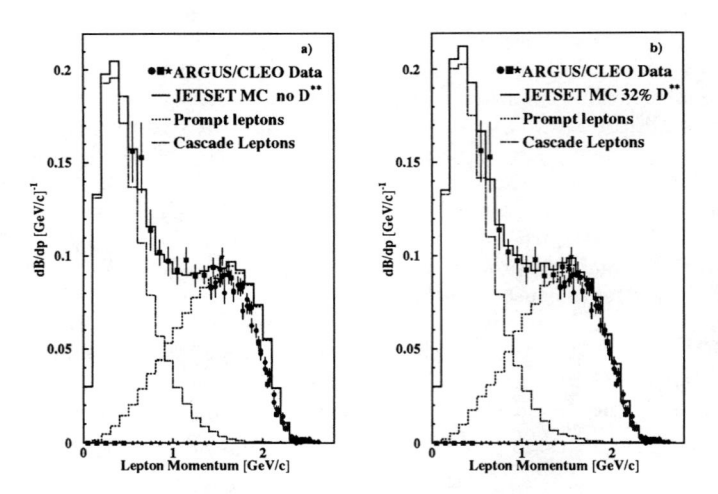

Figure 1: Lepton momentum spectra at the $\Upsilon(4S)$ measured by CLEO and ARGUS compared to JETSET with (a) no D** and (b) 32% of D**.

In order to use the maximum amount of information from the data we fit the p and p_T spectra of the single and dilepton samples to extract Br(b→ℓ). Assuming the standard model value of $\Gamma_{b\bar{b}}$ (378 ± 3 MeV) we find:

$$\text{Br}(b\to\ell) = 0.119 \pm 0.001(\text{stat}) \pm 0.006(\text{sys})$$

Using the ratio fit method we find:

$$\text{Br}(b\to\ell) = 0.118 \pm 0.005(\text{stat}) \pm 0.006(\text{sys})$$

The breakdown on the systematic errors is shown in Table 1. They are dominated by the uncertainties on detector efficiencies and the amount of D** mesons.

Table 1: Breakdown of Systematic Errors.

Contribution	Variation	SM fit	Ratio fit
Simulation and reconstruction		0.0040	0.0040
$\Gamma_{b\bar{b}}$	± 10 MeV	–	0.0006
Br(c → ℓ)	± 0.012	0.0023	0.0005
$\Gamma_{c\bar{c}}$	± 10 MeV	0.0002	0.0001
Background	± 15%	0.0024	0.0019
b fragmentation	$\langle x_E \rangle \pm 0.01$	0.0007	0.0011
c fragmentation	$\langle x_E \rangle \pm 0.04$	0.0005	0.0000
Fitting bias		0.0010	–
D**	.15 – .32	0.0044	0.0045
Total		0.006	0.006

We use the ratio fit value for Br(b→ℓ) combined with those from PETRA and PEP[4] to determine $\Gamma_{b\bar{b}}$. For this measurement we use only the 1990 data and obtain:

$$\Gamma_{b\bar{b}} = 380 \pm 7(\text{stat}) \pm 11(\text{sys}) \pm 17(\text{BR})$$

References

1. B. Adeva *et al.*, *Nucl. Instrum. Methods* **A289** (1990) 35.
2. T. Sjöstrand and M. Bengtsson, *Comp. Phys. Comm.* **43** (1987) 367;
   T. Sjöstrand in "Z Physics at LEP" Vol. III, *CERN report* **89-08**, (1989) 143.
3. S. Henderson *et al.*, *Phys. Rev.* **D45** (1992) 2212
   D. Britton, *SLAC Summer Institute* (1992); Yu. Zaitsev, *Dallas Conference on High Energy Physics* (1992).
4. A compilation can be found in: JADE Collab., W. Bartel *et al.*, *Z. Phys.* **C33** (1987) 339 and references therein.

MEASUREMENT OF THE SEMILEPTONIC BRANCHING RATIOS
Br($b \to l\nu$X) AND Br($c \to l\nu$X) AND B-$\bar{\text{B}}$ MIXING

Leo Bellantoni[*]
University of Wisconsin–Madison
ALEPH Collaboration

ABSTRACT

In a sample of 450,000 hadronic decays of the Z^0 recorded with the ALEPH detector at LEP, the yield of single and dilepton events has been used to measure the B-$\bar{\text{B}}$ mixing rate and the semileptonic branching ratios of b and c hadrons. From a fit to the momentum and transverse momentum spectra, the semileptonic branching ratios have been measured to be Br($b \to l\nu$X) = $(11.0 \pm 0.4 \pm 0.4)\%$, and Br($c \to l\nu$X) = $(8.8 \pm 0.3 \pm 0.9)\%$. The B-$\bar{\text{B}}$ mixing parameter χ has been determined from the ratio of same to oppositely charged prompt dileptons to be $\chi = 0.137 \pm 0.015 \pm 0.007$.

1. Introduction

The LEP collider produces Z^0 bosons at rest which can decay to $b\bar{b}$ and $c\bar{c}$ pairs which form fast ($\beta \sim 10$) beauty and charm hadrons. These hadrons have the decay modes $e\nu$X and $\mu\nu$X which are easily measured[1,2] because the leptons produced have a high momentum and a high momentum perpendicular ($P_\perp$) to the jets produced from the other decay products of the b and c quarks. The $P_\perp$ spectrum for ($b \to l$) is harder than for ($c \to l$) and ($b \to c \to l$) because of the high mass of the b quark. The momentum spectra[3,4] are also different for these three processes; the ($b \to l$) spectrum is the hardest because of the high momentum of the primary b hadron, and the ($b \to c \to l$) spectrum is the softest, due to the multibody cascade nature of this channel.

A fraction of the produced hadrons are B^0 and B_s which change into their own antiparticles through box diagrams. This mixing process can be studied for B^0 at the $\Upsilon(4s)$ resonance, but at LEP there are large numbers of B_s mesons produced. The mixing rate for B_s can thus be inferred from LEP data in conjunction with lower energy measurements.

2. Lepton identification

ALEPH is a large, general purpose detector which has been described in detail elsewhere[5]. Electrons are identified by matching a charged track to an energy deposit with properties consistent with being from an electron in the electromagnetic

---
[*] Supported by the US Department of Energy, contract DE-AC02-76ER00881.

shower calorimeter. Muons are identified by matching a charged track to a pattern of hits in the hadron calorimeter and muon chambers that is consistent with being from a muon[6,7].

The efficiency of electron detection is measured with charged track pairs that originate from γ conversions. The efficiency is typically 47% for the high P, $P_\perp$ electrons of $(b \to l)$, and 42% for electrons due to $(b \to c \to l)$ and $(c \to l)$. The efficiency of muon detection is measured using the process $Z^0 \to \mu^+\mu^-$. The efficiency is typically 62% for $(b \to l)$, and 59% for $(b \to c \to l)$ and $(c \to l)$.

The rate at which hadrons are misidentified as electrons may be found from a study of the ionization in the tracking system of those particles which are identified as electrons by the calorimeter. The fraction of hadrons identified as electrons ranges from about 0.0005 to 0.0013. The rate at which hadrons are misidentified as muons is found from kinematically selected samples of pions from the decays $K_S \to \pi^+\pi^-$, $\tau \to \pi^+\rho^0$, and $\tau \to 3\pi$. The probability that a hadron is misidentified as a muon is typically 0.006.

3. Fit procedure

The semileptonic decay rates could be found from fitting the P and $P_\perp$ spectra of the leptons (after background subtraction) to three terms. The first one would be for the semileptonic decay of the b, the second for the semileptonic decay of the c, and the third for $(b \to c \to l)$. However such a procedure would require assuming the rates of b and c quark production.

Such a procedure would also not measure B-B̄ mixing. To do this, consider events with two leptons in them. The lepton produced in semileptonic decay is negative if the hadron contained a b quark and positive if it contained a $\bar{b}$. If both leptons came from $(b \to l)$ and are of the same electric charge, then either the b or the $\bar{b}$ hadron mixed; if the charges are opposite, then either there was no mixing, or both b hadrons mixed.

To distinguish between mixing and the case where one of the two primary quarks decayed through the cascade channel $(b \to c \to l)$, one may use the different P and $P_\perp$ spectra of the different processes. There is information about $(b \to c \to l)$ in the single lepton spectra. This is our reason for fitting the spectra of the individual leptons and the lepton pairs simultaneously. This method also removes the need to assume rates of b and c production. Lepton pairs where the leptons are on opposite sides of the event (*i.e.* more than 90° apart), are divided into two samples depending on whether the charges are equal or not. This sample is 88% $(b \to l)(b \to l)$ and $(b \to l)(b \to c \to l)$. Lepton pairs on the same side of the event with opposite charges form a third dilepton sample; these events contain information about the decay $b \to l\nu c$ where the c subsequently decays via into $l\nu X$.

For the single lepton sample, the natural variables of the fit are P and $P_\perp$. For the dileptons, the number of spectra to be fit are reduced by using the two variables

$$P_{\perp m} = min(P_\perp^1, P_\perp^2) \quad \text{and} \quad P_\otimes = P_\perp^1 P_\ell^2 + P_\perp^2 P_\ell^1$$

where P_ℓ^i is the component of the momentum of the ith lepton along its jet. If there are many leptons in an event, all possible pairs are used in the analysis. A four lepton event will thus enter in the single lepton sample four times and the dilepton samples six times.

The results given here were obtained using the Altarelli model[3] for $(b \to l)$. The branching ratios for semileptonic decays of charmed mesons are taken from a study of previous measurements, with angular dependences as given by phase space. The heavy flavor fragmentation functions are from the LUND-7.3 parton-shower model[8]. Within the LUND program, the Peterson fragmentation is used at the quark level, for both b and c quarks. The Peterson model parameters ϵ_b and ϵ_c are allowed to float in the fit, as are the partial widths of $Z^0 \to b\bar{b}$ and $c\bar{c}$ as a fraction of the total hadronic width.

4. Fit results

Table 1 lists the fit results from a sample of about 18.6 pb^{-1} of data taken in 1990 and 1991. The covariance matrix of the fit parameters is given in Table 2. Figure 1 shows the result of the fit for the single lepton $P_\perp$ spectrum and the opposite side dilepton $P_\otimes$ spectrum. The mixing is given in terms of χ, the probability that a b hadron which decays semileptonically gives a lepton of the unexpected charge. This result, in conjunction with measurements made at CLEO and ARGUS, is consistent with $\chi_s = 1/2$, which is to say that the rate at which B_s mixes is much greater than the rate at which it decays.

Parameter	Result	Statistical Error	Systematic Error
$\Gamma(b\bar{b})/\Gamma(had)$	0.211	0.007	0.008
$\Gamma(c\bar{c})/\Gamma(had)$	0.170	0.010	0.022
$Br(b \to l\nu X)$	0.110	0.004	0.004
$Br(c \to l\nu X)$	0.088	0.003	0.009
$<x_b>$	0.70	0.01	0.02
$<x_c>$	0.51	0.01	0.02
χ	0.137	0.015	0.007

Table 1: Preliminary results of global fit

The systematic error does have an allowance for the effects of different models, but these are preliminary results. In particular (due to the large, pure sample of single leptons with high $P_\perp$) the most tightly constrained parameter is the product $Br(b \to l\nu X)\,\Gamma(b\bar{b})/\Gamma(had)$. If a $(b \to l)$ decay model which produces a softer spectrum is used, then both $Br(b \to l\nu X)$ and $\Gamma(b\bar{b})/\Gamma(had)$ increase. In comparison, an experi-

ρ	Γ_c	ϵ_b	ϵ_c	$(b \to l)$	$(c \to l)$	χ
Γ_b	-0.26	-0.13	-0.21	-0.94	-0.29	-0.08
Γ_c		-0.14	0.47	0.31	-0.72	0.08
$(b \to l)$			-0.20	0.27	0.21	0.02
$(c \to l)$				0.24	-0.18	0.05
ϵ_b					0.15	0.10
ϵ_c						-0.06

Table 2: Covariance matrix (preliminary)

ment done at the $\Upsilon(4s)$ resonance will apply the same increase to Br($b \to l\nu$X) alone.

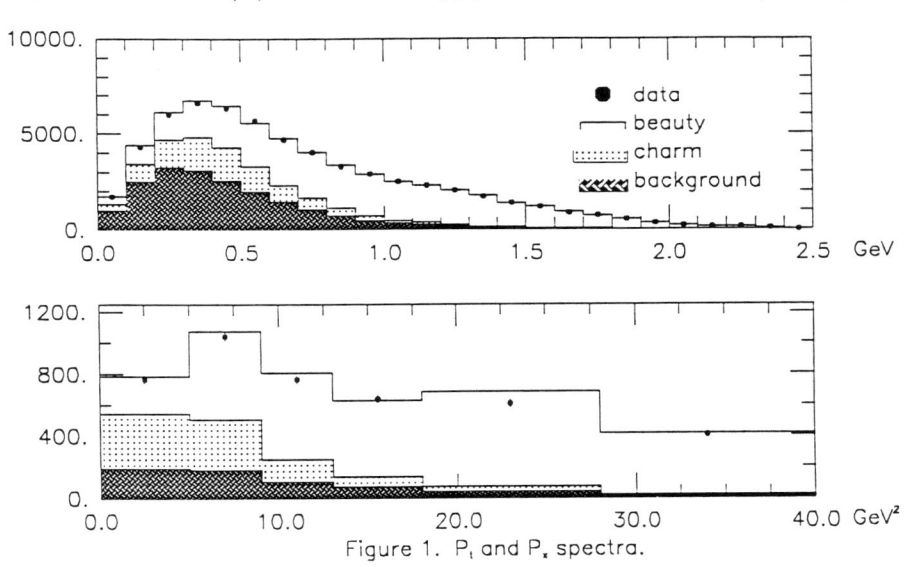

Figure 1. P_t and P_x spectra.

5. References

1. S. Henderson, et al. *Phys. Rev.* **D45** (1992) 2212
2. H. Albrecht, et al. *Phys. Lett.* **DESY-92-146**
3. G. Altarelli, and S. Petrarca, *Phys. Lett.* **B261** (1991) 303
4. N. Isgur, B. Grinstein, D. Scora, and M.Wise, *Phys. Rev.* **D39** (1989) 799
   J. Korner, and G. Schuler *Z. Physik* **C38** (1988) 511
5. ALEPH Collab., D. Decamp, et al. *Nucl. Instr. Meth.* **A294** (1990) 121
6. ALEPH Collab., D. Decamp, et al. *Phys. Lett.* **B244** (1990) 551
7. ALEPH Collab., D. Decamp, et al. *Phys. Lett.* **B263** (1991) 325
8. T. Sjöstrand and M. Bengtsson, *Comp. Phys. Com.* **46** (1987) 43

A STUDY OF THE SEMIMUONIC DECAYS OF THE $D_S^\pm$

DOUGLAS M. POTTER
Physics Department, Carnegie Mellon University
Pittsburgh, PA 15213, U.S.A
(for the E653 collaboration)

ABSTRACT

Preliminary results are presented for the modes $D_S^+ \to \phi\mu^+\nu$ and $D_S^+ \to (\eta\mu^+\nu + \eta'\mu^+\nu)$ observed in π^--emulsion interactions at 600 GeV/c.

Interest in the semileptonic decay modes of the D_S^+ has recently focussed on their role in setting the absolute scale of D_S^+ branching ratios [1]. The technique is to use a quark model prediction for decay rate ratio $\Gamma(D_S^+ \to \phi\mu^+\nu)/\Gamma(D \to \overline{K}^*\mu^+\nu)$, and the measured value of $\Gamma(D \to \overline{K}^*\mu^+\nu)$ to determine the cross section ratio $\sigma(D_S^+)/\sigma(D)$, when both semileptonic modes are observed in the same experiment. It is assumed that the decay rate ratio is correctly predicted by the quark models, despite the fact that predictions for both $\Gamma(D \to \overline{K}^*\mu^+\nu)$ and $\Gamma(D \to \overline{K}^*\mu^+\nu)/\Gamma(D \to \overline{K}\mu^+\nu)$ differ from the measured values[1]. In its more general form, the assumption implies that the quark model correctly relates $\Gamma(D \to \overline{K}^*\mu^+\nu)$ not only to the decay rate for $D_S^+ \to \phi\mu^+\nu$, but also to those for $D \to \rho\mu^+\nu, \omega\mu^+\nu$, and $D_S^+ \to \overline{K}^{*0}\mu^+\nu$, and similarly, relates $\Gamma(D \to \overline{K}\mu^+\nu)$ to the decay rates for $D \to \pi\mu^+\nu, \eta\mu^+\nu, \eta'\mu^+\nu$, and $D_S^+ \to \eta\mu^+\nu, \eta'\mu^+\nu, \overline{K}^0\mu^+\nu$. At a more detailed level, form factor ratios measured for $D^+ \to \overline{K}^{*0}\mu^+\nu$ can be used to predict those for $D_S^+ \to \phi\mu^+\nu$. Thus, there are many possible tests of the technique used to establish the D_S^+ branching ratio scale.

In this paper we both use and test the above assumption with samples of $D_S^+ \to \phi\mu^+\nu$ and $D_S^+ \to (\eta\mu^+\nu + \eta'\mu^+\nu)$ decays. Data were taken at Fermilab by experiment E653, in which a 600 GeV/c π^- interacted in a nuclear emulsion target and the trigger was a penetrating muon.

Evidence for the decay $D_S^+ \to \phi\mu^+\nu, \phi \to K^+K^-$ is provided by Fig. 1, which shows the dikaon mass distribution for 3-prong vertices that include the trigger muon. The two hadron tracks in the vertex were assigned the kaon mass, since particle identification was not available. A clear ϕ signal of 36 events on a background of 16 is observed. These events provide a clean sample of $D_S^+ \to \phi\mu^+\nu$ decays, and a comparison of these to our $D^+ \to \overline{K}^{*0}\mu^+\nu$ signal yields[2] the following result:

$$\left(\frac{\sigma(D_S^+)}{\sigma(D^+)}\right)_{x_F>0} \cdot \left(\frac{\Gamma(D_S^+ \to \phi\mu^+\nu)}{\Gamma(D^+ \to \overline{K}^{*0}\mu^+\nu)}\right) = 0.66 \pm 0.16 \pm 0.15$$

The ISGW model[3] predicts the ratio of decay rates to be 1.02; with this and our measurement[2] of $\sigma(D^\pm)$, we obtain $\sigma\left(\pi^- N \to D_S^\pm; x_F > 0\right) = 5.6 \pm 1.4 \pm 1.9\,\mu$b/nucleon.

---
[1] Throughout this paper, charge conjugation is implied unless otherwise stated.

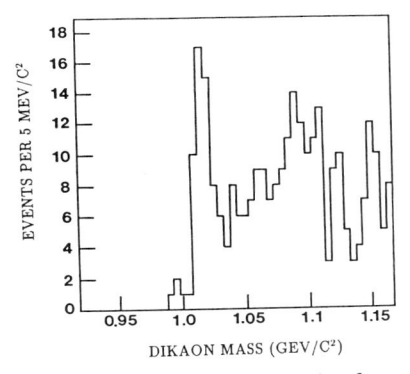

Figure 1. Dikaon mass distribution for a sample of 3-prong vertices which include the trigger muon.

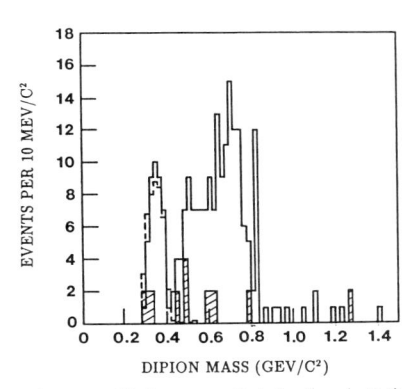

Figure 2. Dipion mass distribution (solid) for a sample of 3-prong vertices which include the trigger muon. Also shown are a simulation (dashed) and the background (hatched), both of which are described in the text.

A fit to the angular and q^2 distributions of the decay yields the form factor ratios, $A_2(0)/A_1(0)$ and $V(0)/A_1(0)$, evaluated at $q^2 = 0$. For $A_2(0)/A_1(0)$, we measure $2.1^{+0.8}_{-0.7}{}^{+0.1}_{-0.2}$, which is larger than that for the $D^+ \to \overline{K}^{*0}\mu^+\nu$ mode[4] $(0.82^{+0.22}_{-0.23} \pm 0.11)$, and also than that predicted by ISGW (1.21). The ISGW prediction, modified according the discussion in the introduction, is that $A_2(0)/A_1(0)$ should be the same for $D_S^+ \to \phi\mu^+\nu$ and $D^+ \to \overline{K}^{*0}\mu^+\nu$. For $V(0)/A_1(0)$, we measure $2.5 \pm 1.1^{+0.3}_{-0.4}$, which is consistent both with the $D^+ \to \overline{K}^{*0}\mu^+\nu$ measurement and with predictions.

Candidates for the $D_S^+ \to (\eta\mu^+\nu + \eta'\mu^+\nu)$ mode consisted of a sample of 3-prong vertices that included the trigger muon. The $D_S^+ \to (\eta\mu^+\nu + \eta'\mu^+\nu)$ signal was extracted by exploiting the fact that the $\pi^+\pi^-\pi^0$ mode of the η, and $\pi^+\pi^-\eta, \eta \to$ *neutrals* modes of the η' produce nearly identical dipion mass distributions which peak near threshold. Figure 2 shows the dipion mass distribution for the data; above 0.4 GeV/c^2 the distribution is dominated by $D^+ \to \overline{K}^{*0}\mu^+\nu$, where the kaon is identified as a pion. Between 0.3 and 0.4 GeV/c^2, there is a contribution attributed to $D_S^+ \to (\eta\mu^+\nu + \eta'\mu^+\nu)$. Figure 2 includes a simulated mass distribution for the 2-prong decays of the η and η', which agrees well with the data. Also shown in Fig. 2 is the background obtained from events in which both hadrons have the same charge.

If the two kaons from the decay of a ϕ are assigned the pion mass, the corresponding dipion mass also peaks between 0.3 and 0.4 GeV/c^2, and ϕ's have been excluded in the final results. However, the dikaon mass distribution for the events in Fig. 2 between 0.3 and 0.4 GeV/c^2 is not dominated by the ϕ. We have found no decay modes which could reasonably account for these events, other than $D_S^+ \to \eta\mu\nu$ and $D_S^+ \to \eta'\mu\nu$.

For the η and η' modes to which this experiment is sensitive, the product of efficiency times branching ratio is the same for $\eta\mu\nu$ and $\eta'\mu\nu$. Since there is no efficient way to distinguish between the two decays, we quote the result:

$$\frac{\Gamma(D_S^+ \to (\eta\mu^+\nu + \eta'\mu^+\nu))}{\Gamma(D_S^+ \to \phi\mu^+\nu)} = 2.4 \pm 1.2$$

The ISGW model, modified as above, predicts 0.88 for this ratio.

Both the form factor ratio, $A_2(0)/A_1(0)$, for $D_S^+ \to \phi\mu^+\nu$ and $\Gamma(D_S^+ \to (\eta\mu^+\nu + \eta'\mu^+\nu))/\Gamma(D_S^+ \to \phi\mu^+\nu)$ are larger than predicted. Although these discrepancies are not large, additional tests of the model are needed before it can be used with confidence to set the absolute scale of the D_S branching ratios.

References

1. D. M. Potter, in *Proceedings of the 1991 Joint International Lepton-Photon Symposium and Europhysics Conference on High Energy Physics*, eds. S. Hegarty, et al. (World Scientific, Singapore, 1992)
2. K. Kodama, et al., *Phys. Lett.* **B284** (1992) 461.
3. D. Scora and N. Isgur, University of Toronto preprint, UTPT-89-29 (1992), D. Scora, *Semileptonic Hadron Decay in the Quark Potential Model*, Ph.D. Thesis, University of Toronto (1992).
4. K. Kodama, et al., *Phys. Lett.* **B274** (1992) 246.

Measurement of $B(D^+ \to \pi^0 l^+ \nu)/B(D^+ \to \overline{K^0} l^+ \nu)$

Alice Bean
Physics Department, UCSB
Santa Barbara, CA. 93106, USA
Representing the CLEO collaboration

ABSTRACT

The branching ratio of the Cabibbo suppressed decay, $D^+ \to \pi^0 l^+ \nu$, relative to the branching ratio of the Cabibbo favored decay, $D^+ \to \overline{K^0} l^+ \nu$, is measured to be $\frac{B(D^+ \to \pi^0 l^+ \nu)}{B(D^+ \to \overline{K^0} l^+ \nu)} = 9.0 \pm 1.8 \pm 1.6\%$, using the CLEO-II detector. The product of the ratio of Kobayashi-Maskawa matrix elements $|V_{cd}/V_{cs}|^2$ and the form factors at $q^2 = 0$ is determined from this ratio to be $0.045 \pm 0.009 \pm 0.008$.

Charm semileptonic decays allow the study of weak transitions without complications from strong interactions for the extraction of CKM matrix elements. By comparing the $D^+ \to \pi^0 l \nu$ rate to the Cabibbo favored partner, $D^+ \to \overline{K^0} l \nu$ rate, the ratio of CKM elements $|V_{cd}/V_{cs}|^2$ can be measured. The current value of V_{cd} is from neutrino experiments and relies on knowledge of model dependent properties of charm production and charm decay.[1] By extracting the ratio of CKM from the ratio of semileptonic branching ratios most of the theoretical and model uncertainties cancel.

The CLEO-II detector is ideally suited to take on the daunting challenge of detecting the Cabibbo suppressed decay, $D^+ \to \pi^0 l^+ \nu$, via the $D^{*+} \to \pi^0 D^+$ tag. The Cabibbo suppressed branching ratio is normalized to $D^+ \to \overline{K^0} l^+ \nu$, which is detected via $\overline{K_s^0} \to \pi^+ \pi^-$, and $D^{*+} \to \pi^0 D^+$ tag. Data for this analysis were recorded with the CLEO-II detector[2] operating in the CESR storage ring at Cornell University. A total 1.7fb^{-1} of e^+e^- collisions were recorded at $\Upsilon(4S)$ and continuum energies below and above the $\Upsilon(4S)$ resonance.

By definition semileptonic decays can not be fully reconstructed. The yield was measured from the pseudo-mass difference distribution, where pseudo-mass difference was defined as $M_{diff} = M_{D^{*+}_{pseudo}} - M_{D^+_{pseudo}} = M(\pi^0_{slw} \pi^0_{fst} l^+) - M(\pi^0_{fst} l^+)$. The mass difference distribution is model independent with a well understood combinatoric background from fake π^0's. However correlated backgrounds from charm daughters that faked leptons or other charm semileptonic decays that passed the cuts peaked in the signal region. These correlated backgrounds were estimated from the well measured lepton fake rates and from generic continuum Monte Carlo.

We placed a number of kinematic cuts on the observed variables. To reduce random $\pi^0_{fst} l^+$ combinations we required that the momentum $P_{\pi^0_{fst} l^+} > 2.5 \ GeV/c$. Since the D^* and the D^+ have almost identical boost, the momentum of the π^0_{slw} can be ignored, this gives; $M(\pi^0_{slw} \pi^0_{fst})^2 \sim 2M^2_{\pi^0} + 2M_{\pi^0} E_{\pi^0_{fst}}$. Thus $M(\pi^0_{slw} \pi^0_{fst})$, was a measure of the π^0_{fst} momentum in the COM of the D+ decay and allowed one to select events with the appropriate π^0_{fst} momentum spectrum. The Monte Carlo $M(\pi^0_{slw}\pi^0_{fst})$ distribution was described well by a Gaussian function, and we required that the data events be within 1.5σ of the Monte Carlo mean. One possible source of background was feeddown from decays of the D^+ or D^0; the π^0_{slw} can tag $D^{*0} \to D^0\pi^0_{slw}$ decays as well. To reduce this feeddown we took all tracks with charge opposite to that of the lepton, and calculated the $M((\pi^0_{fst}l^+)X^-)$ mass, assuming that track X^- was a pion. We required the combination that yielded the mininum mass be greater than $1.9~GeV/c^2$.

The use of the D^{*+} tag allowed an estimate of the D^+ momentum. Continuum production of charm events produces two well defined jets. This thrust or jet axis approximated the D^{*+} direction. Assuming the D^{*+} direction was the thrust axis, the momentum of the D^+ could be estimated from the π^0_{slw} momentum vector and the thrust axis.[3] We required that this momentum estimate, P_{est}, be greater than $2.5~GeV/c$. Knowledge of the D^+ momentum allowed the calculation of the neutrino momentum in the D^+ rest frame, P^*_ν. We required that P^*_ν be less than $1.25~GeV/c$. The final cut imposed required that the mass of the $\pi^0 l^+$ system be greater than $1.3 GeV/c^2$. The efficiency for detecting $D^{*+} \to D^+\pi^0_{slw}, D^+ \to \pi^0_{fst}l^+\nu$ was determined from the Monte Carlo to be $0.412\pm0.019\%$. The selection criteria used for $D^+ \to \overline{K^0_s}l+\nu$ were identical to the criteria used for $D^+ \to \pi^0_{fst}l^+\nu$. The efficiency for detecting $D^{*+} \to D^+\pi^0_{slw}, D^+ \to \overline{K^0_s}l^+\nu$ was determined from the Monte Carlo to be $0.350\pm0.018\%$. The combinatoric background was checked by using random di-photon combinations with the same momentum range as π^0_{slw} and a mass 4σ from the nominal π^0 mass. The extracted yield was very stable to variations in the background parameters and functional form.

Figure 1 shows the background subtracted plot for the M_{diff} projection for the two decay modes. The distributions were fitted to a bifurcated gaussian plus the background function. The centroid and sigmas were fixed to the Monte Carlo values. The dashed line is the background function for random combinations.

The systematic error due to Monte Carlo simulations was determined to 13% by studying well measured D^0 hadronic decays. The lepton fake rate was varied by 3σ of the measured fake rate, and the result change by less than $0.25\sigma_{stats}$. The effect of incorrectly determining the lepton fake rate partially cancels in the ratio. The generic $c\bar{c}$ background amount was increased by a factor of two independently for $\pi^0_{fst}l\nu$ and $K^0_s l\nu$ and the result changed by less than $0.33\sigma_{stats}$. The ratio $\frac{B(D^+\to\pi^0 l\nu)}{B(D^+\to K^0 l\nu)}$ was measured to be $9.0\pm1.8\pm1.6\%$, where the first error is the statistical error (σ_{stats}) and the second error is the systematic error (σ_{sys}). Our value of $9.0\pm1.8\pm1.6\%$ agrees well with the value reported by Mark III, $11.5^{+7.0}_{-3.7}\pm1.2\%$.[4] The increased precision of this measurement makes it unlikely that Cabibbo suppressed channels account for the gap between the inclusive semileptonic rate and the sum of the sum of the exclusive channels.

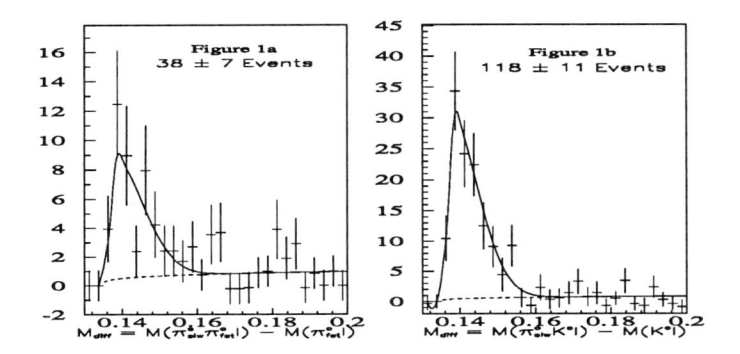

Figure 1: Fitted data of M_{diff} in GeV/c^2 for a) $D^+ \to \pi^0_{fst} l^+ \nu$ and b) $D^+ \to \overline{K^0} l^+ \nu$.

$|V_{cd}/V_{cs}|^2$ is determined from the following relationship,

$$|\frac{V_{cd}}{V_{cs}}|^2 = (\frac{f_+^K(0)}{f_+^\pi(0)})^2 \frac{\int \frac{(E_K^2 - m_K^2)^{3/2}}{(1-q^2/M_{D_s^*}^2)^2} dq^2}{\int \frac{(E_\pi^2 - m_\pi^2)^{3/2}}{(1-q^2/M_{D^*}^2)^2} dq^2} \frac{\mathcal{B}(D^+ \to \pi^0 l^+ \nu)}{\mathcal{B}(D^+ \to \overline{K^0} l^+ \nu)}. \quad (1)$$

We have assumed a simple pole form for the q^2 dependence of the form factors. We have calculated the integrals separately for electrons and muons, since they have different q^2_{min} values. The individual values for $f_+^K(0)$ and $f_+^\pi(0)$ are not well known, however the ratio of $\frac{f_+^\pi(0)}{f_+^K(0)}$ is expected to be unity within 10%. By setting $\frac{f_+^\pi(0)}{f_+^K(0)} = 1$, we obtain $|V_{cd}/V_{cs}|^2 = 0.0452 \pm 0.0090 \pm 0.0080$. Unitarity constraints on the CKM matrix yield a value of 0.051 ± 0.002, consistent with our measurement.[5] The result is also consitent with the new measurement of $|V_{cd}| = 0.209 \pm 0.011 \pm 0.0035$ from the CCFR collaboration.[1]

1. S. A. Rabinowitz, et al., submitted to PRL.
2. Y. Kubota et al., Nucl. Intr. and Meth. A320 (1992) 66.
3. The momentum of the D^+ was determined from the the following equation; $P(D^+) = \gamma \beta M(D^+)$, $\gamma = (P_\parallel^2(\pi^0_{slw}) + M^2(\pi^0))^{1/2}/M(\pi^0)$, $\beta = (1 - 1/\gamma^2)^{1/2}$, where $P_\parallel(\pi^0_{slw})$ was the momentum of the slow π^0 projected onto the thrust axis.
4. J. Adler, et al., Phys. Rev. Lett. 62 (1989) 1821.
5. K. Hikasa et al., Review of Particle Properties Phys. Rev. D 45 pg III.65 1992.

FOUR BODY SEMILEPTONIC CHARM DECAYS

RAY CULBERTSON for the Fermilab E687 Collaboration[1]
Department of Physics
University of Illinois at Urbana-Champaign
1110 W. Green St.
Urbana, Il 61801, USA

ABSTRACT

E687 reports preliminary results on the form factors and polarization in the decay $D^+ \to \overline{K}^{*0} \mu \nu$ (charge conjugates implied); $R_v = 1.46 \pm .24 \pm .18$, $R_2 = .48 \pm .17 \pm .12$, and $\Gamma_l/\Gamma_t = 1.48 \pm .14 \pm .11$. We report a preliminary branching ratio of $\Gamma(D^+ \to \overline{K}^{*0} \mu \nu)/\Gamma(D^+ \to K^- 2\pi) = .537 \pm .039 ^{+.054}_{-.075}$. We report a preliminary branching ratio of $\Gamma(D^0 \to K^{*-} \mu \nu)/\Gamma(D^+ \to \overline{K}^{*0} \mu \nu) = 1.20 \pm .30 ^{+.17}_{-.35}$. We discuss preliminary work in $D_s^+ \to \phi \mu \nu$.

1. Introduction

The E687 detector, which is described in detail elsewhere,[2] is a large aperture multiparticle spectrometer. A silicon microstrip detector allows the separation of primary and secondary vertices. Three multicell, threshold Čerenkov counters are used for particle identification. Muons are identified by a shielded inner detector consisting of three scintillator planes and four proportional tube planes. The average photon energy for the data sample was ≈ 200GeV.

The experiment took data in 1988, '90, and '91. We report on the form factor analysis and $\Gamma(D^0 \to K^{*-} \mu \nu)/\Gamma(D^+ \to \overline{K}^{*0} \mu \nu)$ for the full sample; we report on $\Gamma(D^+ \to \overline{K}^{*0} \mu \nu)/\Gamma(D^+ \to K^- 2\pi)$ using ≈ 50% of the full sample; and the $D_s^+ \to \phi \mu \nu$ signal in ≈ 85% of the full sample. The reconstructed events were skimmed by creating all possible two track microstrip vertices and requiring that at least one pair of vertices were separated by more than 4.5σ. In the analyses, all track combinations are searched for correct sign, mass, lepton and Čerenkov identification combinations to form a charm vertex. This vertex is removed from the event and the remaining tracks are combined into vertices and a primary vertex is selected; we cut on the normalized separation between the primary and secondary vertices (ℓ/σ).

2. $D^+ \to \overline{K}^{*0} \mu \nu$ Form Factors

We require $D^+ \to \overline{K}^{*0} \mu \nu$ candidates to have $\ell/\sigma > 20$ to minimize background contamination. Fig 1a shows the resulting signals for right sign ($Q_K + Q_\mu = 0$) and wrong sign ($Q_K + Q_\mu \neq 0$) combinations. Fig 1b compares the signal's survival *vs* the ℓ/σ cut to the Monte Carlo. The very good agreement at longer lifetimes indicates little contamination from other charm states. Fig 1c shows the signal response *vs* the cut on the secondary vertex confidence level. Some random background which accumulates at low CL is cut by requiring CL > .1.

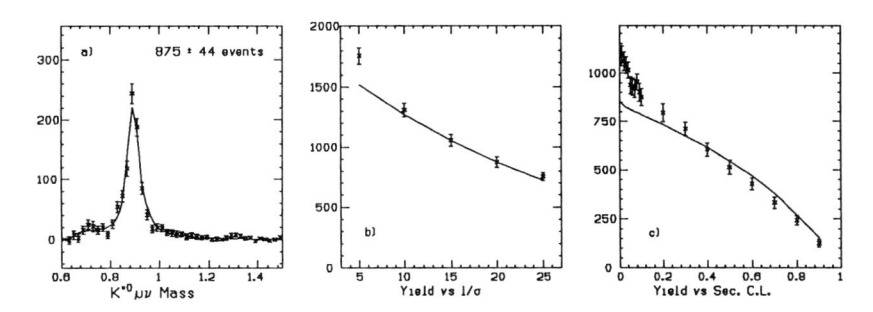

Figure 1. $D^+ \to K^{*0}\mu\nu$ (a) K^{*0} mass (b) signal vs ℓ/σ (c) signal vs secondary CL

The secondary vertex is required to be isolated from over tracks in the event (except the primary vertex tracks). The response to this cut also follows the Monte Carlo indicating there is no contamination from higher charged multiplicity decays. The charged mass distributions agree very well, consistent with no contamination from π^0 modes.

Following published analyses[3], we calculate the kinematic variables, $\cos\theta_v$, the angle between the π and the D in the $K*$ rest frame, $\cos\theta_l$, the angle between the ν and the D in the $\mu\nu$ rest frame, and t, the $\mu\nu$ mass. D^- decays have the same definition of variables and no change is required in the matrix element. Candidates which are reconstructed outside physical limits are recovered by moving the primary vertex to the nearest allowed solution.

We use a binned maximum likelihood technique to fit the form factors. We bin the sample into three bins in $\cos\theta_v$, three in $\cos\theta_v$ and two in t/t_{max}. We do not use the coplanarity angle, χ, in the fit because it provides no significant information. We fit for the ratio of the form factors, $R_v = V/A_1$ and $R_2 = A_2/A_1$ evaluated at $t = 0$ and the background level. The form factors are assumed to have a simple pole dependence with masses $M_A = 2.5$GeV and $M_V = 2.1$GeV. We include the overall factors in the matrix element that arise from a finite muon mass but not the additional (small) terms. The predicted yield in each bin is the integral of $|\mathcal{M}|^2$ over the bin, multiplied by a Monte Carlo correction factor for acceptance and resolution, plus the wrong sign yield in that bin scaled by the background parameter. One addition Poisson term ties the background level to the level of the wrong sign background.

The fit doesn't require parameterization of the background at the cost of a slight loss in statistical power (compared to continuous likelihood fits).

The fit results are $R_v = 1.46\pm.24\pm.18$, $R_2 = .48\pm.17\pm.12$, and $\Gamma_l/\Gamma_t = 1.48\pm.14\pm.11$. The confidence level that the fit results match the data is 19%, and R_v and R_2 are correlated by -14%. Systematics include the effect of the missing mass terms and the third form factor, the possibility of local variations in the muon identification efficiency, and variation in the energy scale of the trigger.

3. $\Gamma(D^+ \to \overline{K}^{*0}\mu\nu)/ \Gamma(D^+ \to K^-2\pi)$

The $K^-2\pi$ signal is found in the same skim with the same vertexing scheme and cuts (where applicable). Background from $\overline{K}^{*0}\pi^+\pi^0$ where the pion is identified as a muon is subtracted from the semileptonic mode. Possible contamination from $\overline{K}^{*0}\pi^0\mu\nu$ is included as a systematic together with signal fitting, nuclear scattering, and triggering energy. The result is $\Gamma(D^+ \to \overline{K}^{*0}\mu\nu)/\Gamma(D^+ \to K^-2\pi) = .537 \pm .039 ^{+.054}_{-.075}$.

4. $\Gamma(D^0 \to K^{*-}\mu\nu)/\Gamma(D^+ \to \overline{K}^{*0}\mu\nu)$

This ratio, which tests the isospin structure of the weak decay in the Cabibbo favored semileptonic decays, is predicted to be 1. The D^0 decay is found using the same methods as the D^+ signal. The wrong sign $(Q_\pi + Q_\mu \neq 0)$ sample is again subtracted. For this mode we require $\ell/\sigma > 5$. The signal is shown in Fig 2a. The presence of background should not be interpreted as non-resonant decays because for the majority of events the K_s decays downstream of the microstrips and cannot be unambiguously assigned to the $\pi\mu$ vertex. It is usually from the recoil charm decay. The signal response to the ℓ/σ cut is shown in Fig 2b; the good agreement implies little contamination from D^+'s. The signal response to the secondary vertex confidence level cut is shown in Fig 2c. The good agreement implies little contamination from higher charged multiplicity decays.

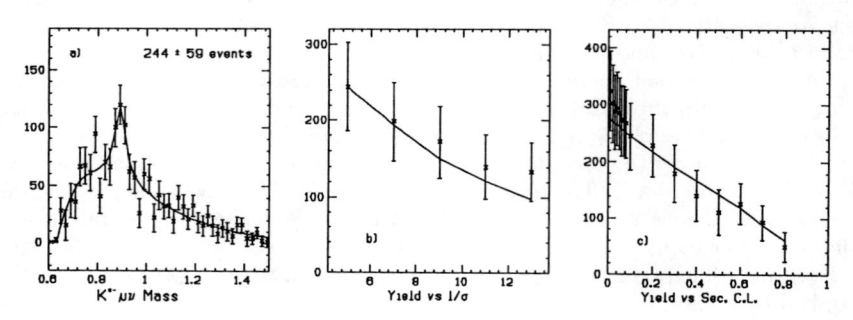

Figure 2. $D^0 \to K^{*-}\mu\nu$ (a) K^{*-} mass (b) signal vs ℓ/σ (c) signal vs secondary CL

Since this is a ratio of a D^0 mode and a D^+ mode we need to use the ratio of the lifetimes, and the ratio of D^+ to D^0 production which we measured to be $.42 \pm .05$. We estimate and subtract backgrounds from $\overline{K}^{*0}\pi^+\pi^0$ and $K^{*-}\pi^+\pi^0$. The result is $\Gamma(D^0 \to K^{*-}\mu\nu)/\Gamma(D^+ \to \overline{K}^{*0}\mu\nu) = 1.20 \pm .30 ^{+.17}_{-.35}$. Since we are taking the ratio of two semileptonic modes, most systematics should cancel. The quoted systematic is based on Čerenkov identification, K_s reconstruction efficiency, and predominantly from the current limits on $BR(\overline{K}^{*-}\pi^o\mu^+\nu)$ and $BR(K^{*-}\pi^o\mu^+\nu)$.

5. $\Gamma(D_s^+ \to \phi\mu\nu)/\Gamma(D_s^+ \to \phi\pi)$

We have isolated a $D_s^+ \to \phi\mu\nu$ sample using the same methods as above. For this decay we require $\ell/\sigma > 3$. Fig 3a is the signal for $\approx 85\%$ of the full sample. Fig 3b is the signal response to the ℓ/σ cut compared to the Monte Carlo showing good agreement with the D_s^+ lifetime. Fig 3c is the signal response to the secondary confidence level cut compared to the Monte Carlo. There appears to be significant background coming in at low confidence level so we require the CL $> .2$ for this sample.

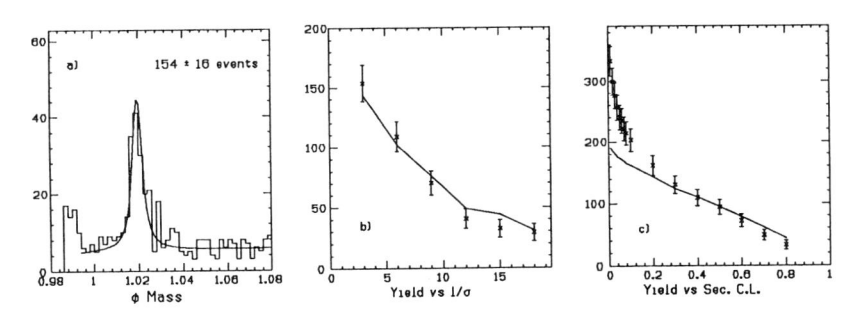

Figure 3. $D_s^+ \to \phi\mu\nu$ (a) ϕ mass (b) signal vs ℓ/σ (c) signal vs secondary CL

Because of the possibility of significant backgrounds, the inability to make a wrong sign subtraction, and the very preliminary nature of the result, we choose to not quote a branching ratio to $\phi\pi$ at this time.

6. Acknowledgements

This work was supported in part by the National Science Foundation, the US Department of Energy, the Italian Istituto Nazionale di Fisica Nucleare and Ministero della Università e della Ricerca Scientifica.

7. References

1. For a complete list of E687 collaborators, see reference 2.
2. E687, P. L. Frabetti et al., Nucl. Instrum. Methods. **A320** (1992) 519.
3. J.C. Anjos, et. al., Phys. Rev. Lett. **65** (1990) 2630.

RECENT RESULTS ON THE SEMILEPTONIC DECAY $D^0 \to K^- \mu^+ \nu_\mu$

WILL E. JOHNS
for the E687 Collaboration[0]
Department of Physics, University of Colorado, Campus Box 390
Boulder, Co. 80309, USA

ABSTRACT

We present a BF($D^0 \to K^- \mu^+ \nu_\mu / D^0 \to K^- \pi^+$) measurement(c.c assumed throughout), and a fit to the single pole form of the f_+ form factor.

1. Introduction

The ultimate goal of investigating semileptonic decays of mesons is to parameterize the form factors that describe the hadronic current and to measure the strength of quark mixing via the CKM element appropriate for the particular decay. This becomes apparent if one looks at the form of the matrix element that describes the semileptonic decay $D^0 \to K^- l^+ \nu_l$,

$$M = G_F V_{cs} \left[f_+(q^2)(p_D + p_K)_\sigma + f_-(q^2)(p_D - p_K)_\sigma \right] \bar{u}_l \gamma^\sigma (1 - \gamma_5) u_\nu, \quad (1)$$

which may be used to calculate the decay rate w.r.t. the kaon energy in the D^0 c.m. system,

$$\frac{d\Gamma}{dE_K} = \frac{G_F^2}{4\pi^3} |V_{cs}|^2 |f_+(q^2)|^2 P_K \left(\frac{W_0 - E_K}{F_0} \right)^2 \left[\frac{1}{3} m_D P_K^2 + \frac{1}{3} m_l^2 \frac{P_K^2}{F_0} + \frac{m_l^2}{8 m_D}(m_D^2 + m_K^2 + 2 m_D E_K) \right.$$
$$\left. + \frac{1}{4} m_l^2 \frac{m_D^2 - m_K^2}{m_D} Re\left(\frac{f_-(q^2)}{f_+(q^2)} \right) + \frac{1}{4} m_l^2 F_0 \left| \frac{f_-(q^2)}{f_+(q^2)} \right|^2 \right],$$
$$W_0 = \frac{m_D^2 + m_K^2 - m_l^2}{2 m_D}, F_0 = W_0 - E_K + \frac{m_l^2}{m_D}, \quad (2)$$

where the matrix element's lepton mass dependence comes from Ref. 1. One notices the importance of measuring both semi-electronic and semi-muonic decays to probe f_- since the f_- terms get weighted by m_{lepton}^2. Assuming a single pole dependence,

$$f_+(q^2) = 1/(1 - q^2/m_{pole}^2) \quad (3)$$

for f_+ and setting f_- equal to 0, we expect $\Gamma_{electron}/\Gamma_{muon}$ to be 98.2%. Also, by measuring the distribution of events w.r.t. the K^- energy in the D^0 center of mass frame, we can measure the pole mass dependence of the f_+ form factor.

2. Data and Analysis

2.1. Branching Fraction

The data were accumulated in the 1990 run of Experiment E687. The E687 spectrometer is described elsewhere.[2] To provide a clean sample of D^0's, we look for

---
[0] see these *Proceedings*

D^{*+}'s through the decay chain $D^{*+} \to D^0 \pi^+$. To find a D^0, we select $K\mu$ candidates by choosing kaons that the Čerenkov system identifies as a definite kaon or kaon/proton ambiguous. This kaon is combined with an opposite charge muon identified by the inner muon system of the E687 spectrometer. Typically, $\sim 1.5\%$ of all pions or kaons are identified as muons due to pattern recognition failures, the decay of the pion, or the decay of the kaon. The kaon and the muon must form a vertex with a confidence level of 1% or better, and have an invariant mass less than 1.855 GeV/c^2 to reduce contamination from $D^0 \to K^-\pi^+$. The remaining tracks in the event are used to find primary vertex candidates. The primary vertex candidate with a significance of separation (l/σ) from the secondary $K\mu$ candidate of 4 or greater and confidence level of fit 1% or greater is retained. To estimate the D^0 momentum, following Ref. 3, we assume the D^0 travels from the primary to the secondary; then boost the $K\mu$ candidate to a frame where $(\bar{P}_\mu + \bar{P}_K) \cdot \hat{l} = 0$ ($\hat{l}$ is the D^0 decay direction), and determine the amount of momentum parallel to the D^0 carried by the missing neutrino. In the boosted frame, we require that $E_\nu > 0$, $(\bar{P}_\nu \cdot \hat{l})^2 = (E_\nu^2 - P_{K\mu}^2) > -.7$ $(GeV/c^2)^2$, and for those events with $-.7 < (E_\nu^2 - P_{K\mu}^2) < 0$ we set $(E_\nu^2 - P_{K\mu}^2) = 0$. Hence, $(\bar{P}_\nu \cdot \hat{l}) = \pm\sqrt{E_\nu^2 - P_{K\mu}^2} = \bar{P}_D$, and one simply boosts the solution into the lab frame to estimate the D^0 momentum. The D^{*+} daughter pion must not be identified by the Čerenkov system as a definite electron, a definite kaon, kaon/proton ambiguous, or a definite proton, and must be included in the primary vertex. Two D^{*+} mass solutions are then formed using the D^0 momenta found with the boost analysis and the lowest mass solution is retained. If more than one D^{*+} is found in an event, again, only the lowest mass D^{*+} candidate is retained. This was found to add no bias to the final result. A fit is then performed that takes microvertex tracks not assigned to the primary or the secondary vertex and gives a confidence level that any of these tracks are consistent with being in the secondary vertex. We require this confidence level to be $< 10\%$. We compare the pion charge to the muon charge and assign $\pi\mu$ like sign events as signal +background and $\pi\mu$ unlike sign events as background, hence the prescription $\pi\mu$ like $- \pi\mu$ unlike $= \#K^-\mu^+\nu_\mu$. Monte Carlo studies show that this prescription underestimates the background in the $\pi\mu$ like signal due to contributions from the decay $D^0 \to K^{*-}\mu^+\nu_\mu(K^{*-} \to K^-\pi^0)(\sim 8\%)$ and $D^0 \to K^-\pi X(\sim 4\%)$ where the π or the X is misidentified by the muon system. The $\pi\mu$ like and $\pi\mu$ unlike distributions are then fitted to the expected Monte Carlo distribution where the $BF(D^0 \to K^{*-}\mu^+\nu_\mu/D^0 \to K^-\mu^+\nu_\mu)$ used in the $\pi\mu$ like excess estimate comes from Ref. 4. A similar analysis is done for the decay $D^0 \to K^-\pi^+$, where the π^+ is limited to the acceptance of the muon system to reduce systematics. The dominant sources of systematic error in the BF measurement come from muon misidentification/decays($^{+5.0\%}_{-3.0\%}$), the $BF(D^0 \to K^{*-}\mu^+\nu_\mu/D^0 \to K^-\mu^+\nu_\mu)(\pm 4\%)$, and the fit to the $D^0 \to K^-\mu^+\nu_\mu$ yield ($\pm 3.0\%$). All sources of systematic error were added in quadrature. After correcting the $D^0 \to K^-\mu^+\nu_\mu$ yield for $K^-\pi X$ excess and the $D^0 \to K^-\pi^+$ for hadronic absorbtion of the pion($\sim 7\%$), we find $338 \pm 24(stat.)$ events in the channel $D^0 \to K^-\mu^+\nu_\mu$ and $525 \pm 27(stat.)$ events in the channel $D^0 \to K^-\pi^+$,

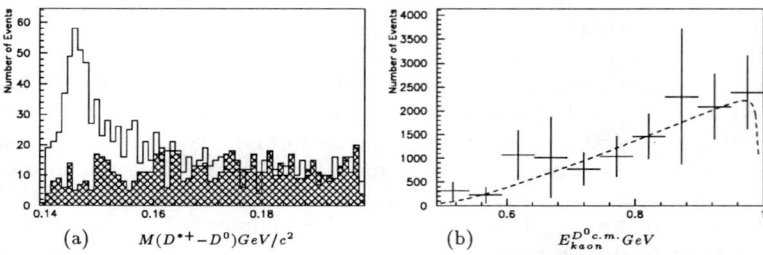

Figure 1. (a) $D^0 \to K^-\mu^+\nu_\mu$ like sign $\pi\mu$ (solid) and unlike sign(hatched) data from 1990 (b) distribution of efficiency corrected, background subtracted events in (a) as a function of $E_K^{D^0 c.m.}$ for $M(D^{*+} - D^0) < .156\ GeV/c^2$ with the fit to the pole mass(described below) as a broken line.

which leads to a $BF(D^0 \to K^-\mu^+\nu_\mu / D^0 \to K^-\pi^+)= .87 \pm .075(stat.)^{+.057}_{-.064}(syst)$ (preliminary). This branching fraction agrees with the CLEO[4] result $.79 \pm .08(stat.) \pm .09(syst.)$.

2.2. Pole Mass

The pole mass dependence of the f_+ form factor (see Eq.(3)) was investigated using the distribution of events vs the energy of the kaon in the D^0 center of mass. Non-physical decays(i.e. those events with $P_\nu^{2boosted} < 0$) were forced to be physical, and the distribution (like - unlike) was corrected for acceptance and backgrounds. A fit to the pole mass was done using Eq.(2) with $f_- = 0$, and our preliminary result $m_{pole} = 2.1^{+.7(stat)+.7(syst)}_{-.3(stat.)-.3(syst)}$ agrees well with the world average $m_{pole} = 2.0^{+.3}_{-.2}$ measured via the semielectronic mode.[5] This result is very preliminary.

2.3. The Future

The $D^0 \to K^-e^+\nu_e$ mode is being analyzed for the 1990 and 1991 data samples and the $D^0 \to K^-\mu^+\nu_\mu$ mode is being analyzed for 1991 as well. We will probably have over 1000 events in both modes and can anticipate a measurement of $\Gamma_{electron}/\Gamma_{muon}$ and a better measurement of the pole mass or a fit to other forms of the form factors.

6. References

1. L. Jauneau, in *Methods in Subnuclear Physics*, ed. M. Nicolic (Gordon and Brach, New York, 1969), p. 125.
2. P. L. Frabetti *et al.*, *Nucl. Instr. and Meth. in Phys. Res., sect.* **A 320** (1992) 519.
3. J. C. Anjos *et al.*, *Phys. Rev. Lett.* **62** (1989) 1587
4. G. Crawford *et al.*, *Phys. Rev.* **D44** (1989) 3394
5. S. Stone, Syracuse University Report No. HEPSY-1-92, to be publ. in *Heavy Flavors*, ed. A. J. Buras and H. Linder (World Scientific, Singapore) (1992)

SEMILEPTONIC DECAYS OF D MESONS AND THE HEAVY QUARK EFFECTIVE THEORY[†]

JAMES F. AMUNDSON and JONATHAN L. ROSNER
*University of Chicago and Enrico Fermi Institute, 5640 S. Ellis Ave.
Chicago, Illinois 60637 USA*

ABSTRACT

We consider the application of heavy quark symmetry to the strange quark in semileptonic decays of D mesons. We find that consistency with experimental data requires substantial ($\simeq 30\%$) corrections due to both perturbative QCD and finite-mass effects. Nonetheless, these corrections are consistent with *a priori* expectations and provide insight into the symmetry-breaking effects in B decays.

The Heavy Quark Effective Theory (HQET) is a useful tool for studying the decays of b quarks to c quarks, as in the decay $B \to D^{(*)} l \nu$. The reason we believe this is true is that corrections to the leading-order HQET are of order $\bar{\Lambda}/2m_Q$. Here m_Q denotes the mass of the heavy quark, while $\bar{\Lambda}$ is a constant of order $\Lambda_{\rm QCD}$. The quark model predicts that $\bar{\Lambda} \simeq 300$ MeV, while sum rule calculations[1] suggest a larger value, $\bar{\Lambda} \simeq 500$ MeV. Either way, the dominant corrections to $B \to D^{(*)} l \nu$ decay, which are of order $\bar{\Lambda}/2m_c$, should be fairly small.

If we we want to apply HQET to $D \to K^{(*)} l \nu$ decays, the situation is less clear. An expansion in $\bar{\Lambda}/2m_s$ might not make any sense at all. If however, we take the quark model prediction for $\bar{\Lambda}$ and a constituent strange quark mass $m_s \simeq 500$ MeV, $\bar{\Lambda}/2m_s$ is "only" about 30% and we can attempt to apply the HQET to the strange quark. Ideally, we want the strange quark to act as a sort of magnifying glass for subleading effects in the HQET. In recent work,[2] which we describe here, we have applied the HQET to semileptonic decays of D mesons in this manner.

In the heavy quark limit, all of the form factors for the decay of a heavy meson H to another heavy meson $h^{(*)}$ are given in terms of the Isgur-Wise function $\xi(w)$, where $w \equiv v \cdot v' = (m_H^2 + m_{h^{(*)}}^2 - q^2)/(2 m_H m_{h^{(*)}})$ and v (v') is the four-velocity of the meson H ($h^{(*)}$). The Isgur-Wise function is not calculable in perturbation theory. We choose to describe it by a single parameter, ρ, with the functional form

$$\xi(w) = \exp\left[-\rho^2(w-1)\right]. \qquad (1)$$

The heavy quark symmetry is broken by both perturbative QCD and finite-mass corrections. The perturbative QCD corrections are calculable, but the finite-mass corrections introduce four new unknown functions and one new unknown constant, $\bar{\Lambda}$.

[†]Presented by James F. Amundson.

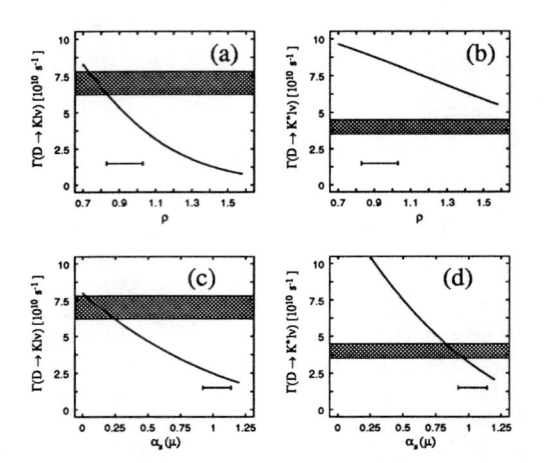

Figure 1: Predictions of heavy-quark symmetry for decay rates of $D \to \overline{K}e^+\nu_e$ (a,c) and $D \to \overline{K}^*e^+\nu_e$ (b,d). Predictions without QCD corrections are shown in (a,b). The ranges of ρ allowed by the fits to B decays are shown by the horizontal error bar. Predictions with QCD corrections are shown in (c,d), where the bars indicate the range of $\alpha_s(\mu)$ obtained in Ref. 2.

In the limit of vanishing lepton mass, there are four measurable form factors in $H \to h^{(*)}l\nu$ decay: f in $H \to hl\nu$ decay and V, A_1, and A_2 in $H \to h^*l\nu$ decay.

The form factor predictions of heavy quark symmetry, including the leading-order perturbative QCD and finite-mass corrections, can be summarized as follows:

$$F_i(w) = k_i(w) \left\{ b_i(w, \alpha_s)\xi(w) + \frac{\overline{\Lambda}}{2m_q} [c_i(w)\xi(w) + \Psi_i(w)] \right\}, \qquad (2)$$

where $k_i(w)$ and $c_i(w)$ are simple kinematic factors, $b_i(w, \alpha_s)$ contains the corrections from perturbative QCD and $\Psi_i(w)$ contains the corrections due to the new unknown functions due to finite mass effects. They obey the condition[3]

$$\Psi_{A_1}(w) = \Psi_V(w) \; ; \; \Psi_{A_1}(w=1) = \Psi_V(w=1) = 0. \qquad (3)$$

In Figure 1 we show the comparison of the leading-order theory with the measured rates. First we ignore all symmetry breaking corrections, varying only ρ, the parameter governing the shape of the Isgur-Wise function. The $D \to K^*$ data cannot be fit for any value of ρ. Next we take $\rho = 0.93$ from fits to B decays and try to see if we can fit the data by including perturbative QCD corrections. Although the situation for $D \to K^*$ is improved for large values of $\alpha_s(\mu)$, there is no value of $\alpha_s(\mu)$ which simultaneously fits both the $D \to K$ and $D \to K^*$ widths.

The preferred value of $\alpha_s(\mu)$ shown in the plot was determined by a procedure similar to that used to extract V_{cb} using heavy quark theory. We obtain $\alpha_s(\mu) = 1.03 \pm 0.11$, which is very large, but not inconsistent with our *a priori* expectations. The actual corrections are of order $\alpha_s(\mu)/\pi \simeq 33\%$.

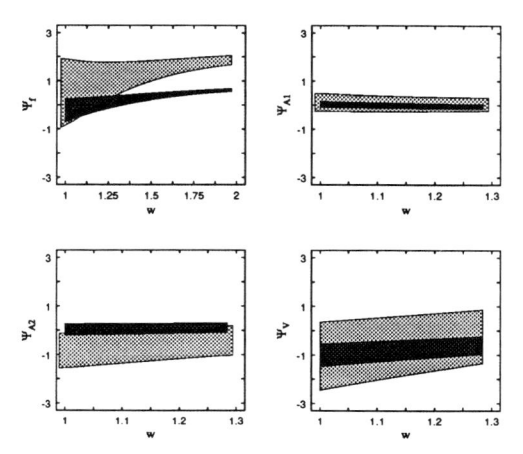

Figure 2: Values of form factors associated with subleading operators obtained from experiment. The light and dark regions correspond to taking $\overline{\Lambda} = 200$ and 400 MeV, respectively. The light regions have been extended horizontally for clarity in some cases.

All of the form factors in $D \to K^{(*)}$ decay have been measured.[4] The only unknown quantity in the form factor $V(w = 1)$ is $\overline{\Lambda}$. Comparison with the measured form factor gives $\overline{\Lambda}/2m_s = -0.05 \pm 0.24$, and $\overline{\Lambda} = -44 \pm 297$ MeV. Unfortunately, the error on this value is too large to be truly useful.

In Figure 2 we have extracted the subleading effects from the data by subtracting the leading-order and perturbative QCD predictions from the measured form factors and plotting the remainder. Since this process depends on $\overline{\Lambda}$, an essentially unknown quantity, we have used two representative values of $\overline{\Lambda}$. We can see that Ψ_f is clearly non-zero for large values of w. This is what is required to simultaneously explain the $D \to K$ and $D \to K^*$ rates. We also see that the conditions in Eq. (3) are better satisfied for the smaller value of $\overline{\Lambda}$.

This work was supported in part by United States Department of Energy under Grant No. DE AC02 90ER40560.

1. M. Neubert, SLAC Report No. SLAC-PUB-5826, June, 1992, to be published in Phys. Rev. D.
2. J. F. Amundson and J. L. Rosner, Enrico Fermi Institute preprint EFI-92-38-Rev, submitted to Phys. Rev. D.
3. M. Luke, Phys. Lett. B **252**, 447 (1990).
4. S. Stone, Syracuse University Report No. HEPSY-1-92, to be published in *Heavy Flavors*, edited by A. J. Buras and H. Lindner, World Scientific, Singapore (1992); E691 Collaboration, J. C. Anjos *et al.*, Phys. Rev. Lett. **67**, 1507 (1991); E653 Collaboration, K. Kodama *et al.*, Phys. Lett. B **286**, 187 (1992).

A QCD 'MANIFESTO' ON INCLUSIVE DECAYS OF BEAUTY & CHARM

I.I.BIGI[a], B.BLOK[b], M.SHIFMAN[c], N.G.URALTSEV[a] and A.VAINSHTEIN[c]

[a] *Physics Department, University of Notre Dame du Lac
Notre Dame, IN 46556, U.S.A.*

[b] *ITP, Univ.of California at Santa Barbara, Santa Barbara, CA 93106, U.S.A.*

[c] *Theoret.Physics Inst., Univ.of Minnesota, Minneapolis, MN 55455, U.S.A.*

ABSTRACT

A selfconsistent treatment of nonperturbative effects in inclusive nonleptonic and semileptonic decays of beauty and charm hadrons is presented. It is illustrated by calculating semileptonic branching ratios, lifetime ratios, radiative decay rates and the lepton spectra in semileptonic decays.

1. Sketch Of General Method

It is the goal of our analysis to calculate transition rates for inclusive nonleptonic and semileptonic decays in terms of the fundamental parameters, namely quark masses, KM parameters and Λ_{QCD} without invoking Voodoo. Nonperturbative effects – namely boundstate dynamics in the initial state and hadronization in the final state – have to be incorporated here. We will do that via an expansion in $1/m_Q$ (m_Q is the mass of the heavy flavour quark Q). For the beauty quark mass is certainly much larger than typical hadronic scales, and an extrapolation down to charm hopefully still makes sense.

The width for the decay of a hadron with the heavy flavor Q into an inclusive final state X is obtained from the transition operator $\hat{T}(Q \to X \to Q)$ describing the forward scattering of a heavy quark Q via an intermediate state X. Then we take the imaginary part of the matrix element of $\hat{T}$ between the state H_Q:

$$\Gamma(H_Q \to X) \propto G_F^2 \langle H_Q | \mathrm{Im}\, \hat{T}(Q \to X \to Q) | H_Q \rangle. \tag{1}$$

One actually proceeds in two steps to evaluate this quantity: **(a)** The nonlocal second-order operator $\hat{T}$ is expanded into a series of local operators $O^{(i)}$ of increasing dimension with coefficients c_i that contain increasing powers of $1/m_Q$

$$\mathrm{Im}\, \hat{T}(Q \to X \to Q) \simeq \sum_i c_i O^{(i)} \tag{2}$$

(Strictly speaking, the expansion parameter is $1/E$ where E is the energy release, rather than $1/m_Q$.) The lowest dimensional operators $O^{(i)}$ thus dominate for large m_Q. **(b)** One has to evaluate the matrix elements $\langle H_Q | O^{(i)} | H_Q \rangle$; it is at this level that one differentiates between the decays of heavy flavor baryons and neutral and charged pseudoscalar mesons, i.e. Λ_Q, P^0 and $P^\pm$. This approach was explicitely formulated in ref.[1] and has been supported by the analysis of ref.[2].

(1) The general expansion of Im $\hat{T}$ is as follows (for details see [1-4])

$$\text{Im } \hat{T}(Q \to X \to Q) = \tilde{c}_3^{(X)} m_Q^5 \bar{Q} Q + \tilde{c}_5^{(X)} m_Q^3 \bar{Q} i\sigma G\, Q + \tilde{c}_6^{(X)} m_Q^2 (\bar{Q}\Gamma q)(\bar{q}\Gamma Q) + \mathcal{O}(m_Q) \quad (3)$$

with $i\sigma G = i\gamma_\mu \gamma_\nu G_{\mu\nu}$, $G_{\mu\nu}$ being the gluonic field strength tensor. The coefficients $\tilde{c}_i^{(X)}$ are calculable dimensionless numbers that depend on the mode X. Once the matrix elements between the states H_Q are formed the first term on the right hand side of eq.(3) yields (among other things) the usual free 'spectator' result; the second one constitutes a new type of 'spectator' contribution; the third term represents 'non-spectator' contributions due to W-exchange ('WA') and interference effects ('PI').

(2) The relevant matrix elements of the operators $\bar{Q}Q$, $\bar{Q}\, i\sigma G\, Q$ and $(\bar{Q}\Gamma q)(\bar{q}\Gamma Q)$ have been evaluated so far. For $\bar{Q}Q$ one employs a nonrelativistic $1/m_Q$ expansion:

$$\bar{Q}Q = v_\mu \bar{Q}\gamma_\mu Q + \frac{1}{4m_Q^2}\bar{Q}\, i\sigma G\, Q - \frac{1}{2m_Q^2}\bar{Q}\left(D^2 - (v\cdot D)^2\right)Q + \mathcal{O}(1/m_Q^3)\ . \quad (4)$$

D_μ denotes here the covariant derivative and v_μ is the 4-velocity vector. One finds:

$$\langle H_Q | \bar{Q}\gamma_\mu Q | H_Q \rangle = 1\cdot v_\mu \quad \left(\text{if } \langle H_Q(\vec{p}\,')|H_Q(\vec{p})\rangle = \frac{E}{M}\cdot(2\pi)^3\,\delta^3(\vec{p}\,' - \vec{p})\right) \quad (5)$$

$$\langle P_Q | \bar{Q}\, i\sigma G\, Q | P_Q \rangle \simeq \frac{3}{2}(M^2(V_Q) - M^2(P_Q)) \quad (6)$$

$$\langle \Lambda_Q | \bar{Q}\, i\sigma G\, Q | \Lambda_Q \rangle \simeq 0\ ;\ \Lambda_Q = \Lambda_b, \Lambda_c\ ;\ P_Q = B, D\ ;\ V_Q = B^*, D^*. \quad (7)$$

The operator $\bar{Q}(D^2 - (vD)^2)Q$ describes the kinetic energy of the heavy quark in the gluon background field; the masses of Λ_Q, P_Q, V_Q yield some information on its size.

Finally we employ the approximation of factorization $\langle P_Q|(\bar{Q}\Gamma q)(\bar{q}\Gamma Q)|P_Q\rangle \simeq \langle P_Q|\bar{Q}\Gamma q|0\rangle\langle 0|\bar{q}\Gamma Q|P_Q\rangle$ with the operators normalized at the low hadronic scale.

2. Qualitative Results

The decay widths of a heavy flavor hadron H_Q look as follows:

$$\Gamma(H_Q) = \Gamma(Q)\cdot[1 + a_2^{(H_Q)}/m_Q^2 + a_3^{(H_Q)}/m_Q^3 + \mathcal{O}(1/m_Q^4)] \quad (8)$$

where $\Gamma(Q)$ is the free quark width with all purely perturbative effects included.
(a) The free spectator ansatz thus holds through terms of order $1/m_Q$.
(b) The first nonperturbative corrections enter on the $1/m_Q^2$ level with

$$a_2^{(\Lambda_b)} \neq a_2^{(B^-)} = a_2^{(B_d)} \simeq a_2^{(B_s)} \quad (9)$$

(c) 'Conventional' non-spectator effects – WA and PI – emerge on the $1/m_Q^3$ level:

$$a_3^{(B^-)} < a_3^{(B_d)} < a_3^{(\Lambda_b)} \quad (10)$$

(d) In charm decays these nonperturbative corrections exhibit similar pattern while being larger by roughly factors of $(m_b/m_c)^2 \sim 10$ and $(m_b/m_c)^3 \sim 30$, respectively.

3. (Semi-)Quantitative Phenomenology

3.1 Semileptonic Branching Ratios: Corrections $1/m_b^2$

The semileptonic and nonleptonic transition operators for $b \to c$ decays in the external gluon field are given by:

$$\hat{\Gamma}_{SL} = F\{z_0 \bar{b}b - \frac{z_1}{m_b^2} \bar{b} i\sigma G b\}, \quad \hat{\Gamma}_{NL} = FN_C\{A_0(z_0 \bar{b}b - \frac{z_1}{m_b^2} \bar{b} i\sigma G b) - \frac{4A_2 z_2}{m_b^2} \bar{b} i\sigma G b\} \quad (11)$$

with $z_0 = 1 - 8x + 8x^3 - x^4 - 12x^2 \log(x)$, $z_1 = (1-x)^4$, $z_2 = (1-x)^3$ and $x = m_c^2/m_b^2$ describing the relative phase spaces, $A_0 = (c_+^2 + c_-^2)/2 + (c_+^2 - c_-^2)/2N_C$ and $A_2 = (c_+^2 - c_-^2)/2N_C$ denoting the QCD radiative corrections (N_C=number of colours) and $F = G_F^2 m_b^5 |V_{cb}|^2 / 192\pi^3$. Thus we find a reduction in the semileptonic branching ratio:

$$\frac{\delta BR_{SL}(B)}{BR_{SL}(B)} \simeq 6 \cdot \frac{M_{B^*}^2 - M_B^2}{m_b^2} \frac{A_2 z_2}{A_0 z_0} \cdot BR_{NL}(B) < 0 \quad (12)$$

This reduction is of the order of 5% in B decays; $BR_{SL}(\Lambda_b)$ remains practically unaffected by nonperturbative corrections on the $1/m_Q^2$ level due to eq.(7).

In charm decays on the other hand one obtains a much larger reduction:

$$\frac{\delta BR_{SL}(D)}{BR_{SL}(D)} \sim -\mathcal{O}(50\%) \ . \quad (13)$$

It is worth noting that in charmed particles some of the $\mathcal{O}(m_c^{-3})$ corrections are numerically as large as the $\mathcal{O}(m_c^{-2})$ ones.

The last term in eq.(11) is produced by an interference between two different color flow amplitudes (it represents a non-factorizable contribution). It is worth noting that it is approximately saturated[4] by non-factorizable contributions to a few exclusive amplitudes that were estimated in ref.[5] arising due to the same operator.

3.2 Lifetime Ratios

Small differences are predicted for the lifetimes of the different beauty hadrons:

$$1.02 \leq \tau(B^-)/\tau(B_d) \leq 1.08 \quad \text{for} \quad 130 MeV < f_B < 250 MeV \ ; \quad (14)$$

these effects are mainly due to 'PI' with 'WA' being rather small[1,2]. A preliminary analysis shows that $\tau(\Lambda_b)$ and $\tau(B)$ could differ by up to 10-15 %.

Extrapolating these findings down to charm one obtains much bigger effects: $\tau(D^+)/\tau(D^0) \sim 2$ mainly due to 'PI' with 'WA' providing a 20% contribution at most. An intriguing 'roller coaster' story thus unfolds behind the semileptonic branching ratios for D mesons: on the m_Q^5 and m_Q^4 levels one gets the parton result $BR_{SL}(D) \simeq 15\%$; $1/m_Q^2$ corrections suppress it roughly by a factor of two: $BR_{SL}(D) \simeq 8\%$; $1/m_Q^3$ effects finally differentiate between D^0 and D^+ decays by suppressing $\Gamma_{NL}(D^+)$ such that $BR_{SL}(D^+) \simeq 16\%$ holds while affecting $BR_{SL}(D^0)$ only a little.

3.3 $b \to s\gamma$

The chromomagnetic dipole operator affects also radiative $b \to s + \gamma$ decays:

$$\hat{\Gamma}_\gamma \propto m_b^5 \{\bar{b}b - 1/m_b^2 \, \bar{b} i\sigma G b\} \ ; \quad (15)$$

yet the ratio $BR(B \to \gamma + (S = -1)) / BR(B \to l\nu X)$ remains practically unchanged.

3.4 Lepton Spectra in Semileptonic Decays

Lepton spectra in semileptonic beauty and charm decays can be treated in an analogous fashion where one relies on an expansion in $1/(p_Q - p_l)^2$ rather than in $1/m_Q^2$ with p_Q [p_l] denoting the momentum of the heavy quark Q [the lepton l]. In the limit of the vanishing quark mass in the final state of $b \to q l \nu$ and neglecting the gluon bremsstrahlung one obtains[6]:

$$\frac{d\Gamma}{dy} \propto y^2 \left[\frac{3}{2} - y + (\frac{5}{3}y + \frac{1}{3}\delta(1-y) + \frac{1}{6}(2y^2 - y^3)\delta'(1-y))\frac{K}{2} + (2 + \frac{5}{3}y - \frac{11}{6}\delta(1-y))\frac{G}{2}\right] \quad (16)$$

where $y = 2E_l/m_b$, $K = 1/m_b^2 \cdot \langle H_b|\bar{b}\vec{D}^2 b|H_b\rangle$ and $G = 1/2m_b^2 \cdot \langle H_b|\bar{b} i\sigma G b|H_b\rangle$. The δ-functions (for $m_q = 0$) reflect the blowup of the expansion near the endpoint. It is important however that the integral over a small region $\Delta y > \mu/m_b$ (μ is a hadronic scale) around the endpoint is correctly reproduced by that of eq.(16).

4. Outlook

Obviously our analysis on the lepton spectra has to be finalized[6]. Beyond that there are two intriguing areas for further study, namely

– the question of $SU(3)_{flavour}$ breaking, e.g. the relation between D^0 and D_s and between B_d and B_s decays;

– the vast realm of heavy flavour baryon decays.

5. Acknowledgements

A.V. is grateful for helpful discussions to L.McLerran and M.Voloshin. This work was supported in part by the NSF under grant number NSF-PHY 92 13313 and in part by DOE under grant number DOE-ER-40105-1100.

6. References

1. M.Voloshin and M.Shifman, Sov.J.Nucl.Phys. **41** (1985) 120; Sov.Phys.-JETP **64** (1986) 698.
2. I.I.Bigi and N.G.Uraltsev, *Phys.Lett.* **B280** (1992) 271.
3. I.I.Bigi, N.G.Uraltsev and A.Vainshtein, *Phys.Lett.* **B293** (1992) 430.
4. B.Blok and M.Shifman, preprints NSF-ITP-92-103, -115.
5. B.Blok and M.Shifman, preprint NSF-ITP-92-76.
6. I.I.Bigi, M.Shifman, N.G.Uraltsev and A.Vainshtein, in preparation.

CONFIRMATION OF CHARMLESS SEMILEPTONIC DECAYS OF B MESONS

FRANZ MUHEIM
Department of Physics, Syracuse University, 201 Physics Building
Syracuse, N.Y., 13244-1130, USA
(Representing the CLEO Collaboration)

ABSTRACT

Using data collected with the CLEO-II detector, we have confirmed charmless semileptonic decays of B mesons. In the lepton momentum interval 2.4 - 2.6 GeV/c the measured rate, averaged for $b \to u\mu\nu$ and $b \to ue\nu$ events, suggests a smaller value of $|V_{ub}|/|V_{cb}|$ than has been inferred from previous studies, ranging from 0.05 to 0.12 for different theoretical models of $b \to u\ell\nu$.

1. Introduction

Charmless semileptonic decays of B mesons were demonstrated by the inclusive production in $\Upsilon(4S)$ decays of leptons with momenta above the kinematic limit for $b \to c\ell\nu$ (2.46 GeV/c)[1, 2]. This demonstrated a nonzero value of the CKM matrix element V_{ub}, which is necessary to explain CP violation in the three-generation standard model. In this paper we describe a study of the endpoint region of the B-meson inclusive lepton momentum spectrum which has been made with the CLEO II detector[3] at CESR. Our sample consists of 923 pb^{-1} of e^+e^- annihilation data at the $\Upsilon(4S)$ resonance (ON), which corresponds to a total number of 935000 $B\bar{B}$ events, and 416 pb^{-1} at total energies 50-60 MeV below the resonance (OFF).

2. Event Selection

Hadronic event-selection criteria include requirements on detected charged energy, energy deposited in the calorimeter, and a reconstructed event vertex consistent with the nominal interaction point. Electrons are selected by requiring an energy deposit in the calorimeter close to the fitted track momentum, and measured specific ionization in the main drift chamber consistent with that expected for electrons. The efficiency to detect a 2.5 GeV/c electron is 92% in the angular region $|cos\theta| < 0.71$, and 70% for $0.71 \leq |cos\theta| < 0.85$. The probability of misidentifying a hadron as an electron is 0.3% - 0.4%. Charged tracks are identified as muon candidates if they are observed to penetrate at least seven nuclear interaction lengths of absorber material. The solid angle coverage for muon detection is 79% of 4π. At 2.5 GeV/c, the efficiency for detecting a muon is 80%, and the probability of a hadron faking a muon is 0.7%.

We apply stringent track quality cuts to lepton candidates to ensure accurate momentum measurement. Requirements include a minimum number of hits in the tracking chambers, a good match to the nominal interaction point, and a small RMS residual in the track fit. Studies of isolated tracks embedded in hadronic events, and of simulated events, showed no appreciable non-Gaussian component in the momentum resolution function.

3. Background Suppression

Production of leptons with momenta around 2.5 GeV/c is dominated by continuum processes. While we can correct the ON lepton yields for this contribution with the OFF totals, this degrades the statistical precision of our measurement. Significant improvement can be achieved by applying continuum-suppressing event-selection cuts. To suppress non-hadronic events such as τ-pairs we demand five well measured charged tracks or four tracks and at least six photon showers. Continuum events are further suppressed by requiring that there be no charged or neutral particle above 3.5 GeV (the kinematic limit for tracks from $B\bar{B}$ events is ≈ 2.8 GeV/c). Beam-correlated QED backgrounds from $e^+e^- \to e^+e^- X$ events, and events with undetected or badly fitted high-momentum tracks near the beam line, are eliminated by requiring the direction of the missing momentum to satisfy $|\cos(\theta_{miss})| < 0.9$. Highly asymmetric $\gamma \to e^+e^-$ pairs are cut by excluding electrons which share a common vertex with an oppositely charged, roughly collinear, track.

Continuum hadronic events are the largest remaining source of high-momentum leptons. The Fox-Wolfram[1] event-shape variable $R_2 \equiv H_2/H_0$ is very effective at distinguishing spherical $B\bar{B}$ events (small R_2) from more jet-like continuum events (larger R_2). In a comparison of continuum events and $b \to u\ell\nu$ events simulated to models of Isgur et al. (ISGW), Körner and Schuler (KS), and Wirbel, Stech and Bauer (WSB)[4], we find that a cut of $R_2 \leq 0.2$ maximizes the statistical significance of a possible $b \to u\ell\nu$ signal. The continuum is suppressed by a factor of 25, while 44% of the $b \to u\ell\nu$ signal is retained.

Additional continuum discrimination achieved with the event missing momentum p_{miss}. The energetic neutrino gives $b \to u\ell\nu$ events a large p_{miss}, while continuum events have considerably smaller p_{miss}. A requirement of 1 GeV/c $< p_{miss} <$ 4 GeV/c reduces the continuum by another factor of 2.3 while losing less than 10% of the signal. We further demand that the missing momentum points into the hemisphere opposite the lepton, removing 25% of the remaining continuum while giving up almost no signal efficiency. Overall, the continuum is suppressed by a factor of more than 70, and the $b \to u\ell\nu$ signal efficiency is 37%.

While this heavy continuum suppression ("strict cuts") gives optimum sensitivity according to our design study, uncertainty in the theoretical description of $b \to u\ell\nu$ makes it essential that we carefully assess possible model dependence. We find the efficiency of the tight R_2 and missing momentum cuts to have a strong dependence on the q^2, which measures the mass squared of the virtual W, of the $b \to u\ell\nu$ decay. Since plausible variations in the theoretical models can produce significant changes in the predicted q^2 distribution, we have analyzed our data with less stringent continuum suppression. Our "R_2-only" analysis relaxes the R_2 cut to less than or equal to 0.3, and eliminates altogether requirements on the magnitude and direction of the missing momentum.

The dominant background from B-meson decays, the $b \to c$ process $B \to \psi X$, followed by $\psi \to l^+l^-$, is suppressed by rejecting leptons that combine with any oppositely charged track with an invariant mass within 60 MeV of the ψ mass. Leakage through this veto ($\approx 10\%$), and the contribution of $B \to \psi' X$, are estimated by Monte Carlo simulation. Semileptonic decays $b \to c l \nu$ do not contribute appreciably above 2.4 GeV/c, and are also estimated by the simulation.

4. Results

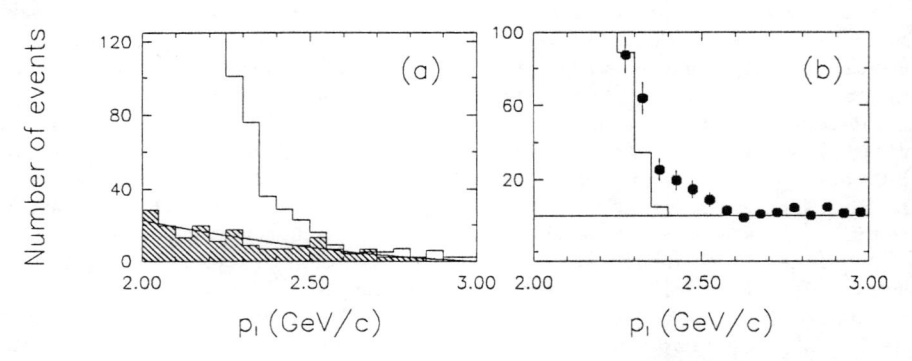

Figure 1: Sum of e and μ momentum spectra (strict cuts) for ON (solid) and scaled OFF data (dashed) in a), after subtraction of fitted continuum (dots) and $b \to c l \nu$ yield (histogram) in b).

Fig. 1a) shows our measured lepton momentum spectra, for the ON (solid line) and the scaled OFF (dashed) data. To minimize the statistical uncertainty associated with the continuum correction, the OFF spectra are fitted to smooth functions before subtraction. The systematic error in this correction is estimated from the spread of various fits. Fig. 1b) shows the lepton spectrum after the subtraction of the fitted continuum background. The expected $b \to c l \nu$ spectrum is shown as the solid histogram. A clear excess of events is seen near 2.5 GeV/c.

Lepton yields and background estimates for the momentum interval 2.4 - 2.6 GeV/c are summarized in Table 1, for both the strict and R_2-only analyses. The fake contributions are determined by multiplying the number of non-lepton tracks by the fake probabilities. The contribution of $b \to c l \nu$ decays is determined by fitting the momentum spectrum (1.5 - 2.4 GeV/c) to the predictions of theoretical models for $b \to c l \nu$[4], ignoring the small $b \to u l \nu$ contribution. The effects of detector smearing and radiative corrections [1] are included in these predictions.

After correcting for all sources of background, we find in the interval 2.4 to 2.6 GeV/c an excess attributable to $b \to u l \nu$ of $42.0 \pm 11.0 \pm 5.7$ events for the strict cuts, and $115 \pm 30 \pm 12$ events for the R_2-only. Efficiencies for detecting electrons and

Table 1: Lepton yields and backgrounds (2.4 to 2.6 GeV/c).

Cuts	Strict	$R_2 < 0.3$
N_{ON}	77 ± 8.8	422 ± 20.6
N_{OFF}	16 ± 4.0	145 ± 12.0
N_{OFF} (Fit)	$14.2 \pm 2.9 \pm 2.6$	$132.5 \pm 9.6 \pm 5.1$
Excess	41.8 ± 12.4	103.4 ± 33.5
Excess (Fit)	$45.9 \pm 10.9 \pm 5.6$	$130.9 \pm 29.4 \pm 11.3$
Fakes	1.6 ± 0.8	5.8 ± 2.6
$B \to \psi X, B \to \psi' X$	1.5 ± 0.7	7.5 ± 1.8
$b \to cl\nu$	$0.8 \pm 0.8 \pm 0.8$	$2.6 \pm 1.3 \pm 2.6$
$b \to ul\nu$ (Fit)	$42.0 \pm 11.0 \pm 5.7$	$115.0 \pm 29.6 \pm 11.6$
Efficiency [%]	21.5 ± 4.3	41.3 ± 6.2
ΔB_{ub} [10^{-6}]	$53 \pm 14 \pm 13$	$74 \pm 19 \pm 13$

muons from $b \to ul\nu$ in this momentum range are estimated by simulations using the ISGW and KS models, restricted to the low-multiplicity modes expected to dominate near the endpoint. For the strict (R_2-only) analysis the electron and muon efficiencies are $(22 \pm 4)\%$ and $(21 \pm 4)\%$ ($(42 \pm 6)\%$ and $(41 \pm 6)\%$), respectively. Possible model sensitivity is the principal component of the quoted errors. The average of the $b \to u\mu\nu$ and $b \to ue\nu$ partial branching ratios for the strict cuts is $\Delta B_u(2.4, 2.6) = (0.53 \pm 0.14 \pm 0.13) \times 10^{-4}$. This is significantly less than the previous CLEO result for this momentum interval, $(1.8 \pm 0.4 \pm 0.3) \times 10^{-4}$. With the R_2-only analysis this branching fraction is $\Delta B_u(2.4, 2.6) = (0.74 \pm 0.19 \pm 0.13) \times 10^{-4}$, somewhat greater than, but consistent with, the measurement obtained with the strict cuts.

We can extract $|V_{ub}|/|V_{cb}|$ from the branching fraction with the equation $|V_{ub}|^2/|V_{cb}|^2 = \Delta B_{ub}(p)/(B_{cb} \cdot d(p))$, where $d(p)$ is derived from the model and varies from 0.05 for ISGW to 0.17 for the KS model. B_{cb} is the branching ratio for $b \to cl\nu$, which is estimated by the semileptonic branching ratio $B_{cb} = (10.8 \pm 0.2 \pm 0.6)$ %[5]. The different models imply a value of $|V_{ub}|/|V_{cb}|$ in the range of 0.05 to 0.12.

5. References

1. R. Fulton et al., *Phys. Rev. Lett.* **64** (1990) 16.
2. H. Albrecht et al., *Phys. Lett.* **B234** (1990) 409, **B255** (1991) 297.
3. Y. Kubota et al., *Nucl. Inst. Meth.* **A320** (1992) 66.
4. N. Isgur et al., *Phys. Rev.* **D39** (1989) 799.
   M. Wirbel et al., *Zeit. Phys.* **C29** (1985) 637.
   J. Körner and G. Schuler, *Zeit. Phys.* **C38** (1988) 511.
   G. Altarelli et al., *Nucl. Phys.* **B208** (1982) 365.
5. S. Henderson et al., *Phys. Rev.* **D45** (1992) 2212.

Search for Exclusive $b \to u$ Semileptonic Decays of B Mesons

Jeffrey D. Richman
Physics Department, UCSB
Santa Barbara, CA. 93106, USA
Representing the CLEO collaboration

ABSTRACT

Using a sample of 935,000 $B\overline{B}$ pairs collected by the CLEO-II detector at the Cornell Electron Storage Ring, we have obtained upper limits on the branching ratios for the $b \to u\, \ell^- \overline{\nu}$ processes $B^- \to \omega\, \ell^- \overline{\nu}$, $B^- \to \rho^0\, \ell^- \overline{\nu}$, and $\overline{B}^0 \to \rho^+\, \ell^- \overline{\nu}$. The combined result using these related modes is $B(B^- \to \rho^0 \ell^- \overline{\nu}) < (1.6 \text{ to } 2.7) \times 10^{-4}$ at 90% C.L., where the range of values is due to model dependence of the detection efficiencies. These measurements yield the limits $|V_{ub}/V_{cb}| < (0.08 \text{ to } 0.13)$.

The decays $B^- \to \omega\, \ell^- \overline{\nu}$, $B^- \to \rho^0\, \ell^- \overline{\nu}$, and $\overline{B}^0 \to \rho^+\, \ell^- \overline{\nu}$ correspond to the highly suppressed transition $b \to u\, \ell^- \overline{\nu}$. These processes are therefore sensitive to the Standard Model parameter V_{ub}, one of the smallest and least well-measured elements of the Cabibbo-Kobayashi-Maskawa (CKM) quark-mixing matrix. Current knowledge of $|V_{ub}|$ is based on measurements[1] of the inclusive energy spectrum of leptons produced in B meson decay. In addition, the ARGUS collaboration has presented preliminary evidence for a $B^- \to \rho^0\, \ell^- \overline{\nu}$ signal.[2]

In the $b \to u$ decay $B^- \to X_u \ell^- \overline{\nu}$, the hadronic system X_u can range over much of the light-quark hadron spectrum, and no single final state is expected to dominate. Theoretical models indicate that, among these rare processes, the rate for $B^- \to \rho^0\, \ell^- \overline{\nu}$ should be one of the largest, representing 3.5% to 14% of the inclusive $B^- \to X_u \ell^- \overline{\nu}$ rate. The three decay modes we have investigated are related to each other:

$$\Gamma(\overline{B}^0 \to \rho^+\, \ell^- \overline{\nu}) = 2\, \Gamma(B^- \to \rho^0\, \ell^- \overline{\nu}) \simeq 2\, \Gamma(B^- \to \omega\, \ell^- \overline{\nu}). \tag{1}$$

(Throughout this paper, charge conjugate modes are implied.)

Our analysis uses 935,000 $B\overline{B}$ pairs (923 pb^{-1} at the $\Upsilon(4S)$) collected by the CLEO-II detector[3] at the Cornell Electron Storage Ring (CESR). To study the continuum background, we use a 416 pb^{-1} data sample accumulated at $\sqrt{s} = 10.52$ GeV.

Quark models predict that the E_ℓ (lab-frame lepton energy) spectrum from $B \to \rho(\omega)\, \ell^- \overline{\nu}$ peaks at high energy, around 2.2 GeV. By requiring $E_\ell \geq 2.0$ GeV, we suppress the dominant background, $b \to c\, \ell^- \overline{\nu}$, which has a substantially softer E_ℓ spectrum. All of the models we have considered predict that the fraction of signal events with $E_\ell > 2.0$ GeV is large: 0.72 in ISGW[4], 0.68 in KS[5], and 0.52 in WSB.[6]

The analysis consists of two main steps. We first select events whose characteristics are consistent with the presence of two B mesons, each nearly at rest, with one decaying into $\pi\pi\ell\nu$ or $\pi^+\pi^-\pi^0\ell\nu$. We optimize the selection cuts separately in two E_ℓ regions, LOLEP: $2.0 \leq E_\ell < 2.3$ GeV and HILEP: $E_\ell \geq 2.3$ GeV. Because the lepton-energy spectrum from $b \to c\, \ell^- \bar\nu$ background falls off sharply around 2.3 GeV, the LOLEP region is dominated by $b \to c\, \ell^- \bar\nu$ processes, whereas the HILEP region has much less total background and is dominated by continuum events. In the second step of the analysis, we fit the resulting $\pi\pi(\pi^+\pi^-\pi^0)$ mass spectra to obtain limits on $B \to \rho(\omega)\, \ell^- \bar\nu$.

Figure 1a shows the $\pi^+\pi^-\pi^0$ HILEP mass spectrum after all cuts from the ω analyses have been applied; figure 1b shows the corresponding $\pi^+\pi^-$ HILEP mass spectrum. Neither shows a clear ω or ρ signal.

To set limits on the number of ω's and ρ's in these spectra, we perform binned maximum likelihood fits. For the ω analysis, we use a Breit-Wigner lineshape convoluted with a Gaussian ($\sigma = 8$ MeV) to describe the ω, and a polynomial to describe the background; the sum of these terms is represented by a solid line in figure 1a. Because the ω is narrow, the $\pi^+\pi^-\pi^0$ fits are insensitive to the background shape. The fits to the $\pi\pi$ mass spectra incorporate three separate background terms in addition to the ρ signal, which is parametrized by a Breit-Wigner. In HILEP, these terms are 1) a term whose shape and normalization is fixed from a fit to the continuum data sample, after the same cuts are applied; 2) a smooth function, which is allowed to vary in both shape and normalization, to represent any background remaining from $b \to c\, \ell^- \bar\nu$ or other sources; and 3) a smooth function, whose shape is fixed by the *signal* Monte Carlo, and which represents the combinatorial background present in signal events when the $\rho\ell$ candidate contains decay products from both B mesons. The normalization of the third term is fixed relative to the area of the ρ Breit-Wigner from a fit to the signal Monte Carlo. The dashed curve in figure 1b shows the sum of terms 1 and 2, the dot-dashed curve represents the sum of terms 1–3, and the solid curve represents the sum of the signal term plus all background terms.

Table 1 gives central values and limits for each mode, assuming efficiencies from a Monte Carlo simulation using the ISGW model. Using the relations given

Table 1: Efficiencies and Fit Results, ISGW-Model. Positive central values cannot be interpreted as evidence for a signal, because there may be ρ or ω contributions from remaining background events. Divide the ρ^+ results by 2 (isospin) to compare with ρ^0.

V	E_ℓ (GeV)	ϵ (%)	$\dfrac{B(B \to Vl^-\bar\nu)}{10^{-4}}$	Limit/10^{-4} (90%C.L.)
ω	≥ 2.3	2.4	$0.5 \pm 1.1 \pm 0.1$	< 2.1
ρ^0	≥ 2.3	7.1	$0.9^{+0.5+0.8}_{-0.8-0.2}$	< 2.1
ρ^+	≥ 2.3	4.1	$2.2 \pm 0.7^{+1.2}_{-0.4}$	< 4.1
ω	$2.0 \leq E_\ell < 2.3$	1.6	$1.4 \pm 2.5 \pm 0.3$	< 5.0
ρ^0	$2.0 \leq E_\ell < 2.3$	8.1	$3.7 \pm 1.5 \pm 2.4$	< 7.5
ρ^+	$2.0 \leq E_\ell < 2.3$	5.4	$-5.8 \pm 3.0 \pm 9.3$	< 12.9

Table 2: Combined Upper Limits for Three Models. Here V^0 represents either a ρ^0 or an ω. As stated in Table 1, positive central values cannot be interpreted as evidence for a signal.

Model	$B(B^- \to V^0 l^- \bar{\nu})/10^{-4}$	Limit/10^{-4} (90% C.L.)	$|V_{ub}/V_{cb}|$ (90% C.L.)
ISGW	$1.0 \pm 0.5 \pm 0.2$	< 1.6	< 0.13
WSB	$1.6 \pm 0.8 \pm 0.3$	< 2.7	< 0.10
KS	$1.3 \pm 0.7 \pm 0.2$	< 2.3	< 0.08

in Eq. (1), we can statistically combine the results for the different channels, which we do for each model in Table 2.

In conclusion, we find, for the set of models considered,

$$B(B^- \to V^0 \ell^- \bar{\nu}) < (1.6 \text{ to } 2.7) \times 10^{-4} \text{ at 90\% C.L.}$$

Our result is inconsistent at the 2.3σ level with a preliminary ARGUS measurement $B(B^- \to \rho^0 \ell^- \bar{\nu}) = (11.3 \pm 3.6 \pm 2.7) \times 10^{-4}$, where the ISGW model was used to obtain the efficiency. Using the partial width predictions for the theoretical models in terms of $|V_{ub}|$, and assuming $\tau_B \times |V_{cb}|^2 = 1.28$ ps $\times (0.041)^2$, we obtain limits on $|V_{ub}/V_{cb}|$ ranging from 0.08 to 0.13, which lowers the allowed range for this parameter.

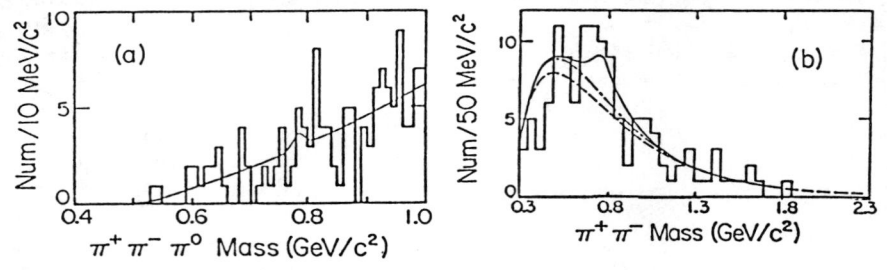

Figure 1. Invariant mass spectra for combinations that pass (a) the ω HILEP cuts and (b) the ρ^0 HILEP cuts. The curves are described in the text.

1. H. Albrecht, et al. (ARGUS Collab.), Phys. Lett. B **234**, 409 (1990); R. Fulton et al. (CLEO Collab.), Phys. Rev. Lett. **64**, 16 (1990).
2. M. Paulini (ARGUS Collab.), in *Proceedings of the Joint International Symposium & Europhysics Conference on High Energy Physics*, edited by S. Hegarty, K. Potter, and E. Quercigh (World Scientific, Singapore, 1992), p. 592.
3. Y. Kubota, et al. (CLEO Collab.), Nucl. Instrum. Meth. A **320**, 66 (1992).
4. N. Isgur, D. Scora, B. Grinstein, and M. Wise, Phys. Rev. **D39**, 799 (1989).
5. J. G. Körner and G. A. Schuler, Z. Phys. C **46**, 93 (1990).
6. M. Wirbel, B. Stech, M. Bauer, Z. Phys. C **29**, 637 (1985).

Ξ and Ω Production in Z Decays

R.P. Johnson, M.A. McNeil
Physics Department, University of California
Santa Cruz, CA   95065
Representing the Aleph Collaboration

ABSTRACT

Inclusive production of Ξ and Ω hyperons has been studied in 460 000 hadronic events observed with the Aleph detector at LEP. Large Ξ^- (Ξ^+) and $\Xi(1530)^0$ ($\bar{\Xi}(1530)^0$) signals are observed, from which the multiplicities and energy spectra have been measured. A small Ω^- ($\bar{\Omega}^+$) signal also is observed, giving a measurement of the multiplicity.

Production of baryons in quark fragmentation is still a poorly understood phenomenon. To increase our understanding of this process, or at least to constrain better our fragmentation models, it is important to measure the production rates of the various baryon species in high-energy e^+e^- annihilation. In particular, it is interesting to measure the rates of production of hyperons in the SU(3) octet and decuplet representations, which provide information on the formation of baryons with one, two, or three strange quarks and with spin-1/2 or spin-3/2. In this paper we present a measurement by the Aleph experiment at LEP of the production rates of Ξ and Ω hyperons in e^+e^- annihilation at the Z resonance.

This analysis relies on the tracking chambers of the Aleph detector, which have been described in detail elsewhere.[1] A total of 458 915 candidates for hadronic Z decays is selected by requiring at least five good charged tracks with a total of at least 10% of the center-of-mass energy. Ξ^- and Ω^- candidates are tagged by the decays $\Xi^- \to \Lambda\pi^-$ and $\Omega^- \to \Lambda K^-$, and the Λ candidates are tagged by the decay $\Lambda \to p\pi^-$. The analysis begins with a search for vertices with radii, transverse to the beam, of greater than 3.5 cm which are consistent with the decay $\Lambda \to p\pi^-$ and inconsistent with being γ conversions. The resulting neutral Λ track is vertexed with all remaining good tracks of the appropriate charge, and Ξ^- (Ω^-) candidates are selected by requiring that the decay length measured from the beam spot be at least 3 cm (1.5 cm). In addition, the Λ decay length is required to be at least 1 cm, and both vertex fits are required to have a χ^2 of no greater than 6. To further reduce background, the measured dE/dx of each track must be within 2σ of the expected value for p and K, and within 3σ for π. The dE/dx cut is made only if the information is available for the track, except in the case of the Ω^- analysis, where at least 50 ionization measurements are required. Also, for the Ω^- selection, candidates are rejected if they fall within 7.5 MeV/c^2 of the Ξ^- mass. The resulting Ξ^- signal is shown in Fig. 1.a. Depending on the Ξ momentum, the mass resolution varies between 2.5 MeV/c^2 and 6 MeV/c^2 and the detection efficiency between 0.05 and 0.20. The background is fit from a linear interpolation of the sidebands, which agree well with the wrong-sign spectrum. Fig. 1.b shows the ΛK^- mass spectrum, where a slight excess of 26±9 events is seen in a region ±4 MeV/c^2 about the Ω^- mass with a resolution consistent with that expected from the Monte Carlo simulation.

For the $\Xi(1530)^0$ analysis, all Ξ^- candidates within 6.4 MeV/c^2 of the Ξ^- mass are paired with all remaining good tracks of the appropriate charge which extrapolate to within 0.8 cm of the origin in the transverse plane. The background shape is obtained by pairing all wrong-sign Ξ^- candidates within 35 MeV/c^2 of the Ξ^- mass with pion candidates of opposite charge. The signal, shown in Fig. 1.c, is fit to a combination of this background, scaled by a free parameter, and a gaussian curve, from which the number of signal events is found to be 109 ± 23.

For the Ξ^- and $\Xi(1530)^0$ signals the efficiencies were calculated by Monte Carlo simulation for each bin in $x_E \equiv E_{\text{baryon}}/E_{\text{beam}}$. The corrected measurements of the x_E distributions are shown in Fig. 1.d, along with the predictions of the Lund Jetset-7.3 model with the parton shower and string fragmentation.[2] As a cross check, the $c\tau$ of the Λ and Ξ^- were measured to be (7.3 ± 0.5) cm and (4.7 ± 0.4) cm respectively, in good agreement with the accepted values. The Ξ^- polarization was measured to be 0.24 ± 0.15, whereas the efficiency was calculated for the expected value of zero polarization. However, an uncertainty of ±0.24 in the polarization introduces a negligible systematic error. The Jetset model was used to extrapolate the results over the unmeasured regions at low x_E to obtain the overall multiplicities:

$$\langle N_{\Xi^-}\rangle + \langle N_{\Xi^+}\rangle = 0.0278 \pm 0.0013 \pm 0.0016,$$
$$\langle N_{\Xi(1530)^0}\rangle + \langle N_{\overline{\Xi}(1530)^0}\rangle = 0.0044 \pm 0.0011 \pm 0.0007,$$
$$\langle N_{\Omega^-}\rangle + \langle N_{\Omega^+}\rangle = 0.0012 \pm 0.0004 \pm 0.0003,$$

where in each case the first uncertainty is statistical and the second is systematic. These results are all consistent with the Jetset-7.3 model and are in reasonable agreement with recently published Delphi (Ξ^- only) and Opal results,[3] except that our measurement of the Ω^- multiplicity is about a factor of four lower than that of Opal. These Aleph results are unpublished and preliminary.

Acknowledgements

This work is a result of the cooperative effort of all of the members of the Aleph collaboration. We are indebted to our colleagues in the SL division, for the fine performance of the LEP storage ring, and to the engineers and technicians at our institutes for their support in constructing and operating Aleph.

References

1. D. Decamp, et al., *Nucl. Instr. Methods* **A294** (1990) 121.
2. M. Bengtsson and T. Sjöstrand, *Phys. Lett.* B **185** (1987) 435; T. Sjöstrand, CERN-TH.6488/92 (1992).
3. P. Abreu, et al., *Phys. Lett.* B **275** (1992) 231; P.D. Acton et al., *Phys. Lett.* B **291** (1992) 503.

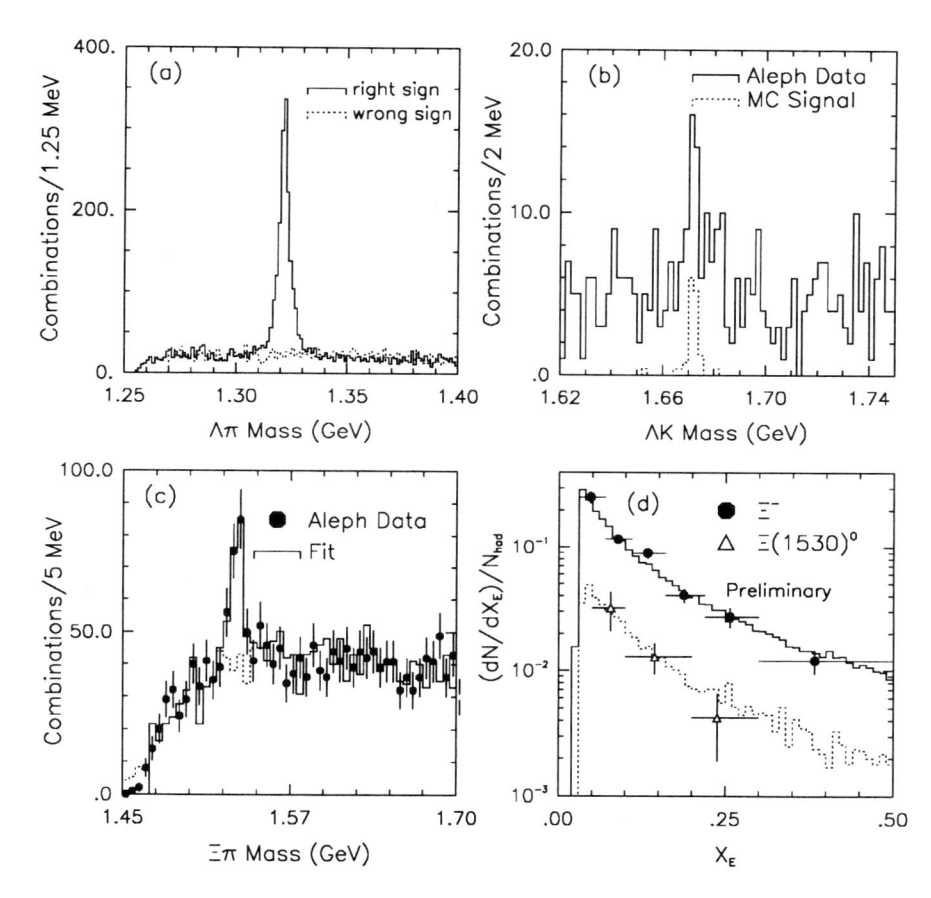

Figure 1: (a) The signal for $\Xi^- \to \Lambda\pi^-$. (b) The ΛK^- mass spectrum, compared with the Jetset 7.3 prediction for Ω^- production, normalized to the luminosity of the data. (c) The signal for $\Xi(1530)^0 \to \Xi^-\pi^+$, fitted to the background prediction from wrong-sign Ξ^- plus a gaussian signal. (d) The measured X_E distributions for Ξ^- and $\Xi(1530)^0$ production, compared with Jetset 7.3 predictions.

PRELIMINARY RESULTS FROM FERMILAB E-800 ON THE POLARIZATION OF Ξ^-'s AND Ω^-'s PRODUCED BY POLARIZED AND UNPOLARIZED NEUTRAL BEAMS

D. M. WOODS, P. BORDER, D. P. CIAMPA, G. GUGLIELMO, K. HELLER, N. B. WALLACE

School of Physics and Astronomy, University of Minnesota, Minneapolis, MN 55455 USA

K. JOHNS

Department of Physics, University of Arizona, Tucson, AZ 85721 USA

R. RAMEIKA

Fermilab, Batavia, IL 60510 USA

Y. T. GAO, M. J. LONGO

Department of Physics, University of Michigan, Ann Arbor, MI 48109 USA

ABSTRACT

A neutral beam was used to produce Ξ^-'s and Ω^-'s at Fermilab. In one method, the hyperons in the neutral beam are polarized and produce polarized Ξ^-'s and Ω^-'s at 0 mrad. In the second method, the unpolarized neutral hyperons produce unpolarized Ξ^-'s and polarized Ω^-'s at 1.8 mrad.

1. Introduction

Since the discovery that Λ hyperons produced by unpolarized high energy protons were polarized[1], similar polarization has been found for most of the stable hyperons ($\Lambda, \Xi^0, \Xi^-, \overline{\Xi^-}, \Sigma^+, \Sigma^0$, and Σ^-)[2,3,4,5,6,7,8]. The $\overline{\Lambda}$ and Ω^- were found to not be polarized[2,9]. The mechanism that creates this polarization is still not well understood, but the model of DeGrand and Miettinen is still a useful guide[10]. In order to further study this mechanism, we measured the polarization of Ξ^-'s and Ω^-'s produced by a neutral beam. In one case, the neutral beam was unpolarized, and in the other case, the neutral beam contained polarized Λ's and Ξ^0's.

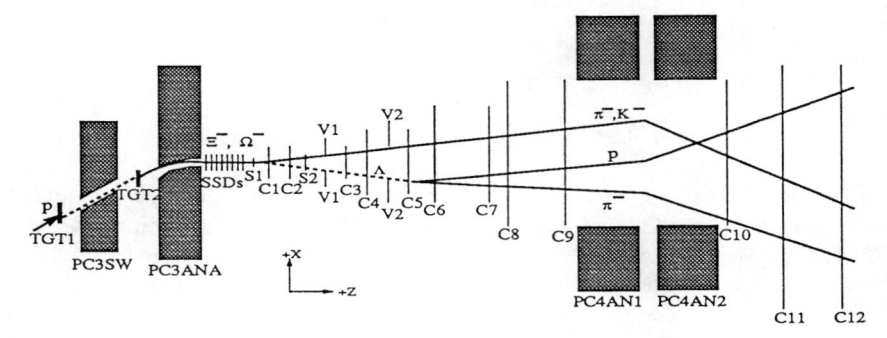

Figure 1. Plan view of the E800 spectrometer. C1 - C12 are MWPCs with 2 orthogonal signal planes

2. Apparatus

At Fermilab, 800 GeV protons were used to produce a beam of neutral particles, which then produced a negative hyperon beam using a curved channel embedded in a large dipole magnet. The charged decay products from $\Omega^- \to \Lambda + K^-$ and $\Xi^- \to \Lambda + \pi^-$ were detected in the spectrometer shown in Figure 1. Because the topologies of these decays are almost identical, the Ξ^-'s and Ω^-'s were detected and analyzed in the same way. The simple trigger required hits in both scintillators S1 and S2, and the characteristic "V" of the Λ with hits in the right half of C11 and the left half of C12.

3. Production Methods

The 3 different methods used to produce the Ξ^-'s and Ω^-'s are shown in Figure 2. In the unpolarized neutral production method, protons strike the first target and a magnet sweeps away all charged particles. The neutral beam, produced at 0 mrad, then strikes the second target producing Ξ^-'s and Ω^-'s at 1.8 mrad. For polarized neutral production, the role of the two angles is reversed. In addition, to allow comparisons with previous experiments, Ξ^-'s and Ω^-'s were also produced directly using a proton beam at 1.8 mrad.

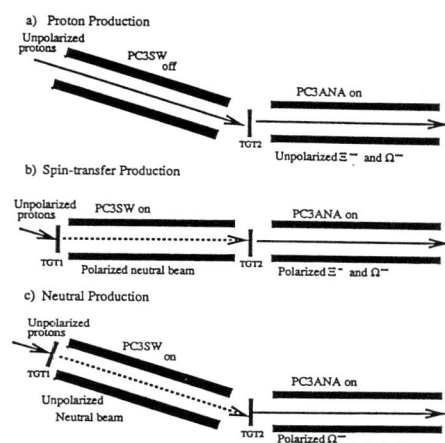

Figure 2. E800 Production Methods.

4. Analysis

The polarization of the Ξ^-'s and Ω^-'s was determined from the decay asymmetry of the daughter Λ. Assuming time reversal invariance ($\beta_\Xi = 0$) and neglecting small terms[4,9], $\vec{P}_\Lambda = \gamma_\Xi \vec{P}_\Xi$ and $\vec{P}_\Omega = \vec{P}_\Lambda$. The polarization of the Λ is measured by examining the distribution of the daughter proton in the Λ rest frame.

5. Results

A preliminary polarization analysis was done on a sample of 1.5 million Ξ^-'s and 78,000 Ω^-'s; this represents about 3% of the total Ξ^- sample and 40% of the total Ω^- sample. The quality of the reconstructed events is shown in Figure 3.

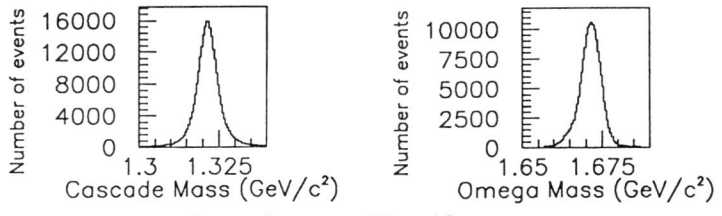

Figure 3. Reconstructed Ξ^- and Ω^- mass.

Figure 4 shows Ξ^- and Ω^- polarization for the neutral production methods together with results from previous measurements[9,11]. The polarization of the Ω^-'s and Ξ^-'s produced by polarized neutrals agrees with previous results[9,11] and with the expectations of models[10]. On the other hand, unpolarized neutral production yields polarized Ω^-'s but unpolarized Ξ^-'s. It is difficult to reconcile this result with models, unless there is a fortuitous cancellation of the Ξ^- polarization produced by neutrons and that produced by Λ's and Ξ^0's.

Preliminary polarization results. The average polarization for all samples is 395 GeV/c.

Spin transfer Ξ^-'s:
P = -0.1172 ± 0.0062

Neutral production Ξ^-'s:
P = 0.0062 ± 0.0042

Spin transfer Ω^-'s:
P = -0.076 ± 0.021

Neutral production Ω^-'s:
P = 0.053 ± 0.012

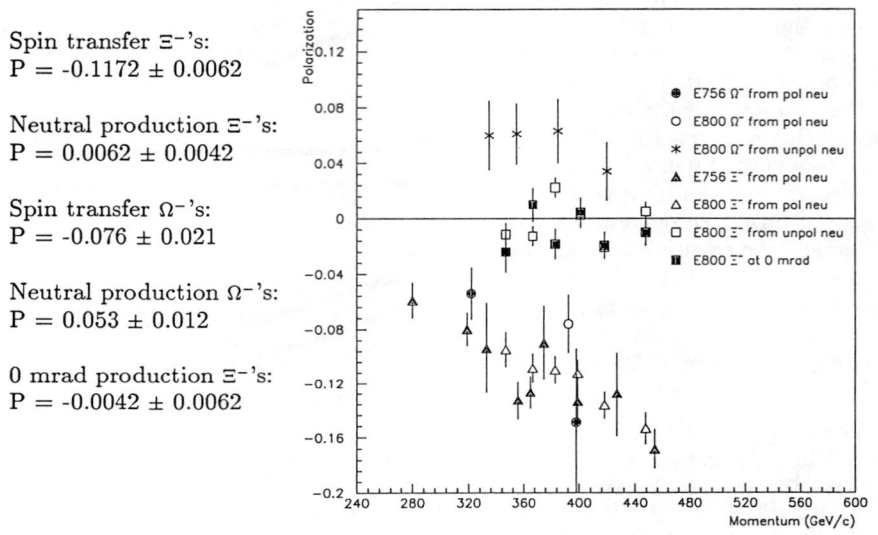

0 mrad production Ξ^-'s:
P = -0.0042 ± 0.0062

Figure 4. Ξ^- and Ω^- polarization results.

6. Acknowledgements

This work was supported by the U.S. Department of Energy. We would like to thank G. Allan, A. Ayala-Mercado, E. Berman, D. Fein, M. Groblewski, J. Jalilian-Marian, E. James, and T. Tynan for their contributions. Also, this work would not have been possible without the support of the Fermilab staff.

1. G. Bunce et al., Phys. Rev. Lett., **36**, 1113 (1976).
2. K. Heller et al., Phys. Rev. Lett., **41**, 607 (1978).
3. K. Heller et al., Phys. Rev. Lett., **51**, 2025 (1983).
4. R. Rameika et al., Phys Rev., **D33**, 3172 (1986).
5. P. M. Ho et al., Phys. Rev. Lett., **65**, 1713 (1990).
6. C. Wilkinson et al., Phys. Rev. Lett., **58**, 855 (1987).
7. L. Deck et al., Phys. Rev., **D28**, 1 (1983).
8. Y. W. Yah et al., Phys. Rev. Lett., **55**, 2551 (1985).
9. H. T. Diehl et al., Phys. Rev. Lett., **67**, 804 (1991).
10. T. DeGrand and H. Miettinen, Phys. Rev., **D24**, 2419 (1981).
11. H. T. Diehl, *Ph.D. thesis, Rutgers University*, (unpublished, 1990).

PRELIMINARY RESULTS FROM FERMILAB E-800 ON THE DECAY ASYMMETRY OF THE Ξ⁻ HYPERON

G. GUGLIELMO, P. BORDER, D. P. CIAMPA, K. HELLER, N. B. WALLACE, D. M. WOODS
School of Physics and Astronomy, University of Minnesota
Minneapolis, MN 55455 U.S.A.

K. JOHNS
Department of Physics, University of Arizona, Tucson, AZ 85721 U.S.A.

Y. T. GAO, M. J. LONGO
Department of Physics, University of Michigan, Ann Arbor, MI 48109 U.S.A.

R. RAMEIKA
Fermilab, Batavia, IL 60510 U.S.A.

ABSTRACT

Previous measurements of the decay asymmetry $\alpha_\Lambda \alpha_{\Xi^-}$ have been shown to be inconsistent. FNAL experiment E-800 has collected samples of Ξ^-s produced by polarized and unpolarized 400 GeV neutral beams. Analysis of 3% of these data has yielded a preliminary measurement of -0.2779 ± 0.0015 for the parameter $\alpha_\Lambda \alpha_{\Xi^-}$.

1. Introduction

Table 1 lists nine previous measurements of $\alpha_\Lambda \alpha_{\Xi^-}$[1]. All six of the lower energy measurements using an incident K^- beam are near -0.250, while the three higher energy proton beam experiments yield values near -0.302. If these measurements are separated into the two groups suggested above, all of the values within each group are consistent with each other to less than one standard deviation. The weighted average for the three proton beam experiments is -0.3018 ± 0.0044, while the six kaon beam experiments have a weighted average of -0.2518 ± 0.0091. These two averages are more than five standard deviations apart and thus indicate a systematic problem.

Table 1. Previous measurements of $\alpha_\Lambda \alpha_{\Xi^-}$.

$\alpha_\Lambda \alpha_{\Xi^-}$ asymmetry	incident beam	$\alpha_\Lambda \alpha_{\Xi^-}$ method
-0.303 ± 0.004 ± 0.004	400 GeV Proton[2]	direct
-0.299 ± 0.007	250 GeV Proton[3]	direct
-0.315 ± 0.026	29.4 GeV Proton[4]	direct
-0.257 ± 0.020	11 GeV K^- [5]	indirect
-0.260 ± 0.017	5 GeV K^- [6]	indirect
-0.239 ± 0.021	4.2 GeV K^- [7]	direct
-0.253 ± 0.028	1.7-2.8 GeV K^- [8]	indirect
-0.252 ± 0.032	1.8 GeV K^- [9]	indirect
-0.243 ± 0.025	1.75 GeV K^- [10]	indirect

2. Apparatus and Method

The Ξ^-s for this measurement were created by a neutral secondary beam on a Be target at a production angle θ_2 and passed through a magnetic field, M2, which provided a means of momentum selection. The neutral beam, obtained by interactions from an 800 GeV proton beam with a Be target, contained neutrons, K^0s, Λs, and Ξ^0s with an average momentum on the order of 400 GeV. The neutral beam was selected by a straight collimator in a magnetic field. Table 2 gives the magnetic field, M1, and the neutral beam production angle, θ_1, together with M2 and θ_2. By varying the production angles at the two targets as well as the fields of the two magnets, samples of Ξ^-s were obtained under a wide variety of production schemes and thus differing background and systematic conditions. Only samples 4a and 4b had polarized beams, and for them both the neutral and Ξ^- beams were polarized.

Table 2. The Ξ^- production schemes.

Set	M1 $\hat{X}$(T)	M2 $\hat{Y}$(T)	θ_1 (mr)	θ_2 (mr)	Set	M1 $\hat{X}$(T)	M2 $\hat{Y}$(T)	θ_1 (mr)	θ_2 (mr)
1a	1.8	-3.33	0.	-1.8	3a	1.8	-3.33	0.	0.
1b	-1.8	-3.33	0.	1.8	3b	-1.8	-3.33	0.	0.
2a	1.8	-2.39	0.	-1.8	4a	-1.8	-3.33	-1.8	0.
2b	-1.8	-2.39	0.	1.8	4b	1.8	-3.33	1.8	0.

The Ξ^-, its decay to $\Lambda + \pi^-$, and the subsequent decay of the Λ to $p + \pi^-$ were detected in a spectrometer[11]. The decay asymmetry can be measured from the angular distribution of the proton in the lambda rest frame. The angular distribution in the lambda rest frame is

$$I(\theta_n, \phi_n) = \frac{1}{4\pi}\left(1 + \alpha_\Lambda \alpha_{\Xi^-} \cos\theta_n\right) \qquad (1)$$

where $\cos\theta_n = -\hat{P}\cdot\hat{\Xi}$ in the lambda rest frame.

3. Results

The reconstruction methods and asymmetry analysis for this measurement are very similar to those employed by this group in previous experiments[12].

The weighted average value for the 86 measurements in Figures 1 and 2 yield $\alpha_\Lambda \alpha_{\Xi^-}$ = -0.2779 ± 0.0015, where the error is statistical only and represents about 3% of the total Ξ^- data. The chi-square per degree of freedom for the fit was 1.35. This measurement disagrees with the previous kaon beam and proton beam results and is nearly midway between them.

Systematic studies are still in progress, and this investigation will be greatly enhanced by a significant reduction in the statistical error provided by the full data set. However, for the preliminary analysis of this subset of E800 data, $\alpha_\Lambda \alpha_{\Xi^-}$ is plotted as a function of Ξ^- momentum in Figures 1 and 2 and no momentum dependence is observed.

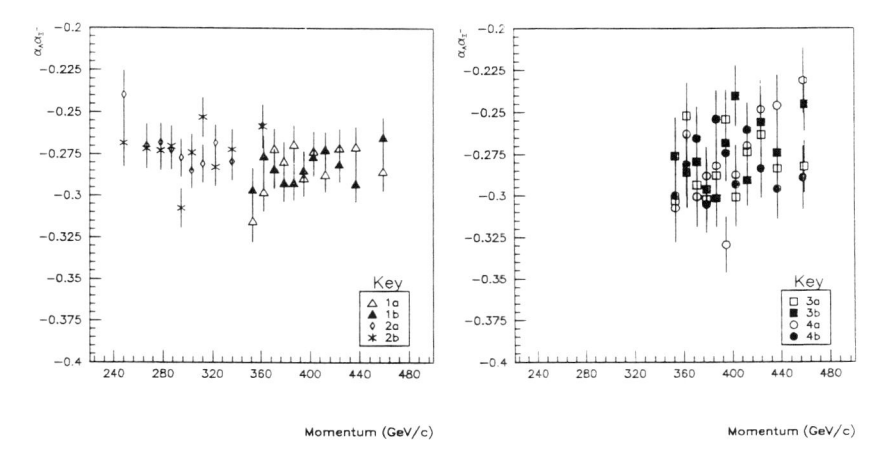

Figure 1. $\alpha_\Lambda \alpha_{\Xi^-}$ for sets 1a,b and 2a,b.   Figure 2. $\alpha_\Lambda \alpha_{\Xi^-}$ for sets 3a,b and 4a,b.

This work was supported by the U. S. Department of Energy and the NSF. We would like to thank G. Allan, A. Ayala-Mercado, E. Berman, D. Fein, J. Jalilian-Marian, E. James, and T. Tynan for their contributions. We would also like to thank the Fermilab staff, especially the Online Data Acquisition Group, for their support.

1. Particle Data Group , *Phys. Rev.*, **D45**, (1992)
2. R. Rameika et al., *Phys. Rev.*, **D33**, 3172 (1986)
3. S. F. Biagi et al., *Phys. Lett.*, **112B**, 265 (1982)
4. W. E. Cleland et al., *Phys. Rev.*, **D21**, 12 (1969)
5. D. Aston et al., *Phys. Rev.*, **D32**, 2270 (1985)
6. J. Bensinger et al., *Nucl. Phys.*, **B252**, 561 (1985)
7. R. J. Hemingway et al., *Nucl. Phys.*, **B142**, 205 (1978)
8. P. M. Dauber et al., *Phys. Rev.*, **179**, 1262 (1969)
9. R. L. Cool et al., *Phys. Rev.*, **D10**, 792 (1974)
10. C. Baltay et al., *Phys. Rev.*, **D9**, 49 (1974)
11. D. M. Woods, These Proceedings
12. J. Duryea, Ph.D. Thesis University of Minnesota (unpublished) (1991)

PRELIMINARY RESULTS FROM FERMILAB E-800 ON THE MAGNETIC MOMENT OF Ω^- PRODUCED BY A NEUTRAL BEAM

N.B. WALLACE, P. BORDER, D.P. CIAMPA, G. GUGLIELMO, K. HELLER, D.M. WOODS

School of Physics and Astronomy, University of Minnesota
Minneapolis, MN 55455 U.S.A.

K. JOHNS

Department of Physics, University of Arizona, Tucson, AZ 85721 U.S.A.

R. RAMEIKA

Fermilab, Batavia, IL 60510 U.S.A.

Y.T. GAO, M. J. LONGO

Department of Physics, University of Michigan, Ann Arbor, MI 48109 U.S.A.

ABSTRACT

E-800 experiment at Fermilab has obtained 230,000 polarized $\Omega^- \to \Lambda K^-$ and has a preliminary measurement of the Ω^- magnetic moment as $-2.1 \pm 0.1\ \mu_N$ using 100,000 events. The uncertainty is statistical only. The systematic errors are still under investigation.

1. Introduction

The magnetic moments of baryons are the physical observables which have been used to test models of the behavior of quarks in hadrons. The static quark model (s.q.m.) predicts hyperon magnetic moments to within 10% of experimental measurements, however most measurements have been made to much higher precision. The current models do not significantly improve this situation.[1,2] Given the simple quark structure of the Ω^-, three identical quarks with spin aligned, a precision measurement of μ_{Ω^-}, could provide a good test of alternative models.

In (s.q.m.) the magnetic moment of a baryon is the sum of the moments of the valence quarks.

$$\mu_B = <B|\sum_i \vec{\mu}_i|B> \qquad (1)$$

Here $<B|$ is the baryon wave function and $\vec{\mu}_i$ are the individual quark magnetic moments. Table 1 compares s.q.m. with previous experimental meausurements. [3]

Table I. Magnetic moment predictions using s.q.m. in units of nuclear magnetons (μ_N) compared to previous measurements.

Hyperon	$\mu_{hyperon}$ in Terms of μ_{quark}	Broken SU(6)	Experimental Result
p	$\mu_{proton} = 4/3\mu_u - 1/3\mu_d$	Input	2.793
n	$\mu_{neutron} = 4/3\mu_d - 1/3\mu_u$	Input	-1.913
Λ	$\mu_\Lambda = \mu_s$	Input	-0.613 ± 0.004
Σ^+	$\mu_{\Sigma^+} = 4/3\mu_u - 1/3\mu_s$	2.74	2.419 ± 0.022
$\Sigma^0 - \Lambda$	$(\mu_d - \mu_u)/\sqrt{3}$	-1.63	-1.61 ± 0.08
Σ^-	$\mu_{\Sigma^-} = 4/3\mu_d - 1/3\mu_s$	-1.21	-1.156 ± 0.014
Ξ^0	$\mu_{\Xi^0} = 4/3\mu_s - 1/3\mu_u$	-1.46	-1.23 ± 0.014
Ξ^-	$\mu_{\Xi^-} = 4/3\mu_s - 1/3\mu_d$	-0.52	-0.6505 ± 0.0025
Ω	$\mu_{\Omega^-} = 3\mu_s$	-1.83	$-1.94 \pm 0.17 \pm 0.14$

2. Method and Apparatus

Given a beam of polarized Ω^-, μ_{Ω^-} can be measured by precessing the Ω^- in a magnetic field.[4] If Φ_{lab} is the difference between the spin precession angle and the momentum precession angle, the magnetic moment of the Ω^- in units of μ_N is given by,

$$\mu_{\Omega^-} = \frac{m_p}{e} \left(\frac{\Phi_{lab}}{\int Bdl} + \frac{-e}{m_{\Omega^-}} \right) S \qquad (2)$$

$\int Bdl$, is the field integral of the precession magnet, m_p and m_{Ω^-} are the proton and Ω^- mass in MeV, and S is the Ω^- spin in units of $\hbar$.

For this measurement the Ω^-s were created by both an unpolarized and polarized neutral secondary beam incident on a be target at a vertical targeting angle of ± 1.8 mrad.

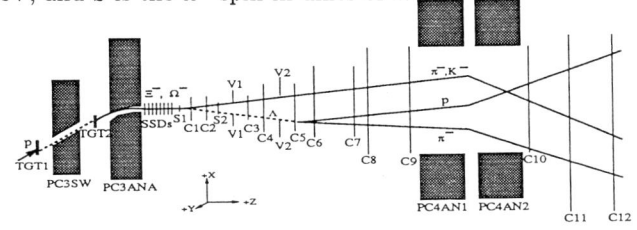

Figure 1. The E800 Spectrometer(plan view) C1-C5 are 1mm MWPCs, C6-C12 are 2mm MWPCs

The charged colliamtor PC3ANA served to precess the Ω^- spin. The Ω^-'s subseqent decay to Λ K^- was detected in the spectrometer shown in Figure 1.

Since the initial direction of the Ω^- spin is perpendicular to the production plane, ($\hat{x}$ direction) and the field is along the $\hat{y}$ axis, the Ω^- spin will precess in the x-z plane.

$$\Phi_{lab} = \tan^{-1} \left(\frac{P_z}{P_x} \right) \qquad (3)$$

where P_z and P_x are the components of the polarization measured in the spectrometer by reconstructing the daughter Λ.[5]

$$\vec{P}_\Lambda = \frac{1}{2(J+1)} [1 + (2J+1)\gamma_\Omega] \vec{P}_\Omega \qquad (4)$$

note that for the Ω^- $J = \frac{3}{2}$, assuming $\gamma_\Omega = 1$, $\vec{P}_\Lambda = \vec{P}_\Omega$.

3. Results

The reconstruction methods, event selection, and polarization analysis for this analysis closely follows those of previous experiments by this group.[6]
Figure 2 illustrates the quality of the 80,000 Ω^-s produced by an unpolarized beam. A sample of 20,000 Ω^- produced by a polarized beam was also analyzed.[4] The average polarization of two the samples is:

$P_{\Omega^-} = 0.053 \pm 0.012$ (unpolarized beam)
$P_{\Omega^-} = -0.076 \pm 0.021$ (polarized beam)

Figure 3 shows Φ_{lab} for the present sample, taken at $\int Bdl = -24.8$ T·m compared to the measurements made by E756 at two lower field integrals. The fitted line, constrained to pass through zero, indicates Φ_{lab} increases with $|\int Bdl|$. Given Φ_{lab} we can compute μ_{Ω^-},

$$\mu_{\Omega^-} = -2.1 \pm 0.1 \; \mu_N \quad \text{(unpolarized beam)}$$
$$\mu_{\Omega^-} = -2.0 \pm 0.1 \; \mu_N \quad \text{(polarized beam)}$$

where the error is statistical only. Possible systematic errors are still being investigated. Figure 4 shows no evidence of momentum dependent instrumental effects. We also measured μ_{Ξ^-} as $-0.653 \pm 0.007 \; \mu_N$ for 260,000 Ξ^- events taken using the polarized neutral beam and analyzed using the same technique as the Ω^-. This is in agreement with the world average of $\mu_{\Xi^-} = -0.6505 \pm 0.0025 \; \mu_N$.

The preliminary result of E800 agrees with our past measurement of 28,000 events from a polarized neutral beam of $\mu_{\Omega^-} = -2.0 \pm 0.17 \pm 0.14 \; \mu_N$.[7] When the full sample is analyzed we expect to have measured μ_{Ω^-} to a precision of $\pm 0.05 \; \mu_N$ or better.

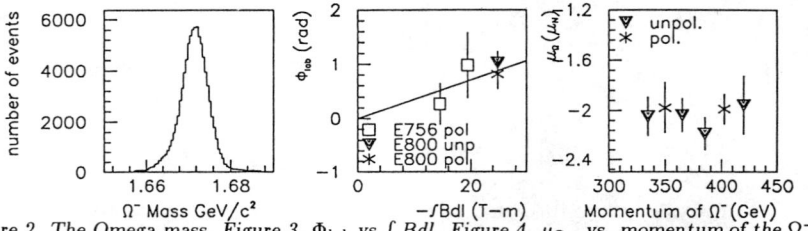

Figure 2. The Omega mass. Figure 3. Φ_{lab} vs $\int Bdl$. Figure 4. μ_{Ω^-} vs. momentum of the Ω^-.

Figure 5 compares magnetic moment predictions made by more complicated models with the experimentally measured values of the magnetic moments using the 3σ error bars for the experimental measurements.[1,2]

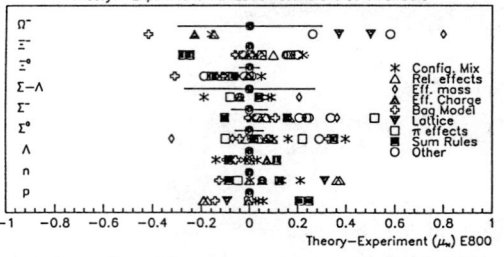

Figure 5. Comparison of models each measurement is shown with a 3σ error bar.

I would like to thank G.T. Allan, J.J. Marian, A.A. Mercado, M. Grobelewski, D. Fein, E. James, E. Berman, L. Morris, T. Tinnan, and especially M. Spagnoli and R. McGriff, and of course the staff at Fermilab.

1. J. Franklin, *AIP Proceedings Part. Ser. 37* and the references therein, **187**, 384 (1988)
2. K. Johns, *AIP Proceedings Part. Ser. 37* and the references therein, **187**, 374 (1988)
3. Particle Data Group, *Phys. Rev. D*, **45**, (1992)
4. D. M. Woods, *These Proceedings*
5. K. B. Luk, *Phys. Rev. D*, **38**, 19 (1988)
6. H. T. Diehl, *Thesis Rutgers University* (unpublished) (1990)
7. H. T. Diehl et al., *Phys. Lett.*, **67**, 804 (1991)

PRELIMINARY RESULTS FROM FERMILAB E-800 ON A SEARCH FOR CHARGED DIBARYONS

Y. T. GAO, M. J. LONGO
Department of Physics, University of Michigan, Ann Arbor, MI 48109, USA

K. JOHNS
Department of Physics, University of Arizona, Tucson, AZ 85721, USA

R. RAMEIKA
Fermi National Accelerator Laboratory, Batavia, IL 60510, USA

P. BORDER, D. P. CIAMPA, G. GUGLIELMO, K. HELLER, N. B. WALLACE, D. M. WOODS
School of Physics and Astronomy, University of Minnesota, Minneapolis, MN 55455, USA

ABSTRACT

The existence of long-lived dibaryon states has been suggested. Both positive and negative results have been reported by previous experiments. Fermilab E-800 has collected a large number of charged hyperon decays that might contain charged dibaryons. We are searching for candidates for the weak decay $\bar{H}^+ \to p + \Lambda^0$, $\Lambda^0 \to p + \pi^-$, with lifetime $\tau_{\bar{H}}^+ \sim 10^{-10}$ sec. No evidence for $\bar{H}^+$ production has been observed in the mass range of $M_{\bar{H}^+} < M_{\Lambda^0} + M_{\Sigma^+}$. For a lifetime $\tau_{\bar{H}} \simeq \tau_{\bar{\Xi}^+}$, the upper limit for the $\bar{H}^+$ production cross section multiplied by the branching ratio is (0.4 - 5.7)% of that for $\bar{\Xi}^+$ production at 90% confidence level. The lifetime $\tau_{\bar{H}}$ dependence of the limit is also estimated.

1. Introduction

A long-lived $S = -2$ neutral dibaryon H^0, predicted by a six-quark model[1], has been sought by many experiments with different results[2,3,4,5]. Theoretical mass estimates, though subject to considerable uncertainty, suggest that $M_{H^0} < 2M_{\Lambda^0}$ (e.g., Ref. 6, 7) so the H^0 would decay weakly. In the Skyrme model it has been argued [8,9] that the lowest-lying $S = -2$ dibaryon state is an I=1 decuplet $\bar{H}$ which contains charged members, rather than the H^0.

Fermilab E-800[10] has collected a large number of charged hyperon decays that might contain charged $\bar{H}^+$ dibaryons, which we define as an $S = -2$ six-quark state, $suusud$. We confine our search to the weak decay mode $\bar{H}^+ \to p + \Lambda^0$, $\Lambda^0 \to p + \pi^-$.

2. Analysis

We look for events with 3 charged tracks, two of which form a Λ^0 and the other is positive. The $\bar{H}^+$ signal would be a peak in the reconstructed $(\Lambda^0 p)$ mass with a width consistent with the experimental resolution.

In analysis, the following criteria for the $\bar{H}^+$ candidates are used: (1) The lowest momentum track must be negatively charged and the two other tracks positively charged; (2) Geometrical $\chi^2 < 65$ for the potential 3-track events; (3) $\tilde{H}^+$ and Λ^0 decay vertices are within the defined decay region (which is from 900 to 2930 cm from the production target along the beam direction); (4) Events originate at the target; (5) Invariant M_{Λ^0}, 1.11 GeV $< M_{\Lambda^0} <$ 1.121 GeV; (6) Removal of anything that reconstructs as $\overline{\Xi}^+$, $\overline{\Omega}^+$, or K^+; (7) Reconstructed $\tilde{H}^+$ momenta $>$ 200 GeV and $<$ 400 GeV, consistent with the momentum band selected by the channel.

With the assumption that $\tau_{\tilde{H}^+} \simeq \tau_{\overline{\Xi}^+}$, Monte Carlo studies show that (1) $R_{eff}^{trig} \simeq 22$, $R_{eff}^{rs} \simeq 1.4$, where R_{eff}^{trig} is the ratio of the triggering efficiencies for the $\overline{\Xi}^+$'s over $\tilde{H}^+$'s, R_{eff}^{rs} is that for reconstruction-selection efficiencies; and that (2) these total efficiencies are approximately uniform within the allowed decay region.

3. Production Limits

For $\tau_{\tilde{H}^+} \simeq \tau_{\overline{\Xi}^+}$, we estimate the relative production cross section limit, at 90% confidence level (CL), as follows:

$$\frac{\sigma_{\tilde{H}^+}^{UP}(\tau_{\tilde{H}^+} \simeq \tau_{\overline{\Xi}^+}) \cdot \Gamma_{\tilde{H}^+ \to \Lambda^0 p}}{\sigma_{\overline{\Xi}^+} \cdot \Gamma_{\overline{\Xi}^+ \to \overline{\Lambda}^0 \pi^+}} \approx \frac{R_{eff}^{trig} \times R_{eff}^{rs} \times S^{CL}(N_{\tilde{H}^+}^{obs})}{N_{\overline{\Xi}^+}} \quad (1)$$

where Γ represents the branching ratio, with $\Gamma_{\overline{\Xi}^+ \to \overline{\Lambda}^0 \pi^+} \simeq 1$; $\sigma_{\tilde{H}^+}^{UP}$ is the upper limit on the $\tilde{H}^+$ production cross section; $\sigma_{\overline{\Xi}^+}$ is the $\overline{\Xi}^+$ production cross section; $N_{\overline{\Xi}^+}$ is the number of reconstructed $\overline{\Xi}^+$'s in the sample; and $S^{CL}(N_{\tilde{H}^+}^{obs})$ is the 90%CL upper limit from Poisson statistics as a function of $N_{\tilde{H}^+}^{obs}$, the observed number of event candidates in a mass range equal to the $\pm 1\sigma$ $M_{\tilde{H}^+}$ resolution (conservatively estimated as 7.5 MeV with Monte Carlo).

At an arbitrary τ_H, the efficiency for accepting decays is determined by how many decays occur within our decay volume. Thus, for other $\tau_{\tilde{H}^+}$, the limits scale as

$$\frac{\sigma_{\tilde{H}^+}^{UP}(\tau_{\tilde{H}^+}) \cdot \Gamma_{\tilde{H}^+ \to \Lambda^0 p}}{\sigma_{\tilde{H}^+}^{UP}(\tau_{\tilde{H}^+} \simeq \tau_{\overline{\Xi}^+}) \cdot \Gamma_{\tilde{H}^+ \to \Lambda^0 p}} \approx \frac{e^{-z_1/\gamma c \tau_{\overline{\Xi}^+}} - e^{-z_2/\gamma c \tau_{\overline{\Xi}^+}}}{e^{-z_1/\gamma c \tau_{\tilde{H}^+}} - e^{-z_2/\gamma c \tau_{\tilde{H}^+}}} \quad (2)$$

where z_1 and z_2 correspond to the beginning and end of the active decay volume, and γ is calculated for the $\tilde{H}^+$'s at the center of the accepted momentum range. (The acceptance and the lifetime factor are both weak functions of $M_{\tilde{H}^+}$.)

To date, for the weak decay mode of $\tilde{H}^+ \to p + \Lambda^0$, $\Lambda^0 \to p + \pi^-$, with lifetime $\tau_{\tilde{H}^+} \sim 10^{-10}$ sec, no evidence of $\tilde{H}^+$ production has been observed in the mass range of $M_{\tilde{H}^+} < M_{\Lambda^0} + M_{\Sigma^+}$.

These results are preliminary, and the limits will be improved by more extensive data selection criteria.

4. Acknowledgements

This work has been supported by the U.S. DOE and NSF, as well as the Fermilab staff. We would like to thank G. Allen, A. Ayala-Mercado, E. Berman, D. Fein, J. Jalian-Marian, E. James and T. Tynan for their contributions. MJL

$$\frac{\sigma^{UP}_{\tilde{H}^+}(\tau_{\tilde{H}^+} \simeq \tau_{\overline{\Xi}^+}) \cdot \Gamma_{\tilde{H}^+ \to \Lambda^0 p}}{\sigma_{\overline{\Xi}^+} \cdot \Gamma_{\overline{\Xi}^+ \to \overline{\Lambda}^0 \pi^+}}$$

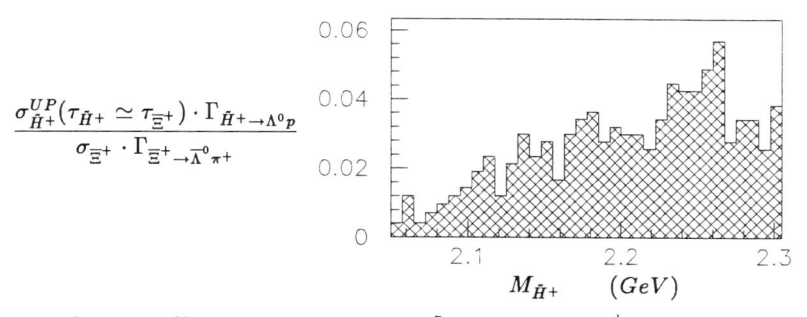

Figure 1: 90% CL limits on the ratio of $\tilde{H}^+$ production to $\overline{\Xi}^+$ vs. $\tilde{H}^+$ mass.

$$\frac{\sigma^{UP}_{\tilde{H}^+}(\tau_{\tilde{H}^+}) \cdot \Gamma_{\tilde{H}^+ \to \Lambda^0 p}}{\sigma^{UP}_{\tilde{H}^+}(\tau_{\tilde{H}^+} \simeq \tau_{\overline{\Xi}^+}) \cdot \Gamma_{\tilde{H}^+ \to \Lambda^0 p}}$$

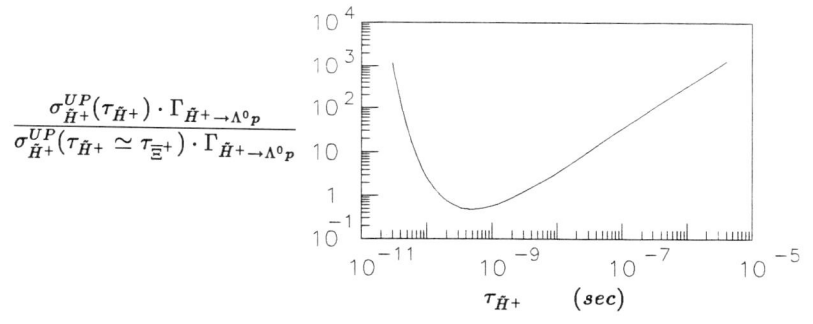

Figure 2: Variation of cross section limits with assumed $\tilde{H}^+$ lifetime, normalized to $\tau_{\tilde{H}^+} = \tau_{\overline{\Xi}^+}$.

and YTG also thank J. Bjorken, S. Cihangir, M. Crisler, C. Dover, G. Golowich, G. Kane, D. Lichtenberg and R. Ray for their valuable comments.

1. R. L. Jaffe, *Phys. Rev. Lett.* **38** (1977) 195.
2. Particle Data Group, *Phys. Lett.* **B170** (1986) 337; **B204** (1988) 472.
3. A. N. Alekseev et al., *Sov. J. Nucl. Phys.* **52**(6) (1990) 1016.
4. B. A. Shahbazian et al., *Phys. Lett.* **B235** (1990) 208.
5. S. Aoki et al., *Phys. Rev. Lett.* **65** (1990) 1729.
6. D. Pal & J. A. McGovern, *Jour. Phys. G: Nucl. Part. Phys.* **18** (1992) 593.
7. U. Straub et al., *Nucl. Phys.* **A508** (1990) 385c.
8. J. Kunz and P. Mulders, *Phys. Lett.* **B215** (1990) 449.
9. C. Dover, *Nuovo Cimento* **A102** (1989) 521.
10. See other E-800 papers (G. Guglielmo et al., N. Wallace et al., and D. Woods et al.) in these Proceedings.

POLARIZATION OF Σ^+ AND ANTI(Σ^+)
PRODUCED BY 800 GeV/c PROTONS

VINCENT J. SMITH
H.H. Wills Physics Laboratory,
University of Bristol, Bristol BS8 1TL, UK

for the Fermilab E761 Collaboration[*]

ABSTRACT

We have measured the polarization of 375 GeV/c Σ^+ and anti(Σ^+) hyperons produced by 800 GeV/c protons incident on a Cu target.
The Σ^+ polarization increases to a maximum of $\approx 16\%$ at $p_T = 1.0$ GeV/c and then decreases to $\approx 10\%$ at $p_T = 1.7$ GeV/c. We compare these results with those for Σ^+ produced in collisions at lower energy.
We have also made the first measurement of anti(Σ^+) polarization. The anti(Σ^+) polarization has the same sign as the Σ^+ but has smaller magnitude.

1. Hyperon and Antihyperon Polarization

The measured values of the polarization of hyperons produced in high–energy collisions of unpolarized protons with unpolarized nuclear targets have not received a convincing theoretical explanation. It is possible to explain the Λ polarization, and to some extent the Ξ and Σ polarizations, in terms of a 'leading' quark or diquark which picks up one or two strange quarks from the sea : the s quark is the one which acquires the polarization. This argument is supported by the observation of zero polarization of the anti(Λ)[1], but is not able to accomodate the recent measurement of anti(Ξ^-) polarization, which was found to be the same sign as, and comparable in magnitude with, the Ξ^- polarization[2].

We have measured the polarization of Σ^+ and anti(Σ^+) produced from 800 GeV/c protons as part of the E–761 experiment, whose main objective was to study the radiative weak decays of hyperons[3].

2. Hyperon Beam

The 800 GeV/c proton beam could be steered through ±5 mrad in the vertical or horizontal plane before hitting the 1 interaction length Cu target at the entrance of a 7.3 m×3.5 T magnet. Thus the direction of polarization could be in the horizontal or vertical direction, and could be reversed at will. A narrow curved channel in the magnet defined a beam of positive or negative charge, at a mean momentum of 375 GeV/c.

---
[*]Fermilab, Carnegie Mellon, SUNY at Albany, U. of Iowa, Yale, USA; U. Federal de Paraiba, CBPF, CNPq, U. de São Paulo, Brazil; PNPI, ITEP, Russia; U. of Bristol, UK; IHEP, PRC.

E761 Sigma Configuration

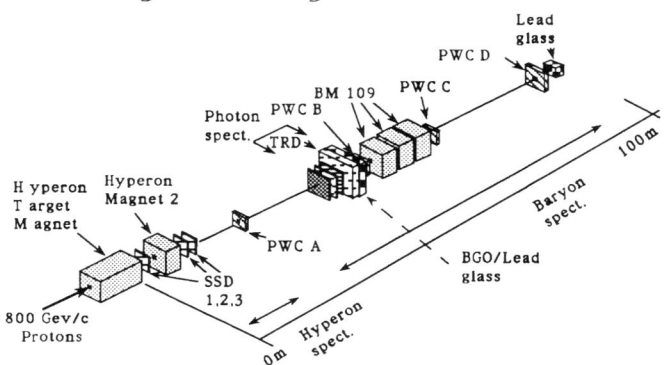

Figure 1: E–761 Experiment

3. Σ^+ and anti(Σ^+) Selection

The E–761 apparatus is shown in fig.1 A full description can be found in ref.3. On leaving the channel, the hyperon track was measured in the hyperon spectrometer (magnet with 3 stations of SSDs) and the decay proton was measured in the baryon spectrometer (3 magnets with 4 stations of PWCs). An electromagnetic shower from one of the photons from the π^0 was used in the trigger. The events were fitted to the hypothesis $\Sigma^+ \to pX^0$. Fig.2 shows the histogram of missing–mass–squared. The data show a very clean π^0 peak, with a shoulder from $\Sigma^+ \to p\gamma$ and a small background from $K^+ \to \pi^+\pi^0$, which are easily removed.

4. Measurement of Polarization

The $\Sigma^+ \to p\pi^0$ decay is a (parity–violating) weak interaction and the asymmetry parameter (α) describing the distribution of the proton direction with respect to the spin of the Σ^+ is known to have the value –0.98 (we assume +0.98 for anti(Σ^+) by CP symmetry). The observed distribution will include a factor for the experimental acceptance,

$$\text{ie} \quad n = \frac{dN}{N\,d\cos\theta} \approx A(\cos\theta)(1 + \alpha P \cos\theta)$$

(where N is the number of events, A is the acceptance, P is the polarization and θ can be any of the three orthogonal directions, x, y or z)

Since we have data with equal and opposite targetting angles (equal and opposite polarizations), we can eliminate the acceptance factor, A, by forming the ratio :

$$\frac{n_+ - n_-}{n_+ + n_-} = \alpha P \cos\theta$$

for $\theta = \theta_x, \theta_y, \theta_z$, to find the component of polarization along any axis.

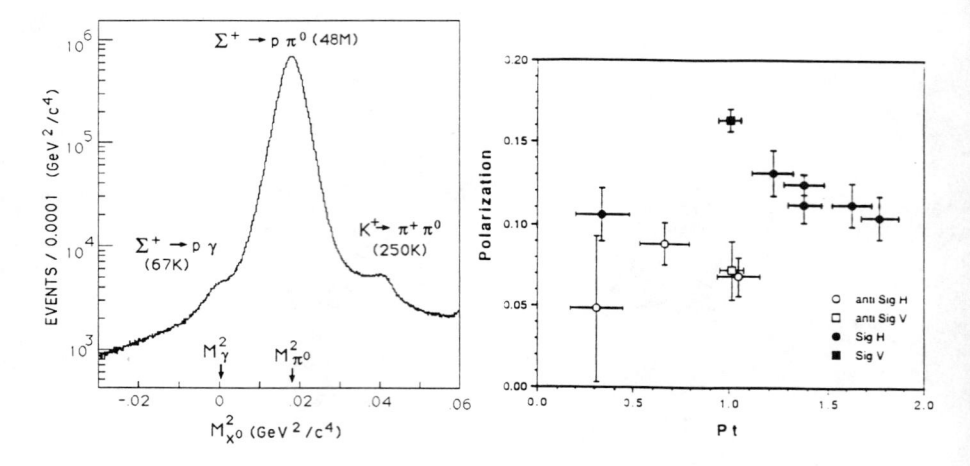

Figure 2: Missing mass

Figure 3: Σ^+ and anti(Σ^+)Polarization

5. Results

The measured values of the polarization are plotted in fig.3, for both Σ^+ and anti(Σ^+), as a function of p_T. For Σ^+, it is seen that the polarization increases with p_T, up to a maximum of $\approx 16\%$ at ≈ 1.0 GeV/c and then decreases. This is the first time such a decrease has been observed, and may indicate that the perturbative QCD regime (for which no polarization is expected) is being reached.

The anti(Σ^+)polarization shows similar behavior, the polarization has the same sign but a smaller magnitude, and reaches its maximum at a lower p_T. This behavior is intermediate between the anti(Λ) and the anti(Ξ^-) cases.

It should be noted that the Σ^+ polarization is a strong function of x_F : our largest sample (at p_T =1.3 GeV/c) shows a variation of polarization from $\approx 11.5\%$ at x_F =0.45 to $\approx 13.5\%$ at x_F =0.50. We also note that the polarization maximum of $\approx 16\%$ for Σ^+ produced from a 800 GeV/c proton beam contrasts with values of ≈ 25–30% for Σ^+ produced from 400 GeV/c protons at similar x_F and p_T [4].

6. References

1. Heller *et al.*, Phys. Rev. Lett **41**, 607 (1978)
2. Ho *et al.*, Phys. Rev. Lett **65**, 1713 (1990)
3. Foucher *et al.*, Phys. Rev. Lett **68**, 3004 (1992)
   (see also the papers presented at this conference by
   A.Morelos, S.Timm, T.Dubbs and R.Carrigan)
4. Ankenbrandt *et al.*, Phys. Rev. Lett **51**, 863 (1983)

MEASUREMENT OF THE BRANCHING RATIO FOR $\Xi^- \to \Sigma^- \gamma$

TIM P. DUBBS
*Department of Physics and Astronomy, University of Iowa
Iowa City, IA 52242*

for the Fermilab E761 Collaboration[*]

ABSTRACT

Hyperon radiative decays represent a class of baryon decays which require strong, weak, and electromagnetic contributions. We have investigated the radiative decay $\Xi^- \to \Sigma^- \gamma$ using a 375 GeV/c beam of Ξ^- produced at the Fermilab Proton Center charged hyperon beam line. A sample of approximately 250 events has been isolated using two high resolution spectrometers, and single photon identification. Previous experimental results yield a total of 11 ± 2 events. Preliminary results for the branching ratio of the radiative Ξ^- decay are presented.

1. Introduction

There has been much interest in the study of weak radiative decays of hyperons in the past twenty years to obtain insight into electroweak theory. Currently there exists no adequate theoretical model for these processes. The decay $\Xi^- \to \Sigma^- \gamma$ is of special interest because it can not proceed via a W exchange mechanism which is believed to play an important role in most other radiative decays[1]. The previous, low statistic, experimental result is also inconsistent with predictions based on single quark exchange, and penguin diagrams[2]. Pole model calculations have been more successful in predicting the observed branching ratio, but it is clear more precise data is needed to guide the theory[3].

2. The Experiment

A 375 GeV/c hyperon beam ($10^3 \Xi^-/s$) was produced by targeting 800 GeV/c protons on a Cu target (1.0 l_i) and momentum selecting with a curved channel in a magnetic field. Two spectrometers were used to measure the position and momentum of the hyperon (Ξ^-) and its charged decay baryon (Σ^-). A photon spectrometer was used to distinguish single photon events from two photon ($\pi^0 \to \gamma\gamma$) events and measure the neutral's energy[4]. For our purposes the essential part of this spectrometer was a segmented lead glass (PbG) and BGO calorimeter downstream of a pair of steel conversion plates. (Details of the E761 Apparatus can be found in ref. 4.) An additional magnet was added downstream of the baryon spectrometer to sweep out soft pions from the secondary decay $\Sigma^- \to n \pi^-$.

---
[*]Fermilab, Carnegie Mellon, SUNY at Albany, U. of Iowa, Yale, USA; U. Federal de Paraiba, CBPF, CNPq, U. de São Paulo, Brazil; PNPI, ITEP, Russia; U. of Bristol, UK; IHEP, PRC.

The trigger demanded a charged track in the hyperon and baryon spectrometers as defined by scintillation counters. It was also required that an electromagnetic shower be started by the conversion of a neutral in one of two 2.54 cm steel plates in the photon spectrometer. This trigger condition accepted the radiative decay $\Xi^- \to \Sigma^- \gamma$ but also allowed the kinematically similar, and dominate background, $\overline{\Sigma}^- \to \bar{p} \pi^\circ$. In addition, a sample of prescaled beam tracks was collected for use in determining the normalization signal $\Xi^- \to \Lambda \pi^-$, and efficiency studies.

3. Analysis and Results

The analysis required that a single track be fitted in each of the hyperon and baryon spectrometers, their decay vertex be within the fiducial region, and a decay angle (Lab) greater than 100 μrad. From these events we reconstructed the squared missing mass (MM^2) of the neutral particle under various charged particle mass hypotheses. All events within the range abs(MM^2) $\leq 0.02 GeV^2/c^4$ (2 million events) under the hypothesis $\Xi^- \to \Sigma^- X$ were selected as candidates. This sample also contains a large fraction of background $\overline{\Sigma}^- \to \bar{p} \pi^\circ$ events which fall in this range. The background is reduced by vetoing events where the decay baryon fires a veto scintillator at the end of the apparatus. For good $\Xi^- \to \Sigma^- \gamma$ events the Σ^- decays to n π^- and the π^- is removed by the downstream sweeper magnet. Thus for these events the veto counter will not fire, while for background events the downstream baryon ($\bar{p}$) will not decay, and will fire the veto. However, due to inefficiencies in the counter, interactions, and scattering, a considerable number of background events survive this cut.

We can further isolate the signal from the background by using information from the photon spectrometer. From the charged track information we reconstruct the expected missing neutral track and extrapolate this track to the PbG system. For background events, the showers from $\pi^\circ \to \gamma\gamma$ will deposit their energy at a larger distance from the extrapolated track than the shower from single γ ($\Xi^- \to \Sigma^- \gamma$) events. Selecting events which have a large fraction of energy in the blocks near the extrapolated track yields a much improved signal to background ratio of 1:1. Figure 1 shows events with $E_{fract.} \geq 85\%$. A clear signal of 211 $\pm$ 40 $\Xi^- \to \Sigma^- \gamma$ events can be seen at MM^2 = 0 above a background consistent with $\overline{\Sigma}^- \to \bar{p} \pi^\circ$. We can define the relative branching ratio as:

$$\frac{\Gamma(\Xi^- \to \Sigma^- \gamma)}{\Gamma(\Xi^- \to \Lambda \pi^-)} = \frac{N_\gamma}{\epsilon_\gamma} \times \frac{\epsilon_\Lambda}{N_\Lambda} \times \frac{1}{Prescale factor} \quad (1)$$

where N_γ is the number of $\Xi^- \to \Sigma^- \gamma$ events determined above, N_Λ is the number of $\Xi^- \to \Lambda \pi^-$ events obtained from the prescaled beam tracks, and $\epsilon_\gamma, \epsilon_\Lambda$ are the efficiencies of the two decay modes determined from Geant Monte Carlo studies. The values of these parameters are summarized in Table 1. Two independent samples, at different targeting angles[4], were analyzed separately and give consistent values for the branching ratio. Differences in the beam phase space account for the variations at opposing angles. Taking a weighted average we obtain a preliminary value for

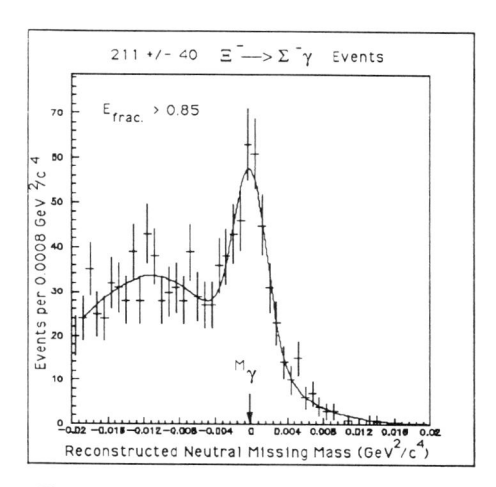

Figure 1: Reconstructed $\Xi^- \to \Sigma^- \gamma$ events

Table 1: Parameters used for branching ratio. ± 2.0 mrad data analyzed separately.

Parameter	+2.0 mrad	-2.0 mrad
N_γ	87 ± 22	124 ± 25
N_Λ	253 ± 46	559 ± 55
ϵ_γ	0.68 ± 0.05 %	0.83 ± 0.04 %
ϵ_Λ	3.7 ± 0.1 %	6.2 ± 0.1 %
Prescale factor	16384 ± 20	16384 ± 20
$\Gamma(\Xi^- \to \Sigma^- \gamma)/\Gamma(\Xi^- \to \Lambda \pi^-)$	$(1.15 \pm 0.38) \times 10^{-4}$	$(1.01 \pm 0.24) \times 10^{-4}$

the $\Xi^- \to \Sigma^- \gamma$ branching ratio.

$$\Gamma(\Xi^- \to \Sigma^- \gamma)/\Gamma(\Xi^- \to \Lambda \pi^-) = 1.05 \pm 0.20 \times 10^{-4}$$

Where the error is statistical only. This value should be compared with the previous experimental measurement of $(2.3 \pm 1.0) \times 10^{-4}$, and is consistent with the unitarity[3] lower bound (1.0×10^{-4}.) Work is still in progress to study the systematics.

4. References

1. R. C. Verma and A. Sharma, *Physica (Utr.)* **38** (1988) 1443.
2. S. F. Biagi et al., *Z. Phys.* **C35** (1987) 143.
3. Y. I. Kogan, and M.A. Shifman, *Sov. J. Nucl. Phys.* **38** (1983) 628.
4. M. E. Foucher et al., *Phys. Rev. Lett.* **68** (1992) 3004.

MAGNETIC MOMENT MEASUREMENTS OF

Σ^+ AND $\bar{\Sigma}^-$

A. MORELOS [*]
*Fermilab, MS219 / E761, P.O. Box 500
Batavia, Il 60510, USA*

for the Fermilab E761 Collaboration [†,1]

ABSTRACT

Preliminary results are presented on a high precision Σ^+ magnetic moment measurement and a first $\bar{\Sigma}^-$ magnetic moment measurement. The magnetic moment is measured using the spin precession technique. Polarized hyperons at 375 GeV/c were produced inclusively with 800 GeV/c protons incident on a Cu target. The hyperon spin precessed while passing through an $\approx$ 20 $T \cdot m$ magnetic field integral. The Σ^+ spin precession is measured with 250000 $\Sigma^+ \to p\pi^0$ decay events providing $\approx$ 0.1 % statistical error on the magnetic moment. Similarly the $\bar{\Sigma}^-$ spin precession is measured with 12000 $\bar{\Sigma}^- \to \bar{p}\pi^0$ decay events providing $\approx$ 1.5 % statistical error.

1. Introduction to Magnetic Moments (μ)

Study of the properties of the confined quarks and the internal structure of the baryons involves precise μ measurements and adequate theoretical models. Up to now the μ of the stable octet baryons (OB) are measured [2] to 1 % or better precision level, see figure 1. There has been a variety of models describing the μ data. The most simple model, the naive quark model (NQM) [3], has a 24 % precision on OB, see figure 2. The more complex models can be classified as (the best precision on all OB is quoted): Lattice Gauge Theory, 20 % [4]; QCD sum rules, 38 % [5]; Bag models, 10 % level [6]; Potential models (not bag), 12.4 % [7]; Static models (NQM plus corrections), 10 % level or better [8]. Today, the best fit to μ data is able to reach a 4 % precision, see figure 3.

The μ of Σ^+ is measured to 2 % [2]. The measurement is dominated by two 1 % measurements [9] and [10], which differ by 3 σ posing an experimental dilemma, see figure 5. We are reporting a preliminary $\approx$ 1 % μ Σ^+ measurement casting some light on the dilemma. We are also reporting the first μ measurement of the $\bar{\Sigma}^-$. Details on these preliminary measurements are in reference [11]. There is work in progress to bring the μ of Σ^+ to a 0.2 % level.

[*] Graduate student from CINVESTAV-IPN, México.

[†] Fermilab, Carnegie Mellon, SUNY at Albany, U. of Iowa, Yale, USA; U. Federal de Paraiba, CBPF, CNPq, U. de São Paulo, Brazil; PNPI, ITEP, Russia; U. of Bristol, UK; IHEP, PRC.

2. Measurement Technique, Apparatus, Signal $\Sigma^+ \to p\pi^0$ and $\bar{\Sigma}^- \to \bar{p}\pi^0$

The equation of motion for a spin in a magnetic field relates the precession angle (ϕ), μ, and the momentum deflection (Ptk) as: $|\mu| = \dfrac{m_p}{m}\left(1 + \beta mc^2 \dfrac{\phi}{\text{Ptk } c}\right)$
where: [μ] = Nuclear Magneton, [ϕ]=radian, [Ptk]=Gev/c, c=speed of light, $\beta = v/c$, v is the hyperon's speed, m_p and m proton and hyperon mass (Gev/c^2). The angle ϕ is measured with the polarization vector and Ptk is given by the field integral.

The apparatus is described elsewhere [1,11]. Data were taken at complementary ± 3 mrad vertical targeting angles.

The neutral mass squared is computed from the reconstructed hyperon (Σ^+) and baryon (p) tracks. The peaks $\Sigma^+ \to p\pi^0$ and $\bar{\Sigma}^- \to \bar{p}\pi^0$ show up prominently, a cut of 2.6 σ defines the signal [1,11].

3. Polarization precession, Preliminary μ of Σ^+ and $\bar{\Sigma}^-$, and Comments

The polarization measurement [1,11] uses a pair of symmetric targeting angle data (see also: V.Smith at this DPF meeting). Figure 4 shows the polarization vector before (along $+\hat{z}$ axis) and after the spin precession for Σ^+ and $\bar{\Sigma}^-$. Figure 5 shows the preliminary μ for Σ^+ and $\bar{\Sigma}^-$.

The μ magnitude of Σ^+ and $\bar{\Sigma}^-$ agree within statistics, as expected from the CPT theorem. The μ error of Σ^+ is dominated by the field integral precision known to 0.8 %. There is work in progress to measure the field integral to 0.2 % level bringing the μ of Σ^+ to 0.2 %.

4. References

1. M.Foucher et al., *Phys. Rev. Lett.* **68** (1992) 3004.
2. Review of Particle Properties, *Phys. Rev.* **D45** (1992) 1.
3. J. Franklin, *Phys. Rev.* **172** (1968) 1807.
4. D.B. Leinweber, *Phys. Rev.* **D45** (1992) 252.
5. B. I. Ioffe et al., *Phys. Lett.* **B133** (1983) 436.
6. S. Theberge et al., *Nucl. Phys.* **A393** (1983) 252. K. Ushio, *Phys. Lett.* **B158** (1985) 71. M. I. Krivoruchenko, *Sov. J. Nucl. Phys.* **45** (1987) 109. H. Hogaasen et al., *Phys. Rev.* **D37** (1988) 1950.
7. M. Bohm, et al., *Phys. Rev.* **D25** (1982) 223.
8. S. K. Gupta et al., *Phys. Rev.* **D36** (1987) 307. J. Franklin, *Phys. Rev.* **D30** (1984) 1542. R. Verma et al., *Phys. Lett.* **B183** (1987) 207. G. Karl, *Phys. Rev.* **D45** (1992) 247.
9. C. Wilkinson et al., *Phys. Rev. Lett.* **58** (1987) 855.
10. C. Ankenbrandt, et al., *Phys. Rev. Lett.* **51** (1983) 863.
11. A. Morelos, *Ph. D. Thesis* CINVESTAV-IPN, México, (1992), Unpublished.

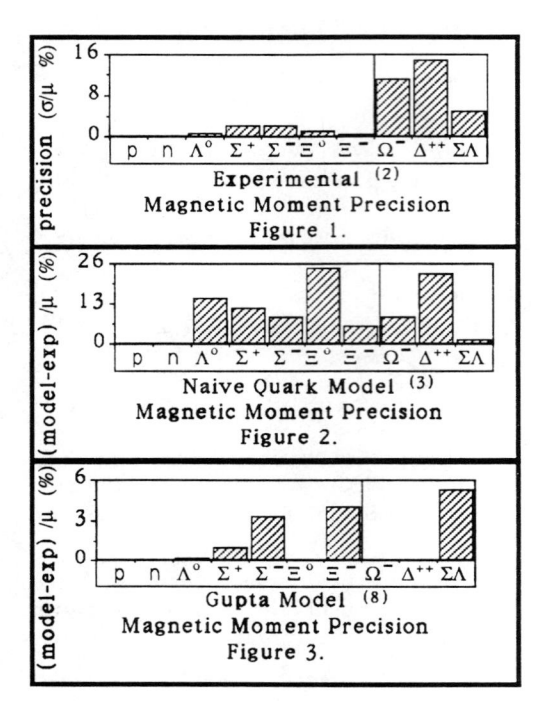

Figure 1. Experimental[2] Magnetic Moment Precision

Figure 2. Naive Quark Model[3] Magnetic Moment Precision

Figure 3. Gupta Model[8] Magnetic Moment Precision

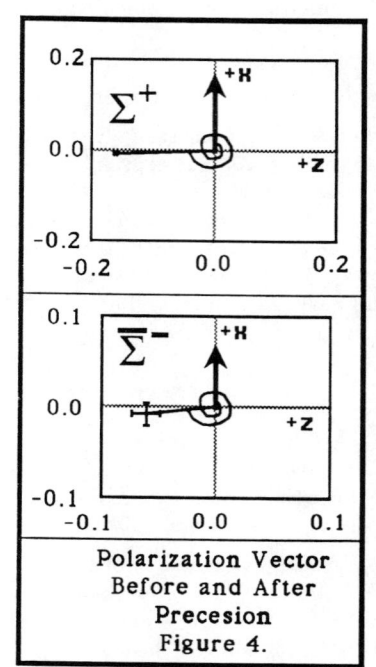

Figure 4. Polarization Vector Before and After Precesion

Figure 5. Magnetic Moment of Σ^+ and $\overline{\Sigma}^-$

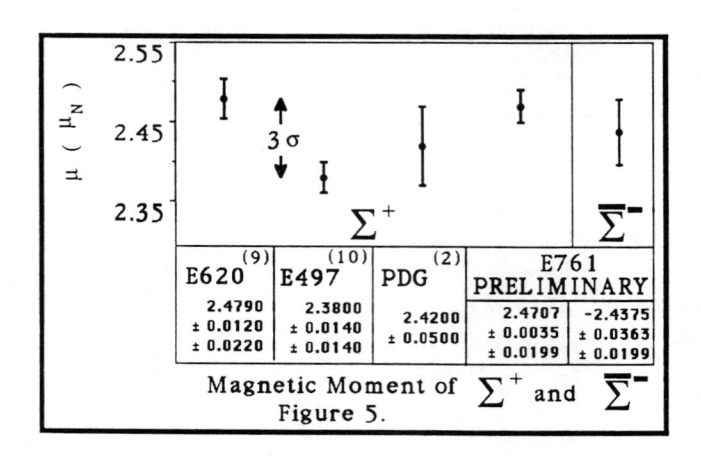

E620[9]	E497[10]	PDG[2]	E761 PRELIMINARY
2.4790 ± 0.0120 ± 0.0220	2.3800 ± 0.0140 ± 0.0140	2.4200 ± 0.0500	2.4707 ± 0.0035 ± 0.0199	−2.4375 ± 0.0363 ± 0.0199

PRELIMINARY MEASUREMENT OF BRANCHING RATIO IN THE RADIATIVE DECAY OF THE Σ^+ HYPERON

Steven C. Timm
*Department of Physics, Carnegie Mellon,
Pittsburgh, PA 15213, USA*

FOR THE FERMILAB E761 Collaboration [*]

ABSTRACT

The branching ratio and the asymmetry of the radiative rare decay $\Sigma^+ \to p\,\gamma$ have proven difficult to predict and measure. In addition to our earlier published measurement of the asymmetry parameter[1], we have measured the branching ratio of the rare decay $\Sigma^+ \to p\,\gamma$ relative to the mode $\Sigma^+ \to p\,\pi^0$. The experiment used the Fermilab 375 GeV/c charged hyperon beam. The radiative decay and reference decay were detected by measuring each charged particle in magnetic spectrometers and a trigger based on the photons converting in iron. We find as a preliminary result that $BR(\Sigma^+ \to p\,\gamma)/BR(\Sigma^+ \to p\,\pi^0) = (2.35 \pm 0.16) \times 10^{-3}$.

Introduction

Fermilab experiment E761 was entitled "An Electroweak Enigma–Hyperon Radiative Decays." The first experiments, with a few hundred events of the decay $\Sigma^+ \to p\,\gamma$ found a large and negative asymmetry in contradiction with SU(3) symmetry and a larger rate than allowed by single-quark transitions. Theoretical progress has been made using QCD sum rules (Balitsky et al)[2] and vector dominance models (Zencyzkowski)[3]. E761 recently published a report of the asymmetry[1] based on 35000 events, and we now present a preliminary result for the branching ratio based on 38208 events.

Of 221 million triggers, 48 million events of $\Sigma^+ \to p\,\pi^0$ survived the minimal cuts. We selected 1/50 of this full sample to analyze that decay. We selected all events consistent with the hypothesis $\Sigma^+ \to p\,\gamma$. We rejected events consistent with $K \to \pi^+\,\pi^0$ and events where the extrapolated hyperon track missed the target.

Measuring the Relative Branching Ratio

Ratio of Efficiencies

We used measured tracks from beam triggers to provide the starting point for a GEANT simulation of geometrical acceptance, reconstruction efficiency, and trigger efficiency. The two targeting angles (POS and NEG) were simulated and analyzed independently because of their different beam phase spaces and geometrical acceptances. Cuts were made in positions of the decay products and decay vertex to improve the agreement of Monte Carlo and data distributions.

---

[*]Fermilab, IHEP Beijing, Petersburg Nucl. Phys. Inst, ITEP Moscow, Iowa, Sao Paulo, Yale, CBPF Rio de Janeiro, CNPq Brazil, SUNY Albany, Bristol, Carnegie Mellon, Paraiba

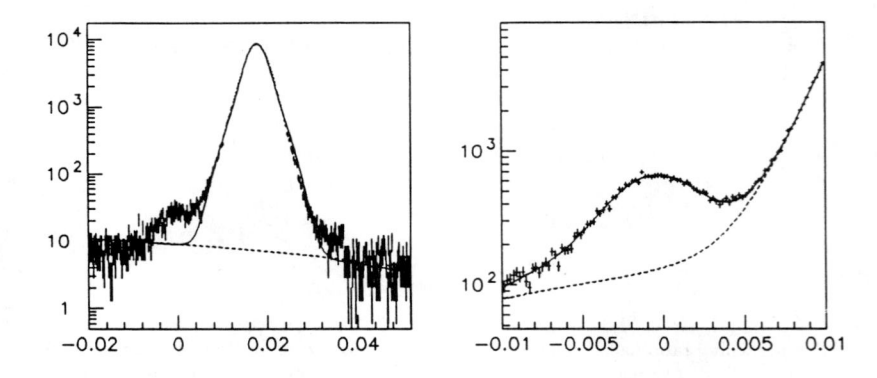

Figure 1: POS angle data, missing mass^2 (GeV^2/c^4), $\Sigma^+ \to pX$
1/50 of all data (left) $\Sigma^+ \to p\,\gamma$ mass region (right)

Efficiency from data was checked using $\Sigma^+ \to p\,\pi^0$ from beam triggers. Random coincidences and beam interactions not included in the Monte Carlo reduce the data efficiency. Various methods of correcting the ratio for this yield a systematic error of 4%. The ratio of efficiencies is seen in Table 1.

Number of $\Sigma^+ \to p\,\pi^0$

We estimate that there are 500 $\Sigma^+ \to p\,\gamma$ events in 1/50 of the sample, shown in Figure 1. We fit a linear background underneath the peak, and declare all other events on the plot to be $\Sigma^+ \to p\,\pi^0$. We bound the systematic error as the size of the background, about 1%. This allows for the background to be all signal or twice as much as the background fit. Totals in Table 1.

Number of $\Sigma^+ \to p\,\gamma$

Single photon-events are isolated by first requiring 70% of lead glass energy near the predicted neutral track. Then a χ^2 is calculated between the predicted track and the quality-weighted clusterized hits in the TRD[1]. The efficiency of TRD χ^2 cuts can be measured by using 2-photon events where one photon showers in the downstream spectrometer and the other goes into the TRD with a predictable direction. 83% of single photons are found to have a TRD $\chi^2 \leq 10$.

The shape of the $\Sigma^+ \to p\,\gamma$ resolution function is found from the shape of the $\Sigma^+ \to p\,\pi^0$ data. The peak is parametrized as two gaussians with fixed relative height and width. This peak plus a linear and exponential background is scaled to fit the data. Results in Figure 1 and Table 1.

The systematic error of the $\Sigma^+ \to p\,\gamma$ fit is determined by dividing the data into five equal-statistics slices in a number of parameters. In each of these slices, the branching ratio is calculated holding the number and efficiency of $\Sigma^+ \to p\,\pi^0$

constant. Then we form the χ^2 that all five measurements are consistent. The mean of the reduced χ^2 distribution is ≥ 1 due to systematic error. The TRD cut is not used in the answer because the systematic errors are larger in that method. The combined answers in Table 1 below treat the 4% systematic error from the efficiency as correlated between the two samples. The other systematic errors are uncorrelated and are included into the weighted average.

In conclusion, we see that we have two consistent answers from samples in which signal to background differs by a factor of two. Our measurements of asymmetry and branching ratio are consistent with the world average. This is a preliminary result. We hope to further understand and reduce the systematic errors by studying the efficiency and fit more carefully.

Table 1:		ALL		TRD≤10	
Result		POS	NEG	POS	NEG
Efficiency ratio		1.585	1.591	1.585	1.591
Stat error		0.003	0.003	0.003	0.003
Syst error		0.063	0.063	.0063	.0063
Number $\Sigma^+ \to p\,\pi^0$ / 50		267415	246222	267415	246222
Stat error		517	496	517	496
Syst error		2624	2478	2624	2478
Number $\Sigma^+ \to p\,\gamma$		19500	18708	16411	15490
Stat error -		1281	1581	961	1168
Stat error +		1402	1660	1064	1219
Syst error (%)		1.40%	5.30%	5.90%	6.10%
Efficiency of TRD		1	1	0.834	0.834
Stat error		–	–	0.012	0.012
Syst error		–	–	0.014	0.014

Sample	REL. BR	Stat-	Stat+	Syst
ALL DATA POS	2.31E-03	-1.50E-04	1.70E-04	1.00E-04
ALL DATA NEG	2.41E-03	-2.00E-04	2.10E-04	1.60E-04
TRD ≤ 10 POS	2.33E-03	-1.60E-04	1.70E-04	1.70E-04
TRD ≤ 10 NEG	2.40E-03	-1.80E-04	1.90E-04	1.80E-04

AVERAGE from ALL DATA
2.35E-03 ± 0.13E-03 ± 0.10E-03
Abs Br[4]: $\Sigma^+ \to p\,\pi^0$ = .5157 ± .0030
Abs Br: $\Sigma^+ \to p\,\gamma$ = 1.21E-03 ± .08E-03
World Avg[4]: 1.24E-03 ± .07E-03

References

1. M. Foucher et al, *PRL* **68** (1992) 3004.
2. I. I. Balitsky et al, *Nucl. Phys.* B **312** (1989) 509.
3. P. Zenczykowski, *Phys. Rev.* D **44** (1991) 1485.
4. Particle Data Group, *Phys. Lett.* B **239** (1990) II.22.

MEASUREMENTS OF $B^0\overline{B}^0$ MIXING AND THE LIFETIME RATIO $\tau(B^+)/\tau(B^0)$ WITH THE CLEO II DETECTOR

DAVID R. PERTICONE
(Representing the CLEO Collaboration.)
School of Physics and Astronomy, University of Minnesota
Minneapolis, MN 55455, U.S.A.

ABSTRACT

Using the CLEO II detector, we have made measurements of $B^0\overline{B}^0$ mixing using dilepton events, and also using a partial reconstruction tag of the decay $\overline{B}^0 \to D^{*+}l^-\overline{\nu}$. These measurements represent substantial improvement over previous results. We have also measured the lifetime ratio $\tau(B^+)/\tau(B^0)$ by counting leptons recoiling against fully reconstructed B meson candidates.

1. Introduction

In this report[1] we will discuss two fundamental properties of non-strange B mesons (B^+, B^0), the rate of $B^0\overline{B}^0$ mixing and the lifetime ratio $\tau(B^+)/\tau(B^0)$. We present two measurements of $B^0\overline{B}^0$ mixing, one analyzing dilepton events, and another using a partial reconstruction tag of $\overline{B}^0 \to D^{*+}l^-\overline{\nu}, D^{*+} \to D^0\pi^+$ (charge conjugate modes are implicit) together with a second lepton to tag the flavor of the other B. We present a measurement of the lifetime ratio $\tau(B^+)/\tau(B^0)$ via the ratio of semileptonic branching fractions b_+/b_0. We tag one B using a fully reconstructed hadronic decay, and then search the event for evidence of semileptonic decay of the $\overline{B}$.

2. The CLEO II Detector

All three measurements utilize the exceptional lepton identification capabilities of the CLEO II detector.[2] In the momentum interval 1.5 GeV/c $\leq |p_l| \leq$ 2.4 GeV/c, electrons are identified in the best region of the calorimeter ($|cos(\theta)| < 0.71$) with efficiency 93% and fake rate 0.2%. Muons are identified with efficiency 77-95% and fake rate 0.1-1.0%. The data sample for the mixing (lifetime ratio) analyses consisted of 951 pb^{-1} (1194 pb^{-1}) taken at the $\Upsilon(4S)$ resonance and 445 pb^{-1} (596 pb^{-1}) taken $\approx$ 55 MeV/c^2 below resonance.

3. The Dilepton Mixing Analysis[3]

We exploit the fact that in semileptonic B decay the sign of the lepton charge tags the flavor of the decaying B meson ($B^0 \to l^+\nu X, \overline{B}^0 \to l^-\overline{\nu} X$). Thus, for $e^+e^- \to \Upsilon(4S) \to B\overline{B}$, like-sign dileptons ($ee, e\mu, \mu\mu$) measure the probability that a produced B^0 will decay as a $\overline{B}^0$. To determine mixing from dilepton events, the like-sign dileptons from mixed events and opposite-sign dileptons from unmixed $B^0\overline{B}^0$ events must be separated from other dilepton sources. These include dileptons from the continuum, fakes, $\psi(\psi') \to l^+l^-$, opposite-sign dileptons from B^+B^- decays, and events where one lepton arises from B semileptonic decay $B \to l^+\nu X$ (primary lepton) and another from a semileptonic decay of a daughter D meson, $\overline{B}{\to}DX, D{\to} l^+\nu Y$ (secondary lepton). The largest background to the like-sign dilepton mixing signal are these like-sign primary-secondary dileptons.

To reduce these backgrounds several constraints were imposed. Both lepton candidates were required to be in the momentum interval 1.5 GeV/c $\leq |p_l| \leq$ 2.4 GeV/c. Events were rejected if more than two identified leptons were found with momentum 1.5 GeV/c $\leq |p_l| \leq$ 2.4 GeV/c. The opening angle between the two leptons is required to satisfy $-0.8 \leq \cos(\theta_{ll}) \leq 0.9$. Finally, we reject events consistent with $\psi(\psi'){\to}l^+l^-$ decay. Real and fake dileptons from the continuum are removed by subtracting the observed dilepton yields in the below resonance data sample. Fake dileptons were estimated using events which passed all cuts but contained a single identified lepton. ψ leakage, as well as events where primary-primary e^+e^- and $\mu^+\mu^-$ were lost due to the ψ veto were estimated using M.C. simulation. Like-sign primary-secondary dileptons were calculated from data, using fits to the single lepton spectrum to determine the fraction of leptons from secondary decays. After all corrections, we find $N(l^\pm l^\pm) = 184.5 \pm 18.9 \pm 23.5$ like-sign dileptons and $N(l^+l^-) = 2169.1 \pm 51.0 \pm 19.1$ opposite-sign dileptons, where the $ee, \mu\mu$, and $e\mu$ modes have been combined. We calculate the mixing parameter $r = N(l^\pm l^\pm)/[N(l^+l^-) - \Lambda(N(l^\pm l^\pm) + N(l^+l^-))]$. The parameter $\Lambda = \frac{f_+ b_+^2}{(f_+ b_+^2 + f_0 b_0^2)}$ (where $(f_{+,0})$ are the $\Upsilon(4S)$ production fractions and and $(b_{+,0})$ the semileptonic branching ratios for charged and neutral B mesons) is used to remove the $N(l^+l^-)$ contribution from B^+B^- decay. We find $r = 0.187 \pm 0.022 \pm 0.025 \pm 0.031$, where the errors are statistical, systematic and systematic due to Λ (which is common to all $\Upsilon(4S)$ dilepton analyses). The errors associated with this measurement are about a factor of two smaller than previous results from ARGUS and CLEO. Our measurement of r corresponds to to $\frac{\Delta M}{\Gamma} = 0.68 \pm 0.10$.

A possible manifestation of CP violation in B decay is an inequality of the mixing rates $\Gamma(B^0{\to}\overline{B}^0{\to}l^-\bar{\nu}X) \neq \Gamma(\overline{B}^0{\to}B^0{\to}l^+\nu X)$. Such a violation would appear as a charge asymmetry in like-sign dileptons, $a_{ll} = \frac{N(l^+l^+)-N(l^-l^-)}{N(l^+l^+)+N(l^-l^-)}$. We find no evidence for a charge asymmetry in the like-sign dilepton yields, and place a 90% C.L. upper limit of $|a_{ll}| < 0.18$.

4. The Partial Reconstruction Mixing Analysis[3]

The partial reconstruction analysis utilizes the correlation of the soft pion and the lepton in the decay chain $\overline{B}^0 \to D^{*+}l^-\bar{\nu}, D^{*+} \to D^0\pi^+$. Because the pion is almost at rest in the D^{*+} center-of-mass, the pion 4-vector allows a crude measurement of the D^{*+} 4-vector, without needing to reconstruct the D^0. We define an effective neutrino missing mass $m_\nu^2 \approx (E_{beam} - E_l - E_{D^*})^2 - |\vec{p}_l + \vec{p}_{D^*}|^2$, where $\vec{p}_B$ has been set to 0. A large enhancement is observed in the right sign combination ($l_{tag}^+\pi^-$) of m_ν^2 while no signal is observed in the wrong sign ($l_{tag}^+\pi^+$). We define the "signal-region" to be $m_\nu^2 > -1.5$. The composition of the tags in the signal region is determined to be 50.4% random background, 42.7% true $\overline{B}^0 \to D^{*+}l^-\bar{\nu}$, and 6.9% $B{\to}D^*\pi l\bar{\nu}$. We then probe the flavor of the other B in the event by searching for a second lepton (l_2). We create two plots of l_2 momentum, one each for $l_{tag}^+l_2^-$ (N_{+-}) and $l_{tag}^+l_2^+$ (N_{++}). We fitted the l_2 spectra with $b\to cl\nu$ and $b{\to}cX, c{\to}sl\nu$ spectra used to fit the single lepton spectrum, in order to determine the primary and secondary components of the l_2 spectra. The fits yielded $N_{++} = 210 \pm 27$ and $N_{+-} = 1213 \pm 54$. Unlike the dilepton analysis, N_{++} and N_{+-} are not trivially connected to the $N(B^0B^0)$, $N(B^0\overline{B}^0)$, and $N(B^+B^-)$ yields, as are the like- and opposite-sign dileptons. To relate N_{++} and N_{+-} to the mixing parameter, we note that the probability of finding a second lepton in the event is proportional to the product of the initial tag fraction times the effective efficiency for finding a second lepton times a function of the mixing parameter. We determine $\frac{r}{1+r} = (0.865 N_{++} - 0.014 N_{+-})/(0.628 N_{++} + 0.696 N_{+-})$, thus $r = 0.200 \pm 0.033 \pm 0.024 \pm 0.015$. This confirms the dilepton result. Because the systematics of this measurement are still under investigation, and because of the large correlation between the event samples and systematic errors, we have not combined them at this time.

5. The Ratio of Lifetimes[4] $\tau(B^+)/\tau(B^0)$

The ratio of the semileptonic branching ratios can be used to determine the ratio of the lifetimes of the B^0 and B^+ mesons, provided the assumption that $\Gamma(\overline{B}^0 \rightarrow l^-\overline{\nu}X) = \Gamma(B^- \rightarrow l^-\overline{\nu}X)$ is valid. By analyzing events containing fully reconstructed B meson candidates, the semileptonic branching ratio can be simply determined by searching the remaining tracks in the event for a lepton with the proper charge to tag a semileptonic decay of the $\overline{B}$. For B^0 decays this requires some caution, however, since in mixed events secondary leptons, not primary, will have the expected charge. Using ≈ 80 decay modes, CLEO is able to reconstruct 853.6 ± 45.6 B^+ candidates and 438.0 ± 31.5 B^0 candidates. For recoil muons, a minimum momentum cut of 1.4 GeV/c is imposed, which is the limit of muon acceptance. For electrons we apply cuts of 0.8 GeV/c for B^+ recoils and 1.4 GeV/c for B^0 recoils, where the stiffer cut is applied to reduced the fraction of secondary leptons making false tags in mixed events. The raw yields are 82 e and 29 μ recoiling against B^+'s and 18 e and 20 μ recoiling against B^0's. These yields are corrected for continuum and $B\overline{B}$ backgrounds, fakes, and efficiency. The leptons recoiling against B^0's are corrected by a factor $(1+r)$ to account for mixing. We then use theoretical models of the $b \rightarrow cl\nu$ spectrum to extrapolate the yields to the entire momentum interval. We find the ratio of the lifetimes to be $\tau(B^+)/\tau(B^0) = 0.92 \pm 0.26 \pm 0.14$ (preliminary), where the errors are statistical and systematic, respectively.

6. Acknowledgements

The author thanks M. Lambrecht and M. Saulnier for their assistance with this report, and Dr. Jim Mueller for his hospitality, computing and otherwise.

7. References

1. For a more detailed summary of this DPF92 presentation see D. R. Perticone, University of Minnesota Preprint UMN-EX-1120/92.
2. Y. Kubota, et al., The CLEO II Detector, *Nucl. Inst. Meth.* **A320** (1992) 66.
3. D. Acosta et al. (CLEO), contributed paper, ICHEP'92 Dallas, Texas (1992).
4. D. Akerib et al. (CLEO), contributed paper, ICHEP'92 Dallas, Texas (1992).

MEASUREMENT OF $B^0\overline{B^0}$ MIXING IN OPAL HADRONIC Z DECAYS

J. FREDERIC KRAL
CERN, PPE Division
CH-1211 Geneva 23, Switzerland

representing

The OPAL Collaboration

ABSTRACT

We measure the average $B^0\overline{B^0}$ parameter in Z decays to be $\chi = 0.125^{+0.017}_{-0.016} \pm 0.015$.

1. Introduction and Method

Both B^0_d and B^0_s are produced in hadronic Z^0 decays, so a measurement of the average mixing parameter probes the CKM matrix elements V_{td} and V_{ts} as well as the production rates of these mesons. This measurement is an important correction to measurements of the forward-backward asymmetry for bottom quarks in hadronic Z^0 decays.

The average $B^0\overline{B^0}$ mixing parameter is defined as

$$\chi = \frac{\mathrm{BR}(b \to \bar{B}^0 \to B^0 \to \ell^+ X)}{\mathrm{BR}(b \to \ell^\pm X)}, \qquad (1)$$

where the denominator includes all b-flavored hadrons produced and ℓ is either an electron or a muon. We measure χ from the ratio R of like-sign dilepton events to all dilepton events using a method described in more detail elsewhere[1]. Important backgrounds to the like-sign mixing signal are events with a secondary b decay $b \to c \to \ell^+$ accompanied by a primary decay $\bar{b} \to \ell^+$ and events containing hadrons misidentified as leptons or leptons which did not originate from heavy quarks. Dilepton events with two primary b decays are enriched by requiring both leptons to have large momenta and large momenta transverse to the b-hadron flight direction. These large momenta result from the relatively large bottom quark mass.

2. Dilepton Event Selection

The data were collected with the OPAL detector at LEP[2]. The most important elements of the detector for this analysis are the central jet chamber inside a solenoidal magnetic field of 0.4 T, the lead-glass electromagnetic calorimeter and the muon chambers. We select nearly 500,000 hadronic Z^0 decays by requiring at least seven charged tracks and seven electromagnetic energy clusters. Using the tracks and clusters we find the directions of the hadronic jets using the JADE cluster algorithm[3]. The direction of a jet containing a lepton candidate serves as an estimate of the parent b-quark flight direction.

We find 5400 dilepton events containing two or more lepton candidates with momenta $p > 2$ GeV/c. The sign of the charge of lepton candidates is required to be measured to 3σ. For each candidate, we construct the transverse momentum p_t relative to the jet containing the lepton.

Muons are identified for $|\cos\theta| < 0.97$, where θ is the angle to the e^- beam direction. Candidates are found by matching tracks with muon-chamber segments. We use dE/dx in the jet chamber to reject kaons. The efficiency is found to be about 80% using our Monte Carlo simulation (MC)[4] and it is cross-checked using $Z \to \mu\mu$ events and two-photon events. The misidentification probability in the MC varies between 0.5 and 0.8% and is checked with pions from $K^0 \to \pi\pi$.

Electrons are identified for $|\cos\theta| < 0.70$ and $0.83 < |\cos\theta| < 0.90$. Candidates are found using dE/dx and matching of tracks with calorimeter clusters[5]. The efficiency varies with p and p_t and is measured to range between 50 and 60% for high p_t. The efficiency is calculated using electrons in radiative Bhabha events and in hadronic events from the data. The misidentification probability is also measured in the data and is found to vary from 0.03 to 0.15%. Electrons from photon conversions are removed with an efficiency of $84 \pm 8\%$.

3. Extraction of the Mixing Signal

To separate out the mixing signal from the background, we use the two leptons in an event with the largest combined p–p_t values,

$$p_{\text{comb}} = \sqrt{(\frac{p}{10})^2 + p_t^2}, \qquad (2)$$

and then assign the minimum value of the two, $p_{\text{comb}}^{\min}$, to each event. Dilepton events with two primary b-hadron decays are enriched for large values of $p_{\text{comb}}^{\min}$ and when the opening angle between the leptons is large. We select events with opening angles greater than 60°. The $p_{\text{comb}}^{\min}$ distribution for such events is shown in Fig. 1. Events with opening angle less than 60° provide a check on the background predictions.

To extract the average mixing parameter χ we select the value of χ which is the best fit to R as a function of $p_{\text{comb}}^{\min}$. The sensitivity of χ to R is indicated in Fig. 2 and the result of our simultaneous fit to the $\mu\mu$, $e\mu$ and ee spectra is $\chi = 0.125^{+0.017}_{-0.016}$.

4. Systematic Errors and Discussion

The largest sources of systematic errors are listed in Table 1. The final result is $\chi = 0.125^{+0.017}_{-0.016} \pm 0.015$, in good agreement with previous measurements[6]. This value is an average weighted by the production rates f of B_d^0 and B_s^0, assuming the semileptonic branching ratios are equal,

$$\chi = f_d \chi_d + f_s \chi_s. \qquad (3)$$

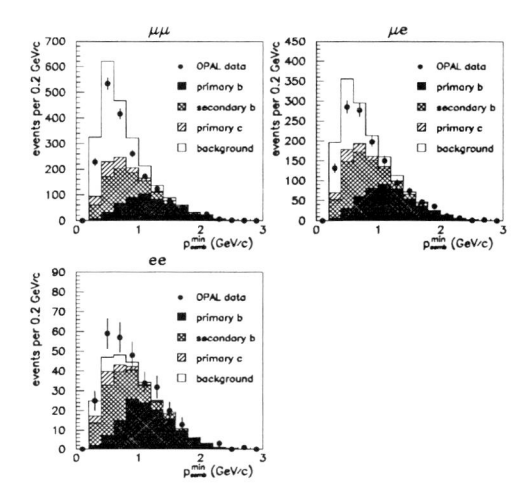

Figure 1: Distributions of $p_{\text{comb}}^{\min}$ for pairs of leptons in the data with predictions.

Combining our χ with the CLEO measurement[7] of $\chi_d = 0.167 \pm 0.019 \pm 0.018$ and assuming $f_u = f_d$ and $f_{\text{baryon}} = 9 \pm 4.5\%$, we find that χ is consistent with full B_s^0 mixing ($\chi_s = 0.5$) for reasonable values of f_s. For full B_s^0 mixing, as favored theoretically, the data imply $f_s = 0.12 \pm 0.06$, in agreement with predictions[8].

5. References

1. OPAL Collaboration, P.D.Acton et al., Phys. Lett. **B 276** (1992) 379.
2. OPAL Collaboration, K.Ahmet et al., Nucl. Instr. and Meth. **A 305** (1991) 275.
3. OPAL Collaboration, P.D.Acton et al., Z. Phys. **C 55** (1992) 191-207.

Source	Variation	Effect on χ
BR($b \to \ell$)	$\pm 10\%$	$^{+0.007}_{-0.009}$
BR($b \to c \to \ell$)	$\pm 16\%$	$^{+0.011}_{-0.010}$
D** fraction	0–32%	± 0.002
Fragmentation, $\bar{x}_E$	0.70–0.74	± 0.003
Muon background	$\pm 30\%$	± 0.003
Electron efficiency	change to a constant 0.5	± 0.003
Monte Carlo statistics		± 0.004
TOTAL (added in quadrature)		± 0.015

Table 1: Systematic errors on the determinations of χ

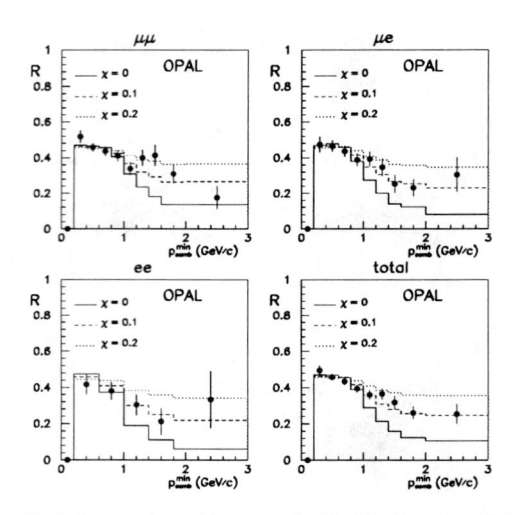

Figure 2: The fraction R of the number of large-angle dilepton events which are like sign versus p^{min}_{comb}, shown separately for $\mu\mu$ events, $e\mu$ events, ee events and the sum of the three channels. Monte Carlo predictions for $\chi = 0$, $\chi = 0.1$ and $\chi = 0.2$ are superimposed. Only statistical errors are included.

4. The JADE cluster algorithm with the E0 recombination scheme[1].
5. The JETSET 7.3 Monte Carlo program with modifications[1].
6. UA1 Collaboration, C.Albajar et al., Phys. Lett. **B 186** (1987) 247;
   MAC Collaboration, H.Band et al., Phys. Lett. **B 200** (1988) 221;
   MARK II Collaboration, A.J.Weir et al., Phys. Lett. **B 240** (1990) 289;
   L3 Collaboration, B.Adeva et al., Phys. Lett. **B 252** (1990) 703;
   ALEPH Collaboration, D.Decamp et al., Phys. Lett. **B 258** (1991) 236;
   UA1 Collaboration, C.Albajar et al., Phys. Lett. **B 262** (1991) 171;
   CDF Collaboration, reported by H.Wenzel at the Third Topical Seminar on Heavy Flavours, San Miniato, Italy, (1991), Fermilab report FL-CONF/91-264-E;
   ALEPH Collaboration, D.Buskulic et al., CERN-PPE/92-48;
   ALEPH Collaboration, reported by J.Kroll, proceedings of Les Rencontres de Moriond, France, 1992.
7. CLEO Collaboration, reported by K.Lingel, proceedings of Les Rencontres de Moriond, France, 1992.
8. Assuming fragmentation parameters consistent with the measured yield of hadrons of various flavours in e^+e^- annihilation at lower energies and at LEP, gives production ratios of 39.5% B_d, 39.5% B_u, 12% B_s and 9% b-flavored baryon[1].

ELECTROMAGNETIC MASS DIFFERENCES FOR HEAVY-LIGHT MESONS*

E. EICHTEN and T. HAN

Fermi National Accelerator Laboratory
P. O. Box 500, Batavia, IL 60510, USA

ABSTRACT

Electromagnetic mass differences for heavy-light mesons such as B, D, and K are calculated based on the Cornell potential model and taking the Breit-Fermi interactions as perturbation. The numerical results consistent with experimental measurements, including the current $B^+ - B^0$ data, can be obtained. Theoretical uncertainties from QCD effects in potential model calculations are shown to be large. A general framework for calculation of the EMD within heavy-light systems is discussed.

The experimentally well-measured value of the electromagnetic mass difference (EMD) for the K system[1] is $K^+ - K^0 = -4.024 \pm 0.032$ MeV. In contrast, recent experimental results[1] have shown that $B^+ - B^0 = -0.1 \pm 0.8$ MeV. This is significantly different from the K system and it signals strong dynamical effects in going from light to heavy-light mesons. We are therefore motivated to re-consider calculations of the EMD for the heavy-light systems.

We start our discussion by examining the EMD in a potential model for a heavy-light meson. We first assume that the lowest order QCD interaction between constituent quarks inside a meson is given by the nonrelativistic flavor-independent Cornell potential[2]. We then take the two-body Breit-Fermi interactions[3] V_{BF} as perturbation. Since there is always a light quark in the system considered, we expect that the relativistic correction to the EMD may be significant. Therefore in our calculation, we have corrected the rest-energy term Δm by $\Delta E = \sqrt{m_1^2 + p^2} - \sqrt{m_2^2 + p^2}$. The total EMD between the two mesons, ΔM, can thus be expressed by

$$\Delta M = \Delta <V_{BF}> + \Delta E.$$

The expectation value of the inverse quark separation r^{-1} is a characteristic quantity. It determines the strength of the Coulombic interaction between the two constituent quarks. $<r^{-1}>$ scales with the reduced mass μ approximately as $\mu^{5/12}$, while for a pure linear confinement potential $<r^{-1}>$ would scale as $\mu^{1/3}$. Therefore, the larger the reduced mass is, the smaller the quark separation will be. This behavior of $<r^{-1}>$ with the reduced mass is general and model-independent.

In evaluating the mass differences, we choose constituent quark masses $m_u = 336$ MeV, $m_s = 540$ MeV, $m_c = 1500$ MeV, and $m_b = 5000$ MeV. There are two more parameters in the potential model calculation: the strong coupling constant α_s, and

---

*Talk presented by T. HAN

the light-quark mass difference $\Delta m = m_d - m_u$. Since the hyperfine splittings between a vector and pseudoscalar meson of the same charge are independent of Δm, but sensitive to α_s, we determine α_s by fitting the experimental hyperfine splittings. We obtain $\alpha_s = 0.353, 0.405, 0.613$ for B, D, and K systems respectively. We then find that if we take $\Delta m = 4$ MeV, the best fits to experimental measurements of the EMD for K, D, and B systems are obtained. The numerical results are shown in Table I.

One would naively expect that the EMD of K and B systems might be similar, because of the same light-quark content and the same electric charge of the heavy quarks in the two systems. However, as discussed earlier, the reduced mass effect considerably increases the value of $<r^{-1}>$ from a light to heavy-light system. Hence the relativistic corrections and the magnetic moment interaction proportional to $<r^{-1}>^3$ become more important. It is these dynamical effects that change the value of EMD from a light to heavy-light system.

Although the agreement between our results and data seems to be rather good except for K^* system, we have gone through a 'fine-tuning' procedure in determining the parameters α_s and Δm. To see to what extent we can trust a potential model calculation, it is physically more instructive to rewrite the EMD as

$$\Delta M = \Delta M_{EM} + Z_G \Delta m,$$

where ΔM_{EM} represents the pure electromagnetic contributions which are those terms proportional to α. Z_G contains non-EM terms from one-gluon exchange as well as dynamical effect on Δm. The numerical results for this separation are also given in Table I. We see that the non-EM dynamical effects are very large. We also notice that there is a large cancellation among the individual terms of the non-EM contributions, which govern the fine-tuning of α_s and Δm. This makes the potential model results more questionable. Indeed, comparing our results with a recent similar calculation[4], we find that the EM terms are close in the two calculations, while the individual non-EM terms show substantial differences. Also, the fitted α_s's in Ref. 4 are rather different from ours and as a result they could not obtain a good fit to the $K^+ - K^0$.

We now take a more general viewpoint. We start from the $SU_C(3) \times U_{EM}(1)$ gauge theory. The action S for the isospin-doublet light quarks (u,d) can be written

Table I. Comparison of the potential model results and experimental data for charged and neutral meson mass differences. $\Delta m = 4$ MeV is used. The EM contribution ΔM_{EM} and the Δm induced contribution are separately shown here.

(MeV)	ΔM_{EM}	$Z_G \Delta m$	Total ΔM	Expt.
$K^+ - K^0$	2.018	-6.056	-4.038	-4.024 ± 0.032
$K^{*+} - K^{*0}$	0.835	-1.362	-0.527	-6.7 ± 1.2
$D^+ - D^0$	2.714	1.95	4.664	4.77 ± 0.27
$D^{*+} - D^{*0}$	1.432	0.269	1.702	2.9 ± 1.3
$B^+ - B^0$	0.805	-0.251	0.555	-0.1 ± 0.8
$B^{*+} - B^{*0}$	0.574	0.279	0.853	–

as
$$S_L(\psi_L) = \int d^4x \bar{\psi}_L \left[i\gamma^\mu \mathcal{D}_\mu - (\bar{m} - \tau_3 \Delta m)\right] \psi_L,$$

where $\bar{m} = (m_u + m_d)/2$. For the heavy-quark sector, the action can be expressed by

$$S_H(\psi_H) = \sum_Q \int d^4x \psi_Q^\dagger \left[i\mathcal{D}_0 - m_Q + \frac{\vec{\mathcal{D}}^2}{2m_Q} - \frac{\vec{\sigma}\cdot\vec{B}}{2m_Q} + R\right] \psi_Q,$$

where $\vec{B}$ is the (color) magnetic fields, and R contains terms of order $1/m_Q^2$.

With the vacuum functional constructed based on these actions, one is able to calculate the two-point correlation function $<0|\mathcal{O}_{HL}(x)\mathcal{O}_{HL}^\dagger(0)|0>$, with the heavy-light meson operator $\mathcal{O}_{HL}(x) = \bar{\psi}_H(x)\Gamma\psi_L(x)$ ($\Gamma = \gamma_5$ for a pseudoscalar). In the Euclidean space, when $x_0 = T$ becomes large, the ground state dominates the correlation function. So in the limit $T \to \infty$,

$$<0|\mathcal{O}_{HL}(x)\mathcal{O}_{HL}^\dagger(0)|0>_E \to \frac{f_M^2 M^2}{2M} e^{-MT} \delta(\vec{x}),$$

where f_M and M are the decay constant and mass of the heavy-light meson, respectively. Therefore one can extract the meson mass M by calculating the correlation function in large T limit. The variation of M with the light quark mass will give a direct determination of the non-EM contribution Z_G.

We have explicitly evaluated the two-point function up to the first order in α and Δm, and to $1/m_Q$, and identified those terms that contribute to the EMD. In order to avoid model-dependent uncertainties, one can implement the formalism into lattice calculations which incorporate the non-perturbative QCD effects in a relativistic way. More details about the formalism and the calculation can be found in our recent work[5].

Acknowledgements

Fermilab is operated by the University Research Association Incorporation under contract with the U. S. Department of Energy. T. Han was supported by an SSC Fellowship from the Texas National Research Laboratory Commission under Award No. FCFY9116.

References

1. Particle Data Group, Phys. Rev. **D45**, No. 11 (1992).
2. E. Eichten, K. Gottfried, T. Kinoshita, K. D. Lane, and T. M. Yan, Phys. Rev. **D17**, 3090 (1978); Phys. Rev. **D21**, 203 (1980).
3. A. De Rújula, H. Georgi, and S. L. Glashow, Phys. Rev. **D12**, 147(1975).
4. R. F. Lebed, LBL-32872 (1992).
5. E. Eichten and T. Han, FERMILAB-PUB-92/319-T (1992).

HEAVY MESON MASSES AND DECAY CONSTANTS

JONATHAN L. ROSNER

Enrico Fermi Institute and Department of Physics, University of Chicago
5640 S. Ellis Ave., Chicago, IL 60637, USA

ABSTRACT

Masses and decay constants of mesons containing a single c or b quark are described within the framework of heavy-quark symmetry. The $B_s^* - B_s$ and $\bar{B}^{*0} - \bar{B}^0$ mass splittings are found equal to within a fraction of an MeV. Decay constants of D and B mesons are estimated using isospin mass splittings in the D, D^*, B, and B^* states to isolate the electromagnetic hyperfine interaction between quarks. A relation following from the use of splittings in kaons is also considered.

1. Introduction

Mesons containing one heavy quark (c, b) are of fundamental importance for the understanding of the strong interactions, since they consist of a single light quark bound to a nearly static source of color. We describe here some recent work on the masses [1] and decay constants [2] of such mesons.

Results on heavy meson masses come from an expansion to first order in α, first order in light-quark masses (m_u, m_d, m_s), and first order in $1/m_Q$, where Q is a heavy quark. We predict one new relation: The photons in $B_s^* \to B_s \gamma$ and $B^{*0} \to B^0 \gamma$ should have equal energies.

Decay constants of heavy mesons are crucial for interpreting data on particle-antiparticle mixing in the neutral B meson system, and for anticipating and interpreting new signatures for CP violation. We describe a method for determination of these constants which relies on the isospin splittings of the D, D^*, B, and B^* mesons. We also consider a relation following from the use of splittings in kaons. The isospin splittings allow one to extract the contributions of the spin-dependent electromagnetic interaction between light and heavy quarks. Additional assumptions about quark masses are required in order to interpret these contributions in terms of decay constants.

2. Masses of D and B mesons

The most general mass operator containing contributions of first order in (a) light quark masses m_q, (b) electromagnetic interactions, and (c) $1/m_Q$, including terms of order m_q/m_Q and α/m_Q, contains 11 terms, not counting ones which can be absorbed into heavy quark masses [1]. One result of this expansion is the familiar relation between the strong hyperfine splitting between the $^3S_1$ and $^1S_0$ D and B states, which says that ΔM^2 should be approximately the same for the two systems.

Aside from this result, we find one new prediction:

$$[B_s^* - B_s] - [\bar{B}^{*0} - \bar{B}^0] = (m_c/m_b)([D_s^* - D_s] - [D^{*+} - D^+]) \quad , \tag{1}$$

where here and below symbols stand for particle masses. Since $D_s^* - D_s = 141.5 \pm 1.9$ MeV [3] and $D^{*+} - D^+ = 140.64 \pm 0.08 \pm 0.06$ MeV [4], we expect the right-hand side of this relation to be about 0.3 ± 0.6 MeV. A recent study suggests that the smallness of the result could be due to accidental cancellation, and that there could be additional contributions of up to a few MeV from effects of higher order in $1/m_Q$ [5].

3. Predictions for decay constants

In the nonrelativistic formula

$$f_M^2 = \frac{12|\Psi(0)|^2}{M_M^2} \tag{2}$$

we seek an estimate of $\Psi(0)$, the nonrelativistic wave function at zero separation of the light and heavy quark. This may be obtained in a constituent quark model from the contribution of electromagnetic hyperfine splitting to meson masses. Specifically, in the limit in which the wave functions of a light quark bound to a c and b quark are the same,

$$\Delta(D) \equiv (D^+ - D^0) - (D^{*+} - D^{*0}) = a + \frac{8\pi\alpha Q_c}{3m_u m_c}|\Psi(0)|^2 \quad , \tag{3}$$

$$\Delta(B) \equiv (\bar{B}^0 - B^-) - (\bar{B}^{*0} - B^{*-}) = \frac{m_c}{m_b}a + \frac{8\pi\alpha Q_b}{3m_u m_b}|\Psi(0)|^2 \quad . \tag{4}$$

Here a denotes the effects of $m_u \neq m_d$ in the color hyperfine interaction and of spin-dependent light-quark electromagnetic self-energies. Now, while we know [4] that $\Delta(D) = 4.80 \pm 0.11$ MeV, the corresponding value [6] for B mesons, $\Delta(B) = 0.12 \pm 0.58$ MeV, is too poorly known to allow us to separate the effects of a and $|\Psi(0)|^2$. In Fig. 1 we show the dependence of predicted decay contants on $\Delta(B)$.

In order to proceed further we use a trick motivated by a result of Cohen and Lipkin [8] which appeals to the similarity between the kaon and B systems. We define

$$\Sigma(B) \equiv (\bar{B}^{*0} + B^{*-}) - (\bar{B}^0 + B^-) \quad , \tag{5}$$

with similar definitions [cf. (4)] for $\Delta(K)$ and $\Sigma(K)$. We then estimate

$$\Delta(B) = \Delta(K)\Sigma(B)/\Sigma(K) = (-0.06 \pm 0.04) \text{ MeV} \quad . \tag{6}$$

As a result, we can separate out the electromagnetic hyperfine term in (2) and (3), finding

$$|\Psi(0)|^2 = (13.8 \pm 1.4) \times 10^{-3} \text{ GeV}^3 \quad , \quad f_D^{(0)} = (290 \pm 15) \text{ MeV} \quad , \quad f_B^{(0)} = (177 \pm 9) \text{ MeV} \quad . \tag{7}$$

4. Comparison with experiment

The Mark III Collaboration finds $B(D \to \mu\nu) \times 10^{-4}$ (90% c.l.), corresponding to $f_D < 290$ MeV. The lowest-order result (7) obtained suggests that f_D may be

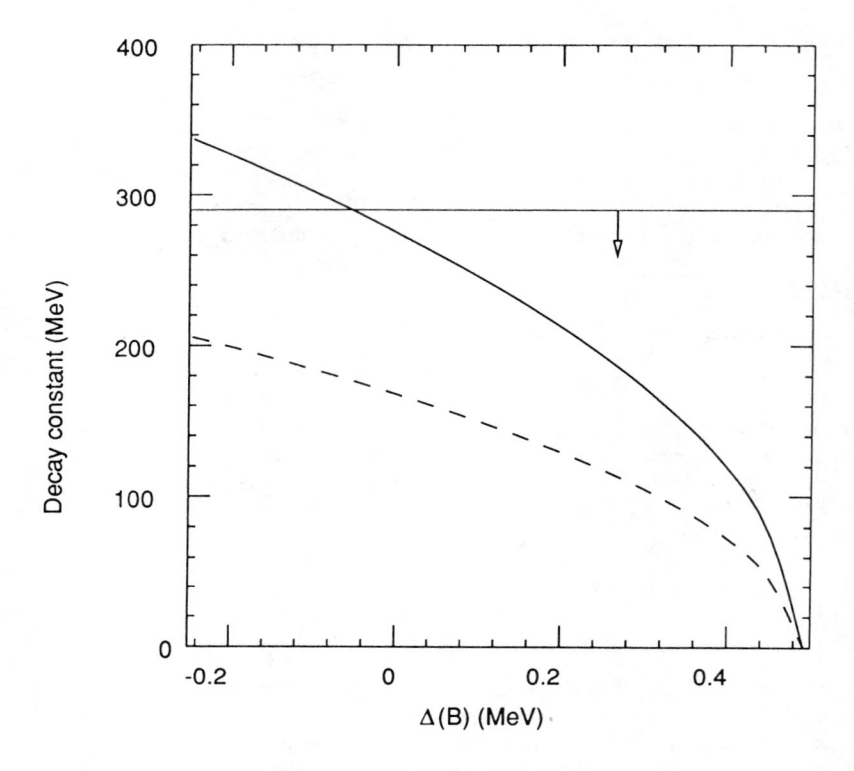

Figure 1: Decay constants $f_D^{(0)}$ (solid curve) and $f_B^{(0)}$ (dashed curve) predicted by the nonrelativistic formula (2) as functions of difference $\Delta(B)$ in isospin splittings between B^* and B mesons. The horizontal line with the arrow pointing downward denotes the upper limit of Ref. [7] on f_D.

close to its present upper limit, so a search for $D \to \mu\nu$ (e.g., through the reaction $e^+e^- \to \psi(3770) \to D^+D^-$ at the Beijing Electron Synchrotron) should prove fruitful.

It may be possible, for example at CLEO, to look for the decay $D \to \mu\nu$ by tagging a $D^\pm$ using the reaction $D^{*\pm} \to \pi^0 D^\pm$, since the π^0 is very soft in the D^* or D center-of-mass system, and helps to label the frame of the decaying D. The signal will show up in a characteristic band of $m(\pi^0\mu)$. One will probably need additional kinematic information to reduce backgrounds (e.g., from semileptonic decays).

Recent evidence for the reaction $D_s \to \mu\nu$ in emulsion [9] rests on the observation of a muon beyond the kinematic endpoint for semileptonic decays of D^+ and D_s. A search for $D_s \to \mu\nu$ using the information from the photon in $D_s^* \to D_s\gamma$ is possible in principle [10]. One needs additional jet or missing energy information.

The WA75 result [9], $f_{D_s} = 232\pm69$ MeV (based on 7 events above background) may be used indirectly to estimate corrections of order $1/m_Q$ to the lowest-order formula (2). First we estimate $|\Psi(0)|_D^2$ using the approximate equality of strong hyperfine splittings in the D and D_s systems, which implies that

$$|\Psi(0)|_D^2/m_u m_c = |\Psi(0)|_{D_s}^2/m_s m_c \quad . \tag{8}$$

With $m_u/m_s = 310$ MeV/485 MeV, we then estimate from the observed value of f_{D_s} that $f_D = 190 \pm 57$ MeV. If the discrepancy with our lowest-order prediction is ascribed to $1/m_Q$ corrections, we may write $f_D = f_D^{(0)}(1 - [\Delta/m_D])$, implying $\Delta/m_D = 0.35 \pm 0.20$ and hence $\Delta/m_B = 0.13 \pm 0.07$ or $f_B = f_B^{(0)}(1 - [\Delta/m_B]) = (154 \pm 17)$ MeV. QCD corrections probably raise this value by about 10%. The most recent range of lattice gauge theory values quoted at this conference [11] puts f_B in the range between 175 and 200 MeV and f_D just slightly above 200 MeV. A value of f_B of about 170 MeV is entirely compatible with recent fits to parameters of the Cabibbo-Kobayashi-Maskawa matrix and $B - \bar{B}$ mixing data.

5. Acknowledgements

I thank Jim Amundson, Nahmin Horwitz, Mike Kelly, Sheldon Stone, and Mark Wise for collaboration on some of the topics mentioned here, and Glenn Boyd and Harry Lipkin for helpful discussions. This work was supported in part by the United States Department of Energy under grant No. DE AC02 90ER40560.

6. References

1. J. L. Rosner and M. B. Wise, *Phys. Rev. D* **47**, January, 1993, to be published.
2. J. F. Amundson, Jonathan L. Rosner, M. A. Kelly, N. Horwitz, and S. L. Stone, Enrico Fermi Institute report EFI-92-31-Rev., September, 1992, submitted to *Phys. Rev. D*.
3. K. Hikasa et al. (Particle Data Group), *Phys. Rev. D* **46** (1992) S1.
4. D. Bortoletto et al. (CLEO Collaboration), *Phys. Rev. Lett.* **69** (1992) 2046.
5. L. Randall and E. Sather, MIT report MIT-CTP#2166, November, 1992 (unpublished).
6. C. Bebek et al. (CLEO Collaboration), *Phys. Rev. D* **36** (1987) 1289; **45** (1992) 21; H. Albrecht et al. (ARGUS Collaboration), *Zeit. Phys. C* **48** (1990) 543.
7. J. Adler et al. (Mark III Collaboration), *Phys. Rev. Lett.* **60** (1988) 1375.
8. I. Cohen and H. J. Lipkin, *Phys. Lett.* **84B** (1978) 323.
9. S. Aoki et al. (WA75 Collaboration), CERN report CERN-PPE/92-157, September, 1992 (unpublished).
10. S. Stone, private communication.
11. S. Sharpe, invited talk, this conference.

COVARIANT DESCRIPTION OF HYDROGEN-LIKE MESONS

Manuel Avila
*Departamento de Física Teórica, Instituto de Física, Universidad Nacional Autónoma de México.
Apartado Postal 20-364, 01000 D.F., MEXICO.*

ABSTRACT

A formalism is presented, covariant up to terms of $O(\frac{1}{M_Q})$ which describes from the center of mass frame a (hydrogen-like) system consisting of a heavy quark (Q) and a light quark (q) whose effective interaction between Q and q is characterized by a color Coulomb-like potential $V = -\frac{\xi}{r}$, a linear scalar potential $S = b \cdot r$ ($b > 0$) and a Breit potential. The formalism is applied to the B- and D- mesons spectroscopy.

1. Introduction

It is well known that the models employed commonly to describe the heavy quark (Q) - light quark (q) systems suffer from a succesful covariant approach. Neither the quark models with effective potentials[1-3] nor the Bag Models and their improved versions[4-8] do take into account center of mass (c.m.) effects which might be important for the spectra of those (Q,q) systems where the light quark is very relativistic (*i.e.* in the limit $\frac{m_q}{M_Q} \to 0$). Up to now there is not a satisfactory way of correcting this c.m. deffect on the Bag Model solutions[4].

With the purpose of describing hydrogen-like systems in a covariant way we present a model inspired in a formalism which was introduced by Grotch and Yennie[9] in the context of atomic physics in the late 60's. According with it the (Q,q) system is described from the c.m. frame by a relativistic light quark q bound to non-relativistic heavy quark Q through a color Coulomb vector potential $V = \frac{\xi}{r}$ a linear potential $S = br$ ($b > 0$) and a Breit potential. It is shown that in the limit of a very heavy quark ($M_Q \to \infty$) there is consistency of the present approach with the new symmetry of QCD called Heavy Quark Symmetry (HQS) which was discovered quite recently by Isgur and Wise[10]. To solve the eigenvalues equation it is done a manipulation of the hamiltonian and as a consecuence of it appear an effective vector ($\tilde{V}$) and scalar ($\tilde{S}$) potentials. These tilde potentials are nonlinear combinations of V and S. The part of the potential depending on the spin of the heavy quark $V'_{\vec{\Sigma}}$ is the responsible of the hyperfine splitting between the $^3S_1$ and $^1S_0$ states. This potential is handled to first order of perturbation theory using as parameter of expansion $\xi(\frac{\epsilon}{M_Q})$ where ϵ is the Q-q binding energy.

To apply the formalism to the D- and B- mesons spectroscopy it is found a very good agreement with the experimental data.

2. Formalism and Applications.

In the c.m. system the (Q,q) hamiltonian is

$$H\psi \equiv \left(\vec{\alpha}\cdot\vec{p} + V + (m_q + S)\beta + \frac{\vec{p}^2}{2M_Q} + \{\frac{\vec{\alpha}\cdot\vec{p}}{2M_Q}, V\} + \frac{1}{4M_Q}[\vec{\alpha}\cdot\vec{p}, [\vec{p}^2, W]] + V'_\Sigma\right)\psi = E\psi, \quad (1)$$

where $W = -\xi r$ and the part of the potential which depends on the spin of the heavy quark ($\vec{\Sigma}$) is

$$V'_\Sigma = i\left(\frac{\xi}{2M_Q}\right)\int d^3\vec{r}\,\psi^\dagger[\vec{\alpha}\times\vec{p},(\frac{1}{r})]\cdot\vec{\Sigma}\,\psi. \quad (2)$$

Note that to take the limit $M_Q \to \infty$ in Eq. (1) this becomes the familiar Dirac equation describing a relativistic light quark subject to the potentials $V + S\beta$. This result is consistent with the Heavy Quark Symmetry[10] predictions in the sense that in this limit both the mass M_Q and the spin $\vec{\Sigma}$ of the heavy quark must appear as internal symmetries of the hamiltonian.

With the use of the identities $V^2 + \frac{1}{2}[V,[\vec{p}^2,W]] = 0$ and $VS + \frac{1}{2}[S,[\vec{p}^2,W]] = 0$, it is possible to rewrite the hamiltonian of Eq. (1) as

$$H \simeq H_1 + \frac{H_1^2 - m_q^2}{2M_Q} + \frac{1}{4M_Q}[H_1,[\vec{p}^2,W]] + O(\frac{1}{M_Q^2}), \quad (3)$$

where

$$H_1 = \vec{\alpha}\cdot\vec{p} + \tilde{V} + (m_q + \tilde{S})\beta - \frac{1}{2M_Q}\{\vec{\alpha}\cdot\vec{p}, S\beta\}, \quad (4)$$

$$\tilde{S} = S - \frac{3}{2}\frac{VS}{M_Q} - \frac{m_q}{M_Q}V, \quad (5)$$

$$\tilde{V} = V - \frac{1}{2}\frac{S^2}{M_Q} - \frac{m_q}{M_Q}S. \quad (6)$$

Now, the problem of finding the energies of the (Q,q) bound system is reduced simply to solve the equation $H_1\psi_0 = \epsilon\psi_0$ since it is possible to show that the solutions of Eq. (1) are

$$\psi \simeq \left(1 - \frac{1}{4M_Q}[\vec{p}^2,W]\right)\psi_0 = \left(1 - \frac{\xi}{2M_Q}\frac{d}{dr}\right)\psi_0 \quad (7)$$

being the respective eigenenergies

$$E = \epsilon + \frac{\epsilon^2 - m_q^2}{2M_Q} + O(\frac{m_q^2}{M_Q^2}). \quad (8)$$

Before of solving the key equation $H_1\psi_0 = \epsilon\psi_0$ one must observe from Eq. (6) that the dependence of the potential $\tilde{V}$ on S^2 would induce non-physical solutions for large values of r. Thereby to find well behaved solutions we impose an effective cutoff $\tilde{V}_{max}$ to $\tilde{V}$. With it the vector potential is

$$\tilde{V} = \begin{cases} V - \frac{1}{2}\frac{S^2}{M_Q} - \frac{m_q}{M_Q}S & \text{for } r \leq r_{max} \\ V_{max} & \text{for } r > r_{max}, \end{cases} \quad (9)$$

where r_{max} is defined as the value of r where the potential of Eq. (6) takes its maximum V_{max}.

Using the convention $\psi_0 = \binom{G(r)}{i\vec{\sigma}\cdot\hat{r}F(r)}\chi_\kappa^m$ then it is possible[11] to solve the equation $H_1\psi_0 = \epsilon\psi_0$ for ϵ. This value of ϵ together with Eq. (8) enables us to know the internal energy of the (Q,q) system without spin effects. To account for the hyperfine splitting in mass between the $^3S_1$ and the $^1S_0$ states we handle the potential V'_Σ of Eq. (2) using first order perturbation theory. Thus the total internal energy of the meson is

$$E_T = M_Q + m_q + \epsilon + \frac{\epsilon^2 - m_q^2}{2M_Q} + <V'_\Sigma>, \tag{10}$$

$$<V'_\Sigma> = (\frac{16\pi}{3})(\frac{\xi}{2M_Q}) \int dr F(r) G(r) <\vec{\sigma}\cdot\vec{\Sigma}>. \tag{11}$$

By assuming that the total angular momentum $\vec{J} = \vec{L} + \vec{s} + \vec{\Sigma}$ is a constant and neglecting heavy quark structure effects one has

$$<\vec{\sigma}\cdot\vec{\Sigma}> = \begin{cases} -3 & J=0 \\ 1 & J=1. \end{cases} \tag{12}$$

Thus on the basis of Eqs. (10), (11) and (12) it is now possible to calculate the masses of the hydrogen-like mesons including of course the hyperfine splitting between the $^3S_1$ and $^1S_0$ states.

The comparison of our results with the predictions of other models and with the values of the physical masses are shown in Table 1.

3. Tables

Table 1. Masses (Gev) for the states $^3S_1$ and $^1S_0$ and their respective splitting (Gev) according to the present model, to the Quark Model with effective potential[1,2], to the Bag Models[4,5] and to the experiment. The input parameters are: $k = -1, b = 0.2\,Gev^2, \xi = 0.445, M_c = 1.3415\,Gev, M_b = 4.7907\,Gev, m_s = 0.12\,Gev$ and $m_u = m_d = m = 0$.

	Present Model	Ref. [1]	Ref. [2]	Ref. [4]	Ref. [5]	Experiment (average)
M_D	1.8674	1.88	1.8515	1.83	1.867	1.867
M_{D^*}	2.0122	2.04	2.012	2.01	2.009	2.009
$M_{D^*} - M_D$	0.1448	0.16	0.1605	0.18	0.142	0.143
M_{D_s}	1.9517	1.98	2.0170	1.92	1.939	1.969
$M_{D_s^*}$	2.1001	2.13	2.1497	2.09	2.148	2.110
$M_{D_s^*} - M_{D_s}$	0.1484	0.15	0.1327	0.17	0.209	0.142
M_B	5.2802	5.31	5.2609	5.27		5.279
M_{B^*}	5.3258	5.37	5.3248	5.34		5.330
$M_{B^*} - M_B$	0.0456	0.06	0.1188	0.07		0.052

5. Acknowledgements

I thank to the Departamento de Física Teórica of the Instituto de Física (UNAM) for the support.

6. References

1. S. Godfrey and N. Isgur, *Phys. Rev.* **D32** (1985) 189.
2. N. Barik and S. N. Jena, *Phys. Lett.* **101B** (1981) 282.

3. P. Colangelo, G. Nardulli and M. Pietroni, *Phys. Rev.* **D43** (1991) 3002.
4. D. Izatt, C. Detar and M. Stephenson, *Nucl. Phys.* **B199** (1982) 269.
5. W. Wilcox, O. V. Maxwell and K. Milton, *Phys. Rev.* **D31** (1981) 1081.
6. P. Singer and G. A. Miller, *Phys. Rev.* **D33** (1986) 141.
7. G. A. Miller, and P. Singer, *Phys. Rev.* **D37** (1988) 2564.
8. P. Singer and G. A. Miller, *Phys. Rev.* **D39** (1989) 825.
9. H. Grotch and D. R. Yennie, *Z. Physik* **202** (1967) 425; *ibid, Rev. Mod. Phys.* **41** (1969) 350.
10. N. Isgur and M. B. Wise, *Phys. Lett.* **B232** (1989) 111; *ibid, Phys. Lett.* **B237** (1990) 527.
11. M. Avila, *Manchester preprint* **M/C.TH.91/25** (1991)

TEST FOR RIGHT-HANDED b QUARK DECAYS[1]

JAMES F. AMUNDSON, JONATHAN L. ROSNER, AND MIHIR P. WORAH
Enrico Fermi Institute and Department of Physics, University of Chicago
5640 S. Ellis Ave., Chicago, IL 60637, USA

and

MARK B. WISE
Lauritsen Laboratory of Physics, California Institute of Technology
Pasadena, CA 91125

ABSTRACT

Gronau and Wakaizumi have proposed a model in which the dominant b decays are due to exchange of a new right-handed gauge boson. A test of this model via the study of polarized Λ_b baryons produced in $e^+e^- \to Z \to \Lambda_b + X$ is suggested.

It is conventionally assumed that the b quark decays left-handedly. However, it turns out to be surprisingly hard to exclude the possibility [1] that the dominant b decays to charm occur via a *right*-handed coupling, as long as the coupling to leptons in such decays is also right-handed. One cannot just look at the beta-decay spectrum, which is the same for $(V - A) \times (V - A)$ and $(V + A) \times (V + A)$ couplings. Instead, one needs to study decays of polarized b quarks.

In the present report, based on the work of Ref. [2], we suggest that the reaction $e^+e^- \to b\bar{b} \to \Lambda_b + \ldots$ is likely to give polarized b's, whose decay to leptons can distinguish among models. We urge, in particular, that the LEP experiments (some of which [3, 4] have already presented evidence for Λ_b) analyze their data with the possibility of $(V + A) \times (V + A)$ couplings in mind. Some aspects of the polarization studies suggested here have been mentioned previously [5, 6].

The reaction $e^+e^- \to Z \to b\bar{b}$ is expected to give rise to b quarks with polarization $\mathcal{P} \simeq -0.93$ for a weak mixing angle $\sin^2\theta = 0.233$. The Λ_b produced in the subsequent fragmentation of these b quarks should retain this polarization in the heavy-quark limit [6], in the absence of hard-gluon emission. The spin of the Λ_b is carried entirely by the b quark; the light quarks in it are coupled up to spin zero. If, on the other hand, the b quark ends up in a (spinless) B meson, information on its polarization is lost.

The inclusive $\Lambda_b \to$ charm semileptonic decay can be treated in the heavy-quark limit as a free-quark decay $b \to ce^-\bar{\nu}_e$. If the b has polarization $\mathcal{P}$, the expression for the normalized decay distribution in the b rest frame may be written

$$\frac{1}{\Gamma}\frac{d^2\Gamma}{dx\, d(\cos\psi)} = \frac{3x^2(1-\zeta)^2}{f(m_c^2/m_b^2)}\left[1 - \frac{2}{3}x + \frac{2x-1}{3}\xi\mathcal{P}\cos\psi\right]$$

[1] Presented by Jonathan L. Rosner.

$$+ \zeta \left\{ 1 - \frac{1}{3}x + \frac{1+x}{3}\xi \mathcal{P} \cos\psi \right\} \right] \quad , \tag{1}$$

where $x \equiv 2E_e^*/m_b$, E_e^* is the electron energy in the b rest frame, ψ is the angle between the electron momentum and the spin quantization axis in this frame, $\xi = \pm 1$ for $V \pm A$ couplings at both vertices, and

$$\zeta \equiv \frac{m_c^2}{m_b^2(1-x)} \quad ; \quad f(y) \equiv 1 - 8y + 8y^3 - y^4 - 12y^2 \log y \quad . \tag{2}$$

The electron spectrum (1) is considerably harder for $\xi\mathcal{P}\cos\psi \simeq 1$ than for $\xi\mathcal{P}\cos\psi \simeq -1$, as one can also see using familiar helicity arguments.

In the reaction $e^+e^- \to Z \to \Lambda_b + X$, the b quark has a large momentum along the axis of a fairly well-defined jet. In order to obtain the signal for Λ_b production, one can select events with a lepton at some minimum transverse momentum p_T with respect to this axis and with an inclusively produced Λ baryon of the appropriate sign [3,4]. In this frame, let us imagine the b spin to be quantized along its direction of motion. The electron transverse momentum and total energy are then $p_T = (m_b x \sin\psi)/2$ and $E_e = m_b x \gamma_b (1 + v_b \cos\psi)/2$, where v_b is the b quark's velocity and $\gamma_b \equiv (1-v_b^2)^{-1/2}$. Using these variables we may transform the distribution (1) to obtain

$$\frac{1}{\Gamma}\frac{d\Gamma}{dE_e}\bigg|_{p_T \geq p_T^{\min}} = \int dx \theta(p_T - p_T^{\min}) \frac{2}{m_b x \gamma_b v_b} \frac{1}{\Gamma} \frac{d^2\Gamma}{dx \, d(\cos\psi)} \tag{3}$$

Examples of this distribution are shown in Fig. 1 for various values of $p_T^{\min}$ and for the two limiting cases $\xi\mathcal{P} = 1$ (close to the standard model) and $\xi\mathcal{P} = -1$ (close to the model of Ref. [1]). We have taken the b quark to have a laboratory energy of 45 GeV, so that $\gamma_b = 9$. We have taken $m_c = 1.66$ GeV, $m_b = 5$ GeV, and have ignored the electron mass. A distinction on the basis of the electron energy spectrum is clearly possible, for example, when $p_T^{\min} = 0.8$ GeV.

The distributions (1) – (3) can be convoluted with more realistic functions for fragmentation of a b quark if desired. These functions are already in use in the Monte Carlo simulations employed in Refs. [3] and [4], so it should be a simple matter to reproduce distributions analogous to those in Fig. 1 which are more appropriate to the actual experiments. The fragmentation of a b quark to a Λ_b is not actually known; the corresponding function for $b \to B$ is peaked around $p_B/p_b \approx 0.7$. A potential source of depolarization is production of Λ_b via the decay of Σ_b^* and Σ_b. If these two resonances are more closely spaced than their natural widths, they can act coherently to preserve the b quark polarization, but if they are too widely spaced, some depolarization will result. (This question has been considered in Ref. [7].) The study of the corresponding spacing between Σ_c and Σ_c^* should shed some light on this question.

We thank M. Gronau and J. Kroll for helpful comments. This work was supported in part by the United States Department of Energy under grant No. DE AC02 90ER40560.

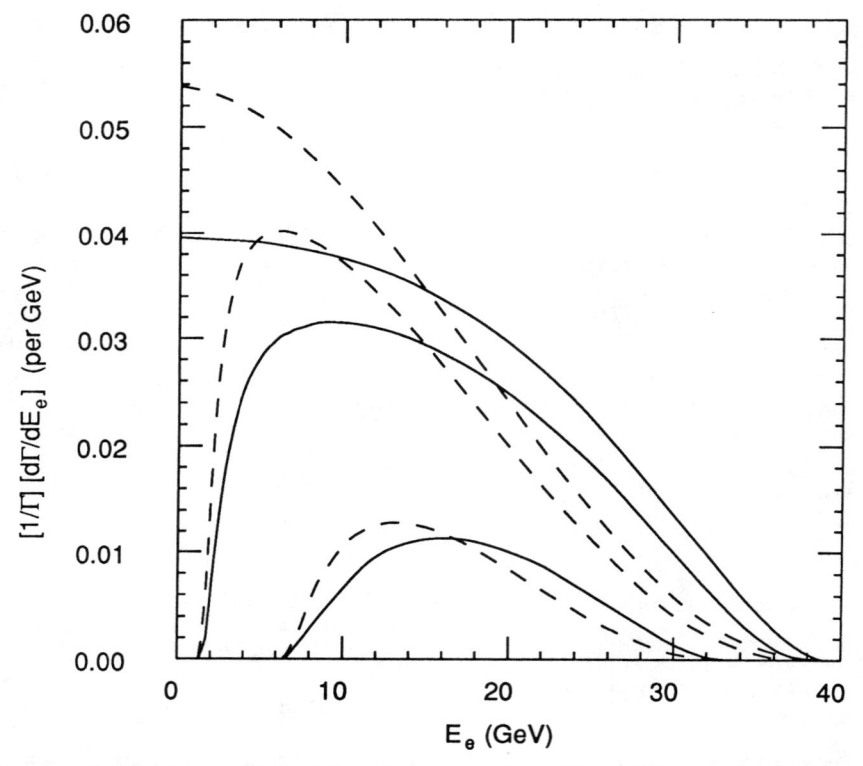

Figure 1: Distributions in electron laboratory energy for semileptonic decays of a b quark with laboratory energy 45 GeV and values of electron $p_T^{min} = 0$, 0.8, and 1.6 GeV (curves in descending order). Distributions are normalized to unit area for $p_T^{min} = 0$. Solid curves: $\xi \mathcal{P} = +1$; dashed curves: $\xi \mathcal{P} = -1$.

1. M. Gronau and S. Wakaizumi, *Phys. Rev. Lett.* **68** (1992) 1992; M. Gronau, *Phys. Lett.* B **288** (1992) 90.
2. J. F. Amundson, J. L. Rosner, M. Worah, and M. B. Wise, *Phys. Rev.* D **47** (1993), to be published.
3. D. Decamp *et al.* (ALEPH Collaboration), *Phys. Lett.* B **278** (1992) 209.
4. P. D. Acton *et al.* (OPAL Collaboration), *Phys. Lett.* B **281** (1992) 394.
5. J. G. Körner and M. Krämer, *Phys. Lett.* B **275** (1992) 495.
6. T. Mannel and G. A. Schuler, *Phys. Lett.* B **279** (1992) 194.
7. F. Close, J. Körner, R. Phillips, and D. Summers, *J. Phys.* G **18** (1992) 1716.

IN CASE THE b QUARK DECAYS RIGHT-HANDEDLY

GEORGE WEI-SHU HOU
Department of Physics, National Taiwan University
Taipei, Taiwan 10764, R.O.C.

ABSTRACT

We extend the scenario of right-handed b decay dominance and find two general class of solutions. Solution I is a direct generalization of the Gronau-Wakaizumi solution, with $b_R \to c_R$, u_R dominance, but V^R_{cd} need not be vanishingly small. Solution II preserves $b_R \to c_R$, but has $b_L \to u_L$ as usual, leading to rather different quark mixing matrices V^L and V^R as compared to Solution I. A third possibility of having normal $b_L \to c_L$ but $b_R \to u_R$ dominance is ruled out by the ε parameter and B_d mixing. Experimental consequences such as Cabibbo suppressed decays and CP violation are discussed. The best way to rule out right-handed $b \to c$ decay dominance is to find $B \to D^{(*)}D^{-(*)}$ modes at the 0.1% level.

1. The Gronau-Wakaizumi Proposal

It is usually assumed that, within the Standard Model (SM) context, the $b \to c$, u transitions are purely left handed, and the long b lifetime is interpreted in terms of small $|V_{cb}|$ and $|V_{ub}|$. This has presumably been tested already. However, it was recently pointed out[1] that in testing the handedness of $b \to c$, u decays, $V - A$ of the associated $\ell\bar\nu$ is usually *assumed*. In fact, experimental tests so far cannot distinguish between $(V-A)(V-A)$ and $(V+A)(V+A)$!

Gronau and Wakaizumi propose that, within the context of $SU_L(2) \times SU_R(2) \times U(1)$ theories, one may have $|V^L_{cb}| = |V^L_{ub}| = 0$, but

$$V^R_{cb}\, G_R = V_{cb}\, G_L, \tag{1}$$

where $G_{L,R}$ are Fermi constants, while V_{cb} corresponds to KM matrix of SM. In this way, long τ_b is due to the heaviness of W_R. Using standard constraints that $\beta_g \equiv G_R/G_L < 0.07$ (or $M^g_R \equiv (g_L/g_R)\, M_R > 300$ GeV), $V^R_{cb} > 1/2$ is needed. On the other hand, one cannot permit $V^R_{cb} \to 1$ for then $V^R_{cs} \to 0$, and would be in conflict with the measured $BR(b \to e\bar\nu X)$ and, especially, the observed $b \to c\bar cs$ type of modes such as $B \to DD_s^-$. To optimize, one chooses $|V^R_{cs}| \simeq |V^R_{cb}| \simeq 1/\sqrt{2}$. With $V^L_{ub} = 0$, $|V^R_{ub}| \simeq 0.09$ is inferred from the present standard value of $|V_{ub}/V_{cb}| \simeq 0.12$. The strongest remaining constraint comes from the two-charm L-R box diagram contribution to K_L-K_S mass difference, which we define as $\Delta m^{LR}_K(c,c)$, leading to the bound

$$|V^R_{cd}| < 0.01. \tag{2}$$

The GW solution for V^R is, therefore,

$$V^R = \begin{bmatrix} c^2 & -cs & s \\ \frac{s(1-c)}{\sqrt{2}} & \frac{c+s^2}{\sqrt{2}} & \frac{c}{\sqrt{2}} \\ -\frac{s(1+c)}{\sqrt{2}} & -\frac{c-s^2}{\sqrt{2}} & \frac{c}{\sqrt{2}} \end{bmatrix} \simeq \begin{bmatrix} 0.9919 & -0.0896 & 0.0900 \\ 0.0003 & 0.7100 & 0.7042 \\ -0.1270 & -0.6985 & 0.7042 \end{bmatrix}, \tag{3}$$

where the numerical values follow from setting $s = 0.09$.

2. A Critique: Two Potential Problems

We wish to explore[2] the GW idea more fully, in particular, we wish to find whether there are loopholes, and what are the best experimental handles.

We first note that $V_{cd}^R \sim 0.0003$ in eq. (3) is in fact much smaller than required from eq. (2). This can be traced to the fact that after choosing "maximal" mixing between 2nd and 3rd generations in the right-handed sector, there still remains two mixing angles, s_{12} and s_{13}. For the purpose of reducing the number of parameters, GW chose $s_{12} = -s_{13}$ such that $V_{cd}^R = (s_{12} - s_{13}c_{12})/\sqrt{2} \to s(1-c)/\sqrt{2} \to s^3/2\sqrt{2} \to 0$, once $s \equiv V_{ub}^R$ is constrained to be small. We immediately see that this artifact can be removed: $s_{13} \sim V_{ub}$ of SM, while eq. (2) implies that s_{12} cannot be very different from this. We call this slight generalization of GW Solution I.

Another interesting point is that not only $|V_{ts}^R| \simeq |V_{cb}^R| \simeq 0.7$ is very large, $|V_{td}^R| \simeq \sqrt{2}|V_{ub}^R| \simeq 0.13$ is also rather large. This is a reflection of having both V_{cb}^L, $V_{ub}^L = 0$. GW argue that this is useful since $x_d^{RR}(t,t)$ and $x_d^{LR}(c,t)$ can account for the observed B_d mixing, with the latter dominating. We note, however, that $x_d^{RR}(t,t)$ is sizable for large m_t. Furthermore, if $W_L - W_R$ mixing is small, $M_R^g \simeq 300-360$ GeV is needed, which also drives up $x_d^{RR}(t,t)$. Because of diagramatic similarities, one may then have a problem in $\Delta m_K^{RR}(t,t) \approx B_K (m_t/130 \text{ GeV})^2 (450 \text{ GeV}/M_R^g)^4 (s/0.09)^2 \, 3.2 \times 10^{-12}$ GeV. For $M_R^g \sim 300$ GeV and $m_t = 130$ GeV, this is about 5 times larger than the experimentally measured value of Δm_K, and gets worse for larger m_t. Can one preserve $V_{cb}^R \sim 0.7$ but avoid these problems?

3. A Second Solution

The problem with Δm_K comes about because V_{td}^R and V_{ts}^R are both large. Note, however, that although experimentally $b \to u$ is much weaker than $b \to c$, it does not imply that $b_R \to c_R$ dominance should be accompanied by $b_R \to u_R$ dominance. We propose to keep $V_{ub}^L \sim V_{ub} \simeq 0.005 \equiv \delta$, and take V_{cb}^L to be of similar order of magnitude or less. Then V_{td}^L and V_{ts}^L should also be of order δ or less. Keeping $V_{cb}^R \sim 0.7$, we take V_{ub}^R and V_{us}^R to be of order a small parameter ι or less. Thus, Solution II consists of

$$V^L \simeq \begin{bmatrix} 1 & \lambda & \delta \\ -\lambda & 1 & \delta \\ -\delta & -\delta & 1 \end{bmatrix}, \quad V^R \simeq \begin{bmatrix} 1 & -\iota & \iota \\ \iota & \frac{1}{\sqrt{2}} & \frac{1}{\sqrt{2}} \\ -\iota & -\frac{1}{\sqrt{2}} & \frac{1}{\sqrt{2}} \end{bmatrix}, \quad (4)$$

where $\delta = V_{ub} \simeq 0.005$ and $\iota < 0.01$ from eq. (2), and should be less than 0.001 when one takes CP violation into consideration.

There are some merits to this solution. Δm_K and Δm_B are all due to standard diagrams. However, although $\Delta m_{B_s} \gg \Delta m_{B_d}$, it is mostly due to $\Delta m_{B_s}^{RR}(t,t)$ and $\Delta m_{B_s}^{LR}(c,t)$ (in Sol. I, $\Delta m_{B_s} \gg \Delta m_{B_d}$ due to scaling from V_{td}^R to V_{ts}^R, just like in SM), i.e., it has different origins as Δm_{B_d}. This should have interesting implications on CP violating effects. In general, ϵ and ϵ' require the tuning of CP violating phases (6 new ones) to 10%. One final thing worthy of note is that, in Sol. II, not only $b \to c\bar{c}d$ is down compared to SM, $b \to c\bar{u}s$ is also quite down.

A third possible solution of having normal $b_L \to c_L$ but $b_R \to u_R$ dominance is ruled out by ϵ and B_d mixing.

4. Experimental Consequences

Although there are many misgivings about the Gronau-Wakaizumi proposal, the key point is that it has not been tested experimentally in a crucial way.

Direct parity violation tests of the $(V+A)(V+A)$ structure is difficult.[3] One way is to measure the E_e spectrum of semileptonic decays of polarized Λ_b's produced in Z decays.[4] Here we propose an indirect test via searching for Cabibbo suppressed b decays. In both models, $b \to c\bar{c}d$ is extremely suppressed vs. $b \to c\bar{c}s$. Similarly, the $b \to c\bar{u}s$ mode is also suppressed compared to SM, but more so in Solution II, hence it can be used to distinguish the two solutions. The point is that exclusive $b \to c\bar{c}s$ modes such as $B \to DD_s^-$, ψK and $D\rho$ have been seen at the $1-3\%$, 0.1% and 1% level, respectively. The corresponding Cabibbo suppressed modes, e.g. $B \to DD^-$, $\psi\pi$ and DK^* should therefore show up at the 0.1%, 0.01% and 0.05% level, respectively, in the near future. If so, right-handed b decay dominance is ruled out.

If they are not found at the SM level, however, one may expect dramatic implications[2] for CP violating effects in the B system, because of the multitude of not-so-well constrained phases. The unitarity triangle becomes quadrangles, a_{CP} of order 40% is possible, B_d and B_s system both exhibit CP violation that are different from SM case, and one has much larger CP asymmetries in $b \to s$ penguins.

Well, let us look diligently into polarized Λ_b decay and $b \to c\bar{c}d$, $c\bar{u}s$ decay modes first!

5. Acknowledgements

I thank Daniel Wyler for collaborating on this work.

6. References

1. M. Gronau and S. Wakaizumi, *Phys. Rev. Lett.* **68** (1992) 1814.
2. W. S. Hou and D. Wyler, *Phys. Lett.* **B292** (1992) 364.
3. M. Gronau and S. Wakaizumi, *Phys. Lett.* **B280** (1992) 79.
4. J. L. Rosner, this proceedings.

E791 STATUS REPORT

For the Fermilab E791 Collaboration[1]

RONALD A. SIDWELL

*Physics Department, The Ohio State University, 174 W. 18th Av.
Columbus, Ohio 43210*

ABSTRACT

The E791 experiment at Fermilab has accumulated a large sample of charm decays in the 1991-2 fixed target run at Fermilab, using a 500 GeV/c π^- beam incident on a segmented target. The highly parallel data acquisition system and fast readout allowed a nearly unbiased trigger, and we recorded 20 billion triggers on 24,000 8mm tapes. We briefly describe the important features of the apparatus, and show signals for some charm decay modes, based on the analysis of 2% of the data.

The goals of the E791 experiment are to collect the largest possible unbiased charm sample in order to search for rare or forbidden charm decays, to study as yet unseen charm decays, and to search for new particle states with charm-like properties. This is the fourth in a series of experiments which have been performed in the Fermilab TPL facility. Previous experiments were E516, E691, and E769. Over 20 billion triggers from interactions of 500 GeV pions in thin widely spaced targets were recorded during a six month span ending in Jan '92. Based on preliminary studies of this huge data set we believe that over 200K useable charm decays will be reconstructed, far surpassing any previous charm particle study.

The large E791 data sample was made possible by the high speed, massively parallel data acquisition system which was capable of the sustained writing of 10K events per second to 42 8mm tape drives in parallel.[1] To exploit this DAQ system, we also were required to reduce the experimental dead time by rebuilding all the data collection systems to achieve a 50 microsecond readout time.

It is not possible in the short space available here to list all the physics potential of the E791 data. I therefore restrict myself to selected topics of interest. In tests of the standard model we intend to search for mixing in the $D^0\overline{D^0}$ system, where we hope to achieve a sensitivity of better than 10^{-3} for this process, or at least 4 times better than the best achieved to date by E691. In order to do this search, the initial particle state must be tagged with the D^* resonance. The limit one can achieve is determined by the statistics available and the cleanliness of the signal. In addition one also enhances the signal to noise by cutting on the D^0 lifetime. Fig. 1

---

[1] **Fermilab E791 Collaboration:** CBPF (Rio de Janeiro), University of California (Santa Cruz), University of Cincinnati, CINVESTAV, Fermilab, Illinois Institute of Technology, University of Mississippi, The Ohio State University, Princeton University, Universidade Federal de Rio de Janeiro, UNESP, Tel Aviv University, Tufts University, University of Wisconsin, Yale University.

shows what has been achieved so far (using $D^0 \to K\pi$ only). The solid curve shows the right sign signal, the dashed curve the wrong sign. At present the wrong sign background under the D* peak is 7%. We ultimately hope to achieve about 2% noise level, after further study of the data. As well as using hadronic decay modes of the D0, we anticipate using semileptonic decays as well. The D* resolution is worse by $\approx$ 50%, but these decays cannot go through double-Cabibbo-suppressed decay (DCSD) modes and therefore can experience no interference between DCSD and mixing. It should also be possible to measure DCSD in these data. In all D^0 decay modes we anticipate about 40,000 D* events, at a signal/noise slightly worse than that shown in the figure.

We have studied the $KK\pi$ spectrum, using 2.5% of the total data to investigate the sensitivity of the experiment for Cabbibo suppressed decays and to decays of the D_s. The results are shown in the four plots of Fig. 2-5. In Fig. 2, we plot the $KK\pi$ spectra, where D^+ and D_s are clearly seen in the data. The next mass spectrum shows the KK mass, with a cut around the D_s of ±30 MeV. The ϕ signal is quite clean. Fig 4 is the $\phi\pi$ mass, and shows D^+ and D_s decays into quasi 2-body mode. Fig. 5 shows the $K\pi$ spectrum, from events with a $KK\pi$ mass consistent with the D_s. There are about 40 events in the K^* peak, over a similar background.

The lepton tagging capability of the TPL facility has been augmented by the addition of a second muon wall of 6 inch high scintillator paddles. This additional hodoscope improves the signal cleanliness by an order of magnitude. We have searched for $D^+ \to K^*\mu\nu$ decays in 2.5% of the data. The $K\pi$ spectrum from these 3 prong decays is shown in Fig. 6. There are about 90 events above background in this channel, corresponding to an extrapolated yield in this mode of perhaps 4000 events. We note that published results for D^+ polarization and form factors for this decay are based on about 300 events. In modes such as $D_s \to \phi l\nu$, we expect 200-300 events, allowing the same level of determination of D_s weak decay parameters as now exists for D^+.

The TPL spectrometer is a two magnet system, with good acceptance of K^0 and Λ decays. The Λ-hadron spectra from 0.3 % of the data are shown for $\Lambda\pi$ in Fig 7, where we see 2600 Ξ^- decays, and in Figure 8 for ΛK where there are about 100 events in the Ω^- above a non-linear background. The potential yield of Ξ^- is nearly 10^6. From about 5×10^8 K^0 and $10^8 \Lambda$ we expect to extract a rich yield of charm baryon decays, for which very little is now known for other than the Λ_c.

To conclude, reconstruction of the data is underway, and significant results are expected by Summer '93.

1. S. Amato, et. al., *The E791 Parallel Architecture Data Acquisition System*, to be published in NIM.

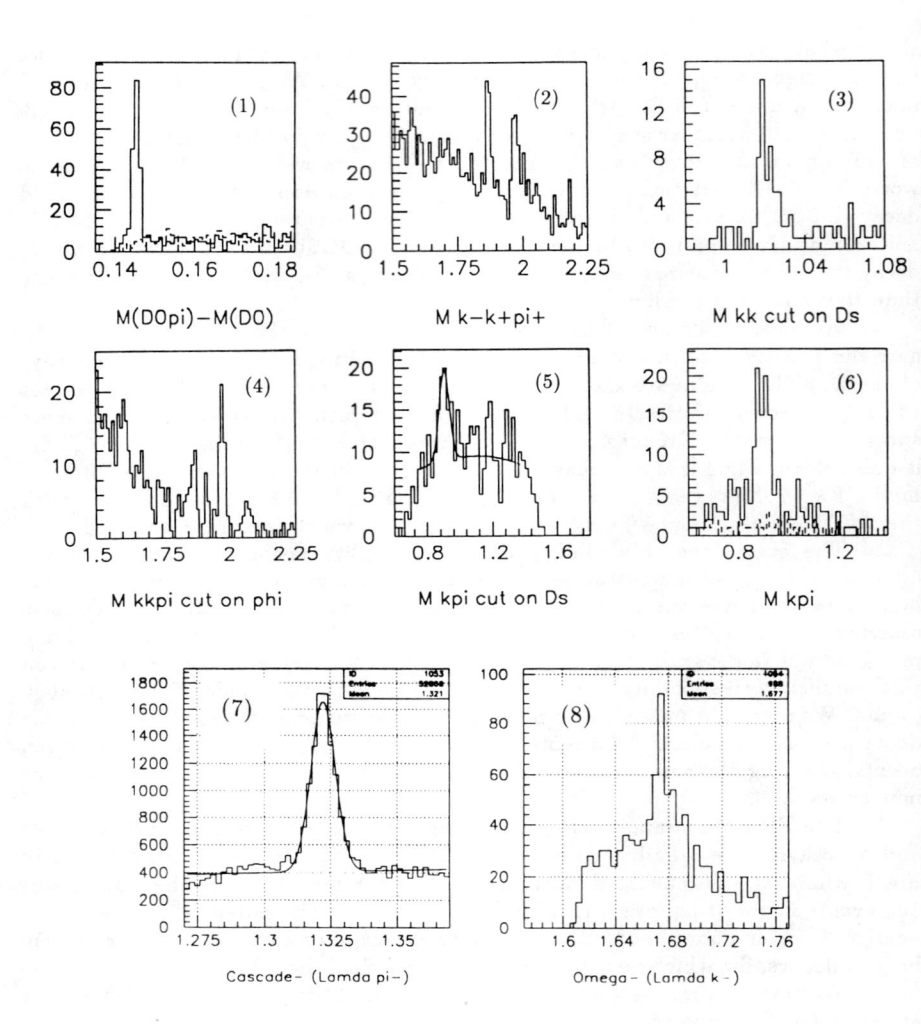

Figure numbers are marked on each plot. The figures are described in the text.

RECENT RESULTS ON L=1 CHARMED MESONS

SHEKHAR SHUKLA
FOR THE THE E687 COLLABORATION*
Fermi National Accelerator Laboratory, U.S.A.

ABSTRACT

The E687 Collaboration at Fermilab has observed the following decays of L=1 charm meson states previously observed by other experiments[1-6] : $D^{**0}(2460) \to D^+\pi^-$, $D^{**0}(2420) \to D^{*+}\pi^-$, and $D_s^{**+}(2536) \to D^{*+}K_s^0$. We present a preliminary measurement for the mass and width of the $D^{**0}(2460)$ and $D^{**0}(2420)$.

1. Introduction

Experiment E687 recorded a large sample of charm in 1990-1991 using a multiparticle magnetic spectrometer that is described elsewhere[7]. The charm was produced by ~200 GeV photons impinging on a beryllium target. Approximately 100 K charm events have been reconstructed using these data. These events have been used to study D** mesons, which are the L=1 bound states of a charm quark and a lighter quark. The quark spins can add to 1 to give the three total angular momentum states, $J^P = 2^+, 1^+$ and 0^+, or to 0 to give the state, $J^P=1^+$. Unless kinematically forbidden, these mesons decay strongly. The allowed 2-body strong decays of the four spin-parity states are listed in Table I. Conservation of angular momentum, parity and isospin prohibits other such decays.

Table I. Allowed 2-body Strong Decays

State	J^P	Decay Mode (D**)	Decay mode (D_s^{**})
$^3P_2$	2^+	$D^*\pi$, $D\pi$	$D^* K$, $D K$
$^3P_1$	1^+	$D^*\pi$	$D^* K$
$^1P_1$	1^+	$D^*\pi$	$D^* K$
$^3P_0$	0^+	$D \pi$	$D K$

We present some preliminary results from the study of the decay modes $D^{**0} \to D^+\pi^-$, $D^{**0} \to D^{*+}\pi^-$, and $D_s^{**+} \to D^{*+}K_s^0$ and state how they were obtained.

2. Event Selection

The decay chains investigated are listed Table II. Here, as in the rest of this report, the charge conjugate decays were also included in the analysis. The selection of the D and the D^{*+} candidates is described elsewhere[8]. The requirement on the minimum separation, L, between the primary and secondary vertices (possible production and decay vertices for the D), scaled by the uncertainty in the separation, σ, is listed in Table II for the various decay chains.

---

* See list of E687 Collaborators in these proceedings.

The selected D^+ or D^{*+} candidate was combined with the pion tracks in the primary vertex, with momentum above a certain minimum threshold (7 GeV for $D^+\pi^-$ and 5 GeV for the $D^{*+}\pi^-$ combination), to give the D^{**} candidate. The cut on the pion momentum was motivated by the observation, from monte carlo simulation and experimental data, that the background in the D^{**} invariant mass plot is mainly due to soft pions combining with the D^+ or D^{*+}, whereas the pion from the D^{**} decay is expected to be relatively hard. The D_s^{**+} candidate was obtained by combining a D^{*+} with the K_s^0 in the event. The difference ΔM in the invariant mass of the D^{**} or D_s^{**+} candidate, and the D or D^{*+} it decays to, is plotted in figures 1 to 3.

Table II. Vertex separation cuts used for the various decay chains.

Decay Chain	Minimum L/σ
$D^{**0} \to D^+\pi^-$, $D^+ \to K^-\pi^+\pi^+$	10
$D^{**0} \to D^{*+}\pi^-$, $D^{*+} \to D^0\pi^+$, $D^0 \to K^-\pi^+$	1
$D^{**0} \to D^{*+}\pi^-$, $D^{*+} \to D^0\pi^+$, $D^0 \to K^-\pi^+\pi^-\pi^+$	3
$D_s^{**+} \to D^{*+}K_s^0$, $D^{*+} \to D^0\pi^+$, $D^0 \to K^-\pi^+$	3
$D_s^{**+} \to D^{*+}K_s^0$, $D^{*+} \to D^0\pi^+$, $D^0 \to K^-\pi^+\pi^-\pi^+$	5

3. The D^{**} mass spectra

The $D^+\pi^-$ invariant mass spectrum (figure 1) shows a pronounced peak at $\Delta M \sim 600$ MeV. This is consistent with being due to the $D^{**}(2460)$ decaying to $D^+\pi^-$. There is an additional enhancements at $\Delta M \sim 420$ MeV. This is believed to be due to the $D^{**0}(2420)$ and $D^{**0}(2460)$ decaying to $D^{*+}\pi^-$, with the D^{*+} subsequently decaying to a D^+ and a π^0. The spectrum was fit with a background function added to three Breit-Wigner peaks, broadened by gaussians of width 7 MeV, to correct for the spectrometer resolution. The masses and widths of the two lower peaks were fixed at values expected,

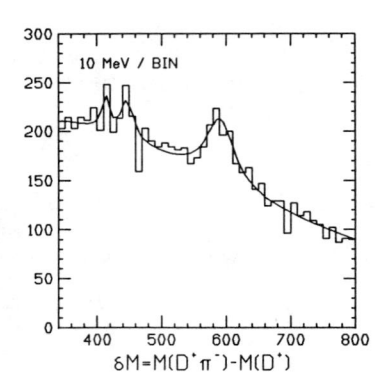

Fig 1. $D^+\pi^-$ mass spectrum

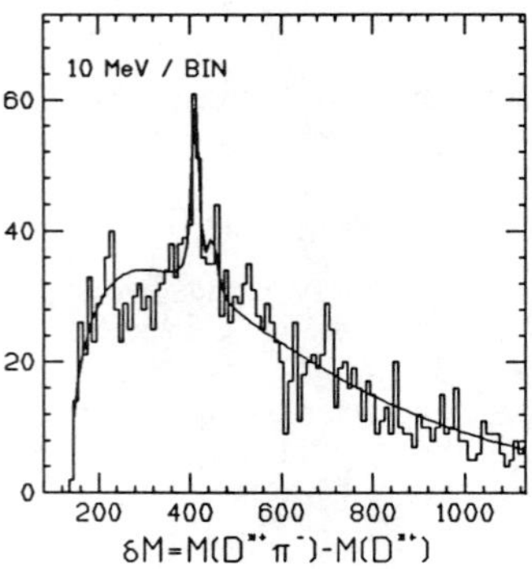

Fig 2. $D^{*+}\pi^-$ mass spectrum

using data from the PDG (Particle Data Group), for D**(2420) and D**(2460). For the remaining peak, we obtain $\Delta M=593\pm4$ MeV, which corresponds to a mass of 2460 ± 4 MeV for the D** state, 42 ± 10 MeV for the natural width, and 501 ± 65 for the number of events.

The 2^+ and the 1^+ states can decay to $D^{*+}\pi^-$. The 2^+ state decays through a D-wave resulting in a distribution in $\cos\alpha$ proportional to $\sin^2\alpha$, where α is the angle between the pions from the decay of the D** and the D*+, measured in the D*+ rest frame. The 1^+ states can decay through an S-wave or D-wave resulting in distributions that are flat and proportional to $(1+3\cos^2\alpha)$ respectively. The 2^+ state was practically eliminated by requiring that $\cos\alpha > .8$. The resulting distribution for $D^{*+}\pi^-$ is shown in figure 2. It was fit with a background function added to two Breit-Wigner peaks, broadened by gaussians of width 4 MeV, the mass and width of one being fixed at values obtained from PDG for the D**(2460). For the other peak, we obtain $\Delta M=412\pm3$ MeV, which corresponds to a mass of 2422 ± 3 MeV for the D** state, 14 ± 8 MeV for the natural width, and 81 ± 26 for the number of events.

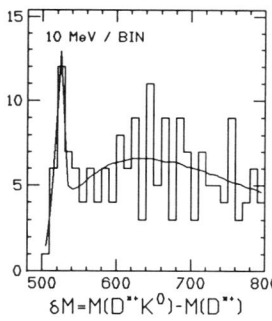

The $D^{*+}K_s^0$ mass spectrum (figure 3) was fit to a background function added to a Breit-Wigner peak broadened with a gaussian of width 5 MeV. We obtain $\Delta M= 525\pm3$ MeV, which corresponds to a mass of 2533 ± 3 MeV for the D_s^{**+} state, 12 ± 6 MeV for the natural width, and 25 ± 7 for the number of events. The systematic error in this measurement of the width is believed to be large compared to the statistical error.

The errors quoted in the measurements in this section are statistical only. The systematic errors are under investigation.

Fig 3. $D^{*+}K_s^0$ mass spectrum

4. Conclusions

We have observed the state D_s^{**+} (2536). The state was previously observed only in e+e- colliding beam experiments[3,5] and a $\bar{\nu}$-n collisions[6]. We have preliminary measurements for the mass and width of the D**0(2460) and the D**0(2420). Previous measurement of the mass and width of the latter come from e+e- colliding beam experiments[3,4].

References

1. J.C.Anjos et al., *Phys. Rev. Lett.* **62** (1989) 1717.
2. H. Albrecht et al., *Phys. Lett.* **B 221** (1989) 422.
3. P. Avery et al., *Phys. Rev.* **D 41** (1990) 774.
4. H. Albrecht et al., *Phys. Lett.* **B 232** (1989) 398.
5. H. Albrecht et al., *Phys. Lett.* **B 230** (1989) 162.
6. A.E. Asratyan, *Z.Phys .C* **40** (1988) 483.
7. P.L.Frabetti et al., *Nucl..Instr.Meth.* **A320** (1992) 519.
8. P.L.Frabetti et al., *Phys. Lett.* **B 263** (1991) 584.
   S. Shukla, *FERMILAB-Conf- 92/139-E*.

LIFETIME DETERMINATION FOR $D_s^\pm$ MESONS

DANILO PUŠELJIĆ for the Fermilab E687 Collaboration[1]
Department of Physics
University of Notre Dame
Notre Dame, IN 46556, USA

Abstract

Data from the 1990-91 run of high energy photoproduction experiment E687 at Fermilab have been analyzed to yield the largest sample presently available of $D_s^\pm$ mesons decaying to $\phi + \pi^\pm$ in a fixed target experiment. We report a preliminary result for the the D_s^+ meson lifetime of $0.47 \pm 0.02 \pm 0.01$ps measured for this decay mode.

Introduction

We have analysed data collected by the Fermilab high energy photoproduction experiment E-687 taken during 1990-91 runs for events containing ϕ mesons. The entire data set consists of $\sim 5 \times 10^8$ hadronic triggers recorded on tape yielding a total of $\sim 10^6\, \phi$ mesons.

The E-687 detector[2] is a large aperture multiparticle magnetic spectrometer with excellent vertex measurement, particle identification, and calorimetric capabilities. This experiment used a high energy photon beam (mean energy 220 GeV) and a Be target. Charged particles coming from the target were tracked by 12 planes of silicon microstrips providing high resolution tracking in the vertex region. Following the microstrip system charged particles passed through two analysis magnets and 3 threshold Čerenkov counters interleaved with 5 stations of multiwire proportional chambers (PWCs).

Event Selection

Initial event selection involved skimming for ϕ candidates identified by the decay $\phi \to K^+ K^-$. A ϕ vertex was formed from every pair of oppositely charge tracks identified as kaons by the Čerenkov system and were linked between the microstrip and PWC systems. The ϕ candidate was required to have the vertex confidence level greater then 1% and two-body invariant mass less than 1.1 GeV/c^2.

This analysis used "candidate-driven" algorithm[2] to find secondary and primary vertices from all 3 track combinations that had the right charge, mass and Čerenkov identification. The pion candidate track was required to be identified as not being a "heavy" (not a proton or a kaon) and not an electron. Both primary and secondary vertices were required to have confidence levels greater then 1%. The ϕ mass was required to be between 1.01 and 1.03 Gev/c^2. However the most powerful tool was the constraint on the significance of separation L/σ between primary and secondary vertices defined as the decay length divided by it's error. And finally we required $|\cos\theta| \geq 0.3$ for the angle between the K and a π in the rest frame of the ϕ.

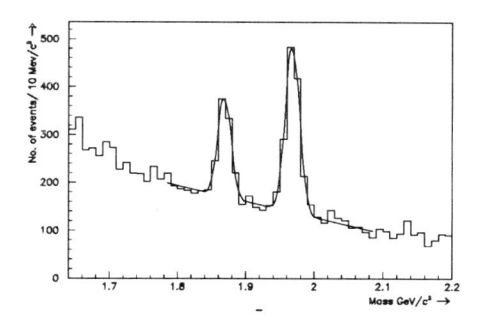

Figure 1. Effective mass distribution for $\phi\pi$ combinations for $L/\sigma > 3.0$

For the final sample in the D_s lifetime determination a cut of $L/\sigma > 3.0$ was imposed. Fig. 1 shows the resulting mass distribution after all the cuts mentioned above were imposed. The mass distribution was fit to a double gaussian with a linear background yielding 900 ± 43 events for the D_s mass peak and width consistent with our resolution.

D_s Lifetime

The D_s lifetime was measured using a binned maximum likelihood technique described elsewhere[3]. A fit was made to the reduced proper time distribution for events which lie within 2σ region of the D_s mass (± 20 Mev/c^2). Reduced proper time is defined as $t' \equiv (L - N * \sigma_t)/\beta\gamma c$ where N represents the significance of detachment cut used. The side-band regions used to represent the lifetime distribution of the background under the signal were chosen $\pm 4\sigma$ away from the peak (1.908 − 28 GeV/c^2 and 2.008 − 28 GeV/c^2) Data was binned in 20 time bins spanning 0 to 3 ps.

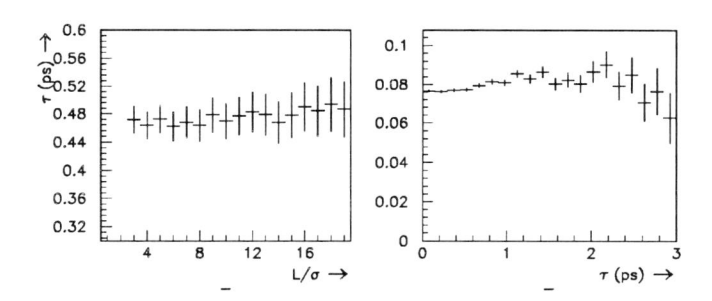

Figure 2. Left:Lifetime versus L/σ, Right:The $f(t')$ correction function for $L/\sigma > 3.0$

A function $f(t')$ was derived from Monte Carlo to correct the signal lifetime evolution for effects of acceptance, skim and analysis cut efficiencies, hadronic absorption, and decay of charm secondaries. Fig.2 on the right shows a plot of $f(t')$ used in the lifetime fit. Tests on Monte Carlo events showed that the statistical bias of the fit is less then 0.002 ps and can thus be ignored. Fig.2 on the left displays the fitted lifetime versus L/σ cut used. For our measurement we will quote the lifetime as $\tau_{D_s} = 0.47 \pm 0.02$, at $L/\sigma > 3.0$ cut. Background subtracted and Monte Carlo corrected lifetime evolution is shown in Fig.3, superimposed on top is a pure exponential function with the above value for the D_s lifetime.

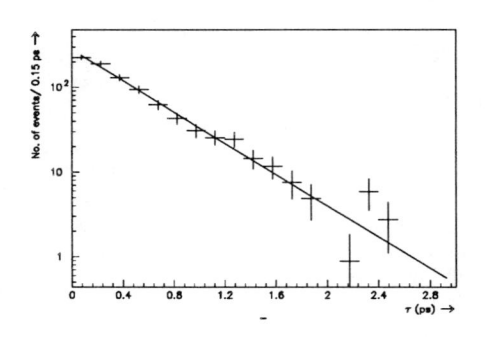

Figure 3. The background subtracted and Monte Carlo corrected lifetime evolution for $L/\sigma > 3.0$

The large sample of detected decays allowed for a number of systematic studies to be performed. We found no systematic effects outside the statistical errors. The studies included uncertainties in: particle-antiparticle lifetimes, target absorption, D_s momentum distribution, background lifetime evolution and possibility of charm background contamination. An upper limit on the systematic error has been estimated and is quoted in the following preliminary result for the D_s lifetime: $\tau_{D_s} = 0.47 \pm 0.02 \pm 0.01$ ps in which first error is statistical and second systematic.

Acknowledgements

This work was supported in part by the National Science Foundation, the US Department of Energy, the Italian Istituto Nazionale di Fisica Nucleare and Ministero della Università e della Ricerca Scientifica.

References

1. For a complete list of E687 collaborators, see reference 2.
2. E687, P. L. Frabetti *et al.*, *Nucl. Instrum. Methods.* **A320** (1992) 519.
3. P.L.Frabetti, *et. al.*, *Phys. Lett.* B **263** (1991) 584.

A DALITZ PLOT ANALYSIS OF D→Kππ DECAYS USING E691 DATA

M. V. PUROHIT
Physics Department, Princeton University
Princeton, NJ 08544, USA

For the E691 collaboration

ABSTRACT

Decays of the D^+ to $K^-\pi^+\pi^+$ and of the D^0 meson to $K^-\pi^+\pi^0$ and $\overline{K}^0\pi^+\pi^-$ have been analysed for resonant substructure. We present results on the amplitudes and phases of each decay mode and compare the results with other measurements. We confirm the highly non-resonant nature of the $D^+ \to K^-\pi^+\pi^+$ decays. The agreement with theoretical models for the branching ratios measured is generally good.

In the decays of charm mesons the phase space is limited and hence one expects the decays to be dominated by 2-body decays.[1,2] We have analyzed some of the 3-body $K\pi\pi$ decays to look for resonant substructure which can only be due to 2-body decays. We used 4149±79 $D^+ \to K^-\pi^+\pi^+$ decays, 174±20 $D^0 \to \overline{K}^0\pi^+\pi^-$ decays and 317±20 $D^0 \to K^-\pi^+\pi^0$ decays (using only D^0 mesons from D^{*+} decays) obtained during experiment E691[3] at Fermilab.

We corrected the data for background and acceptance. Using the known D mass[4] (and in the $K^-\pi^+\pi^0$ case, the π^0 mass as well) as a constraint, we removed most of the smearing in the data. The Dalitz plots for the three decay modes are shown in the figure and the results of a fit to the resonances are listed in the table. The systematic errors come dominantly from the stability of the fit (when removing non-contributing resonances) and from investigating the Monte Carlo simulation by varying the the minimum momentum of the π^0 or K^0_S.

We find that in the $D^+ \to K^-\pi^+\pi^+$ decay the major contribution to the signal is from the non-resonant mode while for the D^0 decays the resonances dominate, in particular the K^* (892) and the ρ (770). Our results are consistent with previous measurements[5] by the Mark III collaboration listed in the table. We allowed for more resonances in the fit to the $D^+ \to K^-\pi^+\pi^+$ decays than were used in ref. 5 (see also the analysis of Mark III data in ref. 6). Still, it is clear that the non-resonant mode dominates this channel, making it unique among the D→Kππ decays. We note that the $D^0 \to K^{*-}\pi^+$ branching ratios measured in the two different final states (see table IV) are consistent with each other and that the branching ratio for $D^+ \to \overline{K}^*(1680)^0\pi^+$ is not inconsistent with our results in 4-body decay modes[7]. Combining the two results yields a branching ratio of $3.02 \pm 0.53\%$. This result can be combined with the decay rates for the modes $D^+ \to \overline{K}^{*0}\pi^+$ and $D^0 \to \overline{K}^{*0}\pi^0$ to yield the isospin amplitudes in $D \to K^*\pi$ decays and their phase difference. We measure $|A_{1/2}| = (3.50 \pm 0.26) \times 10^5/\sqrt{s}$, $|A_{3/2}| = (0.79 \pm 0.09) \times 10^5/\sqrt{s}$, $|A_{1/2}/A_{3/2}| = (4.46 \pm 0.65)$ and $(\delta_{1/2} - \delta_{3/2}) = (64° \pm 22°)$. The ratio of amplitudes and the phase difference agree with the values obtained by Mark III[5]. It is interesting that our measurements are also in good agreement with the values measured for $D \to K\pi$ decays.[5]

We also compare our results with predictions from the effective Lagrangian model of Bauer, Stech and Wirbel[1] (BSW) and the $1/N_C$ model of Lee[8]. These predictions agree well with our measurements within errors. As has been emphasized by many authors, final state interactions can alter predictions in individual decay modes. Therefore it is better to examine predictions for several final states to look for broad agreement between models and predictions, as we have done here.

References

1. M. Bauer, B. Stech and M. Wirbel, Z. Phys. **C34**, 103 (1987).
2. A. N. Kamal, Phys. Rev. **D33**, 1344 (1986).
3. J. R. Raab et al., Phys. Rev. **D37**, 2391 (1988) and additional references therein.
4. K. Hikasa et al., Phys. Rev. **D45** (1992).
5. J. Adler et al., Phys. Lett. **196B**, 107 (1987).
6. M. Diakonou and F. Diakonos, Phys. Lett. **216B**, 436 (1989).
7. J. C. Anjos et al., Phys. Rev. **D46**, 1941 (1992).
8. D. Lee, private communication (paper in preparation). D. Lee, Phys. Lett. **275B**, 469 (1992) and erratum Phys. Lett. **277B**, 529 (1992) describe his model for $D \to P + P$ decays.

Table 1: Comparison to Mark III results[5] and the BSW[1] and Lee[8] models.

Decay Mode	E691 B.R. (%)	Mark III B.R. (%)	BSW prediction (%)	Lee prediction (%)
$K^-\pi^+\pi^+$ final state:				
$D^+ \to (K^-\pi^+\pi^+)_{NR}$	6.7 ± 0.7 ± 2.2	7.2 ± 0.6 ± 1.8	—	—
$D^+ \to \overline{K}{}^*(892)^0\pi^+$	2.0 ± 0.2 ± 0.4	1.8 ± 0.2 ± 1.0	0.3	2.4
$D^+ \to \overline{K}{}_0^*(1430)^0\pi^+$	3.0 ± 0.4 ± 0.2	—	—	—
$D^+ \to \overline{K}{}^*(1680)^0\pi^+$	0.9 ± 0.2 ± 0.4	—	—	—
$K^-\pi^+\pi^0$ final state:				
$D^0 \to (K^-\pi^+\pi^0)_{NR}$	0.41 ± 0.04 ± 0.18	1.2 ± 0.2 ± 0.6	—	—
$D^0 \to \overline{K}{}^*(892)^0\pi^0$	2.4 ± 0.4 ± 0.4	2.6 ± 0.3 ± 0.7	1.4 – 3.9	0.73
$D^0 \to K^*(892)^-\pi^+$	2.8 ± 0.5 ± 0.4	4.9 ± 0.7 ± 1.5	3.7 – 9.1	4.9
$D^0 \to K^-\rho^+$	7.3 ± 0.8 ± 1.7	10.8 ± 0.4 ± 1.7	12.5 – 13.8	8.7
$\overline{K}{}^0\pi^+\pi^-$ final state:				
$D^0 \to (\overline{K}{}^0\pi^+\pi^-)_{NR}$	1.4 ± 0.13 ± 0.22	2.1 ± 0.3 ± 0.7	—	—
$D^0 \to K^*(892)^-\pi^+$	3.9 ± 0.9 ± 1.0	5.3 ± 0.4 ± 1.0	3.7 – 9.1	4.9
$D^0 \to \overline{K}{}^0\rho(770)^0$	1.2 ± 0.3 ± 0.2	0.8 ± 0.1 ± 0.5	0.9 – 1.1	0.38

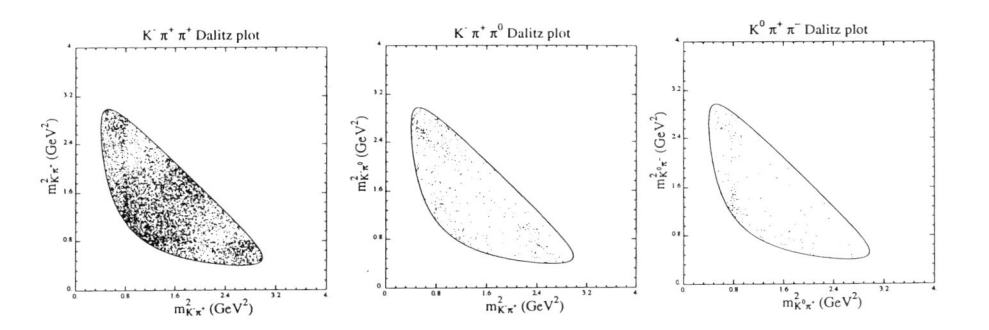

Figure. Dalitz plots for the three modes discussed in the text.

RECENT RESULTS ON CHARMED MESONS FROM CLEO II

PHILIP BARINGER (representing the CLEO Collaboration)
Department of Physics and Astronomy, University of Kansas
Lawrence, KS 66045, USA

ABSTRACT

Recent results from the CLEO II collaboration on hadronic decays of charmed mesons are reported. Among the items presented are new measurements of the production and decay properties of the $D_{s1}^+(2536)$, the branching ratios of the D^0 and D^+ to two pions, some branching ratios of the D^0 into $\bar{K}^0$ or $\bar{K}^{*0}$, and branching ratios of the $D^*(2010)$. Searches for the annihilation processes $D^+ \to \phi K^+$ and $D_s^+ \to \omega \pi^+$, and measurements of the $D^* - D$ mass difference are also mentioned.

1. Introduction

The CLEO II collaboration has accumulated a large data set which corresponds to 1.5 fb^{-1} of e^+e^- annihilations taken at center-of-mass energies between 10.36 and 10.70 GeV. These data contain roughly two million events where $e^+e^- \to c\bar{c}$. We have used these data to study higher mass charmed meson states such as the $D_{s1}^+(2536)$, to look for rare decay modes of the D^0, D^+, and D_s^+ mesons, and to make precision measurements of the $D^*(2010)$ branching ratios and the $D^* - D$ mass difference.

The CLEO II detector has been described elsewhere[1]. In the analyses reported here charged pions and kaons are required to have ionization losses consistent with their expected values. The precise cut varies with the analysis, but is typically 2.5 standard deviations. In the case of the K^+ coming from $D_{s1}(2536)^+ \to D^{*0}K^+$ a time-of-flight within 2.5 standard deviations of that expected was also required. The K^0 is detected via $K_s^0 \to \pi^+\pi^-$ where the two charged pions are required to come from a secondary vertex and the invariant mass is required to be consistent with the known K^0 mass. The π^0 is detected via its decay to two photons. Each photon must have a minimum energy of 30 MeV, the showers must not be associated with charged tracks, and at least one of the photons must be in the barrel region (71% of the solid angle). Photon pairs are selected if they lie within two to three σ of the nominal π^0 mass (the precise cut varies with the particular analysis, σ is typically 5-6 MeV), and the four vectors of the selected pairs are kinematically constrained to the π^0 mass. The η is similarly identified in its $\gamma\gamma$ mode, but with the additional condition that neither of the photons can be paired to form a π^0.

2. $D_{s1}^+(2536)$ Production and Decay

The $D_{s1}^+(2536)$ has been previously observed in the decay channel $D^{*+}K_s^0$. We present here the first observation of the decay $D_{s1}(2536)^+ \to D^{*0}K^+$. The D^0 is reconstructed in the modes $K^-\pi^+$, $K^-\pi^+\pi^0$, and $K^-\pi^+\pi^+\pi^-$. Candidate D^0's are then combined with a π^0 to form a D^{*0}. A cut is made on the mass difference $M(D^0\pi^0) - M(D^0)$, and a peak containing 134 ± 22 events is observed in the $M(D^{*0}K^+) - M(D^{*0})$ plot. We similarly observe 44.1 ± 7.9 events in the mode $D_{s1}(2536)^+ \to D^{*+}K^0$. Correcting for efficiencies, we find that the ratio of branching ratios into $D^{*0}K^+$ and $D^{*+}K^0$ is 1.13 ± 0.30, in agreement with expectations from isospin symmetry.

The $D_{s1}(2536)^+$ fragmentation function has been measured and found to be harder than what has been found for the D_s^+ or D_s^{*+}. We place an upper limit of 2.5 MeV on the width of the $D_{s1}(2536)^+$. This narrow width and our observation of a flat helicity angle distribution support the hypothesis that the spin parity of this state is 1^+.

3. Rare Decays

We now turn to rare decays of the D^0, D^+, and D_s^+.

3.1. D^0 and D^+ to two pions

In this analysis we wish to determine whether the $\Delta I = 1/2$ amplitude $(A_{1/2})$ dominates over the $\Delta I = 3/2$ amplitude $(A_{3/2})$ in the D system as it does in the K system for branching modes into two pions. We search in our data for the three decays $D^+ \to \pi^+\pi^0$, $D^0 \to \pi^0\pi^0$, and $D^0 \to \pi^+\pi^-$. The signal for $D^+ \to \pi^+\pi^0$, which has not been previously observed, is shown in Figure 1.

Figure 1: $\pi^+\pi^0$ invariant mass

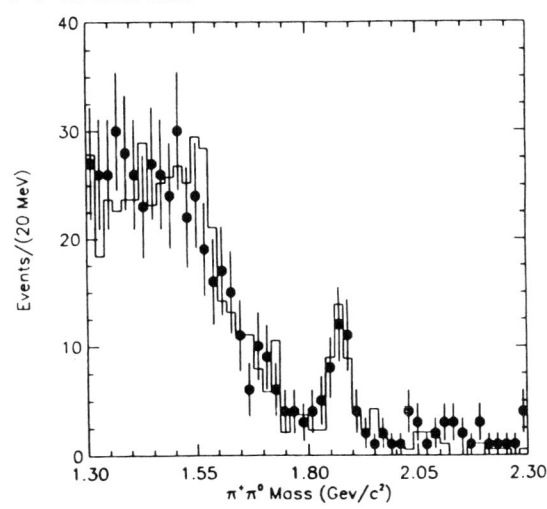

In all of these measurements, in order to reduce combinatoric background, we insist that the D be consistent with being the daughter of a D^{*+}. That is, we make a cut on the mass difference between the D^{*+} and D where we make combinations of D^+ candidates with an additional π^0 and of D^0 candidates with an additional π^+. A cut on $x \geq 0.60$ is also made where $x = p_{D^*}/p_{D^*{max}}$. Yields and branching ratios for the three modes are given in Table 1 in the summary section below. We measure the three branching modes relative to the $K^-\pi^+$ mode for the D^0's and relative to the $K^-\pi^+\pi^+$ mode for the D^+. Absolute branching ratios are obtained by using the Particle Data Group (PDG) values[2] for the normalizing modes.

From these branching ratios we can derive that the ratio of the amplitudes, $|A_{3/2}/A_{1/2}|$, is 0.7 ± 0.2, which shows no evidence for a suppression of $\Delta I = 3/2$ transitions in D meson decays.

3.2. D^0 decays into $\bar{K}^0$ or $\bar{K}^{*0}$

The D^0 can decay into final states with a $\bar{K}^0$ or $\bar{K}^{*0}$ through either an "internal" W spectator process or a W exchange process. Final state interactions may also play a role in these modes. We observe signals in seven decay modes and place an upper limit on an eighth. The η is identified in both the $\gamma\gamma$ and $\pi^+\pi^-\pi^0$ modes; the η' in the $\rho\gamma$ and $\eta\pi^+\pi^-$ modes. A D^{*+} tag is used for the modes containing a $\bar{K}^{*0}$. Yields and branching ratios are presented in Table 1.

The mode $K^-\pi^+\eta'$ is observed here for the first time; no evidence of $\bar{K}^{*0}$ substructure was seen in the signal and an upper limit is placed upon $\bar{K}^{*0}\eta'$. A Dalitz plot analysis of the $\bar{K}^0_s\pi^0\pi^0$ system allows us to extract branching ratios for $\bar{K}^{*0}\pi^0$ and for the non-resonant (NR) system. This non-resonant decay is a first measurement.

3.3. Searches for annihilation modes

The extent to which annihilation diagrams contribute to the decays of the D^+ and D_s^+ is an important open question. We search for the final state ϕK^+ for both the D_s^+ and the D^+, normalizing to $\phi\pi^+$ in each case. Using the PDG values[2] for $D_s^+ \to \phi\pi^+$ and $D^+ \to \phi\pi^+$ we obtain the upper limits cited in Table 1.

We also search for $D_s^+ \to \omega\pi^+$, which is expected to be suppressed by G-parity. The ω is reconstructed from its $\pi^+\pi^-\pi^0$ decay. No signal is seen, and the upper limit given in Table 1 is significantly more restrictive than previous determinations.

4. Precision Measurements

We now briefly advertise two recently published results. The branching ratios of the D^{*0} and D^{*+} have been measured[3] and are presented in Table 1. We require that the sum of the modes for each D^* add to one. Data are not used to determine the $D^0\pi^+$ mode, but rather a theoretical value of the ratio of this mode to the $D^+\pi^0$ mode is used in the calculation of the branching ratios.

We make precise determinations of the $D^{*0} - D^0$ mass difference[4] ($142.12 \pm 0.05 \pm 0.05$ MeV), and the $D^{*+} - D^+$ mass difference ($140.64 \pm 0.08 \pm 0.06$ MeV). Taken together with the previously measured $D^{*+} - D^0$ mass difference we can calculate the isospin mass splittings for $D^{*+} - D^{*0}$ and $D^+ - D^0$. These are found to be

$3.32 \pm 0.08 \pm 0.05$ MeV and $4.80 \pm 0.10 \pm 0.06$ MeV, respectively.

5. Summary of Results

The table below summarizes the branching ratio measurements reported in this paper.

Table 1: Summary of Results

Process	Yield	Branching Ratio (%)
$D^+ \to \pi^+\pi^0$	28 ± 7	$0.28 \pm 0.07 \pm 0.07$
$D^0 \to \pi^0\pi^0$	32 ± 7	$0.091 \pm 0.018 \pm 0.015$
$D^0 \to \pi^+\pi^-$	171 ± 17	$0.142 \pm 0.014 \pm 0.019$
$D^0 \to \bar{K}^0\pi^0$	1942 ± 64	$2.8 \pm 0.1 \pm 0.6$
$D^0 \to \bar{K}^0\eta$	305 ± 32	$0.88 \pm 0.09 \pm 0.16$
$D^0 \to \bar{K}^0\eta'$	594 ± 48	$2.0 \pm 0.15 \pm 0.42$
$D^0 \to \bar{K}^{*0}\pi^0$	$122 ^{+29}_{-23}$	$4.6 ^{+1.1}_{-0.9} \pm 1.1$
$D^0 \to \bar{K}^0\pi^0\pi^0$ (NR)	76 ± 16	$1.0 \pm 0.2 \pm 0.2$
$D^0 \to \bar{K}^{*0}\eta$	214 ± 31	$1.7 \pm 0.3 \pm 0.4$
$D^0 \to K^-\pi^+\eta'$	286 ± 54	$0.85 \pm 0.13 \pm 0.20$
$D^0 \to \bar{K}^{*0}\eta'$		< 0.13 (90% CL)

Process	Yield	Branching Ratio (%)
$D^+ \to \phi K^+$	24 ± 16	< 0.052 (90% CL)
$D_s^+ \to \phi K^+$	16 ± 13	< 0.086 (90% CL)
$D_s^+ \to \omega \pi^+$	7 ± 10	< 0.33 (90% CL)
$D^{*+} \to D^+\gamma$	12 ± 23	$1.1 \pm 1.4 \pm 1.6$
$D^{*+} \to D^+\pi^0$	410 ± 29	$30.8 \pm 0.4 \pm 0.8$
$D^{*+} \to D^0\pi^+$		$68.1 \pm 1.0 \pm 1.3$
$D^{*0} \to D^0\gamma$	621 ± 52	$36.4 \pm 2.3 \pm 3.3$
$D^{*0} \to D^0\pi^0$	1097 ± 59	$63.6 \pm 2.3 \pm 3.3$

In addition we have made the first observation of the decay $D_{s1}(2536)^+ \to D^{*0}K^+$ and have measured the width, fragmentation function, and helicity distribution of this meson.

6. References

1. Y. Kubota et al, *Nucl. Instr. and Meth.* **A320** (1992) 66.
2. Particle Data Group, H. Hikasa et al, *Phys. Rev.* **D45** (1992) 1.
3. F. Butler et al, *Phys. Rev. Lett.* **69** (1992) 2041.
4. D. Bortoletto et al, *Phys. Rev. Lett.* **69** (1992) 2046.

Branching Ratios for $D_s^\pm$ and $D^\pm$ Decays to $\pi^\pm\pi^+\pi^-$

Guinyun Kim
for the Fermilab E687 Collaboration
Department of Physics, University of Notre Dame
Notre Dame, IN 46556, USA

ABSTRACT

Preliminary results from the 1990-91 high energy photoproduction run of Fermilab E687 on decays of D_s^+ and D^+ charmed mesons to $\pi^\pm\pi^+\pi^-$ are presented. The relative branching ratios determined are B($D_s^+ \to \pi^+\pi^+\pi^-$)/B($D_s^+ \to \phi\pi^+$) =0.33 ± 0.08 ± 0.04 and B($D^+ \to \pi^+\pi^+\pi^-$)/B($D^+ \to K^-\pi^+\pi^+$) =0.035 ± 0.006 ± 0.004.

1. Introduction

We report preliminary results for the relative branching ratios of decays of the D_s^+ and D^+ charmed mesons and charge conjugates to the $\pi^\pm\pi^+\pi^-$ final state. The decay processes $D_s^\pm \to \pi^\pm\pi^+\pi^-$ and $D^\pm \to \pi^\pm\pi^+\pi^-$ can occur via the Cabibbo-allowed annihilation subprocess $c\bar{s} \to W^+ \to u\bar{d}$, and via the Cabibbo-suppressed spectator subprocess, respectively. This study utilizes the entire sample of about 500 million hadronic triggers recorded from the Fermilab high energy photoproduction experiment E687 during the 1990-91 fixed target run.

The E687 detector, which is described in detail elsewhere[1] is a large aperture two magnet multiparticle spectrometer with good detection capabilities for charged particles and for photons. A silicon microstrip detector provides high resolution tracking, allowing the separation of primary and secondary vertices. Deflection of charged particles by two analyzing magnets of opposite polarity is measured by five stations of multiwire proportional chambers. Three multicell threshold Čerenkov counters are used for particle identification. The average photon energy for the data sample was $\approx$ 220GeV.

The charm candidates have been selected using a candidate-driven vertex finder where the charm decay particles are assumed to form a secondary vertex and the resulting D momentum vector from these particles is used as a seed track to find the primary vertex. The vertex finder reconstructs the primary vertex by searching for tracks which form high confidence level intersections with the seed track. Tracks are added to the primary vertex as long as the confidence level(CLP) of the resultant vertex exceeds 1%.

2. Event Selection

Events with a three-pion charm-decay candidate are selected using the candidate-driven technique and are required to have the following properties: The three tracks forming the secondary vertex must be reconstructed in both the microstrip and multiwire proportional chamber systems and the two sets of track parameters must agree within measurement errors. Information from the Čerenkov counters is used to identify pions. Pions are required to have a Čerenkov light pattern consistent with that of a charged pion. This allows kaon/pion separation in the momentum range 4.5 to 61 GeV, and proton/pion separation from 0 to 116 GeV. The three microstrip tracks of the three pion combination forming the secondary vertex are required to extrapolate back to a single point with a confidence level (CLD) greater than 2%. In addition, the condition $CLP + 0.5 \times CLD$ greater than 10% was required on the basis of Monte Carlo studies.

The primary vertex was required to be within the target ($-5.5cm < z < -1.0cm$) and the secondary vertex was required to lie upstream of the first scintillator trigger counter($z < 2.4cm$), which is upstream of the first microstrip plane.

The confidence level that any of the three pion tracks extrapolate back to the primary vertex is called CL1. The confidence level that other microstrip tracks not already assigned to the primary and secondary vertices point back to the secondary vertex is called CL2. The large amount of combinatorial background can be greatly reduced by cuts on CL1 and CL2.

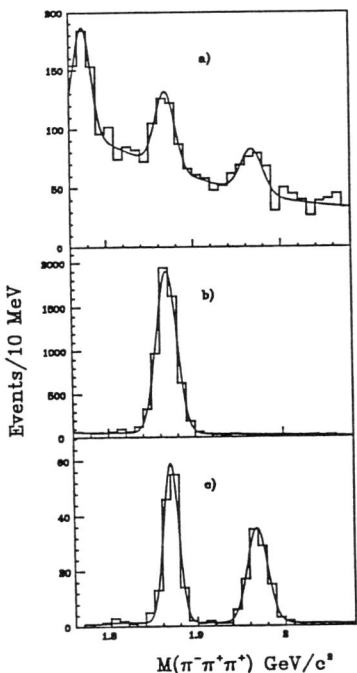

Figure 1. The invariant mass distribution of (a) $\pi^-\pi^+\pi^+$, (b) $K^-\pi^+\pi^+$, and (c) $\phi\pi^+$ with the cuts described in text and with $\ell/\sigma \geq 16.0$.

The momentum of the 3π candidate was required to be greater than 60 GeV/c. In addition, we required that the significance of vertex detachment L/σ_L, where L is the distance between the primary and secondary vertices and σ_L is the error in L, be greater than 16.

The resulting $\pi^+\pi^+\pi^-$ mass distribution is shown in Fig.1(a). There are clear peaks for both the D^+ and the D_s^+. The additional peak around 1.75 GeV/c^2 is due to Cabibbo-allowed decays $D^+ \to K^-\pi^+\pi^+$ where the kaon is misidentified as a pion. The fit to the 3π mass plot, shown in the figure, gives 179 ± 30 D^+ decays and 114 ± 26 D_s^+ decays. The fit includes Gaussian signals and a background shape that is the sum of a second order polynomial term and a Gaussian term for the false peak.

3. Branching Ratios

To reduce systematic effects, the branching fractions for the D_s^+ and D^+ decays were measured relative to the decay modes $D_s^+ \to \phi\pi^+$ and $D^+ \to K^-\pi^+\pi^+$. To obtain signals for these decays, we used a vertex algorithm and cuts identical to those used for the 3π decays with the exception of the Čerenkov requirement for the kaon. For the decay $D_s^+ \to \phi\pi^+, \phi \to K^-K^+$, the K^-K^+ mass was required to be in the range 1.01 to 1.03 GeV/c^2. In Fig. 1 (b) and (c) the mass distributions of the D_s^+ and D^+ signals obtained with these cuts are presented. The signals from the fit correspond to yields of 98 ± 11 $D_s^+ \to \phi\pi^+$ events and 5442 ± 77 $D^+ \to K^-\pi^+\pi^+$ events.

A Monte Carlo simulation was used to determine the ratios of detection efficiencies for the processes. These are $eff(D_s^+ \to \pi^+\pi^+\pi^-)/eff(D_s^+ \to \phi\pi^+) = 0.85\pm0.04$, and $eff(D^+ \to \pi^+\pi^+\pi^-)/eff(D^+ \to K^-\pi^+\pi^+) = 0.94\pm0.02$. The relative measured branching ratios are $B(D_s^+ \to \pi^+\pi^+\pi^-)/B(D_s^+ \to \phi\pi^+) = 0.33\pm0.08\pm0.04$, and $B(D^+ \to \pi^+\pi^+\pi^-)/B(D^+ \to K^-\pi^+\pi^+) = 0.035\pm0.006\pm0.004$. The systematic errors which arise from uncertainties in the Monte Carlo efficiency estimate and from changes in the fitted yield under reasonable variations of the selection and fitting procedures are estimated to be 11%.

Our preliminary results of $B(D_s^+ \to \pi^+\pi^+\pi^-)/B(D_s^+ \to \phi\pi^+) = 0.33\pm0.08\pm0.04$, and $B(D^+ \to \pi^+\pi^+\pi^-)/B(D^+ \to K^-\pi^+\pi^+) = 0.035\pm0.006\pm0.004$ are consistent with previous measurements?

4. Acknowledgements

This work was supported in part by the National Science Foundation, the US Department of Energy, the Italian Istituto Nazionale di Fisica Nucleare and Ministero della Università e della Ricerca Scientifica.

5. References

1. E687, P. L. Frabetti et al., Nucl. Instrum. Methods. **A320** (1992) 519.
2. E691, J. C. Anjos et al., Phys. Rev. Lett. **62** (1989) 125.

RECENT RESULTS ON CHARMED BARYONS

CARLO DALLAPICCOLA
for the Fermilab E687 Collaboration[1]
Dept. of Physics, University of Colorado, Box 390
Boulder, CO 80309, USA

ABSTRACT

New results on charmed baryons are presented. The data were obtained in Fermilab photoproduction experiment E687. The lifetime of the Λ_c^+ is measured to be $0.215 \pm 0.016 \pm 0.010$ ps and the lifetime of the Ξ_c^+ is measured to be $0.41^{+0.11}_{-0.08} \pm 0.02$ ps.

1. Introduction

1.1. Data Collection and Detector

We have analyzed 510 million hadronic triggers collected by the Fermilab experiment E687 during 1990 and 1991 run periods. Charmed baryon states have been reconstructed through their decays into protons, Ξ^-'s and Ω^-'s.

The E687 detector is described in detail in reference 2. Charmed states are photoproduced from the interaction of a photon beam of mean energy 220 GeV impinging on a 4 cm Be target. A microvertex detector consisting of 12 planes of silicon microstrips arranged in three views provides high resolution tracking, allowing the separation of primary (charm production) and secondary (charm decay) vertices. Deflection of charged particles by two analyzing magnets of opposite polarity is measured by five stations of multiwire proportional chambers (PWC's). Three multicell Čerenkov counters operating in threshold mode are used for particle identification.

1.2. Event Selection

We reconstruct Λ^0's through the decay $\Lambda^0 \to p\pi^- + c.c.$ (charge conjugate states should be implicitly included for the rest of this paper). The Λ^0 sample is used to fully reconstruct hyperons through the decays $\Xi^- \to \Lambda^0\pi^-$ and $\Omega^- \to \Lambda^0 K^-$. These decays are reconstructed by intersecting the daughter $\pi^-(K^-)$ track and the Λ^0 and requiring that the resultant momentum vector agree within 2 milliradians with an unmatched microstrip track created by the charged hyperon prior to decay.

All of the charm signals presented in this paper are obtained with a candidate-driven vertex finder using the silicon track information. A full description of this technique can be found in reference 3. A decay length, L, is calculated as the distance between the primary vertex and the secondary vertex. This length is divided by its error, σ_L, to form the *significance of separation* variable, L/σ_L. The significance

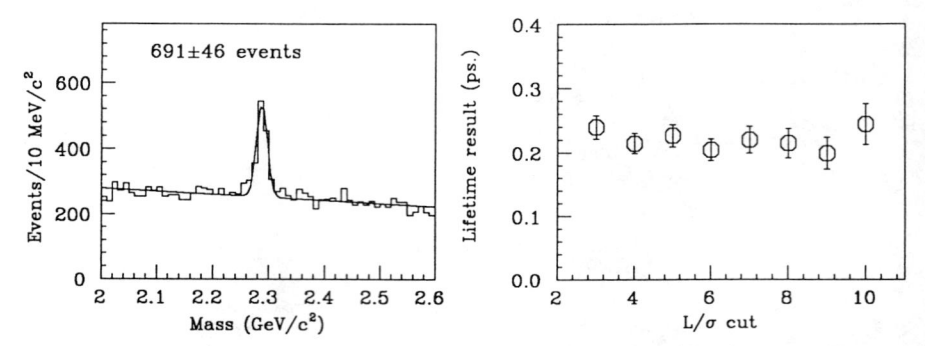

Figure 1. (a) $pK^-\pi^+$ invariant mass plot showing reconstructed Λ_c^+'s. (b) Λ_c^+ lifetime for varying L/σ_L cuts.

of separation is used to reduce background in charm signals.

2. Lifetimes

The Λ_c^+ was reconstructed through the mode $\Lambda_c^+ \to pK^-\pi^+$. The invariant mass plot for $L/\sigma_L > 4$ is given in figure 1(a). The lifetime has been measured using a binned maximum likelihood method (reference 3 gives a detailed description of this technique), based on a sample of 691 ± 46 fully reconstructed Λ_c^+'s. This large sample allows for many detailed systematic studies. Some of the studies done include investigating the effect of background from reflections of D_s^+ and D^+ decays to $K^+K^-\pi^+$ and using various background mass sidebands to measure the background time evolution. We present in figure 1(b) the measured Λ_c^+ lifetime as a function of the L/σ_L cut. We measure the Λ_c^+ lifetime to be $0.215 \pm 0.016(stat.) \pm 0.010(syst.)$ ps.

We have also measured the lifetime of the Ξ_c^+ decaying into $\Xi^-\pi^+\pi^+$, using a binned maximum likelihood method. Figure 2(a) shows the $\Lambda^0\pi^-$ mass plot for reconstructed Ξ^-'s and figure 2(b) shows the $\Xi^-\pi^+\pi^+$ invariant mass plot for $L/\sigma_L > 2.5$. We observe 29.7 ± 7.0 events at a mass of $2464.4 \pm 2.0 \pm 1.2$ MeV/c². The measured Ξ_c^+ lifetime for different L/σ_L cuts is presented in figure 2(c). We measure the Ξ_c^+ lifetime to be $0.41^{+0.11}_{-0.08}(stat.) \pm 0.02(syst.)$ ps.

3. Observation of the Ω_c^0

The first evidence[4] for Ω_c^0 came from CERN experiment WA-62, in which three events in the $\Xi^-K^-\pi^+\pi^+$ mass plot were found to be clustered around 2740 ± 20 MeV/c². Recently the ARGUS collaboration has found further evidence[5] for this channel with 12.2 ± 4.5 events at a mass of $2719.0 \pm 7.0 \pm 2.5$ MeV/c². ARGUS has also found weak evidence[6] for $\Omega_c^0 \to \Omega^-\pi^-\pi^+\pi^+$.

We have examined the $\Omega^-\pi^+$ decay channel. We have chosen this channel because little background is expected. Figure 3(a) shows the Λ^0K^- mass plot, showing

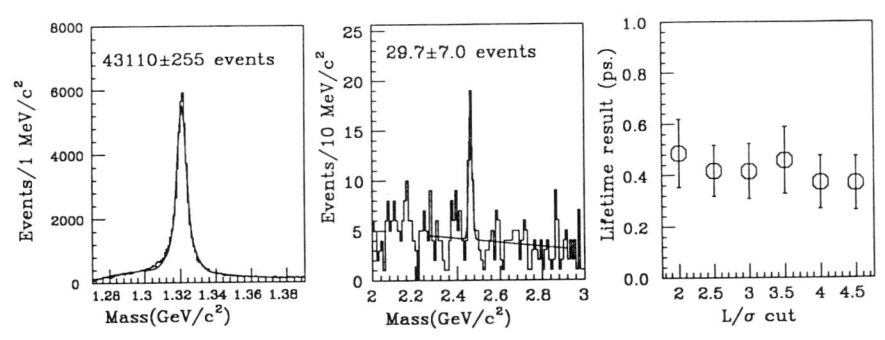

Figure 2. (a) $\Lambda^0\pi^-$ invariant mass plot. (b) $\Xi^-\pi^+\pi^+$ invariant mass plot showing reconstructed Ξ_c^+'s. (c) Ξ_c^+ lifetime for varying L/σ_L cuts.

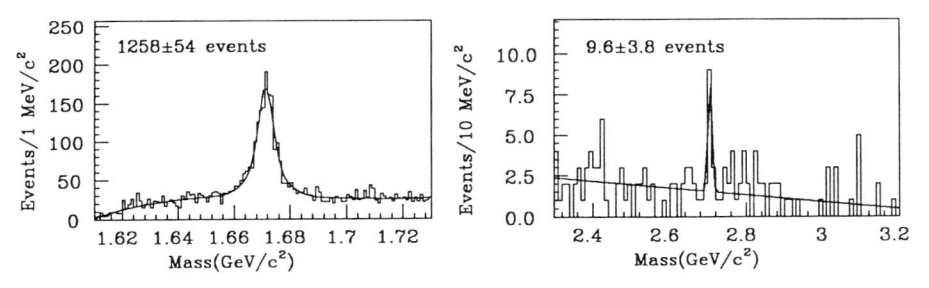

Figure 3. (a) $\Lambda^0 K^-$ invariant mass plot. (b) $\Omega^-\pi^+$ invariant mass plot.

reconstructed Ω^-'s and figure 3(b) presents the $\Omega^-\pi^+$ invariant mass distribution. A total of 9.6 ± 3.8 events above background are found in the peak. The mass of the Ω_c^0 is measured to be $2706.3 \pm 3.0 \pm 2.0$ MeV/c^2, in agreement with the ARGUS mass.

4. References

1. See *These Proceedings* for a complete author list.
2. P. L. Frabetti et al., *Nucl. Instr. and Meth. in Phys. Res.* **A320** (1992) 519.
3. P. L. Frabetti et al., *Phys. Lett.* **B263** (1991) 584.
4. S. F. Biagi et al., *Z. Phys.* **C28** (1985) 175.
5. H. Albrecht et al., DESY Preprint 92-052 (March, 1992).
6. J. Stiewe, ARGUS Collaboration, *Production and decays from ARGUS*, XXVI Int. Conf. on High Energy Physics, Dallas, TX (6-12 Aug. 1992) to be published.

RECENT CHARMED BARYON RESULTS FROM CLEO

BIJAN NEMATI

Physics Department, University at Albany, SUNY,
1400 Washington Ave., Albany, NY 12222

ABSTRACT

We have analysed decays of the charmed baryons Λ_c^+, Σ_c^0, Σ_c^+, Σ_c^{++}, Ξ_c^0, and Ξ_c^+ using data taken with the CLEO II detector at CESR. For the Λ_c^+, we have found eight new decay modes including two W-exchange decay candidates and measured the $\Sigma(1385)^{\pm}\pi\pi$ resonant substructure in $\Lambda_c^+ \to \Lambda\pi^-\pi^+\pi^+$ decays. New measurements of the mass differences among the Σ_c isospin triplet are obtained. Also presented are two new decay modes for each of the the Ξ_c^0 and the Ξ_c^+.

1. Introduction

In recent years there has been an increasing level of interest and activity in understanding the physics of charmed baryon decays. This development is in a great part due to the large number of high quality new measurements which are now becoming available. Improvements in detector technology such as silicon microstrip detectors and crystal calorimeters have had a profound effect on the quality of recent data on charm decays. The CLEO II experiment is a major contributor in this arena because of its being located in the world's highest luminosity e^+e^- storage ring as well as benefiting from some very high performance detector components like its CsI crystal calorimeter. The CLEO II detector is described in detail elsewhere.[1]

The data sample used here consists of 1.6 fb^{-1} taken in e^+e^- collisions at energies near the $\Upsilon(3S)$ and the $\Upsilon(4S)$ resonances. For each charmed baryon decay mode presented, in order to reduce the combinatoric background, only combinations with the fragmentation variable x_p greater than 0.4 or 0.5 are kept depending on the analysis in question. The fragmentation variable x_p is defined to be $x_p \equiv p/p_{max}$, where E and p are the energy and momentum of the charmed baryon, respectively, and $E_{max} = E_{beam}$ and $p_{max} = (E_{beam}^2 - m^2)^{1/2}$ where m is the mass of the charmed baryon. All efficiencies are predicted through Monte Carlo simulation of the production, decay, and propagation of tracks in the detector. For the Monte Carlo simulation, the CERN package GEANT 3.14 is used.[5] All Λ_c^+ results are normalized to the $\Lambda_c^+ \to pK^-\pi^+$ mode, where we observe approximately 4,000–5,000 events, depending on the x_p cut used.

2. Decays of Λ_c^+ with Σ^+ in the final states

The only measurement up to now of a Λ_c^+ decay to a mode with a Σ^+ in the final state has been the 1987 Photon Emulsion Collaboration measurement of

$B(\Lambda_c^+ \to \Sigma^+ \pi^+ \pi^-) = 10 \pm 8\%$.[3] These decay modes can have contributions from both internal W-emission and W-exchange processes as well the spectator decays. The modes studied are $\Lambda_c^+ \to \Sigma^+ \pi^+ \pi^-$, $\Lambda_c^+ \to \Sigma^+ \omega$ and $\Lambda_c^+ \to \Sigma^+ \pi^0$. It is noteworthy that the latter two decay modes cannot have any spectator contributions. For all three of these, a requirement of $x_p > 0.5$ is imposed on each reconstructed Λ_c^+ candidate. The Σ^+ candidates are reconstructed in the $p\pi^0$ final state. The Σ^+ decay vertex is displaced in the event since $c\tau = 2.40$ cm for this particle. Using an iterative technique for determining the Σ^+ vertex 10676 ± 290 Σ^+ candidates are found. Combining with loosely selected pions 369 ± 38 $\Lambda_c^+ \to \Sigma^+ \pi^+ \pi^-$ signal events are observed. For the $\Lambda_c^+ \to \Sigma^+ \omega$ decay mode the ω candidates are reconstructed in the $\pi^+ \pi^- \pi^0$ final state. Applying a 30 MeV/c^2 cut around the nominal ω mass we obtain 87 ± 19 signal events for $\Lambda_c^+ \to \Sigma^+ \omega$. No signal is observed corresponding to the ω sidebands, indicating that the $\Lambda_c^+ \to \Sigma^+ \omega$ signal has no nonresonant contribution. The π^0 candidates for the $\Lambda_c^+ \to \Sigma^+ \pi^0$ decay mode are required to have momentum greater than 500 MeV/c and are further required to be in the same hemisphere as the reconstructed Λ_c^+ as measured in the lab frame. These two requirements remove only 9% of the signal but substantially reduce the combinatoric background. We observe 80 ± 14 signal events in the $\Lambda_c^+ \to \Sigma^+ \pi^0$ decay mode.

3. Decays of Λ_c^+ with Λ or Σ^0 in the final states

Here we have analysed three new decay modes, $\Lambda_c^+ \to \Lambda \pi^+ \pi^0$, $\Lambda_c^+ \to \Sigma^0 \pi^+$, and $\Lambda_c^+ \to \Sigma^0 \pi^- \pi^+ \pi^+$. We have also made new measurements with higher statistics of the decays $\Lambda_c^+ \to \Lambda \pi^+$ and $\Lambda_c^+ \to \Lambda \pi^- \pi^+ \pi^+$. Of these, $\Lambda_c^+ \to \Lambda \pi^+$ and $\Lambda_c^+ \to \Sigma^0 \pi^+$ can not proceed via the internal W-emission diagram, while the others can arise from Spectator, W-exchange, or internal W-emission decays. In the analysis of each of these decay modes, the Λ_c^+ must have $x_p > 0.5$ and the Λ_c^+ daughters are required to be in the same hemisphere as the Λ_c^+ as measured in the lab frame. The latter cut is approximately 90% efficient for the signal while removing as much as 44% of the background, depending on the decay mode. We observe approximately 85,000 Λ signal events in the final state $p\pi^-$. The Σ^0 signal is obtained in the $\Lambda\gamma$ final state, where 7600 events are found. The $\Lambda\pi^+$ mass spectrum, in addition to a clear Λ_c^+ signal, also shows an approximately 100-MeV/c^2-wide enhancement in the mass region below the Λ_c^+, where feed-down from the $\Lambda_c^+ \to \Sigma^0 \pi^+$ decay mode is expected. The fit to the spectrum allows for this feed-down using the expected shape from Monte Carlo simulation with the normalization allowed to vary. A similar procedure is also followed for the fits to the $\Lambda_c^+ \to \Lambda \pi^+ \pi^0$ and $\Lambda_c^+ \to \Lambda \pi^- \pi^+ \pi^+$ mass spectra. The fit yields 337 ± 26 signal events for $\Lambda_c^+ \to \Lambda \pi^+$. For the other previously observed decay mode $\Lambda_c^+ \to \Lambda \pi^- \pi^+ \pi^+$ we obtain 546 ± 61 signal events. Here, clear signals are observed in the $\Lambda\pi^+$ and $\Lambda\pi^-$ mass spectra for $\Sigma(1385)^\pm \pi\pi$ resonant substructure. The fit to each mass spectrum uses the Monte Carlo predicted shapes for the $\Sigma(1385)^\pm$ signal and phase space background. We find $B(\Sigma(1385)^+ \pi^+ \pi^-)/B(\Lambda \pi^- \pi^+ \pi^+) = 0.30 \pm 0.09 \pm 0.07$ and $B(\Sigma(1385)^- \pi^+ \pi^+)/B(\Lambda \pi^- \pi^+ \pi^+) = 0.21 \pm 0.07 \pm 0.05$. Hence we find that $0.51 \pm 0.12 \pm 0.11$ of all $\Lambda_c^+ \to \Lambda \pi^- \pi^+ \pi^+$ decays are from $\Sigma(1385)^\pm \pi\pi$ decays. For the $\Lambda_c^+ \to \Lambda \pi^+ \pi^0$ decay mode we observe 434±56 signal events. The sideband-subtracted $\pi^+\pi^0$ mass spectrum does not show evidence for dominant $\Lambda\rho^+$ resonant substructure. Nor do we find evidence for a strong $\Sigma^*\pi$ component in this case. For the decay mode $\Lambda_c^+ \to \Sigma^0\pi^+$ we observe a clear signal and the fit to the spectrum yields 171 ± 20 signal events. The $\Lambda_c^+ \to \Sigma^0\pi^-\pi^+\pi^+$ mass spectrum show a significantly smaller signal for this mode compared with $\Lambda_c^+ \to \Lambda\pi^-\pi^+\pi^+$. The fit to this spectrum yields 84 ± 20 signal events.

4. W-exchange decays $\Lambda_c^+ \to \Sigma^+ K^+ K^-$ and $\Lambda_c^+ \to \Xi^0 K^+$

Unlike the case in charmed meson decays, W-exchange processes are not expected to be helicity suppressed for charmed baryons. For the Λ_c^+, these decays are also not Cabibbo suppressed. Hence these decay modes may be significant in comparison to spectator or internal W-emission decays. In apparent confirmation of this hypothesis, the world average Λ_c^+ lifetime is currently $1.91^{+.15}_{-.12} \times 10^{-13}$ s, which is less than half of the shortest lived charmed meson.[4] Here we present the observation of two W-exchange decay candidates for the Λ_c^+: $\Lambda_c^+ \to \Sigma^+ K^+ K^-$ and $\Lambda_c^+ \to \Xi^0 K^+$. We have required $x_p > 0.4$ for both modes in this analysis. The Σ^+ candiates are selected as before and combined with loosely identified kaon candidates. The fit to the $\Sigma^+ K^+ K^-$ mass spectrum yields 49 ± 9 events. A fit to the $K^+ K^-$ mass spectrum corresponding to the signal yields 21 ± 8 ϕ events, implying that $44 \pm 16\%$ of the $\Lambda_c^+ \to \Sigma^+ K^+ K^-$ signal is from $\Lambda_c^+ \to \Sigma^+ \phi$. The Ξ^0 candidates are reconstructed in the mode $p\pi^0$, for which the branching ratio is 100%. The fit to the $\Lambda_c^+ \to \Xi^0 K^+$ mass spectrum yields 48 ± 9 events.

5. Observation of the Σ_c^+

The experimental evidence for Σ_c^+ up to now has been limitted to a single event consistent with the decay chain $\Sigma_c^+ \to \Lambda_c^+ \pi^0$ $\Lambda_c^+ \to pK^-\pi^+$ observed in the BEBC bubble chamber in 1980. Here we present the first observation of the Σ_c^+ since the bubble chamber event as well as signals for the Σ_c^{++} and the Σ_c^0. All three Σ_c states decay strongly to $\Lambda_c^+\pi$, but since $M(\Sigma_c) - M(\Lambda_c^+) - M(\pi) \simeq 30$ MeV/c^2, the smallness of the available phase space causes these to be narrow. Four Λ_c^+ decay modes, $\Lambda_c^+ \to pK^-\pi^+$, $\Lambda_c^+ \to p\overline{K}^0$, $\Lambda_c^+ \to \Lambda\pi^-\pi^+\pi^+$ and $\Lambda_c^+ \to \Lambda\pi^+$ are combined to obtain a sample of 2225 ± 91 Λ_c^+'s with sufficiently tight cuts to give a signal/background ratio of about 1:1. In order to reduce systematic errors, the invariant-mass difference $M(\Lambda_c^+\pi^{0,\pm}) - M(\Lambda_c^+)$ is plotted for each case to obtain the signal and the mass measurement. The fits yield 94 ± 15 Σ_c^+ events with $M(\Lambda_c^+\pi^0) - M(\Lambda_c^+) = 168.4 \pm 0.5$MeV/$c^2$, 117 ± 15 Σ_c^{++} events with $M(\Lambda_c^+\pi^+) - M(\Lambda_c^+) = 168.2 \pm 0.3$MeV/$c^2$, and 106 ± 15 Σ_c^0 events with $M(\Lambda_c^+\pi^-) - M(\Lambda_c^+) = 167.3 \pm 0.3$MeV/$c^2$.

6. Evidence for new decay modes of Ξ_c^0 and Ξ_c^+

New decay modes of the charmed strange baryons Ξ_c^0 and Ξ_c^+ have been observed. As of this writing this work is still very prliminary and is in progress.

It has been included here because of its topical nature. For each of the Ξ_c^0 and Ξ_c^+, we have observed two new decay modes along with the previously observed decay modes in which they were originally seen. Only Ξ_c candidates for which $x_p > 0.5$ are included. The Ξ^0 and Ξ^+ candidates are reconstructed in the modes $\Lambda\pi^0$ and $\Lambda\pi^-$, respectively, where we find 1976 ± 91 Ξ^0 events and 2917 ± 66 Ξ^- events. Impact parameter cuts and vertex displacement cuts are employed to reduce the random combinatoric backgrounds. For the decay mode $\Xi_c^0 \to \Xi^-\pi^+$ we obtain 29.2 ± 6.7 signal events with a mean mass of $2463.0 \pm 3.1 \text{MeV}/c^2$. The reasons for this low mass measurement are being studied. In $\Xi_c^0 \to \Xi^-\pi^+\pi^0$ analysis, we observe 45.0 ± 9.5 events with a a mean mass of $2468.2 \pm 2.9 \text{MeV}/c^2$. For the $\Xi_c^0 \to \Xi^0\pi^+\pi^-$ decay mode we observe 30.2 ± 8.1 events and the mean mass is found to be 2471.2 ± 2.6 MeV/c^2. The previously observed decay mode $\Xi_c^+ \to \Xi^-\pi^+\pi^+$ is observed with 50.3 ± 8.8 signal events with mean mass of $2467.1 \pm 2.4 \text{MeV}/c^2$. The signal for the $\Xi_c^+ \to \Xi^0\pi^+$ contains 15.7 ± 4.9 events and the mean mass is measured to be $2470.6 \pm 3.0 \text{MeV}/c^2$. Finally, for the decay mode $\Xi_c^+ \to \Xi^0\pi^+\pi^0$ we obtain 24.5 ± 7.6 Ξ_c^+ events with a mean mass of $2469.9 \pm 4.6 \text{MeV}/c^2$. The fitted signal width for all these modes was found to be consistent with the prediction from Monte Carlo simulation.

7. Conclusion

With a data sample of 1.6 fb^{-1} e^+e^- events taken by the CLEO II detector at CESR, we have made a number of measurements and observations of charmed baryon decays. Eight new modes of the Λ_c^+, totaling $2.4 \times B(\Lambda_c^+ \to pK^-\pi^+)$ have been observed, increasing the fraction of the known Λ_c^+ decays from about 25% to about 35%. For the mode $\Lambda_c^+ \to \Lambda\pi^-\pi^+\pi^+$ we have found that half of the $\Lambda_c^+ \to \Lambda\pi^-\pi^+\pi^+$ decays come from $\Lambda_c^+ \to \Sigma(1385)^\pm\pi\pi$. Two W-exchange candidate decay modes have been observed, $\Lambda_c^+ \to \Xi^0 K^+$ and $\Lambda_c^+ \to \Sigma^+K^+K^-$, with about 44% of the latter mode coming from $\Lambda_c^+ \to \Sigma^0\phi$. Using the world average[4] values for the Λ_c^+ lifetime and $B(\Lambda_c^+ \to pK^-\pi^+)$ we obtain partial widths $\Gamma(\Lambda_c^+ \to \Xi^0 K^+) = 0.13 \pm 0.04 \times 10^{11} s^{-1}$ and $\Gamma(\Lambda_c^+ \to \Sigma^+\phi) = 0.11 \pm 0.04 \times 10^{11} s^{-1}$ which are in agreement with the Körner & Kramer prediction of $0.13 \times 10^{11} s^{-1}$ for both of these modes assuming they arise from the W-exchange process. The Σ_c isospin triplet have each been observed, including 94 ± 15 signal events for Σ_c^+. Finally, preliminary results have been presented for two new decay modes for each of Ξ_c^0 and Ξ_c^+, and new mass measurements will be forthcoming.

References

1. Y. Kubota et al., Nucl. Instrum. Methods **A320**, 66–113 (1992).
2. R. Brun et al., GEANT 3.14, CERN DD/EE/84-1
3. Adamovich, et al., Soviet J. Nucl. Phys. **46**, 447 (1987)
4. K. Hikasa et al., Particle Data Group, Phys. Rev. D **45**, 1 (1992).
5. R. Brun et al., GEANT 3.14, CERN DD/EE/84-1.

PRELIMINARY RESULTS FROM FNAL E690[*]

M.C.BERISSO, E.P.HARTOUNI, M.N.KREISLER, S.LEE, K.MARKIANOS, D.WESSON
*Departmnet of Physics and Astronomy, University of Massachusetts,
Amherst, MA 01003, U.S.A.*

D.C.CHRISTIAN, G.GUTIERREZ, A.WEHMANN
Fermilab,, P.O.Box 500, Batavia, IL 60510, U.S.A.

C.AVILEZ, J.FELIX, G.MORENO, M.ROMERO, M.SOSA
*Instituto de Física, Universidad de Guanajuato,
Apdo. Postal E-143, León , Gto. MEXICO*

A.GARA, B.C.KNAPP
*Columbia University, Nevis Laboratories,
P.O.Box 137, Irvington-on-Hudson, N.Y. 10533, U.S.A.*

ABSTRACT

FNAL E690 studies target dissociation in the reaction $p + p \to p + X$ at 800 GeV/c. The apparatus consists of a high rate, open geometry, multiparticle spectrometer used to measure the target system, and a beam spectrometer system which measures the beam and scattered proton. During the 1991 Fermilab fixed target run, 5.5×10^9 reactions were recorded in 100 days of running. The initial goals of the analysis of these data is the study of heavy flavor production (strange and charm) in target fragmentation. Preliminary results pertaining to this study as well as the performance of the spectrometer will be presented.

1. Introduction

Fermilab E690 studies the production and spectroscopy of hadrons produced in the reactions:

$$p + p \to p + X \qquad (1)$$

where the incoming beam proton has momentum 800 GeV/c ($\sqrt{s}$=38.74 GeV/c). Studies of heavy flavor production in such interactions and at these energies can resolve the issue of the unexpectedly high production cross sections for charm baryon production observed by many experiments at the ISR in the late 1970's. Fermilab E690 is ideally suited to study "forward" heavy particle production from leading particle effects or diffractive processes.
  If the cross sections previously reported are correct, then large numbers of charm baryons should be produced and observed in the "X" system. Strange particle production is already evident in the small samples of data reconstructed so far. Light meson production and spectroscopy has also proven to be possible based on preliminary analyses of this data.
  What follows is a brief description of the apparatus and some features of its performance, a characterization of the data obtained during the 1991 Fermilab fixed target run, and an estimate of the eventual yields for a specific class of final states now under study.

---

[*] This work was funded in part by the National Science Foundation under Grants Nos. PHY89-21320, PHY90-14879; the Department of Energy under contracts Nos. DE-AC02-76CH03000, DE-AS05-87ER40356; and CONACyT de México.

2. Apparatus

The E690 apparatus is located in the Neutrino East (NE) beam line. The beam spectrometer consists of elements located in the enclosures NEB, NEC, NEE (Lab G) and NEF. These elements perform the measurement in two parts: the "incoming" spectrometer measures the beam proton trajectory into the target; the "outgoing" spectrometer measures the scattered proton trajectory through five beam line magnets. The trajectories are measured by drift chambers which use the "mini-drift" technique[1]. The incoming spectrometer has three drift chambers, the outgoing spectrometer has five. The outgoing spectrometer also has five beam magnets (NEFE 1-5) which provide a nominal momentum "kick" of 12 GeV/c. The measurement goal of the beam spectrometer is to provide a 300 MeV/c momentum resolution for the scattered particles. The acceptance of the outgoing spectrometer is from 600 GeV/c to 800 GeV/c longitudinal momentum and ±1 GeV/c transverse momentum.

The "target" spectrometer located in Lab G was moved from Brookhaven National Laboratory where it was used in a series of experiments designated E766. A detailed description can be found elsewhere[2]. The spectrometer was designed with very high segmentation to allow excellent multiparticle detection and measurement efficiency. The geometric acceptance of the spectrometer is ±450 mradians. The spectrometer is capable of measuring particles with momentum in the range of 0.150 to 20.0 GeV/c with less than 1% resolution at 1 GeV/c. The mass resolution of the reconstructed Λ and K_s^0 are 1.75 and 4.5 MeV/c (FWHM) respectively. These numbers are expected to be improved. Time-of-flight hodoscopes and a 96 cell threshold Cerenkov counter provide direct particle identification.

The data acquisition system of this spectrometer system is capable of a digitization and readout rate of 12 Mbytes/sec, corresponding to roughly 12 kevents/sec. The events were "zero suppressed" in the readout stream. These events were written to memory and VHS format tape[3] during the 20 second spill. The tape writing continued off spill recording those events stored in memory. The unique architecture of the data acquisition system allowed for a flexible event "definition" in terms of the types of triggers for the readout, event filters based on simple calculations involving the event data *in real time* and the types of data block information written to tape.

The typical beam rates during the run were nominally 5 MHz (and as high as 10 MHz) of beam protons incident on the 2% liquid Hydrogen target. During the period from August 1991 to January 1992 E690 logged roughly 5.5×10^9 events to tape. Figure 1 shows the number of events accumulated during the run. The triggers which caused these events to be readout were intentionally kept very "open." The major trigger requirements were that at least one of the hodoscope counters outside of the beam region was "on" , that a beam counter hodoscope at the end of the beam line (behind the outgoing beam spectrometer) had an "out of beam" counter coincidence, and that the number of incoming and outgoing beam track hits were consistent with at least one and no more than two beam particles. The "live time" of the data acquisition system was roughly 90% through most of the run (though it varied depending on higher intensity, triggers, etc.).

3. Reconstruction

We are currently reconstructing the primary data. This task is being performed by the Hardware Processor[4]. This device performs a least squares fit to the parameterized particle trajectories for both the beam system spectrometers and the target system spectrometer. The average event has one beam particle in and out, and four charged tracks from the breakup of the target system (though events with 16 tracks are not rare). The rate that the data is reconstructed in this device is limited by the 4 Mbyte/sec read-write rate of the tape drives, corresponding to 2500

---

[1] See D.C.Christian, *et al*, "Hight Rate Drift Chambers", these proceedings.
[2] See M.D.Church, PhD. thesis Nevis R-260 (1986).
[3] Metrum VLDS tape system.
[4] See E.P.Hartouni, *et al*, IEEE Trans. Nucl. Sci., 36 (1989) 1480

events/sec (very approximately 1000 VUPS). This reconstruction step constitutes the largest computation effort.
Vertex reconstruction and particle identification are the two other reconstruction tasks. Analysis of the data at these levels has begun on a subset of the trajectory reconstructed data. Table 1 enumerates the yield of exclusive final states found by these programs for a subset of the final states in 1/40th of the total data sample. Based on estimates from these results it is expected that the final sample of fully reconstructed states will be approximately 10^7 events.

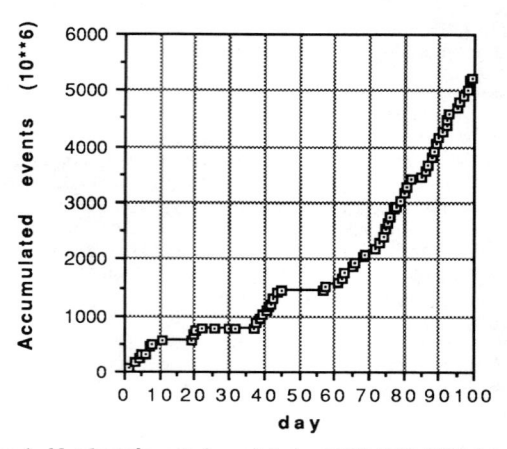

Figure 1. Number of events logged during E690 1991-1992 data run.

We also intend to study inclusive processes such as strangeness production in single dissociation. Current estimates indicate that the full data sample includes roughly 10^7 events containing a Λ and 10^8 events containing a K_s^0.

p + p →	$0(\pi^+\pi^-)$	$1(\pi^+\pi^-)$	$2(\pi^+\pi^-)$	$3(\pi^+\pi^-)$	$4(\pi^+\pi^-)$	$5(\pi^+\pi^-)$	$6(\pi^+\pi^-)$	totals
pp		68307	70579	20558	4418	788	79	164729
ppK^+K^-	25081	21330	6418	1353	229	26		54437
$pp p\bar{p}$	6020	4144	1176	181	20	2		11543
$ppK^+K^-K^+K^-$	779	321	60	19	1			1180
$ppK^+K_s^0\pi^-$	3586	2038	598	126	20			6358
$p\Lambda K^+$	593	1659	511	120	16	2		2901
$ppK^-K_s^0\pi^+$	2589	1589	441	97	18			4734
total								245892

Table 1. Preliminary list of some of the **exclusive** final states isolated in 1/40th of the E690 data sample.

4. Current Status

The primary data sample reconstruction should be completed in late November 1992. During the reconstruction of this data, a sample of 5% of the events was selected which contain 40% of the fully reconstructable events. This sample will be passed through the vertex reconstruction and particle identification stages of the analysis and be available for initial physics studies in December of 1992. Also in December, the vertex reconstruction on the full sample will begin. The exact schedule for completing this analysis awaits additional analysis of current samples, but the task will take approximately 1 year to complete. We anticipate results from the analysis very shortly.

DI-MUON AND SINGLE-MUON EVENTS FROM A BEAUTY EXPERIMENT

W. SELOVE
Physics Department, University of Pennsylvania
Philadelphia, Pa. 19104
for the E771 Collaboration

E771 is an 800 GeV fixed-target beauty experiment. A recent detailed report on the status and capabilities has been given in a Director's Review[1]. Here we show a few features.

A magnetic spectrometer follows an array of inert target foils and an 18-plane silicon vertex detector. Events are triggered by di-muons and by high-p_t single muons. Muons are tracked in the spectrometer and tracks with matching slope(s) are found in the silicon. Figure 1 shows the slope match quality, typically 1/2 to 1 mrad. Fig. 2 shows a J/ψ peak found in the di-muon events. Figure 3 shows a coarse view and a fine view of a typical event with a J/ψ. The dashed tracks are drawn with the slopes found for the muons in the spectrometer, and are drawn to go through the "primary vertex" found by tracking in the silicon. In the expanded view, it can be seen that there are two silicon tracks matching the spectrometer muons, and that these two, and eight other tracks, all intersect within a 50 micron x-interval. (x is one of the two transverse directions; the beam direction is z.) The z-accuracy of the primary is a few hundred microns.

Single-muon events were recorded using a fast high-p_t trigger[2]. The electronics records also the approximate trajectory of the triggering muon; this expedites tracking of the muon. The events are filtered, to select events with a clean secondary vertex as well as a good primary vertex. A sample event of this kind is shown in Figure 4. These events are then studied, analytically and visually. Figure 5a shows the distribution of angle and longitudinal distance, between the primary and secondary vertices, for a sample of 1/400 of the data taken. Fig. 5b shows those surviving events in which the triggering muon is found to correspond to a track which does not come from the primary vertex. Only 6 events survive in the region where the principal concentration would occur for B meson decay. (Theta = 30 ± 15 mrad, z < 40 cm.) All 6 correspond to secondary interactions rather than to heavy-quark decays – the muon comes from a secondary interaction in a target foil.

Analysis of further events is under way.

1. For details contact B. Cox, E771 spokesman, University of Virginia.
2. S. N. Zhang et al., *IEEE Trans. on Nuc. Sci.* **39** (1992) 814.

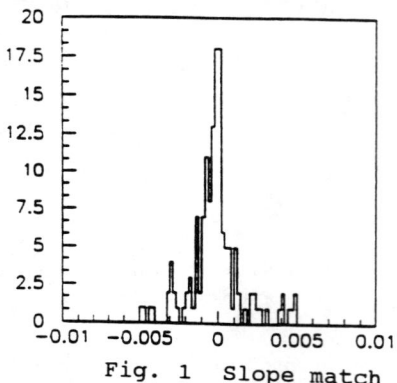

Fig. 1 Slope match distribution

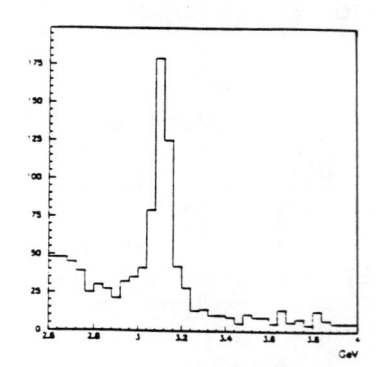

Fig. 2 Di-muon mass distribution

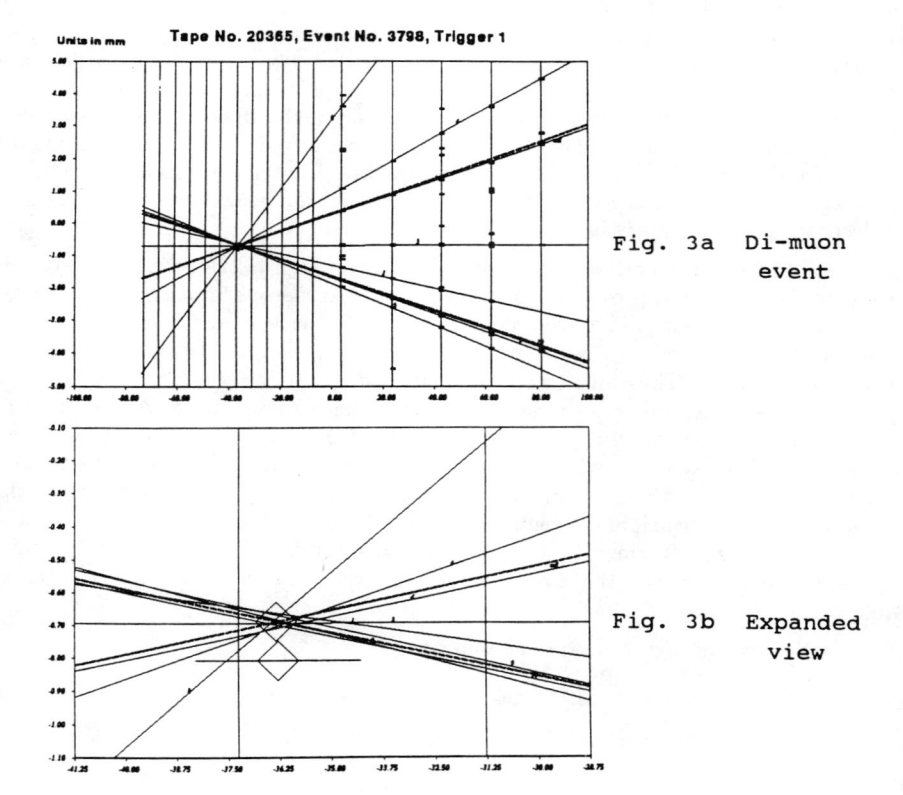

Fig. 3a Di-muon event

Fig. 3b Expanded view

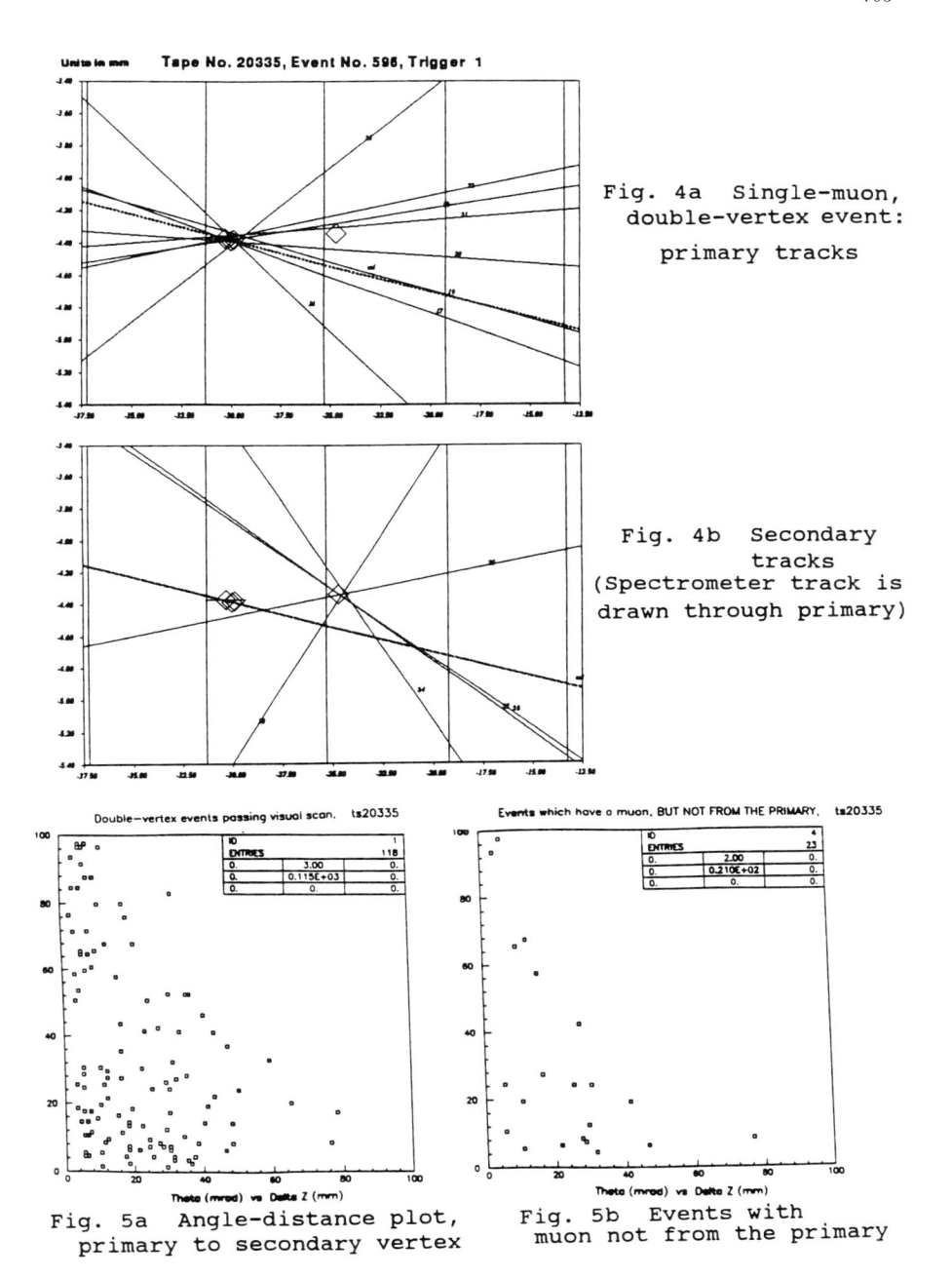

Fig. 4a Single-muon, double-vertex event: primary tracks

Fig. 4b Secondary tracks (Spectrometer track is drawn through primary)

Fig. 5a Angle-distance plot, primary to secondary vertex

Fig. 5b Events with muon not from the primary

FIRST RESULTS FROM FERMILAB EXPERIMENT 789

E789 COLLABORATION

Presented by Martin Schub
*Enrico Fermi Institute, University of Chicago, 5640 S. Ellis Ave.
Chicago, IL 60637, USA*

ABSTRACT

Fermilab Experiment 789, which is designed to study two-prong decay modes of neutral D and B mesons, collected $\sim 1.5 \times 10^9$ events during the 1991 run, using an 800 GeV proton beam incident on gold and beryllium targets. Preliminary values for $\sigma(D \text{or} \bar{D}) \sim 25\mu\text{b}$, the nucleon-number dependence of $\sigma(\text{Au})/\sigma(\text{Be})$, and the $D^0/\bar{D}^0$ production asymmetry will be presented. E789 has also seen evidence for the decay $B \to J/\psi X \to \mu^+\mu^- X$.

1. Introduction

Experiment 789 at Fermilab was designed to measure low-multiplicity decays of B mesons produced in a high-rate fixed-target environment. The existing E605/E772 spectrometer, which was used in previous experiments to detect massive hadron and lepton pairs with good mass resolution and high rate capability, was significantly upgraded for E789: the MWPC's in the first spectrometer station were replaced by drift chambers, and a silicon microstrip vertex spectrometer and a vertex trigger processor were installed. The main goals of the E789 experiment are to measure the B production cross section at 800 GeV via the detection of inclusive $B \to J/\psi + X$ decays, and to search for charmless dihadron decay modes such as $B \to \pi^+\pi^-, K\pi, K^+K^-, \bar{p}p$. The sensitivity for these measurements clearly depends on the rate capability of the spectrometer and on the performance of the silicon microstrip detectors in this high-rate environment (which is similar to those anticipated in future SSC experiments). Preliminary results from analysis of a subset of the data taken in the 1991 fixed-target run are presented in this paper.

2. Apparatus

During the 1991 run, an 800 GeV proton beam was incident on a thin wire target, typically 0.1 mm to 0.2 mm high and 0.8 mm to 3 mm thick. Sixteen silicon microstrip detectors (SMDs) were positioned downstream of the target to cover the angular range from 20 mr to 60 mr above and below the beam axis. The silicon detectors, type 'B' from Micron Semiconductor, had 5×5 cm² area, 300 μm thickness, and 50 μm pitch. Half the SMDs were oriented to measure the Y (vertical) coordinate and the rest to measure U or V coordinates (5° stereo angle). Signals from 8,544 silicon strips were individually read out via Fermilab 128-channel amplifier cards[1] and LBL discriminators[2] synchronized to the accelerator RF. The

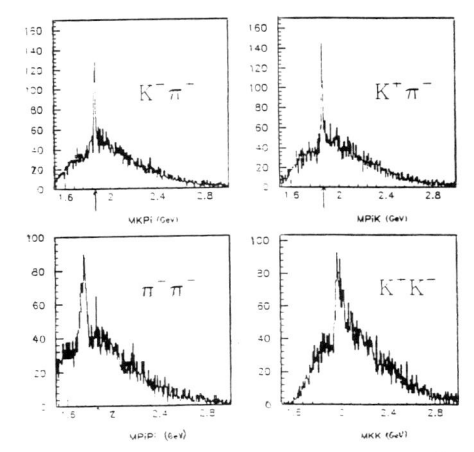

Figure 1. Mass spectra for dihadron events reconstructed with various assumptions for the hadron species. The arrows indicate the D decay peaks.

discriminated signals were then transmitted through $\approx$ 400 ns of multiconductor cables to coincidence registers. A vertex processor[3], which finds tracks in the silicon detectors and selects events with decay vertices downstream of the target, was also implemented and functional. The use of a thin target in vacuum localizes the primary interaction vertex and greatly simplifies the design of the vertex processor, which only needs to search for downstream decay vertices.

3. Summary of E789 1991 Run

The mass acceptance of the E789 spectrometer can be varied by changing the current in the SM12 analyzing magnet. Two different settings of the spectrometer, which separately optimize the acceptance for charm or beauty decays, were used in the 1991 run. The charm running served to check the performance of the SMDs and the vertex trigger processor. In addition, the nuclear dependence of D meson production was measured using beryllium and gold wire targets, providing information related to the origin of the J/ψ A-dependence observed[4] in E772 at the same beam energy. The vertex trigger processor and the upgraded data acquisition system enabled us to take up to 10^{10} protons per beam spill on a 1.5 mm-thick gold target (4 MHz interaction rate).

The efficiency of each silicon plane is found to be better than 90 % and the impact parameter resolution of $\approx$ 30 μm gives a Z-vertex resolution of $\approx$ 1 mm for typical D events. More details on the performance of the SMDs in this high rate experiment have been reported elsewhere[5].

For the beauty running, the spectrometer was set at a configuration to accept both the $B \to J/\psi X$ and the $B \to h^+h^-$ decays. We took data at 5×10^{10} protons per pulse on a 3-mm-thick gold target, corresponding to a 50-MHz interaction rate, without using the vertex trigger processor.

4. Preliminary Charm Results

Figure 1 shows the dihadron mass spectra obtained from an analysis of ≈ 30 % of our charm data sample. To effectively reject the dihadron background, we require that neither track point back to the target, and that the proper lifetime be greater than 0.8 ps. Information from the ring-imaging Cherenkov detector has not yet been used for π/K identification, and the plots in Fig. 1 are obtained by assigning either pion or kaon mass to the hadrons. The $D^0 \to \pi^+ K^-$, $\bar{D}^0 \to K^+ \pi^-$, and $D^0, \bar{D}^0 \to \pi^+ \pi^-$ decays are clearly visible in Fig. 1. The D^0 mass resolution shown in Fig. 1 is consistent with ≈ 6 MeV, and the total number of D^0 and $\bar{D}^0$ events above background is ~ 600. An uncorrected lifetime distribution agrees well with one obtained by reconstructing Monte Carlo data generated assuming a liftime of 0.43 ps.

We estimate the sum of the cross sections for D^0 and $\bar{D}^0$ to be 25 μb, extrapolated to all x_F. The statistical error on this is small, and the systematic error is still under study. This preliminary estimate is consistent with results from other experiments using 800 GeV protons[6]. E789 is sensitive to $0 < x_F < 0.08$. We see essentially no difference in D^0 and $\bar{D}^0$ production; our preliminary estimate of this ratio is 1 ± 0.1 (systematic), and again the systematic errors are under study.

A preliminary value for the exponent in the A-dependence of D^0 production is 0.88 +- 0.04 (systematic). The statistical error is small compared to the systematic. We hope ultimately to achieve an error about half this big. This exponent is consistent with the A-dependence measured by E772 for J/ψ production[7].

5. Preliminary Beauty Analysis

Figure 2 shows the dimuon mass spectrum from a preliminary analysis of ≈ 30 % of our beauty data sample. Good silicon tracks are required for events shown in Fig. 2, but no vertex cuts are applied. Approximately 25,000 J/ψ and 400 ψ' events are observed. To search for $B \to J/\psi X$ events, the impact parameters of both muon tracks are required to be greater than 150 μm and the decay vertex is required to be at least 7 mm downstream of the target (7 mm < Z_{vertex} <5 cm). Fig. 3(a) shows that a total of 41 events, eleven of them in the J/ψ mass region, survive these cuts. These eleven events are considered candidate events for $B \to J/\psi X$ decays. To estimate the background which might be caused by resolution tails or silicon tracking errors, we also select events with decay vertices upstream of the target, namely $-5cm < Z_{vertex} < -7mm$. Fig. 3(b) shows that this background is unimportant. More study of acceptance and efficiency needs to be done before a reliable b-production cross section can be extracted.

In summary, E789 explores the feasibility of studying b-physics in a high-rate fixed-target environment. Preliminary results show that the silicon vertex spectrometer worked well. Eleven $B \to J/\psi X$ candidate events are observed from an

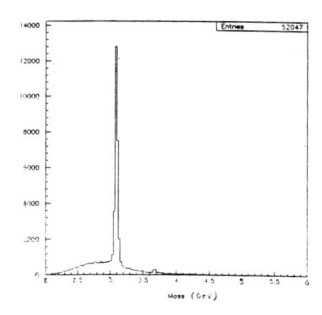

Figure 2. Mass spectrum for dimuon events.

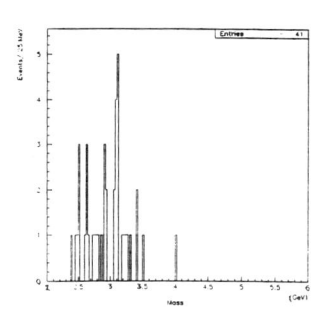

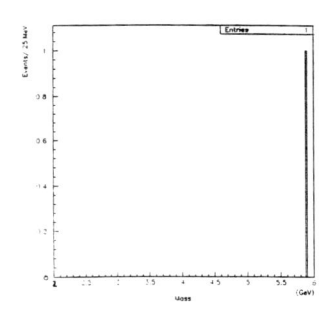

Figure 3. Mass spectra for dimuon events passing a) downstream Z-vertex cuts, b) upstream Z-vertex cut.

analysis of ≈ 30 % of the dimuon data sample.

1. D. Christian et al., *IEEE Trans. Nucl. Sci.* NS-36 (1989) 507.
2. B. T. Turko et al., " A Multichannel Discriminator System for Silicon Strip Detector Readout," *IEEE Trans. Nucl. Sci.*, 39 (1992) 758.
3. C. Lee et al., *IEEE Trans. Nucl. Sci.* 38 (1989) 507.
4. D. M. Alde et al., *Phys. Rev. Lett.* 66 (1991) 133.
5. J. S. Kapustinsky et al., " Radiation Damage Effects on the Silicon Microstrip Detector in E789," presented at the International Conference on Advanced Technology and Particle Physics, Como, Italy, 1992.
6. Ammar et al., Phys. Lett. 178B, 124 (1986); Kodama et al., Phys. Lett. 263B, 573 (1991).
7. D. M. Alde et al., *Phys. Rev. Lett.* 66, (1991) 133.

DOUBLE SEMI-LEPTONIC CHARM DECAY IN
HELIOS-I 450 GeV/c p-Be DATA

AUBRY, PIERRE
Département de Physique, Université de Montréal
Montréal, Quebec, Canada

POMIANOWSKI, PAULA A.
Department of Physics, University of Pittsburgh, 100 Allen Hall
Pittsburgh, PA 15260, USA

ABSTRACT

Data taken in 1989 by HELIOS-I (NA34) at the CERN SPS (450 GeV/c proton beam on Be target) have been examined for $e^{\pm}\mu^{\mp}$ or $\mu^{\pm}\mu^{\mp}$ pairs with associated missing energy. Such pairs arise from semi-leptonic decay of both members of a $c\bar{c}$ pair. The $e\mu$ and $\mu\mu$ samples are consistent with expectations from charm decay, allowing a quantitative limit to be placed on other physics.

1. Introduction

Decay of a $c\bar{c}$ pair can be tagged by looking for an oppositely signed lepton pair in an event with large missing energy (carried off by the two associated neutrinos). However, the study of inclusive charm production in hadronic collisions is complicated by resonance meson decays and the semi-leptonic decay of $\pi^{\pm}$ and $K^{\pm}$. If these background sources are understood, a sample of lepton pairs from double semi-leptonic charm decay can be extracted. This allows the study of other non-charm contributions occurring in the mass region below 3 GeV. In the $\mu\mu$ channel, the amount of non-neutrino events such as Drell-Yan can be compared to charm, whereas the $e\mu$ channel is sensitive to other new physics [1].

2. Experimental Setup

The HELIOS-I setup combined electron identification, muon identification, and measurement of missing energy carried off by neutrinos. A 450 GeV proton beam was focused onto a 4cm long thin (125μm diameter) beryllium wire target. Particle tracking and momentum information was obtained from three drift chambers separated by a magnetic field. Electrons were identified by a coincidence between a silicon pad array, transition radiation detector, and uranium/liquid argon calorimeter (ULAC). Muons were identified using proportional chambers, a magnet for momentum information, and a hodoscope (scintillators separated by an iron wall). Hermetic calorimetry provided a measurement of missing energy.

3. Preliminary Study of $\mu\mu$ Pairs with Missing Energy

Muon spectrometer tracks were matched with drift chamber tracks to improve the mass resolution and reject background muons. The calorimeters were monitored by history flash-ADCs to reject beam particle pileup. Punch-through particles were removed by a cut on muon chamber multiplicity. Background $\pi^\pm$ and $K^\pm$ decays were subtracted using the $\mu^\pm\mu^\pm$ mass, p_T, and missing energy distributions, with absolute normalization and correction for correlated production computed from a Monte Carlo simulation. The total energy resolution ($\sigma_{Etot} = 16.4 \pm 1$ GeV) allows the missing energy events to be separated from the neutrinoless events.

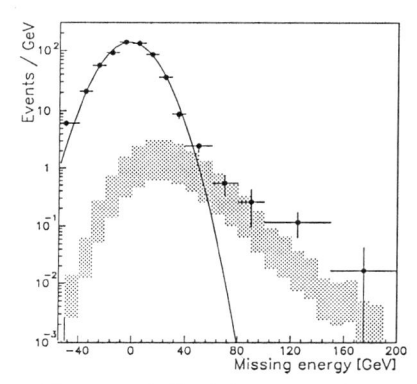

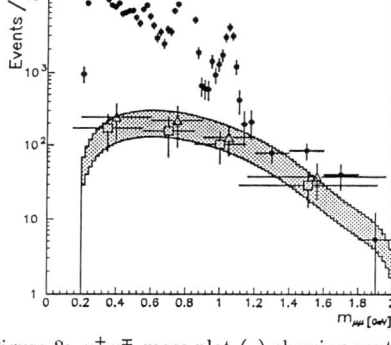

Figure 1: $\mu^\pm\mu^\mp$ missing energy plot

Figure 2: $\mu^\pm\mu^\mp$ mass plot ($\bullet$) showing contribution of missing energy events ($\square,\triangle$)

The $\mu\mu$ missing energy distribution is shown in figure 1. The band, showing the PYTHIA 5.6 computation of semi-muonic decays of $D\bar{D}$ normalized to a cross section of 14.6 μbarns [2], falls only slightly below the data points. Scaling the Monte Carlo to match the data points, and assuming that the data are entirely due to $D\bar{D}$ decays, gives $\sigma_{D\bar{D}}\cdot(BR_{D\to\mu+X})^2 = .35 \pm .12 \pm .15$ μbarns (PRELIMINARY).

The missing energy distribution has been fit in 4 mass bins, assuming a combination of D meson decay and neutrinoless events. This gives a di-muon mass spectrum (figure 2) of double semi-muonic D decays sensitive to the x_F parametrisation of D production. Both $|1-x_F|^6$ (open triangles) and $|1-x_F|^3$ (open squares) show good agreement with the distribution derived from PYTHIA 5.6 normalized to $\sigma_{D\bar{D}}$=14.6 μbarns (gray band). The systematics are under study. An upper limit for Drell-Yan production in the 1.2 – 2.8 GeV mass region is expected.

4. Preliminary Study of $e\mu$ Pairs

For the $e\mu$ data, additional cuts were applied to the electron candidate. An isolated ULAC shower was required which spatially and energetically matched a drift chamber track. Background was further reduced by requiring that the sum of p_T of the leptons be greater than 0.7 GeV/c. The resulting sample of 100±31 $e^{\pm}\mu^{\mp}$ pairs is approximately 3 times the previously published result [1].

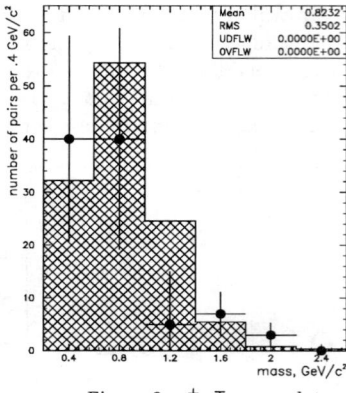

Figure 3: $e^{\pm}\mu^{\mp}$ mass plot

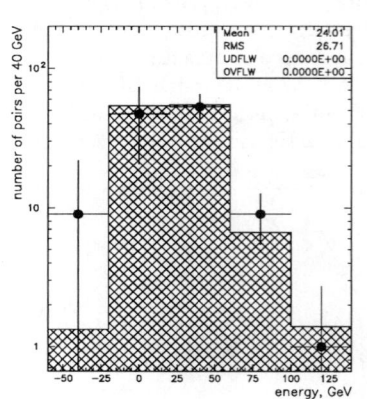

Figure 4: $e^{\pm}\mu^{\mp}$ missing energy plot

The shapes of both the mass (figure 3) and missing energy (figure 4) spectra are consistent with charm. When data (circles in figures) are compared with PYTHIA 5.3 (shaded region), the sample seems free from significant contamination (such as $\pi^{\pm}/K^{\pm}$ decay). The preliminary absolute normalization (required to determine the inclusive $c\bar{c}$ cross section) yields numbers consistent with other experiments [2]. An upper limit for other non-charm physics processes is expected.

5. Conclusions

The $\mu\mu$ and $e\mu$ samples are consistent with expectations from charm decay. Quantitative limits on other physics contributions are under study.

6. Acknowledgments

The HELIOS collaboration thanks the PS-SPS accelerator complex staff, the technical staff of CERN and the collaborating institutes, and the research councils and funding agencies in our home countries. Special acknowledgment is given to the U.S. DOE and Pittsburgh Supercomputing Center (NSF/PSC Grant PHQ7R8P).

7. References

1. Clark et al., *Phys. Lett.* **B77** (1978) 337.
2. M. Aguilar-Benitez et al., *Z.Phys.C.* **40** (1988) 321.

PRODUCTION OF STATES WITH HIDDEN CHARM IN 300 GeV/c π^+, π^-, p, AND $\bar{p}$ COLLISIONS WITH NUCLEI

STEPHEN W. DELCHAMPS

Fermi National Accelerator Laboratory, Batavia, Illinois 60510 USA

for the Experiment 705 Collaboration[*]

ABSTRACT

We discuss the production of charmonium in collisions of 300 GeV/c π^+, π^-, p, and $\bar{p}$ with a natural lithium target. We present inclusive production cross sections for the production of J/ψ and $\psi\prime$ (3685); p_T and x_F dependences are given for the J/ψ. The fraction of J/ψ production from radiative χ decay is reported, as well as the cross sections for χ_1 and χ_2 for π^- beam. We also report the tentative observation of two other states of charmonium, the $^3D_2$ and the $^1P_1$ (recently reported by Fermilab Experiment 760).

1. Introduction

Much of the material in this paper appeared in preliminary form in an earlier conference paper[1]. All of the results presented here will soon appear in much greater detail in several journal articles[2,3,4,5]. The Experiment 705 large acceptance, open geometry spectrometer and high mass dimuon trigger are described in some detail in References 1 and 2. The electromagnetic calorimeter is described briefly in Reference 3, and will be more exhaustively treated in a paper to be submitted to Nuclear Instruments and Methods.

2. J/ψ and $\psi\prime$ Production (see Reference 2)

The J/ψ signals appearing in the dimuon mass spectra for π^+, π^-, p, and $\bar{p}$ beams (the spectrum for π^- data is shown in Figure 1) have been used to obtain the inclusive cross sections per nucleus and per nucleon (assuming atomic weight dependence $A^{0.92}$) for $x_F \geq 0$ given in Table 1. The first and second uncertainties

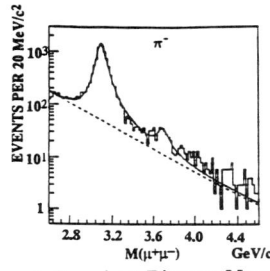

Figure 1. Invariant Dimuon Mass for π^- Li Interactions

Table 1. Inclusive J/ψ Production Cross Section ($x_F \geq 0$)

Beam Type	σ•B(J/ψ –> μμ) (nb / nucleus)	σ (nb / nucleus)	σ•B(J/ψ–>μμ) (nb / nucleon)	σ (nb / nucleon)
π^+	62.5 ± 2.1 ± 5.2	1060 ± 40 ± 90 ±40	10.3 ± 0.3 ± 0.9	179 ± 7 ± 15 ±7
π^-	63.7 ± 2.1 ± 6.9	1080 ± 40 ± 120 ±40	10.5 ± 0.3 ± 1.1	182 ± 7 ± 20 ±7
proton	50.4 ± 1.6 ± 5.3	850 ± 30 ± 90 ±30	8.4 ± 0.3 ± 0.8	143 ± 5 ± 15 ±5
anti-proton	48.2 ± 6.7 ± 4.2	820 ± 110 ± 70 ±30	8.1 ± 1.1 ± 0.7	138 ± 19 ± 12 ±5

---

[*] University of Athens, Duke University, Fermilab, McGill University, Nanjing University, Northwestern University, Prairie View A&M University, Shandong University, University of Virginia

shown in Table 1 are statistical and systematic respectively. In the second and fourth columns, there is an additional uncertainty due to the branching ratio of J/ψ to dimuons.

The corrected distributions for J/ψ production in x_F and p_T were fitted to the forms

$$d\sigma/dx_F \sim (1 - |x_F - x_0|)^n$$

and

$$d\sigma/dp_T^2 \sim \exp(-p_T^2/p_{T0}^2)$$

The parameters n, x_0, $<p_T>$, and $<p_T^2>$ are given in Table 2. For the transverse momentum dependence chosen, the mean square transverse momentum is p_{T0}^2, and the mean transverse momentum is $\sqrt{\pi}p_{T0}/2$. The second uncertainty shown for the transverse momentum fit is due to rescaling of the muon momenta to bring the dimuon mass to the accepted J/ψ value.

Table 2. Fit Parameters for x_F and p_T
Dependences of J/ψ Production

Beam Type	x_0	n	$<p_T>$	$<p_T^2>$
$\pi+$	0.030 ± 0.013	1.99 ± 0.15	1.045± .012± .003	1.39 ± .03 ± .008
$\pi-$	0.062 ± 0.011	2.27 ± 0.27	1.062± .008± .003	1.43 ± .02 ± .008
proton	0.026 ± 0.007	4.14 ± 0.16	0.993± .002± .003	1.255± .005± .008
anti-proton	-0.02 ± 0.10	3.2 ± 1.4	1.08 ± 0.11 ± .003	1.5 ± 0.3 ± .008

We have also measured inclusive cross sections for the production of $\psi\prime$ (3685) using the corrected yields of $\psi\prime$ decaying into dimuons. The inclusive cross sections for J/ψ and $\psi\prime$ are compared in Table 3. The last uncertainty in the second column

Table 3. Comparison of Inclusive J/ψ and $\psi\prime$ Cross Sections

Beam Type	$\sigma\cdot B(\psi' \to \mu\mu)/\sigma\cdot B(J/\psi \to \mu\mu)$	$\sigma(\psi')/\sigma(J/\psi)$
$\pi+$	1.66 ± 0.44 ± 0.04 %	12.0 ± 3.0 ± 0.3 ± 2.0 %
$\pi-$	1.93 ± 0.26 ± 0.05 %	14.0 ± 2.0 ± 0.4 ± 2.0 %
proton	1.88 ± 0.26 ± 0.05 %	14.0 ± 2.0 ± 0.4 ± 2.0 %
anti-proton	3.48 ± 3.04 ± 0.10 %	25.0 ± 22.0 ± 0.7 ± 0.4 %

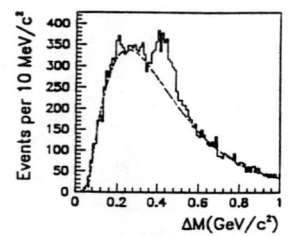

Figure 2. Invariant Mass Difference $M(\mu^+\mu^-\gamma) - M(\mu^+\mu^-)$ for π^-, and pLi Interactions

of the table is due to the branching ratios of the J/ψ and $\psi\prime$ to dimuons.

3. Radiative Decay of χ_1 and χ_2 (see Reference 3)

The mass difference $M(\mu^+\mu^-\gamma) - M(\mu^+\mu^-)$ is shown in Figure 2 for all π^+, π^-, and p beam data. A peak (~1,100 events above background) is evident near the mass difference values (414 and 459 MeV/c^2 respectively) expected for χ_1 and χ_2. Correcting the summed yield of χ_1 and χ_2 for acceptance and efficiency, we calculate the fraction of J/ψ produced through radiative decay of χ_1 and χ_2, given in Table 4. Also shown in Table 4 are the fraction of J/ψ from decay of the $\psi\prime$ and the inferred fraction of J/ψ from all other sources other than χ and $\psi\prime$ decay, presumably mainly direct production at this center of momentum frame energy.

Table 4. Fraction of J/ψ from Various Sources and Inclusive χ Production Cross Section

Beam Type	$(\chi_1+\chi_2 \to \gamma J/\psi)$ /(ψ total)	$(\psi' \to J/\psi X)$ /(ψ total)	Fraction of J/ψ from other sources	$\sigma(\pi-Li \to \chi_1 X)$ (nb/ nucleon)	$\sigma(\pi-Li \to \chi_2 X)$ (nb / nucleon)
$\pi+$	40 ± 4 %	6.4 ± 2.2%	54 ± 5%		
$\pi-$	37 ± 3 %	7.5 ± 1.7%	55 ± 3%	131 ± 18 ± 14	188 ± 30 ± 21
proton	30 ± 4%	7.5 ± 1.7%	62 ± 3%		

By combining the relative yields of χ_1 and χ_2 decaying to J/ψ measured by the CERN WA11 experiment[6] in 185 GeV/c π^-Be collisions with our more precise measurement of the total yield of χ_1 plus χ_2 to J/ψ for π^- beam, and using the known branching ratios of χ_1 and χ_2 to J/ψ, we obtain the inclusive χ_1 and χ_2 production cross sections in the last two columns of Table 4.

A maximum likelihood fit employing our measured resolutions has been used to directly obtain the cross sections for χ_1 and χ_2 for pLi and $\pi^\pm$Li collisions. Differential cross sections in p_T and x_F are also being examined. These results will be presented in a forthcoming paper[5].

4. Other States with Hidden Charm (see Reference 4)

Figure 3 shows the invariant mass distribution for $J/\psi\pi^+\pi^-$ combinations for π^- beam events. Two peaks above background are evident, at masses of 3.678±.006 GeV/c^2 and 3.837±.004 GeV/c^2. The lower mass peak corresponds to the $\psi\prime$. The peak at 3.837 GeV/c^2 lies near the predicted mass for the $^3D_2$ state of charmonium[8].

Figure 4 shows the invariant mass distribution for $J/\psi\pi^0$ for all beam types. There is a two standard deviation excess at 3.527 GeV/c^2, close to the mass of the

$^1P_1$ state of charmonium as reported the Fermilab E760 collaboration[7].

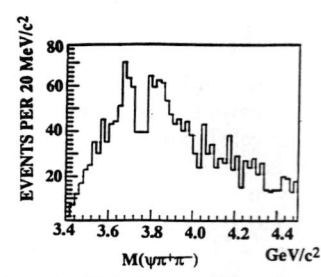

Figure 3. $J/\psi\pi^+\pi^-$ Invariant Mass for π^-Li Interactions

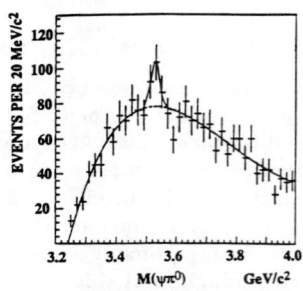

Figure 4. $J/\psi\pi^0$ Invariant Mass for π^+, π^-, and pLi Interactions

5. Acknowledgements

We would like to acknowledge the U.S. Department of Energy, the Natural Sciences and Engineering Research Council of Canada, the Quebec Department of Education, and the Hellenic Science and Technology Agency for their support.

6. References

1. M. Rosati et al., "Production of Charmonium States from Experiment 705 at Fermilab", in *Proceedings of the Vancouver Meeting*, ed. David Axen, Douglass Bryman, and Martin Comyn, (New Jersey: World Scientific,1992). p.672-7.
2. L. Antoniazzi et al., "A Measurement of J/ψ and $\psi\prime$ Production in 300 GeV/c Proton, Antiproton, and $\pi^\pm$ Nucleon Interactions", FERMILAB-Pub-92/141-E, submitted to *Phys. Rev. D*.
3. L. Antoniazzi et al., "Production of J/ψ via $\psi\prime$ and χ Decay in 300 GeV/c Proton and $\pi^\pm$ Nucleon Interactions", FERMILAB-Pub-92/140-E, submitted to *Phys. Rev. Lett.*
4. L. Antoniazzi et al., "Search for Hidden Charm States Decaying into J/ψ or $\psi\prime$ Plus Pions", FERMILAB-Pub-92/265-E, submitted to *Phys. Rev. D*.
5. L. Antoniazzi et al., "Production of χ States via 300 GeV/c Proton and $\pi^\pm$ Interactions on a Lithium Target", to be submitted to *Phys. Rev. D*.
6. Y. Lemoigne et al., *Phys. Lett.* **113B**, 509 (1982).
7. T.A. Armstrong et al., "Observation of the $^1P_1$ State of Charmonium", *Phys. Rev. Lett.* **69**, 2337 (1992).
8. W. Kwong, J.L. Rosner, and C. Quigg, "Heavy-Quark Systems", *Ann. Rev. Nucl. Part. Sci.* **37**, 325-382 (1987).

HEAVY QUARK PRODUCTION RESULTS FROM FERMILAB E653:
BEAUTY PAIRS, AND LIMITS ON DIFFRACTIVE CHARM

N.R. STANTON (For the E653 Collaboration)
Physics Department, The Ohio State University
Columbus, Ohio 43210 USA

ABSTRACT

We report on the production characteristics of 9 beauty pair events produced in emulsion by 600 GeV/c π^-. The pair cross section (assuming A^1) is $33 \pm 11 \pm 6$ nb/nucleon. We also report limits on coherent diffractive production of charm from Si by 800 GeV/c protons.

1. Beauty Hadron Pair Production by 600 GeV/c π^- in Emulsion

For this portion of the experiment, E653 was configured as a hybrid emulsion spectrometer[1]. The electronic spectrometer featured an 18-plane silicon microstrip (SMD) vertex detector, a large aperture dipole magnet, 55 drift chamber planes, and a liquid argon calorimeter. This was followed by a second muon spectrometer, comprised of range steel and 12 drift chamber planes on either side of an iron toroid. The trigger required a muon to penetrate 3900 g/cm² of steel.

The primary interaction and short-lived decays were observed in a nuclear emulsion target 1.5 cm thick. Two thin emulsion-plastic-emulsion sandwiches downstream of the target were used as precision verniers on spectrometer tracks, and improved resolution fivefold for vertices outside the emulsion target. The fiducial decay region (emulsion components and first 6 SMD's) was 12 cm long. In a typical beauty pair event with 4 decays, half of the decays are inside the bulk emulsion target, and half are outside.

A total of 8.2×10^6 events, corresponding to 2.5×10^8 π^- interactions, were recorded on tape. Reconstructed spectrometer events with a muon transverse momentum $p_{T\mu} > 1.5$ GeV/c were scanned in the emulsion[1]. The primary interaction vertex was located for 99.8% of the 6542 events within the emulsion fiducial volume. Unwanted events in which the tagged muon came from the primary interaction (via a π or K decay, e.g.), were rejected by requiring that the trigger muon, as measured in the spectrometer, have slopes different from those of any emulsion track at the primary vertex. Decays were located in the surviving 359 events by three methods: tracks from the primary vertex were followed down in the emulsion; vertices outside the emulsion were reconstructed with an interactive program; and unmatched spectrometer tracks were projected back into the emulsion. A detailed Monte Carlo simulation of both the spectrometer and of the emulsion procedure determined detection efficiencies and resolutions. Because E653 beauty and charm

---
[1] A scan requiring $p_{T\mu} > 0.8$ GeV/c, now underway, should double the beauty sample.

decays generally have unseen neutrals, momenta were estimated by matching the topology, prong count, and momenta in each data event to a large sample of Monte Carlo decays. The momentum distribution of the matched Monte Carlo events was taken to be the probability distribution for the momentum of the data event.

There are 12 neutral and 6 charged decays in the final beauty pair sample; lifetimes from these decays are reported elsewhere[2]. All but 3 of these 9 events have 4 decay vertices. The semileptonic decays all have low multiplicity and a muon with high decay $p_\perp$. There are 5 $D^{*\pm}$ among the 8 D^0 from beauty decays. The level of background in the beauty sample was estimated to be 0.15 events from the number and characteristics of data events which passed looser criteria than the final sample, and from using a Monte Carlo simulation to understand the effectiveness of the tighter criteria in rejecting such backgrounds. Lifetime measurements on the 175 charm events found during the beauty scan were used to verify the validity of the momentum estimator and the absence of significant scanning bias for decays.

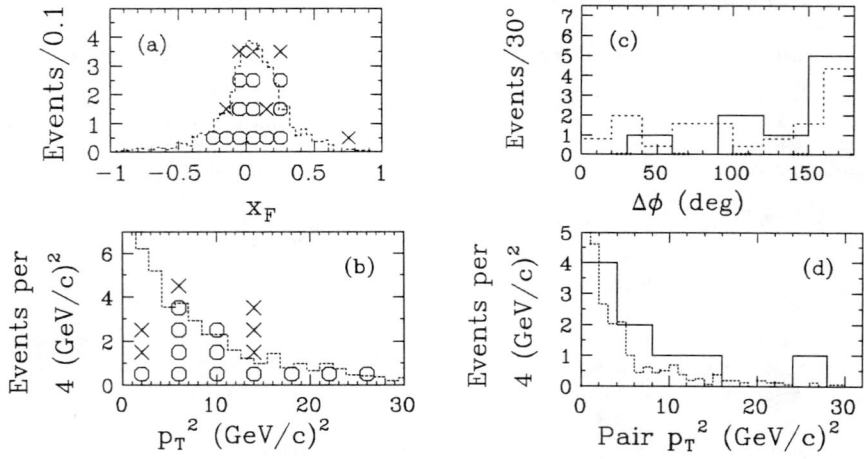

FIG. 1. (a) Histogram of inclusive x_F for the 6 neutral (circles) and 6 charged (crosses) beauty hadrons. The dashed histogram is a simulation with $n = 5.0$ and $x_0 = 0.06$. (b) Histogram of inclusive p_T^2. The dashed histogram is a simulation with $b = 0.13$. (c) Azimuthal opening angle $\Delta\phi$ between members of the 9 beauty pairs (solid histogram), compared with those for 35 charm pairs[4] (dashed). (d) Pair p_T^2 for the 9 pairs (solid), compared with a simulation with pair $p_T^2 = 0$ (dashed).

The production properties of the beauty events are summarized in Fig. 1. The pair cross section, assuming linear A dependence, is $33 \pm 11 \pm 6$ nb/nucleon, about 1/700 of that for charm[3] at 600 GeV/c. The inclusive x_F distribution (Fig. 1a), which is measured with good efficiency for $-0.6 < x_F < 0.9$, is described by $d\sigma/dx_F = (1 - |x_F - x_0|)^n$, with $n = 5.0^{+2.7+1.5}_{-2.1-0.9}$, similar to charm at this energy[3] and a positive offset (as expected in π^- production) of $x_0 = 0.06^{+0.06+0.0}_{-0.07-0.02}$. The inclusive

p_T^2 distribution (Fig. 1b) is much broader than that for charm, as expected; it is described by $d\sigma/dp_T^2 = \exp{-bp_T^2}$, with $b = 0.13^{+0.05+0.00}_{-0.04-0.02}$. The distribution in azimuthal opening angle $\Delta\phi$ between members of each pair (Fig. 1c) shows a strong tendency for back-to-back production, more so than for charm pairs[4]. The $p_{T_{pair}}^2$ distribution of the pairs (Fig. 1d) is described by $b_{pair} = 0.2 \pm 0.1$ $(\text{GeV}/\text{c})^2$, i.e. the mean $p_{T_{pair}}^2$ is nonzero but is smaller than the mean inclusive p_T^2.

2. Search for Coherent Charm Production by 800 GeV/c Protons on Si

This portion of the experiment searched for forward production of charm in which the target nucleus recoiled without breaking up. The beam was 800 GeV/c protons, the emulsion target was replaced by a 16-wafer active Si target, and a multiplicity jump trigger replaced the muon trigger: the multiplicity of charged particles (measured by Si wafers) was required to increase by at least 2.5 minimum ionizing particles within a 10 cm decay region[2]. A total of 0.5×10^6 triggers, corresponding to 1.7×10^7 interactions, was recorded with this E653 configuration. Simulations showed this trigger to be 50% efficient for diffractive charm. Coherent p-Si interactions were selected offline by requiring no evidence for nuclear breakup in the active Si target. No charm signals were seen in these events in the channels $D^+ \to K^-\pi^+\pi^+$, $D^0 \to K^-\pi^+, K^-\pi^+\pi^-\pi^+$, or $\Lambda_c \to pK^-\pi^+$. The resulting upper limits (90% CL) for coherent diffractive production of D^+, D^0, and Λ_c are respectively 20, 42, and 420 μb/Si nucleus. These limits correspond to $< 2\% (< 4\%)$ of the total inclusive cross section for production of D^+ (D^0) from individual nucleons (A^1 assumed), and to $< 0.17\% (< 0.33\%)$ of the total p-Si diffractive cross section with $M > M_{c\bar{c}}$.

Acknowledgements

This work was supported in part by the US Department of Energy; the US National Science Foundation; the Japan Society for Promotion of Science; the Japan-US Cooperative Research Program for HEP; the Ministry of Education, Science and Culture of Japan; the Korea Science and Engineering Foundation; and the Basic Science Research Institute Program, Ministry of Education, Republic of Korea.

References

1. K. Kodama et al., Nucl. Instr. & Meth. **A289** (1990) 146.
2. K. Kodama et al., "Measurement of the Lifetimes of Charged and Neutral Beauty Hadrons", Ohio State preprint OHSTPY-HEP-E-92-019 (Sept., 1992), submitted to Prog. Theor. Phys.
3. K. Kodama et al., Phys. Lett. **B284** (1992) 461.
4. K. Kodama et al., Phys. Lett. **B263** (1991) 579.

---

[2] The trigger decision was made on the basis of the smaller of the two pulse heights in each of two pairs of Si wafers, with one pair at either end of the decay region.

Atomic Mass Dependence of $D^{\pm}$ and $D^0, \overline{D}^0$ Production in 250 GeV $\pi^{\pm}$-Nucleon Interactions

Gilvan A. Alves

Laboratório de Física Experimental de Altas Energias (LAFEX), CBPF
Rua Xavier Sigaud, 150 5° andar
Rio de Janeiro, RJ 22290, Brazil

Representing the Fermilab E769 Collaboration[†]

ABSTRACT

We report on the relative yields of charmed D-mesons produced in $\pi^{\pm}$ interactions with Be, Al, Cu and W. Based on 1400 fully reconstructed decays, of the types $D^0 \to K^-\pi^+$, $D^+ \to K^-\pi^+\pi^+$ (and charge conjugates), we find that the per nucleus cross section is well fit by the form $\sigma_c = \sigma_0 A^\alpha$ where A is the atomic mass and $\alpha = 1.00 \pm 0.05$. We find no significant dependence of α on the transverse or longitudinal momentum of the D-meson nor on the charge of either the incident particle or the produced one.

1. Introduction

Measurement of the nuclear target dependence of the hadroproduction of charm mesons allows one to probe the distance scale important in the production and hadronization of charmed quarks. Also, since in the Standard Model the dominant sub-process contributing to charm quark production is gluon-gluon fusion, this measurement provides a means for studying the distribution of gluons in nuclear matter. If the distance scale is small compared to the size of a nucleon, and if the gluon distribution is the same in different nuclei, then the cross section per nucleon should not depend on the target type. If the dependence of the cross section per nucleus on atomic mass, A, is parameterized by the form A^α, then the behavior described above is characterized by $\alpha = 1$. In contrast, for the total inelastic cross section in pion-nucleon collisions[1], $\alpha = 0.75$, which can be compared to the value of 2/3 expected from scattering by a totally absorbing sphere. The target dependence of the charm cross section is also important in comparing results from experiments with different target materials and in choosing the target material for future heavy quark experiments.

The measurements presented here are from Fermilab experiment E769. This experiment utilized a $\pi^{\pm}$, secondary beam of momentum 250 GeV. The A dependence measurement was made by simultaneously exposing foils of Be, Al, Cu, and W with total nuclear interaction length of 2%. The high Z materials were located most upstream to minimize multiple scattering effects. The Be, Al, and Cu foils were each 250 μm thick, and the W foils were each 100 μm thick. The foils were

---
[†]Centro Brasileiro de Pesquisas Físicas - Fermi National Accelerator Laboratory - University of Mississippi - Northeastern University - University of Toronto - Tufts University - University of Wisconsin - Yale University

separated by 1.6 mm gaps along the beam direction. The coincident exposure of all targets allowed cancellation of systematic errors associated with beam conditions, experimental deadtime, and relative luminosity. Since the total nuclear interaction length through all the target foils was only 2%, nearly all the beam struck each target foil. More detailed descriptions of the apparatus can be found in the references cited in our previous paper[2].

2. The Data Analysis

The charm mesons are detected by fully reconstructing the decays $D^0 \to K^-\pi^+$, $D^+ \to K^-\pi^+\pi^+$, and charge conjugates. (In this article, reference to a decay implicitly includes the charge conjugate.) To select events with these decays, we required that the particles from the decay form a vertex separated from the interaction point by more than 8σ. Other analysis cuts include: The summed P_T^2 of the decay tracks, with P_T measured relative to the direction of the parent, had to be > 0.5 GeV^2 (0.7 GeV^2) for charged (neutral) decays. The distance between the primary vertex and the line of flight of the parent D, had to be < 80 μm for both charged and neutral decays. Using Cerenkov counters, we excluded identified pions as candidate kaons from charm decay. The resulting invariant mass plots for the two decay channels are shown in Fig. 1. The number of reconstructed decays is 776 ± 35 D^+ and 650 ± 36 D^0 as determined from fits to the invariant mass distributions.

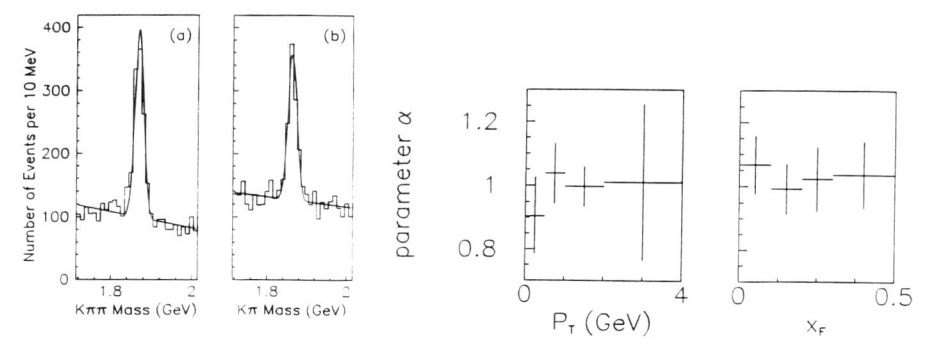

Fig. 1. Invariant mass distributions for (a) D^+ and (b) D^0.

Fig.2. Dependence of the parameter α on P_T and x_F for D^+ and D^0.

3. Results

Using the data sample of Fig. 1, we obtained the relative cross section for D^+ and D^0 combined, in each of our targets. The four data points are well fit by a function of the form A^α, giving $\chi^2/d.o.f.$ of 0.7 with $\alpha = 1.00 \pm 0.05$.

Table 1: Comparison of the values of α measured in this experiment with others using π^- beams.

Expt.	P(beam) (GeV)	detected charm	α	x_F range
E769	250	D^0, D^+	1.00 ± 0.05	> 0.0
WA82	340	D^0, D^+	0.92 ± 0.06	> 0.0
WA78	320	inclusive μ^-, μ^+	0.81 ± 0.05	> 0.2

We studied the size of systematic errors due to uncertainties in the target composition, misidentification of the target material due to primary vertex resolution, attenuation of the beam flux from interactions in the foils, trigger efficiency, detector efficiencies, and signal estimation from fitting the mass plots. We estimate the overall systematic error due to these effects to be ±0.02, which is negligible in comparison with the statistical errors in the data. In the discussion below, we quote only the statistical error in α.

The dependences of α on the transverse momentum (P_T) of the D and the longitudinal momentum fraction (Feynman-x or x_F) are shown in Fig. 2, for the same data set as in Fig. 1. The values of α for D^0 and D^+, separately, are 1.05 ± 0.07 and 0.95 ± 0.06, respectively. The values of α for π^- and π^+, separately, are 1.00 ± 0.05 and 1.03 ± 0.15, Thus, there is no significant dependence of α on the transverse or longitudinal momentum of the D-meson, the type of D-meson (neutral or charged) or the beam polarity.

A comparison of our results with other measurements of α for charm production by pions is shown in Table 1. The measurement of α from WA78[3], based on the inclusive muon spectrum, suggested that the A dependence for charm production was similar to that for the total inelastic cross section. However, our result, together with the measurement from WA82[4], suggests that α is close to 1. This reinforces the picture that charm production and fragmentation are short-range processes and that the nucleon gluon distributions in various nuclei, in the x-range probed by charm production, are the same.

We gratefully acknowledge funding from the U.S. Department of Energy, the U.S. National Science Foundation, the Brazilian Conselho Nacional de Desenvolvimento Científico e Tecnológico, and the National Research Council of Canada.

5. References

1. S. Fredriksson et al., *Phys. Rep.* **144**, 187 (1987).
2. E769 Collaboration, G.A. Alves et al., submitted to Phys. Rev. Lett., Fermilab Pub-92/208 (1992).
3. WA78 Collaboration, H. Cobbaert et al., *Phys. Lett.* **B191**, 456 (1987).
4. WA82 Collaboration, M. Adamovich et al., *Phys. Lett.* **B284**, 453 (1992).

Feynman-x and Transverse Momentum Dependence of $D^{\pm}$, $D^0/\overline{D}^0$, and $D^{*\pm}$ Production in 250 GeV π-N Interactions

Stephen F. Takach [1]
J.W. Gibbs Laboratory, Yale University, 260 Whitney Ave.
New Haven, CT 06511, USA

Representing the Fermilab E769 Collaboration [2]

ABSTRACT

We have measured the differential cross-section with respect to Feynman-x (x_F) and transverse momentum (p_t) for charm meson production using targets of Be, Al, Cu, and W. We obtained our samples for $D^{\pm}$, $D^0/\overline{D}^0$ from our π^- beam data and for $D^{*\pm}$ from both $\pi^{\pm}$ beam data. In the range $0.1 < x_F < 0.7$, the form $(1-x_F)^n$ with $n = 3.9 \pm 0.3$ fits well the $D^{\pm}$, $D^0/\overline{D}^0$ data for $d\sigma/dx_F$. Similarly, for $D^{*\pm}$ we have found a preliminary result of $n = 3.5 \pm 0.3$ over the range $0.1 < x_F < 0.6$. In the lower p_t range, < 2 GeV, the form $\exp(-bp_t^2)$ fits $d\sigma/dp_t^2$ well for $D^{\pm}$, $D^0/\overline{D}^0$, and $D^{*\pm}$. We have found $b(D^{\pm}, D^0/\overline{D}^0) = 1.03 \pm 0.06$ GeV^{-2} and the preliminary result $b(D^{*\pm}) = 0.70 \pm 0.07$ GeV^{-2}. In the higher p_t range, 0.8 to 3.6 GeV, the form $\exp(-b'p_t)$ with $b' = 2.76 \pm 0.08$ GeV^{-1} describes well the $D^{\pm}$, $D^0/\overline{D}^0$ data.

1. Charm Hadroproduction

At leading order (LO) in QCD, only the short-distance processes $gg \to c\bar{c}$ and $q\bar{q} \to c\bar{c}$ contribute to the hadroproduction of charm. At the next-to-leading order (NLO), processes with real and virtual gluon emission also contribute. Nason, Dawson, and Ellis (NDE) [3] have calculated the differential cross sections for charm quarks at NLO. Generally, they find steeply-falling cross sections in x_F and p_t, which are dominated by the gg process at E769's beam energy. Furthermore, their model does not contain any special effects such as leading production or target dependent shapes. Although at NLO the total cross section for charm increases by a factor of roughly 3 over the LO result, the shapes of the differential distributions are nearly identical to the LO results.

E769 has focussed on investigating these and other aspects of charm hadroproduction. In the experiment, we employed a 250 GeV/c beam of $\pi^{\pm}$, $K^{\pm}$, and $p/\bar{p}$, which impinged on 26 foils of Be, Al, Cu, and W. A differential Čerenkov counter and a transition radiation detector identified beam particle species. Downstream of the target, 11 SMD planes comprised our vertexing system. Reference 4 and references therein detail more completely the apparatus. With this spectrometer and a fast data acquisition system, we gathered roughly 170M negative beam and 230M positive beam events. From this large sample of hadroproduced events, E769 has extracted results for the x_F and transverse momentum shapes of the $D^{\pm}$, $D^0/\overline{D}^0$ differential distributions from π^- beam data and preliminary results for the shapes

Beam	Sample	n	b (GeV^{-2})	b' (GeV^{-1})
π^-	$D^\pm, D^0/\overline{D}^0$	3.9 ± 0.3	1.03 ± 0.06	2.66 ± 0.11
π^-	D^- (leading)	3.3 ± 0.5	1.05 ± 0.08	2.67 ± 0.18
π^-	D^+ (nonleading)	4.4 ± 0.5	0.92 ± 0.08	2.55 ± 0.21
$\pi^\pm$	$D^{*\pm}$	3.5 ± 0.3	0.68 ± 0.07	—
$\pi^\pm$	leading $D^{*\pm}$	3.0 ± 0.4	0.57 ± 0.09	—
$\pi^\pm$	nonleading $D^{*\pm}$	4.1 ± 0.6	0.79 ± 0.09	—

Table 1: Differential Cross Section Parameters. Section 3 gives an explanation of the fitting. The fit ranges used to extract the parameters are $0.1 < x_F < 0.7$, $0.0 < p_t^2 < 4.0$ GeV^2, $0.8 < p_t < 2.4$ GeV for $D^\pm, D^0/\overline{D}^0$, and $0.1 < x_F < 0.6$, $0.0 < p_t^2 < 4.0$ GeV^2 for $D^{*\pm}$. $D^{*\pm}$ values are preliminary.

of the $D^{*\pm}$ distributions from $\pi^\pm$ beam data.

2. Signal Extraction

To select our sample of charged and neutral D events, we applied a set of analysis cuts optimized for the kinematics and relatively long lifetime of charm decays. We searched for the all-charged decay modes $D^\pm \to K^\mp \pi^\pm \pi^\pm$ and $D^0/\overline{D}^0 \to K^\mp \pi^\pm$. A forthcoming publication details these cuts more extensively [4]. After fitting the resultant mass histograms with a gaussian signal and a linear background, we find 700 ± 34 $D^\pm$ and 607 ± 41 $D^0/\overline{D}^0$. To obtain a sample of $D^{*\pm}$, we searched for the decay $D^{*\pm} \to \pi^\pm D^0/\overline{D}^0$ by matching a charged pion with a neutral D. We searched in both our $\pi^\pm$ beam data for three decay modes of the neutral D: $D^0/\overline{D}^0 \to K^\mp \pi^\pm$, $D^0/\overline{D}^0 \to K^\mp \pi^\pm \pi^0$, and $D^0/\overline{D}^0 \to K^\mp \pi^\mp \pi^\pm \pi^\pm$. The resultant signals are 243 ± 18 in the $K\pi$ mode, 147 ± 15 in the $K\pi\pi^0$ mode, and 129 ± 15 in the $K3\pi$ mode.

3. Physics Results

To study our acceptance and efficiencies, we produced a sample of Monte Carlo (MC) events using a leading order QCD generator for the $c\bar{c}$ pair, FRITIOF 1.3 for the underlying portion of each event, and JETSET 6.3 for the parton fragmentation. We projected the $D^\pm$ and $D^0/\overline{D}^0$ data signals into bins of x_F, p_t^2, and p_t and the $D^{*\pm}$ data signals into bins of x_F and p_t^2. In each bin of x_F or transverse momentum, we then extracted the signal using a binned maximum likelihood fitter for the mass distribution. In this fit to the data, we fixed the D mass to its known value and the mass resolution according to our MC modelling. We then combined the acceptance corrected numbers of $D^\pm$ and $D^0/\overline{D}^0$ and fit them to the forms: $\frac{d\sigma}{dx_F} \propto (1 - x_F)^n$, $\frac{d\sigma}{dp_t^2} \propto e^{-bp_t^2}$, and $\frac{d\sigma}{dp_t} \propto e^{-b'p_t}$. We fit the $D^{*\pm}$ distributions only to the first two of these forms.

Figure 1 shows the differential cross sections in x_F and p_t for $D^\pm$, $D^0/\overline{D}^0$. In the x_F plot, the theoretical curve is a fit to the NLO distribution,[3] normalized to the data, for *unfragmented* charm quarks of mass 1.5 GeV. The fits to both the data and the theory use the same form and the same range. They yield $n(D^\pm, D^0/\overline{D}^0) = 3.9 \pm 0.3$ and $n_{theory} = 4.25$. The lower curve is the theoretical distribution fragmented with

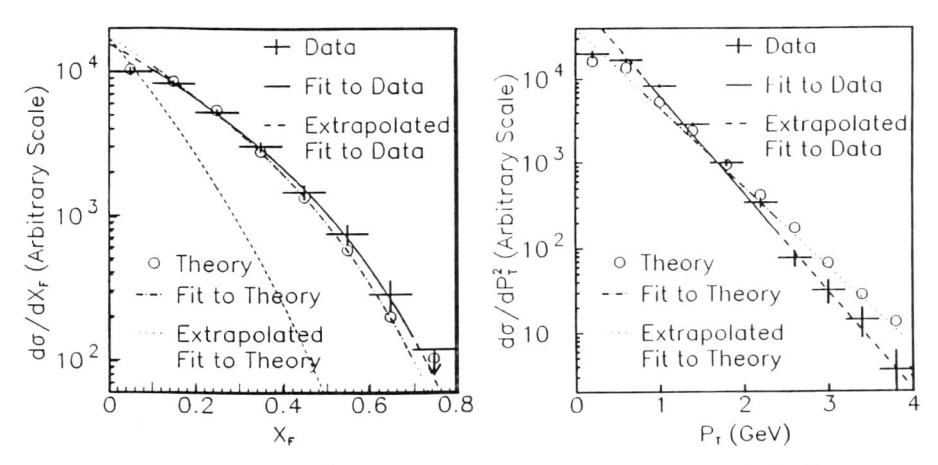

Figure 1: $D^{\pm}$ and $D^0/\overline{D}^0$ x_F and p_t Differential Cross Sections. See text for details.

the Peterson fragmentation function[7]. Given that the theoretical distribution is for unfragmented c-quarks as opposed to mesons, the agreement between the two is surprising and raises the question of what role fragmentation plays in hadroproduction. We found that the form $e^{-b'p_t}$ is better in describing the large p_t behavior of $\frac{d\sigma}{dp_t^2}$ than the form $e^{-bp_t^2}$. The theoretical curve on the p_t distribution is a fit to the LO distribution[5] for unfragmented charm quarks of mass 1.2 GeV. Although the exponential form describes both the theory and the data well, the exponents differ. The fits yield $b'_{theory} = 2.16$ GeV^{-1} and $b' = 2.66 \pm 0.11$ GeV^{-1} for the $D^{\pm}, D^0/\overline{D}^0$ data. We restricted the range of this fit to $0.8 < p_t < 2.4$ GeV for consistency with the smaller subsamples of our data shown in table 1. When fitting over the largest range of significant data points, $0.8 < p_t < 3.6$ GeV, we find $b' = 2.76 \pm 0.08$ GeV^{-1}.

Figure 2 shows preliminary $D^{*\pm}$ differential cross sections in x_F and p_t^2 for the dominant mode in our sample, $D^{*\pm} \to (K^{\mp}\pi^{\pm})\pi^{\pm}$. We find that the shape of the x_F distribution agrees well with that for the $D^{\pm}$, $D^0/\overline{D}^0$ sample. The shape of the p_t^2 distribution, however, is apparently harder than that for the $D^{\pm}$, $D^0/\overline{D}^0$. Table 1 shows some results for the shape parameters from our fits. We report only statistical errors in the table. We have found that the systematic errors are negligible for $D^{\pm}$, $D^0/\overline{D}^0$. Although we are still studying systematic effects for the $D^{*\pm}$ results, we anticipate that they too will be small compared to statistical errors.

Besides comparing with theory, we have also examined the data for target dependence in the shapes and for leading particle effects. Our sample of 1300 $D^{\pm}$, $D^0/\overline{D}^0$ was large enough to divide into subsamples for each target material without compromising too much the statistical quality of our results. If short-distance processes govern the hadroproduction of charm and if the gluon distributions are the same between different nuclei, then the x_F, p_t, and p_t^2 distributions should not display any dependence on atomic mass. In fact, we do not observe such effects. We also studied our $D^{\pm}$ and $D^{*\pm}$ data for leading effects by comparing D^+ to D^- and leading-D^* to nonleading-D^*. We found $\Delta n_{\pm} = 1.1 \pm 0.7$ and a preliminary $\Delta n_* = 1.1 \pm 0.7$ for $D^{\pm}$ and for $D^{*\pm}$, respectively. These results disagree with NA27's report of a large

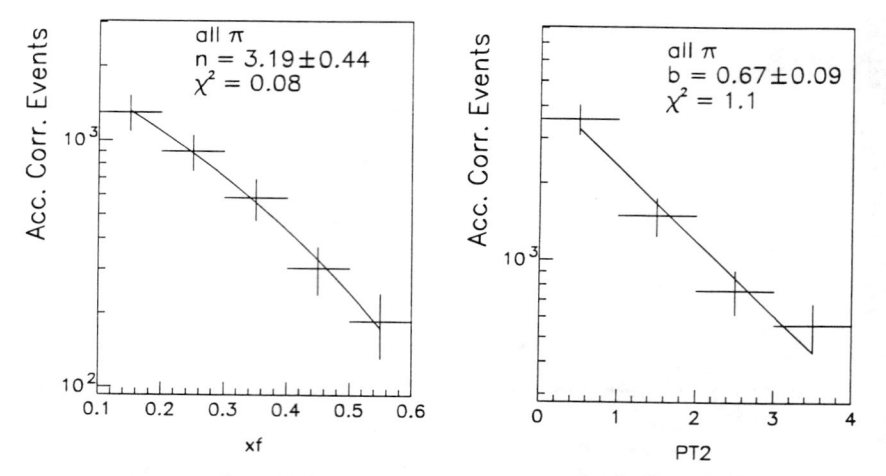

Figure 2: Preliminary $D^{*\pm} \to (K^{\mp}\pi^{\pm})\pi^{\pm}$ Differential Cross Sections in x_F and p_t^2. See text for details.

leading effect of $\Delta n = 6.1 \pm 1.6$ in its D meson data.[6] Although leading effects in the shapes of the differential distributions are not significant in our data, we further investigate the total asymmetry $A(x,y) = [\sigma(x) - \sigma(y)] / [\sigma(x) + \sigma(y)]$ for states x, y. In this expression, $\sigma(x) \propto$ the total cross section for state x, acceptance corrected as a function of x_F for $x_F > 0$. We find $A(D^-, D^+) = 0.18 \pm 0.06$ and preliminarily $A(\text{leading } D^{*\pm}, \text{nonleading } D^{*\pm}) = 0.07 \pm 0.05$.

4. Acknowledgements

I thank my fellow-collaborators on E769 for all their efforts. I especially thank Sandra Amato (CBPF), Jussara Miranda (CBPF), and Ali Rafatian (U. of Mississippi) for providing the latest $D^{*\pm}$ results for this talk. This research was supported by the U.S. Department of Energy, the U.S. National Science Foundation, The Brazilian Conselho Nacional de Desenvolvimento Científico e Tecnológico, and the National Research Council of Canada.

5. References

1. Address: MS 219, WH11W, Fermi National Accelerator Lab, Batavia, IL 60510
2. CBPF (Rio de Janeiro), FNAL, U. of Mississippi, Northeastern U., U. of Toronto, Tufts U., U. of Wisconsin, Yale U.
3. Nason, P., Dawson, S., Ellis, R.K., *Nuclear Physics* B327, 1989, p. 49.
4. Alves, G.A., *et al.* (E769 Collaboration), "Feynman-x and Transverse Momentum Dependence of $D^{\pm}$ and $D^0/\overline{D}^0$ Production in 250 GeV π^--Nucleon Interactions", Fermilab-Pub-92/208-E, to be published in *Physical Review Letters*.
5. Ellis, K., in proc. of *Les Rencontres de Physique de la Vallée d'Aoste: Results and Perspectives in Particle Physics*, M. Greco, ed., 1987, p. 187.
6. Aguilar-Benitez, M., *et al.*, *Physics Letters* 161B, 1985, p. 400.
7. Bortoletto, D., *Physical Review* D37, 1988, p. 1719.

A Study of Beauty and Charm Production in 250 GeV π^+-nucleon Interactions Using Semi-electronic Decays

Chris L. Darling
Physics Department, Yale University, P. O. Box 6666
New Haven, CT 06511

Representing the Fermilab E769 Collaboration

Abstract

Results from an analysis of high transverse momentum(p_T) electrons are presented in which a two dimensional distribution of electron candidates in p_T^2 and impact parameter to the primary vertex is fit in order to extract the total charm and beauty production cross sections per nucleon. The preliminary results are $\sigma_{b\bar{b}} < 97 nb$ @ $90\% C.L.(stat + syst)$, and $\sigma_{c\bar{c}} = 13.5 \pm 2.3(stat) \pm 1.4(syst) \mu b$ assuming effective semi-electronic branching ratios of 0.222 for charm and .214 beauty. The systematic errors do not include the uncertainties in these branching ratios.

The few existing measurements of the beauty hadroproduction cross section at fixed target energies are based on the observation of opposite sign high transverse momentum(p_T) muons[1, 2]. An alternative method is presented here, based on the impact parameter(ip) distribution of single high p_T electrons. The E769 spectrometer[3], used for this measurement, consists of silicon microstrip detectors and drift chambers for tracking, two magnets for momentum measurement, and segmented electro-magnetic(EM_{cal}) and hadronic(HAD_{cal}) calorimeters. A transition radiation detector distinguishes beam pions and protons.

We analyze the subset of E769 data recorded with a trigger requiring a total transverse energy($E_{T\ TOT}$) of at least 4.5 GeV, and at least 0.5 GeV of E_T deposited in one EM_{cal} strip of the non-bend view. With this trigger, 15 million π^+ interactions were recorded. Electrons are identified offline from three tests using calorimeter information. First, the track momentum and its calorimeter energy are compared. Second, the amount of energy deposited in the EM_{cal} and HAD_{cal} are compared. Finally, the transverse shower shape in the EM_{cal} is required to be consistent with that of an electron shower. From a study of $K_s \to \pi^+\pi^-$ decays and $\gamma \to e^+e^-$ conversions in data we determine the electron identification efficiency and the pion misidentification probability to be 0.19 and 0.001 respectively.

The analysis sample consists of all tracks passing the electron identification cut in events with at least three reconstructed vertices which fall into the two dimensional track parameter space defined by $2 \leq p_T^2 \leq 10 (GeV/c)^2$ and $50 \leq ip < 1000 \mu m$. After these cuts are imposed, 358 tracks remain.

The data are fit with three terms: one each for electrons from charm, electrons from beauty, and background tracks. The binned maximum likelihood method is used. All of the parameters which describe the p_T and ip dependence(called shape parameters) are fixed in the fit, while the amplitudes of the three terms are allowed to vary. In a MC simulation, charm hadrons are generated with the measured E769

x_F and p_T distributions taken from exclusive decays of D mesons[3]. Beauty hadrons are generated with the x_F and p_T distributions of b quarks predicted by perturbative QCD[4, 5]. It is from these simulations that the shape parameters for electrons from charm and beauty are taken. The shape parameters for the background are taken from a sample of minimum bias events in the data, as there is no MC model that can reliably predict the p_T distribution in the range required for this analysis. Possible sources of background are misidentified pions, electrons from photon conversions and strange particle decays.

The breakdown of the fit for the 358 tracks is shown in column 1 of Table 1. Since the beauty signal is not significant, the fit was repeated without the beauty term(see column 2 of Table 1). For the fit including a beauty term, Figure 1. shows the data and fit projected onto the p_T^2 and ip axes. The production fractions of different particle species used in this analysis are shown in Table 2. The semi-electronic branching fractions used are nearly identical to the current PDG values. The preliminary cross section results are given in Table 1. Note in the case of beauty that an upper limit is quoted as well. The systematic errors quoted here only include the uncertainties in the shape parameters. The uncertainty in the production fractions shown in Table 2 are not included.

Table 1: Preliminary results.

Item	From Fit With Beauty Term	From Fit Without Beauty Term
Background Tracks	235^{+23}_{-22}	242^{+23}_{-22}
Electrons from Charm	80^{+24}_{-23}	116^{+20}_{-19}
Electrons from Beauty	43^{+20}_{-18}	—
χ^2/DOF of fit	1.19	1.21
$\sigma_{b\bar{b}/nucl.} \times B(b\bar{b} \to eX)$	$12 \pm 5(stat) \pm 2(syst)nb$	—
$B(b\bar{b} \to eX)$	.214(no error estimate)	—
$\sigma_{b\bar{b}/nucl.}$	$56 \pm 23(stat) \pm 9(syst)nb$	—
Limit on $\sigma_{b\bar{b}/nucl.}$	$< 97nb@90\%C.L.$	—
$\sigma_{c\bar{c}/nucl.} \times B(c\bar{c} \to eX)$	$2.0 \pm .6(stat)^{+.3}_{-.2}(syst)\mu b$	$3.0 \pm .5(stat) \pm .3(syst)\mu b$
$B(c\bar{c} \to eX)$	.222(no error estimate)	.222(no error estimate)
$\sigma_{c\bar{c}/nucl.}$	$9.0 \pm 2.7(stat)^{+1.4}_{-.9}(syst)\mu b$	$13.5 \pm 2.3(stat) \pm 1.4(syst)\mu b$

Table 2: Assumed production fractions of hadrons.

Hadron	Fraction	Hadron	Fraction
D^0	59 %	B^0	46 %
D^+	29 %	B^+	44 %
D_s^+	9 %	B_s^0	7 %
Λ_c^+	3 %	Λ_b^0	3 %

Table 3: Data from references 6-9.

Experiment	$\sigma(\pi^- N \to D, x_F > 0), \mu b$
E769, 250GeV	$10.6 \pm .4(stat)$
NA32, 200GeV	$6.7^{+.9}_{-.8}(stat + syst)$
NA32, 230GeV	$9.5 \pm 1.9(stat + syst)$
NA27, 360GeV	$15.8 \pm 2.7(stat)$
E653, 600GeV	$30.7 \pm 5.4(stat + syst)$

The charm cross section reported here is consistent with the cross section for D meson production for $x_F > 0$ measured in this experiment and others, which are shown in Table 3. Although the method employed here does not provide sensitivity to the beauty cross section at fixed target energies, this method should prove useful at hadron colliders.

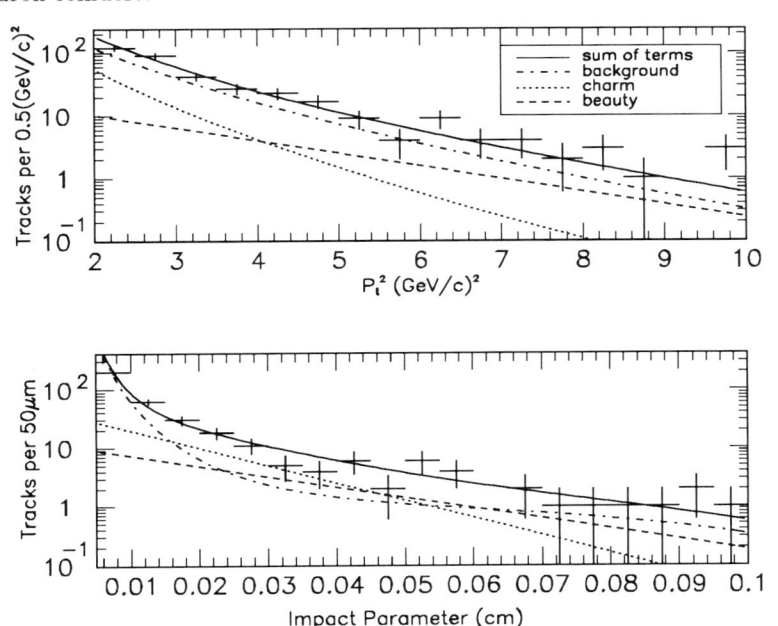

Figure 1. p_T^2 and ip distribution from data. The curves are for the fit projections. The legend applies to both plots.

1. P. Bordalo, et.al., Z. Phys. **C39** (1988) 7.
2. M. G. Cantanesi, et.al., Phys. Lett. **B202** (1988) 453.
3. G. A. Alves, et.al., The E769 Collaboration, Phys. Rev. Lett., to be published.
4. R. K. Ellis and C. Quigg, FNAL Report N. FN-445 (1987).
5. P. Nason, S. Dawson and R. K. Ellis, Nucl. Phys. **B327** (1988) 49.
6. Preliminary result.
7. S. Barlag, The NA32 Collaboration, et.al., Z. Phys., **C49** (1991) 555.
8. M. Aguilar-Benitez,The NA27 Collaboration, et.al., Z. Phys., **C31** (1986) 491.
9. K. Kodama, The E653 Collaboration, et.al., Phys. Lett., **B284** (1992) 461.

MEASURING CHARM AND BOTTOM QUARK MASSES

THOMAS J. WEILER
Department of Physics & Astronomy, Vanderbilt University
Nashville, TN 37235 USA

and

KRASOOS GHAFOORI-TABRIZI
Department of Physics, University of Shahid Beheshty
Eween, Tehran 19834 Iran,
and Center for Theoretical Physics and Mathematics
Atomic Energy Organization of Iran, Tehran, Iran

ABSTRACT

The meaning and the extraction of heavy quark masses are discussed. A simple production model is presented which incorporates the running of the heavy quark mass into perturbative calculations. The model offers the possibilities of (i) understanding the differing charmed mass values extracted from different experiments, (ii) determining the short-distance mass relevent to quark mass matrix and mixing angle studies, and (iii) determining the long-distance charm mass, which determines the charm quark threshold and sensitively affects the extraction of $\sin^2 \theta_w$. Threshold and forward angle production offer the best possibilities to test the model and extract meaningful charm/bottom masses.

1. Quark Masses and QCD

This year, the Particle Data Group (PDG) introduced into the *Review of Particle Properties* a "Quark Table," in which they list values for the quark masses[1]. The d-, u-, and s-quark mass values are "current-quark masses" extracted from pion and kaon masses using chiral symmetry. The c- and b-quark mass values are potential model masses estimated from charmonium, bottomonium, D, and B masses; they are not the running masses derivable from the QCD Lagrangian. Moreover, the masses are poorly determined: m_c is given a range of 1.3 to 1.7 GeV, and m_b is given a range of 4.7 to 5.3 GeV. The PDG say that "since the subject of quark masses is controversial, the purpose of the table is to provoke discussion."

Experiments on quark scattering and production can provide the PDG with running QCD masses, with the running scale provided by the subprocess invariants $\hat{s}$, $\hat{t}$, and $\hat{u}$. Because of the running of QCD, one expects to find (i) scattering quark masses smaller than the potential model masses listed above, and (ii) extracted mass values that change with scale and with reaction channel. Point (i) expresses the fact tha QCD is asymptotically free. At large scale one expects a measured mass to be the bare current mass in the electroweak Lagrangian; this mass originates from the Higgs mechanism and has nothing to do with QCD. Point (ii) reflects running, but also the fact that different reaction channels have different intrinsic scales.

For example, in Drell–Yan or e^+e^- production, the quark lines are external and the quarks are constituent–like; while in heavy quark production via boson–boson fusion there is an internal quark line and the associated quark is a short–distance, off–shell (by $\hat{t} - m_Q$) current quark. Reactions with t– or u–channel quark exchange will yield lighter quark mass values than reactions without.

Unfortunately, the extraction of scattering masses is necessarily model–dependent, for "hadronization" or "fragmentation" of the final state quarks is inherently nonperturbative (hadrons and jets do not appear in the QCD Lagrangian), and nonperturbative QCD must be modelled rather than calculated.

2. Models for Heavy Hadron Production

One way to view the model dependence of the perturbative/nonperturbative QCD interface is to ask, at what stage in the calculation do nonperturbative effects enter? In conventional QCD phenomenology, a common mass parameter is used everywhere in the Feynman diagrams and hadronization is added on in a classical fashion. The charmed mass value that emerges from fits to hadroproduction data (where gluon–gluon fusion is dominant) appears to us to be too large. Fits with lowest order QCD give $m_c = 1.2\ GeV$, which is fine, but fits with loop-corrected QCD give $m_c = 1.5\ GeV$, which is as large as the mass determined from potential models! Furthermore, in a one–mass model there is no possibility to understand the different mass values that seem to emerge from different reaction channels. And finally, there is no possibility for running the mass into the nonperturbative region where the running is greatest.

Thus, there is motivation to look at other models for the perturbative/nonperturbative interface. One simple approach is to admit the heavier, dressed, constituent mass in the phase space limits. A more motivated two–mass model has recently been introduced by us[2]. It models running of the heavy quark mass at the Feynman diagram level: the mass in quark propagators is identified with the short–distance mass arising from electroweak symmetry breakdown, and the mass in the "free" Dirac spinors and in the phase space limits is identified with the long–distance/constituent mass. Specifically, quark propagators are $(\not{p} - m_{SD})^{-1}$, while quark spinors satisfy the Dirac equations $(\not{p} - m_{LD})u(p, m_{LD}) = 0$ and $(\not{p} + m_{LD})v(p, m_{LD}) = 0$. SD and LD denote short and long distance, respectively. An immediate prediction is that charm-masses extracted from reaction channels dominated by graphs with (without) internal charm-quark lines will have smaller (larger) values.

The LD constituent mass in the Dirac spinor encompasses some of the nonperturbative physics of color bleaching, fragmentation, and hadronization. It may also be viewed as arising from a mass insertion on external quark legs due to interactions with QCD vacuum condensates. As such, it is a simple representation of highly complicated physics. The successes of the nonrelativistic quark model in describing static hadron properties argue that constituent quarks do behave like Dirac particles, a result supported by current algebra[3].

Assigning different masses to internal and external lines creates nonconserved currents, which break gauge invariance. This becomes an issue in higher order calculations where internal gauge boson lines are present. The breaking of gauge invariance can be avoided by retaining $(\not{p}-m_{SD})u(p, m_{LD}) = 0$ and $(\not{p}+m_{SD})v(p, m_{LD}) = 0$. Then the LD mass shows up only in the relations $u(p, m_{LD})\bar{u}(p, m_{LD}) = \not{p} + m_{LD}$ and $v(p, m_{LD})\bar{v}(p, m_{LD}) = \not{p} - m_{LD}$, and in the phase space limits. Alternatively, one may note that when nonperturbative effects turn on, the physics that results looks nothing like any known extrapolation from the QCD Lagrangian. Hence it may make sense to allow nonperturbative effects to break gauge invariance in any perturbative calculation, with the faith that an all orders calculation will produce the exact gauge invariant physics. (Just this philosophy is adopted in some versions of light–cone QCD.) This point of view motivates calculating in physical gauges, where unitarity is manifest. Further discussion on this issue is contained in ref.2.

3. Experimental Comparison of Heavy Hadron QCD Models

In ref.2 it is shown that m_{SD} determines the peak magnitude and the asymptotic magnitude of the subprocess $gg \to c\bar{c}$ cross section, while m_{LD} determines the threshold energy. Thus, in principle both masses are measureable. The running-mass model gets both the threshold and the rate correct with $m_{SD} \sim 1.2$ GeV and $m_{LD} \gtrsim 1.5$ GeV. To quantitatively distinguish between conventional perturbative QCD and this model, it may be necessary to compare across reaction channels; we have mentioned that this model predicts a lighter charm mass only for those reactions having a t- and/or u-channel charmed line. It may also be possible to distinguish between the two models by examing a single reaction cross section near threshold where the greatest differences in shapes occurs[2], or near the forward scattering angle, where $\hat{t}$ most closely approaches the SD charmed-mass pole. It may be possible to experimentally determine $\hat{s}$ and $\hat{t}$ (or θ_{cm}) on an event by event basis, through final state measurements. Eventually, photon-photon charm-production data will become available; in this reaction, $\hat{s}$ and $\hat{t}$ are measureable, and there is no dependence on an initial state gluon distribution. The forward scattering peak is quite sensitive to the charmed mass[2].

We encourage charm and bottom production experimenters to analyze data with the model discussed here. If it turns out that this model and the conventional QCD model both fit the data and yield differing charm masses, then available experiments are insufficient to quantitatively determine the short–distance charm mass. But if a detailed study should show a preference for one model over the other, then Nature will have spoken, and we will have listened.

4. References

1. Particle Data Group, *Phys. Rev.* **D45** (1992) II.4.
2. K. Ghafoori–Tabrizi and T. J. Weiler, *Phys. Rev.* **D**, to appear Dec. 1, 1992.
3. S. Weinberg, *Phys. Rev. Lett.* **65** (1990) 1181.

NEUTRAL STRANGE-PARTICLE PRODUCTION IN NEUTRINO-NEON CHARGED-CURRENT INTERACTIONS AT THE FERMILAB TEVATRON

M. KALELKAR (for the E632 Collaboration[*])
Department of Physics and Astronomy
Rutgers University
New Brunswick, NJ 08903

[*]E632 Collaboration: Berkeley, Birmingham, Brussels, CERN, Chandigarh, Fermilab, Hawaii, IHEP Serpukhov, Illinois Tech., Imperial Coll., ITEP Moscow, Jammu, Munich (MPI), Moscow State Univ., Oxford, Rutgers, Saclay, Stevens, Tufts

ABSTRACT

A study has been made of K^0, Λ, and $\bar{\Lambda}$ production in charged-current neutrino interactions at higher energy ($<E_\nu> = 150$ GeV) than any previous study. The experiment was done at Fermilab using the 15-ft. bubble chamber, and the data sample consists of 968 observed neutral strange particles. Production rates per event have been measured to be $(40.8\pm4.8)\%$ for K^0, $(12.7\pm1.4)\%$ for Λ, and $(1.5\pm0.5)\%$ for $\bar{\Lambda}$; they are significantly higher than in lower-energy experiments. The dependence of rates on event variables has been measured, and single-particle distributions obtained as well. Comparisons have been made with previous experiments.

1. Introduction and Experimental Procedure

There have been a number of published results[1] on neutral strange particle production in charged current (CC) ν_μ and $\bar{\nu}_\mu$ interactions. However, most of these experiments have been at average neutrino energies of about 50 GeV. Here we report results from an experiment (E632) at the Fermilab Tevatron featuring higher neutrino energies than any previous work. The quadrupole triplet train was used for the beam, which produced ν and $\bar{\nu}$ CC events in a ratio of 6 to 1, and with mean energies of 150 GeV and 110 GeV respectively.

The detector for E632 was the Fermilab 15-ft. bubble chamber filled with a neon-hydrogen mixture. CC events were selected by requiring a muon identified in the External Muon Identifier (EMI),[2] the muon's momentum exceeding 5 GeV/c, and the event's total hadronic mass exceeding 2 GeV. Vees were required to make constrained fits to the event vertex, and to be at least 1 cm away. Vee vertices also had to be at least 20 cm from the chamber wall. Fit ambiguities were resolved by comparing relative probabilities and making selections so as to produce an isotropic K_s decay angular distribution.[3]

A total of 968 vees comprised the final sample. The numbers of K_s, Λ, and $\bar\Lambda$ were 502, 285, and 27 respectively from 6263 ν CC events, and the corresponding numbers from 1115 $\bar\nu$ CC events were 93, 57, and 4.

2. Production Rates

To determine inclusive production rates, the vees were weighted for random scan loss, geometric detection efficiency, loss due to interaction before decay, loss at small flight times, energetic vee loss, and Λ loss due to low-momentum decay π^-. Average experimental weights were 1.87 for K_s, 1.99 for Λ, and 2.56 for $\bar\Lambda$. An additional weight for decay branching ratio was then also applied, and the fully corrected average multiplicities per ν CC event are 0.408±0.048 for K^o, 0.127±0.014 for Λ, and 0.015±0.005 for $\bar\Lambda$. The corresponding rates per $\bar\nu$ CC event are 0.454±0.078 for K^o, 0.118±0.019 for Λ, and 0.010±0.007 for $\bar\Lambda$. (K^o includes $K^o + \bar K^o$). The quoted errors include statistical errors as well as the uncertainties in calculating each of the correction factors, and the uncertainty in the ambiguity resolution algorithm. The ratio of Λ to K^o production is 0.31±0.05 for ν, and 0.26±0.06 for $\bar\nu$.

3. Differential Rates

Fig. 1 shows the K^o and Λ production rates as a function of neutrino energy. For comparison, published results from previous experiments are also shown. For $E_\nu < 100$ GeV, our results are consistent with these older results. Above 100 GeV, however, where there are no previous measurements, we observe a significant increase in neutral strange particle production, especially for the K^o.

To obtain information on production mechanisms, we have examined various single-particle distributions. There is significant production of K^o at higher values of rapidity than in previous experiments; the asymmetry between the numbers of forward (F) and backward (B) K^o is A = (F-B)/(F+B) = 0.35±0.02, which is appreciably greater than the value of 0.16±0.02 reported by the highest-statistics previous experiment.[4] The Λ is mainly produced in the target fragmentation region, although there is some central production as well. The forward-backward asymmetry is A = -0.47±0.03, compared to A = -0.71±0.02 for Ref. 4.

Fig. 2 shows the ratio of K^o to π^- normalized rapidity distributions. The π^- is believed to be almost exclusively produced centrally in ν CC interactions, because it does not contain the u quark which is in the current jet. The K^o/π^- ratio in Fig. 2 unambiguously indicates enhanced production of K^o as the rapidity increases. In the very forward direction, about one-quarter of the particles might be kaons.

This work was supported in part by the U.S. Dep't. of Energy and the National Science Foundation, and by the U.K. Science and Energy Research Council.

4. References

1. The most recent paper, which includes a list of all previous ones, is S. Willocq et al., Z. Phys. C 53, 207 (1992).
2. Details about the EMI are given in V. Jain et al., Phys. Rev. D 41, 2057 (1990).
3. For more details about the event selection criteria, see D. DeProspo, Ph.D. Thesis, Rutgers University, 1991.
4. N.J. Baker et al., Phys. Rev. D 34, 1251 (1986).

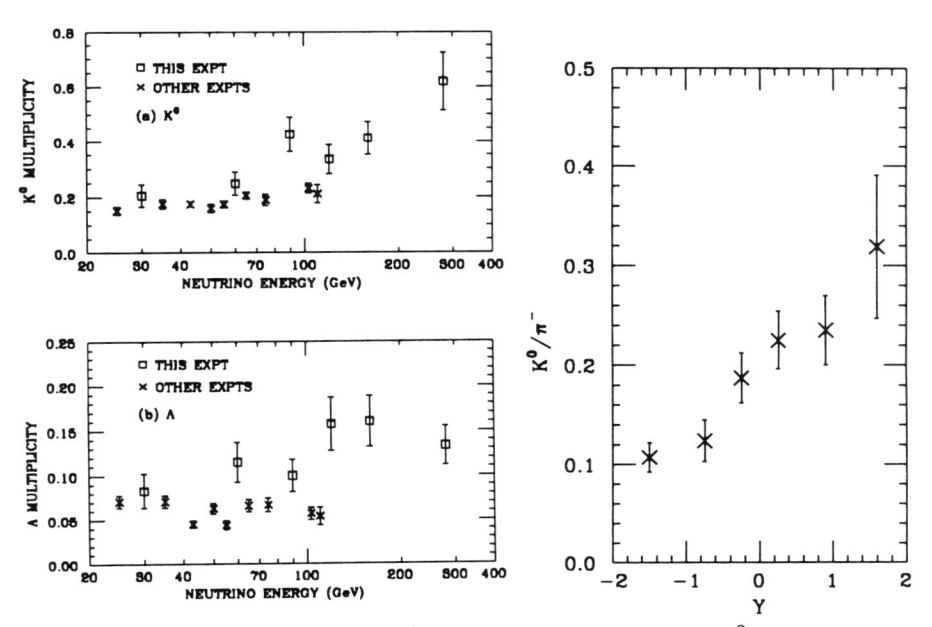

Figure 1. Average multiplicities of (a) K^0 and (b) Λ as a function of neutrino energy.

Figure 2. Ratio of K^0 to π^- normalized rapidity distributions.

EVIDENCE FOR TWO $J^P = 2^-$ STRANGE MESON STATES IN THE $K_2(1770)$ REGION DECAYING TO $K^-\omega$ [1]

The LASS E135 Group [2]

represented by

D. ASTON

Stanford Linear Accelerator Center, Stanford, California 94309, U.S.A.

ABSTRACT

Evidence is presented for two $J^P = 2^-$ strange mesons; one at ~ 1.77 and the other at ~ 1.82 GeV/c^2. These states have been observed in a partial wave analysis of the $K^-\omega$ system in the reaction $K^-p \to K^-\pi^+\pi^-\pi^0 p$ where the strange mesons decay into $K^-\omega$ and the ω then decays to $\pi^+\pi^-\pi^0$. The data set contains $\sim 10^5$ $K^-\omega p$ events at 11GeV/c taken with the LASS spectrometer at SLAC.

1. Introduction

Evidence for the quark model is very strong, but the correct $q\bar{q}$ model assignment of all the known mesons is far from clear, and a number of states are experimentally "missing," even in the low spin multiplets. The strange meson spectrum is the best understood of any $q\bar{q}$ system but, even there, the suggested assignments of the Particle Data Group[1] show that the expected level structure is only complete for the $L = 0$ and $L = 1$ ground states. Completing the D-wave ($L = 2$) singlet and triplet levels would sharpen comparison of the experimental data with the models considerably,[2] particularly for the spin-dependent forces.

In this paper, we present evidence for two strange 2^- states in the $K_2(1770)$ region. These results are taken from a high-statistics study of the $K\omega$ system produced in the reaction

$$K^-p \to K^-\pi^+\pi^-\pi^0 p \qquad (1)$$

at 11GeV/c. The data were obtained with the Large Aperture Superconducting Solenoid (LASS) spectrometer at SLAC, which is described in detail elsewhere.[3] Since the LASS spectrometer was not equipped with a photon detector, the π^0 in the final state is not seen directly, but is reconstructed in the missing π^0 channel. The $K^-\omega p$ sample of $\sim 10^5$ events obtained in this experiment is at least 25 times larger than that obtained in any previous experiment.

2. Data and Analysis

The $\pi^+\pi^-\pi^0$ mass spectrum of Figure 1 shows a clear ω signal, with signal to background ratio about one to one in the signal region (0.72–0.84 GeV/c^2). It is clear from the Dalitz plot (not shown) that the high-mass $K^-\omega$ region overlaps with

---

[1] Work supported by Department of Energy contract DE-AC03-76SF00515; the National Science Foundation under grant Nos. PHY82-09144, PHY85-13808, and the Japan-US Cooperative Research Project on High-Energy Physics.
[2] SLAC, Nagoya University, University of Cincinnati and, INS Tokyo. A complete list of the authors can be found in Reference 4.

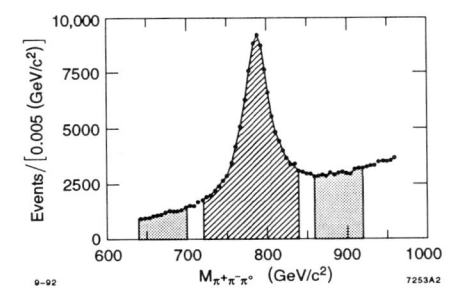

Figure 1: The $\pi^+\pi^-\pi^0$ invariant mass distribution; the signal region is diagonally lined while the background region is shaded.

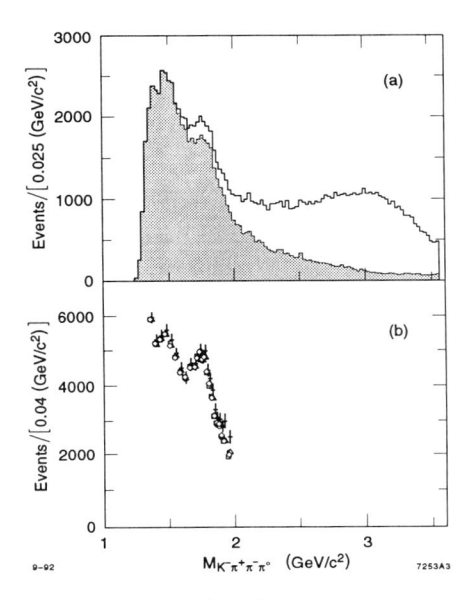

Figure 2: The $K^-\pi^+\pi^-\pi^0$ invariant mass distribution for events with $0.1 < |t'| < 2.0 (\text{GeV/c})^2$; (a) the unshaded curve contains all events that satisfy $0.72 < M_{3\pi} < 0.84$ GeV/c^2 while the shaded portion contains events with $M_{p\omega} > 2.28$ and $M_{pK} > 2.0$ GeV/c^2; (b) the background-subtracted and acceptance-corrected mass distribution; the points with error bars are the measured values and the other points are the values obtained in the PWA fit discussed in the text.

substantial production of several baryon resonances, so events with $M_{p\omega} < 2.28$ or $M_{pK} < 2.0$ GeV/c^2 are eliminated. The $K^-\pi^+\pi^-\pi^0$ effective mass distribution in the ω region (Fig. 2(a)) shows peaks in the $K^-\omega$ threshold region and in the region around 1.75 GeV/c^2. The shaded histogram shows the events with the baryon resonance region removed. Most of the high mass $K^-\omega$ events lie in the overlap region and are removed by this cut.

The partial wave analysis (PWA), more details of which can be found elsewhere,[4] is performed using joint decay spherical-harmonic moments in the $K^-\omega$ Gottfried-Jackson frame and the ω rest frame, using the normal to the decay plane as the analyser. The $\pi^+\pi^-\pi^0$ mass spectrum shown in Fig. 1 contains a significant background under the ω peak region (0.72–0.84 GeV/c^2). Each moment is background subtracted using the ω sideband regions indicated (0.64–0.70 GeV/c^2 and 0.86–0.92 GeV/c^2) and acceptance corrected, after which the partial waves for J^P of the $K^-\omega$ system up to 3^- are determined.

The background and acceptance corrected $K^-\omega$ mass distribution obtained is shown in Fig. 2(b). The main features are similar to those observed for the uncorrected data. There is a strong peak at threshold, and a large bump in the 1.7 to 1.8 GeV/c^2 region, with some evidence for a smaller structure around 1.5 GeV/c^2.

3. The Partial Wave Structure

The low mass $K^-\omega$ region is dominated by 1^+ waves (not shown), while the mass bump around 1.75 GeV/c^2 is dominantly 2^-. Figure 3 shows the incoherently summed intensity of all the 2^- waves. There is a large and rather broad bump centered around 1.75 GeV/c^2. The much smaller $K^-\omega$ decays of the leading $K_2^*(1430)$ (not shown) and the $K_3^*(1780)$ are also observed with branching ratios which are consistent with predictions from SU(3). Figure 4 shows the real and imaginary parts of the PWA amplitudes for the $J^P = 2^-$ and 3^- waves that are significant in the 1.75 GeV/c^2 region. In addition to the bump in the 3^- amplitude corresponding to $K_3^*(1780)$ production, there is a substantial and rather complicated structure in the different 2^- amplitudes. However, this structure can be explained in a straightforward manner as follows: first, the 3^- amplitudes are fit to a single Breit-Wigner resonance model to define a phase reference in the 1750 MeV/c^2 mass region; then the 2^- and 3^- amplitudes are fit simultaneously with their relative phases and magnitudes as free parameters. Two different

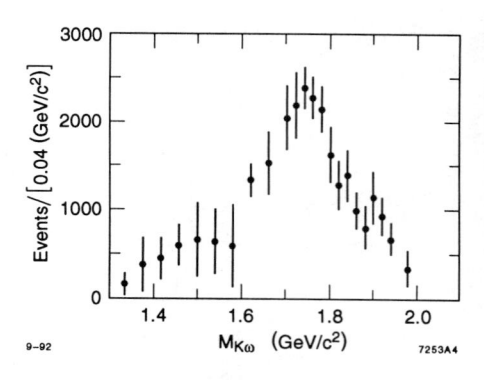

Figure 3: The summed intensities of the 2^- waves.

models are compared: (1) that the 2^- waves observed in the 1750 mass region come from a single resonance and; (2) that they result from two interfering resonances. The dotted curves in Fig. 4 show the fit results of hypothesis (1). The fitted mass and width of the 2^- resonance are 1728 ± 7 MeV/c^2 and 221 ± 22 MeV/c^2, respectively. The χ^2 is 128.9 for 116 degrees of freedom. The one-resonance fit does not reproduce the 2^-1^+F wave at all well. Moreover, the dip at ~ 1.84 GeV/c^2 in the $Re(2^-0^+P)$ and the tail of $Re(2^-0^+F)$ are not well represented by the fit.

On the other hand, the fit results of hypothesis (2) represented by the solid curves in Fig. 4 reproduce all of the amplitudes very well and provide a significantly better fit to the data with a χ^2 of 70.6 for 110 degrees of freedom. The fitted masses of the two resonances are 1773±8 and 1816±13 MeV/c^2 and the fitted widths are 186±14 and 276±35 MeV/c^2, respectively. In this model, the 2^-1^+F wave is almost entirely the higher mass resonance, but the other amplitudes contain rather large contributions from both resonances, and overall, each resonance is observed with nearly equal strength into P and F waves. The χ^2 difference is almost 60 units between the one and two resonance models, which is a nominal "Gaussian" significance level for the second resonance of more than 7σ. In fact, since the PWA typically has a number of nearby solutions, the error bars shown and used in the fit tend to be overestimated compared to Normal errors. Thus, the absolute values of the χ^2 for these fits, the difference between the models, and the significance of the second resonance in the fit, will all tend to be underestimated. Clearly, the data strongly prefer the model with two 2^- resonances.

4. Summary

A partial wave analysis of a high-statistics sample of $\sim 10^5 K^-\omega p$ events provides very good evidence for two 2^- strange resonances with masses around 1773 and 1816 MeV/c^2. This is the only $q\bar{q}$ D-wave spectrum with good candidates for all ground state singlet and triplet levels. The singlet/triplet classification of these states is unclear since strange mesons are not eigenstates of charge conjugation C, and the experimental states can therefore be mixed (as are the $^1P_1$ and $^3P_1$ strange states). It is interesting that Godfrey and Isgur[2] predict masses of 1780 and 1810 MeV/c^2 for the unmixed $^1D_2$ and $^3D_2$ states respectively, remarkably close to the

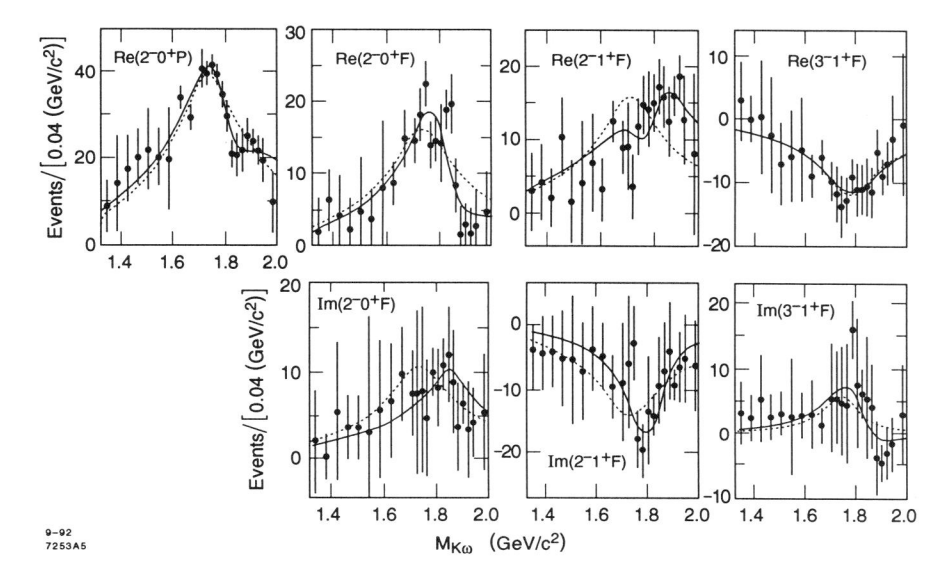

Figure 4: The real and imaginary parts of the $K^-\omega$ 2^- and 3^- amplitudes; the lines show the results of the fits described in the text.

experimental values. Kokowski and Isgur[5] also predict that the pure states are essentially decoupled, with the lower mass state decaying mostly to P-wave and the higher mass state to F-wave. Experimentally, production can complicate matters, but the 2^-1^+F wave is explained as mostly the higher mass state, as predicted. On the other hand, both resonances contribute significantly to the other P and F-wave amplitudes and, overall, the resonances appear with roughly equal total strengths in P and F waves.

5. References

1. K. Hikasa et al., *Phys. Rev.* **D45** (1992).
2. See, for example, S. Godfrey and N. Isgur, *Phys. Rev.* **D32** (1985) 189.
3. D. Aston et al., *SLAC-REP-298* (1986).
4. D. Aston et al., *SLAC-PUB-5634* (1991); also see the Ph.D. thesis of Y. Kwon (in preparation, to be published as a SLAC report).
5. R. Kokowski and N. Isgur, *Phys. Rev.* **D35** (1987) 907.

MEASUREMENT OF THE STRANGE SEA CONTENT OF THE NUCLEON BY CCFR

A.O. BAZARKO, C.G. ARROYO, K.T. BACHMANN, T. BOLTON, C. FOUDAS,
B.J. KING, W.C. LEFMANN, W.C. LEUNG, S.R. MISHRA, E. OLTMAN, P.Z. QUINTAS,
S.A. RABINOWITZ, F.J. SCIULLI, W.G. SELIGMAN, M.H. SHAEVITZ;[a] F.S. MERRITT,
M.J. OREGLIA, B.A. SCHUMM;[b] R.H. BERNSTEIN, F. BORCHERDING, H.E. FISK,
M.J. LAMM, W. MARSH, K.W.B. MERRITT, H.M. SCHELLMAN, D.D. YOVANOVITCH;[c]
A. BODEK, H.S. BUDD, P. DE BARBARO, W.K. SAKUMOTO;[d]
T. KINNEL, P.H. SANDLER, W.H. SMITH[e]

[a] *Columbia University, New York, NY 10027*
[b] *University of Chicago, Chicago, IL 60637*
[c] *Fermilab, Batavia, IL 60510*
[d] *University of Rochester, Rochester, NY 14627*
[e] *University of Wisconsin, Madison, WI 53706*

ABSTRACT

We present the first measurement of the Q^2 dependence of the nucleon strange quark distribution, $xs(x)$, based on a high-statistics study of opposite-sign dimuon events induced by neutrino-nucleon scattering at the Fermilab Tevatron. A sample of 5044 ν_μ and 1062 $\bar{\nu}_\mu$-induced $\mu^\mp\mu^\pm$ events with $30 \leq E_\nu \leq 600$ GeV and $\langle Q^2 \rangle = 22.2$ GeV^2/c^2 is observed. The data support the slow-rescaling model of charm production with $m_c = 1.31 \pm 0.24$ GeV/c^2. We measure the CKM matrix element $|V_{cd}| = 0.209 \pm 0.012$ and the nucleon fractional strangeness content $\eta_s = 0.064^{+0.008}_{-0.007}$.

A charged-current neutrino interaction with a nucleon strange or down quark may produce a charm quark, which fragments into a charmed hadron. The semileptonic decay produces a second muon, of opposite sign from the muon at the leptonic vertex. This distinctive opposite sign dimuon signature allows a unique and highly sensitive study of charm particle production dynamics and the strange sea content of the nucleon. Scaling violations of the strange quark distribution, measured here for the first time, are of particular interest in the exploration of nucleon structure, while the threshold behavior associated with the heavy charm mass is critical to the extraction of the weak mixing angle, $sin^2\theta_W$, from the ratio of neutral-current to charged-current $\nu - N$ cross sections.

The effect of the massive charm quark is parameterized in the slow-rescaling model,[1] wherein ξ, the momentum fraction carried by the struck quark, is related to the kinematic variable x by the expression $\xi = x(1 + m_c^2/Q^2)$. The cross section for neutrino production of dimuons on an isoscalar target may be written:

$$\frac{d^2\sigma(\nu N \to \mu^-\mu^+ X)}{d\xi\, dy} = \frac{G^2 M E_\nu}{\pi}\left\{[\xi u(\xi) + \xi d(\xi)]|V_{cd}|^2 + 2\xi s(\xi)|V_{cs}|^2\right\}\left[1 - \frac{m_c^2}{2ME_\nu\xi}\right]D(z)B_c \quad (1)$$

where $\xi s(\xi)$ and $\xi d(\xi)$ are the fractional momentum distributions of the nucleon s and d quarks. The Peterson function[2] $D(z) \propto (z[1 - (1/z) - \epsilon/(1-z)]^2)^{-1}$ describes the fragmentation of a charm quark into a charmed hadron and B_c is the semileptonic branching ratio for charmed hadron decay. The analogous equation for antineutrinos is found by substituting $u(\xi) \to \bar{u}(\xi)$, $d(\xi) \to \bar{d}(\xi)$ and $s(\xi) \to \bar{s}(\xi)$.

This analysis combines data gathered during two experiments, E744 and E770, which ran in 1985 and 1988, by the Columbia-Chicago-Fermilab-Rochester collaboration at the Fermilab Tevatron using the quadrupole triplet neutrino beam.[3] The detector[4] combines a 690 ton steel/scintillator calorimeter target with a 420 ton toroidal magnetic spectrometer, with drift chambers for muon tracking. Previously published results from E744 alone[5] described data for $30 \leq E_\nu \leq 600$ GeV with $P_\mu \geq 9$ GeV/c and $\theta_\mu \leq 250$ mrad for both muon tracks. By combining the E744 and E770 samples, requiring $E_{had} \geq 10$ GeV, and lowering the cut on P_{μ_2} to 5 GeV/c for $E_{had} \leq 130$ GeV, 5044 ν_μ and 1062 $\bar{\nu}_\mu$-induced $\mu^\mp\mu^\pm$ events are observed, yielding more than a threefold increase in the event sample.

Single muon and dimuon events are simulated using Monte Carlo techniques. Quark and antiquark momentum densities are obtained from the CCFR structure functions[6] using a modified Buras-Gaemers parameterization.[7] The strange quark x dependence is parameterized as $xs(x) \propto (1-x)^\beta$, and it and the non-strange sea distributions evolve together in Q^2, with the strange quark magnitude set by the parameter $\kappa = 2S/(\bar{U}+\bar{D})$ (where $S = \int_0^1 xs(x)dx$, etc.). The parameters m_c, β, B_c, and $\eta_s = 2S/(U+D)$ are obtained from a multiparameter χ^2 minimization comparing the data and Monte Carlo events binned in five E_{vis} and ten x_{vis} bins.

Muonic decays of π and K mesons in the hadron shower of the charged-current events constitute the primary source of dimuon background. Hadronic test beam muoproduction data and Monte Carlo simulations predict a π/K decay background of 796.5±11.5 ν_μ and 118.0±2.1 $\bar{\nu}_\mu$ events.[8] The largest source of systematic uncertainty is the charm quark fragmentation, which is modeled by the Peterson function, whose argument $z = P_D/P_c$ is the ratio of the charmed meson and quark momenta. The Monte Carlo is fit to the data for various fixed values of the adjustable Peterson parameter ϵ, and a study of the distribution of $z_{vis} = E_{\mu_2}/(E_{\mu_2}+E_{had})$ combined with an analysis of E531 neutrino emulsion data[9] yields a neutrino average $\epsilon = 0.20 \pm 0.04$.

Other systematic errors are estimated by varying the fit parameters within their uncertainties. These include: π/K decay background, the relative E_μ and E_{had} energy scale, dimuon data selection, $R_{LONG} = \sigma_L/\sigma_T$, and the d/u quark ratio.[10] Assuming $|V_{cd}| = 0.220 \pm 0.003$ and $|V_{cs}| = 0.9744 \pm 0.0008$, the multiparameter fit yields:

$$m_c = 1.31^{+0.20+0.12}_{-0.22-0.11} \text{ GeV}/c^2 \qquad \beta = 9.45^{+0.60+0.36}_{-0.55-0.25} \qquad (2)$$

$$B_c = 0.105 \pm 0.007 \pm 0.005 \qquad \eta_s = 0.064^{+0.008}_{-0.007} \pm 0.002$$

with χ^2 of 42.5 for 46 degrees of freedom.

The difference between the strange sea exponent $\beta = 9.45$ and that of the total sea $\alpha = 6.95$ at $Q^2 = 22.2$ GeV$^2/c^2$, where $x\bar{q}(x) \propto (1-x)^\alpha$, provides a quantitative indication that the strange sea is softer than the $\bar{u}$ and $\bar{d}$ sea. The strange sea content with respect to the non-strange sea quarks is found by combining η_s with the measured antiquark fraction[6] $\bar{Q}/Q = 0.198$ at $Q^2 = 22.2$ GeV$^2/c^2$ to yield $\kappa = 0.373^{+0.048}_{-0.041} \pm 0.018$.

If the CKM matrix elements are not assumed then the results of the fit in (2) can be expressed in terms of the product $|V_{cd}|^2 B_c = (5.09 \pm 0.32^{+0.17}_{-0.16}) \times 10^{-3}$. Substitution of the neutrino world average charm branching ratio[11] $B_c = 0.116 \pm 0.010$ yields $|V_{cd}| = 0.209 \pm 0.011 \pm 0.004$.

The Q^2 dependence of the strange quark momentum distribution $xs(x)$ is found from the observed dimuon event distributions assuming the leading-order formalism described above. The observed data is corrected for acceptance, missing energy associated with the decay neutrino, neutrino/antineutrino misidentification and charm mass effects. The predicted down quark contribution to the dimuon sample is subtracted, resulting in event distributions due exclusively to the nucleon strange sea. The combined neutrino and antineutrino results for $xs(x)$ are displayed in Figure 1, which shows the Q^2 variations in $xs(x)$ for each value of x (the lines are power-law fits to the data). This measurement of the scaling violations of the strange sea may be used to test perturbative-evolution predictions and evaluate flavor asymmetry in the nucleon quark sea.

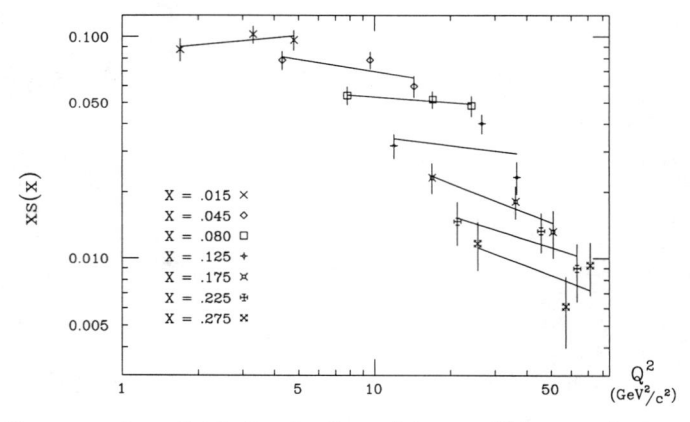

Figure 1: Strange quark sea distribution function $xs(x)$ versus Q^2 for several values of x. The lines are power-law fits to the data. Errors are statistical. An additional $^{+14\%}_{-12\%}$ scale error arises due to the uncertainty in κ.

1. H. Georgi and H. Politzer, *Phys. Rev.* **D14** (1976) 1829; R.M. Barnett, *Phys. Rev.* **D14** (1976) 70.
2. C. Peterson, et al., *Phys. Rev.* **D27** (1983) 105.
3. S.A. Rabinowitz, et al., sub. to *Phys. Rev. Lett.*; S. Rabinowitz, Ph.D. Thesis, Columbia U. (1992).
4. W.K. Sakumoto, et al., *Nucl. Inst. Meth.* **A294** (1990) 179; B.J. King, et al., *Nucl. Inst. Meth.* **A302** (1991) 254.
5. C. Foudas, et al., *Phys. Rev. Lett.* **64** (1990) 1207.
6. S.R. Mishra, et al., Nevis Preprint 1459, submitted to *Phys. Rev. Lett.*
7. A.J. Buras, K.J.F. Gaemers, *Nucl. Phys.* **B132** (1978) 249.
8. P.H. Sandler, et al., Wisconsin Preprint WISC-EX-92-324, submitted to *Z. Phys.* **C**.
9. N. Ushida, et al., *Phys. Lett.* **B121** (1983) 292.
10. D. Allasia, et al., *Phys. Lett.* **B249**, (1990) 366.
11. M.H. Shaevitz, Neutrino '90, *Nucl. Phys.* (Proc. Suppl.) **B19** (1991) 270.

VECTOR MESON AND CHIRAL LOOP CONTRIBUTIONS TO THE DECAYS $V^0 \to P^0 P^0 \gamma$

ALBERT BRAMON

Universitat Autònoma de Barcelona, 08193 Bellaterra (Barcelona), Spain

AGNES GRAU

Departamento de Física Teórica y del Cosmos, Universidad de Granada, 18071 Granada, Spain

and

GIULIA PANCHERI

INFN, Lab.Naz.Frascati, Frascati, Italy

ABSTRACT

The contribution of intermediate vector mesons to the decays $V^0 \to P^0 P^0 \gamma$ is calculated and compared with previous estimates. For some decays, like ϕ or $\omega \to \pi^0 \pi^0 \gamma$ our results update the existing numbers. For the decays $\phi \to K^0 \bar{K}^0 \gamma$ and $\phi, \omega \to \pi^0 \eta \gamma$, we find values different from the ones in the literature and discuss the origin of the discrepancy.In an attempt to extend Chiral Perturbation Theory to these radiative decays the contributions of (chiral) loops are calculated and found to be important.

1. Introduction

With a high-luminosity, low-energy e^+e^--machine like Daϕne, rare decays of vector mesons with branching ratios even smaller than 10^{-6} can be studied. Indeed, since the Frascati Φ-Factory is expected to provide $\sim 10^{10} \phi$-decays per year thus allowing for analyses of final states such as $\pi^0\pi^0\gamma$, $\pi^0\eta\gamma$ and, in principle, $K^0\bar{K}^0\gamma$. Their dynamics includes the effects of well-known vector mesons and of largely unknown scalar mesons, whose effects will probably manifest themselves in radiative ϕ-decays. Our first purpose is to provide a rather exhaustive analysis of the vector meson contributions. Previous studies [1, 2, 3, 4] are based on old data and turn out to be rather incomplete or not free of contradictions. Our second aim is an attempt to extend Chiral Perturbation Theory (χPT) to radiative vector-meson decays into two neutral pseudoscalars, $V^0 \to P^0 P^0 \gamma$. The relation of χPT amplitudes to the VMD ones is introduced in terms of the (VM-)resonance saturation of counterterms in the chiral lagrangian. The effects of (chiral) loops are found to be important in some cases. Unambiguous predictions are given for $\phi \to \pi^0\pi^0\gamma, \pi^0\eta\gamma$ and $\rho \to \pi^0\pi^0\gamma$.

2. The VMD Approach

In conventional VMD models, the amplitude for the process $V^0 \to P^0 P^0 \gamma$ is obtained from the two well-known lagrangians obeying the SU(3)-symmetry dictates

$$L(V\gamma) = -2egf^2 A^\mu \ tr(QV_\mu) \qquad L(VVP) = \frac{G}{\sqrt{2}} \epsilon^{\mu\nu\alpha\beta} \ tr(\partial_\mu V_\nu \partial_\alpha V_\beta P) \qquad (1)$$

Table 1: Global contribution of intermediate vector mesons to decay rates (in eV) and branching ratios (last column) for different $V^0 \to P^0 P^0 \gamma$ transitions as predicted by several authors. Experimental upper limits are also quoted.

Decay rates (in eV)	EXP [6, 7]	Ref. [3]	Ref. [4]	Ref. [1]	This calculation Γ	B.R.
$\Gamma(\rho \to \pi^0\pi^0\gamma)$	—	$(2.5)1.6 \cdot 10^3$	—	$4.3 \cdot 10^3$	$1.6 \cdot 10^3$	$1.1 \cdot 10^{-5}$
$\Gamma(\rho \to \pi^0\eta\gamma)$	—	—	—	593	0.061	$4 \cdot 10^{-10}$
$\Gamma(\omega \to \pi^0\pi^0\gamma)$	$< 3.4 \cdot 10^3$	(350) 227	—	690	235	$2.8 \cdot 10^{-5}$
$\Gamma(\omega \to \pi^0\eta\gamma)$	—	—	—	53	1.39	$1.6 \cdot 10^{-7}$
$\Gamma(\phi \to \pi^0\pi^0\gamma)$	$< 4.4 \cdot 10^3$	(250) 54	45	153	51	$1.2 \cdot 10^{-5}$
$\Gamma(\phi \to \pi^0\eta\gamma)$	$< 11 \cdot 10^3$	—	35	228	23.9	$5.4 \cdot 10^{-6}$
$\Gamma(\phi \to K^0\bar{K}^0\gamma)$	—	—	—	0.18	$1.2 \cdot 10^{-5}$	$2.7 \cdot 10^{-12}$

where A^μ is the photon field, Q is the quark charge matrix, V stands for the vector meson nonet, $G = 3\sqrt{2}g^2/(4\pi^2 f)$ is the $\rho^0\omega\pi^0$ coupling constant and $f_\rho = f_\omega/3 = -\sqrt{2}f_\phi/3 = \sqrt{2}g = 5.9$, $f = 132 MeV$

Our results using the full VMD amplitudes ([5]) are shown in the two last columns of Table 1. For comparison we also include the upper limit for the three experimentally studied decay rates [6, 7] and the predictions of other authors [1, 3, 4] who have worked in our same context. An important point is that we disagree in the complete list of numerical predictions quoted in ref.[1] even if the initial expressions for the lagrangians are the same (notice that our coupling constant g has been defined as 1/2 of that in ref.[1]).

Concentrating on ϕ-decays one first observes that our vector-meson dominated mechanism predicts a completely negligible $\Gamma(\phi \to K^0\bar{K}^0\gamma)$, contrasting with the (four orders of magnitude larger) prediction from ref.[1]. We believe that the $\phi \to K^0\bar{K}^0\gamma$ decay is predicted to be exceptionally suppressed not only by the obviously scarce available phase-space but also due to an almost complete destructive interference in the amplitude.

If $\phi \to K^0\bar{K}^0\gamma$ is detected at Daϕne this would signal decay mechanisms different from ours, such as $\phi \to f_0, a_0\gamma \to K^0\bar{K}^0\gamma$ or other final-state interactions in $\phi \to K^+K^-\gamma \to K^0\bar{K}^0\gamma$. Similarly, only this kind of alternative mechanisms could produce sizable even-wave $K^0\bar{K}^0$ contaminations to the p-wave $\phi \to K^0\bar{K}^0$ decay (pure in K_L-K_S) thus disturbing CP-violation experiments [8]. On the contrary, our mechanism predicts sizable contributions to $\phi \to \pi^0\pi^0\gamma$ and $\eta\pi^0\gamma$ decays.

3. Chiral loop contributions

Implementing the strict χPT lagrangian [9] –dealing solely with pseudoscalar and electroweak currents– with the effects of meson-resonances may lead to a more complete and realistic scheme with a largely increased predictive power. In particular, it can incorporate and improve most of the VMD results so far discussed. Vector-mesons can be incorporated along the lines of the work by Bando et al.[10]

Table 2: Contribution of Chiral loops and intermediate vector mesons to decay rates (in eV) and branching ratios (last column) for different $V^0 \to P^0 P^0 \gamma$ transitions.

Decay rates (in eV)	χ-loops	VMD	Total	B.R.
$\Gamma(\rho \to \pi^0\pi^0\gamma)$	1.42×10^3	1.62×10^3	3.88×10^3	26×10^{-6}
$\Gamma(\rho \to \pi^0\eta\gamma)$	0.006	0.061	$\simeq$VMD	VMD
$\Gamma(\omega \to \pi^0\pi^0\gamma)$	1.8	235	$\simeq$VMD	VMD
$\Gamma(\omega \to \pi^0\eta\gamma)$	0.013	1.39	$\simeq$ VMD	VMD
$\Gamma(\phi \to \pi^0\pi^0\gamma)$	224	51	281	64×10^{-6}
$\Gamma(\phi \to \pi^0\eta\gamma)$	131	23.9	151	34×10^{-6}
$\Gamma(\phi \to K^0\bar{K}^0\gamma)$	0.033	1.2×10^{-5}	$\simeq \chi$- loops	7.6×10^{-9}

or other (for our purposes) equivalent contexts [11].

In Table 2 we show the result of this calculation [12] and its comparison with the pure VMD results.

In summary, the well understood contributions of intermediate vector mesons in $V^0 \to P^0 P^0 \gamma$ decays have been discussed. Vector Meson Dominance alone predicts $BR(\phi \to \pi^0\pi^0\gamma) = 12 \times 10^{-6}$ and $BR(\phi \to \pi^0\eta\gamma) = 5.4 \times 10^{-6}$, and a characteristic photonic spectrum (peaked at higher energies) in the first decay. Similarly, an exceptionally small contribution is predicted (and its physical origin understood) for the branching ratio $BR(\phi \to K^0\bar{K}^0\gamma)$, namely, $\sim 2.7 \times 10^{-12}$. Other VMD predictions are $BR(\omega \to \pi^0\pi^0\gamma) \simeq 28 \times 10^{-6}$ and $BR(\rho^0 \to \pi^0\pi^0\gamma) \simeq 11 \times 10^{-6}$. We also find that some vector meson decays into two neutral pseudoscalars and a photon could receive important contributions from chiral loops.

6. References

1. S.Fajfer and R.J.Oakes, Phys. Rev. D42 (1990) 2392.
2. P.Singer, Phys. Rev. 128 (1962) 2789; 130 (1963) 2441; 161 (1967) 1694(E).
3. F.M.Renard, Nuovo Cim. 62A (1969) 475.
4. N.N.Achasov and V.N.Ivanchenko, Nucl Phys. B315 (1989) 465.
5. A. Bramon, A. Grau and G. Pancheri, Phys. Lett. B283 (1992) 416.
6. *Particle Data Group*, Phys. Lett. B239 (1990) 1.
7. S.I.Dolinsky et al., Phys. Rep. 202 (1991) 99.
8. The DAΦNE Physics Handbook. Edited by L.Maiani, G.Pancheri, N.Paver. INFN-Laboratori Nazionali di Frascati. Frascati 1992.
9. J. Gasser and H. Leutwyler, Ann. Phys. 158 (1984) 142.
10. M.Bando, T.Kugo and K.Yamawaki, Phys. Rep.164 (1988) 217.
11. A. Bramon, E. Pallante and R. Petronzio, Phys. Lett. B271 (1991) 237.
12. A. Bramon, A. Grau and G. Pancheri, Phys. Lett. B289 (1992)97.

SOLVING THE f_0 PUZZLE AT DAΦNE

PAULA J. FRANZINI
Laboratoire de Physique Théorique ENSLAPP,[#1]
B.P. 110, F-74941 Annecy-Le-Vieux Cedex, France

WON KIM
SUNY at Stony Brook, Stony Brook, New York 11794

and

JULIET LEE-FRANZINI
Laboratori Nazionali di Frascati dell'INFN, Frascati, Italy
SUNY at Stony Brook, Stony Brook, New York 11794

ABSTRACT

We summarize the excellent prospects for study of the $f_0(975)$ scalar meson at the Frascati ϕ-factory DAΦNE, in the reaction $e^+e^- \to \phi \to f_0\gamma \to \pi\pi\gamma$.

Beginning in 1995, DAΦNE[1] will deliver a luminosity $\mathcal{L} \approx 10^{32} cm^{-2} s^{-1}$, yielding some five billion ϕ's in four months of machine-on time. While the main goal of this high luminosity e^+e^- collider is the study of CP violation, an important complementary goal is spectroscopy. The $f_0(975)$,[2] the lightest scalar ($I^G J^{PC} = 0^+0^{++}$) meson, has been a puzzle since the 1970's. If it is assumed to be a $q\bar{q}$ bound state, many predictions fail, such as the total width (500 MeV rather than the measured 30 MeV), two photon couplings and so on. Other structures, such as four-quark bound states or $K\bar{K}$ "molecules," have been proposed for the f_0. The current predictions[2] for the branching ratio of $\phi \to f_0\gamma$ (BR$_{\phi f_0\gamma}$) vary from $\mathcal{O}(10^{-4})$ for various four quark states, to $\mathcal{O}(10^{-5})$ for $s\bar{s}$ states, to $< \mathcal{O}(10^{-5})$ for diffuse $K\bar{K}$ systems. The experimental upper bound is currently 2×10^{-3} at 90% c.l. In this talk we will consider BR$_{\phi f_0\gamma}$'s ranging from 1×10^{-6} to 2.5×10^{-4}, and a running period with 5×10^9 ϕ's. With several thousand to a million produced f_0's per year, DAΦNE is an ideal place to study the f_0.[3]

One observes f_0's through their decay to pions, a 78% branching ratio. We will first consider the decay to neutral pions, which is simpler than the charged pion case. The signal is then five photons, with one low energy photon of about 50 MeV, and the other photons reconstructing to two nearly back-to-back pions. The primary background process (A_1) is $\phi \to \pi^0\pi^0\gamma$ via an intermediate ρ. Even pessimistically taking the rate at the experimental upper limit (1×10^{-3}) rather than the theoretical estimate which is two orders of magnitude smaller, this background is easily controlled. Smaller backgrounds come from processes such as $\phi \to \pi\rho, \rho \to \eta\gamma, \eta \to \gamma\gamma$, yielding five photons but with different kinematics; or events such as $\phi \to \gamma\eta, \eta \to \pi\pi\pi$, which is a background when two photons are missing.

Our simulations have been done in KLOE,[4] a large general purpose detector

---

[#1] *URA 14-36 du CNRS, associée à l'E.N.S. de Lyon, et au L.A.P.P. d'Annecy-le-Vieux*

with a magnetic field, which covers a solid angle of 98% of 4π, resulting in a geometrical acceptance for five photons of 0.92. For $BR_{\phi f_0 \gamma}$ from 1×10^{-6} to 2.5×10^{-4} the anticipated fractional error in $BR_{\phi f_0 \gamma}$ varies from $\sim 4\%$ to 0.2%.

For the case of $f_0 \to \pi^+\pi^-$, additional backgrounds come from continuum processes such as coupling of the initial e^+e^- state to the tail of the ρ, an *initial state radiation process* (A_2), and $e^+e^- \to \mu^+\mu^-\gamma$, if muons are mistaken for pions. Furthermore, the ϕ can produce a pair of pions through off-shell ρ production with one of the pions radiating a γ, a *final state radiation process*. We shall call A_{ρ^*} the amplitude for this process and A_{f_0} the amplitude for $\phi \to f_0\gamma \to \pi^+\pi^-\gamma$.

While A_2 only contributes an incoherent background, as it is the only process antisymmetric under pion exchange ($C_{\pi^+\pi^-} = -1$), the amplitudes A_{ρ^*} and A_{f_0} interfere, since they are both $C_{\pi^+\pi^-} = +1$ processes.[5,6] The sign of the interference term (i.e., the sign of the $\phi f_0 \gamma$ coupling) is one of the unknown facets of the f_0. While the magnitude of $|A_{\rho^*}|^2$ is approximately one tenth of that of $|A_2|^2$, $|A_{f_0}|^2$ is comparable to or smaller than $|A_{\rho^*}|^2$, by as much as a factor of ten to one hundred. The interference term can drastically alter the f_0 signal in ϕ decays, both in shape and in magnitude. If the interference is destructive, the f_0 signal becomes very small, and was believed to disappear in Ref. 6. However, since the shape of the interference term and its angular distributions[7] are different from those from $|A_{f_0}|^2$, the presence of an f_0 signal can always be recognized, even when cancellation is maximal. We only lose sensitivity to the presence of f_0's in ϕ decays when $BR_{\phi f_0 \gamma}$ becomes smaller than about 3×10^{-7}. In addition, the shape of the signal allows in general to determine the sign of the $\phi f_0 \gamma$ coupling.

The $\mu^+\mu^-\gamma$ background, while much larger than the signal, can be easily removed in a detector such as KLOE by appropriate kinematical cuts. $|A_1|^2$ is negligible compared to the other backgrounds. $|A_2|^2$, the largest source of background, is peaked very sharply at small angles between the photon and the beam, $\theta_{\gamma, \text{beam}}$; we thus reduce its contribution by a factor of ~ 7 by a cut $|\cos\theta_{\gamma, \text{beam}}| < 0.9$. $|A_{\rho^*}|^2$ is peaked at small values of the angle between the the pions and the photon in the dipion rest frame, $\theta_{\pi\gamma}$. We therefore restrict $|\cos\theta_{\pi\gamma}|$ to be less than 0.9. With these cuts combined, we retain 80% of the signal and improve the signal to background ratio by a factor of 5 – 6. The angular dependence of $|A_{f_0}|^2$ is $(1 + \cos^2\theta_{\gamma, \text{beam}})$. The interference term $2\Re(A_{\rho^*} A_{f_0}^*)$ is slightly peaked along the beam direction and slightly suppressed along the pions. For small $BR_{\phi f_0 \gamma}$ the interference term dominates in absolute value over the f_0 term, while the reverse is true for the largest $BR_{\phi f_0 \gamma}$. This cross-over occurs because $|A_{f_0}|^2 \propto BR_{\phi f_0 \gamma}$, while $2\Re(A_{\rho^*} A_{f_0}^*) \propto \sqrt{BR_{\phi f_0 \gamma}}$. Thus, even for destructive interference, the contribution of $|A_{f_0}|^2 - 2\Re(A_{\rho^*} A_{f_0}^*)$ to the total cross section is not always negative. For $BR_{\phi f_0 \gamma} \sim 1.75 \times 10^{-4}$, the integrated contribution to the $\pi^+\pi^-\gamma$ cross section vanishes; however, a dip appears at low γ energies and an enhancement at high γ energies, allowing detection of the f_0 signal.

Fig. 1 shows the MC simulated photon spectrum which would be observed in KLOE (after cuts) for $\phi \to f_0\gamma \to \pi^+\pi^-\gamma$ for the two cases, constructive (solid) and destructive (dashed) interference, for $BR_{\phi f_0 \gamma} = 2.5 \times 10^{-4}$. The incoherent background contribution is also shown (dotted).

We use the *a priori* error estimate method for the maximum likelihood solution[8] to find the fractional accuracy, shown in Fig. 2, for constructive (dashed) and destructive (solid) interference. Even at the smallest $BR_{\phi f_0 \gamma}$ considered and with destructive interference, the fractional accuracy in the measurement of $BR_{\phi f_0 \gamma}$ is ten percent. In addition we note that the differential rate $d^3\Gamma/dE_\gamma d\cos\theta_{\gamma,beam} d\cos\theta_{\pi\gamma}$ clearly contains more information than the integrated cross section, thus it is possible to improve on the results presented. The study of $\phi \to f_0 \gamma \to \pi^0 \pi^0 \gamma$ provides an independent measure of the the strength of the $\phi f_0 \gamma$ coupling and therefore a check on the determination of its sign in the $\pi^+\pi^-$ case, thus completing the picture of the f_0.

We wish to thank Paolo Franzini for many helpful discussions.

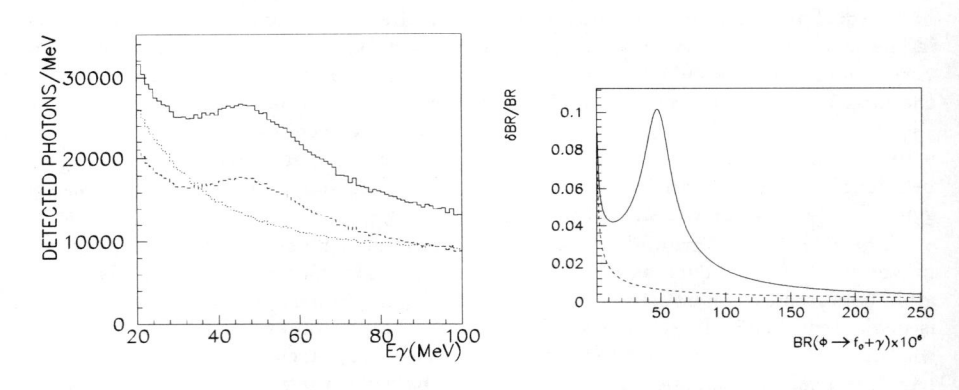

Figs. 1. γ spectrum from $\phi \to \pi^+\pi^-\gamma$ **2.** Fractional error on $BR_{\phi f_0 \gamma}$ vs. $BR_{\phi f_0 \gamma}$

References

1. G. Vignola, in the *Proceedings of the XXVIth ICHEP*, Dallas, 1992.
2. N. Brown and F. E. Close, in the *DAΦNE Physics Handbook*, ed. L. Maiani (INFN Frascati, Frascati, 1992), and references therein.
3. For further details and full references see P. J. Franzini, W. Kim, and J. Lee-Franzini, Phys. Lett. **B287** (1992) 259 and in the *DAΦNE Physics Handbook*.
4. P. Franzini, "The KLOE detector," these Proceedings.
5. M. J. Creutz and M. B. Einhorn, Phys. Rev. D1 (1970) 2537.
6. A. Bramon, G. Colangelo, and M. Greco, Phys. Lett. **B287** (1992) 263; these authors and P. J. Franzini, in the *DAΦNE Physics Handbook*.
7. P. J. Franzini, G. Colangelo, Phys. Lett. **B289** (1992) 189.
8. P. Franzini, in the *DAΦNE Physics Handbook*, p. 15.

SVX b PHYSICS PROSPECTS

S. Dell'Agnello
University and INFN - Pisa
Via Livornese 582/A, San Piero a Grado, Pisa, 56010, ITALY

for The CDF Collaboration

ABSTRACT

CDF has enhanced its capabilities for b-physics with the installation of a silicon vertex detector (SVX)[1], which provides precise 2-dimensional tracking. The SVX impact parameter (IP) resolution ($\sim 13\mu$m for $P_t > 10$ GeV) is well suited to detecting displaced secondary vertices (SV) from b-hadron decays ($c\tau_B \simeq 390\mu$m). In this paper we show evidence of SV detection using the $\Psi \to \mu^+\mu^-$ sample, which is b-enriched, and describe some prospects of b physics opened by the SVX with 25 pb^{-1}, the goal integrated luminosity of present run.

1. Vertex Finding with the SVX

The search for SV's takes advantge of the good SVX IP and primary vertex (PV) resolution. The IP resolution can be parametrized as $\sigma_{IP} = \sqrt{(a/P_t)^2 + b^2}$. The P_t dependence is due to multiple scattering and is estimated to be $a = 39\mu$m GeV from simulation. Given the SVX geometry, simulation studies predict that $b \simeq$ intrinsic position resolution. With current alignment constants, the position resolution that we extract from track residuals in the data is $\simeq 13\mu$m $\simeq b$.

At CDF the PV position averaged over a data taking run is known with $\sigma_{PV} \simeq 40 \mu$m, which is the size of the Tevatron transverse luminous region. If the IP is calculated wrt the average PV, from the data we measure $\sigma_{IP}(P_t > 5\text{GeV}) = 561 \pm 13\mu$m without the SVX and $44 \pm 1\mu$m with the SVX (dominated by σ_{PV}). We also try to reconstruct the PV event by event: in a $t\bar{t}$ ($b\bar{b}$) Montecarlo sample 35 (13) tracks are used in the average to determine the PV and $\sigma_{PV} \simeq 12\mu$m ($\simeq 35\mu$m). The efficiency of this algorithm ($\simeq 70\%$) is dominated by the SVX geometrical acceptance and the longitudinal spread of the luminous region ($\simeq 30$ cm).

We estimated the rate of fake SV's from the inclusive jet sample, which is b-depleted, and found a result consistent with Montecarlo expectations. We found, instead, a statistically significant excess of displaced SV's in b-enriched samples, like the inclusive electron and the $\Psi \to \mu^+\mu^-$ samples.

3. Physics with the $\Psi \to \mu^+\mu^-$ Sample

At the Tevatron Collider a significant fraction of Ψ's come from B-meson decays. Using the 1989 Ψ sample, CDF identified the exclusive decay $B^\pm \to \Psi + K^\pm$ and measured $\sigma(b)$, the b-quark production cross section[2]. With current run CDF will enlarge the size of the Ψ sample thanks to the improved muon detection, which is providing a factor 5.3 increase of the $\mu\mu$ trigger rate. In addition, the measurement of the Ψ decay length with the SVX allows discriminating $B \to \Psi$ from zero lifetime $\chi \to \Psi$ decays. The expected yield of Ψ's in the SVX ($\sim 50\%$ acceptance) is of the order of 45,000. With this sample we will measure $\sigma(b)$, F_B, the fraction of Ψ's from B, the inclusive B lifetime and separate B lifetimes from exclusive decays.

We analyzed a limited sample of Ψ's ($\sim 1,000$ events) to study the feasibility of a lifetime measurement. Results reported below are preliminary and not corrected for systematic effects. We compute the $\mu^+\mu^-$ invariant mass requiring the muons to come from a common vertex. We use SVX + CTC (outer central tracking chamber) and CTC tracking only, getting respectively 17 Mev and 26 MeV resolution, the improvement being due to the increased tracking lever arm provided by the inner SVX hits. We define the signal ($/Psi$) region to be $\pm$ 50 MeV around the central vaule of $M(\mu^+\mu^-) = 3.093$ GeV. We then look at the 3-dim. signed decay length for the signal and the side band regions, which will serve as a measure of the non-Ψ background (fig. 1). We observe a long tail for positive decay lengths, which is a clear indication of non-zero lifetime in the sample. Negative decay lengths are due to: 1) non-Ψ background and prompt-χ contributions, which we assume symmetric around zero with width equal to the decay length resolution; 2) smearing of $B \to \Psi$ events from the convolution of a falling exponential with the resolution function. In fig. 2 we show the Ψ decay length after side band subtraction and correction for the average parent b-hadron $\beta\gamma$, determined with the ISAJET+CLEO Montecarlo as a function of $P_t(\Psi)$. This quantity, $c\tau$, is expected to represent the proper b-hadron decay length for $c\tau > 0.05$ cm (Montecarlo estimate). The $c\tau$ distribution is indeed exponentially falling for large values and within the statistical error it is consistent with the world average measurement of the inclusive b-hadron lifetime. This result shows that lifetime measurements at CDF are becoming feasible thanks to the SVX.

The yields of exclusive B decays in the SVX suffer from large uncertainties on F_B for the $P_t(\Psi) > 3.0$ GeV region now accessible with the trigger. We expect approximately 180-360 $B^\pm \to \Psi + K^\pm$, 140-280 $B^\circ \to \Psi + K^*$ (both already observed by CDF), $\sim$ 40-80 $B_S \to \Psi + \Phi \to \mu^+\mu^- K^+K^-$ and ≤ 100 $\Lambda_b \to \Psi + \Lambda \to \mu^+\mu^- p\pi^-$ events. The limit on Λ_b comes from CDF 90% CL upper limit on Λ_b production. The SVX will provide excellent combinatoric background rejection by requiring a common displaced vertex for the decay products. This will be very effective for B_S (four particle SV plus Ψ, Φ mass constraints). For the Λ_b search the SVX can also help by increasing the angular/P_t acceptance with standalone tracking and identifying a Λ_c signal (LEPwise) from the cascade decay $\Lambda_b \to l\nu\Lambda_c \to l\nu + pK\pi$.

2. QCD Topics

The b-quark production dynamics can be tested by studying the spectrum of Φ, η, P_t and invariant mass correlations of $b\bar{b}$ pairs[3]. For example, study of small $\delta\Phi(b\bar{b})$ for $P_t(b) > 20$ GeV will allow measuring the amount of gluon splitting[4] ($g \to b\bar{b}$). We estimate that for $P_t(b) > 20$ GeV, the SVX will provide $\sim$ 600 double b-tags in the inclusive lepton sample.

QCD predicts large variations in the behavior of b-hadron production cross section in jets, $\sigma(jet)BR(jet \to b\text{-hadron}+X)$, vs. the fragmentation variable, $z = E(b\text{-hadron})_\parallel/E_{jet}$. Three very different regimes can be distinguished depending on E_{jet}: 1) for $E_{jet} \ll 100$ GeV the production rate vs. z follows the Peterson model, with the typical peak for $z \to 1$ due to direct $b\bar{b}$ production; 2) for $E_{jet} \sim 100$ GeV two peaks are predicted ($z \to 0,1$), with the low z peak due to gluon splitting; 3) for $E_{jet} \gg 100$ GeV, the $z \to 1$ peak disappers and b production behaves just like the π fragmentation function, with the important difference that the b-hadron fragmentation function can be calculated in QCD from first principles. Quantitative predictions for these three regimes are known for supercollider energies[5], but the same qualitative behavior is expected at the Tevatron[6].

4. Conclusions

A preliminary analysis of data taken in three months of running shows that the SVX is opening to CDF interesting b physics prospects. With 25 pb^{-1} some of these prospects include EWK measurements (inclusive and exclusive b-hadron lifetimes with the $\Psi \to \mu^+\mu^-$ sample), QCD measurements ($b\bar{b}$ correlations, b production in jets) and identification of B_S and Λ_b hadrons.

6. References

1. F. Bedeschi et al, Publ. Proc. XXVIth International Conference on High Energy Physics, Dallas, TX, August 1992.
2. The CDF Collaboration, F. Abe et al, *Phys. Rev. Lett.* **68** (1990) 3403.
3. M. L. Mangano, P. Nason and G. Ridolfi, *Nucl. Phys.* **B373** (1992) 295.
4. M. L. Mangano and P. Nason, *Phys. Lett.* **B285** (1992) 160.
5. J. P. Guillet, P. Nason and H. Plothow-Besch, Publ. Proc. Large Hadron Collider Workshop, **Vol. II** p. 116, Aachen, Germany, 1990.
6. M. L. Mangano, private communication.

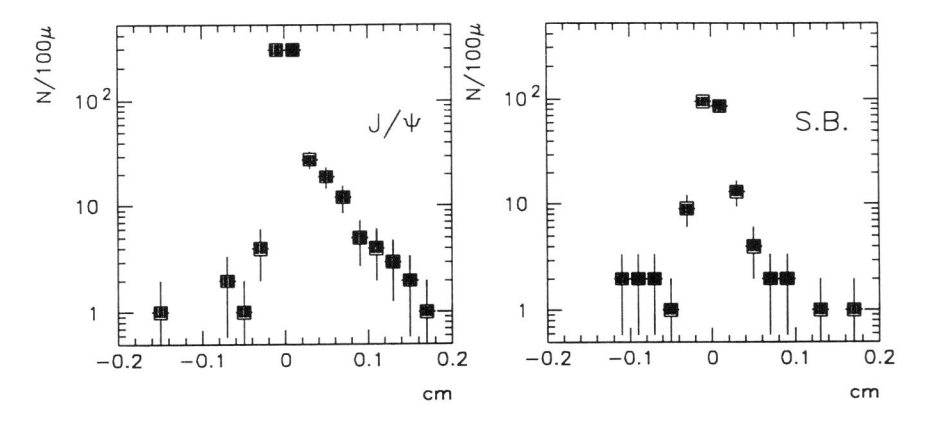

Figure 1: Decay length distribution of the signal (J/Ψ) and side band (S.B.) region.

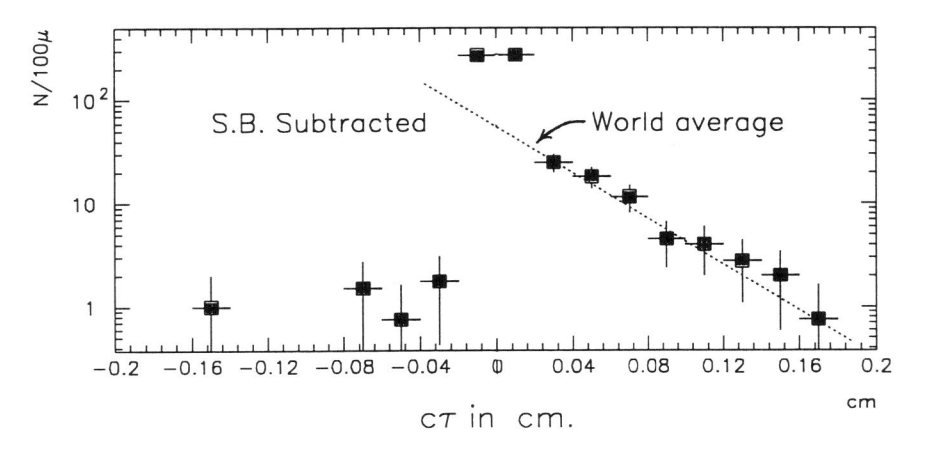

Figure 2: Ψ decay length side band subtracted and corrected for kinematics.

INCLUSIVE SINGLE MUONS AT DØ

Kamel A. Bazizi, for the DØ Collaboration
University of California, Riverside
Riverside, CA 92521, USA

ABSTRACT

We report preliminary results on b-quark production in $p\bar{p}$ collisions at $\sqrt{s} = 1.8$ TeV from the current Run 1a of the Tevatron collider. Using an inclusive muon data sample which corresponds to an integrated luminosity of 50–70 nb^{-1} and by further requiring the muon to be accompanied by a jet we obtain an almost background free sample of muons consistent with $b\bar{b} \to \mu X$ decay. A preliminary p_T^μ spectrum and some characteristics of this decay, compared to the Monte Carlo expectations, are presented.

1. The DØ Detector

The DØ detector consists of a tracking system, a calorimeter and a muon detection system. The central tracking chambers play an important role in muon identification. The calorimeter is utilized to measure jet energies and the minimum ionizing energy along the muon track which also aids in muon identification. The muon system, which includes proportional drift tubes and toroidal magnets, is used to reconstruct muon tracks and determine the corresponding momenta. The properties and performance parameters of the DØ detector are described in references [1] and [2].

2. The Muon Trigger

A description of the DØ trigger system can be found in a paper submitted to these proceedings [3]. The muon trigger, [4], consists of two hardware triggers, a coarse centroid trigger (level 1.0) and a fine centroid trigger (level 1.5), and one software trigger (level 2.0). The centroids are based on patterns of hits from discriminated and latched cathode pad signals. Centroid combinations consistent with tracks pointing to the interaction region are programmed into the trigger logic. The effective p_T threshold for the level 1.0 trigger is currently 5 GeV and is expected to be lowered to 3 GeV, (for level 1.5 it is about 7 GeV). At level 2.0 the muon track is reconstructed and selection cuts can be applied on the track quality and transverse momentum p_T. The data considered in this analysis was collected with a single muon trigger inside of a pseudo rapidity range of $|\eta| < 1.7$ with a prescaling factor of 5 and a p_T minimum of 7 GeV at level 2.0.

3. Offline Event Selection

The offline muon identification consists of a full reconstruction of the muon track and a selection on the quality of the fit parameters. The track is required to include hits in all three layers of muon chambers and have good fits. The track must extrapolate to within 15 cm of the vertex and match with at least one track in the central detector.

Backgrounds for muons include hadron punchthrough, decay in flight of pions and kaons, and cosmic rays. The calorimeter and toroids are about 13 to 20 interaction lengths deep. Therefore punchthrough background is small. Decay in flight probability is reduced considerably by the small decay path in the central detector. To eliminate any residual background from cosmic ray and in flight decay muons the muon track is required to have an associated jet within $\Delta R = 0.6$. The jet reconstruction uses a fixed cone algorithm ($R = 0.7$) and a minimum transverse jet energy of 8 GeV.

4. Preliminary Results

The muon p_T spectrum for the final sample, in the range $7\,GeV < P_T^\mu < 20\,GeV$, where the best momentum resolution is currently achieved, is shown in Fig. 1. The shape of the spectrum is consistent with monte carlo expectations for $b\bar{b}$ and $c\bar{c}$ decays.

Fig. 2 shows the distribution of the separation of the muon and the accompanying jet ($\Delta R = \sqrt{\Delta\eta^2 + \Delta\phi^2}$). The data agrees with the monte carlo model for $b\bar{b} \to \mu X$ decay. This is an indication that the data sample consists largely of b decay muons. The dominance of b decays with a $P_T^\mu > 7\,GeV$ is expected [5].

Fig. 3 shows the distribution of the muon transverse momentum with respect to the jet axis (p_T^{rel}) which is also consistent with the monte carlo prediction (ISAJET) for b decays. This distribution is sensitive to the fragmentation of the parent quark. Since b quarks have a higher Q value than c quarks, this parameter can be used on a statistical basis to remove any residual c quark decay background [5].

5. Conclusions

Based on a very small sample of muon data, DØ has observed muons in association with hadronic jets with characteristics consistent with $b\bar{b}$ decays. By extending the muon trigger coverage out to the region $1.7 < |\eta| < 3.4$ and by lowering the p_T threshold, the DØ experiment, in the course of Tevatron collider Runs 1a and 1b, is expected to collect high statistics data for the study of many aspects of b Physics.

6. References

1. DØ Design Report Fermilab (1984)
2. C. Brown, et al., *Nucl. Instrum. and Meth.* **A279** (1989) 331.
3. J.T. Linneman, *Triggering the DØ Detector*, these proceedings.
4. M. Fortner, et al., *Nucl. IEEE Transactions on Nuclear Science,* **38** (1991) 480.
5. C.Albajar, et al., *Phys. Lett. B,* **256** (1991) 121.

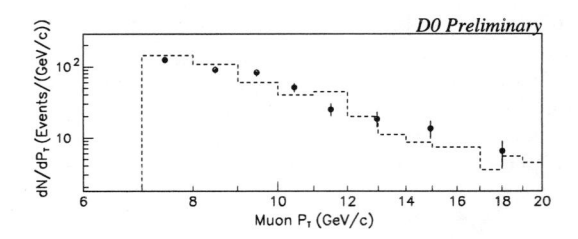

Figure 1: The muon p_T spectrum where the points are the data and the histogram represents the Monte Carlo (ISAJET) model for $b\bar{b} + c\bar{c} \to \mu X$ decays.

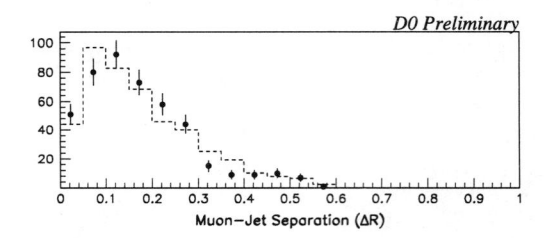

Figure 2: The distribution of the muon-jet separation $\Delta R = \sqrt{\Delta\eta^2 + \Delta\phi^2}$. The points are the data and the histogram represents ISAJET prediction for $b\bar{b} \to \mu X$ decay.

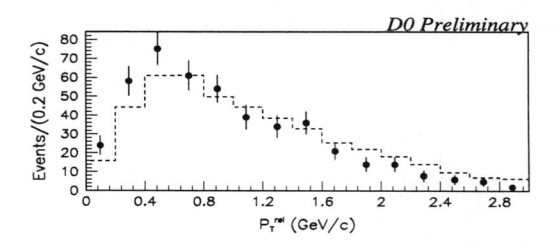

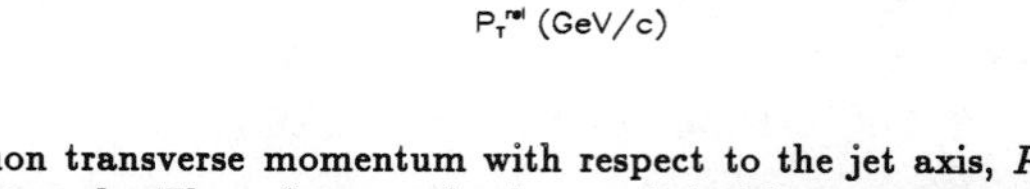

Figure 3: The muon transverse momentum with respect to the jet axis, $P_T^{rel} = P^\mu \sin\theta^{rel}$, where θ^{rel} is the muon-jet angle. The points are the data and the histogram represents ISAJET prediction for $b\bar{b} \to \mu X$ decay.

DIMUON PRODUCTION in DØ

Susumu Igarashi for the DØ Collaboration
Physics Department, Fermilab, M.S.122 P.O.Box 500
Batavia, IL 60510, U.S.A.

ABSTRACT

Dimuon events with associated jets were analysed using the DØ detector at the Fermilab Tevatron $\bar{p}p$ collider. We report preliminary results on the dimuon invariant mass spectrum and opening angle distribution. The observed ratio of the production rates for the same sign and opposite sign muon pairs is consistent with CDF and UA1 results and implies a strong $B^0\overline{B^0}$ mixing.

1. Physics Interest

Non-isolated dimuon events are expected to arise from the pair production of c or b quarks, with subsequent semileptonic decays producing two muons. Above $p_t = 7 GeV$, these events are more likely to be from the b quark production processes[1].

The QCD mechanisms in heavy quark production can be inferred from the angular correlation of the two muons. In the lowest order diagrams $b\bar{b}$ are produced back to back in the transverse plane relative to the beam axis, and the two muons are expected to be almost back to back. Through higher order processes, however, the opening angle of $b\bar{b}$ can be anything and it can even be collinear through a process called gluon splitting.

In the absence of $B^0\overline{B^0}$ mixing, leading decays of $b\bar{b}$ events produce opposite sign dimuon events. Same sign dimuon events are also produced when one of the muons is from a sequential decay, $b \to c \to \mu$. The probability of observing a secondary decay muon is low, because such muons are expected to be of lower p_t than the leading decay muons. The process of $B^0\overline{B^0}$ mixing also produces same sign dimuon events through leading decays. Therefore, the charge ratio is sensitive to $B^0\overline{B^0}$ mixing.

2. Event Selection

DØ and its muon detector have been described in detail elsewhere[2-6]. This analysis is based on a data sample collected last September and October and corresponding to an integrated luminosity of $600 nb^{-1}$. The trigger requirements included: (a) a single muon in the central pseudorapidity region ($|\eta| < 1.0$) or two muons in the $|\eta| < 1.7$ region (hardware Level 1 trigger) and (b) two muons with $p_t > 7 GeV$ and $|\eta| < 1.7$ (software Level 2 trigger). The offline selection of good muon candidates was based on quantities such as χ^2 of the track fit, the vertex projection of the track, energy deposit in the calorimeter along the muon track, no back to back muon track within $\Delta\theta > 170°$ and $\Delta\phi > 160°$ and $|\eta|$ cut of 1.7. Jets were then searched using the fixed cone algorithm with a radius ΔR of 0.7 in the η - ϕ space. At least one muon must be associated with a jet within a cone of 0.7 in ΔR.

3. Preliminary Results

The invariant mass distribution for opposite sign and same sign dimuon events are shown in Figure 1. Cosmic rays are rejected by the back to back track cut. Drell-Yan events are rejected because of the requirement of jet association. Pion and kaon decays and charmed decays are suppressed by the muon $p_t > 7 GeV$ cut. Because B mesons have a decay channel to ψ, there is evidence for ψ production in the opposite sign dimuon distribution. Same sign dimuon events are featureless as expected.

The opening angle distributions of the two muons are shown in Figure 2. From the lowest order diagrams for $b\bar{b}$ pair production, the opening angle is expected to be 180° if both muons are from leading decays. The opening angle can be 0° if the muons are from the sequential decay of the b quark. Higher order processes can make this angle anything from 0–180°. The prediction of the ISAJET Monte Carlo is shown in Figure 2. It is similar to the data. Note that ISAJET simulates the lowest order $b\bar{b}$ production and the parton shower and may not be a good simulation for the higher order production processes. Clearly, opposite sign dimuons have $\Delta\phi \sim 0°$ and same sign dimuons have $\Delta\phi \sim 180°$, indicating sequential decays and mixing respectively.

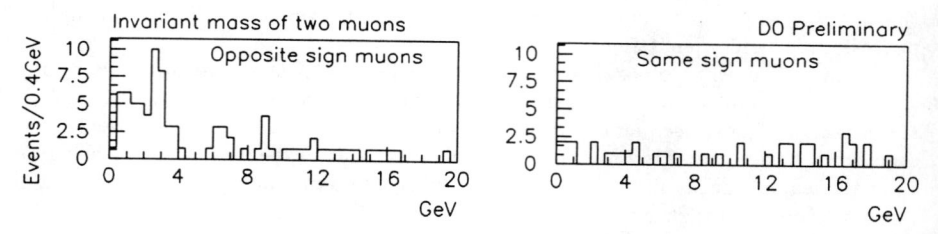

Figure 1: The invariant mass of two muons (a. opposite sign dimuons, b. same sign dimuons)

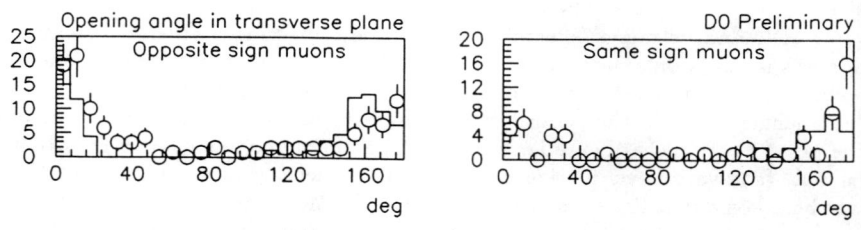

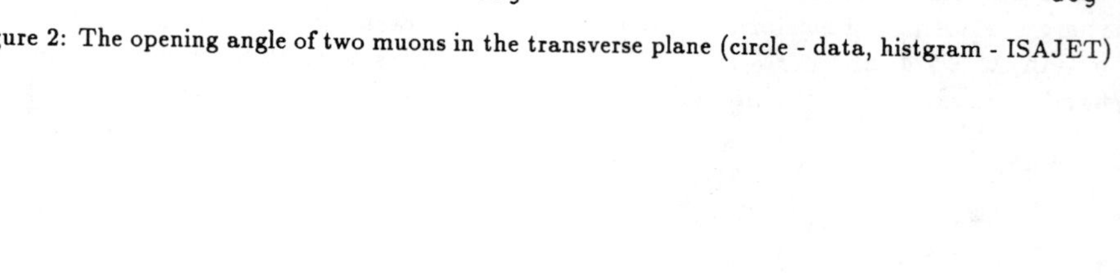

Figure 2: The opening angle of two muons in the transverse plane (circle - data, histgram - ISAJET)

The ratio of the number of same sign events to the number of opposite sign events is measured to be $0.65 \pm 0.16(stat.)$ for dimuon events with invariant mass $M_{\mu\mu} > 6 GeV/c^2$. The invariant mass cut is applied to reduce the contribution due to small angle sequential dimuon events. ISAJET, which does not have mixing, predicts a ratio of 0.17, including a charm quark background of 8%. Our measurement does not agree with a model without $B^0\overline{B^0}$ mixing, and it is consistent with CDF and UA1 mixing measurements[7-8].

The systematic uncertainty in the $B^0\overline{B^0}$ mixing measurement may be reduced in the future using the opening angle and invariant mass distributions. For the same sign dimuon events with a large opening angle, the invariant mass distribution can be separated statistically into $B^0\overline{B^0}$ mixing events and sequential dimuon events. A mixing produces leading decay muons and sequential dimuon events have one softer secondary muon.

The muon transverse momentum relative to the jet axis depends on whether it is from the leading b decay, sequential b decay, c decay or background such as decay in flight of π/K hadrons. The distribution for the dimuon sample with same sign and large opening angle will help to separate the $B^0\overline{B^0}$ mixing process and the other processes. This will reduce the systematic uncertainty for the mixing measurement.

4. Summary

We observed dimuon events with jets which are likely signals of $b\bar{b}$ production events. The DØ detector is a good detector for this study, because the muon identification in jets is excellent. Backgrounds from decay in flight and punchthrough are expected to be very small. The ratio of the number of same sign dimuon events to the number of the opposite sign dimuon events is consistent with CDF and UA1 mixing measurements. While muons with $|\eta| < 1.7$ only are used in this analysis, we are now extending the trigger and reconstruction capability to our full coverage of $|\eta| < 3.2$. Using the good muon identification and the wide η coverage of the DØ detector, the QCD mechanisms in b quark production will be studied in detail in the future.

5. References

1. C.Albajar, et al., *Phys. Lett. B* **186** (1987) 237.
2. *DØ Design Report* Fermilab (1984).
3. C.Brown, et al., *NIM* **A279** (1989) 331.
4. J.M.Butler, et al., *NIM* **A290** (1990) 122.
5. D.Green, et al., *NIM* **A244** (1985) 356.
6. M.Fortner, et al., *IEEE Transactions on Nuclear Science* **38** (1991) 480.
7. F.Abe, et al., *Phys. Rev. Lett.* **67** (1991) 3351.
8. C.Albajar, et al., *Phys. Lett. B* **262** (1991) 171.

HADRONIC PRODUCTION OF χ_c MESONS

HECTOR MENDEZ
Department of Physics
University of Illinois at Chicago
801 W. Taylor Street, Room 2236
Chicago, Il 60607, USA
for the E672/E706 Collaboration

ABSTRACT

We report a preliminary study of χ_c mesons produced in π^--nucleon collisions at 530 GeV/c observed via the final state J/ψ plus photon. The J/ψ particles have been identified through the decay $J/\psi \to \mu^+\mu^-$. Muons were detected in a muon tracking system, and photons either in a liquid-argon calorimeter or through conversion into an e^-e^+ pair. The fraction of J/ψs produced via this radiative decay mode is measured and compared with previous experiments at lower energies.

1. Introduction

Radiative decays of charmonium states (χ_c) are well suited for testing QCD predictions of the processes involved in J/ψ production [1]. In hadron collisions, this production can occur through the production and subsequent cascade decay of χ_c mesons. This contribution to the J/ψ cross section seems to be significant but not dominant. In this paper, we present preliminary results on χ_c production, observed via $\chi_c \to J/\psi + \gamma$, in a sample of data from 530 GeV/c π^- incident on Cu and Be targets. The data was obtained during the 1990 Fermilab fixed target run using the Meson West spectrometer [2]. The spectrometer was employed simultaneously by E672 and E706. Experiment E672 is designed to study hadronic processes yielding high mass dimuons and associated particles, while E706 is designed to measure the production of direct photons at large transverse momentum.

During the 1990 run, we collected 5.5 million dimuon triggers. The opposite sign dimuon mass spectrum in the J/ψ region is shown in Fig. 1a. This analysis is based on about 75% of the full sample. For our χ_c analysis, we chose events with a dimuon mass in the range (3.097 ± 0.3) GeV/c^2 and constrained the dimuon mass to the nominal J/ψ mass $(3.097$ $GeV/c^2)$.

2. χ_c Analysis

To search for radiative χ_c decays, we examined photons associated with the J/ψ event sample. We have two independent methods to detect photons in our spectrometer: 1) we identified photons in the electromagnetic section of the liquid argon calorimeter (EMLAC) and 2) we identified photons in the tracking system through the photon conversion into e^-e^+. A preliminary description of the χ_c analysis done

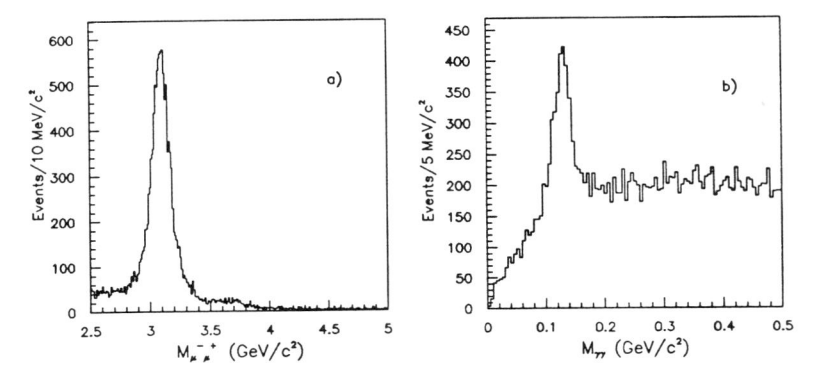

Figure 1. a) The opposite sign dimuon mass spectrum above 2.5 GeV/c^2. b) Two photon mass spectrum.

with photon identified in the tracking system has been presented elsewhere [3]. The analysis shows that the fraction of J/ψs produced via the radiative decay of $\chi_{c1} + \chi_{c2}$ is (44 ± 9 ± 8)% and the relative production of χ_{c1} to χ_{c2} is 1.3 ± 0.6.

In the EMLAC, two cuts were applied to identify showers as originating from photons. We selected only showers that were not associated with charged tracks within a 0.5 cm circle at the calorimeter front face, and deposited at least 60% of the total energy of the shower in the front section of the EMLAC in order to reduce hadron contamination. Showers that satisfy both cuts are called "photons". A clear π^0 peak is observed in the resulting $\gamma\gamma$ mass spectrum (Fig. 1b), where the transverse momentum of the pair is required to be greater than 700 MeV/c.

A $J/\psi + \gamma$ mass spectrum formed with dimuons in the J/ψ region is shown in Fig. 2a, where reconstructed photons close to the edge of the EMLAC have been eliminated to avoid partially detected photon energies. In order to reduce the background resulting from combining all possible photons in an event with the J/ψ, an asymmetry cut ($\alpha \leq 0.8$) was applied to obtain the $J/\psi + \gamma$ mass distribution. The asymmetry, defined as $(E_{J/\psi} - E_\gamma)/(E_{J/\psi} + E_\gamma)$, is related to the decay angle θ_γ^* of the photon in the χ_c center of mass by; $\alpha = 0.76 - 0.24 \beta \cos\theta_\gamma^*$, where this quantity has been evaluated at 3.555 GeV/c^2, the mass of χ_{c2} state. The impact of this asymmetry cut on the accepted photon energy is shown in Fig. 2b where the energy spectrum of the photons that survive the cut are shown in the shaded region.

The estimated background (dashed curve in Fig. 2a) was obtained by combining photons with J/ψs from different events. The background was then normalized to the number of events in the mass region 3.70 GeV/c^2 to 5.70 GeV/c^2. An excess of 63 ± 17 events exists in the χ_c region (3.45 GeV/c^2 to 3.6 GeV/c^2).

We interpret this excess of events as evidence of the production and radiative decay of the $\chi_{c1}(3.510)$ and $\chi_{c2}(3.555)$ states. We have calculated the acceptance and mass resolution in a GEANT Monte Carlo study [4]. The χ_c states were generated with the same x_F and p_t distribution as for J/ψ mesons. Based upon the Monte Carlo simulation, the overall detection efficiency was found to be 1.8% assuming the ratio $\sigma(\chi_{c1})/\sigma(\chi_{c2})$ to be 1.3 [3]. The resulting mass spectrum (not normalized)

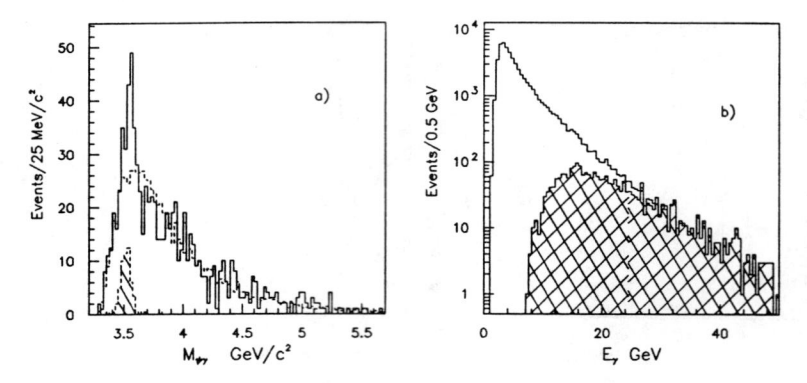

Figure 2. a) $J/\psi + \gamma$ invariant mass. b) Photon energy Spectrum.

expected from our Monte Carlo calculation is shown by the shaded region in Fig. 2a. The major acceptance loss is due to photons passing through the central hole of the EMLAC. Using the computed Monte Carlo acceptance for the χ_c, the fraction of produced J/ψs coming from the radiative decay $\chi_{c1}+\chi_{c2}$ is (37 ± 11 ± 10)%, where the first uncertainty is statistical only and the second represents the systematic uncertainty due to background subtraction. This is in good agreement with our results from photon conversion and with similar experiments at lower energies [5]. At this stage of the analysis, the systematics are still under investigation.

3. References

1. C. E. Carlson and S. Suaya, *Phys. Rev.* **D18**, 760 (1978).
2. V. Abramov et al., FERMILAB-PUB-91/62-E, Mar, 1991; G. Alverson et al., "Production of Direct Photons and Neutral Mesons at Large Transverse Momenta by π^- and p Beams at 500 GeV/c", in preparation.
3. R. Li et al., "Hadroproduction of χ_c States in the Collision of 530 GeV/c Pions with Nuclear Targets", Presented at the XXVI International Conference on High Energy Physics, Dallas, TX, Aug. 6-12, 1992.
4. V. Abramov, "Monte Carlo Study of χ_c Particle Production at E672 Experiment", E672 Internal Note, 17 Dec 1991.
5. S. R. Hahn et al., *Phys. Rev.* **D30**, 671 (1984); J. H. Cobb et al., *Phys. Lett.* **72B**, 497 (1978); F. Binon et al., *Nucl. Phys.* **B239**, 311 (1984); C. Kourkoumelis et al., *Phys. Lett.* **81B**, 405 (1979); D. A. Bauer et al., *Phys. Rev. Lett.* **54**, 753 (1985); Y. Lemoigne et al., *Phys. Lett.* **113B**, 509 (1982); and L. Antoniazzi et al., FERMILAB-PUB-92/140-E, May, 1992

HADRONIC PRODUCTION OF B MESONS

LORETTA J. DAUWE

Department of Physics, University of Michigan at Flint
Flint, MI 48502-2186, USA

for the Fermilab E672/E706 Collaboration

We investigated $B \to J/\psi + X$ decays in π^--nucleon collisions at 530 GeV/c by analyzing events in which J/ψs originate at a secondary vertex. The preliminary $B\overline{B}$ cross section is (28±9±8) nb/nucleon for $x_F >$ 0.1. We also show evidence for the exclusive B decay modes $J/\psi K^\pm$ and $J/\psi K^{0*}$.

1. Introduction

Experimental observation of heavy-quark production in hadronic interactions yields important information on strong interactions. Fermilab experiments E672/E706 have the capability to measure processes which result in final states containing muons: specifically, charmonium and b-quark production. Based upon a preliminary analysis of the dimuon triggers, we report on $B \to J/\psi + X$ decays.[1] These data were collected using the Fermilab Meson West spectrometer during the 1990 fixed target run with a 530 GeV/c π^- beam incident on Cu and Be targets. The sensitivity of this sample is 6.6 events/pb.

2. J/ψs from Secondary Vertices

Of the 11×10^3 reconstructed J/ψ events, 11% have more than one vertex. In 64% of these events, there was a possibility that both muons came from a secondary vertex. A vertex refit was done for dimuons in the mass range 2.85 GeV/$c^2 < M_{\mu\mu} <$ 3.35 GeV/c^2 constraining the dimuon mass to 3.097 GeV/c^2. The resulting vertex was used as a seed for an iterative vertex-fitting that associated other charged tracks to this vertex. The reconstructed J/ψ vertex Z-position distribution is shown in Fig. 1a. The target consists of two 0.8 mm thick pieces of Cu, followed by two pieces of Be, 3.71 and 1.12 cm thick respectively.

This sample contains 857 events in which this dimuon vertex was downstream of the primary vertex. Several cuts were applied to clean the sample: Only events with > 2 reconstructed tracks from the primary were kept (631 events survived). Fiducial-volume cuts were made for both primary and secondary vertices (577 events survived). A separation significance > 3 was required for both the longitudinal and transverse separations between the primary and secondary vertices. A longitudinal separation of 3 mm was also required (121 events survived). Secondary J/ψ vertices with > 4 associated hadrons were discarded to reduce the background from secondary interactions. The Z-position of the primary- and secondary-vertex for the 73 events passing these cuts are shown in Fig. 1b and 1c, respectively. The background from reconstruction of false vertices is estimated to be 4±2 events. A preliminary Monte Carlo simulation indicates that 25 to 40 events containing secondary-interactions remain in this sample.

There are two large gaps in the target vicinity where only air is present. The positions in the Y-Z plane of the J/ψ secondary vertices in these gaps are shown in Fig. 2. There are 10 events in which the J/ψ vertex is at least three standard deviations from solid target. Assuming the false vertices are distributed uniformly across the volume, 1±1 of the 4±2 background events from false vertex reconstruction occur in the gaps. Thus, we report a preliminary signal of 9±3 secondary-vertex J/ψ events in which the secondary vertex occurs in a region where only air is present.

Extrapolating from the 9 gap events, we estimate 26 ± 10 $B \to J/\psi + X$ events in the entire fiducial volume. This number added to the estimated number of events from secondary interactions (33) and false vertex reconstruction (4) gives a total of 63 events, quite consistent with the 73 ± 9 events found.

Based on the 9 ± 3 $B \to J/\psi + X$ candidates in the gaps, we estimate the $B\bar{B}$ cross section using the J/ψ cross section for normalization.[2] Assuming that B production has linear A dependence, and employing the $B \to J/\psi + X$ branching ratio of 1.57×10^{-3}, combined with Monte Carlo estimates of $B \to J/\psi + X$ acceptance (0.28) and reconstruction efficiency (0.15), yields a preliminary value of $\sigma_{B\bar{B}}(x_F > 0.1) = (28\pm9\pm8)$ nb/nucleon where the first uncertainty is statistical. The last uncertainty is systematic, which includes uncertainties in the x_F-distribution of the B, reconstruction efficiencies, the J/ψ production cross section and the branching ratios.

3. Exclusive B Decay Modes

The decay modes $B^\pm \to J/\psi + K^\pm$ and $B \to J/\psi + K^{0*}$ have significant channels that contain only charged particles in the final state, allowing full reconstruction of the B. Our $B^\pm \to J/\psi + K^\pm$ candidates satisfy the following cuts: (a) Only charged tracks with a transverse impact parameter < 20 μm with respect to the secondary dimuon vertex were used. A quality cut ($\chi^2<4$) was imposed on the three-prong vertex fit. (b) Monte Carlo-based momentum cuts were imposed on the candidate kaon to reduce the background of hadrons from the underlying event; the track's p_T with respect to the beam axis must be > 0.5 GeV/c, and the track's momentum must be ≤ 150 GeV/c. (c) All of the cuts of the secondary vertex J/ψ analysis described previously were used in this analysis, with a secondary-vertex hadron multiplicity requirement of ≤ 2 tracks. (d) The total momentum vector of the secondary-vertex tracks must join the primary vertex such that the transverse impact parameter is < 120 μm. The invariant mass distribution of the four surviving events is shown as the shaded entries in Fig. 3.

The search for the exclusive decay mode $B \to J/\psi + K^{0*}$ (and its charge conjugate) proceeded as follows: K^{0*}s were observed by their decays into $K^\pm \pi^\mp$ pairs. A kinematic criterion for kaon identification was used to reduce combinations: if one of the tracks in a pair had momentum greater than half of the other, it was assigned to be the kaon. Charged track pairs from the secondary vertex J/ψ sample in the observed K^{0*} mass region were combined with the J/ψ in the same manner as in the $K^\pm$ analysis. Only $K^\pm\pi^\mp$ pairs with $p_T>0.5$ GeV/c with respect to the beam axis were kept, and the candidate B momentum was required to pass the primary vertex within 200 μm. Five events remained after these cuts, three of which have masses in the B-signal range (see Fig. 3).

There is a clear excess of events near the nominal B-meson mass in Fig. 3. A background analysis using primary vertex events subject to the described cuts shows no evidence for enhancement in the B-mass region due to the cuts imposed.

4. Conclusion

In a sample of dimuon triggered data generated by 530 GeV/c π^- beam incident on nuclear targets, we have observed 73 J/ψs from secondary vertices including 10 in air gaps. Based upon the observed secondary vertices in these gaps, the preliminary $B\bar{B}$ cross section is $(28\pm9\pm8)$ nb/nucleon for $x_F > 0.1$. Evidence for fully reconstructed B mesons in the $J/\psi K^\pm$ and $J/\psi K^{0*}$ decay modes has also been presented.

5. References

1. R. Jesik *etal.*, *Proceedings of XXVI International Conference on High Energy Physics*, Dallas (1992), To be published.
2. V. Abramov *etal.*, FERMILAB-Pub-91/62-E (1991). The branching ratio times $\sigma_\psi(x_F>0.0)$ of (11 ± 2) nb/nucleon is a revised value for our 1988 data and is consistent with our analysis of the 1990 data sample.

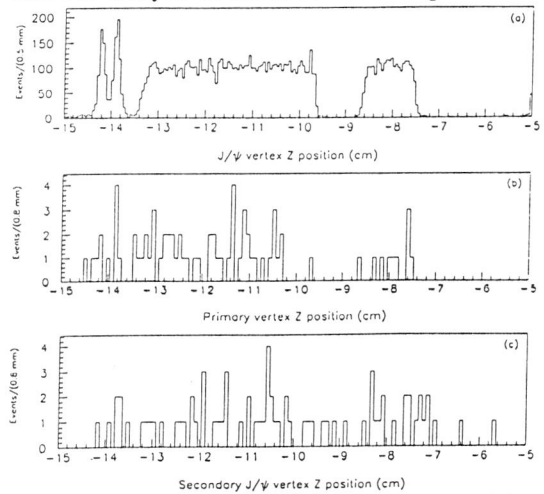

Fig. 1. Vertex Z-position distributions: (a) J/ψ vertex position for all events; (b) primary vertex position for the 73 events passing cuts; (c) secondary J/ψ vertex position.

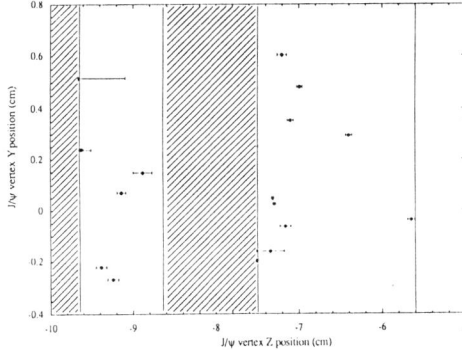

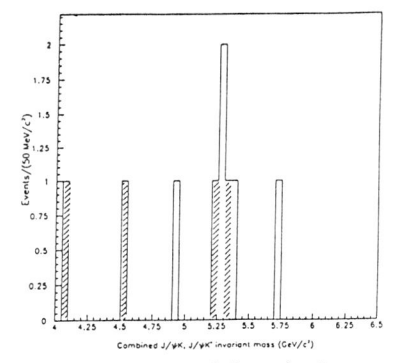

Fig. 2. Secondary J/ψ vertex position in the Y-Z plane showing events with vertices in air gaps. Hatched areas represent solid target material; the line at -5.6 cm represents a Mylar-foil window.

Fig. 3. Reconstructed invariant mass distribution for $J/\psi K^\pm$ and $J/\psi K^{0*}$ combined. The $J/\psi K^\pm$ combinations are shaded.

STUDIES OF FULLY RECONSTRUCTED $D\overline{D}$ EVENTS IN HIGH ENERGY PHOTOPRODUCTION

ROB GARDNER for the Fermilab E687 Collaboration[1]
Department of Physics
University of Illinois at Urbana-Champaign
1110 W. Green St.
Urbana, Il 61801, USA

ABSTRACT

Results on charm production dynamics from the Fermilab photoproduction experiment E687 are presented. Included are comparisons of p_t^2 and Feynman x distributions to other experimental data. Correlations between fully and partially reconstructed $D\overline{D}$ pairs can be used to test production models.

1. Inclusive D Distributions

We have analyzed data collected by the Fermilab high energy photoproduction experiment E687[2] for events containing one or two fully reconstructed charmed mesons. Inclusive p_t^2 and Feynman x distributions are studied using decay modes of the D mesons which are copiously produced with high acceptance, namely, $D^+ \to K^-\pi^+\pi^+$, $D^0 \to K^-\pi^+$, $D^0 \to K^-\pi^+\pi^+\pi^-$, together with their charged conjugates. The sample consists of approximately 10,000 charmed particles with a signal-to-noise ratio of 6. In Fig. 1 the invariant mass, p_t^2 and x_f distributions are plotted for the combined sample. The p_t^2 distribution was fit to the the form $dN/dp_t^2 = A\ exp(ap_t^2 + bp_t^4)$. The result (see Table 1) is in good agreement with our Monte Carlo[3] (based on the photon-gluon fusion mechanism and the Lund model[4] for fragmentation) but is slightly harder (due to our higher beam energy $E_\gamma \approx 200$ GeV) than that of experiment E691[5] The the acceptance-corrected x_f distribution is fairly consistent with E691 but softer than the Monte Carlo prediction.

2. $D\overline{D}$ Correlations

Correlations between two fully reconstructed D's can be exploited to test QCD production models and the effects of charm quark dressing. The $D\overline{D}$ signature is shown in the scatter plot of Fig. 2a in which the normalized D invariant mass appears on the vertical axis and the normalized $\overline{D}$ invariant mass on the horizontal. After subtracting background, the number of fully reconstructed $D\overline{D}$ pairs was 325 ± 23 with a signal to noise ratio of ≈ 15. Fig. 2b shows the $M_{D\overline{D}}$ distribution from data (points), and the Monte Carlo (solid). The $M_{D\overline{D}}$ distribution is related to the photon-gluon center of mass energy in the context of the photon gluon fusion model[6] The acoplanarity angle $\Delta\phi$, plotted in Fig. 2c, is the azimuthal angle between the D

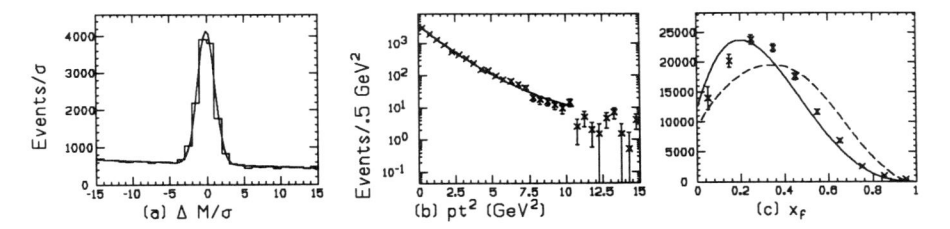

Figure 1. (a) Normalized D invariant mass $\Delta M/\sigma$; (b) p_t^2 (solid curve is the fit result); (c) acceptance corrected x_f (solid curve: E691 parameterization,[5] dashed curve: Monte Carlo.)

Table 1: Fits to p_t^2 for $D \to Kn\pi$ Decays.

	a	b	$<p_t^2>$
E687	-0.85 ± 0.02	0.03 ± 0.01	1.51 ± 0.02
E691[5]	-1.07 ± 0.05	0.04 ± 0.01	1.16 ± 0.04
Monte Carlo[3]	-0.87 ± 0.01	0.03 ± 0.01	1.55 ± 0.01

and $\overline{D}$ momentum vectors in the plane transverse to the photon direction. The data peaks at π radians corresponding to back to back $D\overline{D}$ production, though tends to be somewhat flatter than the Monte Carlo.

Correlations can also be studied using a fully reconstructed $D^{\mp}$ produced against a kinematically selected soft pion $\tilde{\pi}$ from the decay $D^{*\pm} \to \tilde{\pi} D$. Taking advantage of the low Q value, the soft pion will have a lab momentum nearly collinear to the the parent $D^{*\pm}$ and can be scaled up to serve as a measurement of its momentum. Since the $D^{*\pm}$ and recoil D should roughly balance in p_t, one expects that the $\tilde{\pi}$ pions from $D^{*\pm}$ should balance the recoil charm $(D^{\mp})$ momentum vector $\vec{P}^{(r)}$ causing enhancements near 0 in the variables:

$$\Delta_x = 13.8 P_x^{(\pi)} + P_x^{(r)} \quad \text{and} \quad \Delta_y = 13.8 P_y^{(\pi)} + P_y^{(r)}.$$

The factor 13.8 is obtained from the average energy fraction of the parent $D^{*\pm}$

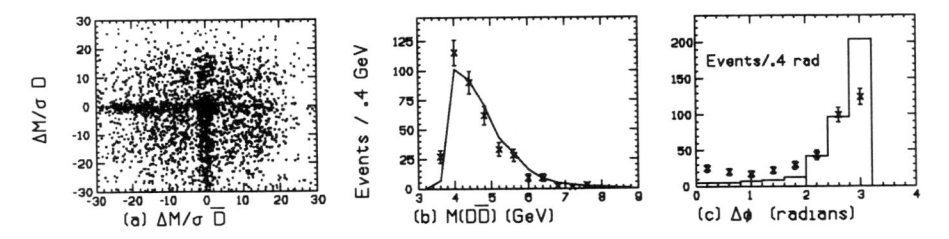

Figure 2. (a) Normalized D vs. $\overline{D}$ invariant mass scatter plot; (b) $M_{D\overline{D}}$; (c) $\Delta\phi$. (Solid curve and histogram are Monte Carlo predictions.)

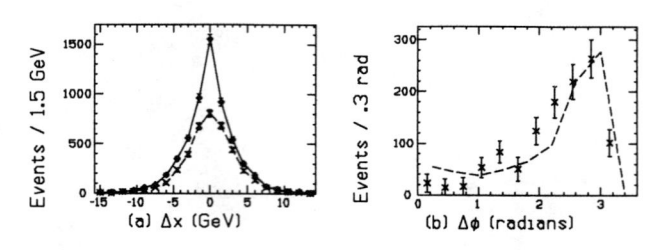

Figure 3. Soft $\tilde{\pi}$ tagged sample: (a) Δ_x (solid: right sign; dashed: wrong sign); (b) $\Delta\phi$ (dashes are for fully reconstructed events).

carried by the $\tilde{\pi}$. Using a sample of $\approx$ 6,000 $D^{\mp}$ mesons, the enhancement in Δ_x (requiring $|\Delta_y| < 2$ GeV) is shown in Fig. 3a where the correct charge correlation is the solid upper curve and the wrong correlations is the dashed lower curve. The corresponding $\Delta\phi$ distribution of Fig. 3b (wrong sign candidates were subtracted) is in agreement with the fully reconstructed $D\overline{D}$ sample.

3. Conclusions

The p_t^2 distribution of our sample of photoproduced D mesons is consistent with a Monte Carlo based on the photon-gluon fusion mechanism and the Lund model. However, the x_f distribution is somewhat softer than predicted and is in fair agreement with other experimental data[5] The acoplanarity $\Delta\phi$ between fully and partially reconstructed $D\overline{D}$ pairs is somewhat flatter in the data than Monte Carlo and indicates that dressing effects may be more severe than expected.

4. Acknowledgements

This work was supported in part by the National Science Foundation, the US Department of Energy, the Italian Istituto Nazionale di Fisica Nucleare and Ministero della Università e della Ricerca Scientifica.

5. References

1. For a complete list of E687 collaborators, see Ref. 2.
2. E687 Collaboration, P. L. Frabetti *et al.*, *Nucl. Inst. Meth.* **A320** (1992) 519.
3. The Monte Carlo consists of the Lund packages[4] PYTHIA 5.6 for the charm photoproduction and JETSET 7.3 for fragmentation, combined with simulation algorithms for the E687 apparatus?
4. T. Sjostrand, *Computer Phys. Comm.* **39** (1986) 347. H.-U. Bengtsson, *Computer Phys. Comm.* **46** (1987) 43.
5. J.C. Anjos *et al.*, *Phys. Rev. Lett.* **62** (1989) 513.
6. L.M. Jones, H.W. Wyld, *Phys. Rev.* **D17** (1978) 759.

INCLUSIVE J/ψ, $\psi(2S)$ AND b-QUARK PRODUCTION IN $\bar{p}p$ COLLISIONS AT $\sqrt{s} = 1.8$ TeV [*]

CDF Collaboration[†]
Presented by Theresa A. Fuess
SSC Laboratory
2550 Beckleymeade Avenue
Dallas, Texas 75237

ABSTRACT

Inclusive J/ψ and $\psi(2S)$ production has been studied in $\bar{p}p$ collisions at $\sqrt{s} = 1.8$ TeV using the Collider Detector at Fermilab. The products of production cross section times branching fraction have been measured as functions of P_T for $J/\psi(\psi(2S)) \to \mu^+\mu^-$ in the kinematic range $P_T^{J/\psi(\psi(2S))} > 6$ GeV/c and $|\eta^{J/\psi(\psi(2S))}| \leq 0.5$. The products of the integrated cross section times branching fraction are calculated and used to obtain an inclusive b-quark production cross section.

1. Introduction

The reactions $\bar{p}p \to J/\psi(\psi(2S))X \to \mu^+\mu^- X$ at $\sqrt{s} = 1.8$ TeV were studied using 2.6 ± 0.2 pb^{-1} of data taken with the Collider Detector at Fermilab (CDF) during the 1988-1989 running period of the FNAL $\bar{p}p$ collider[1]. This is the first measurement of $J/\psi(\psi(2S))$ cross sections at Tevatron energies. These cross sections are important for the investigation of charmonium production mechanisms in $\bar{p}p$ collisions[2], for the study of the production of b-quarks at low P_T[3,4], and are used to obtain an inclusive b-quark production cross section.

2. The J/ψ and $\psi(2S)$ Data Sample

The components of the CDF detector[5] relevant to this analysis are the central tracking chamber which is in a 1.4116-T axial magnetic field, the central muon chambers which provide muon identification in the pseudorapidity region $|\eta^\mu| < 0.61$, and a multi-level central dimuon trigger. From events passing the trigger, pairs of opposite sign muons were selected with the following cuts: $P_T^\mu > 3.0$ GeV/c for each muon, $|\eta^{\mu^+\mu^-}| \leq 0.5$ and $6.0 < P_T^{\mu^+\mu^-} < 14.0$ GeV/c for each muon pair, and track quality criteria. The resulting J/ψ and $\psi(2S)$ mass distributions were each fit to

---
[*] Supported by the U.S. Dept. of Energy, contract number DE-AC02-76CH03000.
[†] The CDF Collaboration: ANL, Brandeis, UCLA, U. Chicago, Duke, FNAL, INFN-Frascati, Harvard, U. Ill., Johns Hopkins, KEK, LBL, MIT, U. Mich. INFN-Padova, U. Penn., INFN-Pisa, Purdue, Rochester, Rockefeller, Rutgers, SSCL, Texas A&M, Tufts, Tsukuba, U. Wisconsin

a Gaussian line shape plus a linear background. The number of J/ψ candidates above background is 889±30; the number of $\psi(2S)$ candidates above background is 35 ± 8.

3. The J/ψ and $\psi(2S)$ Cross Sections

The J/ψ and $\psi(2S)$ differential cross sections are displayed in the figure below together with the theoretical predictions for two processes expected to dominate J/ψ and $\psi(2S)$ production. The circles in the figure correspond to the data. The solid curve is the B-production model (BPM), a next-to-leading-order calculation of b-quark[6] production leading to B-mesons[7] which decay to $J/\psi(\psi(2S))$. The dashed curve, the charmonium production model (CPM), corresponds to $J/\psi(\psi(2S))$'s from direct charmonium production[2,8]. A fit of the sum, BPM plus CPM, to the J/ψ data with no normalization constraints suppresses the BPM contribution because of the difference in slope between the BPM curve and the data. However, another CDF study[4] found that the BPM calculation underestimates the b-quark cross section by a factor of 5.5 ± 2.8. When this datum is added to the fit we find that ~42% J/ψ's result from B-production. The 90% C.L. upper limit on the BPM contribution is ~60%. If future measurements exceed this value, then one must conclude that not only the normalization of BPM, but also the P_T-dependence of at least one of the models is wrong.

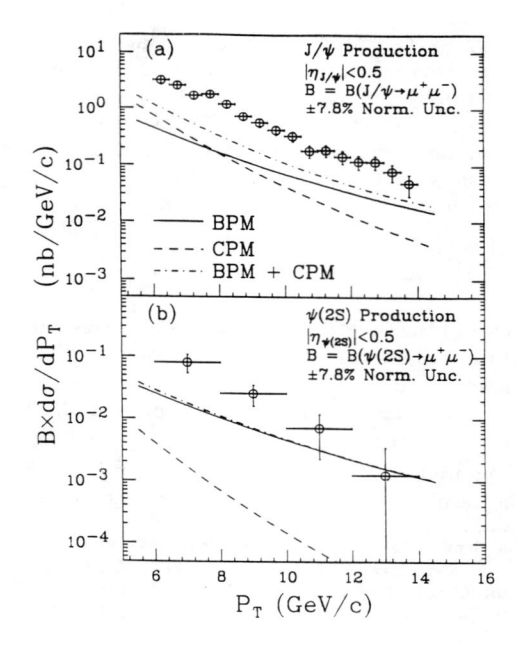

The products of the inclusive production cross section times branching fraction in the kinematic range $P_T^{J/\psi(\psi(2S))} > 6$ GeV/c and $|\eta^{J/\psi(\psi(2S))}| \leq 0.5$ are

$$\sigma(\bar{p}p \to J/\psi\, X) \times B(J/\psi \to \mu^+\mu^-) = 6.88 \pm 0.23(stat)\, ^{+0.93}_{-1.08}\, (syst)\, \text{nb} \text{ and}$$

$$\sigma(\bar{p}p \to \psi(2S)X) \times B(\psi(2S) \to \mu^+\mu^-) = 0.232 \pm 0.051(stat)\, ^{+0.029}_{-0.032}\, (syst)\, \text{nb}.$$

4. The b-Quark Cross Section

The b-quark inclusive production cross section is calculated using the $J/\psi(\psi(2S))$ inclusive production cross sections, the ratio of $J/\psi(\psi(2S))$ to b-quark cross sections as determined by the BPM Monte Carlo technique[6,7,9,10,11], and the fraction f_B of $J/\psi(\psi(2S))$'s from B meson decays. The b-quark P_T^{min} is chosen such that in the BPM, 90% of the $B \to J/\psi(\psi(2S))$ events having $P_T^{J/\psi(\psi(2S))} > 6$GeV/c also have $P_T^b > P_T^{min}$. In this analysis P_T^{min} is 8.5 GeV/c. Assuming the fraction f_B to be unity, believed to be true for $\psi(2S)$[2,8,12] but not for the J/ψ[13], we find

$$\sigma^b(P_T^b > 8.5\text{GeV/c}, |y^b| < 1) = 18.9\, ^{+4.7}_{-5.0}\, \mu\text{b} \text{ using } J/\psi \text{ and}$$

$$\sigma^b(P_T^b > 8.5\text{GeV/c}, |y^b| < 1) = 10.5\, ^{+5.0}_{-5.1}\, \mu\text{b} \text{ using } \psi(2S).$$

The b-quark cross section we get using $\psi(2S)$ is in reasonable agreement with other CDF measurements[4,13,14,15].

5. References

1. F. Abe et al., to be published in *Phys. Rev. Lett.*
2. E.W.N.Glover, A.D.Martin, W.J.Stirling, *Z. Phys.* **C38** (1988) 473.
3. C. Albajar et al., *Physics Letters* **B256** (1991) 121.
4. F. Abe et al., *Phys. Rev. Lett.* **B68** (1992) 3403.
5. F. Abe et al., *Nucl. Inst. Meth.* **A271** (1988) 387.
6. P. Nason, S. Dawson, and R.K. Ellis, *Nucl. Phys.* **B303** (1988) 607.
7. C. Peterson et al., *Phys. Rev.* **D27** (1983) 105.
8. E.W.N.Glover, personal communication.
9. N. Ellis and A. Kernan, *Physics Reports* **195** (1990) 23.
10. H. Schroder, personal communication.
11. W. Chen, Ph.D Thesis, Purdue University, May, 1990.
12. S. D. Ellis et al., *Phys. Rev. Letters* **36** (1976) 1263.
13. C. Boswell, these DPF proceedings.
14. B. T. Huffman, these DPF proceedings.
15. S. Vejcik, these DPF proceedings.

INCLUSIVE χ_c PRODUCTION
IN $\bar{p}p$ COLLISIONS AT $\sqrt{s} = 1.8$ TeV

Christopher M. Boswell
*Department of Physics and Astronomy, The Johns Hopkins University
Baltimore, Maryland 21218, USA*

for

The CDF Collaboration

ABSTRACT

We report the full reconstruction of χ_c mesons through the decay chain $\chi_c \to J/\psi\gamma$, $J/\psi \to \mu^+\mu^-$, using data obtained at the Collider Detector at Fermilab in $\bar{p}p$ collisions at $\sqrt{s} = 1.8$ TeV. This sample, the first observed at a hadron collider, is then used to measure the χ_c meson production cross section times branching fractions. We obtain $\sigma \cdot Br = 3.2 \pm 0.4(\text{stat}) \pm 1.1(\text{syst})$ nb for χ_c mesons with $P_T > 7.0$ GeV/c^2 and pseudorapidity $|\eta| < 0.5$. From this and the inclusive J/ψ cross section we calculate the inclusive b-quark cross section.

1. Introduction

This talk reports the first full reconstruction of χ_c mesons at a hadron collider, through the decay chain $\chi_c \to J/\psi\gamma$, $J/\psi \to \mu^+\mu^-$. The technique exploits the easily implemented $\mu^+\mu^-$ trigger and cleanly identified $J/\psi \to \mu^+\mu^-$ signal to compensate for the small decay branching fraction. The observed χ_c sample is used to measure the χ_c production cross section times branching fractions. This value, in combination with the J/ψ production cross section measured previously by the authors [1], is then used to calculate the b-quark production cross section under the assumption that direct J/ψ production contributes negligibly to the total J/ψ rate. The results are based upon data from $\sqrt{s} = 1.8$ TeV $\bar{p}p$ collisions observed at the Collider Detector at Fermilab (CDF).

2. Data Selection

To reconstruct χ_c mesons, we first identified J/ψ mesons by requiring two oppositely charged muon candidates, each with $P_T > 3.0$ GeV/c. For each muon, we then calculated the difference in both the transverse and longitudinal directions between the position of the muon chamber track and the CTC track extrapolated to the muon chamber position. These differences were weighted by the uncertainty expected from measurement errors, energy loss and multiple scattering. Requiring these matching variables to be less than 3.0 removed the majority of the background to the $\mu^+\mu^-$ signal. We fit the resulting $\mu^+\mu^-$ mass distribution (Figure 1) to a Gaussian plus a constant background. The width of the Gaussian is $\sigma = 0.18$

GeV/c^2. Defining our J/ψ sample as those events with dimuon mass between 3.05 and 3.15 GeVc^2, we observe 896±32 reconstructed J/ψ events above a background of 45±8.

Photon candidates were selected by demanding an electromagnetic energy cluster in excess of 1 GeV and a cluster in the central electromagnetic strip chambers. We rejected photon candidates that occurred in the same calorimeter tower traversed by one of the muons. The photon direction was determined from the position of the strip chamber cluster and the muon pair vertex. The energy and direction of the photon candidate were combined with the muon momenta to determine the invariant mass of the $\mu^+\mu^-\gamma$ system. The mass difference [ΔM = mass($\mu^+\mu^-\gamma$) - mass($\mu^+\mu^-$)] distribution is shown in Figure 2. A clear χ_c signal is present, although the individual angular momentum states cannot be resolved.

The shape of the background spectrum was estimated using real J/ψ events containing charged tracks other than muons. The momenta of these tracks were used as input to a Monte Carlo that generated decays of neutral pions to two photons. The ΔM spectrum of these simulated photons and the J/ψ, weighted by the photon finding efficiency, was normalized to the sideband region of the observed spectrum.

The number of events was determined using a binned maximum likelihood technique to fit the ΔM distribution to a Gaussian signal plus the independently determined background shape. The fit resulted in a mean mass difference of .406 ± .013 GeV/c^2 with 67 ± 8 (statistical) signal events within one standard deviation of the expected average value. Uncertainty in the background shape contributes to the uncertainty in the observed number of χ_c mesons.

3. Efficiency Determination

Photon reconstruction efficiencies were measured by examining a sample of conversion electrons in which one of the electrons was selected using only tracking information. We calculate the electron efficiency from the number of electron tracks that pass the calorimeter and strip chamber criteria for photons. The resulting electron efficiency was corrected for a difference in calorimeter response between electrons and photons.

The combined χ_c detection efficiency for $\chi_c \to J/\psi\gamma$, $J/\psi \to \mu^+\mu^-$ is 0.80±0.22% where the uncertainty represents the sum in quadrature of all the systematic effects listed in the preceding discussion.

4. χ_c Production Cross Section

The cross section times branching fractions is determined using the formula:

$$\sigma(\bar{p}p \to \chi_c X \to J/\psi\gamma X \to \mu^+\mu^-\gamma X) = \frac{N_{\chi_c}}{\epsilon L}$$

where N_{χ_c} is the number of observed number of χ_c events, ϵ is the χ_c detection efficiency and L is the integrated luminosity. We obtain

$$\sigma(\bar{p}p \to \chi_c X \to J/\psi\gamma X \to \mu^+\mu^-\gamma X) = 3.2 \pm 0.4(\text{stat}) \pm 1.1(\text{sys}) \text{ nb},$$

where the result is the sum of the χ_c angular momentum states. The first uncertainty is statistical and the second combines in quadrature the systematic uncertainties due to the fitting procedure, the efficiency calculation, and the luminosity measurement.

5. b-quark Production Cross Section

To determine the b-quark cross section, recall that χ_c and B-meson decays dominate the total J/ψ production rate[1]. Thus, we can use the above result to subtract from the inclusive J/ψ cross section that portion due to χ_c decays, leaving the observed cross section times branching ratio for B-meson decay to J/ψ. The two cross sections can be compared directly since the two analyses used identical J/ψ samples. By multiplying the observed cross section by the ratio, obtained from Monte Carlo, of the b-quark cross section to the J/ψ cross section observed with a full detector simulation[1], we extract the b-quark cross section:

$$\sigma^b_{exp} =$$

$$\frac{Br(J/\psi \to \mu^+\mu^-)\sigma(\bar{p}p \to J\psi X)R}{2Br(B \to J\psi X|_{no\chi_c})Br(J\psi \to \mu^+\mu^-)},$$

where

$$R = \frac{\sigma^b_{MC}(P^b_T > P^{min}_t, |y^b| < 1)}{\sigma^{J/\psi}_{MC}(P^{J/\psi}_T > 6\ GeV/c, |\eta^{J/\psi}| < 0.5)}.$$

This implies

$$\sigma^b(P^b_T > 8.5\ GeV/c, |y^b| < 1) = 12.0 \pm 4.5\ \mu b.$$

6. References

1. F. Abe et al., submitted to Physical Review Letters.

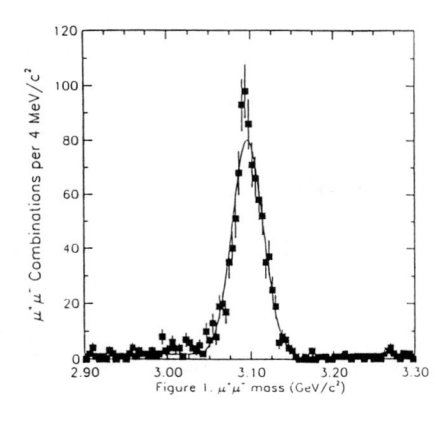

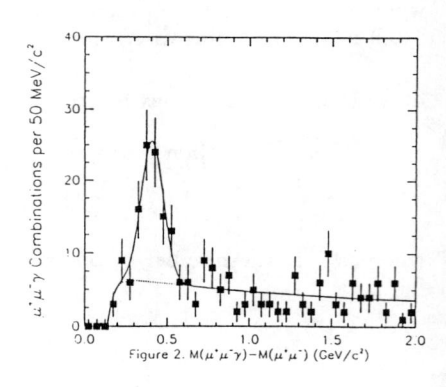

Figure 1. $\mu^+\mu^-$ mass (GeV/c^2)

Figure 2. $M(\mu^+\mu^-\gamma) - M(\mu^+\mu^-)$ (GeV/c^2)

THE BOTTOM QUARK CROSS SECTION IN $P\text{-}\overline{P}$ COLLISIONS FROM INCLUSIVE DECAYS TO MUONS

CDF Collaboration Presented by
B. TODD HUFFMAN
Physics Department, Purdue University
West Lafayette, IN 47907, USA

ABSTRACT

The study of b quarks at high energy hadron colliders tests the Standard Model in regions of small x and high transverse momentum. The method used to measure the b quark cross section using the semileptonic decay to muons is outlined. A preliminary CDF muon cross section is given using data from the 88-89 run, and a plot of the measured b quark cross section compared to other CDF preliminary results is shown.

1. Introduction

1.1. Motivation

The physics of heavy quarks in hadron colliders is calculable in the Standard Model.[1] At CDF the region of small x and high p_t is explored. The measurement of the b quark cross section provides experimental tests of the Standard Model in this region. In these proceedings we present the preliminary measurement of the b quark and muon cross sections using a data sample with an integrated luminosity of $3.79 \pm .26$ pb^{-1}.

1.2. Muon Data Set

The CDF detector is described elsewhere.[2, 3] Muons are collected by a multilevel trigger system.[4, 5] The first level required a track in the muon chamber above a p_t threshold. The second required the muon chamber track to match a charged track in the central tracking chamber (CTC) within $\pm 15°$. Level 3 required the intercepts of the CTC track and the muon track be within 10 cm in the local muon coordinate system.[4]

The following cuts were applied to the muon sample. We required the muon track had $p_t > 12$ GeV/c, that the z position of the track was within 10 cm of the event vertex, and that the impact parameter was less than .15 cm. Additionally the tower traversed by the muon candidate was required to have less than 5.0 GeV of hadronic energy.

Two other cuts required a match between the CTC and the muon tracks. A χ^2 variable was formed of the difference in slope and intercept in the $r\text{-}\phi$ plane weighted by the expected variance from multiple scattering. Additionally we cut on the weighted intercept difference in the $r\text{-}z$ plane. We required $\chi^2 < 10.0$ and

Table 1: The fraction of muons measured using a fit to muon and hadron distributions in $|\eta|$. The χ^2 per degree of freedom is also shown (there are 18 degrees of freedom).

p_t bin	muon+DIF frac.	fit error	χ^2 per D.O.F.
12 – 17 GeV/c	.55	±.01	.69
17 – 22 GeV/c	.47	±.04	.64

$|\Delta I_z/\sigma_{I_z}| < 3.0$.

2. Backgrounds

2.1. Non-interacting Punch-through

A kaon or pion may pass through the calorimeter without showering. In order to measure this background one uses the fact that a track with larger $|\eta|$[1] passes through more steel. The punch-through probability (P) goes as:

$$P = \exp(-\Lambda/\sin\theta) \qquad (1)$$

where Λ is the number of absorption lengths at normal incidence. After correcting for edge effects, Eq.(1) plus a line function with a slope of $-.17$ are fit to the data distribution in $|\eta|$ yielding the relative proportion of hadrons and muons+decays (DIF). Table 1 shows the fit results for the two muon transverse momentum bins. There is an additional estimated systematic uncertainty of ±.027 in the muon fractions.

2.2. Decays-in-Flight

There is no straightforward method of measuring the decay background in the muon data. Using the inclusive charged particle spectrum one can, however, calculate the decay-in-flight background. The inclusive charged particle spectrum was collected under a special trigger that required a track in the CTC above a p_t threshold of 7 GeV/c.

5000 kaons and pions were each simulated at integer p_t from 6 to 31 GeV/c and forced to decay prior to reaching the inner wall of the muon chamber. Hadrons showering before decaying were not included. The tracks were reconstructed and the offline cuts applied. The result was weighted by the inclusive charged particle spectrum and is insensitive to the K/π ratio. This is corrected for the offline cut efficiencies and subtracted from the muon candidates after removal of the hadronic background.

3. The Muon Cross Section

The background subtracted sample of muons must be divided by the trigger efficiency (ϵ_{trig}), the offline cut efficiency (ϵ_{off}), the acceptance in $-1 < y < 1$, and

---
[1] $\eta = \ln\cot(\theta/2)$ where θ is measured from the beam line.

Table 2: The preliminary muon cross section from b quarks integrated over 5 GeV/c bins.

σ_μ from $b+\bar{b}$ quarks integrated over 5 GeV/c	
p_t	σ_μ
12 – 17 GeV/c	$3.83 \pm .27 \pm .51$ nb
17 – 22 GeV/c	$.54 \pm .13 \pm .08$ nb

the integrated luminosity of the muon data. Additionally, the fraction of muons from charm decays must be estimated and removed.

The offline cut efficiency was measured using cosmic rays, W and Z bosons, and J/Ψ decays. The hadron energy cut was estimated using a detector simulation and the ISAJET b-$\bar{b}$ Monte Carlo. The combined cut efficiency is about 75% based on those sources. The trigger efficiency was measured elsewhere[6] and a value of $\epsilon_{trig} = .90 \pm .02$ was used here. The detector acceptance is $.421 \pm .002 \pm .011$ in a rapidity range from $-1 < y < 1$.

The charm fraction was estimated at $N_c/N_b = .15 \pm .08$ using the ISAJET Monte Carlo and varying the relative fragmentation of b and c quarks to B and D mesons. The muon cross section from b quark decays is shown in Table 2 with the statistical and estimated systematic errors.

4. b Quark Cross Section

$$\sigma_{p_t^b > p_t^{min}} = \frac{1}{2} \sigma_{\mu\, data} \frac{\sigma_{MC}(p_t^b > p_t^{min})}{\sigma_{MC}(12 < p_{t\mu^-} < 17)} \qquad (2)$$

Eq.(2) shows the method used to convert a muon cross section into a b cross section.[7] The value of p_t^{min} is set by running ISAJET and requiring 90% of the b quarks have $p_t^b > p_t^{min}$ that decayed into muons with transverse momentum in the given range. The factor of 1/2 corrects for using both μ^+ and μ^- in the data. The final result with the other CDF measurements is displayed in the article by Dr. Avi Yagil.[8]

6. References

1. P. Nason, S. Dawson, and R.K. Ellis, *Nucl. Phys.* **B327** (1989) 49.
2. F. Abe et al., *Nucl. Inst. and Meth.* **A271** (1988) 387.
3. G. Ascoli et al., *Nucl. Inst. and Meth.* **A286** (1988) 33.
4. G. Ascoli et al., *Nucl. Inst. and Meth.* **A269** (1988) 63.
5. G. W. Foster et al., *Nucl. Inst. and Meth.* **A269** (1988) 93.
6. F. Abe et al., *Phys. Rev. Lett.* **67** (1991) 2609.
7. C. Albajar et al., *Phys. Lett.* **B213** (1988) 405.
8. A. Yagil, these proceedings.

PRODUCTION OF J/ψ IN Z^0 DECAYS

Yuan-Hann Chang
Physics Department, Massachusetts Institute of Technology
Cambridge, MA 02139, USA

Representing the L3 Collaboration

ABSTRACT

Measurement on the production of J/ψ from the Z^0 decays by the L3 detector is presented. The branching ratios $Br(Z^0 \to J/\psi + X)$, $Br(Z^0 \to q\bar{q}g^*, g^* \to J/\psi + X)$, and $Br(B \to J/\psi + X)$ are determined. The b quark fragmentation function is also studied through $b \to J/\psi + X$ decays.

1. Introduction

The inclusive production of J/ψ in hadronic Z^0 decays is mainly from $Z^0 \to b\bar{b}$ decays where the b-quarks subsequently decays inclusively to J/ψ. This process is suppressed because the color of the two c quarks have to be the same to form a J/ψ. This suppression, however, could be reduced because of soft gluon radiation which corrects the color factor [1]. Measurement of the branching ratio therefore provides the information on the effect of soft QCD processes in hard quark production.

A second process of J/ψ production is through a hard virtue gluon radiates from one of the quarks from Z^0 decays. The gluon is subsequently converted to a J/ψ with soft fluon radiation to correct the color factor [2]. This process has low branching ratio because the virtue gluon is heavy and the color suppression. This process, however, gives a very distinctive signature as the J/ψ are produced with large angle relative to the quark jets.

This study measures the inclusive production of J/ψ from Z^0 decays through the above mentioned channels. Results on the branching ratios is shown.

2. The data sample

Data used in this analysis is collected by the L3 detector [3] at LEP. The L3 detector includes, from inside out, a time projection tracking chamber, BGO electromagnetic calorimeter, Uranium/gas proportional tube hadron calorimeter, and three layers of precision muon chambers. The whole detector is enclosed in a large magnet of 0.5 Tesla field.

Di-electron and Di-muon decay channels are used to identify the J/ψ signal in a jet. The electrons are identified by the shower profile in the BGO calorimeter and requiring a good matching between the track measured in the tracker and the BGO cluster. The momentum of the electrons are measured by the BGO. The muons are measured and identified by the muon chambers. The angle between the muon tracks are measured by the corresponding tracks in the central tracking chamber.

Data used in this analysis are collected during the LEP 1991 run, corresponding to ~ 410,000 hadronic events. The events are selected from the hadronic events requiring in addition two opposite sign electrons or muons with more than 2 GeV momentum in the same hemisphere. Due to energy resolution, only barrel detectors are used for this analysis. Monte-Carlo events based on JETSET 7.3, with full detector simulation by GEANT 3.15, are used to estimate the detection efficiency and the background contribution. The acceptance for $J/\psi \to e^+e^-$ coming from $b \to J/\psi + X$ is calculated to be 0.15 ± 0.01(stat). The acceptance of $J/\psi \to \mu\mu$ is calculated to be 0.28 ± 0.01(stat). In efficiency of the detector components are not simulated, but are calculated using the data. We find the efficiency to two electrons and two muons are $\epsilon_{ee} = 0.82 \pm 0.02$(stat) and $\epsilon_{\mu\mu} = 0.92 \pm 0.02$(stat), respectively.

Major background comes from the cascade semileptonic decays of the b-quarks, where the two decayed leptons reconstructed to the right invariant mass. Other backgrounds include one lepton from semileptonic b or c decay and one misidentified electron or muon; or two misidentified electrons or muons.

To determine the number of the J/ψ events, we fit the invariant mass distribution of the di-lepton pair with a gaussian for the J/ψ peak and a polynomial for the backgrounds. The polynomial and the width of the gaussian are determined from Monte-Carlo study. From the fit, we find 43 ± 8 dimuon events and 15 ± 5 dielectron events.

2. Determination of $\mathrm{Br}(Z^0 \to J + X)$

The branching ratio $\mathrm{Br}(Z^0 \to J + X)$ is determined by normalizing the observed J/ψ events to the total hadronic events:

$$\mathrm{Br}(Z^0 \to J + X) = \frac{N_J}{\epsilon_J \cdot \epsilon_{\ell^+\ell^-}} \cdot \frac{\epsilon_h}{N_h} \cdot \frac{\Gamma_h}{\Gamma_Z} \cdot \frac{1}{\mathrm{Br}(J \to \ell^+\ell^-)}$$

where N_J and N_h are the number of the J meson signal events and the total number of hadronic Z^0 decays, respectively, and ϵ_h is the selection efficiency for hadronic events [4]. ϵ_J denotes the geometric and kinematic acceptance for the J meson, while $\epsilon_{\ell^+\ell^-}$ takes into account detector inefficiencies that are not included in the Monte Carlo simulation.

Combining the ee and $\mu\mu$ channels, and using the recent result $\mathrm{Br}(J \to \ell^+\ell^-) = 0.0590 \pm 0.0015$ (stat.) ± 0.0019 (sys.) from Mark-III [5], we find:

$$\mathrm{Br}(Z^0 \to J + X) = (4.1 \pm 0.7 \text{ (stat.)} \pm 0.3 \text{ (sys.)}) \times 10^{-3}.$$

Systematics are estimated by varying the selection cuts and including the errors in $\mathrm{Br}(J \to \ell^+\ell^-)$.

3. Upper limits of $\mathrm{Br}(Z^0 \to q\bar{q}g^*; g^* \to J + X)$

The J/ψ production from virtual gluon radiation is characterized by the large angle between the J/ψ and the quark jets. We define the angle between the

J/ψ to the most energetic jet to be θ_J. To enhance the signals from the virtual gluon production, we selected the events by requiring $20° < \theta_J < 160°$. The resulting θ_J distribution are then fitted with the MC distribution. We found that the fraction of events from the virtual gluon radiation is

$$f_g = 0.03^{+0.08}_{-0.06} \text{ (stat.)} \pm 0.02 \text{ (sys.)}$$

which is consistent with 0. We therefore set the upper limit of J/ψ production from gluon radiation to be

$$\text{Br}(Z^0 \to q\bar{q}g^*; g^* \to J + X) < 7.0 \times 10^{-4}$$

at 90% confidence level.

4. Determination of $\text{Br}(b \to J + X)$

The branching ration $\text{Br}(b \to J + X)$ is determined by

$$\text{Br}(b \to J + X) = \frac{\Gamma_Z}{2 \cdot \Gamma_{b\bar{b}}} \cdot (1 - f_g) \cdot \text{Br}(Z^0 \to J + X).$$

We used the values of Γ_Z and $\Gamma_{b\bar{b}}$ from L3 measurements, and find

$$\text{Br}(b \to J + X) = (1.3 \pm 0.2 \text{ (stat.)} \pm 0.2 \text{ (sys.)}) \times 10^{-2}.$$

5. b-quark Fragmentation

Since the J/ψ is produced dominantly from the B-mesons, the momentum distribution of J/ψ carrys information of the momentum of the B-mesons. It is therefore a good channel to study the fragmentation function of the b-quarks. We assumed the Peterson fragmentation function and determine the parameter ϵ_b by maximal likelihood fit to the momentum spectrum of the J/ψ. We obtain

$$\epsilon_b = 0.044^{+0.026}_{-0.018} \text{ (stat.)}^{+0.009}_{-0.013} \text{ (sys.)},$$

corresponding to the fraction of beam energy carried by b-hadrons, $\langle x_B \rangle$, of

$$\langle x_B \rangle = 0.70 \pm 0.03 \text{ (stat.)}^{+0.02}_{-0.01} \text{ (sys.)}.$$

6. Summary

The analysis of J/ψ production through B-meson decay and virtual gluon radiation at Z^0 peak is carried out. The branching ratios of J/ψ production and the b-quark fragmentation has been studied. We obtained:

$$\text{Br}(Z^0 \to J + X) = (4.1 \pm 0.7 \text{ (stat.)} \pm 0.3 \text{ (sys.)}) \times 10^{-3}.$$

$$\text{Br}(Z^0 \to q\bar{q}g^*; g^* \to J + X) < 7.0 \times 10^{-4}$$

at 90% confidence level.

$$Br(b \to J + X) = (1.3 \pm 0.2 \,(\text{stat.}) \pm 0.2 \,(\text{sys.})) \times 10^{-2}.$$

$$\langle x_B \rangle = 0.70 \pm 0.03 \,(\text{stat.})^{+0.02}_{-0.01} \,(\text{sys.}).$$

7. References

1. J. H. Kühn, S. Nussinov and R. Rückl, Z. Phys. **C 5** (1980) 117;
   J. H. Kühn and R. Rückl, Phys. Lett. **B 135** (1984) 477;
   M. B. Wise, Phys. Lett. **B 89** (1980) 229;
   P. H. Cox et al., Phys. Rev. **D 32** (1985) 1157;

2. G. C. Branco, H. P. Nilles and K. H. Streng, Phys. Lett. **B 85** (1979) 269.
3. L3 Collaboration, B. Adeva et al., Nucl. Inst. and Meth. **A289** (1990) 35.
4. L3 Collaboration, B. Adeva et al., Z. Phys. **C 51** (1991) 179.
5. MARK-III Collaboration, D. Coffman et al., Phys. Rev. Lett. **68** (1992) 282.

THE RATE FOR $e^+e^- \to BB^{\pm}\pi^{\mp}$

AND ITS IMPLICATION FOR THE STUDY OF CP VIOLATION

LAURENT LELLOUCH,[1] LISA RANDALL[†] AND ERIC SATHER
*Center for Theoretical Physics, Department of Physics, Massachusetts Institute of Technology
Cambridge, MA 02139, U.S.A.*

ABSTRACT

H. Yamamoto[1] has proposed using B mesons produced with a charged pion at an Υ resonance to study CP violation in the B^0-$\bar{B}^0$ system at a symmetric e^+-e^- collider. The pion charge tags the neutral B meson. We estimate the branching ratio for this process using the combined heavy-quark and chiral effective field theory and find that it is insufficient for CP-violation studies at the known Υ resonances. However, at energies just above the resonance region this may be a useful method of tagging neutral B's for CP-violation studies at a symmetric collider.

1. Introduction

On the $\Upsilon(4S)$ resonance, measurement of a CP-violating asymmetry in the decays of B^0 and $\bar{B}^0$ into a CP eigenstate requires an asymmetric e^+-e^- collider. Because the B mesons are produced in a $C = -1$ state, the time-integrated asymmetry, accessible to a symmetric collider, is zero. However, the time-integrated asymmetry is not zero if the B mesons are in a $C = +1$ state. For example, above the 4S one can produce $B^{*0}\bar{B}^0$ (or $B^0\bar{B}^{*0}$); then $B^* \to B\gamma$ leaving $B^0\bar{B}^0$ with $C = +1$ (since $C_\gamma = -1$).

An alternative, proposed by H. Yamamoto,[1] is to produce B and B^* mesons accompanied by a charged pion. The pion charge tags the single neutral B meson as B^0 or $\bar{B}^0$. Neutral B^* mesons can also be used since they decay into pseudoscalars. Unlike the two methods listed above, almost all the events are tagged.

To assess the usefulness of $\Upsilon \to BB^{\pm}\pi^{\mp}$ for CP-violation studies, we estimate the $BB^{\pm}\pi^{\mp}$ branching ratio using heavy-quark and chiral methods. Our calculation also allows us to estimate the background for B_s production at the $\Upsilon(5S)$.

2. Effective Theory

In our description of $BB^{\pm}\pi^{\mp}$ production we directly apply heavy-quark effective theory (HQET). In the resonance region, interactions between the heavy quarks imply that the assumptions that lead to HQET are not fully realized, and so our results are only qualitative at these energies. Beyond the resonances, however, our calculation should be accurate, at least when restricted to the region of phase space where the pion energy is small enough that we can trust first-order chiral perturbation theory.

---

[1]Present address: Department of Physics, University of Southampton, Highfield, Southampton, SO9 5NH, U.K.

Since $e^+e^- \to BB^\pm\pi^\mp$ proceeds through a virtual photon or, for some energies, via an Υ resonance, we treat the initial state as a vector source, S^μ, that couples to the bottom quarks in the B mesons. The cross section is proportional to the source width. While interactions with the light quarks cannot flip a heavy-quark spin, interactions between the heavy quarks can flip their spins. The total spin of the heavy quarks is conserved, however, and hence the spin of the source is transferred entirely to the heavy-quark spins. This is incorporated in the HQET by coupling the B-field heavy quark labels to the source as $\overline{\mathbf{B}}(v)S^\mu\gamma_\mu\underline{\mathbf{B}}(v)$. Here $\mathbf{B}(v)$ is the field of $\bar{B}$ mesons and $\underline{\mathbf{B}}(v)$ is the field of B mesons. (Because we treat the heavy mesons as nonrelativistic, we take both heavy-quark velocities to be $v^\mu = (1,0,0,0)$.)

We work to lowest order in the chiral expansion and treat the B mesons as nonrelativistic. These are reliable approximations except at high energy. Our effective lagrangian is

$$\mathcal{L}_{\text{eff}} = -i\text{tr}\{\overline{\mathbf{B}}_a(v)v^\mu\partial_\mu\mathbf{B}_a(v) + \overline{\underline{\mathbf{B}}}_a(v)v^\mu\partial_\mu\underline{\mathbf{B}}_a(v)\} + g\text{tr}\{[\overline{\mathbf{B}}_a(v)\mathbf{B}_b(v) + \underline{\mathbf{B}}_a(v)\overline{\underline{\mathbf{B}}}_b(v)]A^\nu_{ba}\gamma_\nu\gamma_5\}$$
$$+ (-i\lambda/2)S^\mu\text{tr}\{\gamma_\mu\overline{\mathbf{B}}_a(v)\overleftrightarrow{D}^\nu_{ab}\gamma_\nu\underline{\mathbf{B}}_b(v)\} + \lambda S^\mu g'\text{tr}\{\gamma_\mu\overline{\mathbf{B}}_a(v)A^\nu_{ab}\gamma_\nu\gamma_5\underline{\mathbf{B}}_b(v)\} \quad (1)$$

Here $D = \partial + V$ is the chiral covariant derivative, and V and A are the vector and axial fields constructed from the pion fields. Since B mesons produced alone must be in at least a p-wave in order to conserve parity, the leading term in the decay of the source into B mesons is proportional to $\Delta k = k - k'$, where k and k' are the residual momenta of the B mesons.

The kinetic and axial coupling terms for the B mesons have been discussed before and are the straightforward result of heavy-quark and chiral effective theory.[2]

3. Calculation of $\sigma(e^+e^- \to BB^\pm\pi^\mp)/\sigma(e^+e^- \to B\bar{B})$

To compare $BB^\pm\pi^\mp$ with $B\bar{B}$ as a source of neutral B mesons, we divide the $BB^\pm\pi^\mp$ cross sections by $\sigma_0 \equiv \sigma(e^+e^- \to B^0\bar{B}^0,\ B^0\bar{B}^{*0},\ B^{*0}\bar{B}^0,\ \text{or}\ B^{*0}\bar{B}^{*0})$. We consider

$$R_{\text{PP}} = \sum_\pm \sigma(e^+e^- \to B\bar{B}\pi^\pm)/\sigma_0, \qquad R_{\text{VV}} = \sum_\pm \sigma(e^+e^- \to B^*\bar{B}^*\pi^\pm)/\sigma_0,$$
$$R_{\text{PV}} = \sum_\pm \sigma(e^+e^- \to B\bar{B}^*\pi^\pm\ \text{or}\ B^*\bar{B}\pi^\pm)/\sigma_0, \quad (2)$$

and their sum, $R = R_{\text{PP}} + R_{\text{PV}} + R_{\text{VV}}$. The subscripts denote the heavy-meson content of the $BB^\pm\pi^\mp$ final state, with a P for each pseudoscalar and a V for each vector. In the ratios, R_α, λ and kinematic factors associated with the initial state cancel out.

The $B\bar{B}$ cross sections are, apart from a common factor, each a product of a p-wave phase-space factor and a spin-counting factor.[3] Hence σ_0 is proportional to a sum of such products: $\sigma_0 \propto r_{\text{PP}}^{3/2} + 4r_{\text{PV}}^{3/2} + 7r_{\text{VV}}^{3/2} \equiv P(s)$. Here r_α is the center-of-mass energy that remains after supplying the rest-mass energies of the heavy mesons: $r_{\text{PP}} = \sqrt{s} - 2M_B$, $r_{\text{PV}} = \sqrt{s} - M_B - M_{B^*}$ and $r_{\text{VV}} = \sqrt{s} - 2M_{B^*}$. Note that we include heavy-quark symmetry violation via the B-B^* mass splitting, $\Delta M = 46\,\text{MeV}$, which significantly affects the phase space and the off-shellness of intermediate B mesons.

Our results are

$$R_\alpha(s) = \frac{2g^2}{3\pi^2 f_\pi^2 P(s)} \int_{m_\pi}^{r_\alpha} dE_\pi p_\pi^3 (r_\alpha - E_\pi)^{3/2} \times \begin{cases} (E_\pi - \Delta M)^{-2}, & \alpha = \text{PP}; \\ \frac{7}{4}(E_\pi - \Delta M)^{-2} + \frac{3}{4}(E_\pi + \Delta M)^{-2} \\ \quad + E_\pi^{-2} + \frac{1}{2}(E_\pi^2 - (\Delta M)^2)^{-1}, & \alpha = \text{PV}; \\ 5E_\pi^{-2} + 2(E_\pi + \Delta M)^{-2}, & \alpha = \text{VV}. \end{cases} \quad (3)$$

Because the B mesons are so much more massive than the pion, the maximum pion energy is essentially r_α. For $\Delta M \ll r_\alpha \ll M_B$, $R_{\text{PP}} : R_{\text{PV}} : R_{\text{VV}} :: 1 : 4 : 7$. (From the formula above for σ_0, we see that the relative probabilities of producing heavy mesons with either 0, 1, or 2 as vector mesons do not depend on whether a pion is emitted from one of the heavy mesons.) For $g^2 = 0.5$, R is only 0.3% at the $\Upsilon(5S)$ and 2% at the $\Upsilon(6S)$. But R grows with energy to order unity at about 12 GeV as the limited phase space for pion production is overcome. We need to ask whether lowest-order chiral perturbation theory can be trusted at such large energies. We find that for a large fraction of phase space the pion energy is sufficiently small for our calculations to be reliable.

Our calculation also allows us to estimate the background for B_s production at the $\Upsilon(5S)$. Anticipated studies of B_s mesons would distinguish them from the lighter, nonstrange B mesons by their smaller momenta. Nonstrange B mesons produced with a pion also have less momentum and are background for B_s identification. For a large B_s-B mass splitting (130 MeV) the background is about 1/2, but for smaller splittings it should be negligible.

4. Conclusion

At the known $\Upsilon(5S)$ and $\Upsilon(6S)$ resonances the pion-tagging method is not competitive with the favored method for CP-violation studies at a symmetric collider, $\Upsilon \to B^0 \bar{B}^0 \gamma$. However, around 12 GeV, a pion should accompany the B pair as often as not. Although beyond the resonances, this might be the best place to search for CP violation in the $B^0 \bar{B}^0$ system at a symmetric collider.

This work is supported in part by Texas National Research Laboratory Commission #RGFY92C6 and U. S. Department of Energy #DE-AC02-76ER03069.
[†]National Science Foundation Young Investigator Award.
Department of Energy Outstanding Junior Investigator Award.
Alfred P. Sloan Foundation Research Fellowship.

References

1. H. Yamamoto, Cornell University note CBX 92-94, to be published.
2. M. B. Wise, *Phys. Rev.* **D45** (1992) 2188.
3. A. De Rújula, H. Georgi and S. Glashow, *Phys. Rev. Lett.* **37** (1976) 398.

D. Rare Decays, CP and T Violation

Conveners: I. I. BIGI (U. of Notre Dame)
L. S. LITTENBERG (BNL)
Liaison: B. WINSTEIN (U. of Chicago)

STRINGY CPT VIOLATION AND THE $K\bar{K}$ SYSTEM

V. ALAN KOSTELECKÝ[1]
*Physics Department, Indiana University,
Bloomington, IN 47405, U.S.A*

and

ROBERTUS POTTING
*U.C.E.H., Universidade do Algarve, Campus de Gambelas,
8000 Faro, Portugal*

ABSTRACT

This talk outlines our results on CPT in string theories, including dynamical CPT invariance and spontaneous CPT violation. If realized in nature, stringy CPT violation could appear at levels detectable in the next generation of experiments. We present an estimate of the induced values of parameters for CPT violation in the $K\bar{K}$ system.

1. Introduction

Any description of the fundamental forces and interactions must eventually face the issue of whether it predicts physical effects that are unique to the theory and are experimentally observable. Such effects are to be expected in string theory, at least at the string scale, because a string is qualitatively different from a particle. However, there is a folklore to the effect that they are unobservable in current experiments because present energy scales are at best only about 10^{-17} of the natural string scale. While it must be true that the low-energy effective theory is well approximated by a four-dimensional renormalizable gauge field theory, this folklore overlooks the possibility of tiny but observable corrections to the low-energy effective theory that could not appear in a purely particle model.

Although definitive statements about such corrections are difficult to make in the absence of a satisfactory realistic string theory, it is nonetheless feasible to address the possibility of their existence. Given the presence of the suppression factor 10^{-17}, it is reasonable to focus on possible violations of results believed to be exact in particle theory that can be measured in high-precision experiments.

The CPT theorem[1] is a general theoretical result holding for local relativistic point-particle field theories satisfying a few mild restrictions. Experimentally, the present limit on CPT violation arises from observations of the $K\bar{K}$ system, where the figure of merit is currently[2] $(m_K - m_{\bar{K}})/m_K \lesssim 5 \times 10^{-18}$. The extended nature of strings makes it unclear a priori whether they satisfy the CPT theorem, so the generality of the theoretical result for particle physics along with the precision of the

---
[1]Speaker

experimental limit make CPT violation a natural candidate for a string signature.

2. Dynamical CPT for Strings

Our earlier work[3] includes a study of the field theory of the open bosonic string[4] and the class of field theories for the open superstring.[5] We define a consistent set of C, P, and T transformations at the level of the string fields and obtain suitable Fock-space operator representations. To verify dynamical CPT invariance, it suffices to demonstrate invariance under these transformations of the actions and of the interacting-theory quantization. We find that the open bosonic string is invariant under C, P, T, and CPT. In contrast, the actions proposed for the open superstring violate each of the three symmetries independently, but nonetheless preserve CPT. The violations of P and T are to be expected in a ten-dimensional theory with massless chiral fermions, but the C violation is not. To avoid this, a modified action can be found that does not violate C or CPT.

Most of the basic assumptions made in our analysis are standard, such as the reality of observables and the correct spin-statistics assignment (including in this case the use of the GSO projection). Normal ordering is unnecessary, however, due to the cyclic symmetry of the string vertices. In any event, the qualitative differences between the particle and string quantum field theories are apparently insufficient to cause dynamical CPT violation.

3. Spontaneous CPT Breaking and the $K\bar{K}$ System

The remaining issue is that of invariance of the vacuum. This is nontrivial because string theory has a natural mechanism for spontaneous breaking of Lorentz invariance,[6] which can also induce CPT violation. Briefly, the point is that there exist couplings in string field theory that are forbidden in standard models by particle gauge invariance but that are compatible with the full string gauge invariance. When scalars acquire expectation values, these couplings can induce instabilities in the effective potentials for Lorentz tensors. Nonzero expectation values for one or more Lorentz tensors may result, breaking Lorentz symmetry. If the tensors in question change sign under CPT, the shifted lagrangian also violates CPT.

The issue of interest here is whether any observable effects could arise from spontaneous CPT breaking. If so, they must be heavily suppressed to be compatible with current limits. Suppose that there is a realistic effective four-dimensional model based on a fundamental string theory in which spontaneous CPT violation occurs. A crude estimate of the scale of the effects can be made. One expects a suppression related to the ratio of the relevant light scale to the string (Planck) scale. Presumably, the light scale is the electroweak scale or smaller, so one might expect a suppression of at least 17 orders of magnitude.

To make this more explicit, consider interactions appearing in the realistic four-dimensional low-energy effective theory of the form $\lambda m_P^{-k} T \cdot \bar{\psi} \Gamma (i\partial)^k \chi$ with $k \geq 0$. Here, λ is a dimensionless coupling, T is a four-dimensional Lorentz tensor, ψ and

χ are (possibly different) four-dimensional fermions, Γ represents a gamma-matrix structure, and $(i\partial)^k$ represents k derivatives. Suppose T acquires a vev $\langle T \rangle = r^l m_P t$, where t represents a numerical matrix, $r = m_l/m_P$ is the ratio of the light scale to the Planck scale and the term r^l allows for the suppression of the vev of T in line with the known hierarchy in nature. If the fermions are assumed light, then $k + l \geq 1$. Furthermore, if T carries nontrivial Lorentz structure a realistic model presumably has $\langle T \rangle \ll m_l$, i.e., $l \geq 2$. The issue is then whether $k = 0, l = 2$ terms are observable.

A candidate system for observing effects from such terms is the $K\bar{K}$ system. One example of an interaction affecting this system is $\lambda T_{\lambda\mu\nu}\bar{\psi}\gamma^\lambda\gamma^\mu\gamma^\nu\chi$, where the fermions ψ and χ are taken as the d and/or s quarks. Here, an expectation value lying along T_{000} results in energy changes for the quarks and in d-s mixings. The energy changes induce opposite-sign shifts in the diagonal terms of the $K\bar{K}$ effective hamiltonian. An analysis[3] shows that the result is a nonzero contribution to the parameter δ that measures CPT violation, given by $\delta \simeq i(h_d - h_s)e^{i\phi_\epsilon}/(\sqrt{2}\Delta m)$, where $\Delta m \simeq (3.522 \pm 0.016) \times 10^{-15}$ GeV and $\phi_\epsilon \simeq 43.68 \pm 0.14°$ are experimentally measured quantities.[7] The contribution to h_s and h_d from this sample term has the form $h_{d,s} = r_{d,s}\lambda_{d,s}tm_l^2/m_P$, with $r_{d,s}$ representing QCD correction factors allowing for the confinement of the d and s quarks in the kaons. We see that with real energy shifts Re $\delta \simeq -$ Im δ, and a realistic model might have contributions to δ of order 10^{-6} to 10^{-4}. Note that because the quark-energy shifts do not enter directly into matrix elements of decays, the only effects expected arise from the contributions to δ in the mass matrix and the decay parameters. Values for δ within the range cited are likely to be probed in Φ factories such as those proposed at Frascati or Novosibirsk or the novel asymmetric Φ factory under consideration at UCLA.[8]

4. Acknowledgments

We thank David Cline, Julia Thompson, and Stuart Samuel for discussions.

5. References

1. See, for example, R.F. Streater and A.S. Wightman, *PCT, Spin and Statistics, and All That*, Benjamin Cummings, Reading, 1964.
2. R. Carosi et al., Phys. Lett. B **237** (1990) 303.
3. V.A. Kostelecký and R. Potting, Nucl. Phys. **B359** (1991) 545; Indiana University preprint IUHET 236 (October 1992).
4. E. Witten, Nucl. Phys. **B268** (1986) 253.
5. C. Preitschopf, C.B. Thorn and S.A. Yost, Nucl. Phys. **B337** (1990) 363; I.Ya. Aref'eva, P. Medvedev and A. Zubarev, Nucl. Phys. **B341** (1990) 464.
6. V.A. Kostelecký and S. Samuel, Phys. Rev. D **39** (1989) 683; Phys. Rev. Lett. **63** (1989) 224; Phys. Rev. D **40** (1989) 1886.
7. Review of Particle Properties, Phys. Rev. D **45** (1992) no. 11-II.
8. D.B. Cline, UCLA preprint CAA0091 (May 1992).

Preliminary Results from the Analysis of K^0 and $\bar{K}^0$ Semileptonic Decays from the CPLEAR Collaboration

D. Zimmerman
Boston University, 590 Commonwealth Ave. Boston, MA

Representing

The CPLEAR Collaboration

R. Adler[2], T. Alhalel[11], A. Angelopoulos[1], A. Apostolakis[1], E. Aslanides[7,11], G. Backenstoss[2], C.P. Bee[7], J. Bennet[9], V. Bertin[11], J.K. Bienlein[17,a], P. Bloch[7], Ch. Bula[16], P. Carlson[14], J. Carvalho[4], E. Cawley[9], S. Charalambous[15], M. Chardalas[15], G. Chardin[13], M. Danielsson[14], S. Dedoussis[15], M. Dejardin[7], J. Derre[13], M. Dodgson[9,b], J.-C. Dousse[6], J. Duclos[13], A. Ealet[11], B. Eckart[2], C. Eleftheriadis[15], I. Evangelou[8], L. Faravel[6], P. Fassnacht[11], J.L. Faure[13], C. Felder[2], R. Ferreira-Marques[4], W. Fetscher[17], M. Fidecaro[7], A. Filipčič[10], D. Francis[13], J. Fry[9], C. Fuglesang[14,c], E. Gabathuler[9], R. Gamet[9], D. Garreta[7,13], T. Geralis[16], H.-J. Gerber[17], A. Go[3], P. Gumplinger[17,d], C. Guyot[13], P.F. Harrison[9,e], P.J. Hayman[9], W.G. Heyes[7,f], R.W. Hollander[5], K. Jansson[14], H.J. Johner[6,g], K. Jon-And[14], A. Kerek[14], J. Kern[6], P.R. Kettle[16], C. Kochowski[13], P. Kokkas[8], R. Kreuger[5], T. Lawry[3,h], R. Le Gac[12], A. Liolios[15], E. Machado[4], P. Maley[9], I. Mandić[10], N. Manthos[8], G. Marel[13], M. Mikuž[10], J. Miller[3], F. Montanet[11], T. Nakada[16], A. Onofre[4], B. Pagels[2], P. Pavlopoulos[2], F. Pelucchi[11], J. Pinto da Cunha[4], A. Policarpo[4], G. Polivka[2], H. Postma[5], R. Rickenbach[2], B.L. Roberts[3], E. Rozaki[1], T. Ruf[17], L. Sacks[9], L. Sakeliou[1], P. Sanders[9], C. Santoni[2], K. Sarigiannis[1], M. Schäfer[17], L.A. Schaller[6], A. Schopper[7], P. Schune[13], A. Soares[13], S. Szilagyi[14,i], L. Tauscher[2], C. Thibault[12], F. Touchard[12], C. Touramanis[15], F. Triantis[8], D.A. Tröster[2,j], E. Van Beveren[4], M. Van den Putte[5], C.W.E. Van Eijk[5], G. Varner[3], S. Vlachos[9], P. Weber[17], O. Wigger[16], C. Witzig[17,k], M. Wolter[17], C. Yeche[13], D. Zavrtanik[10] and D. Zimmerman[3].

[1]University of Athens, GR-10680 Athens, Greece, [2]University of Basle, CH-4056 Basle, Switzerland
[3]Boston U., Boston, MA 02215, USA, [4]LIP and University of Coimbra, P-3000 Coimbra, Portugal
[5]T U Delft, 2629 JB Delft, Netherlands, [6]University of Fribourg, CH-1700 Fribourg, Switzerland
[7]CERN, CH-1211 Geneva 23, Switzerland, [8]University of Ioannina, GR-45110 Ioannina, Greece
[9]University of Liverpool, Liverpool L69 3BX, UK, [10]J. Stefan Institute and Department of Physics, University of Ljubljana, YU-61111 Ljubljana, Slovenia
[11]CPPM, IN2P3-CNRS et Université d'Aix-Marseille II, F-13288 Marseille, France
[12]CSNSM, IN2P3-CNRS, F-91405 Orsay, France, [13]DAPNIA/SPP, CE Saclay, F-91191 Gif-sur-Yvette, France
[14]MSI, S-10405 Stockholm, Sweden [15]University of Thessaloniki, GR-54006 Thessaloniki, Greece
[16]PSI, CH-5232 Villigen, Switzerland, [17]ETH-IMP Zürich, CH-8093 Zürich, Switzerland
[a]Permanent address: DESY, Hamburg, Germany, [b]Now at ECP/SA, CERN, Switzerland
[c]Now at ESA/EAC, Köln, Germany, [d]Now at TRIUMF, Vancouver, Canada
[e]Now at QMW, U of London, England, [f]Now at CEBAF, Newport News, VA, USA
[g]Now at SUeR, Fribourg University, Switzerland, [h]Now at University of Virginia, USA
[i]Permanent address: Atomki, Debrecen, Hungary, [j]Now at SBS, Basle, Switzerland
[k]Now at Brookhaven National Laboratory, LI, NY, USA

ABSTRACT

The CPLEAR experiment at CERN studies CP violation in the neutral kaon system by tagging the K^0 and $\bar{K}^0$ states produced in proton antiproton annihilations at rest. CP violation can be observed for different final states through the difference in partial decay difference between the particles and antiparticles. Preliminary results from the analysis of the semileptonic decay channels are presented.

1. The CPLEAR Experiment

By observing the partial decay rates of K^0 and $\bar{K}^0$ into different final states $|f>$, the CPLEAR experiment can measure many of the parameters describing CP violation in the neutral kaon system [1]. Among these parameters are:

- In the $\pi^+\pi^-$, final state: $|\eta_{+-}|$ and φ_{+-}, a phase angle describing CP violation in the $K^0 \to |\pi^+, \pi^- >$ decay, in addition to a test of CPT invariance.

- In the $\pi^+\pi^-\pi^0$, final state: $|\eta_{+-0}|$ which measures the CP violating component of the CP = -1 eigenstate.

In particular, from the semileptonic decay channels, the analysis of which will be presented here, one can extract the values of the following CP violation parameters, (following the parameterization used in [1]).

- ϵ_T, which is a direct measure of T violation [3].

- ϵ_S, the parameter which describes the CP violating component of the K_S eigenstate.

- δm, the mass difference between K_S and K_L which is an important quantity for the determination of φ_{+-}.

- The parameter x, which provides a test of the $\Delta S = \Delta Q$ rule [1].

The CPLEAR experiment measure particle-antiparticle decay asymmetries of K^0 and $\bar{K}^0$ decays into a number of final states. The K^0 and $\bar{K}^0$ are produced in proton-antiproton annihilation at rest through the interactions:

$p\bar{p} \to K^-\pi^+K^0$, $Branching Ratio = 2 \times 10^{-3}$
$p\bar{p} \to K^+\pi^-\bar{K}^0$ $Branching Ratio = 2 \times 10^{-3}$

The antiprotons are provided by the LEAR accelerator at CERN. Because of strangeness conservation in the strong interaction, the strangeness of the neutral kaon can be tagged by measuring the charge of the accompanying charged kaon.

All charged particles in the event are reconstucted by tracking chambers and all neutrals are reconstructed by an electromagnetic calorimeter. Full particle identification is done by the PID detector [4], a scintillator/cerenkov sandwich. In order to deal with the low branching ratios for our production channels, and large backgrounds, full event reconstruction is performed online by custom processors. For a complete description of the detector refer to [2].

2. The Semileptonic Analysis.

This experiment offers a unique opportunity for the study of CP violation in the kaon system. In particular, it allows the first opportunity to directly measure time reversal (T) violation symmetry.

Thus far, the phenomenon of CP violation has been observed in the neutral kaon system only in the decays of K_L into two pions and in the charge asymmetry of K_L semileptonic decays. Assuming CPT invariance, one expects T symmetry to be violated to the same extent as the CP symmetry. This expected T violation is measured directly using the semileptonic decays of the neutral kaons by detecting a possible difference in the transition rates $R(\overline{K^0} \to K^0)$ and $R(K^0 \to \overline{K^0})$ [3]. This difference is measurable because the semileptonic decay of the neutral kaon is, in the Standard Model, governed by the $\Delta S = \Delta Q$ rule, according to which the following semileptonic decay channels are allowed

$$K^0 \to \pi^- l^+ \nu_l \tag{1}$$
$$\overline{K^0} \to \pi^+ l^- \overline{\nu_l} \tag{2}$$

and the following decay channels are forbidden

$$K^0 \to \pi^+ l^- \overline{\nu_l} \tag{3}$$
$$\overline{K^0} \to \pi^- l^+ \nu_l. \tag{4}$$

Assuming this rule, the strangeness of the decaying K^0 ($\overline{K^0}$) is tagged by the sign of the charged lepton. Neutral kaons produced with a given strangeness can decay according to (3) and (4) due to oscillations between K^0 and $\overline{K^0}$. By comparing the rates for each of these channels as a function of the eigentime of the decay, we have extracted values for the parameters that characterize the oscillations between K^0 and $\bar{K}^0$ [1]. We have measured: δm, the K_L-K_S mass difference, x, the parameter which describes the violation of the $\Delta S = \Delta Q$ rule and ϵ_S, the parameter describing the CP violating component of the K_S. In addition to these measurements, we have a preliminary value for the first measurement of ϵ_T, the parameter which describes directly the T violating part of the kaon decay amplitude.

2. The Data Analysis

In the current analysis the electrons and positrons are identified using the particle identification detector (PID). [4]. We have used the Cherenkov and scintillator pulse heights to separate secondary $e^\pm$ from $\pi^\pm$ in the momentum range up to

250 MeV/c. In the future the use of the electromagnetic calorimeter should enable identification of $e^{\pm}$ in the full momentum range, thus increasing the efficiency of detecting $e^{\pm}$ by almost a factor of two. To further clean the semileptonic event sample kinematic constrained fits are used.

The results presented here are based on a sample of 42000 events which passed the selection criteria as $K^0(\overline{K^0}) \to \pi^{\pm}e^{\mp}\overline{\nu}_e(\nu_e)$ events. The residual contamination is estimated at about 2% for $\pi^+\pi^-$ decays and about 0.5% for $\pi^+\pi^-\pi^0$ decays.

2.1. Results

These data were corrected for the kaon normalisation and the particle identification efficiency ratio and fitted to compute the follwing parameters:

$$\begin{aligned}
\Delta m &= [0.523 \pm 0.018(stat.)^{+0.007}_{-0.001}(syst.)] \times 10^{10}\hbar s^{-1} \\
Re(x) &= -0.11 \pm 0.065(stat.)^{+0.02}_{-0.006}(syst.) \\
Im(x) &= [22 \pm 32(stat.) \pm 12(syst.)] \times 10^{-3} \\
Re(\epsilon_S) &= [4.0 \pm 2.7(stat.) \pm 2.3(syst.)] \times 10^{-3}. \\
Re(\epsilon_T) &= [2.1 \pm 1.1(stat.) \pm 3.9(syst.)] \times 10^{-3}.
\end{aligned}$$

2.2. Systematic Errors

The main contributions to the systematic errors are the statistical uncertainties in the value of the $\overline{K^0}/K^0$ flux ratio and the efficiency for detecting a secondary $e^-\pi^+$ pair to that of detecting an $e^+\pi^-$ pair. Work is in progress to improve the precision of the secondary identification background using calibration samples of pions from multipionic annihilations and electrons and positrons from photon conversions. The presented systematic errors should be considered as the present upper limits. The full statistics and the dedicated calibrations of the detector will reduce these systematic errors to practically one fourth of the present world average precisions.

4. Conclusions

The results of the analysis of a low statistics sample of $K^0, \overline{K}^0$ semileptonic decays in CPLEAR have been presented. The measured value of mass difference, Δm, is in good agreement with the world average value of $(0.5351 \pm 0.0024) \times 10^{10}\hbar s^{-1}$. [5]. First measurments of ϵ_T, ϵ_S, and x have also been presented. Further study of the particle identification backgrounds will be made in 1993 which will improve our understanding of the systematic errors. In addition to these studies, the implementation of the full trigger and readout improvements have been made in the beginning of 1992. Thus, data accumulation until the end of 1993 should allow a considerable improvement of the significance of the present measurements (by a factor ≈ 6 in statistical precision).

1. T. D. Lee and C. S. Wu, Annual Rev. of Nucl. Science **11**
2. L. Adiels et al., proposals CERN/PSCC 85-6 P82 (1985) and CERN/PSCC 85-3 P82 Add.1(1985); Memorandum CERN/PSCC 86-34 M263 (1986)
3. P. K. Kabir, Phys. Rev. **D2** (1970) 540.
   (1966) 511.
4. A. Angelopoulos et al., (CPLEAR Collaboration), Nucl. Instr. and Meth. **A311** (1992) 78.
5. Review of Particles Properties, Phys. Rev. **D45**, Part 2 (1992).

791

NEW MEASUREMENTS OF $Re(\varepsilon'/\varepsilon)$ AND OTHER $K \to \pi\pi$ DECAY PARAMETERS

Lawrence K. Gibbons

The Enrico Fermi Institute, The University of Chicago, 5640 S. Ellis Avenue Chicago, IL 60637

for the
FNAL-E731 Collaboration

ABSTRACT

The FNAL E731 has completed its measurement of the CP-violation parameter $Re(\varepsilon'/\varepsilon)$, finding $Re(\varepsilon'/\varepsilon) = (7.4 \pm 5.2 \pm 2.9) \times 10^{-4}$. The method used also allowed precise determinations of several other kaon decay parameters. We find the K_S lifetime to be $\tau_S = (0.8929 \pm 0.0016) \times 10^{-10} s$, the $K_L - K_S$ mass difference to be $\Delta m = (0.5286 \pm 0.0028) \times 10^{10} \hbar s^{-1}$, the phase of η_{+-} to be $\Phi_{+-} = 42.2° \pm 1.4°$, and the difference of the phases of η_{+-} and η_{00} to be $\Delta\Phi = -1.6° \pm 1.2°$.

1. Introduction

The primary goal of the E731 experiment has been a precise measurement of the CP-violating parameter $Re(\varepsilon'/\varepsilon)$. Until recently, all manifestations of CP violation have been consistent with time-asymmetric oscillations (parametrized by ε) between the K^0 and $\bar{K}^0$. The Standard Cabbibo-Kobayashi-Maskawa (CKM) model[1] can naturally accommodate CP violation, but then also predicts direct CP violation, wherein a particle of one CP eigenstate can decay directly to a final state of opposite CP. Alternative models, such as the "superweak"[2] model which hypothesizes a new $\Delta S = 2$ interaction, can explain the observed mixing effects but predict no direct CP violation, so it is important to refine searches for direct CP violation. While evidence[3] for direct CP violation in the $\pi\pi$ decays of the neutral kaon was given in 1988 by the CERN NA31 experiment, our collaboration reported a result[4] in 1990, based upon 20% of the data discussed here, which favored no direct CP violation. In preliminary results for much larger data sets presented[5] at the 1991 DPF meeting by both groups, this discrepancy persisted. In light of this, we chose to significantly enlarge our fiducial volume for the $2\pi^0$ decay mode, almost doubling the sample of our then statistically-limiting $K_L \to \pi^0 \pi^0$ mode. The results presented here were finalized shortly after the DPF 1992 conference.

The presence of direct CP violation, parametrized by ε', would shift the ratio η of CP-violating to CP-conserving decay amplitudes of the charged relative to the neutral final state. Thus the following double ratio of rates would differ from unity:

$$\frac{|\eta_{+-}|^2}{|\eta_{00}|^2} = \frac{\Gamma(K_L \to \pi^+\pi^-)/\Gamma(K_S \to \pi^+\pi^-)}{\Gamma(K_L \to \pi^0\pi^0)/\Gamma(K_S \to \pi^0\pi^0)} \approx 1 + 6Re(\varepsilon'/\varepsilon). \quad (1)$$

In the CKM model, the expected[6,7] level for $Re(\varepsilon'/\varepsilon)$ is of order 0.001.

It is interesting to probe CPT symmetry in addition to CP violation. While it is very difficult to build a realistic local quantum field theory that does not automatically satisfy this symmetry, it is possible that the topology of string theories could lead to a violation of CPT symmetry[8]. In the neutral kaon system, CPT symmetry coupled with Unitarity implies that the K_S and K_L lifetimes and the $K_S - K_L$ mass difference Δm should be related to the phases of η_{+-} and η_{00} via

$$\Phi_{+-} \approx \Phi_{00} \approx \tan^{-1} \frac{2\Delta m}{\Gamma_S - \Gamma_L}, \qquad (2)$$

where $\Gamma_{S(L)}$ is the $K_{S(L)}$ decay rate and $\Phi_{+-(00)} \equiv \arg(\eta_{+-(00)})$. The righthand expression is commonly known as the superweak phase Φ_{SW}. Accurate measurements of Δm and τ_S are necessary not only for the verification of (2), but also for accurate experimental determination of the phases Φ_{+-} and Φ_{00}. One can also directly compare the charged and neutral phases, which are expected to be equal to within a fraction of a degree, $\Delta \Phi \equiv \Phi_{00} - \Phi_{+-} \approx 0$. Recent $\Delta \Phi$ measurements [9, 10] are consistent with zero, with the average having an error of $\pm 2.0°$. The average value for Φ_{+-} of $46.5° \pm 1.2°$ is higher than the value predicted from (2) of $43.7° \pm 0.2°$.

2. Method and Detector

To minimize systematics in the measurement of the double ratio in (1), $K \to \pi\pi$ decays to either the neutral or charged final state were collected simultaneously. The experiment used two parallel K_L beams, and K_S were produced in one of them by coherent regeneration. This gave K_S and K_L with identical spatial and similar momentum distributions. The regenerator alternated between the two beams to make any biases from asymmetries in the beams or detector negligible. Because the decays from the two beams are collected simultaneously, the ratio of rates in the two beams is largely insensitive to accidental activity and to changes in detector or accelerator performance on any time scale during the run. However, the difference in the K_S and K_L lifetimes requires that the detector acceptance as a function of decay vertex be well understood. Many decays to the $\pi^{\pm} e^{\mp} \nu_e$ (Ke3) and $3\pi^0$ final states were collected to aid in the acceptance determination. It is important that the event trigger, reconstruction and selection criteria were *independent* of the beam from which the kaon decayed.

Detailed descriptions of the detector and of reconstruction techniques can be found in the other publications[4, 11]. The $\pi^+\pi^-$ decays were reconstructed by measuring the pions in a magnetic drift chamber spectrometer with a spatial resolution of 100μm and an average momentum resolution of 0.7%. For $2\pi^0$ decays, the energies and positions of the four photons in the final state were measured in a lead glass calorimeter with an energy resolution of $2.5\% + 5\%/\sqrt{E(\text{GeV})}$. The photons were paired using the π^0 mass as a constraint to find the kaon decay position.

The backgrounds for the $\pi^+\pi^-$ were small. Backgrounds in the pure K_L beam (vacuum beam) were mainly from semileptonic decays and could be rejected by use of a muon filter (for $\pi^{\pm}\mu^{\mp}\nu_{\mu}$) and the ratio of track momentum to electomagnetic shower energy (for $\pi^{\pm}e^{\mp}\nu_e$). Backgrounds in the regenerator beam were almost entirely from noncoherent regeneration. After transverse momentum and mass cuts, residual backgrounds were $0.326\% \pm 0.014\%$ ($0.155\% \pm 0.011\%$) in the vacuum (regenerator) beam.

For $2\pi^0$ decays, there were backgrounds from kaons scattering in the regenerator or in a trigger plane located near the center of the neutral fiducial volume, from neutron interactions in the trigger plane, and from $3\pi^0$ decays with missing or overlapping photons. Eleven planes of veto counters helped detect photons escaping the detector to reduce the $3\pi^0$ background. The background shapes were determined with our Monte Carlo (MC) simulation, using the transverse momentum spectrum for kaons scattering in the regenerator measured with $\pi^+\pi^-$ decays as input. The total vacuum beam background of 5.16% ± 0.06% was dominated by roughly equal contributions from scattering and $3\pi^0$ backgrounds. The regenerator beam background of 2.63% ± 0.04% was dominated by regenerator scattering.

A highly detailed Monte Carlo (MC) simulation was used for the acceptance determination as well as for simulation of some of the backgrounds. The acceptance was largely determined by two planes of active counters whose positions could be accurately measured with the Ke3 sample. The full nonlinear response of the calorimeter was modelled. The agreement between our MC and data distributions in the $2\pi^0$ and $\pi^+\pi^-$ decay modes, as well as in the much more copious $3\pi^0$ and Ke3 modes are all excellent.

3. Extracting the Parameters

At a distance z downstream of the regenerator, the decay rate for a kaon of momentum p is given by

$$\frac{d\Gamma_R}{dpdz} \propto F(p)|\rho(p)e^{-z(\Gamma_S/2+i\Delta m)/\gamma c} + \eta e^{-z\Gamma_L/2\gamma c}|^2, \qquad (3)$$

where c is the speed of light and γ is the kaon Lorentz boost. The incident flux of kaons $F(p)$ is identical to that in the vacuum beam. The regeneration amplitude $\rho(p)$ is expected to have the form $\rho(p) \propto p^\alpha \exp(-i\pi(2+\alpha)/2)$, where the phase $\phi_\rho = \pi(2+\alpha)/2$ follows from analyticity. In all the fits we will discuss, we constrain the regeneration to have this momentum dependence with the regeneration amplitude and the power α made parameters of the fits. Above 40 GeV, the deviation of the regeneration phase from that expected by anlayticity is negligible, while for the charged fits down to 20 GeV we have added an extra systematic uncertainty on all measurements corresponding to 0.5° uncertainty on this phase.

We can fit for Δm and τ_S in the charged and neutral modes separately. We binned the data in 10 GeV bins in the range 20–160 GeV in charged mode and 40–160 GeV in neutral mode. The fiducial regions in z start downstream of the regenerator to reduce systematic biases. Our trigger and fiducial z cuts let us probe out to proper times of $7\tau_S$ in the $\pi^+\pi^-$ mode, while the new extended fiducial volume in the $2\pi^0$ mode lets us probe out to almost $11\tau_S$. We used the vacuum beam to constrain the flux of kaons $F(p)$ incident on the regenerator. The charged and neutral results were $\tau_S = (0.8952\pm0.0015\pm0.0020)\times10^{-10}$s, $\Delta m = (0.5311\pm0.0044\pm0.0020)\times10^{10}\hbar s^{-1}$ and $\tau_S = (0.8912\pm0.0017\pm0.0012)\times10^{-10}$s, $\Delta m = (0.5274\pm0.0030\pm0.0017)\times10^{10}\hbar s^{-1}$), where the first error is statistical and the second error is systematic in all cases. CPT was implicit in these fits through the use of (2). The systematic error is dominated by uncertainty in the detector acceptance in the charged fits, while in the neutral fits it is dominated by the photon energy measurement. Combining the charged and neutral fits gives $\tau_S = (0.8929 \pm 0.0016) \times 10^{-10}$s and $\Delta m = (0.5286 \pm 0.0028) \times 10^{10} \hbar s^{-1}$. τ_S agrees well with the current world average, while Δm is about 2 standard deviations lower than the world average.

For the $\Delta\Phi$ measurement, the charged and neutral sets were fit simultaneously and $Re(\varepsilon'/\varepsilon)$ and Φ_{+-} were parameters of the fit as well. The binnings and momentum and z ranges were the same as above. We use our own values for τ_S and Δm in this fit, and use a similar fit floating Δm so we may quote a value for Φ_{+-}. We obtain $\Delta\Phi = -1.6° \pm 1.0° \pm 0.7°$ from the first fit and $\Phi_{+-} = 42.2° \pm 1.4°$ from the second. Uncertainties in acceptance and photon energy reconstruction again dominate the systematic error. Our results are in good agreement with the expectations of (2). Furthermore, using the quoted sensitivities to Δm and our new Δm result to correct previous measurements of Φ_{+-} gives an average of $\Phi_{+-} = 42.8° \pm 1.1°$, in good agreement with our measurement and (2).

To fit for $Re(\varepsilon'/\varepsilon)$ the data were binned only in momentum, the $2\pi^0$ and $\pi^+\pi^-$ data were fit simultaneously. The momentum range in both modes was 40–160 GeV. We obtained $Re(\varepsilon'/\varepsilon) = (7.4 \pm 5.2 \pm 2.9) \times 10^{-4}$, which is completely consistent with the preliminary result using the smaller fiducial region, and with the previously published result on the 20% sample. The systematic is dominated by the uncertainty in the neutral energy scale, with acceptance and background having the next most significant uncertainties. The superweak hypothesis cannot be ruled out with this result, and we do not confirm the positive effect seen by NA31.

References

1. M. Kobayashi and T. Maskawa, *Prog. Theor. Phys.* **49** (1973) 652.
2. L. Wolfenstein, *Phys. Rev. Lett.* **13** (1964) 569.
3. H. Burkhardt et al., *Phys. Lett. B* **206** (1988) 268.
4. J.R. Patterson et al., *Phys. Rev. Lett.* **64** (1990) 1491.
5. B. Winstein, proceedings of the 1991 Division of Particles and Fields Meeting, edited by D. Axen, D. Bryman and M. Comyn, World Scientific (1992).
6. M. Ciuchini et al., University of Rome "La Sapienza" preprint 911 (Nov. 23, 1992).
7. J. Heinrich et al., *Phys. Lett. B* **279** (1992) 140.
8. See, for example, V.A. Kostelecký and R. Potting, *Nucl. Phys.* **B359** (1991) 545.
9. R. Carosi et al., *Phys. Lett. B* **237** (1990) 303.
10. M.K. Karlsson et al., *Phys. Rev. Lett.* **64** (1990) 2976.
11. L.K. Gibbons et al., EFI 93-06, submitted to Phys. Rev. Lett.

MEASUREMENT OF THE PROPERTIES

OF THE DECAY $K_{L,S} \to \pi^+\pi^-\gamma$

ERIK J. RAMBERG
Physics Department, Fermilab, PO Box 500
Batavia, Illinois 60510 USA

ABSTRACT

In this report we discuss the latest results from experiment 731 at Fermilab on the radiative decay of neutral kaons: $K_{L,S} \to \pi^+\pi^-\gamma$. These results include the first measurement of two new CP violation parameters: $|\eta_{+-\gamma}| = (2.15\pm0.26\pm0.20)\cdot10^{-3}$ and $\phi_{+-\gamma} = (72\pm23\pm17)°$. The K_L direct emission photon energy spectrum shows a distinct shift from the pure M1 expectation, which indicates the possible presence of a rho propagator in the form factor.

1. Physics of the Decay $K_{L,S} \to \pi^+\pi^-\gamma$

The $\pi^+\pi^-\gamma$ decay for both K_L^o and K_S^o can occur through the radiative process termed inner bremsstrahlung, or "IB", where the photon is emitted by one of the final state pions through an E1 transition. Because this process is similar to the $\pi^+\pi^-$ decay mode, the CP characteristics should be similar, namely CP conserving for K_S and CP violating for K_L. However, another type of decay can occur. The direct emission, or "DE" decay, has a photon arising directly from the decay vertex, through an M1 transition. This type of decay should be CP conserving for K_L and CP violating for K_S.[1] There have been several recent theoretical analyses of the K_L DE decay.[2-4] Presently, they disagree on whether the amplitude for this decay contains a significant dependence on the photon energy, beyond the standard M1 amplitude. Specifically, it has been postulated that a rho propagator form factor will be present for this decay.[5] The CP violation parameters for the $\pi^+\pi^-\gamma$ decay should be the same as for the $\pi^+\pi^-$ decay, once the presence of the DE decay has been taken into account.

2. The Data

The data for this analysis was obtained from experiment 731 at Fermilab. A description of the apparatus can be found elsewhere.[6] The trigger for charged decays, of which the $\pi^+\pi^-\gamma$ decays are a subset, demanded that two charged tracks traversed the detector on either side of the vertical midplane, as determined by the second set of drift chambers and a hodoscope array before the lead glass. Each event was required in the offline analysis to contain two reconstructed tracks of between 7 and 80 GeV/c in momentum and have exactly one cluster of energy of at least 1.5 GeV in the lead glass calorimeter not associated with either track. The photon

Table 1: Measured Branching Ratios for $K_{L,S} \to \pi^+\pi^-\gamma$.

Decay Mode	No. of Evts.	$\frac{\Gamma(K \to \pi^+\pi^-\gamma)}{\Gamma(K \to \pi^+\pi^-)}$	B.R.
K_L	3136 ± 58	$(23.0 \pm 0.6) \cdot 10^{-3}$	$(4.66 \pm .15) \cdot 10^{-5}$
K_L-DE only	1937 ± 65	$(15.7 \pm 0.7) \cdot 10^{-3}$	$(3.19 \pm .16) \cdot 10^{-5}$
K_L-IB only	1199 ± 58	$(7.31 \pm 0.38) \cdot 10^{-3}$	$(1.49 \pm .08) \cdot 10^{-5}$
K_S	3723 ± 64	$(7.10 \pm 0.16) \cdot 10^{-3}$	$(4.87 \pm .11) \cdot 10^{-3}$
K_S-($E_\gamma^* > 50$ MeV)	1286 ± 39	$(2.56 \pm 0.09) \cdot 10^{-3}$	$(1.76 \pm .06) \cdot 10^{-3}$

energy in the center of mass system had to be at least 20 MeV. To exclude electrons from the sample, we required $\frac{E}{p} < 0.8$, where E is the cluster energy associated with a track and p is the momentum of that track. Each event was also required to pass the same cuts as for analyzing the $\pi^+\pi^-$ events, which included a total kaon energy between 30 and 160 GeV, a reconstructed mass between 484 and 512 MeV/c² and a total transverse momentum squared of less than 250 (MeV/c)².

Only a small amount of background remains after the selection cuts, mostly associated with the vacuum beam. There are 7042 decays that pass all of the cuts, 3841 of which are associated with the regenerator beam and 3201 from the vacuum beam. The background under the mass peak was estimated to be 65 ± 10 for the vacuum beam and 25 ± 15 for the regenerator beam by studying the p_T^2 distribution of events on either side of the mass peak.

3. Analysis of the Data

To isolate the separate components of the K_L decay into DE and IB, the shape of the photon energy spectrum was used. The K_S spectrum was normalized to fit the K_L spectrum. The normalized K_S spectrum can then be associated with the IB component of the K_L decays. When subtracted from the total spectrum the DE component for K_L decays is then determined. After determining the numbers of each type of decay, we corrected these numbers according to their acceptance. We normalized the number of $\pi^+\pi^-\gamma$ decays to the $\pi^+\pi^-$ sample, corrected for its own acceptance.

The final results for the numbers of events (after all selection cuts, background subtractions and corrections) and branching ratios of neutral kaons into $\pi^+\pi^-\gamma$ are given in Table 1. All errors quoted are combined statistical and systematic. Systematic errors include the errors in background subtraction and extra cluster correction quoted above and an estimate for an error in acceptance correction of 1.5%.

A comparison of the shape of the K_L DE photon energy spectrum to the one predicted by two different models for the decay was made. This comparison showed that the data supports a modification to the standard M1 amplitude that includes a ρ propagator form factor.

4. The CP Violation Characteristics of the Decay

Downstream of the E731 regenerator, the number of decays into the CP-even IB final state can be described as a function of proper time, τ, as

$$\frac{dN}{d\tau} \propto |\rho|^2 e^{-\Gamma_S \tau} + |\eta_{+-\gamma}|^2 e^{-\Gamma_L \tau} + \\ 2|\rho| \cdot |\eta_{+-\gamma}| \cos(\Delta m \tau + \phi_\rho - \phi_\eta) e^{-\frac{(\Gamma_S + \Gamma_L)}{2}\tau} \quad (1)$$

where Γ_L and Γ_S are the decay widths of the K_S^0 and K_L^0 and Δm is their mass difference. The parameter ρ is the regeneration amplitude. The parameter $\eta_{+-\gamma}$ is the CP violating amplitude for the $\pi^+\pi^-\gamma$ decay mode and $\phi_{+-\gamma}$ is its phase.

The presence of the DE type of decay can possibly complicate the analysis. If no mixing occurs between the DE and IB forms of decay, then the DE decay will modify Equation 1 by adding a term $\frac{f}{(1-f)}|\eta_{+-\gamma}|^2 e^{-\Gamma_L \tau}$ where f is the fraction of K_L^0 decays that occur through the DE process. If, however, mixing does occur between the two forms of decay (meaning E1 transitions occur for the DE process), then the interference term of Equation 1 will also be affected, thus forcing the fit value of $\eta_{+-\gamma}$ to differ from η_{+-}. This would indicate that direct CP violation exists in this decay mode, with $\epsilon'_{+-\gamma} \neq 0$.

The regenerator beam data sample described above was summed into bins of momentum and z vertex with bin widths of 10 GeV and 2 meters, respectively. An acceptance correction was applied to each bin as determined from a Monte Carlo analysis. A fit was then performed using a modified form of equation 1 with the DE addition given above and with the variable τ replaced by the seperate variables of momentum and z vertex. The variables allowed to float in the fit were $\eta_{+-\gamma}$ and $\phi_{+-\gamma}$ and the overall amplitude.

The result of the fit is

$$|\eta_{+-\gamma}| = (2.15 \pm 0.26 \pm 0.20) \cdot 10^{-3}$$
$$\phi_{+-\gamma} = (72 \pm 23 \pm 17)° \quad (2)$$

The first error is from the statistical uncertainty of the fit as determined by the fitting program while the second error is an estimate of the systematic error which was obtained by varying quantities in the fit, and by varying the acceptance in both momentum and z vertex. The χ^2 of the fit is 46 for 54 degrees of freedom.

These results imply that the level of direct CP violation in this decay is small. If all of the difference between the fit value of $\eta_{+-\gamma}$ and the known value of η_{+-} were to be attributed to a direct CP violation effect in the DE decay, and if the phase angles of these two parameters are assumed to be the same, then a limit of

$$|\epsilon'_{+-\gamma}| < 7 \cdot 10^{-4} \quad (3)$$

can be placed at the 90% confidence level.

5. References

1. G. Costa and P.K. Kabir, Nuovo Cimento A **51**, 564 (1967)
2. L.M. Sehgal and L. Wolfenstein, Phys. Rev. **162**, 1362 (1967)
3. C. Picciotto, Phys. Rev. D **45**, 1569 (1992)
4. P. Ko and T.N. Truong, Phys. Rev. D **43**, R4 (1991)
5. Y.C.R. Lin and G. Valencia, Phys. Rev. D **37**, 143 (1988)
6. M. Woods *et al.*, Phys. Rev. Lett. **60**, 1695 (1988)

Study of the Decay $K_L \to \pi^{\pm}\pi^0 e^{\mp}\bar{\nu}(\nu)$

Gregory Makoff, FNAL Experiment E731
*Department of Physics, University of Chicago, 5640 S. Ellis
Chicago, IL 60637, U.S.A*

ABSTRACT

We have observed 729 examples of the decay $K_L \to \pi^{\pm}\pi^0 e^{\mp}\bar{\nu}(\nu)$. Based on a fit to the form factors describing the decay we find the K_{e4} branching ratio is $5.16 \pm .20_{stat} \pm .22_{sys} \times 10^{-5}$.

1. Introduction

The kaon decay, $K_L \to \pi^{\pm}\pi^0 e^{\mp}\bar{\nu}(\nu)$, commonly known as the K_{e4} decay, is an excellent system for studying the long-distance contributions to $K\pi\pi$ in the P-wave. Isospin symmetry and the $\Delta I=1/2$ rule dictates that the final state $\pi\pi$ system in this decay is predominantly in a P-wave state. A measurement of the branching ratio of this process allows a clean determination of the parameter L_3 in the $O(p^4)$ chiral lagrangian[1]. The branching ratio for this mode has been predicted in a parameter-free way in a vector meson symmetry calculation[2].

The matrix element can be factored into hadronic and leptonic parts[3]

$$M = \frac{G_F}{\sqrt{2}} sin\theta_C \bar{\nu}\gamma_\mu (1-\gamma_5) e \langle \pi\pi | V_\mu + A_\mu | K \rangle,$$

where G_F is the Fermi coupling constant and θ_c is the Cabbibo angle. The hadronic part of the matrix element may be parametrized by the 4 form factors F, G, H, and R as

$$\langle \pi\pi | A_\mu | K \rangle = \frac{1}{M_K}[F(p_1+p_2)_\mu + G(p_1-p_2)_\mu + R(k-p_1-p_2)_\mu],$$

$$\langle \pi\pi | V_\mu | K \rangle = \frac{1}{M_K^3}[H\epsilon_\mu^{\nu\alpha\beta}k_\nu(p_1+p_2)_\alpha(p_1-p_2)_\beta],$$

where p_1, p_2, and k are the momenta of the $\pi^{\pm}$, π^0 and the kaon respectively. The decay is described in terms of five kinematic variables: the two masses $M_{\pi\pi}$, $M_{e\nu}$, and the three angles θ_π, θ_e, and Φ.

Since the four form factors are in general complex numbers we write $F = f_s e^{i\delta_s} + f_p cos(\theta_\pi)e^{i\delta_p}$, $G = ge^{i\delta_p}$, and $H = he^{i\delta_p}$ where δ_s and δ_p are the S and P-wave final state phase shifts. The contributions of the R and H terms to the total decay rate are small and the F contribution is suppressed by isospin symmetry. As a result, this decay allows a clean measurement of the G form factor as well as its possible $M_{\pi\pi}$ dependence which can be parametrized by λ_G where $g(M_{\pi\pi}) = g(0)(1+\lambda_G q^2)$ and $q^2 = \frac{M_{\pi\pi}^2 - 4M_\pi^2}{4M_\pi^2}$.

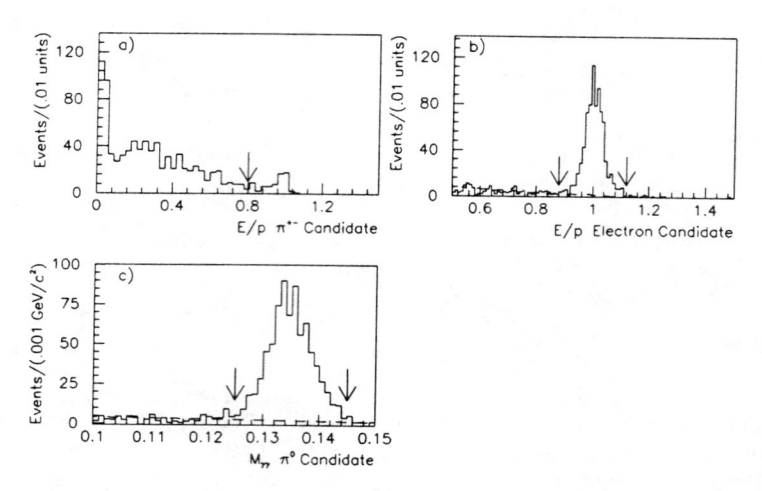

Figure 1: a) Charged pion candidate E/p. b) Electron candidate E/p. The dashed histogram shows the $\pi^+\pi^-\pi^0$ background estimated using kinematically selected $\pi^+\pi^-\pi^0$ events. c) $M_{\gamma\gamma}$ spectrum for the π^0 candidates.

2. Event Selection

We identified K_{e4} decays by looking for events with a charged π candidate with $E/p < 0.8$ and an $e^\mp$ candidate with $0.88 < E/p < 1.12$. The events were also required to have two extra clusters combining to form the π^0 candidate with $M_{\gamma\gamma}$ in the range $125 < M_{\gamma\gamma} < 145(MeV/c^2)$. We also require that $M_{\pi\pi e} < M_K$ and that the neutrino momentum transverse to the kaon line of flight, p_t, not exceed its kinematic limit by more than 15 MeV/c.

To reject background from $K_L \to \pi^+\pi^-\pi^0$ in which one of the charged pions showers in the lead glass and fakes an electron in the E/p identification we reconstructed the invariant mass of the observed particles, assuming that both charged particles were pions. We then rejected events in which the $p_t < 77 MeV/c$ and $475 < M_{3\pi} < 530 (MeV/c^2)$. In the region $M_{3\pi} < 525(MeV/c^2)$ we remove remaining $\pi^+\pi^-\pi^0$ events characterized by small $\pi^+\pi^-$ momentum transverse to the kaon line of flight by cutting all events in which this quantity is less than its kinematic limit.

Background events due to $K_{e3} + 2\gamma_{Extra}$ events with extra clusters due to internal or external bremsstrahlung were rejected by cutting all events with small $p_e \cdot p_\gamma$, where p_e is the electron four-momentum, and p_γ is the four-momentum of either photon detected in the calorimeter. We also required that each of the unmatched clusters comprising our π^0 candidate leave at least 2 GeV/c^2.

Figure 1 shows the reconstructed $M_{\gamma\gamma}$ and E/p distributions, showing clean $\pi^\pm$, $e^\mp$, and π^0 signals in the data. The background in the E/p figure is estimated from the sidebands to be 38+/-10 events and the background in the $M_{\gamma\gamma}$ spectrum

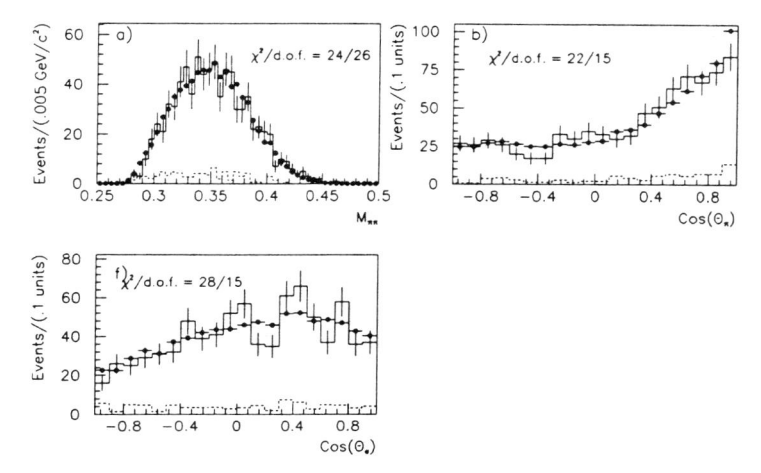

Figure 2: The three kinematic variables included in the fit to the K_{e4} decay distribution. a) $M_{\pi\pi}$, b) θ_π, and c) θ_e. The solid histograms show the data and the points show the Monte Carlo simulation of the decay using the results of the fit. The background (which is included in the Monte Carlo plot) is shown seperately on the plots as a dashed histogram.

is estimated to be 43+/-11 events. We are left with 729 ± 15 K_{e4} events.

3. Branching Ratio Results

The K_{e4} branching ratio was normalized to the known K_{e3} decay rate. The K_{e4} acceptance was 1.47%, based upon a simulation using form factors measured in a maxmimum likelihood fit. Figure 2 shows a comparison the K_{e4} data in three of the five kinematic variables with a Monte Carlo calculation based on the results of a form factor fit. Using the known K_{e3} decay rate, we find that the branching ratio for K_{e4} is $5.16 \pm .20_{stat} \pm .22_{sys} x 10^{-5}$.

Our branching ratio result agrees within errors with the 1980 result of Carrol et al of based on 16 events[4]. In chiral perturbation theory the K_{e4} decay rate depends strongly on the unknown parameter L_3. Using our measured decay rate we determine $L_3 = 3.4 \pm .4 x 10^{-3}$. A recent prediction, including vector meson exchange effects in a framework called "vector meson symmetry", predicts that the K_{e4} branching ratio should be $5.2 x 10^{-5}$, in agreement with our measurement[2].

4. References

1. C.Riggenback et al., *Phys. Rev* **D43** (1991) 127.
2. P.Ko, *Enrico Fermi Institute Preprint* **EFI-91-40** (1991).
3. A.Pais and S.B. Tremain, *Phys. Rev.* **168** (1968) 1858.
4. A.S.Carroll et al., *Phys. Lett.* **96B** (1980) 407.

Determination of Branching Ratio of the Decay $\pi^0 \to e^+e^-$

A.Deshpande,[4] C. Alliegro,[4] V. Chaloupka,[3] J. Egger,[2] H.A. Gordon,[1] N.J. Hadley,[4],[a]
W.D. Herold,[2], H. Kaspar,[2] A.M. Lee,[4],[b] D.M. Lazarus,[1] H.J. Lubatti,[3] H. Ma,[1] P.
Rehak,[1] A. Shukla,[3] M.E. Zeller,[4] T. Zhao[3]

[1] Brookhaven National Laboratory, Upton, New York 11973
[2] Paul Scherrer Institute (Swiss Institute for Nuclear Research), CH-5234 Villigen, Switzerland
[3] Department of Physics, University of Washington, Seattle, Washington 98195
[4] Department of Physics, Yale University, New Haven, Connecticut 06511
a. Present address: University of Maryland, College Park, MD 20742
b. Present address: Duke University, Durham, NC, 27706.

ABSTRACT

Employing the decay chain $K^+ \to \pi^+\pi^0$; $\pi^0 \to e^+e^-$ in an experiment at the Brookhaven AGS, E851, we have observed approximately 21 events of the decay $\pi^0 \to e^+e^-$. Normalizing to the decay $K^+ \to \pi^+e^+e^-$, we measure the branching ratio for $\pi^0 \to e^+e^-$ to be $(6.7 \pm 2.0) \times 10^{-8}$.

The decay $\pi^0 \to e^+e^-$ has a somewhat checkered history. Calculations of the ratio of the rate of this decay to that of $\pi^0 \to \gamma\gamma$ to lowest order in QED yields the "unitary limit" of 4.75×10^{-8}.[1] The 1988 Particle Data Table listed the measured ratio as $18^{+7}_{-6} \times 10^{-8}$, large enough to suggest the presence of other physics. A measurement by the SINDRUM collaboration at PSI in 1989 yielded an upper limit of 13×10^{-8} which is now the value accepted in the PDT.[2] Employing the decay chain $K^+ \to \pi^+\pi^0$; $\pi^0 \to e^+e^-$ in an experiment at the Brookhaven AGS, E851, we have made a new measurement of the rate of $\pi^0 \to e^+e^-$ normalized to $K^+ \to \pi^+e^+e^-$.

The E851 apparatus is described in previous publications[3]. It resided in an unseparated beam of momentum $(6\pm0.03)GeV/c$ containing about 10^7 K^+ mesons/sec, accompanied by 2×10^8 π^+ and protons. The detector consisted of a dipole spectrometer with two proportional chamber packages (x,u,v per package) on either side. This system was capable of determining the momentum of trajectories with a resolution of $\delta P/P \simeq 0.01P$, where P ranged from 0.6 to $4.0 GeV/c$. Particle identification consisted of tandem Cerenkov counters filled with hydrogen at atmospheric pressure, plus a Pb-scintillator shower counter 11 radiation lengths thick. Electrons were required to fire both Cerenkov counters and to have a signal in the shower counter whose amplitude was consistent with the measured energy (momentum) in the spectrometer. Pions were required not to fire either Cerenkov counter. The probability of particle misidentification was less than 10^{-5}.

Events selected were those having $\pi^+e^+e^-$ particle identification, particle trajectories consistent with having originated from a common vertex, and a reconstructed momentum vector of the sum of the trajectories consistent with having come from the production target after being tracked back through the beam magnets.

Figure 1a is a scatter plot of the πee invariant mass, $M_{\pi ee}$, vs. the ee invariant mass, M_{ee}, for selected events. The band of events with $M_{ee} > 0.15 GeV/c^2$ are direct $K^+ \to \pi^+e^+e^-$ events. Figure 1b displays the $M_{\pi ee}$ distribution for these events. One sees a signal to background ratio of about 20:1 for this decay mode. The published branching ratio for this mode is 2.7×10^{-7}.[3]

For $M_{ee} < 0.15 GeV/c^2$ Fig. 1a is dominated by $K^+ \to \pi^+\pi^0$ events with a subsequent decay of the π^0 to $e^+e^-\gamma$, Dalitz decays, and $e^+e^-e^+e^-$, double Dalitz decays. These events have $M_{\pi ee} < M_K$ due to the undetected photon or e^+e^- pair. As the momenta of these missing particles approaches zero, however, $M_{\pi ee}$ approaches M_K. These events are the dominant background to $\pi^0 \to e^+e^-$, but their effect can be reduced by biasing the data sample selection to events with high values of $M_{\pi ee}$.

Figure 1c shows the M_{ee} distribution for events in Fig. 1a with $M_{\pi ee} > 0.474 GeV/c^2$. The histogram in this figure is a Monte Carlo calculation using the distributions and the published branching ratios for Dalitz and double Dalitz modes and normalized to the direct $K \to \pi ee$ events with $M_{ee} > 0.15 GeV/c^2$. This normalization, the only free parameter, is same for all subsequent plots.

Figure 2 is a series of M_{ee} distributions in the M_{ee} region of the π^0 mass with $M_{\pi ee} < 0.504 GeV/c^2$ and successively higher cuts on the lower bound of $M_{\pi ee}$. The dashed histogram is the Monte Carlo simulation of the mass spectrum without inclusion of the process $K^+ \to \pi^+\pi^0$; $\pi^0 \to e^+e^-$. The dotted histogram is the same including Monte Carlo $\pi^0 \to e^+e^-$. For $M_{\pi ee} > 0.490 GeV/c^2$, Fig. 2(c), the χ^2 value for the former comparison is 35, and that for the latter is 13, for 10 degrees of freedom. The strength of the $\pi^0 \to e^+e^-$ contribution to the Monte Carlo spectrum was determined by a maximum likelihood fit as described below.

In searching for the decay $\pi^0 \to e^+e^-$, we employed a peak finding algorithm which used three input components: the data and the dashed Monte Carlo mass spectra of Fig. 2(c), and an M_{ee} spectrum for a short lived neutral particle, X^0, of mass M_{X^0} decaying to e^+e^-. The peak finder sought to maximize the likelihood of the fit of the summed Monte Carlo M_{ee} spectrum to that of the data by varying the number of events in the X^0 peak, N_X, and its central mass, M_{X^0}. The result of this analysis was $N_{X^0} = 21 \pm 7$ at $M_{X^0} = 0.134 \pm 0.001$. M_{X^0} was thus found to be consistent with the mass of the π^0.

In order to determine the BR($\pi^0 \to e^+e^-$), the ratio of number of events of $K^+ \to \pi^+ e^+ e^-$ to the number of events of $K^+ \to \pi^+\pi^0$; $\pi^0 \to e^+e^-$ at the input to the Monte Carlo was adjusted to simulate the observed number of events, N_{X^0}, through the entire analysis chain. From the above ratio and the published branching ratios of $K^+ \to \pi^+ e^+ e^-$ and $K^+ \to \pi^+\pi^0$ we measure the BR($\pi^0 \to e^+e^-$) to be $(6.7 \pm 2.0) \times 10^{-8}$ where the error is statistical only. The systematic uncertainty is still under study with a current estimate being approximately $\pm 1 \times 10^{-8}$. The measured branching ratio is consistent with the unitarity limit and does not contradict the published 90% confidence level upper limit of 13×10^{-8}.[2]

References

1. L.Bergström *et al.*, *Phys. Lett.*, **B126**, (1983) 117.
2. G.Niebuhr, *et al.*, *Phys. Rev*, **D40**, (1989) 2796.
3. C.Alliegro, *et al.*,*Phys. Rev. Lett.*, **68**, (1992) 278.

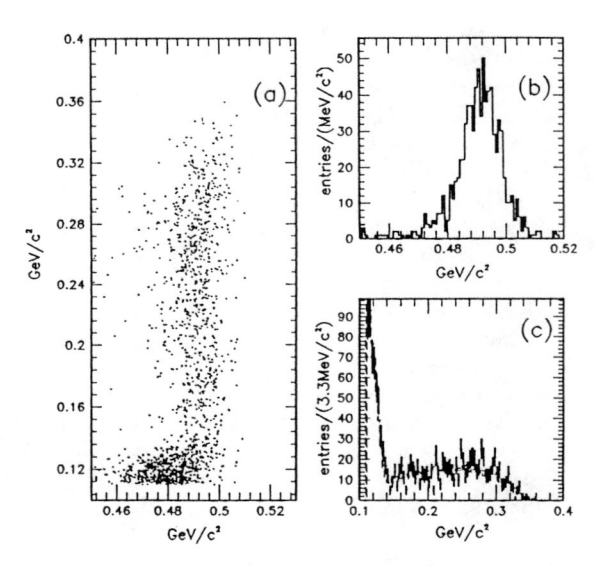

Figure 1: (a) $M_{\pi ee}$ vs. M_{ee} ,(b) Data $M_{\pi ee}$ for $M_{ee} > 0.15 GeV/c^2$ (c) Monte Carlo M_{ee} superposed on data for $M_{\pi ee} > 0.474 GeV/c^2$.

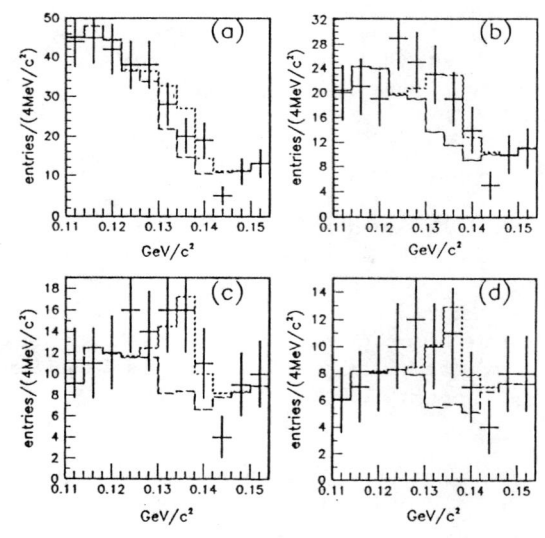

Figure 2: Monte Carlo without (dashed) and with (dotted) $\pi^0 \to e^+e^-$ superposed on data (with error bars), $M_{\pi ee} < 0.504 GeV/c^2$ and (a) $M_{\pi ee} > 0.483 GeV/c^2$ (b) $M_{\pi ee} > 0.487 GeV/c^2$ (c) $M_{\pi ee} > 0.490 GeV/c^2$ (d) $M_{\pi ee} > 0.4916 GeV/c^2$.

A NEW MEASUREMENT OF THE BRANCHING RATIO OF $\pi^0 \to e^+e^-$

presented by

Kevin S. McFarland
*The Enrico Fermi Institute, The University of Chicago, 5640 S. Ellis Avenue
Chicago, IL 60637*

for the
FNAL-E799 Collaboration

ABSTRACT

The FNAL E799 Collaboration has carried out a search for the rare decay $\pi^0 \to e^+e^-$. We observe a signal of nine events with approximately one event background, and from this we measure a branching ratio of $(7.8 \pm 3.1\,(stat) \pm 1.2\,(syst)) \times 10^{-8}$ (*preliminary*). This measurement represents a significant improvement over past experiments in both its high sensitivity and its low background level. The QED unitarity bound for $\pi^0 \to e^+e^-$ is 4.75×10^{-8}, and most theoretical predictions fall in the range between 6×10^{-8} and 7×10^{-8}.

1. Introduction

First calculated by Drell[1] in 1959, the rare decay $\pi^0 \to e^+e^-$ has been of considerable theoretical interest because of its very small predicted branching ratio. Because all Standard Model processes proceed through the intermediate two-photon state, this decay is suppressed by a factor of $\alpha^2(\frac{m_e}{m_{\pi^0}})^2$ relative to $\pi^0 \to \gamma\gamma$. The contribution to the rate from on-shell photons is easily calculated in QED and leads to a branching ratio prediction of 4.75×10^{-8}, the 'unitarity limit' for $\pi^0 \to e^+e^-$. Model-dependent calculations that include terms from off-shell photons typically yield predicted branching ratios between 6×10^{-8} and 7×10^{-8} [2,3]. This low branching ratio provides a window through which one might be able to view non-Standard Model processes, such as interactions mediated by other pseudoscalar bosons like the axion[4], or effects from lepto-quarks[5].

Experimentally, this decay has presented some significant challenges, and left experimenters with controversial results. In particular, Fisher et al.[6] used π^0's from $K^+ \to \pi^+\pi^0$ at CERN to search for $\pi^0 \to e^+e^-$ and measured the branching ratio to be $(2.23^{+2.4}_{-1.1}) \times 10^{-7}$ (90% confidence errors). Another experiment, Frank et al.[7] at LAMPF, used a different reaction to produce π^0's, $\pi^-p \to n\pi^0$, and found a branching ratio consistent with that of the CERN measurement, $(1.7 \pm .6\,(stat) \pm .3\,(syst)) \times 10^{-7}$. These two measurements suggest that the branching ratio is well above both the unitarity limit and Standard Model predictions, which could indicate contributions from non-Standard-Model effects. However, a recent experiment from the SINDRUM collaboration[8], using the same technique as the Frank et al. measurement, has placed an upper limit on the branching ratio of 1.3×10^{-7} at 90% confidence, apparently contradicting these earlier results.

At FNAL-E799, a rare K_L decay experiment, a K_L beam is produced by interactions of $800\,GeV$ protons from the Fermilab Tevatron in a Be target $100\,m$

from the E799 detector. The search for $\pi^0 \to e^+e^-$ uses π^0's from the common decay $K_L \to \pi^0\pi^0\pi^0$. This technique has considerable advantages over the techniques of previous experiments. First, the mean π^0 momentum is large, approximately 25 GeV, allowing more efficient rejection of background resulting from other π^0 decays. Second, there is no significant background from the continuum e^+e^- production process, $K_L \to \pi^0\pi^0 e^+e^-$, analogous to the backgrounds from $K^+ \to \pi^+e^+e^-$ and $\pi^-p \to ne^+e^-$ which plague the K^+ and π^-p experiments, respectively. Because of these two factors, E799 can make this measurement in an almost background-free environment.

2. Experimental Apparatus and Event Selection

The E799 detector was originally designed for experiment E731 which studied CP violation in the $K^0, \overline{K}^0 \to 2\pi$ system in both neutral and charged final states. Because both photon calorimetry and charged particle momentum resolution were important for E731, the detector was well-suited to the task of fully reconstructing the four photon and two electron final state of $K_L \to \pi^0\pi^0\pi^0$, $\pi^0 \to e^+e^-$. For charged particle reconstruction, a spectrometer consisting of four drift chambers and an analyzing magnet with a 200 MeV kick was used. The single hit resolution in the drift chambers was approximately 100 μm, and the observed momentum resolution was $.5\% \oplus \frac{.014p}{1 GeV}\%$, where the first contribution is from multiple-scattering in material inside the spectrometer, and the second is from the resolution of the chambers. To detect photons and electromagnetic showers from charged particles, an array of 804 Lead-Glass (PbG) blocks, $(5.8cm)^2 \times 18.7$ radiation-lengths long, was employed. The resolution, on average, for electrons in the lead-glass was approximately $3.8\% \oplus \frac{5\%}{\sqrt{E(GeV)}}$.

Candidate events were selected on-line using a trigger designed to select events with two electrons and at least one photon. In order to satisfy the fast (Level 1) trigger, events were required to leave at least 55 GeV in the calorimeter and have two hits in scintillator banks directly upstream of the PbG. In addition, there were counters in veto to reject events with charged particles escaping from the detector, events with photons pointing down the beam holes of the PbG, and events with hadron showers in the calorimeter. The hardware processing trigger (Level 2) required at least 3 clusters of energy in the PbG and sufficient hits in the drift chambers to make possible the reconstruction of two tracks.

Offline, events were selected by first locating tracks in the drift chambers. If these tracks pointed to clusters of energy in the calorimeter, and the ratio of the energy of the cluster to the track momentum is close to unity, these tracks are identified as electron candidates. For the $\pi^0 \to e^+e^-$ signal, two electron candidates and four photon candidates in the calorimeter were required. Using the charged tracks to locate the decay vertex, one can then reconstruct kinematic quantities, such as the total two electron and four photon invariant mass, the two electron mass, the component of observed momentum transverse to the direction of the parent kaon, and a χ^2 for the hypothesis that the four photons can be paired to form two π^0's in the calorimeter. Cuts on these quantities can then be chosen by looking at events generated in a Monte Carlo simulation of the detector. In addition, events with signals in the photon veto counters, which indicate a photon escaping the PbG fiducial region, were removed from the event sample.

3. Backgrounds to $\pi^0 \to e^+e^-$

The two important backgrounds to this measurement of $\pi^0 \to e^+e^-$ are the π^0 Dalitz Decay ($\pi^0 \to e^+e^-\gamma$) and processes involving four electrons from two low-mass e^+e^- pairs where one electron from each pair is lost and the remaining two electrons form a 'fake' high-mass e^+e^- pair. Fortunately, in the case of the Dalitz background, the e^+e^- mass spectrum of these decays strongly favors low e^+e^- mass, and only a 6×10^{-7} fraction will satisfy the mass cut. The e^+e^- mass spectrum for Dalitz decays (Figure 1) is well-modelled by our detector simulation, and the prediction of the

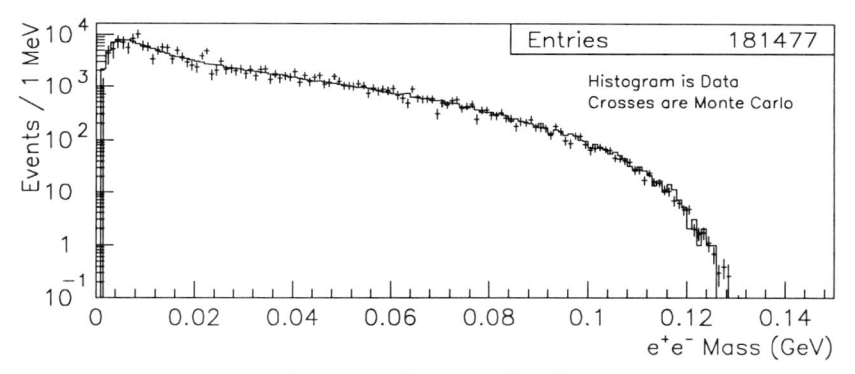

Figure 1: The e^+e^- invariant mass of $\pi^0 \to e^+e^-\gamma$ candidates

Monte Carlo is used to subtract this background, which occurs at approximately the one event level in the data. The four electron backgrounds, although potentially troublesome, are effectively rejected by cutting on extra in-time hits in the second drift chamber which are left by the extra soft electrons. Before such a cut, these backgrounds dominate the signal region; after the cut, the level of background from four electron processes is quite small, contributing about one-quarter of an event to the total background. In addition to these two backgrounds which are modelled in Monte Carlo, possible additional backgrounds are studied by looking in kinematic sidebands around the signal region. From this study, an upper limit on these backgrounds of .4 events at the 90% confidence level is obtained, and this result is folded into our systematic error.

4. Extraction of the $\pi^0 \to e^+e^-$ Branching Ratio

After all cuts, nine events are observed in the signal region (Figure 2). The sensitivity to the $\pi^0 \to e^+e^-$ decay is computed using the sample of π^0 Dalitz decays (Figure 1) with e^+e^- mass above 70 MeV as a normalization sample. Using the Monte

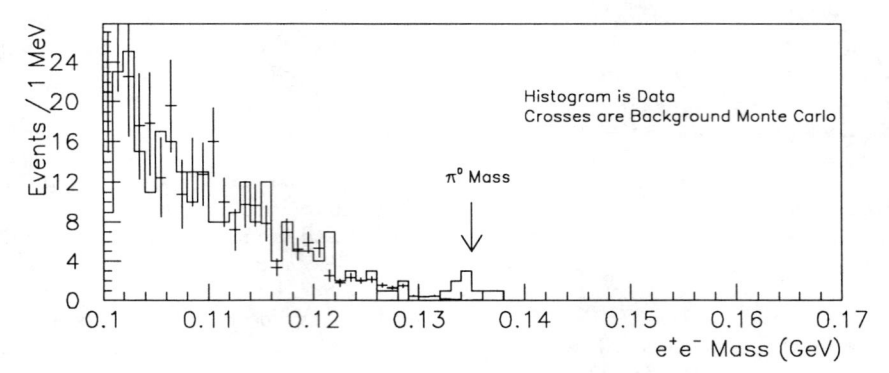

Figure 2: The e^+e^- mass of $\pi^0 \to e^+e^-$ candidates and the background Monte Carlo prediction

Carlo to predict the ratio of acceptances for the signal and normalization modes, we obtain a single event sensitivity of approximately 1×10^{-8}.

The systematic errors at this point are inflated because of possible uncertainties in the preliminary analysis of the effect of accidental activity in the detector. The dominant systematic effects that will remain once this correction is finalized will be the dependence of the branching ratio measurement on our choice of e^+e^- mass cut and the limits set on additional non-simulated background processes which were discussed earlier. Also considered are the effects of systematic uncertainties in the understanding of the calorimeter, the charged spectrometer and π^0 electromagnetic form-factor slope, and these are found to be negligible. We have not yet considered the effects of radiative corrections to the processes $\pi^0 \to e^+e^-$ and $\pi^0 \to e^+e^-\gamma$ which may give corrections as large as 10% in the branching ratio.

The E799 preliminary measurement of the branching ratio is

$$\mathrm{BR}(\pi^0 \to e^+e^-) = (7.8 \pm 3.1\,(stat) \pm 1.2\,(syst)) \times 10^{-8}.$$

References

1. S. D. Drell, *Nuovo Cimento* **11** (1959) 693.
2. L. G. Landsberg, *Physics Reports* **128** (1985) 301-376.
3. L. Bergström et al., *Physics Letters* **126B** (1983) 117.
4. E. Massó, *Physics Letters B* **181** (1986) 388.
5. J. Pati and A. Salam, *Phys. Rev. D* **11** (1975) 1137.
6. J. Fisher et al., *Phys. Lett.* **73B** (1978) 364.
7. J. S. Frank et al., *Phys. Rev. D* **28** (1983) 423.
8. C. Niebuhr et al., *Phys. Rev. D* **40** (1989) 2797.

A MEASUREMENT OF THE BRANCHING RATIO OF $K_L \to e^+e^-e^+e^-$

Ping Gu
Rutgers, the State University of New Jersey
Piscataway, NJ 08855

for the
FNAL E799 Collaboration

ABSTRACT

A measurement of the branching ratio for the decay $K_L \to e^+e^-e^+e^-$ has been carried out in Phase I of Fermilab experiment E799. Based on the observation of 31 events with approximately two events background, the branching ratio for $K_L \to e^+e^-e^+e^-$ is measured to be $(4.47 \pm 0.85(stat.)) \times 10^{-8}$(preliminary).

The rare decay $K_L \to e^+e^-e^+e^-$ could be described in the Standard Model through $K_L\gamma^*\gamma^*$ vertex with two virtual photons going to two electron-position pairs. The form factor of the $K_L\gamma^*\gamma^*$ vertex is interesting from both theoretical and experimental points of view because of its nontrivial structure[1]. The QED prediction[2] for the branching ratio of $K_L \to e^+e^-e^+e^-$ is 3.6×10^{-8}, obtained from the measured branching ratio [3] of $K_L \to \gamma\gamma$ with no regard the structure of $K_L\gamma^*\gamma^*$ form factor and radiative corrections. The branching ratio of $K_L \to e^+e^-e^+e^-$ was measured in three previous experiments[4,5,6], where two of them were based on the observation of two and six fully reconstructed events, respectively, and the third one was based on the analysis of e^+e^-X events. A new measurement for the branching ratio of $K_L \to e^+e^-e^+e^-$ in Phase I of Fermilab experiment E799 is reported here.

Experiment E799 had almost the same setup as that of experiment E731. The detailed characteristics of the E731 detector have been described elsewhere[7]. Here we only give brief description of the relevant elements of the detector used in this analysis. Two K_L beams were produced by 800GeV protons striking a Be target. The trajectories and momenta of charged particles were reconstructed by using four drift chambers and an analyzing magnet which imparted a horizontal transverse momentum (P_t) kick of about 200MeV/c. Each drift chamber consisted of two X planes and two Y planes; the cell size of the chambers was 0.635cm and each plane had a resolution of approximately 100μm. A roughly circular array of 804 lead glass blocks was used to measure the energies and positions of electrons and photons. Each block was 5.82cm× 5.82cm in cross section, and was about 19 radiation lengths long. The average energy resolution for electrons was approximately $3.8\% + 5\%/\sqrt{E}$(GeV). In the lead glass array, there were two 11.6cm by 11.6cm beam holes whose centers were 11.6cm above and below the center of the array, through which the neutral beam passed. There were altogether twelve planes of photon veto counters at different positions in the spectrometer which were used to detect decay products outside the chamber and calorimeter acceptance.

Twelve types of triggers were collected simultaneously during data taking in order to study various K_L rare decays. The data from the two-electron trigger were used in this analysis. The two-electron trigger required at least two hits in each trigger counter, at least two groups of isolated hits in X and Y view of each chamber, and also more than three isolated clusters in lead glass with cluster energy above 2GeV. The trigger also required the total energy deposited in lead glass to be larger than 40GeV, and no signal on each photon veto and muon banks.

$K_L \to e^+e^-e^+e^-$ candidates were selected from two-electron trigger data according to the following criteria:

1) That there be four tracks, two positively charged and two negatively charged.

2) That each track match a cluster in the lead glass having $0.80 < E/p < 1.2$, where E was measured from lead glass and p was measured from drift chambers.

3) That there be no extra neutral cluster in the lead glass with energy larger than 2.0GeV.

4) That the total χ^2 for the common vertex fitting from the four tracks be less than 10.0, and the fitted Z vertex be within in the 49m fiducial decay region beginning at 110m from target.

The events which passed the above cuts are plotted in scatter plot P_t^2 vs. M_{eeee} shown in Figure 1 a, where P_t was defined as the projection of K_L momentum in the plane which was perpendicular to the direction from target to the reconstructed vertex, and M_{eeee} was the invariant mass of four electrons. In the final sample of $K_L \to e^+e^-e^+e^-$, we required that $P_t^2 < 300\text{MeV}^2 (3\sigma)$, and $478\text{MeV} < M_{eeee} < 511\text{MeV}$ (3σ), where the asymmetric mass cut was resulted from the energy loss by radiative soft photons. The distribution of M_{eeee} after $P_t^2 < 300\text{MeV}^2$ cut is shown in Figure 1 b, also shown is the Monte Carlo simulation distribution. There were 31 events in the data signal region.

The major background for $K_L \to e^+e^-e^+e^-$ was from $K_L \to e^+e^-\gamma$ with γ converting to e^+e^- pair in the material before the first chamber. The material in the decay region before the first chamber was about 0.41% radiation length. This background was heavily suppressed by requiring that all tracks were separated from each other by one cell on the second chamber in X view or Y view. The rejection factor for $K_L \to e^+e^-\gamma$ by this cut was about 20 and the expected background was about 6%. The background from $K_L \to \gamma\gamma$ with external conversion of both γ's was negligible.

A possible background from lower mass side was $K_L \to \pi^\pm e^\mp \nu e^+e^-$ by misidentifying one charged pion as an electron. There were two possible sources. One was radiative $Ke3$ decay with the photon externally converting. With the reconstructed K_L mass by assuming four charged particles to be electrons, $M_{eeee} < 450\text{MeV}$, there were no events in the defined signal region from this source. Another one was similar to radiative $Ke3$ decay but with photon internally converting. and its branching ratio could be roughly estimated to be 9.5×10^{-5}. Although no measurement of this decay has been established so far, no events would be expected in the defined signal region by the same argument as in radiative $Ke3$ decay.

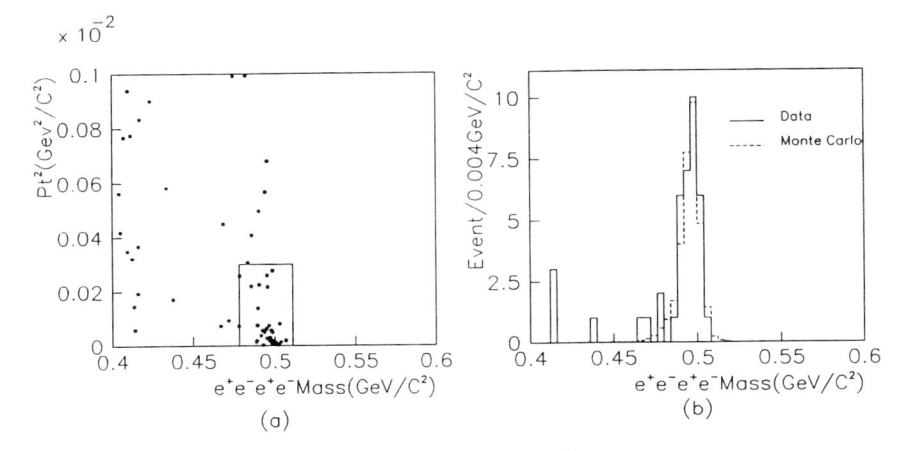

[Figure 1: (a) Event scatter plot of P_t^2 vs. M_{eeee} (b) M_{eeee} distribution after $P_t^2 < 300 MeV^2$ cut]

There were other possible backgrounds, for example, $K_L \to \pi^0\pi^0\pi^0, \pi^0\pi^0$ with two π^0 Dalitz decays, and random background from two $Ke3$ decays in the same RF bucket, but they were found to be negligible.

The $K_L \to e^+e^-e^+e^-$ events were normalized to $K_L \to \pi^0\pi^0\pi^0$ events with two π^0 Dalitz decay (called $K_L \to \pi^0\pi_D^0\pi_D^0$) which were found in the same trigger data. The $K_L \to \pi^0\pi_D^0\pi_D^0$ events were selected by the same basic cuts as in $K_L \to e^+e^-e^+e^-$ except that four extra neutral clusters were required instead of no neutral cluster. Since M_{eeee} in this mode was smaller than in $K_L \to e^+e^-e^+e^-$ decay, a loose χ^2 cut was used, i.e., $\chi^2 < 20.0$. To reconstruct $K_L \to \pi^0\pi_D^0\pi_D^0$, we also required that the reconstructed π^0 mass from $\gamma\gamma$ and $e^+e^-\gamma$ was between 115MeV and 155MeV. the major background was from $K_L \to \pi^0\pi^0\pi^0$ with $\pi^0 \to e^+e^-e^+e^-$ (called $K_L \to \pi^0\pi_D^0\pi_{DD}^0$), however, it could be rejected by requiring M_{eeee} not between 120MeV and 150MeV. Another background was from $K_L \to \pi^0\pi^0\pi^0$ with one π^0 Dalitz decay and one of photons externally converting, so the same separation cut of tracks in the second chamber as in $K_L \to e^+e^-e^+e^-$ was used here. Finally we required that P_t^2 of the K_L be less than 1000MeV^2 and the K_L mass between 400MeV and 600MeV. There were 2191 events selected by above cuts, where the background from $K_L \to \pi^0\pi_D^0\pi_{DD}^0$ was expected to be <0.5%, and the background from $K_L \to \pi^0\pi^0\pi_D^0$ was about 7%.

The branching ratio of $K_L \to e^+e^-e^+e^-$ was calculated follows:

$$BR(K_L \to e^+e^-e^+e^-) = BR(K_L \to \pi^0\pi_D^0\pi_D^0)\frac{N(K_L \to e^+e^-e^+e^-)}{N(K_L \to \pi^0\pi_D^0\pi_D^0)}\frac{A(K_L \to \pi^0\pi_D^0\pi_D^0)}{A(K_L \to e^+e^-e^+e^-)}$$

The acceptances were obtained by Monte Carlo simulation. The average ratio, $A(K_L \to \pi^0\pi_D^0\pi_D^0)/A(K_L \to e^+e^-e^+e^-) = 0.0342$. The number of observed $K_L \to e^+e^-e^+e^-$ events, $N(K_L \to e^+e^-e^+e^-) = 31-2.0 = 29.0$, and the number of observed $K_L \to \pi^0\pi_D^0\pi_D^0$ events, $N(K_L \to \pi^0\pi_D^0\pi_D^0) = 2191 - 154 = 2037$, where the expected backgrounds from Monte Carlo simulation were subtracted, respectively. The statistical error for the branching ratio was 19%, mostly from $K_L \to e^+e^-e^+e^-$.

The systematic error study has not been finished yet. The major systematic error will be from the relative acceptance of $A(K_L \to \pi^0\pi_D^0\pi_D^0)/A(K_L \to e^+e^-e^+e^-)$. Even though the two modes had similar final charged particles which could cancel out some systematic error in tracking, they had different patterns in the lead glass which were sensitive to accidental activity in lead glass. Another possible systematic error will be from background subtraction. An uncertainty from the radiative corrections also gave an uncertainty in the acceptance of $K_L \to e^+e^-e^+e^-$ because the radiative events had larger P_t^2 and wider mass resolution. In current calculation, the radiative corrections for $K_L \to e^+e^-e^+e^-$ were made by using program PHOTOS[8]. All these systematic errors are still being investigated. Given the above numbers, we have the preliminary result for the branching ratio of $K_L \to e^+e^-e^+e^-$ where only the statistical error is quoted:

$$BR(K_L \to e^+e^-e^+e^-) = (4.47 \pm 0.85(stat)) \times 10^{-8}(preliminary)$$

Our result is consistent with previous measurements[3, 4, 5], and is also compatible with the theoretical prediction[2].

References

1. R. Battiston, et al. *Phys. Rep.* **214**, (1992) 294, also see references quoted in this paper.
2. T. Miyazaki and E. takasugi, *Phys. Rev.* **D8**, (1973) 2051.
3. Particle Data Group, K. Hikasa et al.,*Phys. Rev.* **D45**,(1992) S1.
4. G. D. Barr, et al. *Phys. Lett.* **B259**, (1991) 389.
5. M. R. Vagins, et al. *YAUG-A- 93/1.* (submitted to *Phys. Rev. Lett.*)
6. T. Akagi, et al. *KEK Preprint* **92-35**, *May* 1992. (submitted to *Phys. Rev. Lett.*)
7. J. R. Patterson, et al. *Phys. Rev. Lett.* **64**,(1990) 1491.
   J. R. Patterson, Ph. D thesis (University of Chicago, 1991).
8. E. Barberio, et al. CERN-TH-5857/90.

MEASUREMENT OF THE $K_L \to \mu^+\mu^-\gamma$ BRANCHING FRACTION, AND SEARCH FOR $K_L \to \pi^0\mu^+\mu^-$ DECAY

ROBERT S. TSCHIRHART
Physics Department, Fermilab, PO Box 500
Batavia, Illinois 60510 USA

ABSTRACT

In this report we present the first clear observation and measurement of K_L muonic Dalitz decay, $K_L \to \mu^+\mu^-\gamma$, with a branching fraction of $3.88 \pm 0.32 \times 10^{-7}$, *(statistical errors only)*. The observed decay form factor is consistent with the hypothesis of Dalitz decay. In addition, we have searched for the decay $K_L \to \pi^0\mu^+\mu^-$, which potentially has a large CP violating component. We present a limit on this process of 1.7×10^{-8} at the 90% confidence level *(statistical errors only)*, which represents a factor of ×70 improvement over previous limits.

1. Physics of the Decays $K_L \to \mu^+\mu^-\gamma$ and $K_L \to \pi^0\mu^+\mu^-$

The decay $K_L \to \mu^+\mu^-\gamma$ is expected to proceed through internal conversion of the radiative decay, $K_L \to \gamma\gamma^*$ (Dalitz decay). The decay amplitude is described with the baseline QED Kroll-Wada form factor modified by (π^0, η) pole terms and a contribution from the weak vector transition, $K_L \to \gamma(K^* \to (\rho, \omega, \phi))$ [1,2]. The QED component of the decay can be reliably calculated to be $3.0 \pm 0.15 \times 10^{-7}$, where the uncertainty is due to the precision of the measured root $K_L \to \gamma\gamma$ branching fraction. Long-distance modifications to the QED component from pole terms and K^* transitions are more difficult to calculate, and are expected to enhance the baseline QED branching fraction by 30%[2]. Hence measurements of the $K_L \to \mu^+\mu^-\gamma$ decay serve as an excellent probe of the long-distance structure of radiative K_L decays. Measurements of the K_L long-distance radiative structure are of particular importance in extracting the short-distance second order weak component from the measured $K_L \to \mu^+\mu^-$ [2,3]. branching fraction. In addition, extraction of the weak vector transition amplitude is of interest in probing the origin of the $\Delta I = \frac{1}{2}$ rule in kaon decays [2]. The $K_L \to \pi^0\mu^+\mu^-$ decay amplitude potentially has large CP-violating component. In contrast, the direct CP-violating component of the $K_L \to 2\pi$ decay amplitude is less than 2.0×10^{-3} at the 90% confidence level [4]. The magnitude of the $K_L \to \pi^0\mu^+\mu^-$ branching fraction is expected to be very small; at the 10^{-11} level in the context of the Standard Model.

2. Experiment and Data

The data used in this analysis were collected by the E799 experiment during the 1991 fixed target running cycle at Fermilab. The principle focus of the E799 experiment is to search for the $K_L \to \pi^0 e^+ e^-$ decay, which is expected to have a CP violating component of the decay amplitude that is large, and greater than that in $K_L \to \pi^0 \mu^+ \mu^-$. The E799 detector inherited a large acceptance for four-body decays as well as excellent charged tracking and electromagnetic calorimetry from the preceding experiment E731, which searched for direct CP violation through a precision measurement of $Re(\frac{\epsilon'}{\epsilon})$. A general discussion of the E799 apparatus can be found in these proceedings [5].

In order to address a broad range of rare K_L decays the E799 detector ran many physics triggers in parallel. Of particular importance to this analysis are the 2μ trigger, a prescaled minimum bias two-track trigger, and a random trigger that measured the accidental activity in the detector. The minimum bias two-track trigger required that hit wires in the drift chamber system and hit counters in a trigger hodoscope be consistent with at least two charged tracks through the spectrometer. In addition, the minimum bias two-track trigger required that there be no activity in the veto system that surrounds the decay volume. The 2μ trigger required the following conditions: (1) The minimum bias two-track trigger. (2) At least 6 GeV of energy deposited in the lead glass electromagnetic calorimeter. (3) At most 5 minimum ionizing equivalents of energy deposited in a hadronic veto hodoscope downstream of the lead glass array. (4) At least two non-adjacent hit counters in a muon hodoscope downstream of a 3m iron muon filter.

3. Analysis

Approximately 60 million 2μ triggers were collected during the duration of the E799 run. These 60 million events were reduced to the final data set through the following selection criteria: (1) To suppress backgrounds from $(\pi^\pm \to \mu^\pm \nu_\mu)$ decays, two high quality tracks through the spectrometer are required. In searching for $K_L \to \pi^0 \mu^+ \mu^-$, both tracks must have no missing hits in the bending plane of the spectrometer. (2) The momenta of each track must be greater than 7 GeV/c to ensure tractable trajectories through the muon filter. (3) The total energy in the calorimeter must be greater than 10 GeV in order to avoid detailed simulation of the online trigger requirement of 6 GeV in the lead glass array. In addition, the energy sum of candidate photon clusters must be greater than 6 GeV to suppress accidental photons which predominately have lower energy. (4) The energy of calorimeter clusters that are associated with charged tracks must be less than 3.0 GeV in order to reject non-minimum ionizing particles. (5) The separation of track clusters and photon clusters in the lead glass array must be greater than 20 cm to suppress the contribution of hadronic showers to photon clusters in the array. (6) In searching for $K_L \to \pi^0 \mu^+ \mu^-$, The invariant mass of the two charged tracks must be inconsistent with the $\Lambda \to p^+ \pi^-$ hypothesis. In addition, the invariant mass of the two photons must be greater than 120 MeV/c^2 and less than 150 MeV/c^2. (7) The transverse momentum of candidate events with respect to the production target must be less than 150 MeV/c.

The mass distribution of the surviving $K_L \to \mu^+ \mu^- \gamma$ candidates is shown in figure 1. A clear signal of 167 events is seen, with a background level of 3%-5%. The background is well modeled by $K\mu3$ decay and an accidental photon where the pion decays in flight. Figure 2 shows the mass distribution of $K_L \to \pi^0\mu^+\mu^-$ candidates. The background at low mass is due to $K_L \to \pi^+\pi^-\pi^0$ decays where the pions are misidentified as muons from decay in flight and/or muon filter punch-through.

The sensitivity of the experiment is determined from $K_L \to \pi^+\pi^-\pi^0$ decays that populate the prescaled minimum bias two-track trigger. The acceptance of $K_L \to \mu^+\mu^-\gamma$ and $K_L \to \pi^0\mu^+\mu^-$ decays is determined from a Monte Carlo simulation of these processes where a Kroll-Wada form factor is assumed in $K_L \to \mu^+\mu^-\gamma$, and flat phase-space is assumed for the $K_L \to \pi^0\mu^+\mu^-$ process. Accidental events are overlaid on Monte Carlo events to correctly account for the effect of accidental energy deposits. The measured branching fraction and limit is:

$$B(K_L \to \mu^+\mu^-\gamma) = 3.88 \pm 0.32 \times 10^{-7}, \text{ (stat errors only)}$$
$$B(K_L \to \pi^0\mu^+\mu^-) < 1.7 \times 10^{-8}, 90\% \text{ C.L., (stat errors only)}$$

Evaluation of systematic errors are in progress now, where the dominant sources of systematic error are the effects of accidental energy deposits, and understanding of the absolute efficiency of the 2μ trigger.

References

1. L. Bergstrom et al, Phys. Lett. **131B**, 1983, 229.
2. P. Singer, Nucl. Phys. **A527**, 1991 713.
3. See these proceedings, (Schartz).
4. See these proceedings, (Gibbons).
5. See these proceedings, (McFarland).

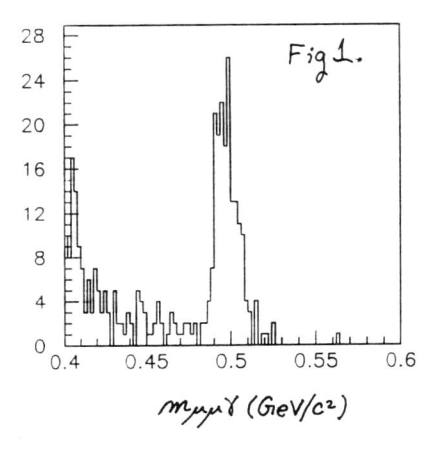

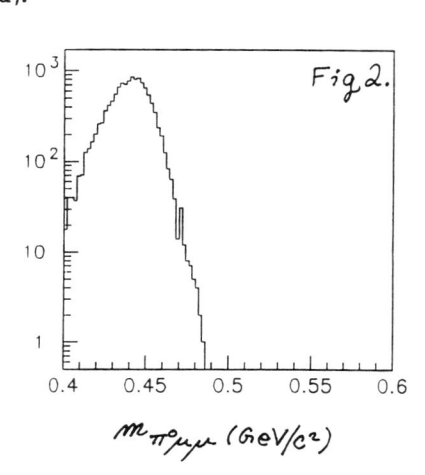

MEASUREMENT OF BR($K_L \to \mu^+\mu^-$): OVERALL RESULTS FROM BNL E791

A. J. SCHWARTZ
*Physics Department, Princeton University
Princeton, New Jersey 08544*

(for the E791 Collaboration)

ABSTRACT

Using our overall sample of 707 $K_L \to \mu^+\mu^-$ candidates collected during our three running periods, 1988, 1989, and 1990, we measure a branching fraction $BR(K_L \to \mu^+\mu^-) = (6.86 \pm 0.37) \times 10^{-9}$. The sample used is the largest to-date of $K_L \to \mu^+\mu^-$ events. The result is very close to the unitarity bound 6.83×10^{-9} coming from an absorptive $\gamma\gamma$ intermediate state.

1. Introduction

We have measured the branching ratio for $K_L \to \mu^+\mu^-$ using all three of our data sets: that recorded in 1988, 1989, and 1990. The yields of $\mu^+\mu^-$ candidate events are 87, 274, and 346, respectively. The latter two samples have been subjected to a common analysis, described here, with similar errors and efficiencies. The measured rate for $K_L \to \mu^+\mu^-$ is interesting because the amplitude receives contributions from a top-dominated quark loop. The real (or dispersive) part of $A(K_L \to \mu^+\mu^-)$ received contributions from the short-distance electroweak diagrams of Figure 1, while the imaginary (or absorptive) part is dominated by a $\gamma\gamma$ intermediate state. The latter contribution factors into two pieces, $\Gamma(K_L \to \gamma\gamma) \cdot \Gamma(\gamma\gamma \to \mu^+\mu^-)$, and using the measured value[1] $BR(K_L \to \gamma\gamma) = 5.70 \times 10^{-4}$ and the QED result[2] $\Gamma(K_L \to \gamma\gamma \to \mu^+\mu^-)/\Gamma(K_L \to \gamma\gamma) = 1.20 \times 10^{-5}$, one calculates $BR(K_L \to \mu^+\mu^-)_{\text{abs}} = 6.83 \times 10^{-9}$. This value, called the unitarity bound, is the minimum rate at which $K_L \to \mu^+\mu^-$ is expected to occur.

The electroweak diagrams of Figure 1 contain a quark loop receiving contributions from u, c, and t quarks. Because top is so heavy ($m_t > 91$ GeV/c^2 at 95% confidence[3]), it dominates the loop such that contributions from lighter quarks can be neglected; the amplitude is then proportional to[4] $(m_t/m_W)^2 |\text{Re}(V_{td}^* V_{ts})|^2$. Thus a precise measurement of $BR(K_L \to \mu^+\mu^-)$

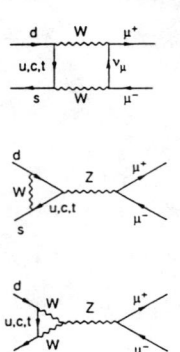

Figure 1: Short-distance contributions to $K_L \to \mu^+\mu^-$.

allows one to constrain the product of Kobayashi-Maskawa matrix elements $|\text{Re}(V_{td}^*V_{ts})|$ given the top quark mass m_t, or vice-versa.[5]

2. Detector and Event Selection

The E791 collaboration consists of physicists from UC Irvine, UCLA, LANL, Stanford, Temple, Texas, and William and Mary. The apparatus, described in detail in reference 6, consists of a 24 GeV proton beam incident on a copper target tilted at 2.75° with respect to the horizontal. The secondary beam emitted horizontally is accepted by a series of collimators, sweeping magnets, and thin lead foils which define the beam to lie within a solid angle of 65 μsr, sweep away charged particles and convert photons. The beam subsequently enters an 8 m vacuum tank in which accepted kaons decay. Downstream of the tank is a 2-magnet spectrometer which makes 2 independent momentum measurements. Following the spectrometer are particle ID detectors consisting of a Čerenkov counter and lead-glass array for electron identification, and a 1 m iron wall, scintillator hodoscope, and 13 m rangestack for muon identification. The first-level trigger used to record $\mu^+\mu^-$ events requires hits in trigger scintillator counters placed upstream and downstream of the Čerenkov counter, hits in both arms of the first 3 drift chambers, and hits in both arms of the muon hodoscope.

The offline analysis consists first of a pattern recognition algorithm requiring 2 oppositely-charged tracks, one in each spectrometer arm, which point back to a common vertex. Events which pass are subjected to track and vertex fits using the complete magnetic field maps, and cuts are made on the χ^2 of the fits to reject pion decays in-flight. Some fiducial volume cuts are made to ensure that decays originate in the decay volume and that tracks do not traverse material or rapidly varying regions of the magnetic field, e.g. near the coils. Events surviving up to this point have their tracks projected to particle ID counters and the responses noted. The particle ID cuts used to select the $\mu^+\mu^-$ sample require (for each track) in-time hits in those paddles of the muon hodoscope to which the track projects, and penetration of the muon rangefinder to within 3 gaps of that expected based on the momentum measurement. A $\pi^+\pi^-$ sample used to normalize the sensitivity of the experiment is selected from minimum bias triggers analyzed through fiducial volume cuts.

3. Final $\mu^+\mu^-$ Sample

Figure 2 shows a scatter plot of the 1990 $\mu^+\mu^-$ sample plotted in the variables θ_c^2 versus reconstructed $\mu\mu$ mass. The 1989 sample look similar. The colinearity angle θ_c is defined as the angle between a line drawn from target to K_L decay vertex and the reconstructed kaon momentum vector $\vec{p}_K$. For 2-body decays, $\vec{p}_K$ points back to the target and $\theta_c \simeq 0$. For 3-body decays the reconstructed $\vec{p}_K$ does not include the neutrino's momentum and does not necessarily point back; θ_c is then large.

The figure shows a large clustering of events at low θ_c^2 near $m_K = 498$ MeV/c^2.

Also visible is a relatively small amount of background extending to high $\mu\mu$ mass. The background is dominated by K_{e3} decays where the pion decays in-flight and the electron is mis-identified as a muon. The mis-identification can produce a large 2-body invariant mass equal to or exceeding m_K. The background also contains a small number of mis-measured $K_{\mu3}$ decays which for perfect mass resolution have a kinematic endpoint of 489 MeV/c^2. To subtract off these backgrounds two boxes are defined: a signal box extending ± 6 MeV/c^2 around the kaon mass and from 0–2 mrad^2 in θ_c^2, and a 'background' box covering the same region of $m_{\mu\mu}$ but extending from 2.5–6.5 in θ_c^2. There are 370 events in the signal box and 29 events in the background box. Of this latter group 16 have one of the muons satisfying electron ID and are thus identified as K_{e3} decays. Since the electron efficiency in this kinematic region is 88.7% (measured from a separate study), the most-likely number of K_{e3} events in the background box is 18, leaving 11 $K_{\mu3}$ events.

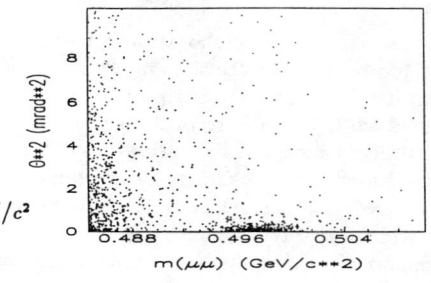

Figure 2: θ_c^2 vs. $m_{\mu\mu}$ for final $\mu^+\mu^-$ sample.

To extrapolate the K_{e3} background into the signal box one selects from the $\mu\mu$ trigger sample those events which satisfy offline electron ID rather than muon ID. Of these K_{e3} events, those with $|m_{\mu\mu} - m_K| < 6$ MeV/c^2 are plotted as a function of θ_c^2 (Figure 3a). The extrapolation factor needed is then the ratio of the number of events with $0 < \theta_c^2 < 2$ mrad^2 to the number with $2.5 < \theta_c^2 < 6.5$ mrad^2. The factor is 1.03, giving an estimated number of K_{e3} events in the signal box of 18.5.

To extrapolate the $K_{\mu3}$ background one plots the dimuon events of Figure 2 which have $|m_{\mu\mu} - m_K| < 6$ MeV/c^2 and which *do not* have an electron (Figure 3b). This sample has little K_{e3} contamination and consists essentially of $K_L \to \mu^+\mu^-$ decays at low θ_c^2 and $K_{\mu3}$ decays at higher θ_c^2. The distribution of $K_{\mu3}$ events appears roughly constant in $dN/d\theta_c^2$ and the 11 events in the background box are extra-

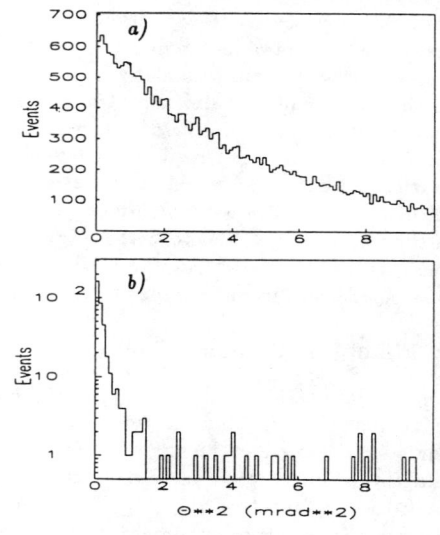

Figure 3: θ_c^2 spectrum of a) $K \to \pi e \bar{\nu}$ events, b) $\mu^+\mu^-$ events with electron veto.

polated as such into the signal box to give an estimated $K_{\mu 3}$ background of 5.5 events. The final number of $\mu^+\mu^-$ candidates for 1990 is $370-18.5-5.5=346$. The final number for 1989 is 274.

4. Final $\pi^+\pi^-$ Sample and Normalization

To count the number of $\pi^+\pi^-$ candidates one defines for the minimum bias sample a signal box identical to that used for $\mu^+\mu^-$. For 1990 data there are 40485 events in this box, of which a significant fraction is background due to the lack of particle identification in the minimum bias sample. To estimate the background, all events with $\theta_c^2 < 2$ mrad^2 are projected onto the $m_{\pi\pi}$ axis (Figure 4a) and all events with $|m_{\pi\pi} - m_K| < 6$ MeV/c^2 are projected onto the θ_c^2 axis (Figure 4b). A large sample of Monte Carlo K_{e3} and $K_{\mu 3}$ decays are generated and the mass and θ_c^2 Monte Carlo lineshapes are matched to the respective data spectrum by normalizing to the number of events away from the $\pi^+\pi^-$ peak. For the mass spectrum the normalization region is 482–490 and 505–520 MeV/c^2 while for the θ_c^2 spectrum the normalization region is 3–10 mrad^2. The resultant number of Monte Carlo semileptonic events in the signal box is 8269 for the mass lineshape and 8069 for the θ_c^2 lineshape; averaging the two values gives 8169 background events or $40485 - 8169 = 32316$ $\pi^+\pi^-$'s for 1990. The number for 1989 is 15245, which is lower because of less sensitivity and a larger prescale of minimum bias events.

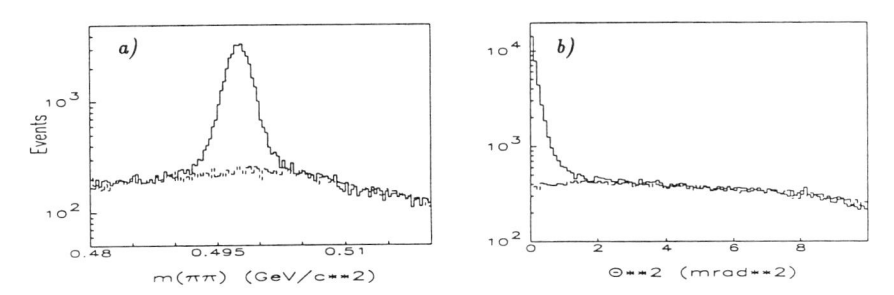

Figure 4: Matching Monte Carlo $K \to \pi \ell \bar{\nu}$ spectra (dashed) to data. a) Events with $\theta_c^2 < 2$ mrad^2, b) events with $|m_{\pi\pi} - m_K| < 6$ MeV/c^2.

5. Likelihood Fit for Result

The $K_L \to \mu\mu$ branching ratio is calculated as:

$$BR = \frac{N_{\mu\mu}}{N_{\pi\pi} \cdot P} \left(\frac{A_{\pi\pi}}{A_{\mu\mu}}\right) \left(\frac{\epsilon_{\pi\pi}^{L3}}{\epsilon_{\mu\mu}^{L3}}\right) \left(\frac{1}{\epsilon_{\mu\mu}^{L1}}\right) \left(\frac{1}{\epsilon_{\mu\mu}^{PID}}\right) (\delta_{\text{int}}) BR(K_L \to \pi^+\pi^-) \quad (1)$$

where $N_{\mu\mu}$ is the number of $\mu\mu$ candidates, $N_{\pi\pi}$ is the number of $\pi\pi$ candidates, P is a prescale factor (4000 for 1990 data, 6000 for 1989), $A_{\pi\pi}/A_{\mu\mu}$ is the acceptance of $\pi\pi$ relative to $\mu\mu$, $(\epsilon_{\pi\pi}{}^{L3})/(\epsilon_{\mu\mu}{}^{L3})$ is the Level 3 trigger efficiency for $\pi\pi$ relative to $\mu\mu$, $\epsilon_{\mu\mu}{}^{L1}$ is the Level 1 trigger efficiency for $\mu\mu$ (accounting for deadtime, etc.), $\epsilon_{\mu\mu}{}^{PID}$ is the offline $\mu\mu$ particle ID efficiency, δ_{int} is a correction for the fraction of $\pi\pi$ events lost due to pion-nucleon interactions in detector material, and $BR(K_L \to \pi^+\pi^-)$ is the measured $K_{\pi\pi}$ rate as listed in the Particle Data Book.[1] The number $N_{\pi\pi}$ contains a 1.1% correction to account for $K_S \to \pi^+\pi^-$ contamination. The acceptance ratio $A_{\pi\pi}/A_{\mu\mu}$ is calculated via Monte Carlo, where the momentum spectrum used to generate K_L's is tuned to give an accepted spectrum which closely matches the $\pi^+\pi^-$ data. Inserting in (1) the 1990 values $N_{\mu\mu} = 346 \pm 20$, $N_{\pi\pi} = 32,316 \pm 250$, $A_{\pi\pi}/A_{\mu\mu} = 1.148 \pm 0.024$, $(\epsilon_{\pi\pi}{}^{L3})/(\epsilon_{\mu\mu}{}^{L3}) = 1.011 \pm 0.003$, $\epsilon_{\mu\mu}{}^{L1} = 0.977 \pm 0.004$, $\epsilon_{\mu\mu}{}^{PID} = 0.911 \pm 0.002$, $\delta_{\text{int}} = 0.957 \pm 0.005$, and $BR(K_L \to \pi^+\pi^-) = (2.03 \pm 0.04) \times 10^{-3}$, one calculates $BR_{1990} = 6.78 \pm 0.40 \text{ (stat.)} \pm 0.23 \text{ (syst.)} \times 10^{-9}$. Inserting 1989 values in (1) gives $BR_{1989} = 7.45 \pm 0.48 \pm 0.34 \times 10^{-9}$.

To combine these results and also include our 1988 data (which alone gives $BR_{1988} = 5.8 \pm 0.6 \pm 0.6 \times 10^{-9}$), we use the method of maximum likelihood, including all numbers of candidates, backgrounds, efficiencies, and their respective errors in constructing the likelihood function. The most-likely value and 68.3% likelihood interval around this value give an overall result:

$$BR(K_L \to \mu^+\mu^-)_{1988+1989+1990} = 6.86 \pm 0.37 \times 10^{-9}.$$

The total number of $\mu^+\mu^-$ candidates is 707. This measurement is consistent with, but much closer to the unitarity bound than, previous measurements made with significantly smaller samples.[7]

6. References

1. K. Hikasa et al. (Particle Data Group), *Phys. Rev.* **D45** (1992) VII.93.
2. B. R. Martin, E. de Rafael and J. Smith, *Phys. Rev.* **D2** (1970) 179.
   L. M. Sehgal, *Phys. Rev.* **183** (1969) 1511.
3. F. Abe et al. (CDF Collaboration), *Phys. Rev.* **D45** (1992) 3921.
4. R. E. Shrock and M. B. Voloshin, *Phys. Lett.* **87B** (1979) 375.
5. P. Ko, *Phys. Rev.* **D45** (1992) 174.
   G. Bélanger and C. Q. Geng, *Phys. Rev.* **D43** (1991) 140.
   C. S. Kim, J. L. Rosner, and C. P. Yuan, *Phys. Rev.* **D42** (1990) 96.
   L. Bergström, E. Massó, and P. Singer, *Phys. Lett.* **249B** (1990) 141.
6. C. Mathiazhagan et al., *Phys. Rev. Lett.* **63** (1989) 2181.
   R. D. Cousins et al., *Nucl. Instr. and Meth.* **A277** (1989) 517.
7. A. J. Schwartz, in *Intersections Between Particle and Nuclear Physics*, ed. W. T. H. Van Oers (AIP, New York, 1992).
   A. P. Heinson et al., *Phys. Rev.* **D44** (1991) 1.
   C. Mathiazhagan et al., *Phys. Rev. Lett.* **63** (1989) 2185.
   T. Akagi et al., *Phys. Rev. Lett.* **67** (1991) 2618.

PHYSICS AT DAΦNE

JULIET LEE-FRANZINI
Laboratori Nazionali di Frascati dell'INFN, I-00044, Frascati, Italy
SUNY at Stony Brook, Stony Brook, New York 11794

Abstract

Experimental measurements which can be done at DAΦNE, the ϕ-factory under construction at the Laboratori Nazionali di Frascati dell'INFN, are briefly discussed.

1. Introduction

The Frascati ϕ–factory, DAΦNE, is a "factory" of neutral K's which are in a well prepared quantum state, and of charged K pairs, as well as of ρ's, η's and the rarer η''s. The high luminosity of DAΦNE will also allow measurements of rare ϕ radiative decays.[1] Another feature at DAΦNE is that, because the ϕ's decay at rest, neutral kaons are produced in collinear pairs, with momenta of 110 MeV/c. The observation of one K guarantees the existence of the other, with determined direction and identity, *i.e.*, K's can be "tagged". By using the KLOE detector proposed for DAΦNE,[2] which has a K_S decay fiducial volume of radius $\sim$8 cm, and a K_L decay fiducial volume of radius $\sim$150 cm, up to 10^{10} tagged K mesons can be collected per year. One has beams of K_S, with no background, and thus can dramatically improve knowledge of K_S branching ratios (most are not measured yet). Searches for $K_S \to \pi^0 \nu \bar{\nu}$, $e^+ e^- \gamma$, $\mu^+ \mu^- \gamma$, $\pi^0 e^+ e^-$, $\pi^0 \mu^+ \mu^-$ etc., down to 10^{-8} or better are possible.

2. CP and CPT at DAΦNE

The KLOE program at DAΦNE is aimed at measuring CP and possible CPT violation in the $K^0, \bar{K}^0 - K_S, K_L$ system, with a sensitivity comparable to the next generation fixed target experiments ($\sim 10^{-4}$), both by using pure K_S, K_L beams obtained from tagging, and also by taking advantage of the coherent K_S, K_L states produced, which allows performance of *kaon-quantum-interferometry*, determining most parameters of the neutral kaons such as $\Re(\epsilon'/\epsilon)$, $\Im(\epsilon'/\epsilon)$, Δm, $|\eta_{\pi\pi}|$, $\phi_{\pi\pi}$, with improved accuracy. Diagonalizing the K^0-$\bar{K}^0$ mass matrix (which has non-diagonal elements from $K^0 \rightleftharpoons \bar{K}^0$) we get the physical states K_S and K_L, which we can write (adopting the notation of Ref. 3), without assuming CPT, as $|K_S\rangle \propto (1 + \epsilon_K + \delta_K)|K^0\rangle + (1 - \epsilon_K - \delta_K)|\bar{K}^0\rangle$, $|K_L\rangle \propto (1 + \epsilon_K - \delta_K)|K^0\rangle - (1 - \epsilon_K + \delta_K)|\bar{K}^0\rangle$, where the (small) complex ϵ_K and δ_K characterize respectively the CP violating and CPT violating parameters in the effective Hamiltonian. Using the usual defintions of amplitude ratios and epsilon parameters:[4] $\eta_{+-} = \epsilon + \epsilon'$, $\eta_{00} = \epsilon - 2\epsilon'$ where η's and ϵ's are all complex, experimental observation of $\epsilon' \neq 0$ would be proof that CP is violated in the decay amplitude. The relationships between $\eta_\pm$, η_{00} and ϵ, ϵ', when one allows CPT violation, remain as above, since they depend only on isospin decomposition, *albeit* both ϵ, ϵ' each acquire terms which violate CP and CPT separately.[3]

At DAΦNE $K^0\bar{K}^0$ are produced in a C-odd state. In vacuum the $K^0\bar{K}^0$ pair remains a pure K_S, K_L state. Defining $\eta_i = \langle f_i|K_L\rangle/\langle f_i|K_S\rangle$, $\Delta t = t_1 - t_2$, $t = t_1+t_2$, $\Delta\mathcal{M} = \mathcal{M}_L - \mathcal{M}_S$ (where $\mathcal{M}_{S,L} = M_{S,L} - i\Gamma_{S,L}/2$ are the complex masses of K_S and K_L), and $\mathcal{M} = \mathcal{M}_L + \mathcal{M}_S$, the amplitude for decay to states f_1 at time t_1 and f_2 at time t_2, without identification of K_S or K_L, is: $\langle f_1, t_1, \mathbf{p}; f_2, t_2, -\mathbf{p}|i\rangle \propto \left(\langle f_1|K_S\rangle\langle f_2|K_S\rangle e^{-i\mathcal{M}t/2}\right) \times \left(\eta_1 e^{i\Delta\mathcal{M}\Delta t/2} - \eta_2 e^{-i\Delta\mathcal{M}\Delta t/2}\right)$. The decay intensity $I(f_1, f_2, \Delta t = t_1 - t_2)$ to final states f_1 and f_2 is obtained from the above equation by integrating over all t_1, t_2, with Δt constant. For $\Delta t > 0$:

$$I(f_1, f_2; \Delta t) = \frac{1}{2}\int_{\Delta t}^{\infty} |A(f_1, t_1; f_2, t_2)|^2 dt = \frac{1}{2\Gamma}|\langle f_1|K_S\rangle\langle f_2|K_S\rangle|^2$$

$$\times \left(|\eta_1|^2 e^{-\Gamma_L \Delta t} + |\eta_2|^2 e^{-\Gamma_S \Delta t} - 2|\eta_1||\eta_2| e^{-\Gamma\Delta t/2} \cos(\Delta m \Delta t + \phi_1 - \phi_2)\right),$$

with $\eta_i = A(K_L \to f_i)/A(K_S \to f_i) = |\eta_i|e^{i\phi_i}$, exhibiting interference terms sensitive to phase differences. We can perform "kaon-interferometry" by using the decay intensity of the previous equation with appropriate choices of the final states f_1, f_2. For example: 1) $f_1=f_2$: we can measure Γ_S, Γ_L and Δm, since all the phases disappear. Rates can be measured to $\times 10$ improvement in accuracy and Δm to $\times 2$. 2) $f_1 \neq f_2$: a) $f_1=\pi^+\pi^-$, $f_2=\pi^0\pi^0$: we can measure $\Re(\epsilon'/\epsilon)$ and $\Im(\epsilon'/\epsilon)$, the former by concentrating on large time differences, the latter for $|\Delta t| \leq 5\tau_s$. b) $f_1 = \pi^+\ell^-\nu$ and $f_2 = \pi^-\ell^+\nu$: we can measure the CPT-violation parameter δ_K, the real part by concentrating on large time difference regions; and the imaginary part for $|\Delta t| \leq 10\tau_s$. c) $f_1 = 2\pi$, $f_2 = K_{\ell 3}$, this leads to measurements of CP and CPT violation parameters at large time differences, since we measure the asymmetry in K_L semileptonic decays. At small time differences, we obtain Δm, $|\eta_{\pi\pi}|$ and $\phi_{\pi\pi}$. 3) By choosing $f_1 = \pi\pi$, and $f_2 =$ all other decay channels of the other K, the "inclusive method," we obtain the best measurements of the magnitudes of η_{+-} and η_{00} as well as $\Re\epsilon_K + i\Im\delta_K$. 4) By choosing $f_1 = \pi^\pm\ell\nu$, and $f_2 =$ all other decay channels of the partner K we obtain the best measure of the $\langle K_S|K_L\rangle$ overlap, i.e., determine both $\Re\epsilon_K$ and $\Im\delta_K$. 5) We can measure the asymmetry in the semileptonic decays of the K_S. The difference between this asymmetry, and that in the semileptonic decays of the K_L's, measures the real part of the CPT-violation parameter δ_K. 6) By measuring the difference in rates into two positive same sign leptons of the K pair from that into two negative same sign leptons, we probe the K^0-$\bar{K}^0$ mass difference to 1×10^{-18}.[3]

In addition, we can also use the classical method of the double ratio $\mathcal{R}^\pm/\mathcal{R}^0 = 1 + 6\times\Re(\epsilon'/\epsilon)$, and other ways of measuring $\Re(\epsilon'/\epsilon)$ from selected final states. Thus, at DAΦNE we can improve the present knowledge of all sixteen observables in the K_S, K_L system by up to one or two orders of magnitudes, and, by measuring the real part of δ_K, we can separate all the individual CPT violating parameters.[3] If the $\Delta S = \Delta Q$ rule is relaxed, so that 4 new parameters are added to describe the neutral kaon system, only one other experimental input (involving tagging strangeness without use of semileptonic decays of K's) is needed to completely disentangle all eight CP and CPT violating parameters.[5]

3. Other CP Violations at DAΦNE

So far the only CP violation has been observed in the K_L system. Observation of $K_S \to 3\pi^0$ would constitute a new proof of CP violation. KLOE can collect ~ 30 events in one year, with zero background. KLOE can also easily measure the difference in rates between $(K_S \to \pi^\pm \ell^\mp \nu)$ to 4×10^{-4}. Evidence for direct CP violation can be also be obtained from the decays of charged kaons which are copiously produced at DAΦNE. CP requires equality of the partial rates for $K^\pm \to \pi^\pm \pi^+ \pi^-$ ($\tau^\pm$) and for $K^\pm \to \pi^\pm \pi^0 \pi^0$ ($\tau'^\pm$). We can improve the present rate asymmetry by two orders of magnitude. We can also observe differences in the Dalitz plot distributions for K^+ and K^- decays in both the τ and τ' modes; here KLOE could reach sensitivities of $\sim 10^{-4}$. Differences in rates in the radiative two pion decays of $K^\pm$, $K^\pm \to \pi^\pm \pi^0 \gamma$, are also proof of direct CP violation. The KLOE sensitivity is $\sim 1.4\times 10^{-3}$.

4. Chiral Perturbation Theory

In the last decade chiral perturbation theory (CHPT) has been extended to the next order terms in the chiral expansion ($\mathcal{O}(m^4)$, $\mathcal{O}(p^4)$, $\mathcal{O}(m^2 p^2)$). Many new amplitudes can then be predicted.[6] At lowest order the CHPT relation predicts the slope of the scalar form factor, λ_0. There is at present disagreement from experiment with the CHPT prediction, 0.017 ± 0.004. KLOE can measure λ_0 for K_L to an accuracy of 1.4×10^{-5}. Similar accuracy are obtained for $K^\pm$ and for λ_+. There is only one measurement of the relevant $K_{\ell 4}$ form factors. These decays also provide another opportunity for the determination of the $\pi\pi$ phase shifts. The amplitudes for $K_{\ell 2,\gamma}$, $K_{\ell 2, e^+ e^-}$ and $K_{\ell 3,\gamma}$ depend on the K charge radius. The rate for $K^\pm \to \pi^\pm \gamma\gamma$ and the $\gamma\gamma$ distributions are uniquely predicted by the chiral lagrangian approach. Dalitz type decays of K mesons and two photon production of pions are also of great interest. KLOE can improve vastly on all these topics.

5. Acknowledgements

I wish to thank Paolo and Paula J. Franzini for help in preparing this paper.

6. References

1. P. J. Franzini,"Solving the f_0 Puzzle at DAΦNE", these Proceedings.
2. P. Franzini, " The KLOE Detector", these Proceedings.
3. C. Buchanan et al., Phys. Rev. **D45**, 4088 (1992).
4. T. T. Wu and C. N. Yang, Phys. Rev. Lett. **13**, 380 (1964).
5. L. Maiani, in *DAΦNE Physics Handbook*, ed. L. Maiani et al., LNF, Frascati.
6. For all references on CHPT, see *DAΦNE Physics Handbook*, ed. L. Maiani et al., LNF, Frascati.

RARE η DECAYS

B.M.K. NEFKENS
Physics Department, UCLA
Los Angeles, CA 90024-1547

The rare decays of the η-meson offer a large variety of precision tests of C, CP, T, and even CPT invariance as shown in Table I which lists 13 different cases. Furthermore, rare η decays provide new opportunities in the quest for exotica such as leptoquarks, second class weak currents, and lepton-family violating transitions, see Table II. Some not-so-rare η decays make good cases for significant tests of chiral perturbation theory. Several examples are listed in Table II.

The exceptional suitability of η decays for the above physics is due to three factors:

(a) The η is an eigenstate of the C and CP operators. This is a rarity in nature and it explains the current paucity of direct tests of C and CP invariance of the strong and electromagnetic interaction of hadrons. Detailed analysis shows that the experimental limit is only $A_{\cancel{C}} < \frac{1}{10} A_C$, where $A_{\cancel{C}}$ is the C-violating and A_C the C-conserving amplitude.

(b) The elementary-particle assignments $I^G, J^{PC} = 0^+, 0^{-+}$ together with the low value of the mass, $m_\eta = 547.3$ MeV, result in the η having a relatively long mean life, the decay width $\Gamma(\eta \to \text{all}) = 1.2$ keV. This allows precision tests of strong and electromagnetic interactions and even of weak interactions which are expected at the level BR$\sim 10^{-9}$.

(c) The additive quantum numbers of the η are zero, $J = Q = I = S = B = L = 0$, J = spin, Q = electric charge, I = isospin, S = strangeness (also charm, beauty, and topness), B = baryon number, and L = lepton number. η decays allow the study of vacuum-like transitions. They are not subject to the restrictions that hamper flavor-changing transitions which one encounters in the popular K- and B-meson decays.

A novel test of C, charge conjugation, is a search for lepton charge asymmetry in the decay $\eta \to \pi^0 \ell \bar{\ell}$, where ℓ is μ or e. The lowest order electromagnetic interaction could occur by way of the one photon intermediate state, $\eta \to \pi^0 \gamma \to \pi^0 \ell \bar{\ell}$, which is however forbidden by C-conservation, the amplitude for this is $A_{\cancel{C}}(1\gamma)$. The rate is $\sim \alpha^2$ which implies that BR$(\eta \to \pi^0 \mu^+ \mu^-) \sim 10^{-4}$. The next order is based on the two photon intermediate state $\eta \to \pi°\gamma\gamma \to \pi°\ell\bar{\ell}$, the amplitude is $A_C(2\gamma)$. The rate is now $\sim \alpha^4$, the decay is allowed by C and CP and an estimate of the branching ratio based on the unitarity lower bound is $BR(\eta \to \pi°\ell\bar{\ell}) \sim 10^{-9}$. The lepton charge asymmetry is $\mathcal{A} \sim A_{\mathcal{C}}(1\gamma)\, A_C(2\gamma) \sin\phi$ where ϕ is the interference phase, expected to be large. The Standard Model predicts $\mathcal{A} < 10^{-5}$. A nonzero value for $\mathcal{A}$ thus is unequivocal evidence for C violation and New Physics.

Time reversal (T) invariance can be tested by searching for a transverse μ^+ polarization in the decay $\eta \to \pi°\mu^+\mu^-$. Such a polarization would be the result of the amplitude $A_T \sim \vec{\sigma}_{\mu^+} \cdot (\vec{p}_{\mu^+} \times \vec{p}_{\mu^-})$, which is odd under T.

A novel test of CPT invariance is based on a particular symmetry in the decay spectrum of $\eta \to \pi°\mu^+\mu^-$. The reason that one can test CPT is a consequence of the η being an eigenstate of C and CP. The decay symmetry follows from the physical meaning of the CPT operator which is to reverse all spins and interchange the spins and momenta of $\ell\bar{\ell}$. It requires a certain regularity in the decay spectrum specifically if $theta$ is the angle of the $\pi°$ in the dilepton c.m. frame, then the decay spectrum should have only even powers of $\cos\theta$.

Besides testing the discrete symmetries P, T, and C, the rare η decays offer a host of interesting possibilities for confronting the Standard Model. Consider the decay $\eta \to e^+e^-$. This is an α^4 type decay which is suppressed by the helicity factor $(m_e/m_\eta)^2$. Estimates are $BR(\eta \to e^+e^-) \simeq 5 \times 10^{-9}$. A branching ratio much larger than this would be a significant hint for new physics such as the speculative leptoquark which is a novel intermediate boson that connects directly quarks with leptons. The present experimental limit is merely $BR(\eta \to e^+e^-) < 3 \times 10^{-4}$.

Next, we consider the decay $\eta \to \pi\ell\nu$. The simplest interaction responsible for this decay is the speculative second-class weak current with vector-type coupling. The branching ratio for a typical, allowed weak decay would be about 10^{-9} with a possible suppression by the $(m_\ell/m_\eta)^2$ factor due to helicity conservation. Second-class weak currents are not easily renormalizable and they are not compatible with modern gauge theories. Experimental tests of gauge invariance, which underlies the Standard Model, are hard to find. Thus the decay $\eta \to \pi\ell\nu$ is of fundamental interest as it provides a possible, unambiguous test of gauge invariance. Observation of these decays at the level 10^{-11} would point uniquely to new physics.

A tagged η source of $10^8 - 10^9 \eta/\text{day}$ is already available at Saturne (Saclay). It is based on the production reaction $pd \to {}^3He\,\eta$ at $1\frac{1}{2}$ MeV above threshold. There exists an exciting possibility for an excellent η source at the AGS and PILAC (LAMPF) based on $\pi^+p \to \eta n$ or $\pi^+d \to pp\eta$ at $p_\pi = 730$ MeV as $\sigma \sim 2$ mb. It is also possible to have a strong η source at FNAL. Some details of the above are given in Ref. [1]. Useful reference on η decay physics can be found in Refs. [2-6].

References

[1] B.M.K. Nefkens in *New Vistas with High Energy Pion Beams*, Santa Fe, N.M., Oct. 1992. To appear in World Scientific.

[2] B.M.K. Nefkens, "Physics of Light Mesons," in AIP Conference Proceedings 243, Intersections between Particle and Nuclear Physics, edited by W.T.H. van Oers, AIP (1991) p. 647.

[3] B.M.K. Nefkens, "Rare and Not-so-Rare-Decays of Light Mesons," in Meson Production, Interaction and Decay, edited by A. Magiera et al., World Scientific (1991), p. 40.

[4] Proceedings of the Workshop on Physics with Light Mesons, edited by W.R. Gibbs and B.M.K. Nefkens, Los Alamos, LAMPF LA-11184-C (1987).

[5] "Production and Decay of Light Mesons," Paris 1988, edited by P. Fleury, World Scientific (1988).

[6] "Rare Decays of Light Mesons," Gif-sur-Yvette 1990, edited by B. Mayer, Editions Frontières (1990).

TABLE I Testing C, CP, T, and CPT

Decay	Symmetry	Observable
$\eta \to \pi^0 \ell^+ \ell^-$	C	1st order rate
$\eta \to \pi^0 \ell^+ \ell^-$	C, CP	charge asym.
$\eta \to \pi^0 \mu^+ \mu^-$	T	μ^+ trans. pol.
$\eta \to \pi^0 \ell^+ \ell^-$	CPT	decay correl.
$\eta \to 3\gamma$	C	rate
$\eta \to \mu^+ \mu^-$	P, CP	μ^+ long. pol.
$\eta \to \pi^+ \pi^-$	P, CP	rate
$\eta \to \pi^0 \pi^0$	P, CP	rate
$\eta \to 4\pi^0$	P, CP	rate
$\eta \to \pi^+ \pi^- \ell \bar{\ell}$	P, CP	decay correl.
$\eta \to \pi^+ \pi^- \gamma$	P, CP	spectr. shape
$\eta \to \pi^+ \pi^- \pi^0$	C	charge asym.
$\eta \to \pi^+ \pi^- \gamma$	C	charge asym.

TABLE II Other interesting rare η decays

Decay Mode	New Physics	Needed Sens.
$\eta \to e^+ e^-$	leptoquark	$BR \sim 10^{-9}$
$\eta \to \mu e$	lepton fam. viol.	$BR \sim 10^{-10}$
$\eta \to \pi \ell \nu$	2nd class current	$BR \sim 10^{-11}$
$\eta \to K e \nu$	ΔS weak int.	$BR \sim 10^{-13}$
$\eta \to \pi \pi \nu \nu$	neutr. weak current	$BR \sim 10^{-10}$
$\eta \to \ell^+ \ell^- \gamma$	form factor	$BR \sim 10^{-4}$
$\eta \to \pi^0 \gamma \gamma$	chiral perturb. th.	5% in spectr.
$\eta \to \pi^+ \pi^- \gamma$	chiral perturb. th.	5% in spectr.
$\eta \to 3\pi^0$	chiral perturb. th.	1% in spectr.

ATOMIC PHYSICS CALCULATIONS OF
WEAK INTERACTION EFFECTS

J. SAPIRSTEIN
Department of Physics, University of Notre Dame
Notre Dame, IN 46556, USA

ABSTRACT

Information about weak interactions can be obtained from atomic physics experiments on heavy atoms. Reliable atomic structure calculations are required for the interpretation of parity nonconservation and atomic electric dipole moment measurements. The nature of these calculations will be described and applied to give limits on the electron edm and to put constraints on new physics from an accurate measurement of PNC in atomic cesium.

While atomic physics has a long history of testing Quantum Electrodynamics (QED), it has until recently not played a role in testing the weak interactions. However, as pointed out first by the Bouchiats[1], weak neutral currents can induce a measurable parity nonconserving transition in heavy atoms, in particular cesium. In addition, Sandars[2] found that an electron electric dipole moment (edm) d_e could induce a much larger atomic edm d_A in heavy atoms, allowing stringent constraints on d_e. As examples of the particle physics utility of these tests, the weak charge of cesium has been determined to be[3,4]

$$Q_W = -71.04(1.58)[0.88], \qquad (1)$$

where the first error is experimental and the second from the uncertainty in atomic theory. This is to be compared with the almost top mass independent standard model theory prediction[5]

$$Q_W = -73.20(13). \qquad (2)$$

While the experimental error is at present too large to make this test of the standard model competitive with other more accurate tests, it is of interest that some technicolor theories have a Q_W closer to -75, and are close to being ruled out by this experiment.

Because of an accurate calculation of the edm enhancement factor in thallium by Liu and Kelly[6], the experimental limit[7]

$$d_{Tl} = (1.6 \pm 5.0) \cdot 10^{-24} e \cdot cm \qquad (3)$$

can be interpreted in terms of an electron edm as

$$d_e = (-2.7 \pm 8.3) \cdot 10^{-27} e \cdot cm. \qquad (4)$$

It is clearly important to be sure of the atomic theory part of these results. However, while the underlying theory of such atoms is of course QED, the practical problem of carrying out accurate calculations is quite challenging. However, considerable progress has been made in recent years: this paper will sketch some basic ideas, and the interested reader is referred to references 4 and 6 for a more detailed description.

The basic problem in calculating the properties of an N-electron atom is to solve $H\psi = E\psi$, where ψ is a many-electron wave function and

$$H = \sum_{i=1}^{N}(\vec{\alpha}_i \cdot \vec{p}_i + \beta_i m - \frac{Z\alpha}{r_i}) + \sum_{i<j} \frac{\alpha}{|\vec{r}_i - \vec{r}_j|}. \quad (5)$$

The last term makes this too complicated to solve for directly, so one makes the rearrangement $H = H_0 + V_C$, where

$$H_0 = \sum_{i=1}^{N}(\vec{\alpha}_i \cdot \vec{p}_i + \beta_i m - \frac{Z(r_i)\alpha}{r_i}) \quad (6)$$

and

$$V_C = \sum_{i<j} \frac{\alpha}{|\vec{r}_i - \vec{r}_j|} - \sum_{i=1}^{N} \frac{(Z - Z(r_i))\alpha}{r_i}. \quad (7)$$

Here $Z(r)$ is an effective nuclear charge felt equally by each electron: for example, it can be modeled for cesium as the Tietz potential, derived from Thomas-Fermi theory,

$$Z(r) = 1 + \frac{54}{(1 + 2.0453r)^2} e^{-0.2445r}. \quad (8)$$

At small r an electron sees the full nuclear charge, and at very large r only the unit charge of the nucleus screened by the other electrons. (While in actual calculations the non-local Hartree Fock potential is used, this potential serves to illustrate the way calculations are carried out.) It is trivial to solve $H_0\psi_0 = E_0\psi_0$ for an atom with a set of occupied orbitals, with the energy the sum of the eigenvalues coming from numerical solution to the Dirac equation in the Tietz potential, and the wave function a Slater determinant of the respective wave functions. This lowest order wave function is conveniently represented using second quantization:

$$|\psi_0> = a_v^\dagger |0_C> \quad (9)$$

where $a_v^\dagger$ creates a valence electron v and $|0_C>$ the filled xenon-like core. It is a remarkable fact that this very simple model of the atom gives fairly good results for a variety of properties. Adjusting the Tietz parameters to fit two energies gives other valence removal energies accurate to a few percent, and hyperfine constants and oscillator strengths to about 20%. However, it is clearly necessary to include the effect of the real physics of the atom, which has been put aside as the perturbation V_C. This can be done with standard Rayleigh-Schrödinger perturbation theory, with the effect of the presence of many-electrons handled again with second quantization. This procedure, known as many-body perturbation theory (MBPT), actually had its genesis in QED. In the early 1950's, workers in the nuclear many-body field realized that the then recently developed diagrammatic technique for field theory could be carried over to the many-body problem[8]. The main difference is that instead of fully covariant Feynman diagrams time-ordered diagrams known as Goldstone diagrams are used, and external legs have to be interpreted differently when they refer to occupied states, and are treated similarly to positron states. As an example of MBPT, a first order correction to the wave function is

$$|\psi_1> = \sum_{amn} \frac{g_{avmn}}{(\epsilon_a + \epsilon_v - \epsilon_m - \epsilon_n)} a_m^\dagger a_n^\dagger a_a |0_C> \qquad (10)$$

where a refers to a summation over the xenonlike core and m and n are complete summations over states excluding that core and negative energy states. Implementing the rule that negative energy states are not summed over avoids a problem with the full Hamiltonian, which is that it does not 'know' the negative energy sea is filled. This rule remedies that problem, though it leaves out small radiative corrections that are not important for most atomic calculations. The above correction schematically annihilates a core state a and replaces it with a linear combination of excited states m, at the same time replacing v with states n. An important technical step in carrying out MBPT calculations is dealing with sums over excited states with the use of finite basis sets. While in principal the sums over excited states include an infinite number of bound states and a continuous infinity of scattering states, for a given angular momentum about 40 finite basis sets can reproduce the exact sum to very high accuracy. Thus, after carrying out an angular momentum reduction exploiting the spherical symmetry of the atom, MBPT calculations are readily evaluated as finite sums over the basis set. However, in higher orders sums over as many as 4 excited states are quickly encountered, so that the computer demands are at the tens of CRAY hour level. More serious is the fact that the number of MBPT diagrams increases very rapidly with order. The practical limit for a complete evaluation of energy diagrams is probably fourth order, since the third order calculation is already a very large scale one. The situation is worse for the more physically relevant case of matrix elements. For this reason, methods that sum infinite classes of MBPT diagrams are used for the most accurate calculations: these methods at present when applied to energies reproduce every diagram through third order, along with a wide class of higher order diagrams. The basic idea of the approach can be seen by writing

$$|\psi_v> = [\sum_m \rho_{mv} a_m^\dagger + \sum_{amn} \rho_{avmn} a_m^\dagger a_n^\dagger a_a]|0_C>. \qquad (11)$$

Here the states are still eigenfunction of H_0, but now when this wavefunction is substituted into $H|\psi_v> = E|\psi_v>$, a set of coupled equations for ρ_{mv}, etc. results. When expanded in perturbation theory, for example, the second term can be seen to exactly reproduce Eq. (10), but if the coupled equations are solved iteratively, higher and higher order diagrams are automatically accounted for. However, while a very large set of diagrams are included with this method, important effects arise also from *triple* excitations, defined by

$$|\delta\psi_v> = \sum_{abmnr} \rho_{abvmnr} a_m^\dagger a_n^\dagger a_r^\dagger a_a a_b |0_C>. \qquad (12)$$

At present this term has been included only approximately, so that a set of fourth-order energy diagrams has been left out. However, this calculation is sufficiently complete that agreement with experiment for a wide variety of parity conserving properties of cesium is found at under the 1% level. This of course does not guarantee that a PNC calculation will be as accurate, though the fact that hyperfine constants, which, like PNC, are sensitive to small distance behavior of the wave function, agree well with experiment, is an important test. It is also possible to include the missed diagrams in an approximate manner by rescaling the ρ coefficients: when this rescaling is carried out, it is seen that the PNC prediction changes by less than 1%[4]. Present research on this problem is focused on treating ρ_{abvmnr} more exactly. Such a treatment would then include every MBPT diagram for energies through fourth order along with a very wide class of higher order diagrams, and will hopefully allow calculations accurate at the few tenths of a percent level.

In conclusion, atomic experiments coupled with many-body theory already place the most stringent bound on d_e and provide a top mass independent test of the standard model. As experiments and theory improve, atomic physics can be expected to play a more and more significant role in extending our understanding of the weak interactions.

Acknowledgements

This research was carried out in collaboration with Steve Blundell and Walter Johnson, and is being supported in part by NSF grant PHY-92-04089.

References

1. M.A. Bouchiat and C. Bouchiat, *J. Phys. (Paris)* **35** (1974) 899.
2. P.G.H. Sandars, *J. Phys.* **B1** (1968) 511.
3. M.C. Noecker, B.P. Masterson, and C.E. Wieman, *Phys. Rev. Lett.* **61** (1988) 310.
4. S.A. Blundell, W.R. Johnson, and J. Sapirstein, *Phys. Rev.* **D45** (1992) 1602.
5. W.J. Marciano and J.L. Rosner, *Phys. Rev. Lett.* **65** (1990) 2963.
6. Z.W. Liu and H.P. Kelly, *Phys. Rev.* **A45** (1992) R4210.
7. K. Abdullah, C. Carlberg, E.D. Commins, H. Gould, and S.B. Ross, *Phys. Rev. Lett.* **65** (1990) 2347.
8. J. Goldstone, *Proc. Roy. Soc. (London)* **A239** (1957) 267.

THE ORIGIN OF STRONG CP VIOLATION

R. G. SACHS

Enrico Fermi Institute and Physics Department, University of Chicago, 5640 South Ellis Avenue Chicago, IL 60637, USA

1. Remarks on Gauge Field Topology

In quantum field theory the states of a system are described in a functional "Hilbert space" which is spanned by the eigenstates of a complete set of commuting kinematic observables Q having the set of eigenvalues q. In QCD the (non-Abelian) gauge invariance requires that these states also be eigenstates of the unitary operator generating the gauge transformation of winding number n. These eigenstates are $|q,\theta\rangle$, where $n\theta$ are the eigenphases, and the values of θ lie between $-\pi$ and π. The parameter θ characterizes the topology of the associated gauge (gluon) field. I have assumed that none of the quark masses vanishes.

A superselection rule associated with the gauge invariance forbids non-vanishing matrix elements of physical observables between distinct values of θ. A state of given θ that is a solution of the dynamics of QCD may be viewed as a state generated by the dynamics from the gluon vacuum state having topology θ (the θ vacuum). Therefore the dynamical solution space is divided into non-communicating sectors $S(\theta)$ of the Hilbert space each sector corresponding to one distinct value of θ.

In the conventional language of QCD θ is described as a "new (fixed) physical constant". This implies selection of $S(\theta)$, with a particular value of θ, as the physical sector. Sectors corresponding to other values of θ are assumed to be non-existent in the physical universe. In particular the θ vacuum for this θ is the physical vacuum state. This is an assumed boundary condition (determined by Nature) selecting a set of physical solutions from among all the mathematical solutions.

2. Properties under C, P and T

The usual unitary (antiunitary) transformations C, P, (T) give $P|\theta,q\rangle = |-\theta,q'\rangle$, $T|\theta,q\rangle = |-\theta,q''\rangle*$, $C|\theta,q\rangle = |\theta,\bar{q}\rangle$, where the asterisk denotes the conjugate complex and the notations q', q'' and $\bar{q}$ denote the eigenvalues corresponding to q of the transformed operators $Q = PQP^{-1}$, $Q'' = TQT^{-1}$, and $\bar{Q} = CQC^{-1}$.

Thus the physical vacuum state is transformed into an unphysical state by P and T so that both P and T are violated by the conventional boundary condition, hence by the entire set of physical solutions. This suggests that it is the topological boundary condition that is responsible for strong CP violation.

However this interpretation introduces a paradox. Since P changes the sign of θ its matrix element between a θ state and a $-\theta$ state is non-vanishing, violating the superselection rule. Therefore P is not a physical observable. This result is consistent with the fact that the parity of the vacuum is not an observable since only relative parity can be measured by experiments.

The paradox is that, for $\theta \neq 0$, P and T-violating physical observables, like the edm of the neutron, are calculated to be non-vanishing, a result giving physical meaning to the operator P. The calculated edm is proportional to $sin\theta$.

As it turns out measurement of the neutron edm places an upper limit on it, yielding $|\sin\theta| \leq 10^{-1}$, and it might be argued that the physical value is $\theta = 0$ so that there is no paradox because there is no strong CP violation.

3. Resolution of the Paradox

There is a better resolution of the paradox, independent of the measured value of θ. It makes use of the fact that a physical parity ('intrinsic parity') operator can always be defined by $P_i |q,\theta\rangle = |q,\theta\rangle$. P_i does not affect the vacuum state so it is the operator representing the physical parity observable.

The physical P violation may now be understood by noting that there exists a correspondence $U(\theta)$ between states of different θ sectors: $U(\chi)|q,\theta\rangle = |q,\chi+\theta\rangle$ and $U(\chi)$ is the chiral rotation $-\chi$ of the quark fields. If it is assumed that, before the change of representation the quark masses appeared as a scalar term in the Hamiltonian, $U(\chi)$ transforms the scalar quark mass term in the Hamiltonian into the sum of scalar and pseudoscalar mass terms with coefficients $\cos\theta$ and $\sin\theta$, respectively, while also transforming $|vac,\theta\rangle$ to $|vac,0\rangle$, which is invariant under P. The new mass term introduces a dynamical P and T violation which leads to the physical effect. Thus strong CP violation has its physical origin through the dynamics rather than through the topological aspects of the vacuum.

This conclusion introduces another puzzle: the topology of the gauge fields has an entirely different physical meaning from that of a chiral rotation of the quarks but they appear to be physically indistinguishable for purely mathematical reasons. In fact, if an ad hoc pseudoscalar mass term arising from the chiral rotation $-\chi/2$ is introduced into the Lagrangian it can be removed by applying the change of representation $U(\chi)$ to the states, changing $S(\theta)$ into $S(\theta+\chi)$. This demonstrates that the two distinct physical parameters θ and χ are physically indistinguishable in general if the physical topology is fixed by the conventional boundary condition.

In particular the experimental upper limit on the neutron edm leads to $|\sin(\theta+\chi)| \leq 10^{-9}$, suggesting again that there is no strong CP violation. This result requires a remarkable coincidence between two different physical effects.

4. Proposed Alternative

There is an alternative to the assumed boundary condition having the advantage that it separates these two physical effects and therefore enriches the theory. It involves no change in the dynamics. Results of calculations are related to established results by trivial algebra. Topological P and T violation are eliminated. The physically correct choice between the alternatives can only be determined by experiment.

The alternative is the boundary condition yielding a physical sector S(phys) that is the union $S(\theta) \cup S(-\theta)$. Note that the two sectors have the same energy spectrum. P no longer violates the superselection rule. Its eigenvalues are the product of the parity of the vacuum, which is not observable, and the intrinsic parity.

Matrix elements of all physical observables that were functions $f(\chi+\theta)$ become the average $[f(\chi + \theta) + f(\chi - \theta)]/2$. Thus the edm is proportional to $cos\theta sin\chi$ and it will vanish if either $\chi = 0$ or $\theta = \pi/2$. The phenomenological effects of the two parameters are different so that they may, in principle, be determined separately by two measurements.

5. Origin of Observed CP Violation?

This alternative boundary condition opens a new way to account for the observed (weak) CP violation: a phenomenological theory based on the standard model with real KM matrix, two Higgs doublets and invoking an ad hoc chiral rotation of the quark fields. If the neutron edm is taken to be zero the assumption $\theta = \pi/2$ allows χ to be chosen freely as the parameter leading to the observed CP violation.

The ad hoc introduction of this parameter may be circumvented by requiring maximal T violation, which fixes the parameter at the value $\chi = \pi/4$. This phenomenological theory makes it possible to calculate other CP-violating effects in terms of ϵ, the only well-measured such effect. Order of magnitude estimates give $|\epsilon\prime/\epsilon| \leq 10^{-7}$ and a neutron edm of the order of 10^{-27}e cm. For the neutral B meson the ratio of mixing coefficients is $p/q = e^{i\varphi}, 10° \leq \varphi \leq 40°$. The range of values reflects the uncertainty in the ratio of B to K form factors. Charge asymmetries in neutral B meson phenomena manifest relatively large direct and indirect CP violation.

RECENT PROGRESS IN CP VIOLATING GLUONIC OPERATORS AND NEUTRON ELECTRIC DIPOLE MOMENT

DARWIN CHANG
Department of Physics, Northwestern University,
Evanston, IL 60208, U.S.A.

ABSTRACT

Recent results on the contributions of various gluonic operators to the neutron electric dipole moment are summarized. In particular, the relative importance of the contributions due to the θ-term, the dimension-6 and 8 gluonic operators and dimension-8 photo-gluonic operators are analyzed.

How can neutron get its electric dipole moment(D_n)? A photon coming into a collision course with neutron will see the constituent light quarks, the sea quarks(light and heavy) and, indirectly, the gluons. The fundamental mechanism of CP violation(CPX) in a given theory typically involves heavy particles like the top quark in Kobayashi-Maskawa model, the right handed boson in the left-right models, the Higgs bosons in Higgs-mediated theories or the susy particles in the supersymmetric theories[1]. At the energy scale of the W boson mass or below, these heavy particles can be integrated out and the resulting effective theory may contain many new operators that can be used to account for the CPX effect of these heavy particles at low energy. For D_n, the operators to look for in this effective Lagrangian are the CPX, flavor neutral operators involving strongly interacting particles listed above.

A catalogue of such operators includes the θ-operator[2,3], $\mathcal{O}_\theta = (g_s^2/64\pi^2) G^a_{\mu\nu} G^a_{\rho\sigma} \epsilon^{\mu\nu\rho\sigma}$, the electric and chromo-electric dipole moments of the light quarks, $\mathcal{O}_q^\gamma = (e/2) G^a_{\mu\nu} \bar{q} i\sigma^{\mu\nu} \gamma_5 q$ and $\mathcal{O}_q^c = (g_s/2) G^a_{\mu\nu} \bar{q} i\sigma^{\mu\nu} \gamma_5 (\lambda^a/2) q$, or those of the heavy quarks, $\mathcal{O}_Q^\gamma = (e/2) G^a_{\mu\nu} \bar{Q} i\sigma^{\mu\nu} \gamma_5 Q$ and $\mathcal{O}_Q^c = (g_s/2) G^a_{\mu\nu} \bar{Q} i\sigma^{\mu\nu} \gamma_5 (\lambda^a/2) Q$, the dimension-6, chromo-electric dipole moment operator for gluons[4] $\mathcal{O}_g = (g_s^3/6) f_{abc} G^a_{\mu\alpha} G^{b\alpha}{}_\nu G^c_{\rho\sigma} \epsilon^{\mu\nu\rho\sigma}$, and the dimension-8, purely gluonic operators of Morozov[5,6]

$$\begin{aligned} O_{8,1} &= g^4 \tfrac{1}{12} \tilde{G}^a_{\mu\nu} G^{a\mu\nu} G^b_{\alpha\beta} G^{b\alpha\beta} \\ O_{8,2} &= g^4 \tfrac{1}{12} \tilde{G}^a_{\mu\nu} G^{b\mu\nu} G^a_{\alpha\beta} G^{b\alpha\beta} \\ O_{8,3} &= g^4 \tfrac{1}{12} d_{abe} d_{ecd} \tilde{G}^a_{\mu\nu} G^{b\mu\nu} G^c_{\alpha\beta} G^{d\alpha\beta} \end{aligned} \quad (1)$$

d_{abc} is the totally symmetric tensor of $SU(3)$. In addition, there are also two dimension-8 operators[7,8] with one electromagnetic field strength, $F^{\mu\nu}$, and three $G^{a\mu\nu}$'s

$$\begin{aligned} O_{8,1}^{\gamma-c} &= eg^3 \tilde{F}_{\mu\nu} G^{a\mu\nu} G^b_{\alpha\beta} G^{c\alpha\beta} d_{abc} \\ O_{8,2}^{\gamma-c} &= eg^3 F_{\mu\nu} G^{a\mu\nu} G^b_{\alpha\beta} \tilde{G}^{c\alpha\beta} d_{abc} \end{aligned} \quad (2)$$

three operators with two[9] $F^{\mu\nu}$'s and two $G^{a\mu\nu}$'s and one with four $F^{\mu\nu}$'s. There are also many four fermion operators.

There are two levels one can ask questions related to these operators. (1)Given an operator, how important is its contribtuion to D_n? That is, one likes to know the relative importance of various operators. Also, given the experimental limit of about $D_n \leq 8 \times 10^{-26}$, what is the limits on the coefficients of these operators assuming no cancellation between various contributions. (2)Given a model of CPX, which operators will be prominantly induced at low energy? This will allow one to constrain the CPX parameters in the theory.

Before we plunge into the details of recent results, let's first step back and ask what have we learned about D_n from all these analyses? The answer is unfortunately not very much. We have learned a lot of theoretical insights about how complex the issue is. We have a good qualitative, semi-model independent view of the relative importance of various operators. About the limits on models, one should be reminded that first of all, in the Standard (Kobayashi-Maskawa) Model, all the operators mentioned above come with negligible coefficients(except maybe the illusive $\mathcal{O}_\theta$ operator). That will make the observation of D_n a potential signal from "beyonds". On the other hand, current experimental limits only place moderate constraints on the CPX parameters of most models. The exceptions are a couple of minimal models. These minimal models have only one fundamental source of CPX. The parameter associated with this source is fixed by the observed ϵ parameter of nertral kaons and thus give relatively precise(modulo our ignorance about the matrix elements) predictions for ϵ' and D_n. Therefore they are more prone to be ruled out. For example in the minimal Weinberg-Branco charged Higgs model with spontaneous CPX, a recent analysis[10] concluded that it is most likely ruled out. Another example is the minimal left-right symmetric model, again with spontaneous CPX, proposed about 10 years ago[11]. The model is probably on the borderline of being ruled out. A more detailed analysis is needed to draw definite conclusion.

In this report, I like to summarize three recent results related to the gluonic operators. First of all, it was pointed out that there is an importance source of the dimension-4 operator, $\mathcal{O}_\theta$, induced by the dimension-5 CEDM operator through the operator mixing in the RG evolution[3,5,12]. This mechanism gives rise to the strongest constraint on the CEDM of b (and possibly c) quark. To show this, one parametrizes the CP violating effective Lagrangian at the electroweak scale as $\mathcal{L}_{CP} = \tilde{d}_g G_F \mathcal{O}_g(M_W) + \tilde{d}_b G_F m_b \mathcal{O}_b^c(M_W) + (\theta)_{M_W} \mathcal{O}_\theta(M_W)$, where the parameters $\tilde{d}_g$ and $\tilde{d}_b$ are dimensionless. After integrating out various thresholds[12], the neutron electric dipole moment induced at low energy is related to the parameters in the effective Lagrangian as $D_n = \left[(1.3 \times 10^4 (\theta)_{M_W} + 29 \tilde{d}_b - 4 \tilde{d}_g) \xi_\theta + (0.74 \tilde{d}_g - 0.0067 \tilde{d}_b) \xi_g \right] \times 10^{-20} e$ cm. where $r = 0.36$ for $m_d = 9$MeV, $m_u = 5$MeV. ξ_g and ξ_θ parametrize the uncertainties in the matrix elements of the operators $\mathcal{O}_g$ and $\mathcal{O}_\theta$ respectively. ξ_g, ξ_θ are normalized to one in a naive estimate method called the naive dimensional analysis(NDA)[13] with scale chosen to be such that $g(\mu) = 4\pi/\sqrt{6}$. (More elaborated analyses[2] give $|\xi_\theta| \simeq 7.7$ and [14] $|\xi_g| \simeq 1/30$.) These results imply that the NEDM associated with $\mathcal{O}_b^c(M_W)$ and $\mathcal{O}_g(M_W)$ may be dominated by the RG induced $\mathcal{O}_\theta(\mu)$, instead of $\mathcal{O}_g(\mu)$ at the hadronic scale μ. For models with Peccei–Quinn symmetry[2] our analysis poses no problem since in these models the θ at low energy can be rotated away by a Peccei–Quinn transformation. In addition, the RG induced contribution calculated here and the radiatively induced contribution that is usually calculated through the argument of the determinant of the quark mass matrix, $ArgDetM$, should be considered independent contributions.

Secondly we have calculated the effective operators of dimension 6 and 8 induced if one integerates out a quark with CEDM of mass m. It can be written as,

$$S_{\text{eff}} = S_{QCD} + S_{\text{light quarks}} + \int d^4x \left[C_6 O_6 + \sum_{i=1}^{3} C_{8,i} O_{8,i} \right] , \qquad (3)$$

$$C_6 = \frac{C}{32\pi^2 m}, \quad C_{8,1} = -\frac{C}{96\pi^2 m^3}, \quad C_{8,2} = 0, \quad C_{8,3} = -\frac{C}{64\pi^2 m^3}, \qquad (4)$$

where C is the coefficient of the CEDM operator. In the subsequent RG evolution, the three operators mix and the three eignvalues of the anomalous dimension matrix are 4.82, −42.98, and −20.84. The operator which is RG enhanced is mainly composed of $O_{8,1}$. After these operators are evolved further down to hadronic scale, only one of them remains significant. The hadronic matrix element and the size of the NEDM can be estimated using the naive dimensional analysis[13] If the quark integrated out is the b quark, the resulting numerical ratio of the resulting NEDM due to $O'_{8,i}$ and those due to O_6 is about 3.6, using the same set of input parameters as in Ref. 4. More elaborate methods[14] for the hadronic matrix elements give about the same ratio. This indicates that the contributions from the dimension-8 operators can be potentially more important than the dimension-6 one. suppression which is expected of the higher dimensional operator is dictated by the b quark mass which is not very heavy and the highly suppressive effect of the R.G. evolution on the dimension-6 operator. Operators with even higher dimension are not expected to be competitive with the dimension-8 ones unless some surprising R.G. enhencement effect occurs.

We have also checked[8] the anomalous dimensions of the dimension-8 photo-gluonic operators. Our resulting anomalous dimension matrix is symmetric with eigenvalues -24 and -22 which are somewhat different from the values obtained previously[7]. The contributions of these operators are relatively small compared to the dimension-6 one unless one artificially evolves the RG equations to a scale much below the chiral symmetry scale.

I wish to acknowledge all my collaborators K. Choi, W.-Y. Keung, T. Kephart, C. S. Li, I. Phillips and T. C. Yuan. I wish to thank E. Braaten, M. Booth, M. Chemtob, H.-Y. Cheng, O. Pene, L. Wolfenstein for discussions.

References

1. For a review of various CP violating models see D. Chang, in *The Standrad Model and Beyond–Ninth Sorak Symposium* ed. J. E. Kim, (World Scientific, Singapore, 1991).
2. For a review see J. E. Kim, *Phys. Rep.* **150** (1987) 1; H. Y. Cheng, *Phys. Rep.* **158** (1988) 1; R. D. Peccei, *DESY Report* No. DESY 88-109, 1988, and references cited there.
3. D. Chang, K. Choi, and W.-Y. Keung, *Phys. Rev.* **D44**, (1991) 2196.
4. S. Weinberg, *Phys. Rev. Lett.* **63** (1989) 2333; E. Braaten, C. S. Li, and T. C. Yuan, *Phys. Rev. Lett.* **64** (1990) 1709; E. Braaten, C. S. Li, and T. C. Yuan, *Phys. Rev.* **D42** (1990) 276 .
5. A. Yu. Morozov, *Sov. J. Nucl. Phys.* **40**(3) (1984) 505; M. Booth, *Phys. Rev.* **D45** (1992) 2518.
6. D. Chang, T. W. Kephart, W.-Y. Keung, and T. C. Yuan, *Phys. Rev. Lett.* **68** (1992) 439.
7. A. de Rujula, M. B. Gavela, O. Pene, and F. J. Vegas, *Phys. Lett.* **B245** (1990) 640.
8. D. Chang, W.-Y. Keung, I. Phillips and T. C. Yuan, *Phys. Rev.* **D46** (1992) 2270;
9. D. Chang, T. W. Kephart, W.-Y. Keung, and T. C. Yuan, *Nucl. Phys.* **B** (1992) to appear.
10. H. Y. Cheng, *Int. J. Mod. Phys.* **A7** (1992) 1059.
11. D. Chang, *Nucl. Phys.* **B214** (1983) 435; see also G. Branco, J.-M. Frere and Gerard, *Nucl. Phys.* **B221** (1983) 317; G. Ecker, W. Grimus and H. Neufeld, *Nucl. Phys.* **B258** (1985) 328.
12. D. Chang, W.-Y. Keung, C. S. Li, and T. C. Yuan, *Phys. Lett.* **B241** (1990) 589; G. Boyd, A.K. Gupta, S.P. Trivedi, and M.B. Wise, *Phys. Lett.* **241B** (1990) 884.
13. A. Manohar and H. Georgi, *Nucl. Phys.* **B234** (1984) 189; H. Georgi and L. Randall, *Nucl. Phys.* **B276** (1986) 241.
14. I. I. Bigi and N. G. Uraltsev, *Nucl. Phys.* **B353** (1991) 321; M. Chemtob, *Phys. Rev.* **D45** (1992) 1649.

DIMENSION EIGHT OPERATORS, CP VIOLATION AND THE NEUTRON ELECTRIC DIPOLE MOMENT

MICHAEL J. BOOTH[*]
*Enrico Fermi Institute and Department of Physics
University of Chicago, Chicago, Illinois 60637*

ABSTRACT

In the past year, it has been shown that dimension-eight operators may give important contributions to the neutron electric dipole moment.[1] Here some recent work involving dimension eight operators and CP violation is summarized. The coefficient of the dimension-six gluonic operator is argued to vanish exactly in the standard model and the coefficients of the dimension-eight operators are estimated. The observation of these operators in atomic systems is discussed and a brief discussion of the anomalous dimensions is included.

1. The Standard Model and Electric Dipole Moments

In the standard KM model of CP violation, all CP violation amplitudes may be written as $M = \sum_{u_1,u_2,d_1,d_2} \Phi^{u_2 d_2}_{u_1 d_1} M^{d_1 d_2}_{u_1 u_2}$, where $\Phi^{u_2 d_2}_{u_1 d_1} = \text{Im}(V_{u_1 d_1} V^*_{u_2 d_1} V_{u_2 d_2} V^*_{u_1 d_2})$ and u and d are flavor indices. Φ has two important properties[2]: it is antisymmetric in (u_1, u_2) and (d_1, d_2) and the sum over any index, *eg.* u_1, vanishes. The properties of Φ, which are often called the GIM mechanism, force any CP violating partial amplitude $M^{d_1 d_2}_{u_1 u_2}$ to depend on four quark masses and to be antisymmetric under the exchange of up or down quark masses. This antisymmetry leads to cancellations among the contributions of different quarks and is responsible for suppressing CP violation in the SM.

As an example of this, Shabalin[3] was able to show that the quark electric dipole moment vanishes to two loops in the SM. The essence of Shabalin's work was to show that because of gauge invariance, the GIM mechanism (combined with the purely left-handed coupling of the the W-bosons) eliminates not only the $O(k^0)$ term in the photon vertex (which is to be expected) but also the $O(k)$ term which would generate the electric dipole moment. In fact, Shabalin's result is more general[4] and is not limited to the neutron EDM. It can be interpreted as the statement that the one-loop weak corrections to the process $W q \to W q\gamma$ are a symmetric function of the intermediate quark masses (to first order in the photon momentum), and thus

---
[*]Electronic address: booth@yukawa.uchicago.edu

CP even.* Considered in this way, Shabalin's result has implications for the W-boson EDM and thus the electron EDM. By a simple extension of Shabalin's argument, one can also show that the dimension six Weinberg operator, (or the chromo-electric dipole moment of the gluon[1]), vanishes to three loop order in the SM. One must then either go to four loops[5] and suffer the extra suppression that comes with the extra loop or consider dimension-eight operators.[4] The SM thus provides an interesting example where the dimension-eight operators may naturally be expected to dominate, because the lower dimension operators are actually of higher order in the strong coupling constant. Unfortunately, this is a rather academic point because the coefficient is still impossibly small.

2. Atomic T Violation and Dimension-Eight Operators

Although one usually thinks of searching for low energy CP violation in the electric dipole moments of elementary particles, it may also be manifest in atoms. It is interesting to see how the some of these higher dimension operators will contribute. Consider the photonic-gluonic operators[6]†

$$\mathcal{W}_1^{(8)} = \frac{\kappa_1 \alpha_S \alpha}{M^4} G^a_{\mu\nu} G^a_{\mu\nu} F_{\sigma\rho} \tilde{F}_{\sigma\rho},$$
$$\mathcal{W}_2^{(8)} = \frac{\kappa_2 \alpha_S \alpha}{M^4} G^a_{\mu\nu} \tilde{G}^a_{\mu\nu} F_{\sigma\rho} F_{\sigma\rho}. \tag{1}$$

There are also two operators with the structure $GGG\tilde{F}$, but these will contribute directly to the $NDEM$, and furthermore their hadronic matrix elements are uncertain.[1] The operators $\mathcal{W}_{1,2}^{(8)}$ are particularly interesting because they will not contribute to the neutron electric dipole moment and evaluation of the hadronic matrix elements is straightforward. Using QCD low-energy theorems, one may replace the gluonic part of $\mathcal{W}_{1,2}^{(8)}$ with nucleonic operators. For example,

$$\langle \overline{N} | \mathrm{tr}(G_{\mu\nu} G^{\mu\nu}) | N \rangle = -\frac{8\pi}{b\alpha_S} m_N \langle \overline{N} | \overline{N} N | N \rangle, \tag{2}$$

where $b = 11 - \frac{2}{3} n_L$, n_L being the number of quarks in the effective low energy theory. Thus $\mathcal{W}_1^{(8)}$ gives rise to a P and T violating nucleon polarizability, $\overline{N} N F \tilde{F}$ (the operator $\mathcal{W}_1^{(8)}$ involves a nuclear spin-flip and is thus suppressed by a factor of m_e/m_N). This may contribute to a number of phenomena, but consider the contribution to the atomic EDM which arises by coupling both photons to a single electron. The resulting loop diagram gives rise to an effective nucleon-electron interaction, which in the long distance limit looks like

$$\mathcal{O}_{eeNN} = \frac{\alpha^2 \kappa}{b} \frac{m_N}{M^4} \frac{1}{m_e} t \ln(\frac{-t}{m_e^2}) \overline{N} N \bar{e} i \gamma_5 e. \tag{3}$$

---
*for a more detailed discussion, see Shabalin's paper and ref. (4).
†Recently, one of these operators has also been considered by W. Fischler et al.[7] in the context of the minimal supersymmetric standard model, though their treatment differs.

This operator will mix levels of different parity in the atom. Considering for simplicity ^{55}Cs, one finds

$$| d_{\text{Cs}} | = (3.3 \times 10^{-24} \text{ e cm})\kappa_1 \left[\frac{100 \text{ GeV}}{M}\right]^4. \quad (4)$$

The current limits on such a dipole moment are $d_{\text{Cs}} < 7.2 \times 10^{-24}$ e cm. The implied limit on the operator coefficient is $\kappa_1^{1/4} \left(\frac{90 \text{ GeV}}{M}\right) < 1$. This limit is even stronger than it first appears since one typically has $M^4 \simeq \Lambda^2 m_Q^2$ where Λ is the scale of the new physics, typically a mass in the Higgs sector, and m_Q is the mass of the heavy quark which is integrated out, i.e. the bottom quark.

It is interesting to compare the effects of $\mathcal{O}_{eeNN}$ to that of an atomic dipole induced through the $NEDM$. Both are long-range, but $\mathcal{O}_{eeNN}$ couple to the atomic number, not just the nuclear spin. And in contrast to an EDM induced interaction, $\mathcal{O}_{eeNN}$ is not suppressed by Schiff's theorem. Consequently, the enhancement in heavy atoms of an $\mathcal{O}_{eeNN}$ induced atomic EDM will be greater by at least a factor of A.

3. Anomalous Dimensions

The last year has shown that despite what one might expect, dimension-eight operators can be important to low energy CP violation as some of the lower-dimension operators. To date, only gluonic and mixed gluonic-photonic[6] operators have been considered. However, a consistent analysis requires the inclusion of fermionic operators. In order to do this one needs the anomalous dimensions of those operators. This has been done by Morozov[8] through dimension seven, and partially checked[9] and extended to include operators with photons.[1] The extension of Morozov's work to include all dimension-eight operators is in progress.[10]

This work was supported by DOE grant AC02 80 ER 10587.

References

1. For a survey of recent work, see the paper by Darwin Chang in these proceedings.
2. For a more detailed discussion of the symmetry properties, as well as further references, see: I. Dunietz, *Ann. Phys.* **184** (1988), 350.
3. E. P. Shabalin, *Sov. J. Nucl. Phys.* **32** (1980), 129.
4. M. J. Booth, "A note on Weinberg Operators in the Standard Model", preprint EFI-92-13.
5. I. Bigi and N. G. Uraltsev, *Sov. J. Nucl. Phys.* **73** (1991), 198
6. M. J. Booth and G. Jungman, T and P Violation From Certain Dimension-Eight Operators, preprint EFI-92-51.
7. W. Fischler, S. Paban and S. Thomas, *Phys. Lett.* **B289** (1992), 373.
8. A. Yu. Morozov, *Sov. J. Nucl. Phys.* **40** (1984), 505.
9. M. J. Booth, *Phys. Rev.* **D45** (1992), 2018.
10. M. J. Booth, work in progress.

A SEARCH FOR LEPTON FLAVOUR VIOLATION IN Z^0 DECAYS

KENNETH ÖSTERBERG

Research Institute for High Energy Physics (SEFT), Siltavuorenpenger 20 C
SF-00170 Helsinki, Finland

Representing the DELPHI Collaboration

ABSTRACT

A search for lepton flavour violation through the decays $Z^0 \to e\mu, e\tau$ and $\mu\tau$ was made with the DELPHI detector at LEP, using a sample corresponding to an integrated luminosity of 11.2 pb^{-1}. The number of candidates was consistent with the estimated background. The upper limit on the branching ratio for $Z^0 \to e\mu$ was 3.2 10^{-5}, for $Z^0 \to e\tau$ was 10.8 10^{-5} and for $Z^0 \to \mu\tau$ was 13.5 10^{-5}.

1. Introduction

Lepton flavour conservation is a feature of the Minimal Standard Model, however extensions to it may include processes were the family specific lepton flavour is not conserved [1]. Limits originating from low energy experiments are based on the failure to observe neutrinoless $\mu \to eee$, $\tau \to eee$ and $\tau \to \mu\mu\mu$. Direct searches can be performed at LEP using a large amount of Z^0 decays. The following report is based on data taken with the DELPHI detector [2] during the 1990 and 1991 runs. A momentum resolution of 3.4% was obtained for μ from $Z^0 \to \mu^+\mu^-$ decays. The electromagnetic energy resolution for e from $Z^0 \to e^+e^-$ was 8.3%.

2. Analysis

A sample of low multiplicity events was selected. Further criteria were then applied to search for lepton flavour violating events with two jets (as defined below) with different lepton flavour. For each lepton species a reference sample was selected from the data using loose selections. These samples were used to compute the efficiencies of single jet selections used in the search. An iterative jet algorithm was used to define single leptons (including τ), which started from the most energetic particle. All particles within 20° were included and afterwards the second jet was formed in the same way with the unused particles. The selections for any two leptons required events to have between 2 and 6 charged particles making 2 jets and collinear within 10°.

2.1. Selections

Selection criteria for single electron, muon and tau jets used in the search were the following: The e jet was selected requiring a jet with $0.9 < E_{em}/E_b < 1.4$

and p/p_b greater than 0.7, where p_b and E_b is the beam momentum and energy. The observed longitudinal shower profile in the electromagnetic calorimeter had to be compatible with an e of the same energy. A μ jet had to have one or more associated hits in the muon chambers and $0.9 < p/p_b < 1.4$. A candidate τ jet in the $e\tau$ (respectively $\mu\tau$) search had to have p/p_b below 0.6 (respectively 0.7). In addition a $\tau \to \mu\nu_\mu\nu_\tau$ candidate had to have one or more associated hits in the muon chambers. A $\tau \to h\nu_\tau$ candidate had to have additionally a hadron like longitudinal shower profile and no associated hits in the muon chambers. A $\tau \to e\nu_e\nu_\tau$ candidate had to have E_{em}/E_b between 0.05 and 0.9 and a compatible shower profile.

The τ single jet identification had to be treated differently in $Z^0 \to e\tau$ and $Z^0 \to \mu\tau$ searches. For $Z^0 \to e\tau$, only the decays $\tau \to \mu\nu_\mu\nu_\tau$ and $\tau \to h\nu_\tau$ were considered because if the decay $\tau \to e\nu_e\nu_\tau$ was allowed, the background from $Z^0 \to e^+e^-$ would increase substantially. Conversely, in the search for $Z^0 \to \mu\tau$ only $\tau \to e\nu_e\nu_\tau$ and $\tau \to h\nu_\tau$ were considered. The searches for $Z^0 \to e\tau, e\mu$ was made in the whole barrel while the search for $Z^0 \to \mu\tau$ was restricted to the central region within the acceptance of the barrel muon chambers.

3. Search for lepton flavour violation

No candidate was found for $Z^0 \to e\mu$, five were found for $Z^0 \to e\tau$ and six for $Z^0 \to \mu\tau$. The main background to $Z^0 \to e\tau$ and $\mu\tau$ arises from one of the τ in $Z^0 \to \tau^+\tau^-$ giving a high momentum e or μ. Another source of background is radiative e (in $Z^0 \to e^+e^-$ events) or μ (in $Z^0 \to \mu^+\mu^-$ decays) passing the selections for a $\tau \to h\nu$. The number of candidates is compatible with the total number of background events as seen in Table 1. Upper limits on the numbers of produced $Z^0 \to e\mu$, $e\tau$ and $\mu\tau$ at 95% confidence level are given in Table 1. The upper limit on the branching ratio for Z^0 decays (to $e\mu$ for instance) was calculated as:

$$\mathrm{BR}(Z^0 \to e^-\mu^+ + e^+\mu^-) < N_{e\mu} BR(Z^0 \to e^-e^+)/\varepsilon_e\varepsilon_\mu N_{e^+e^-}$$

,where $N_{e\mu}$ upper limit on $e\mu$ events, ε_e and ε_μ single e and μ efficiency respectively, $N_{e^+e^-}$ number of $Z^0 \to e^+e^-$ events within the geometrical acceptance corrected for selection efficiencies, $Z^0 \to \tau^+\tau^-$ contamination and t-channel contribution. Upper limits on the branching ratios are given in Table 2, where the published limits obtained in other LEP experiments are also shown [3].

5. References

1. E. Glover and J. Van der Bij, in *Z physics at LEP1*, eds G. Altarelli, R. Kleiss and C. Verzegnassi (CERN 89-08, Vol.II, 1989).
2. DELPHI Collaboration, The Delphi Detector at LEP, *Nucl. Instr. & Meth.* **A303** (1991) 233.
3. OPAL Collaboration, M.Z. Akrawy et al., *Phys. Lett.* **B254** (1991) 293; L3 Collaboration, B. Adeva et al., *Phys. Lett.* **B271** (1991) 453; ALEPH Collaboration, D. Decamp et al., *Phys. Reports* **216 No 5&6** (1992).

Table 1 : Number of candidate events, background contribution and upper limit on predicted number of events for $Z^0 \to e\mu$, $Z^0 \to e\tau$ and $Z^0 \to \mu\tau$.

Z^0 decay mode	$e\mu$	$e\tau$	$\mu\tau$
Number of candidates	0	5	6
e^+e^- background	0	1.6±1.1	0
$\mu^+\mu^-$ background	0	0	1.5±0.6
$\tau^+\tau^-$ background	0	5.7±1.3	5.3±1.2
Upper limit on # of events	3.0	5.4	6.3

Table 2 : Upper limits on branching ratios for $Z^0 \to e\mu$, $Z^0 \to e\tau$ and $Z^0 \to \mu\tau$.

	$BR(Z^0 \to e\mu)$	$BR(Z^0 \to e\tau)$	$BR(Z^0 \to \mu\tau)$
Low energy exp.	7.5 10^{-13}	10.0 10^{-5}	6.0 10^{-5}
OPAL	4.6 10^{-5}	7.2 10^{-5}	35.0 10^{-5}
L3	2.4 10^{-5}	3.4 10^{-5}	4.8 10^{-5}
ALEPH	2.6 10^{-5}	12.0 10^{-5}	10.0 10^{-5}
DELPHI	3.2 10^{-5}	10.8 10^{-5}	13.5 10^{-5}

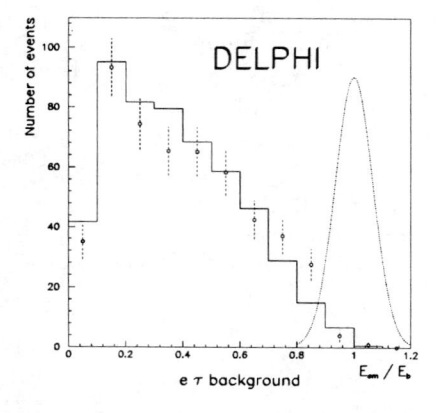

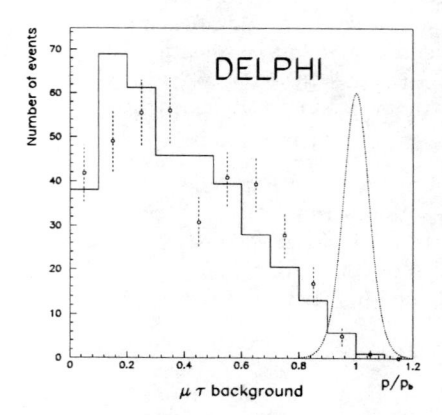

Figure 1: Electromagnetic energy and momentum scaled to beam energy, for the e (respectively μ) jet when the cut on E_{em} (respectively p) is removed from the selections for $Z^0 \to e\tau$ (respectively $Z^0 \to \mu\tau$), for data (dots). The solid lines are Monte Carlo simulated events that have passed the same cuts. The Gaussians indicates the measured resolution of electromagnetic energy and momentum.

SEARCH FOR LEPTONIC B DECAYS
AND $\tau^- \to \mu^-\gamma$ AT CLEO

D. Cinabro
Harvard University
Representing the CLEO Collaboration

ABSTRACT

Using the large integrated luminosity accumulated by the CLEO II detector at CESR, we search for the decays $B^- \to \ell^- \bar{\nu}$ and the lepton number violating decay $\tau^- \to \mu^-\gamma$. We set 90% confidence level upper limits of $B(B^- \to e^- \bar{\nu}) < 1.3 \times 10^{-5}$, $B(B^- \to \mu^- \bar{\nu}) < 2.0 \times 10^{-5}$, $B(B^- \to \tau^- \bar{\nu}) < 0.013$, and $B(\tau^- \to \mu^-\gamma) < 4.2 \times 10^{-6}$.

The CLEO II detector at the Cornell e^+e^- storage ring, CESR, has collected a large integrated luminosity of e^+e^- collisions at a center of mass energy near 10 GeV. Most of this data has been collected on the $\Upsilon(4S)$ (collision energy of 10.6 GeV) resonance, 954 pb^{-1}. This corresponds to roughly 925,000 $B\bar{B}$ events. A substantial amount of data has also been taken 60 MeV below the $\Upsilon(4S)$ for subtraction of continuum production from the on resonance sample to isolate the effects of B meson decays. Other data has been taken at the $\Upsilon(3S)$ and above the $\Upsilon(4S)$ for a total of 1.5 fb^{-1}. This total corresponds to 1.44×10^6 $e^+e^- \to \tau^+\tau^-$ events. This large sample of B and τ decays compels us to search for some interesting decays of the B^- (Charge conjugation is implied throughout the text unless otherwise mentioned.) meson and the τ^- that are rare or forbidden within the framework of the Standard Model. This contribution reports on our searches for the fully leptonic decay modes of the charged B meson: $B^- \to e^-\bar{\nu}$, $B^- \to \mu^-\bar{\nu}$, and, $B^- \to \tau^-\bar{\nu}$; and for the lepton number violating decay of the tau lepton $\tau^- \to \mu^-\gamma$.

The CLEO II detector has been described in detail elsewhere[1]; here only a brief description of the sub-systems most critical to these searches is given. Charged particles are detected in three wire drift chambers with 67 total tracking layers immersed in an axial magnetic field of 1.5 T. The tracking system gives a resolution of $(\delta p/p)^2 = (0.0015p)^2 + (0.005)^2$, where p is measured in GeV. The acceptance for charged tracks is approximately 92% of 4π down to a momentum of 70 MeV. Charged particles are identified through their specific ionization (dE/dx) in the main drift chamber and time-of-flight to scintillation detectors outside of the tracking detectors. The dE/dx system has a resolution of 7.0% for tracks in hadronic events, and the time-of-flight system has a timing resolution of 150 ps. The two systems combined give a π-K separation of two standard deviations throughout most of the momentum range of interest. The tracking system is surrounded by a CsI crystal calorimeter which has resolution of $\sigma_E/E = 0.0035/E^{0.75} + 0.019 + 0.001E$, with E in GeV, for electromagnetic showers in the barrel region of the detector ($|\cos\theta| < 0.71$) down to energies of 30 MeV. The calorimeter's performance is slightly degraded in the endcaps due to more material in front of the crystals. Electrons are identified by matching charged tracks to electro-magnetic showers in the calorimeter. Outside of the magnet coil is a muon system consisting of over one meter of steel with three layer of streamer tubes embedded within for penetrating charged particle tracking. Muons are identified by matching charged tracks to penetrating tracks in the muon system.

The fully leptonic decays of the B^- proceed via the internal annihilation of the b and $\bar{u}$ quarks to a virtual W^- that decays to a lepton-anti-neutrino pair. The calculation of these branching ratios is straight forward[2] and depends on $f_b^2|V_{ub}|^2$, where f_b is the decay constant of the B meson and V_{ub} is the CKM matrix element between the b and u quarks. Neither of these two parameters are well measured by experiment or well predicted by theory. Taking $f_b = (200 \pm 100)$ MeV and $|V_{ub}| = 0.0045 \pm 0.0021$ yields

$$\text{Br}(B^- \to \tau^- \bar{\nu}_\tau) = (1.04 \pm 0.71) \times 10^{-4} \tag{1}$$

$$\text{Br}(B^- \to \mu^- \bar{\nu}_\mu) = (3.7 \pm 2.5) \times 10^{-7} \tag{2}$$

$$\text{Br}(B^- \to e^- \bar{\nu}_e) = (8.6 \pm 5.8) \times 10^{-12}. \tag{3}$$

Limits on these branching ratios will limit the product $f_b|V_{ub}|$ and provide insight into other elements of the CKM matrix.

The decays $B^- \to \mu^- \bar{\nu}_\mu$ and $B^- \to e^- \bar{\nu}_e$ are two body decays of the B meson. At the $\Upsilon(4S)$ the B mesons are nearly at rest ($\beta = 0.06$) and thus the leptons in these decays are nearly monoenergetic. Thus we begin our search for these decay modes by choosing events that contain identified leptons in the momentum range 2.45 to 2.85 GeV. By comparing data taken on the $\Upsilon(4S)$ resonance to that taken on the nearby continuum it is clear that these selected events have little $B\bar{B}$ contribution. To reduce the continuum contribution we require the ratio of the second and zero-th Fox-Wolfram moments[3], calculated with charged tracks and neutral calorimeter showers, to be less than 0.30. This rejects two jet-like events. We then form the event's missing momentum, $\vec{p}_{\text{mis}}$, and require it to not point along the beam direction ($|\cos\theta_{\text{mis}}| < 0.9$ to be accepted). We then consider the correlation between $\Delta P \equiv |\vec{p}_{\text{lepton}} + \vec{p}_{\text{mis}}|$ and $\Delta E \equiv E_{\text{lepton}} + |\vec{p}_{\text{mis}}| - E_{\text{beam}}$. For the signal ΔE is zero, while ΔP is the momentum of the B meson, 300 MeV. Background has ΔE below zero and ΔP larger than the B momentum. We cut at $\Delta P < 800$ MeV and -200 MeV $< \Delta E < 400$ MeV, where these cuts were optimised on our Monte Carlo simulation of the signal and continuum background.

Two events are observed in the $B^- \to \mu^- \bar{\nu}_\mu$ decay mode in the on $\Upsilon(4S)$ data and one event in the continuum data just below the resonance where we have about half the integrated luminosity as the on-resonance sample. No events are observed in the $B^- \to e^- \bar{\nu}_e$ decay mode. The efficiency for observing these decays with the analysis described here is taken from our Monte Carlo simulation and is 20% for the $\mu^- \bar{\nu}_\mu$ mode and 21% for the $e^- \bar{\nu}_e$ mode. The resolution on ΔE and ΔP predicted by the Monte Carlo simulation is in good agreement with the data in $B^- \to D^{*0} \ell^- \nu$ tagged events[4]. We place 90% confidence level (CL) upper limits based on less than 4.04 signal events in the $\mu^- \bar{\nu}_\mu$ channel and 2.31 signal events in the $e^- \bar{\nu}_e$ channel.

Combining these limits with our efficiency and a sample of 925,000 charged B decays we find $B(B^- \to e^- \bar{\nu}) < 1.3 \times 10^{-5}$ and $B(B^- \to \mu^- \bar{\nu}) < 2.0 \times 10^{-5}$ at the 90% CL.

The decay $B^- \to \tau^- \bar{\nu}_\tau$ is more of an experimental challenge. There are at least two neutrinos in the final state so $p_{\rm mis} \neq E_{\rm mis}$, and such a signature can be easily faked by missing some of the decay products of the B. To minimize the possibility of fakes from missing decay products, we consider a sample of tagged events that contains a reconstructed charged B meson[5]. We find 1401 ± 37 fully reconstructed charged B mesons in the on 4S sample and 325 ± 25 in the continuum sample. The number in the continuum sample has been scaled up by the ratio of the two samples integrated luminosities times continuum cross sections. We also estimate, from our Monte Carlo simulation of $B\bar{B}$ events for the shape and the reconstructed B energy sidebands for the normalization, that there are a further 359 ± 115 background events from mis-reconstructed decay chains to this tagged sample. This gives us a total of 716 ± 123 tagged charged B mesons. The errors on the number of tags is dominated by systematic uncertainty in the number of background tags from mis-reconstructed $B\bar{B}$ events. This uncertainty is estimated by varying the subtraction method.

We then look opposite the reconstructed B for a unique signature of the $B^- \to \tau^- \bar{\nu}_\tau$ decay. We select events with one and only one additional charged track, besides those in the reconstructed B. This selects the τ to one prong decays of the signal. The total charge of the event must be zero. We then require that there be no neutral showers in the crystal calorimeter that are not part of the reconstructed B with energy greater than 200 MeV. This selects the τ to one charged particle and nothing else portion of the signal. We find no such events in the data. We use our Monte Carlo simulation of the signal compared with generic $B\bar{B}$ events to select this last cut value, measure the probability to tag a charged B when it is opposite a $B^- \to \tau^- \bar{\nu}_\tau$ decay relative to when it is opposite a generic decay, and measure the efficiency to find the $B^- \to \tau^- \bar{\nu}_\tau$ decay once an event has been tagged. Good agreement between the data and simulation is noted for the distribution of number of charged tracks the energy spectrum of neutral showers opposite the reconstructed tag at all stages of the analysis. Our efficiency to find the signal is $(26.0 \pm 3.3)\%$ in tagged events. The error on this efficiency is dominated by Monte Carlo statistics for determining the relative tagging probabilities for signal versus background. We set a 90% CL upper limit of $B(B^- \to \tau^- \bar{\nu}) < 0.013$.

In the Standard Model lepton number violating decays can only proceed if the neutrinos have non-zero mass and mix with each other as the quarks do via the CKM matrix. For neutrinos with $m_\nu \approx 100$ eV we expect $B(\tau^- \to \mu^- \gamma) \leq 10^{-40}$. Extensions to the Standard Model can enhance this branching ratio. Recent predictions in a superstring model[6] were obtained by extrapolating physics at the Planck scale to the low energy regime. Predictions of absolute branching ratios are not possible, but the model does give the relation $B(\tau^- \to \mu^- \gamma) \simeq 2 \times 10^5 B(\mu^- \to e^- \gamma)$ based on mass dependent couplings with the enhancement varying as $(m_\tau/m_\mu)^5$. The best upper limit on $B(\mu^- \to e^- \gamma)$ is 4.9×10^{-11} at the 90% CL[7]. Thus searches for $\tau^- \to \mu^- \gamma$ with sensitivities to the branching ratio in the 10^{-5} range will be of value in defining possible extensions to the Standard Model.

Our search for the $\tau^- \to \mu^-\gamma$ decay[8] will take advantage of the facts that energy of the $\mu^-\gamma$ system equals the beam energy and the invariant mass of the $\mu^-\gamma$ system reconstructs to the τ mass. Due to the boost of the τ's at CESR energies the energy of the photon is uniformly distributed between 0.1 and 5.1 GeV and the angle between the μ and the γ is less than 90°. We tag τ-pair events by reconstructing one of the τ's in an exclusive decay topology and then looking for a $\mu\gamma$ pair in the rest of the event. We begin with a sample of well contained, low track multiplicity events. Seven different τ^+ decay modes ($e^+\nu_e\bar{\nu}_\tau$, $\mu^+\nu_\mu\bar{\nu}_\tau$, $\pi^+\bar{\nu}_\tau$, $\pi^+\pi^0\bar{\nu}_\tau$, $\pi^+\pi^+\pi^-\bar{\nu}_\tau$, $\pi^+\pi^0\pi^0\bar{\nu}_\tau$, and $\pi^+\pi^+\pi^-\pi^0\bar{\nu}_\tau$) are used as tags and we are sensitive to 99.5% of all τ decays due to feed down from other modes. Tagging cuts include requiring the total visible energy to be below the center of mass energy (to remove QED mediated events), minimum energy requirements on photon candidates, and π^0 mass within 25 MeV of the nominal. For the $\mu^+\nu_\mu\bar{\nu}_\tau$ tag the missing energy and momentum and tagging muon must reconstruct to within 600 MeV of the tau mass. Besides the tag there must also be a well identified muon track and a photon of at least 100 MeV in the event. There are 52,900 tagged events.

We then require that the energy of the remaining muon and photon be within 150 MeV of the beam energy; 930 events remain after this cut. The requirement that the remaining muon and photon be in the same hemisphere leaves 48 events. According to our Monte Carlo simulation signal events reconstruct to the tau mass with $\sigma = 23$ MeV after the selection sketched above. No events are found within three standard deviations of the tau mass. The 48 events that survive before looking in the region of the tau mass are consistent in both number and distribution in reconstructed tau mass with the predictions of our Monte Carlo simulation of generic $\tau^+\tau^-$ background events. Other sources of background ($\gamma\gamma$, $\mu\mu\gamma$ for example) are predicted to give negligible contribution at this point. We measure the efficiency for each tagging mode in our Monte Carlo and calculate the sum of efficiencies times branching ratios to be (20.5±1.3)%. The error on this is efficiency is dominated Monte Carlo statistics and the branching ratios of the tau. The number of $\tau^+\tau^-$ events is calculated with our measured integrated luminosities and known cross sections at different center of mass energies yielding $N_{\tau\tau} = (1.44 \pm 0.03) \times 10^6$. Reducing the efficiency and number of taus by one standard deviation we obtain

$$B(\tau^- \to \mu^-\gamma) < 4.2 \times 10^{-6} \text{ at 90\% CL}. \tag{4}$$

This upper limit is roughly an order of magnitude improvement over the previous best limit on this process[9].

In summary we have searched for the fully leptonic decay modes of the charged B meson. No evidence has been found for such decays and we set 90% CL upper limits on the branching ratios. We note that the limit on B($B^- \to \mu^-\bar{\nu}$) corresponds to an upper limit of 5.6 MeV on $f_b|V_{ub}|$, and that these are the only existing experimental limits on these processes. We have also set a 90% CL upper limit on the lepton number violating decay $\tau^- \to \mu^-\gamma$. Independent of this limit's impact on extensions to the Standard Model, it is the most stringent test of τ lepton number conservation to date.

References

1. Y. Kubota et al. (CLEO Collaboration), *Nucl. Inst. and Meth.* **A320** (1992) p. 66.
2. J. L. Rosner in *B Decays* ed. S. Stone (World Scientific, River Edge, NJ, 1992), p. 312, contains a review of the importance of the leptonic B^- decays and measurements of the CKM matrix elements.
3. G. Fox and S. Wolfram, *Phys. Rev. Lett.* **41** (1978) p. 1581.
4. G. Sanghera et al. (CLEO Collaboration), submitted to *Phys. Rev. Letters*.
5. D. Perticone et al. (CLEO Collaboration), contribution to this conference, N. Katayama in, *Proceedings of the International Conference on Computing in High Energy Physics 1991* ed. Y. Watase and F. Abe, p. 439.
6. R. Arnowitt and P. Nath, *Phys. Rev. Lett.* **66** (1991) p. 2708.
7. R. D. Bolton et al., *Phys. Rev.* **D38** (1988) p. 2077.
8. A. Bean et al. (CLEO Collaboration), submitted to *Phys. Rev. Letters*.
9. H. Albrecht et al. (ARGUS Collaboration), submitted to *Z Phys.* **C**.

RARE HADRONIC DECAYS OF B MESONS

STEPHEN M. PLAYFER
Department of Physics, Syracuse University, 201 Physics Building
Syracuse, N.Y., 13244-1130, USA
representing the CLEO collaboration

ABSTRACT

Using 0.98 fb^{-1} of data taken on the $\Upsilon(4S)$ with the CLEO II detector at the Cornell Electron Storage Ring, searches have been made for a number of rare decays of the B meson to final states with no charmed mesons. Upper limits (90% C.L.) of 4.8×10^{-5}, 5.6×10^{-5}, 2.9×10^{-4}, and 1.1×10^{-4} are presented for the modes $B^0 \to \pi^+\pi^-$, $B^0 \to K^+\pi^-$, $B^0 \to \pi^+\rho^-$ and $B^0 \to K^+\rho^-$ respectively.

1. Introduction

This paper describes a search for the rare hadronic decays $B^0 \to \pi^+\pi^-$, $B^0 \to K^+\pi^-$, $B^0 \to \pi^+\rho^-$ and $B^0 \to K^+\rho^-$, and their charge conjugate decays. The decays $B^0 \to \pi^+\pi^-$ and $B^0 \to \pi^+\rho^-$ are examples of exclusive b→u transitions produced primarily by the spectator diagram (Fig. 1a), where the small CKM matrix element V_{ub} replaces the element V_{cb} which describes the usual B decays of the form b→c. Published values of V_{ub}/V_{cb} of about 0.1 from measurements of the endpoint of the inclusive lepton spectrum[1] lead to branching ratio predictions of about 2×10^{-5} for $B^0 \to \pi^+\pi^-$ and 6×10^{-5} for $B^0 \to \pi^+\rho^-$[2]. The decays $B^0 \to K^+\pi^-$ and $B^0 \to K^+\rho^-$ are expected to be

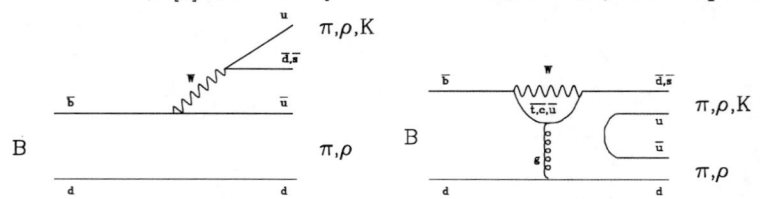

Figure 1: Diagrams for rare B decays (a) Spectator (b) Penguin
(a) (b)

dominated by "penguin" diagrams (Fig. 1b), although there is also a contribution from a Cabibbo suppressed spectator diagram (Fig. 1a). Penguin diagrams have been invoked to explain the $\Delta I = \frac{1}{2}$ rule in $K \to \pi\pi$ decays, and may also play a role in ϵ'/ϵ. The integral rate for all processes of the form b→sg depends on the top mass, and on details of the gluon couplings between the quarks. There are difficulties in calculating the fractions of the integral rate expected in each individual decay mode, reflected in a wide variety of theoretical predictions. The most recent predictions for $B^0 \to K^+\pi^-$ and $B^0 \to K^+\rho^-$ are about 1×10^{-5}[3].

These modes have attracted special attention in recent years due to their potential use for the observation of CP violation at a B factory. The $\pi^+\pi^-$ channel is a CP eigenstate which may be sensitive to one of the angles in the unitary triangle describing CP violation in the the framework of the CKM matrix. Interference between penguin and spectator amplitudes could also lead to the observation of direct CP violation.

2. Event Selection

The CLEO II detector[4] at the Cornell Electron Storage Ring, has taken a data sample of 980 pb^{-1} at the $\Upsilon(4S)$, and 425 pb^{-1} just below the resonance. The detector has three concentric drift chambers in a 1.5T magnetic field, which measure charged particles with a resolution of $(\delta p_\perp/p_\perp)^2=(0.0015p_\perp)^2+0.005^2$. A CsI calorimeter provides excellent energy and angular resolution for photons.

All the decays in this paper involve two light mesons produced by the decay of a B meson which is essentially at rest. The final state mesons are nearly collinear and have energies of about 2.6 GeV. Candidate events must satisfy standard hadronic event selection criteria, and the tracks forming the two mesons must satisfy additional requirements on track quality intended to reject poorly measured tracks. Photon candidates are selected from showers in the barrel calorimeter which are not matched to a charged track, have an energy of at least 30 MeV, and have a lateral energy distribution consistent with that expected for photons. Candidate π^0's are selected from pairs of photons with an invariant mass within 2σ of the known π^0 mass. By making a cut on the polar angle θ of the thrust axis of the two mesons at $\cos\theta<0.8$ we remove a region of the detector where the measurements of both tracks and photons have degraded resolution.

Candidate B decays are identified using the variables ΔE and M_B where ΔE is the summed energy of the two mesons, which should be equal to the beam energy, and $M_B=\sqrt{E_{beam}^2-(\Sigma\vec{p_i})^2}$ is the beam-constrained mass. For the modes without π^0's the resolution in ΔE is 27±2 MeV, which is less than the difference of 42 MeV in the energy of 2.6 GeV/c kaons and pions. This helps separate the different decay modes. For the modes with π^0's the ΔE resolution varies between 35 and 45 MeV, depending on the π^0 energy. The resolution of 3 MeV/c^2 in M_B is dominated by the beam energy spread of the machine. We define a signal region within 2σ of the expected values of ΔE and M_B. The background in the signal region is estimated by studying a two-dimensional sideband in ΔE and M_B.

We use dE/dx information from the main drift chamber for particle identification. At momenta of 2.6 GeV/c, kaons and pions are on the relativistic rise portion of the dE/dx curve, and the separation between them is about 2σ. The high momentum track recoiling against the ρ^- is identified as a π or a K according to the most probable hypothesis with 80% efficiency for correct identification. In the case of $\pi^+\pi^-$ and $K^+\pi^-$ final states, we construct a χ^2 for each of four hypotheses ($K\pi$, πK, $\pi\pi$, and KK) using the dE/dx information from both tracks, and identify the event with the most probable hypothesis. There are 65% correct identifications, 9% misidentifications of $K\pi$ as $\pi\pi$, and 18% misidentifications of $\pi\pi$ as $K\pi$.

For the analyses involving ρ mesons, there are two additional variables, the ρ

mass and the ρ decay helicity angle (α). The ρ mesons are fully polarized and decay with a helicity distribution proportional to $\cos^2\alpha$, resulting in asymmetric decays with one fast and one slow pion. Very asymmetric decays with the slow pion energy below 200 MeV are rejected because of large combinatorial backgrounds. The signal region is defined by 620<m_ρ<920 MeV/c^2, and $|\cos\alpha|$>0.5.

The dominant source of background is from continuum $q\bar{q}$ jets. B decays contribute negligibly small backgrounds to the processes studied here, since the highest allowed momentum in a b→c decay is below the lowest momentum that is required by the kinematics of the rare decays. The continuum background can be studied using the sample of data taken slightly below the Υ(4S). The distribution of continuum events is a smooth function in ΔE and M$_B$, which is well described by our continuum Monte-carlo. The observed background events in the sideband regions of the Υ(4S) data sample, can be accounted for by scaling the off-resonance data by the appropriate luminosity ratio.

The continuum background is suppressed by a cut on the angle, ψ, between the thrust axis of the candidate decay, and the thrust axis of the rest of the event, $\cos\psi$<0.7. For the $K^+\pi^-$ and $\pi^+\pi^-$ channels further suppression has been achieved by combining the the direction of the the candidate thrust axis, the flight direction of the candidate B, and nine variables characterizing the energy flow of the event, to form a Fisher discriminant[5]. After using Monte-carlo samples to determine the coefficients, distributions of the Fisher discriminant are produced for signal and continuum events. A cut is made that retains 85% of the signal, and only 43% of the continuum background.

3. Results

Figure 2 shows the beam-constrained mass distributions for the four rare decays, for the events that lie inside a 2σ cut on ΔE. There are no significant signals at the B mass of 5.280 GeV/c^2. In Table 1 the numbers of events in the signal region are given. The background is estimated from the sideband using the shape of the continuum background distribution to extrapolate into the signal region. This gives the numbers of background events in Table 1, with a systematic uncertainty due to knowledge of the background shape. The detection efficiency has been determined by Monte-carlo. Where possible the efficiencies have been checked using data. As an example, we have embedded $e^+e^-\to\mu^+\mu^-$ events in hadronic events to check the efficiency for finding tracks. These checks are used to estimate a systematic uncertainty in the efficiencies given in Table 1. To obtain 90% confidence level upper limits we conservatively account for the systematic errors in the detection efficiency, and the background subtraction, by reducing both the background and the efficiency by the systematic error.

The upper limits are compared with previous published limits in Table 1. The large data sample taken by CLEO II leads to significant reductions in the limits, particularily for the modes with π^0's, since CLEO II has excellent photon detection. The limits are approaching recent theoretical predictions, and already

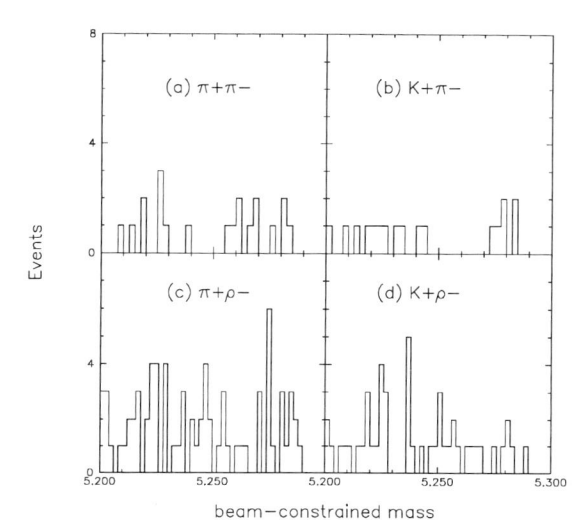

Figure 2: Mass distributions of events inside the summed energy window

B decay Channel	Monte-Carlo Efficiency	Event Yields Signal	Event Yields Background	90% CL Upper Limits This Result	90% CL Upper Limits Previous Results
$\pi^+\pi^-$	0.190±0.030	4	1.2±0.2	4.8×10^{-5}	9.0×10^{-5}
$\pi^+\rho^-$	0.085±0.015	14	6.2±0.7	29.0×10^{-5}	52.0×10^{-5}
$K^+\pi^-$	0.190±0.030	5	1.4±0.2	5.6×10^{-5}	9.0×10^{-5}
$K^+\rho^-$	0.085±0.015	5	3.6±0.4	11.0×10^{-5}	none

Table 1: Upper limits for rare hadronic B decays

exclude some earlier predictions[6].

4. References

1. R. Fulton et al., Phys. Rev. Lett. **64** (1990) 16.
   H. Albrecht et al., Phys. Lett. **B234** (1990) 409.
2. M. Bauer et al., Zeit. Phys. **C34** (1987) 103.
3. L.L. Chau et al., Phys. Rev. **D43** (1991) 2176.
   N.G.Deshpande and J.Trampetic, Phys. Rev. **D41** (1990) 895.
4. Y. Kubota et al., Nucl. Inst. Meth. **A320** (1992) 66.
5. M.G.Kendall and A.Stuart, "The Advanced Theory of Statistics", Volume III, Hafner Publishing, New York (1968).
6. M.B. Gavela et al., Phys. Lett. **B154** (1985) 425.

RADIATIVE DECAYS OF THE B-MESONS: CP VIOLATION AND CONSTRAINTS ON $|V_{td}|$

JOÃO M. SOARES
*Physics Department, Carnegie Mellon University
Pittsburgh, PA 15213, USA*

ABSTRACT

The CP-violating asymmetries in the radiative decays of the B-mesons are investigated, on the framework of the standard CKM model. An estimate based on a quark level calculation gives asymmetries of the order $(0.1 - 1)\%$ and $(1 - 10)\%$ for the $b \to s\gamma$ and the $b \to d\gamma$ decays, respectively. Another appealing feature of these decays is that the ratio of the decay rates for $B \to \rho\gamma$ and $B \to K^*\gamma$ can provide an alternative measurement of the CKM matrix element $|V_{td}|$. The theoretical uncertainty is mainly in the light-quark contribution to the decay diagrams, which is also at the origin of the CP-violating asymmetry.

1. Decay Amplitudes

The decay amplitudes for the radiative decays $B \to K^*\gamma$ and $B \to \rho\gamma$ are dominated by the spectator process shown in fig. 1, with $q = s$ and $q = d$ respectively. The relevant operator in the effective Hamiltonian is then

$$H_{eff} = \frac{G_F}{\sqrt{2}} \frac{e}{4\pi^2} m_b F(x_t + x_u r) \bar{q} \frac{1+\gamma_5}{2} \sigma^{\mu\nu} b F_{\mu\nu}$$
$$x_i \equiv V_{iq}^* V_{ib} \qquad (q = s, d). \tag{1}$$

The contribution of the virtual t-quark in the loop is dominant, and gives the term

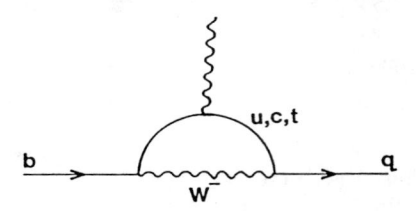

Figure 1

proportional to x_t. The corresponding form factor F includes QCD corrections [1] that enhance the decay rate by about a factor of two: for $m_t = 140 GeV$, $F = 0.31$. The coefficient r of the x_u term is GIM suppressed: it is discussed in the following sections. For the inclusive processes, eq. (1) gives (with $m_t = 140 GeV$) $BR(b \to s\gamma) = 4 \times 10^{-4}$ and $BR(b \to d\gamma) = (1-4) \times 10^{-5}$. (The range of values corresponds to the presently allowed values for the CKM parameters. For other values of m_t, the results are of the same order.) For the exclusive decays, the rates are more uncertain as it is necessary to estimate the hadronic matrix element of the quark operator in H_{eff}. The rates should be smaller by about one order of magnitude [2]: $BR(B \to K^*\gamma)$ is then close to the present experimental upper bound, and $BR(B \to \rho\gamma)$ is in the range of future B-factories.

2. CP violation

The interference between the two terms in eq. (1) gives the CP-violating asymmetry [3]

$$a_{CP} \equiv \frac{\Gamma(\bar{b} \to \gamma \bar{q}) - \Gamma(b \to \gamma q)}{\Gamma(\bar{b} \to \gamma \bar{q}) + \Gamma(b \to \gamma q)} \simeq 2 \frac{Im\{x_t x_u^*\}}{|x_t|^2} Im\{r\}. \tag{2}$$

(which is the same for inclusive and exclusive decays). The contributions to r come from order α_S diagrams such as that shown in fig. 2. These QCD corrections are known [4] to attenuate the GIM suppression, and give a dependence on the light quark masses more significant than that from fig. 1. Moreover, these diagrams now have an absorptive part: $Im\{r\}$ has contributions from the on-mass-shell intermediate states qg, $qu\bar{u}$ and $qc\bar{c}$. The decay amplitude for $b \to qg$ is QCD suppressed, and the scattering $q\gamma \to qc\bar{c}$ is phase space suppressed. Therefore, the asymmetry is mostly due to the $qu\bar{u}$ intermediate state. It gives [3] $Im\{r\} \simeq \alpha_S/(4F)$, and the asymmetry is in the range $(0.1 - 1)\%$ and $(1 - 10)\%$ for the $b \to s\gamma$ and the $b \to d\gamma$ decays, respectively (with opposite signs). The single hard photon is a clear signature, but the small branching ratios make the asymmetries only marginally acessible to upcoming experiments.

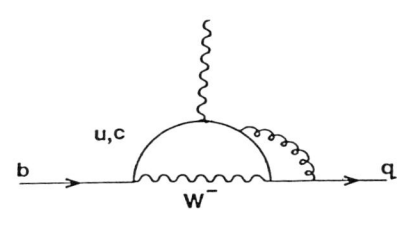

Figure 2

It must be pointed out that the quark-level, perturbative, calculation of the correction term r in the decay amplitude is a crude estimate of the final state interactions that involve both real and virtual intermediate hadronic states. In this sense, this term should be viewed as a long-distance contribution that involves physics below the m_b scale. The quantitative result is therefore uncertain, but the qualitative features are striking: a non-zero asymmetry is expected; the light quark masses should be compared to m_b, and not M_W, and so the magnitude of r can be significant.

3. Constraints on $|V_{td}|$

The present constraints on $|V_{td}|$, from the $B^0 - \bar{B}^0$ mixing, are hindered by large theoretical uncertainties. An alternative measurement may be obtained from the ratio [5]

$$\Omega \equiv \frac{BR(B \to \rho\gamma) + BR(\bar{B} \to \bar{\rho}\gamma)}{BR(B \to K^*\gamma) + BR(\bar{B} \to \bar{K}^*\gamma)} \tag{3}$$

(the branching ratios of particles and anti-particles are added for improved statistics). The poorly known hadronic matrix elements in each decay cancel in the ratio, in the $SU(3)_{flavor}$ symmetric limit. The branching ratios are evaluated from eq. (1). For $B \to K^*\gamma$, the term in x_u is doubly-Cabibbo suppressed and can be ignored, but it should be kept for $B \to \rho\gamma$. Then,

$$\Omega \simeq T^2 \left[\frac{|V_{td}|^2}{|V_{ts}|^2} + 2Re\{r\} \frac{Re\{V_{tb}^* V_{ub} V_{ud}^* V_{td}\}}{|V_{ts} V_{tb}^*|^2} \right] \tag{4}$$

T measures the $SU(3)_{flavor}$ symmetry breaking that occurs in the evaluation of the hadronic matrix elements. Its estimate is model dependent: the BSW model gives $T \simeq 0.92$. $Re\{r\}$ can be calculated from the quark-level approximation that was used above, and it should be of the order of $Im\{r\}$. Due to the long-distance nature of this term, a reliable estimate is hard to obtain. The main theoretical uncertainty in the measurement of $|V_{td}|$ is then the second term of eq. (4). The measurement of the asymmetry, that probes $Im\{r\}$, may provide some control over its magnitude.

1. B. Grinstein, R. Springer and M. B. Wise, *Nucl. Phys.* **B339** (1990) 269.
2. T. Altomari, *Phys. Rev.* **D37** (1988) 677; N. G. Deshpande, P. Lo and J. Trampetic, *Z. Phys.* **C40** (1988) 369; C. A. Dominguez, N. Paver and Riazuddin, *Phys. Lett.* elevenbf B214 (1988) 459.
3. J. M. Soares, *Nucl. Phys.* **B367** (1991) 575.
4. M. A. Shifman, A. I. Vainshtein and V. I. Zakharov, *Phys. Rev.* **D18** (1978) 2583; S. Bertolini, F. Borzumati and A. Masiero, *Phys. Rev. Lett.* **59** (1987) 180; N. G. Deshpande et al., *Phys. Rev. Lett.* **59** (1987) 183.
5. A. Ali and C. Greub, *Phys. Lett.* **B287** (1992) 191; J. M. Soares, preprint CMU-HEP92-13, June 1992.

FSI PHASES AND CP ASYMMETRIES IN BEAUTY: QCD POINT OF VIEW

N.G.URALTSEV
Physics Department, University of Notre Dame
Notre Dame, IN 46556, USA
and
St.Petersburg Nuclear Physics Institute
Gatchina, St.Petersburg District, 188350, Russia

ABSTRACT

Inclusive and exclusive decays of heavy flavours look quite different from a theoretical viewpoint. We argue that inclusive decays can be treated quantitatively and report on the calculation of the perturbative corrections to the Final State Interaction phases in connection to their impact on effects of CP violation.

Present expectations for the observation of the CP nonconservation in beauty are based on the search for those CP odd effects in B mesons that appear due to $B^0 - \bar{B}^0$ mixing. Some modes – like $B_d \to \psi K_s$, $\pi^+\pi^-$ have the additional advantage of being "clean" from a theoretical point of view. Of much practical interest is another kind of effects where the $B^0 - \bar{B}^0$ mixing is not important, say in decays of $B^\pm$ or Λ_b. However the simplest CP odd asymmetries in such decays are rather obscure as they depend crucially on the CP even phases generated by the strong interactions in the final state (the FSI phases). (For a general review see e.g. ref.[1]).

The decays mediated by the $b \to u\bar{u}s$ transitions look most promising. The main reason is that here the "Penguin" amplitudes due to the $b \to s + (c\bar{c}, t\bar{t})_{virt} \to s + q\bar{q}$ chain also contribute, and their magnitude must be close to the strength of the doubly KM suppressed tree level amplitude[2]. The relevant Penguin amplitude has literally a CP even phase δ_P, $\tan \delta_P \simeq \pi/\log \frac{m_t^2, M_W^2}{m_b^2}$, or numerically $\delta_P \simeq 0.5$; however including the sizeable mass of the c quarks reduces the estimate to $\delta_P \simeq 0.1$.

There is a popular opinion that other FSI phases are negligible and one can rely on the Penguin phase δ_P. Simultaneously the opposite point of view can be found in the literature – that in spite of the large b quark mass and energy release the FSI phases are generally large in heavy flavour decays. In such a case however it is hardly possible to predict theoretically even the sign of the effect.

We believe[3] that *a priori* there are no sound grounds to consider FSI phases as small, at least as compared to δ_P. This should be especially the case for a generic exclusive process where the result depends crucially not only on the hadronization details but also on the actual dynamics of the formation of the particular final state at the "hard" stage[2]. For instance for color suppressed decays the hard part of the process can naturally involve a hard gluon exchange; if so one might expect the FSI phase to be of the order of $\pi/2$. On the contrary for inclusive processes the QCD language of quarks and gluons is adequate[4]: perturbative corrections are governed by the parameter $\alpha_s(m_b^2)$ and nonperturbative effects are power-like suppressed; therefore here the δ_P based estimate is a reasonable first approximation.

Exploring this idea we concentrated[3] on the CP odd inclusive width difference for the decays of b and $\bar{b}$ quarks into the states without heavy quarks. We calculated higher order QCD effects and found them to reduce the asymmetry only slightly (by 10-20%). This disagreed with the result of the paper[5] where the strong cancellation of the effect had been claimed.

We start with the main equation for the CP odd width difference

$$\Delta\Gamma \equiv \Gamma(\bar{b} \to \bar{s}q\bar{q}) - \Gamma(b \to sq\bar{q}) = -4\mathrm{Im}(\lambda_i\lambda_j^*) \cdot \sum_F \mathrm{Im}(A_i(b \to F) \cdot A_j^*(b \to F)), \qquad (1)$$

where F are the final states included for the process, $A_{i,j}$ are the decay amplitudes with the KM factors factored out and $\lambda_{i,j}$ are the corresponding KM factors. The S matrix unitarity enables one to express the absorptive parts of the amplitudes A as a sum over the set I of real intermediate states for the $b \to F$ transitions:

$$\Delta\Gamma = -2\mathrm{Im}(\lambda_i\lambda_j^*) \cdot \sum_F \sum_I \{A_i(b \to I)A^*(F \to I)\mathrm{Re}A_j(b \to F) -$$
$$- A_j(b \to I)A^*(F \to I)\mathrm{Re}A_i(b \to F)\}, \qquad (2)$$

with $A(F \to I)$ being generated by strong interactions.

In the perturbative QCD expansion $\Delta\Gamma$ appears in order α_s and does not contain $\log(m_t^2/m_b^2)$. In the spirit of the standard LLA we have calculated all the corrections of the form $\alpha_s^{n+1}\log^n(m_t^2/m_b^2)$. The result appears to be very simple. To calculate $\Delta\Gamma$ one should consider only the one-gluon rescattering amplitude $c\bar{c}X \to q\bar{q}X'$, thus almost reproducing the lowest order estimate based on the Penguin phase δ_P. The account for the higher orders reduces merely to using the weak decay amplitudes $A_{i,j}(b \to F, I)$ obtained by the *effective* $\Delta B = 1$ weak interaction Lagrangian normalized at the scale $q^2 = -m_b^2$ rather than by the bare one defined at $q^2 = -M_W^2$.

To prove this prescription one can consider all possible states F and I (such as $s+g$, $sq\bar{q}$, $sq\bar{q}+g$ ...) step by step and count the powers of g_s in the the corresponding 'strong' amplitudes $A(F \to I)$. The important point here is that owing to the on-shellness of both F and I the strong amplitude $A(F \to I)$ cannot contain large logs, $\log\frac{m_t^2, M_W^2}{m_b^2}$, provided it is expressed in terms of the α_s normalized at $q^2 = -m_b^2$. In fact this statement is nothing but the renormalizability of QCD.

The states I without a $c\bar{c}$ pair cannot contribute to $\Delta\Gamma$. The rescattering amplitude $A(F \to I)$ therefore describes a transition from a charmless state to a state with hidden charm and so it contains at least one power of α_s. For that reason the leading contribution is obtained only if the single gluon amplitude is considered whereas in the remaining weak amplitudes $A_{i,j}$ any extra power of the strong coupling is accompanied by the 'ultraviolet' *log*. The letter requirement defines exactly the 'standard' LLA renormalized weak decay amplitudes.

Actually the renormalization of the weak amplitudes not only modifies their strength but also makes new states possible on the quark level – say $d\bar{d}$ can now appear as well as $\bar{u}u$; all they should be taken into account. The following observation[3] simplifies the analysis further: the states like $gg + s$, $ggg + s$ etc. *are absent* in the LLA.

Indeed, the Penguin operator which appears in the effective Lagrangian due to the integration over the virtual states with $q^2 \gg m_b^2$ has the form $\bar{b}\gamma_\mu\frac{\lambda^a}{2}s \cdot \nabla_\nu G_{\mu\nu}^a$. In the absence of the light quark legs the equation of motion $\nabla_\nu G_{\mu\nu}^a = 0$ tells the vanishing of its matrix element for purely gluon final states in the leading order in α_s. For the $gg + s$ states, in particular, it corresponds to the LLA cancellation for real gluons of the contributions of two possible graphs.

Finally the first nontrivial correction to $\Delta\Gamma$ generated in two loops reads as

$$\Delta\Gamma \propto \frac{\alpha_s}{3\pi}\text{Im}\,[\log\frac{m_t^2}{m_b^2} + i\pi\zeta(m_c^2/m_b^2)] \to$$

$$\to \frac{\alpha_s(m_b^2)}{3\pi}\text{Im}\,[\log\frac{m_t^2}{m_b^2} + i\pi\zeta(m_c^2/m_b^2)\cdot(1 - \frac{\alpha_s}{3\pi}(n_f+1)\log\frac{m_t^2}{m_b^2} + \ae(c_\pm))]\,, \qquad (3)$$

where n_f is the number of light flavours excluding c quark, $\zeta \simeq 0.2$ is the phase space suppression factor, $\ae \simeq 2\alpha_s/4\pi \cdot \log M_W^2/m_b^2$ is the 'ordinary' correction factor due to the renormalization of the standard color factors $c_\pm$ in the effective Lagrangian. (In a sense the last term $\ae$ in the eq.(3) together with the unity added to n_f can be attributed to the moduli of the interfering amplitudes rather than to the phases). For $n_f = 3$ and $\alpha_s(m_b^2) = 0.18$ the first term (representing the less trivial correction) is about -0.17, however it is strongly canceled by the trivial corrections, $\ae \simeq 0.13$. The summation of all orders in the LLA practically does not change the conclusion: the total correction to $\Delta\Gamma$ if taken literally appears to be near -2% for $\Lambda_{QCD} = 0.1 \div 0.3 GeV$. Numerically for the inclusive asymmetry one has

$$\frac{\Gamma(\bar{b} \to \bar{s} + charmless) - \Gamma(b \to s + charmless)}{\Gamma(\bar{b} \to \bar{s} + charmless) + \Gamma(b \to s + charmless)} \simeq -1.9 \cdot \zeta \cdot \left|\frac{V_{ub}}{V_{cb}}\right| \cdot \sin\alpha \simeq -2\cdot 10^{-2}\,, \qquad (4)$$

where $\alpha = arg(V_{cb}^* V_{cd} V_{ub} V_{ud}^*)$ is one of the angles of the Unitarity Triangle[1], $\alpha \simeq 0.55$ at $|V_{ub}/V_{cb}| = 0.1$ if one assumes $f_B \simeq 140\,MeV$. The total probability of such decays $BR(b \to s + charmless)$ is in this case about $2.5 \cdot 10^{-3}$.

In the similar way one calculates also the CP odd inclusive width differences in the decays $b \to q s\bar{s}$, which are nonzero owing to the different phase space for the $c\bar{c}$ and $u\bar{u}$ intermediate states. Under the same numerical assumptions the rate asymmetry for $b \to ss\bar{s}$ is about $-1.8\cdot 10^{-2}$ at $BR(b \to ss\bar{s}) \simeq 5\cdot 10^{-4}$ and for the channel $b \to ds\bar{s}$ the asymmetry is near $+1.3\cdot 10^{-1}$ while $BR(b \to ds\bar{s}) \simeq 7\cdot 10^{-5}$.

The measurement of the inclusive CP odd asymmetries in beauty particles seems to be an extremely difficult experimental problem and similar analysis for exclusive few body modes would be more relevant for experiment. Nevertheless the QCD calculations we have made are not useless. For these corrections enter any quark diagram that proceeds via Penguins. Our caution to apply directly similar calculations to exclusive decays is in fact no more but the statement that in that case there could be other and even larger sources for the FSI phases.

Aknoledgements

I am grateful to my coauthor on paper[3] Yu.Dokshitzer for collaboration and to I.Bigi for pursuing me to address the problem of FSI phases from the positions of QCD. This work was supported in part by National Science Foundation under grant number NSF-PHY 92 13313.

References

1. I.I.Bigi, V.A.Khoze, A.I.Sanda, N.G.Uraltsev, In: C.Jarlskog (Ed.) *CP Violation* (World Scientific, Singapore, 1988), p. 175.
2. A.E.Blinov, V.A.Khoze, N.G.Uraltsev, *Int.J.Mod.Phys.* **A4** (1989) 1933.
3. Yu.L.Dokshitzer, N.G.Uraltsev, *ZhETF Lett.* **52** (1990) 509.
4. I.I.Bigi, N.G.Uraltsev, *Phys.Lett.* **B280** (1992) 271;
   I.I.Bigi, N.G.Uraltsev, A.I.Vainshtein, *Phys.Lett.* **B293** (1992) 430.
5. J.-M.Gerard, W.-S.Hou, *Phys.Rev.Lett.* **62** (1989) 855.

USING GLUON FUSION TO PROBE CP VIOLATION IN THE HIGGS SECTOR

John F. Gunion

Davis Institute for High Energy Physics
Department of Physics, U.C. Davis, Davis CA 95616

ABSTRACT

A technique for directly probing CP violation in the Higgs sector of a multi-doublet model using gluon-gluon collisions at the SSC is reviewed.

1. Introduction

Understanding the Higgs sector is one of the fundamental missions of future high energy colliders such as the SSC and LHC. In particular, it will be important to know if CP violation is present in the Higgs sector. Generally, either spontaneous or explicit CP violation can be present if the Higgs sector consists of more than the single doublet field of the Standard Model (SM). (For a review of this and other issues summarized below, see Ref. [1], and references therein.) The presence of significant CP violation would provide strong constraints on possible models. For instance, although CP violation is certainly possible in a general two-Higgs-doublet model (2HDM), it does not arise (either explicitly or spontaneously) in the restricted version of the 2HDM that emerges in the Minimal Supersymmetric Model (MSSM). Indeed, observation of large CP violation in the Higgs sector is generally very difficult to reconcile with a supersymmetric theoretical structure. Thus, it will be of great interest to determine the CP nature of any Higgs boson that is found.

Although there are a variety of experimental observables that are indirectly sensitive to CP violation in the Higgs sector, direct probes of CP violation in the Higgs sector are sorely needed. Here we describe a *production rate* asymmetry that directly probes the CP nature of any (observed) Higgs boson that is produced via gluon-gluon fusion at the SSC/LHC. (The proposed asymmetry is closely analogous to that developed previously for collisions of polarized back scattered laser beams at a future linear e^+e^- collider.[2]) The primary experimental requirement is the ability to polarize the colliding protons. The difference between Higgs boson production rates for colliding beams of different polarizations can be quite large in a general 2HDM, and arise as follows. First, note that in the neutral Higgs sector a CP-violating phase for one of the neutral field vacuum expectation values leads to mass matrix mixing between the CP-even scalar fields and the CP-odd scalar fields. Since the gg coupling to CP-even scalars is not very different in magnitude from that to CP-odd scalars (both arising at one loop, see below) there is clear opportunity for large interference effects when the Higgs mass eigenstate (ϕ) contains substantial components of both types. Asymmetries larger than 10% are quite typical.

2. Gluon Fusion

The basic production mechanism in question is gluon fusion through a triangle diagram. In gluon fusion, any colored particle which acquires its mass via the Higgs mechanism can appear in the loop. In particular, a heavy quark does *not* decouple when its mass is much greater than the Higgs boson mass. Thus, in the SM the top quark typically dominates. Of course, additional quarks and other types of colored particles appearing in extended models can also contribute. In the computations quoted here, we consider the model in which the only extension of the SM occurs in the Higgs sector, but clearly the rates and consequent detectability of CP-violating asymmetries could be very much larger in theories containing many heavy fermions.

At hadron colliders, the gluons within the hadrons provide a large effective gluon-gluon collision luminosity. The procedure for computing the $gg \to$ Higgs cross section in leading order is well-known.[1] Crucial to our discussion is the degree of polarization that can be achieved for gluons at the SSC. The amount of gluon polarization in a positively-polarized proton beam, defined by the structure function difference $\Delta g(x) = g_+(x) - g_-(x)$, is not currently known with any certainty. (Here, the $\pm$ subscripts indicate gluons with $\pm$ helicity, and $g(x) = g_+(x) + g_-(x)$ is the unpolarized gluon distribution function.) Many models used to describe the EMC data require a significant amount of the proton's spin to be carried by the gluons. A value for $\Delta g = \int \Delta g(x)\,dx$ of $\Delta g \sim 3$ is not atypical. In the results to be quoted, we shall employ the form:[3] $\Delta g(x) = g(x)$ $(x > x_c)$, $\Delta g(x) = \frac{x}{x_c} g(x)$ $(x < x_c)$, where $x_c \sim 0.2$ yields a value of $\Delta g \sim 3 - 3.5$ over the Higgs mass range (which determines the momentum transfer scale at which $g(x)$ is evaluated) that we consider. (Strictly speaking, $\Delta g(x)$ should be chosen to be of this form at some given Q_0 and then evolved to obtain the form at other Q values — we ignore this subtlety here.) Although this form maximizes $\Delta g(x)$ at large x, the x values most important for Higgs production are substantially below 0.2.

3. Asymmetry and Results

The asymmetry we compute is simply $A \equiv [\sigma_+ - \sigma_-]/[\sigma_+ + \sigma_-]$, where $\sigma_\pm$ is the cross section for Higgs production in collisions of an unpolarized proton with a proton of helicity $\pm$, respectively. $\sigma_+ - \sigma_-$ is proportional to the integral over x_1 and x_2 (with $x_1 x_2 = m_\phi^2/s$) of $g(x_1)\Delta g(x_2)\left[|\mathcal{M}_{++}|^2 - |\mathcal{M}_{--}|^2\right]$, while $\sigma_+ + \sigma_-$ is determined by the integral of $g(x_1)g(x_2)\left[|\mathcal{M}_{++}|^2 + |\mathcal{M}_{--}|^2\right]$. (We have assumed that it is proton 2 that is polarized.) Now, $|\mathcal{M}_{++}|^2 - |\mathcal{M}_{--}|^2$ vanishes for a CP eigenstate, but can be quite large in a general 2HDM; the difference is proportional to Im(eo^*), where e (o) represents the gg coupling to the CP-even (-odd) component of ϕ.

To obtain a numerical indication of the observability of A, we have proceeded as follows. First, we maximize $(\sigma_+ - \sigma_-)/\sqrt{\sigma_+ + \sigma_-}$ (which determines the statistical significance of our observation) by choosing an optimum value for x_F^{cut} such that only $x_2 - x_1 > x_F^{cut}$ is included in our integrals; such a cut pushes the integrals into the region where $\Delta g(x_2)/g(x_2)$ is less suppressed — x_F^{cut} near 0.05 typically yields optimal results. Second, we assume that ϕ can only be detected in the $\phi \to ZZ \to l^+l^-X$ modes. Third, we have searched (at fixed $\tan\beta = v_2/v_1$) for the parameters of the most general CP-violating 2HDM that yield the largest achievable statistical significance, N_{SD}^{max}, for measuring A in the $ZZ \to l^+l^-X$ mode — the need for keeping a large rate in the ZZ mode competes with the requirement of keeping Im(eo^*) large.

The results for N_{SD}^{max} at the SSC with integrated luminosity of 10 fb^{-1} are extremely encouraging. For example, computations using the above form of $\Delta g(x)$ at

$\tan\beta = 2$ and 10 yield N_{SD}^{max} values in excess of 3 for m_ϕ between 180 and 650 GeV at $m_t = 150$ GeV. Detection of this asymmetry is clearly not out of the question. Indeed, the Higgs sector parameters required to achieve such N_{SD}^{max} values are not at all fine tuned. Large ranges of parameter space yield values very nearly as big. It should be noted that for the parameter choices which yield these maximal results, the production rate for ϕ at $\tan\beta = 2$ is quite similar to that for production of a SM Higgs boson of the same mass, once $m_\phi > 2m_t$, and that the branching ratio for $\phi \to ZZ, WW$ decays is close to the SM value. Thus, without this asymmetry measurement, distinguishing between a ϕ which is a CP mixture and the SM Higgs boson could be difficult. At $\tan\beta = 10$, the ϕ production rate becomes increasingly suppressed relative to the SM value at larger m_ϕ, and would alone indicate a non-SM scenario.

Our ability to detect A may be either better or worse than that indicated by the sample results stated above. If only partial polarization for the proton beam can be achieved N_{SD}^{max} would worsen. Limited acceptance for the final states of interest would also cause N_{SD}^{max} to decrease. If additional decay modes could be employed (e.g. WW decay channels with one W decaying leptonically) or if enhanced luminosity can be used, N_{SD}^{max} could be improved. Of course, if only the $ZZ \to l^+l^-l^+l^-$ channel can be employed then the statistical significance is decreased (by a factor of roughly 5.5); a higher luminosity would definitely be required to detect the asymmetry. However, we are optimistic that once a Higgs boson is found and its mass known, techniques for employing more than just the gold-plated $4l$ mode will be found.

4. Conclusion

The ability to polarize one of the proton beams at the SSC will provide a unique opportunity for determining the CP nature of any observed neutral Higgs boson. Indeed, if the Higgs boson has both significant CP-even and CP-odd components, then a large asymmetry between production rates for positively versus negatively polarized protons will arise. If measurable CP violation is found in the Higgs sector many otherwise very attractive models will be eliminated, including the Standard Model and most supersymmetric models. This should provide a rather strong motivation for expending the relatively modest monetary amounts needed to achieve polarized SSC beams.

5. Acknowledgements

The results described here were obtained in collaboration with T.-C. Yuan and B. Grzadkowski. This work has been supported in part by the Department of Energy.

References

1. J.F. Gunion, H.E. Haber, G. Kane and S. Dawson, *The Higgs Hunter's Guide*, Frontiers in Physics Lecture Note Series #80, (Addison-Wesley Publishing Company, Redwood City, CA, 1990).

2. J.F. Gunion and B. Grzadkowski, preprint UCD-92-18, *Phys. Lett.* **B** (1992) in press.

3. E.L. Berger and J. Qiu, *Phys. Rev.* **D40** (1989) 778.

FINAL-STATE INTERACTIONS IN THE TOP-QUARK SEMILEPTONIC DECAY

JIANG LIU
Department of Physics, University of Pennsylvania
Philadelphia, Pennsylvania 19104, USA

ABSTRACT

Final-state interactions in the top-quark semileptonic decays are discussed, with emphasis on their implications on the spin-momentum correlation and on the validity of the Breit-Wigner approximation for unstable particle propagators.

Final-state interactions play an important role[1] in the determination of CP and T violation. A test for T violation is to observe a "T-odd correlation" such as those of the form $\vec{\sigma} \cdot (\vec{p}_1 \times \vec{p}_2)$ where $\vec{\sigma}$ is a spin and $\vec{p}_1$ and $\vec{p}_2$ are momenta. This correlation can be produced by final-state interactions even if T invariance holds. To use such correlations as a test of T violation the final-state-interaction effect must be negligible or calculable.

The computation of final-state-interaction effects on the T-odd correlation has long been of interest[2]. Early examples of the calculation involved nuclear β decay, hyperon semileptonic decay and $K^{\pm,0}_{\ell 3}$ decays. In terms of weak-current interactions the t-quark semileptonic decay $t \to bW^+ \to b\nu_\ell \bar{\ell}$ is analogous in many respects to nuclear β decay but with an unsuppressed recoil. Accordingly, one may define a parameter, which is often referred to as the D parameter, for the correlation in the decay spectrum[3]. The dominant contribution to D comes from $bW \to bW$ rescattering by exchanging a photon and a Z. An simple analytic result for D is given in Ref. 3. Numerically D lies between 1×10^{-3} to 6×10^{-3} for m_t between 100 GeV and 200 GeV. This effect is considerably larger than the maximal-allowed T violation effect in a large class of theoretical models. To get rid of this pure final-state interaction effect one may consider comparing the asymmetry parameter for both $t \to bW^+$ and $\bar{t} \to \bar{b}W^-$.

Another interesting test for CP violation is to compare the partial decay rates of a particle and its antiparticle. In this case final-state interactions are necessary since in their absence the partial decay rates are equal from CPT even if CP is violated. Examples of special interest are those involving an intermediate unstable particle, in which the final-state interaction enters into the standard calculation as the width of the unstable particle. In this case the Breit-Wigner approximation is usually introduced, under which the W gauge boson propagator is given in the unitary gauge by

$$iD_{\mu\nu}(k)_{BW} = \frac{-i}{k^2 - M_W^2 + i\Gamma_W M_W}\left[g_{\mu\nu} - \frac{k_\mu k_\nu}{M_W^2}\right], \qquad (1)$$

where M_W and Γ_W are the W mass and total width, respectively.

This approximation violates CPT invariance and its effect can be very large[4]. Consider the difference of the following partial rates of the t decays

$$\Delta_{b\nu_\tau \bar{\tau}} \equiv \Gamma(\bar{t} \to \bar{b}\bar{\nu}_\tau \tau) - \Gamma(t \to b\nu_\tau \bar{\tau}) \qquad (2)$$

in the CP-violating Higgs model of Weinberg[5]. Neglecting the neutral Higgs sector, the lowest order CP-violating asymmetry $\Delta_{b\nu_\tau\bar\tau}$ is produced by the interference of the tree-level W and charged-Higgs exchange diagrams. Assuming, for simplicity, that the effect is dominated by one of the charged-Higgs exchange and that the final-state interaction effect due to the charged-Higgs boson width is insignificant, one finds from the Breit-Wigner approximation that

$$\Delta_{b\nu_\tau\bar\tau} = \frac{-g^4}{512\pi^3}\left(\frac{m_\tau}{M_W}\right)^2 \frac{\tilde\Gamma_W}{M_W} \frac{m_t^3 M_W^2 \, Im(Y_1 Z_1)}{(M_W^2 - M_{H_1^+}^2)^2 + \Gamma_W^2 M_W^2} F\left(\frac{M_W^2}{m_t^2}, \frac{M_{H_1^+}^2}{m_t^2}\right), \tag{3}$$

with

$$F(x,y) = \left[\frac{y}{x} - 1\right]\left[(1-x)^2 \ln\frac{1-x}{x} - (1-y)^2 \ln\frac{1-y}{y} + (x-y)\right], \tag{4}$$

where $\tilde\Gamma_W = \Gamma_W - \Gamma(W \to \nu_\tau\bar\tau) \approx \frac{8}{9}\Gamma_W$, and Y_1 and Z_1 are dimensionless parameters arising from the diagonalization of the mass matrix of the charged scalars. In reaching Eq. (3) we have assumed that $\Gamma_W M_W \ll |M_W^2 - M_{H_1^+}^2|$.

Under the Breit-Wigner approximation $\Delta_{b\nu_\tau\bar\tau}$ is the largest CP asymmetry that can be produced by the standard weak currents and the charged-Higgs boson interaction. The analogous asymmetries of other t decays are completely negligible. As a consequence, the lifetime of t would not be the same as the lifetime of $\bar t$, in violation of CPT invariance.

CPT violation occurred in the calculation discussed above is a consequence of the Breit-Wigner approximation, which misses an important final-state interaction phase. Consider the W propagator in the unitary gauge. The tree-level result is

$$iD_{\mu\nu}^{(0)}(k) = \frac{-i}{k^2 - M_W^2}\left[g_{\mu\nu} - \frac{k_\mu k_\nu}{M_W^2}\right]. \tag{5}$$

Parameterizing the one-loop W self-energy as $\Pi_{\mu\nu}(k) = g_{\mu\nu}F_1(k^2) + (k^2 g_{\mu\nu} - k_\mu k_\nu)F_2(k^2)$, we find that the regularized (but unrenormalized) W propagator is

$$iD_{\mu\nu}^{(1)}(k) = \frac{-i[1 - F_2(k^2)]^{-1}}{k^2 - [M_W^2 + F_1(k^2)][1 - F_2(k^2)]^{-1}}\left[g_{\mu\nu} - k_\mu k_\nu \frac{1 - F_2(k^2)}{M_W^2 + F_1(k^2)}\right]. \tag{6}$$

It then follows from the unitarity of S-matrix, which implies

$$Im F_1(M_W^2) + M_W^2 Im F_2(M_W^2) = -\Gamma_W M_W, \tag{7}$$

and the standard on-shell renormalization procedure that

$$iD_{\mu\nu}^{(1)}(k) = \frac{-iQ(k^2)}{k^2 - M_W^2 + i\Gamma_W M_W - \Sigma_R(k^2)}\left[g_{\mu\nu} - \frac{k_\mu k_\nu}{M_W^2 - i\Gamma_W M_W + \Sigma_R(k^2)}\right], \tag{8}$$

where $Q(k^2) = [1 - F_2(k^2) + F_2(M_W^2)]^{-1}$, and $\Sigma_R(k^2) = [F_1(k^2) - F_1(M_W^2)] + M_W^2[F_2(k^2) - F_2(M_W^2)]$ are the renormalized weak charge correction and self-energy, respectively.

Compared to the Breit-Wigner approximation, the result given by Eq. (8) has an important difference: the width term $i\Gamma_W M_W$ is always in company with the mass term M_W^2 everywhere in the formula. Other modifications include (1) an over all screening factor $Q(k^2)$ for the weak charge, and (2) a renormalized self-energy $\Sigma_R(k^2)$. Both $Q(k^2)$ and $\Sigma_R(k^2)$ can have a final-state interaction phase, but their effects are likely to be less significant as they vanish at the pole: $k^2 = M_W^2 - i\Gamma_W M_W$.

For the CP-violating asymmetries in the t decays, effects arising from $Q(k^2)$ and $\Sigma_R(k^2)$ are negligible, and the W propagator can be approximated as

$$iD_{\mu\nu}(k) \approx \frac{-i}{k^2 - M_W^2 + i\Gamma_W M_W}\left[g_{\mu\nu} - \frac{k_\mu k_\nu}{M_W^2 - i\Gamma_W M_W}\right]. \tag{9}$$

The phase in the longitudinal part of the propagator is crucial in restoring CPT invariance of the calculation. It introduces a correction to $\Delta_{b\nu_\tau\bar\tau}$ given by Eq. (3). The correction has the same amplitude but with the opposite sign and thus cancels completely, as it should.

Because of the large cancellation imposed by CPT, the size of the CP-violating asymmetries induced by the mechanism discussed above turns out to be purely academic. The order-of-magnitude of the leading terms is further suppressed by a factor $\sim |Y_1|^2 m_c^2/M_W^2$, where m_c is the c-quark mass, and is about 10^{-4} times smaller. Furthermore, $\Delta_{b\nu_\tau\bar\tau} = -\Gamma(\bar t \to \bar bcs) - \Gamma(t \to bc\bar s)$. Although the calculations of the decay rates $\Gamma(t \to b\nu_\tau\bar\tau)$ and $\Gamma(t \to bc\bar s)$ are very different, there is a complete correspondence imposed by CPT when we calculate the rate difference.

In general, neglecting the phase in the $k_\mu k_\nu$ part of the W propagator will have an important implication for CP asymmetries generated from interactions involving an interference that requires a small mass insertion. Finally, the propagator of an unstable fermion with mass m and width Γ is

$$iS(k) = \frac{i}{\not{k} - m + i\Gamma/2 - \Sigma_R(k^2)} \approx i\frac{\not{k} + m - i\Gamma/2}{k^2 - m^2 + i\Gamma m}, \tag{10}$$

where $\Sigma_R(k^2)$ is the renormalized self-energy of the fermion. The approximation in the second step of Eq. (10) corresponds to neglecting $\Sigma_R(k^2)$. The phase factor $i\Gamma/2$ in the numerator has so far been ignored in the literature. Its consequence should be examined carefully. Little change is expected from an unstable scalar, whose propagator is the same as the standard Breit-Wigner form if one ignores its renormalized self-energy.

Acknowledgements

I wish to thank M. Cvetic, B. Kayser, P. Langacker, J.F. Gunion and L. Wolfenstein for valuable discussions and suggestions. This work was supported in part by the U.S. Department of Energy under the contract DE-ACO2-76-ERO-3071 and the SSC National Fellowship.

References

1. L. Wolfenstein, *Ann. Rev. Nucl. Part. Sci.* **36** (1986) 137; *Phys. Rev.* **D43** (1991) 151.
2. N. Byers, S. W. MacDowell and C. N. Yang, in *High Energy Physics and Elementary Particles* (IAEA, Vienna, 1965) p953; C. G. Callan and S. B. Treiman, *Phys. Rev.* **162** (1967) 1494; L. B. Okun and I. B. Khriplovich, *Sov. J. Nucl. Phys.* **6** (1968) 919.
3. J. Liu, *University of Pennsylvania preprint*, UPR-0517T (1992).
4. J. Liu, *University of Pennsylvania preprint*, UPR-0525T (1992).
5. S. Weinberg, *Phys. Rev. Lett.* **37** (1976) 657.

CP VIOLATING EFFECTIVE GLUON-TOP QUARK COUPLINGS

David Atwood
SLAC, Stanford CA 94309

and

Amarjit Soni
BNL, Upton NY 11973

ABSTRACT

The general form of CP violating effective couplings between the gluon and top quark is considered. Those operators which are relevant to top production at hadron super colliders through $gg \to t\bar{t}$ are categorized. In this way the limits which may be placed on the scale of new CP violating physics at the SSC are considered. The Weinberg 3 Higgs doublet model is considered as an illustration of the utility of this approach.

The next generation of hadron supercolliders will hopefully shed light on any TeV scale physics which exists beyond the standard model. One possible way to achieve this goal is to concentrate on experimental quantities where the standard model contribution is small. In this way any positive signal will be important evidence of new physics.

In this talk we consider signals for CP violation in the hadronic production of top quarks. Since the main production mode of top quarks at supercolliders is $gg \to \bar{t}t$ such a signal would indicate violation of CP in the gluon top effective coupling. In analogy to the fermion electric dipole moment (EDM) the standard model would only contribute to such couplings at a level of three or more loops[1] leaving the possibility that contributions from new physics may be large and not subject to SM backgrounds.

In order to describe CP violation in top production in a model independent manner, we proceed as follows: First we expand the effects of the new physics on the top-gluon system with an effective lagrangian expansion. We then isolate the operators relevant to the case of top production. These operators therefore give rise to form factors in the top-gluon interaction; we then examine the sensitivity which might be achieved experimentally. This sensitivity may then be compared to values of these form factors calculated in the literature.

In this case the effective lagrangian formalism as discussed for example in [2], describes new physics at a energy scale Λ as an expansion in Λ^{-1} of non-renormalizable gauge invariant operators constructed out of top-quark and gluon fields. An important feature of such an expansion[2,3] is that operators proportional to the QCD equations of motion for the top or gluon fields may be eliminated by a field redefinition. Thus operators related by such equations of motion are redundant.

In order for an operator to be relevant to CP violation in top production, it must satisfy certain restrictions: (1) It must violate CP; (2) Its Feynman rules must include couplings to two or less gluons; (3) It must not be proportional to q^2 of one of the on shell gluons in the initial state. In addition our set of operators should be complete and not redundant under equations of motion. Furthermore we shall not consider purely gluonic operators since they are constrained much more effectively by light physics (eg neutron EDM) and the effects on the top quark is expected to be small.

There are of course several ways one might express the list of operators which pass the above strictures; we choose the following:

$$O_a = (1/2)\bar{t}\ i[f_a(-\Box)\mathbf{F}^{\mu\nu}]\sigma_{\mu\nu}\gamma_5\ t$$
$$O_b = \bar{t}\ i[f_b(-\Box)F_i^{\mu\nu}F_{\mu\nu}^i]\gamma_5\ t$$
$$O_c = \bar{t}\ \epsilon_{\alpha\beta\gamma\delta}[f_c(-\Box)F_i^{\alpha\beta}F_i^{\gamma\delta}]\ t$$
$$O_d = \bar{t}\ i[f_d(-\Box)F_j^{\mu\nu}F_{\mu\nu}^k]\gamma_5 d^{ijk}T^i\ t$$
$$O_e = \bar{t}\ \epsilon_{\alpha\beta\gamma\delta}[f_e(-\Box)F_j^{\alpha\beta}F_k^{\gamma\delta}d^{ijk}]T^i]\ t$$

where $\Box = D^\mu D_\mu$ where the analytic functions $h_a, \ldots, h_e$ are roughly form factors dependent on q^2. Note however that f_a, for example, also contains additional dependence on the gauge fields.

As an illustrative example, let us now consider the operator O_a in somewhat more detail. This operator is essentially the chromoelectric dipole moment (CEDM) form factor analogous to the static quantity discussed in [3]

Let us now expand the Feynman rules for this operator. For the one gluon interaction, the vertex is

$$ih_a(q^2)\ \bar{t}\sigma^{\mu\nu}\gamma_5 T^i t\ q_\mu E_\nu^i$$

which is completely analogous to the EDM form factor. There is however a two gluon coupling given for on shell gluons by

$$g\ \bar{t}\sigma^{\mu\nu}\gamma_5 T^i t\ F^{ijk}\left[h_a(q^2)E_{1\mu}^j E_{2\nu}^k + \left[\frac{h_a(q^2)-h_a(0)}{q^2}\right](q_2 \cdot E_1^j q_{2\mu}E_{2\nu}^k - q_1 \cdot E_2^k q_{1\mu}E_{1\nu}^j)\right]$$

where $q = q_1 + q_2$. Note the peculiar second term needed to maintain gauge invariance. An important property of f_a (as with any of these form factors) is that the constant piece $f_a(0)$ must be real while at $q^2 \neq 0$ f_a may have an imaginary piece due to absorbtive effects. In fact precisely these kinds of effects have been considered in [4] in the case of an extended Higgs model. In a previous work[3] we considered extensively the phenomenology of the static CEDM (ie. $f_a(0)$). We determined that in an ideal detector given 10^7 $t\bar{t}$ pairs both of which decay leptonically, a precision of $5 \times 10^{-20} g_s - cm$ for this quantity could be achieved. We have extended this analysis in the following way: assuming that f_a is roughly constant above the $t\bar{t}$ threshold, we define the quantity $f' = f_a(4m_t^2) - f_a(0)$. We find that the precision to which $Re(f')$ can be measured under ideal conditions is 4×10^{-20} while for $Im(f')$ it is 3×10^{-20}.

In [5] the case of the analogous EDM form factor is calculated using a version of the Weinberg model for an extended higgs sector. The source of CP violation is taken to be through neutral higgs exchange. Since O_a is the only operator which gives a one gluon Feynman rule, the electromagnetic form factor calculated their to one loop is the same as the quantity f_a except e is replaced by g_s. There results thus translated into QCD give the real part of f_a roughly constant at 5×10^{-20} and the imaginary part at roughly the same level above threshold. Thus it is conceivable that such a model would give an experimental signal though the experimental challenge is likely to be formidable.

Acknowledgements

The authors would like to acknowledge useful conversations with Cliff Burgess, Carl Im, Andre Aeppli and Blake Irwin. The work of AS was supported by DOE contract DE-AC02-76CH00016 while the work of DA was supported by the SSC fellowship program, DOE contract DE-AC02-76CH00016 and DOE contract DE-AC03-76SF00515.

6. References

1. J. Donoghue, *Phys. Rev.* **D18**, 1632 (1978); E. P. Shabalin, *Sov. J. Nucl. Phys.* **31**, 864 (1980); I. Khriplovich and M. Pospelov, *INP Novosibirsk*, 90-123 (1990).
2. C. P. Burgess and J. A. Robinson, Proceedings of BNL summer Study on CP violation, 205 (1990).
3. D. Atwood, A. Aeppli and A. Soni, *Phys. Rev. Lett.* **69**, 2754 (1992).
4. C. R. Schmidt and M. W. Peskin, *Phys. Rev. Lett.* **69**, 410 (1992).
5. A. Soni, R. M. Xu, *Phys. Rev. Lett.* **69**, 33 (1992).

CP-MIXED TOPONIA STATES

David HOCHBERG and Thomas J. WEILER
*Department of Physics and Astronomy, Vanderbilt University
Nashville, TN 37235, USA*

and

Krasoos GHAFOORI-TABRIZI
*Department of Physics, University of Shahid Behehshty
Eween, Tehran 19834, Iran
and
Center for Theoretical Physics and Mathematics
Atomic Energy Organization of Iran
P.O. Box 1135-8486, Tehran, Iran*

ABSTRACT

We calculate possible mixing among CP-even and CP-odd toponia states, due to a CP-nonconserving scalar/Higgs sector. The resulting mass eigenstates in the top system cannot be classified by $^{2S+1}L_J$ or by J^{PC}, but rather are mixtures of the S, L, P, and CP quantum numbers. The toponia states are particularly vunerable to CP-mixing, because the Yukawa couplings to top are large, and the top and Higgs mass scales are comparable.

Mass eigenstates for mesons built from $q\bar{q}$ are labeled by their total spin J and intrinsic parity P= ±. In the nonrelativistic quark model (NRQM), J is resolved into quark total spin S and $q\bar{q}$ relative orbital angular momentum L; the notation employed is just that used in atomic spectroscopy: $^{2S+1}L_J$. The classification of states by nonrelativistic L and S quantum numbers is valid as long as the q-$\bar{q}$ binding energy is small compared to the rest mass $2m_q$. Mesons with hidden flavor (i.e. mesons with no electric, strange, charm, ... charges) are further labeled by their charge conjugation eigenvalue C= ±. The mass eigenstates are labeled as J^{PC}. Conservation of J is guaranteed by the rotational invariance of Nature, whereas conservation of the eigenvalues C and P results from the symmetry of the QCD lagrangian which provides the force binding the $q\bar{q}$ state. Like QCD, QED commutes with charge conjugation and parity operators, and so electromagnetic corrections do not mix the meson bound states having differing J^{PC} quantum numbers. The weak interaction does violate C and P, but to a very good approximation conserves the product CP[1]. So presumably the weak interaction causes a small mixing of states with differing C and P values, but a common CP value. The enlarged scalar/Higgs sector of non-standard electroweak models may in fact violate P and CP, and so mix states of differing CP eigenvalues.

In this talk we report on a calculation of possible CP-mixed mass eigenstates resulting from CP-noninvariance in the scalar/Higgs sector. Since the Higgs particles' couplings to quarks grow with the quark mass, it is in the top-quark sector where the largest mixing effects may occur. Toponia spectroscopy offers the possibility for the first observation of CP-noninvariance outside of the kaon system.

The argument for CP-violation in the scalar sector is two-fold. First of all, in all models the origin of fermion masses can be traced to a scalar sector. The scalar sector provides, via dynamical or spontaneous symmetry breakdown, a Lorentz-invariant mass scale in the vacuum. Secondly, there are no symmetries that prohibit complex self-couplings and mass parameters in the scalar sector, so in fact T-violation is natural. Then, by the CPT theorem, CP-violation is also naturally present. Thus, a good place to look for CP-violation beyond the kaon system is in fermion systems coupled strongly to the scalar sector. The top system is the obvious candidate.

For definiteness, consider the J=1 sector of toponium. Ignoring for the moment the principle quantum number n, there are four NRQM mesons with J=1, namely $^3S_1, ^1P_1, ^3P_1$, and $^3D_1$, with J^{PC} values $1^{--}, 1^{+-}, 1^{++}$, and 1^{--}, respectively. The ^1P state is CP-odd, the others are CP-even. The C-even ^3P state will not mix with the ^1P state because the scalar sector conserves C. So we are left with a 3×3 mixing problem. As we are interested in the CP-violating contribution to the mass matrix, it is sufficient to use the pure QCD-generated bound state masses as the diagonal entries, and to calculate only the CP-violating off diagonal contributions. There are two independent off-diagonal terms: $< ^3S_1|L_{CP}|^1P_1 >$ and $< ^3D_1|L_{CP}|^1P_1 >$, where L_{CP} is the CP-violating part of the effective Lagrangian L_{eff}. The bound states are continuum normalized as

$$< ^{2S'+1}L'_{J'}, \vec{p}'\,|\,^{2S+1}L_J, \vec{p} > = \delta_{S',S}\delta_{L',L}\delta_{J',J}(2\pi)^3 2p^0 \delta^{(3)}(\vec{p}' - \vec{p}), \tag{1}$$

where

$$|n, ^{2S+1}L_J >_{J_z} = \frac{1}{\sqrt{V}} \int \frac{d^3\vec{p}}{(2\pi)^3 2p^0} \sum_{m_L+m_S=J_z} C(L, m_L; S, m_S|J, J_z)\, \phi_{n\,L\,m_L}(\vec{p})|S, m_S, \vec{p} > \tag{2}$$

is the momentum space representation of a bound state carrying the given quantum numbers. As indicated, these are built up from products of total spin (S) and Fourier-transformed spatial wavefunctions ($\phi_{n\,L\,m_L}$) in the CM frame. The sum is over the appropriate Clebsch-Gordan coefficients C. The spatial volume V is included only for purposes of normalization and gets cancelled out at the end of the calculations.

We consider a CP-violating mixing amplitude coming from scalar exchange. The t-channel scalar φ is a mixture of scalar (0^{++}) and pseudoscalar (0^{-+}). We parameterize its coupling to the top-quark as $L_{wk} = \varphi \bar{t}(a + ib\gamma_5)t$. The effective Lagrangian is then second order in this interaction: $L_{eff} = \frac{i^2}{2}\int d^4x \int d^3y\, T(L_{wk}(y)L_{wk}(x))$. The CP-violating piece will be proportional to the product $a \times b$.

The reduced mass $m_{top}/2$ of the t-$\bar{t}$ system is sufficiently heavy to bring the quark orbit well within the Coulomb $1/r$ part of the QCD potential. Thus, the functional form of the t-$\bar{t}$ bound state wave function is hydrogenic. We use these hydrogenic wave functions in our estimates of the diagonal and off-diagonal mass entries. (These entries must also include the particle width, but we omit treating them here for lack of space[2]).

Now we consider the effects of the principle quantum number n. For n=1, only the S=1, L=0 state is present. For n=2, S and P states are present, and for n > 2, S, P, and D states are present. We show elsewhere[2] that mixing among states with differing n is small, for n not too large (just as in hydrogen). Thus we may ignore such mixing and consider n to be a good quantum number. Then, we infer from Eqn(1) that the n=1 ground state is unmixed, while the n=2 states are $^3S/^1P$ mixed, and the n >2 states are $^3D/^1P$ and $^3S/^1P$ mixed.

The matrix elements are calculated by inserting between each bound state and the operator a complete set of free t-$\bar{t}$ states:

$$1 = \sum_{s,\bar{s}} \int \frac{d^3\vec{p}}{(2\pi)^3 2p^0} \int \frac{d^3\vec{\bar{p}}}{(2\pi)^3 2\bar{p}^0} |t_s(p)\bar{t}_{\bar{s}}(\bar{p})><t_s(p)\bar{t}_{\bar{s}}(\bar{p})| \qquad (3)$$

The factor $< t_s(p)\bar{t}_{\bar{s}}(\bar{p})|L_{CP}|t_s(p)\bar{t}_{\bar{s}}(\bar{p}) >$ is calculated perturbatively, using the Feynman rules appropriate for the short distance contributions. Factors of the type $< {}^{2S+1}L_J|t_s(p)\bar{t}_{\bar{s}}(\bar{p}) >$ resolve the bound state into a wave function in the relative momentum $\vec{p}-\vec{\bar{p}}$ of the $t\bar{t}$ constituents. As noted earlier, these wave functions are to a good approximation hydrogenic, and we take them to be so. The calculation[2] leads to the conclusion that for scalar and pseudoscalar couplings a and b of order the weak coupling g_2, and for typical values of the scalar and top quark masses, say, $m_S \approx 300 GeV$ and $m_{top} \approx 100 GeV$, the mixing in the amplitude is rather small, at about the 10^{-4} to $10^{-3}\%$ level. The values for a and b which we assume here are in accord with the unitarity limit[3] on the magnitude of CP-violation in the Higgs sector.

Signatures must face the annoying fact that heavy $m_{top} \gtrsim 140\ GeV$ decays as a free quark before it has time to form the toponium bound state[4]. There are claims in the literature that the perturbative calculation of the top width overestimates the width by a factor of about two[5], in which case toponium would form even with a top mass exceeding 140 GeV. So there is hope for an expanded relevance of our calculation and conclusions. This research was supported by US DOE grant DE-FG05-85ER40226.

1. CP-violation enters the minimal electroweak interaction through the charged-current KM-matrix, and vanishes unless all three generations of quarks are present in a graph. For state mixing, this means the effect is a highly suppressed loop contribution.
2. Complete details of our calculations will appear in a forthcoming paper.
3. S. Weinberg, Phys. Rev. **D42**, 860 (1990).
4. I. Bigi, Y. Dokshitzer, V. Khoze, J. Kühn and P.M. Zerwas, Phys. Lett. **181B**, 157 (1986).
5. P. Jain, D.W. McKay and H.J. Munczek, Kansas preprint KUHEP-92-11 (1992).

Could Large CP Violation Be Detected at Colliders?

C. J.-C. Im and G. L. Kane
Randall Laboratory of Physics, University of Michigan
Ann Arbor, MI 48109/U.S.A.

ABSTRACT

Systematic searches for large CP-violation effects at hadron and electron colliders should be undertaken, not only because such large effects are not excluded by present limits, but also because attempts to generate the baryon asymmetry at the weak scale normally require some large CP-violating operators. We argue that CP-violation effects smaller than about a percent are probably undetectable at colliders. Consequently only operators giving effects that interfere with tree–level SM amplitudes can be detected. In this paper we emphasize detection at the FNAL collider. We list the operators whose effects could be detected there, and the reactions with two or three body final states that could show such effects there (treating W, Z, t, and h as single particles). At present or future hadron and electron colliders several operators that could generate a baryon asymmetry could be detected.

1. Introduction

Our understanding of how the baryon asymmetry of the universe was generated is at an exciting stage of development. All such ideas that have gone beyond the speculative stage to construct models so far have found that large CP-violating interactions are required, for example, a CP-violating term in the Lagrangian with coefficients of the same order as the gauge couplings.

If such interactions exist, their presence may be directly detectable in collisions at the electroweak scale. The purpose of this paper is to suggest several processes that can be studied at present and future colliders to search for large CP–violating effects with emphasis on FNAL in this paper. We think that many of the processes which could show such effects can be studied at colliders. While the possibility of relating such effects to the origin of the baryon asymmetry is particularly exciting, motivation for studying such processes is also provided by the simple observation that at the present time published limits do not exist for the size of CP-violating processes at the 100 GeV scale and that present limits allow large($\sim$ 50%) CP-violation at high energy hadron colliders.

In order to parameterize effects detected at a collider (or upper limits if none are detected) and the CP–violating operators entering the models for generating the baryon asymmetry we will formulate our arguments in terms of $SU(3) \times SU(2)_L \times U(1)$–invariant CP–violating operators of dimensions less than or equal to six.

2. CP Violation at Colliders

A number of analyses of possible CP–violation effects at colliders have been published. There is, however, a major constraint that we feel has not been considered sufficiently. For both theoretical and experimental reasons, we think that it is probably not possible to detect CP–violation effects smaller than about a percent in collider experiments.

The first reason is that the detectors will not be CP–invariant. Systematic studies can be done to determine at what level electric and magnetic fields could induce CP–asymmetries. It is not clear at what level to worry about such systematic asymmetries. Certainly to argue they were smaller than one percent level would require experimental "proof." Even if such systematic asymmetries can be understood to below one percent level, there are no event–by–event observables of CP–violation. Thus in order to establish a CP–violating effect of order 10^{-3} at 2σ, for example, one would need to average over about 10^7 events of interest. Even at the SSC, an event sample of size 10^7 for any realistic CP–observable would be very difficult to achieve.

Second, there is a variety of theoretical effects that are difficult or impossible to eliminate. First, whenever one is studying CP–violation by actually studying T–violation and assuming CPT–invariance, one has to be sure that spurious T–violating effects such as final state interactions are not present[2]. For example, gluon exchange induces a parity–violating transverse polarization of order 1% ~ 2% in $t\bar{t}$ production. The process $u\bar{d} \to t\bar{b}$ is another example. For this reaction, one can search for CP–violation by studying $u\bar{d} \to t\bar{b}$ and looking for T–violating observables formed from momenta and the top spin. Then final state QCD interactions and top width effects both induce such observables at about the 1 percent level. Moreover, QCD and EW interactions between quarks will cause final state interactions in the background that could mimic a CP–asymmetry, perhaps at the one-half or even one percent level. For example, the Wjj–channel, perhaps plus softer jets, will be a background for $t\bar{t}$ that cannot be entirely eliminated, giving rise to a spurious CP–violating effect that can easily be of order 1%.

Because of these arguments we conclude that it is unlikely that it will be possible to reliably detect new CP–violating effects below about one percent at colliders.

CP–violating effects arises from interferences between diagrams and fall into four categories: tree–tree, tree–loop, loop–tree, and loop–loop. But all loops in the SM are already suppressed by factors smaller than 10^{-2}. Thus if it is correct that this is effectively a lower limit on what could be discovered, we conclude that only new CP–violating effects that interfere with SM tree amplitudes could be detected. Strictly speaking, the CP–violating operators of dimensions five and higher could also be generated by loops in some fundamental theory, but here we do not assume that such a theory is necessarily weakly interacting.

Given this conclusion, we can enumerate all processes in which new CP–violating effects could be observed at the tree–level for a given set of external particles. To this end, the general condition for interference between two tree–level amplitudes can be formulated in terms of whether they are even or odd under a particular discrete transformation. Using this general condition, it can be shown that all CP–violating operators of dimension six or less that contain fermion fields lead to CP–violating effects that are proportional to the fermion masses.

Some of the processes that exhibit tree–level observables are shown in the following section. Fortunately all interesting vertices in the SM are present, though very large luminosity would be required to study them all down to the one percent level. In the second column of table 1, we only show the hypothetical new CP–violating piece. These interfere with the CP–even contribution from the SM to yield tree–level CP–odd observables.

3. Examples

We list some of the two and three body processes that can be tested at FNAL to detect large CP–violation. The second column gives one of the CP–violating operators that contribute to the process, and the final column lists what is required to observe the effect. In all cases, ↑, ↓ donote the top spin in the direction of $p_{proton} \times p_t$ and θ is the angle between the proton beam momentum and p_t. For $q\bar{q} \to ZH$, p_l is the momentum of the lepton coming from the Z. The coefficients Δ's measure the strengths of the CP–violating operators. Note that Δ_{Wt}, Δ_{Zh}, Δ_g, and Δ_{gt} have dimensions of M^{-2}, while Δ_{ht} is dimensionless.

Reaction	CP − odd Operator	Observables
$u\bar{d} \to t\bar{b}$	$i\Delta_{Wt} W^+_{\mu\nu} \bar{t}_L \gamma^\mu \partial^\nu b_L$	$\sigma_\uparrow(\theta) - \sigma_\downarrow(\theta), \sigma_\uparrow(\theta) - \bar{\sigma}_\downarrow(\theta)$
$q\bar{q} \to ZH$	$\Delta_{Zh} H \epsilon^{\mu\nu\sigma\eta} \tilde{Z}_{\mu\nu} Z_{\sigma\eta}$	$p_l \cdot (p_Z \times p_q)$
$gW^+ \to t\bar{b}$	$i\Delta_{gt} G^a_{\mu\nu} \bar{t} \gamma^\mu \lambda^a \partial^\nu t$	$\sigma_\uparrow(\theta) - \sigma_\downarrow(\theta), \sigma_\uparrow(\theta) - \bar{\sigma}_\downarrow(\theta)$
$bW^+ \to tH$	$i\Delta_{ht} H \bar{t} \gamma_5 t$	$\sigma_\uparrow(\theta) - \sigma_\downarrow(\theta), \sigma_\uparrow(\theta) - \bar{\sigma}_\downarrow(\theta)$
$qq \to gqq$	$\Delta_g f_{abc} \epsilon^{\mu\nu\sigma\eta} G^{a\rho}_\mu G^b_{\rho\nu} G^c_{\sigma\eta}$	$\vec{p}_{q,in} \cdot (\vec{p}_{q,out} \times \vec{p}_{\bar{q},out})$

5. Acknowledgements

C. I. thanks the theory groups at the Fermi Laboratory and the Brookhaven Laboratory, where a part of this work was done, for kind hospitality. G. K. appreciates conversations with A. Dolgov, M. Voloshin, and D. Amidei. This work was supported in part by the U.S. Department of Energy.

6. References

1. A. De Rujula, M. B. Gavela, O. Pene, and F. J. Vegas, *Phys. Lett.* **B245** (1990) 640; *Nucl. Phys.* **B357** (1991) 311.
2. Jiang Liu, in *"Final–State–Interaction Simulation of T–Violation in Top Quark Semileptonic Decay,"*, University of Pennsylvania Preprint, UPR–0517T, 1992.

AUTHOR INDEX

Akchurin, N.	1687	Boyer, J.	1388
Alexopoulos, T.	1164	Brambilla, N.	515
Allen, T. J.	1537	Brock, I. C.	587
Allport, P. P.	1724	Brock, R.	421
Alves, G.	718	Brown, D. S.	968
Amundson, J. F.	607	Burger, W.	1510
Aston, D.	1657,734	Cahill, K.	1418,1468,1519
Astur, R. V.	993	Caldwell, D. O.	1353
Atwood, D.	864	Cartiglia, N.	1752
Avery, P.	1705	Cassel, D. G.	213
Avila, M.	662	Chaney, R. C.	1644
Babu, K. S.	1311,1314	Chang, C. Y.	1225
Baer, H.	1188	Chang, D.	1250,834
Bagger, J.	357	Chang, Y.	774
Baker, M.	932	Cherney, M.	1177
Baker, O. K.	1772	Chisholm, J. S. R.	1534
Balitsky, I.	1077	Christian, D. C.	1775
Ball, S.	533	Cinabro, D.	843
Baltay, C.	109	Clemen, M.	1746
Barao, F.	1281	Cline, J. M.	1358
Baringer, P.	684	Coan, T.	1278
Barnett, R. M.	491	Cohen, A.	1405
Bathas, G.	1555	Collins, J.	1032
Baur, U.	362	Conrad, J. M.	1020
Bazarko, A.	738	Contopanagos, H. F.	1042
Bazizi, K. A.	750	Conway, J. S.	298
Bean, A.	597	Cormack, R.	1379
Behrends, S.	999	Crawford, G.	314
Bellantoni, L.	338,590	Crawford, J. P.	1531
Bender, C. M.	1549	Crosetti, G.	1271
Benlloch, J.	1091	Culbertson, R.	600
Bern, Z.	901	Cumalat, J. P.	197
Bernstein, R.	411	Dai, H.	1382
Bhat, P. C.	1681	Dallapiccola, C.	691
Bhatti, A.	1699	Darling, C.	725
Bigi, I.	610	Dauwe, L.	759
Biller, S.	1361	Dawson, S.	487
Bird, D. J.	1385	De Alwis, S. P.	1576
Blazey, G. C.	996	De Barbaro, P.	1702
Blok, B.	537	Del Duca, V.	990
Bodwin, G. T.	1063	Delchamps, S. W.	711
Boehm, F.	1291	Dell'Agnello, S.	747
Boettcher, S.	1522	Deshpande, A.	802
Booth, M. J.	837	Dhina, M.	875
Boswell, C.	768	Di Ciaccio, L.	583

Di Leo, L.	1528	Haeri, B.	1552
Diaz, M. A.	1194	Hahn, M.	893
Dombeck, T.	1625	Hahn, R. L.	1442
Doncheski, M. A.	1039,366	Haller, K.	1583
Draper, T.	1494	Halling, A. M.	1635
Dubbs, T.	639	Hallman, T.	1179
Duboscq, J.	579	Halverson, P.	1337
Dunlea, J. M.	965	Halzen, F.	1394
Edwards, K.	527	Han, T.	655
Eigen, G.	1719	Hansmann, U.	1507
Einhorn, M. B.	1234	Haridas, P.	1342,1711
Elias, V.	1071,1206	Harris, R. M.	975
Ellis, R. K.	167	Harton, J. L.	397
Engel, J.	1303	Hartouni, E.	1161
Falbo-Kenkel, M. K.	1586	Hartouni, E. P.	698
Fan, C.	898	Heinson, A. P.	1731
Fast, J. E.	507	Heintz, U.	501
Fields, T.	1141	Henderson, S.	318
Fisher, P.	305	Henkes, T.	1653
Fortney, L.	1684	Hewett, J.	1185
Frampton, P. H.	1259	Hewett, J. L.	496
Frankle, S.	1605	Hime, A.	1349
Franzini, P.	1737	Hindi, H.	1599
Franzini, P. J.	744	Hinshaw, D.	332
Fuess, S.	920	Hochberg, D.	867
Fuess, T.	765	Hou, G. W.	446,669
Fulcher, L. P.	521	Howell, B.	408
Gabella, W.	1610	Huet, P.	1401
Gallas, E.	1218	Huffman, B. T.	771
Gangopadhyaya, A.	1525	Igarashi, S.	753
Gao, Y.	553	Im, C.	870
Gao, Y. T.	633	Incandela, J.	450
Gardner, R.	762	Jacobsen, R.	405
Gay-Ducati, M. B.	1135	Jaffe, A. H.	1456
Gibbons, L. K.	791	Jain, P.	1148,1540,436,518
Golterman, M.	1467	Ji, X.	1036
Gondolo, P.	1435	Johns, W. E.	604
Gonin, M.	1170	Johnson, J. M.	484
Goodman, M.	1300	Johnson, R. P.	621
Gottlieb, S.	1500	Jungman, G.	1256
Graf, N. A.	387	Junk, T.	884
Grant, A. K.	511	Kahana, D. E.	477
Grassi, M.	1453	Kalelkar, M.	731
Green, K. D.	1367	Kamionkowski, M.	1409
Gregory, R.	1568	Kang, K.	1082
Gross, D. J.	265	Kao, C.	1191
Gu, P.	809	Kaplan, D.	1734
Guglielmo, G. M.	627	Kass, R.	1765
Gui, M.	1690	Kauffman, R.	1023
Gunion, J. F.	1231,858	Kearns, E.	1376
Gupta, S.	1125	Keeble, L.	1002

Kennedy, D.	1200	Mani, S.	1728
Kennedy, R. D.	942	Mann, W. A.	1330
Keranen, R.	1275	Marciano, W. J.	185
Kim, G.	688	Marco, J.	378
Kim, S.	1491	Markeloff, R.	393
King, M. E.	1669	Mattingly, A. C.	909
Kiskis, J.	1481	Mawhinney, R. D.	1478
Klein, S.	1364	McDonough, J.	1708
Klein, S. R.	1138	McFarland, K. S.	805
Klima, B.	453	McGrath, G.	1306
Knowles, I. G.	1247	McGrew, C.	1334
Kosowsky, A.	1415	McKay, T. A.	1370
Kostelecky, V. A.	783	McNulty, R.	308
Kowalewski, R.	289	Mendez, H.	756
Kral, J. F.	651	Meng, R.	954
Kronfeld, A. S.	1060	Merritt, K. W.	1265
Kuhn, J. H.	439	Meschi, E.	1117
Laenen, E.	987	Meurice, Y.	1562
Langacker, P.	1326	Michael, D. G.	1323
Lauber, J. A.	881	Miller, R.	1761
Leblanc, P.	1114	Milton, K. A.	1580
Lederman, L. M.	277	Mir, R.	548
Lee-Franzini, J.	821	Mirabito, L.	325
Levin, E.	938	Mishra, C.	1619
Levin, J. J.	1412	Morelos, A.	642
Lew, H.	1253	Moulding, S.	1268
Lewis, R. A.	1647	Muheim, F.	614
Li, H.	1057	Murphy, C. T.	1615
Li, Y.	887	Murray, W. J.	1749
Lin, L.	1461	Nandi, S.	1203
Lincoln, D.	926	Naples, D.	948
Linnemann, J. T.	1641	Narain, M.	1678
Liu, J.	861	Narayanan, R.	1484
Liu, K.	1471	Nardi, E.	1240
Longley, N. P.	1373	Nath, P.	1197
Loomis, C.	1155	Nefkens, B.	824
Lopez-Fernandez, A.	1221	Nemati, B.	694
Lu, H. J.	917	Nico, J. S.	1446
Luebke, W.	1638	Nojiri, M. M.	1244
Lundberg, W. R.	1589	Norman, E. B.	1450
Luo, M.	951	Ogren, H.	1785
Lykken, J. D.	1572	Olness, F. I.	981
Ma, E.	474	Olson, C. L.	524
Ma, H.	1696	Ong, B.	1053
Maas, P.	978	Orr, L. H.	432
Mackenzie, P. B.	1503	Osterberg, K.	840
Madaras, R.	19	Oyang, J. Y.	1664
Maehlum, G.	567	Pan, J.	1158
Makoff, G. D.	799	Pancheri, G.	443,741
Malchow, R.	1778	Pantaleone, J.	1317,1320
Mangano, M.	427	Papadopoulou, T.	1262

Park, H.	1607	Siegemund-Broka, S.	1513
Partridge, R.	456	Simon, J. Z.	1421
Paterno, M.	1228	Sinclair, D.	123
Perticone, D.	648	Singh, V.	1497
Peterson, K. A.	370	Sjostrand, T.	1111
Piccioni, O.	1346	Smith, G. A.	1005
Playfer, S. M.	848	Smith, V. J.	636
Pomianowski, P. A.	708	Snow, G. R.	971
Potter, D.	594	Soares, J. M.	852
Prosperi, G. M.	1086	Song, L.	464
Purohit, M. V.	681	Sopczak, A.	470
Puseljic, D.	678	Spartiotis, C.	1286
Qiu, J.	957	Springer, R. W.	1675
Radel, G.	415	Stanev, T.	1308
Raja, R.	1012	Stanton, N. R.	715
Rajagopal, K.	1474	Steinberg, R. I.	1296
Ralston, J.	1045	Stephens, R.	545
Ramberg, E. J.	795	Strauss, M. G.	1758
Renken, R.	1464	Stubbs, C.	1424
Ressell, M. T.	1432	Stutte, L.	1661
Rey, S.	1565	Su, D.	342
Rice, D.	1595	Surguladze, L. R.	906
Richman, J.	618	Swamy, P. N.	1543
Riemersma, S.	984	Syphers, M. J.	1629
Riesselmann, K.	481	Tajima, H.	1755
Rind, O.	961	Takach, S. F.	721
Rodrigo, T.	1097	Takai, H.	1693
Rosner, J. L.	352,658,666	Taylor, L.	576
Rudaz, S.	1339	Taylor, T. R.	1558
Ryan, J. J.	929	Tchikilev, O.	1107
Sachs, R.	831	Tepikian, S.	1622
Sakumoto, W.	935	Thaler, J. J.	1715
Sanghera, S.	912	Tigner, M.	155
Sapirstein, J.	827	Timm, S.	645
Sather, E.	778	Ting, S. C. C.	53
Schmitt, M.	293	Toki, W. H.	235
Schneider, O.	1743	Torres, M.	1672
Schub, M. H.	704	Trost, H.	1782
Schubnell, M.	1439	Tschirhart, R.	813
Schumm, B. A.	348,890	Uraltsev, N.	855
Schwartz, A.	816	Valencia, G.	1237
Schwiening, J.	1104	Van Bibber, K.	1428
Sciulli, F. J.	37	Veenhof, R.	1008
Seligman, W. G.	923	Vilanova, D.	563
Selove, W.	701	Wainer, N.	1120
Sharpe, S. R.	247	Wakely, A. B.	1074
Shaw, N. M.	459	Wallace, N. B.	630
Shen, Y.	541	Walsh, M.	301
Shukla, S.	675	Wayne, M.	1650
Shuryak, E.	1067,1144,1152	Wear, J.	1740
Sidwell, R. A.	672	Weber, A.	1215

Weber, F.	558, 571
Weerasundara, D. D.	1016
Weiler, T. J.	728
Weingarten, D.	1487
Wells, P.	335
White, A. R.	383
Wiencke, L.	1167
Wilkerson, J. F.	137
Wilkinson, C. A.	1603
Willenbrock, S.	1026
Wittek, W.	1101
Wood, D.	390
Woods, D. M.	624
Worah, M.	1209
Worden, H.	1048
Wright, D.	329
Wu, Q.	504
Xue, S.	321
Yagil, A.	3
Yu, J.	1094
Yuan, C.	1029
Yuan, Y.	1212
Zeppenfeld, D.	374
Zhang, H.	1546
Zhao, T.	1769
Zhou, B.	467
Zhu, Q.	945
Zimmerman, D.	786